# Catalogue of

## MODEL TOYS

### TWELFTH EDITION

# Originator and Editor
# John Ramsay

# Technical Editor
# John King

1st Edition published 1983
2nd Edition published 1986
3rd Edition published 1988
3rd Edition Update published 1989
4th Edition published 1991
5th Edition published 1993
6th Edition published 1995
7th Edition published 1997
8th Edition published 1999
9th Edition published 2001
10th Edition published 2003
11th Edition published 2005
12th Edition published 2007

Copyright © 2007 by Warners Group Publications plc.

ISBN: 978-0-9556194-0-3

Book designed by John King.
Origination by Warners Group Publications plc.
Printed by Warners Midlands plc., Bourne, Lincs.

Models featured on the front cover:
Dinky Toys No. 919 Guy Van 'Golden Shred' and
Post-war Tri-ang Minic 24M Luton Delivery Van 'Minic Transport'

# Contents

# Guide to Advertisers

# Acknowledgements

The Editor would like to express appreciation to the following collectors, auctioneers and traders who very kindly took the time and trouble to provide updating information and photographs about new entries and colour variations, etc.

John King, Norwich.
John Kinchen, Hampshire.
David Cooke, DTCA.
Derek Barratt, Norwich.
Bruce Hoy, Queensland, Australia.
Bryan Goodall and Simon Smith.
 Vectis Auctions Ltd, Stockton-on-Tees.

Hugo Marsh, Christie's Auctioneers.
Terry Durrant, Lacy Scott & Knight
 Model Auctions, Bury St Edmunds.
Glenn Butler and Ray Strutt,
 Wallis & Wallis, Lewes, Sussex.
Barry Potter of Barry Potter Auctions.
Robert Newson, Wood Green, London.
Mike and Sue Richardson, Windsor.
Susan Pownall, Corgi Club.
Herbert Bell, Western Australia.
Andy Woodhall, Bury St Edmunds.
Phillipe Salmon, Collectoys, France.
Andrew Hilton and Nigel Mynheer,
 Special Auction Services, Reading.
Vincent Espinasse, France.

Horace Dunkley, Stamford, Lincs.
Nigel Cooper, Basingstoke.
Trevor Bannister, Seaford.
Leigh Gotch, Bonhams Auctioneers.
Kevin McGimpsey (MICA),
 Deeside, Flintshire.
Tony Murphy, DTCA.
Norman Warnars, Tegelau, NL.
Kevin Barwick, DTCA.
Pierre Jacques Dujardin, France.
Hans Nuis, DTCA.
Major H.B (Bev) Stevens, Dorset.
Graham Hamilton,
 www.rockertron.co.uk.

**DTCA - The Dinky Toys Collectors Association.**
Details from: DTCA, PO Box 60, Norwich, NR4 7WB.
Website: www.dtca.org.uk.    E-mail: info@dtca.org.uk

**Dinky News - Australia.** Bruce Hoy, PO Box 249 Aspley, Queensland 4034, Australia. Tel/Fax: +61-7-3264-4227.
E-mail: dinkynews@yahoo.com.au

# Introduction

Welcome to the 12th Edition of 'British Diecast Model Toys Catalogue', brought to you by the publishers of Diecast Collector and Collectors Gazette.

During the summer of 2007, and nearly 25 years after the launch of the first edition, Warners Group Publications plc took over the publishing responsibility for the Catalogue. However the work involved in compiling the guide has continued to be done by John Ramsay and John King.

**Updating and revision of the 12th Edition**
The 12th Edition model listings have, where applicable, been completely revised and improved.

The Guide includes over 500 new items never before listed.

The 'Market Price Range' prices have been revised and amended by a team of valuation experts and show hundreds of meaningful auction results selected from a wide range of specialist auction houses and the internet.

The 12th Edition includes more colour pages of some of the finest models sold through auction since the previous edition.

**The Future**
It is the new publisher's intention to grow the publication with the inclusion of modern issue releases and, through the quarterly Price Guide (given away with Diecast Collector magazine in January, April, July and September issues) endeavour to update collectors of variations and any new models uncovered.

# Market Price Range Grading System

Based on the findings of the Market Surveys undertaken since 1983 virtually all the models have been given a 'Market Price Range'. The price gap between the lower and higher figures indicates the likely price range a collector should expect to pay for the model.

Models qualifying for a price at the top end of the range could include:
- Boxed models where both the model and the box are in pristine condition,
- A scarce or unusual colour
- An unusual component such as special wheels
- A model with pristine decals where this is unusual
- A model in an unusual or special box
- A model priced by a trader who disagrees with the price range quoted in the Catalogue (which is only a guide).

## PRICES FOR MODELS IN LESS THAN 'MINT BOXED' CONDITION

Many boxed models seen for sale fail to match up to the exacting standards on which the Market Price Range has been based, having slight model or box damage. In these instances models may be priced at 50% to 60% of the Market Price Range shown, and this is particularly relevant when a model is common. Boxed models with considerable damage or models lacking their original box will be priced much lower.

**Note:** It cannot be over-emphasised that irrespective of the price guidance provided by this Catalogue, collectors should not always expect to see prices asked within the price ranges shown. Traders will ask a price based on their trading requirements and will NOT be governed by any figures shown in this Catalogue, nor could they be reasonably expected to do so.

## MODELS NOT GIVEN A 'MARKET PRICE RANGE'

It has not been possible to give every model a price range and these exceptions are as follows:

## NPP   No Price Possible

This is shown alongside models never encountered in the survey or about which there is doubt as to their actual issue, even though a model may have been pictured in a catalogue. Readers will appreciate that unlike postage stamps or coins, no birth records are available in respect of all the die-cast models designed or issued.

## NGPP   No Grading Possible at Present

Price grading may not be possible at present because:
i) The model or gift set is particularly rare and has not come to market in recent times. Consequently, no price grading has been shown as the Compiler believes that to attempt one would be carrying rarity and value assessment into the realms of pure guesswork. As and when information becomes available concerning these rarities it will be included in the Catalogue.
ii) The model may have been recently introduced or announced in the model press or in a manufacturer's own literature, but a price has not yet been suggested or communicated to us.

## GSP   Gift Set Price

If a model forms part of a Set (and is not available separately) the price range will be shown against the entry in the relevant Gift Set section and will refer to the complete set.

## DESCRIPTION OF MODEL COLOURS

The descriptions of the various colours used to describe model colour variations have been derived from the following sources:
i) Manufacturers colour descriptions.
ii) Colours commonly used and known to refer to certain models over a period of many years
iii) Colours which we in consultation with the trade or specialist collectors decide most closely describes a previously unrecorded genuine colour variation
iv) Colours given a model by an bonafide auction house. If this model is a previously unrecorded colour variation we will include the variation in future catalogue listings provided that:
a) The auctioneers are themselves satisfied that the model is genuine and not a repaint
b) Specialist dealers and collectors who view the model are satisfied that the colour variation is genuine and is not a repaint.

## SCARCE COLOURS AND VARIATIONS

Collectors or traders who know of other variations which they believe warrant a separate listing are invited to forward this information to the Editor together with any supporting evidence.

## AUCTION PRICE REALISATIONS

Prices of common models sold are often less than the Market Price Range figures shown. In many instances, the models have been purchased by the trade who will add their own mark-up.

# Model and Box Valuation Guidelines

The research has produced the following comparative price information concerning the values of both unboxed models and separate boxes in the various condition classifications.

The guidelines have been based on the 'General Condition' grading system as described in the previous section. The percentage value ranges are designed to reflect the relatively higher values of the rarer models and boxes.

| UNBOXED MODEL CONDITION | % VALUE OF MINT BOXED MODEL |
|---|---|
| Mint | 50% - 60% |
| Excellent | 40% - 50% |
| Good | 20% - 40% |
| Fair | 10% - 20% |
| Poor | 0% - 10% |

| BOX CONDITION | %VALUE OF MINT BOXED MODEL |
|---|---|
| Mint | 40% - 50% |
| Excellent | 30% - 40% |
| Good | 20% - 30% |
| Fair | 10% - 20% |
| Poor | 0% - 10% |

Note: The same model may have been issued in two or more types of box (Yesteryears for example). The model in the earlier box is usually (though not always) the more valuable.

**Rare Models and Sets**

The exceptions to the foregoing guidelines are in respect of rare models or boxes, or models seldom found in first class condition such as some pre-war models. In these situations rarity commands a premium and the asking price or the price realised at auction will certainly reflect it.

# Classifying the condition of models and boxes

The condition of a model and its accompanying box does of course have a direct bearing on its value which makes accurate condition grading a matter of key importance.

Unlike other collecting hobbies such as stamps or coins, no one universal grading system is used to classify the condition of models and boxes. Nevertheless, whilst several versions exist, there are really two main systems of condition classification in the UK as follows:

### 1. The 'Specific Condition' Grading System

The following example is fairly typical of the types of descriptions and gradings seen on Mail Order lists.

| | | | |
|---|---|---|---|
| M | Mint | AM | Almost Mint |
| VSC | Very Slightly Chipped | SC | Slightly Chipped |
| C | Chipped | VC | Very Chipped |

If a model is described as Mint Boxed, the condition of its box is not normally separately described. However, it is expected to be in first class and as near original condition as is possible, bearing in mind the age of the model concerned.

If a box is damaged the flaws are usually separately described. This method has always seemed to work out quite well in practice, for all reputable dealers automatically offer a 'Sale or Return if not satisfied' deal to their clients, which provides the necessary safeguard against the misrepresentation of the model's condition. The Compiler would stress that the foregoing is only an example of a mail order condition grading system and stricter box grading definitions are known to exist.

### 2. The 'General Condition' Grading System

This method is often used by auctioneers although it is also to be seen used on the occasional mail order list.

| | | | | | |
|---|---|---|---|---|---|
| (M) | Mint | (E) | Excellent | | |
| (G) | Good | (F) | Fair | (P) | Poor |

Usually these gradings are separately applied to describe firstly the condition of the model and secondly the condition of the box. From our observations and purely for guidance purposes, we would suggest the following descriptions approximately represent the different grades.

### MODEL CONDITION GRADINGS

*1. MINT (M)* The model must be complete and as fresh, new and original in appearance as when first received from the manufacturers.

*2. EXCELLENT (E)* The model is almost in mint condition and is only barred from that classification by having a few slight flaws, e.g., slight paintwork chipping in unimportant areas.

*3. GOOD (G)* The model is in a complete and original condition and retains an overall collectable appearance despite having a few chips or rubbed paintwork.

*4. FAIR (F)* The model may not be in its original state having, for example, a broken bumper, replacement radiator or windscreen, or it may have signs of metal fatigue. The paintwork may be faded, well chipped, retouched or repainted. There may be signs of rust. Unless the model is rare it is in a barely collectable condition.

*5. POOR (P)* The model may be damaged, incomplete, repainted, altered, metal fatigued, or have a rusted baseplate or heavily chipped paintwork, etc. Unless the model is rare it has little real value to a collector other than as a candidate for a complete restoration or use as spares.

### BOX CONDITION GRADINGS

*1. MINT (M)* The box must be complete both inside and out and contain all the original packing materials, manufacturer's leaflet and box labels. It should look as fresh, new and original in appearance as when first received from the manufacturers.

*2. EXCELLENT (E)* The box is in almost mint condition but is only barred from that classification by just the odd minor blemish, e.g., there may be slight damage to the display labels caused by bad storage. The original shop price label may have been carelessly removed and caused slight damage. The cover of a bubble pack may be cracked or there may be very slight soiling etc.

*3. GOOD (G)* The box is complete both inside and out, and retains an overall attractive collectable appearance. Furthermore, despite showing a few signs of wear and tear, it does not appear 'tired'.

*4. FAIR (F)* The box will have a 'tired' appearance and show definite signs of wear and tear. It may be incomplete and not contain the original packing materials or leaflets. In addition it may not display all the exterior identification labels or they may be torn or soiled or a box-end flap may be missing or otherwise be slightly damaged. In this condition, unless the model is particularly rare, it will not add much to the model's value.

*5. POOR (P)* The box will show considerable signs of wear and tear. It will almost certainly be badly damaged, torn, incomplete or heavily soiled and in this condition, unless it is very rare, is of little value to a collector.

# Catalogue omissions

Accurate birth records do not exist in respect of all the die-cast models issued. Therefore whilst every effort has been made to provide comprehensive information it is inevitable that collectors will have knowledge of models which have not been included. Consequently the Compiler and Editors will be pleased to receive details of these models in order that they may be included in future editions. Naturally, supporting evidence regarding authenticity will be required.

This Catalogue has been prepared solely for use as a reference book and guide to the rarity and asking prices of die-cast model toys.

Whilst every care has been taken in compiling the Catalogue, neither the Editors nor the publishers can accept any responsibility whatsoever for any financial loss which may occur as a result of its use.

# Buying and Selling models

### SELLING MODELS TO THE TRADE:

The model value figures produced by the Price Grading system always refer to the likely *asking prices* for models. They have been prepared solely to give collectors an idea of the amount they might reasonably expect to pay for a particular model.

The figures given are *not* intended to represent the price which will be placed on a model when it is offered for sale to a dealer. This is hardly surprising bearing in mind that the dealer is carrying all the expense of offering his customers a collecting service which costs money to maintain.

Collectors should not therefore be surprised when selling models to the trade to receive offers which may appear somewhat low in comparison with the figures shown in the Catalogue. Dealers are always keen to replenish their stocks with quality items and will as a result normally make perfectly fair and reasonable offers for models. Indeed, depending on the particular models offered to them, the actual offer made may well at times exceed the levels indicated in the Catalogue which are only *guidelines* and not firm figures.

One last point: when selling models to the trade, do get quotations from two or three dealers, especially if you have rare models to sell.

### BUYING and SELLING MODELS AT AUCTION:

Collectors wishing to acquire or dispose of model toys are reccommended to contact auctioneers advertising in this Catalogue and ask for their terms of trade. Most have their own websites where much information may be obtained concerning their rates of commission and forthcoming auction dates, etc.

# Abbreviations

## A
| | |
|---|---|
| A.E.C. | Associated Equipment Company |
| AA | Anti-aircraft |
| A.A. | Automobile-Association |
| ABC-TV | Associated British Cinemas (Television) |
| A.F.S. | Auxiliary Fire Service |
| AG | Amber glass |
| AMC | American Motor Corporation |
| APC | Armoured Personnel Carrier |
| artic. | articulated |
| ATV | Associated Television |

## B
| | |
|---|---|
| BA | British Airways |
| BAC | British Airways Corporation |
| BB | Black base |
| BBC | British Broadcasting Corporation |
| BEA | British European Airways |
| BG | Blue glass |
| bhp | brake horsepower |
| BLMC | British Leyland Motor Corporation |
| BMC | British Motor Corporation |
| BMW | Bayrische Motoren-Werke |
| B.O.A.C. | British Overseas Airways |
| BP | British Petroleum |
| BPT | Black plastic tyres |
| BPW | Black plastic wheels |
| BR | British Railways |
| BRM | British Racing Motors |
| BRS | British Road Services |
| B.S.M. | British School of Motoring |
| BWW | Black WhizzWheels |

## C
| | |
|---|---|
| CG | Clear glass |
| CLE | Certificated Limited Edition |
| cv | chevaux-vapeur. (a measure of power; translated into English, it literally means 'horse-steams') |
| C.W.S. | Co-operative Wholesale Society |
| cwt. | hundred-weight |
| CWW | Chrome WhizzWheels |

## D
| | |
|---|---|
| DCMT | Die Casting Machine Tools |
| DH | De Havilland |
| Dk. | Dark (shade of colour) |
| DUKW | An amphibious military vehicle developed by General Motors in WWII. The letters are not initials or an abbreviation - just part of an early drawing office reference. |

## E
| | |
|---|---|
| EEC | European Economic Community |
| e.g. | exempli gratia (= 'for example') |
| EMI | Electrical & Musical Industries |
| ER | Elizabetha Regina, (E II R, Queen Elizabeth II) |
| ERF | Edwin Richard Foden |
| Est. | Established (or estimate/d) |

## F
| | |
|---|---|
| Fiat | (or FIAT) Fabbrica Italiana Automobile Torino |
| fig(s) | figure(s) |

## G
| | |
|---|---|
| GB | Green box, or Grey base |
| G.B. | Great Britain |
| GER | Great Eastern Railway |
| GG | Green glass |
| GMC | General Motors Corporation |
| GP | Grand Prix |
| GPO | General Post Office |
| GPW | Grey plastic wheels |
| GR | Georgius Rex |
| GS | Gift Set |
| GSP | Gift Set price |
| GTO | Gran Turismo Omologato |
| GTV | Gran Turismo Veloce |
| GWR | Great Western Railway |

## H
| | |
|---|---|
| HM | His/Her Majesty |
| HMS | His/Her Majesty's Ship |
| H.M.V. | 'His Masters Voice' |
| hp | horse-power |
| H.W.M. | Hersham & Walton Motors |

## I
| | |
|---|---|
| ICI | Imperial Chemical Industries |
| int. | interior |
| INTER | (or INTL) International |
| I.O.M. | Isle of Man |

## J
| | |
|---|---|
| JB | James Bond |
| JCB | Joseph C. Bamford |

## K
| | |
|---|---|
| K.D.F. | Kraft durch Freude |
| K.L.G. | Kenelm Lee Guinness |
| K.L.M. | Koninklijke Luchtvaart Maatschappij NV (Dutch airline) |

## L
| | |
|---|---|
| L.A.P.D. | Los Angeles Police Department |
| LE | Limited Edition |
| l/h | left hand |
| LM | Le Mans |
| LMS | London Midland & Scottish Railway |
| LNER | London & North Eastern Railway |
| LNWR | London & North Western Railway |
| Lt. | Light (shade of colour) |
| Ltd. | Limited Liability Company |
| LWB | Long wheel-base |

## M
| | |
|---|---|
| MB | Matchbox |
| Met. | Metallic |
| MG | Make of car, ('Morris Garages') |
| M.I.C.A. | Matchbox International Collectors Association |
| mm. | millimetres |
| MOY | Models of Yesteryear |
| MPR | Market Price Range |
| MW | Metal wheels |

## N
| | |
|---|---|
| N | North |
| NAAFI | Navy, Army & Air Force Institutes |
| N.A.S.A. | National Aeronautics & Space Administration |
| NB | nota bene ('mark well') |
| NCO | Non-Commissioned Officer |
| NGPP | No guide price at present |
| nhp | (or n.h.p.) nominal horsepower |
| No. | Number |
| NPP | No price possible |
| NS | (or n/s) Nearside |

## O
| | |
|---|---|
| OG | Orange glass |
| OS | (or o/s) Offside |

## P
| | |
|---|---|
| PB | Propeller blade(s) |
| PG | Purple glass |
| P.I. | Private Investigator |
| PLC | Public Limited Company |
| PO | Post Office |
| PP | Packing piece(s), or plated parts |
| PSV | Public service vehicle |
| P.T.T. | Postes-Telephones-Telegraphes |

## R
| | |
|---|---|
| RAC | Royal Automobile Club |
| RAF | Royal Air Force |
| R.C.M.P. | Royal Canadian Mounted Police |
| r/h | right hand |
| RHD | Right-hand drive |
| RM | Routemaster (bus) |
| RN(s) | Racing or Rally number(s) |
| RNLI | Royal National Lifeboat Institution |

## S
| | |
|---|---|
| S | South |
| SB | Silver base |
| SBRW | Solid black rubber wheels |
| SBX | Special box |
| SPW | Silver plastic wheels |
| SR | Southern Railway |
| St. | Saint or Street |
| SWB | Short wheel-base |
| SWRW | Solid white rubber wheels |

## T
| | |
|---|---|
| TC | Twin carburettors |
| TDF | Tour de France |
| TK | Type of Bedford truck |
| TP | Twin Pack |
| TS | 'Touring Secours' |
| TT | Two-tone (or Tourist Trophy) |
| TV | Television |

## U
| | |
|---|---|
| UB | Unboxed, or Unpainted base |
| UK | United Kingdom |
| UN | United Nations |
| US | United States (of America) |
| USA | United States of America |
| USAAF | United States Army Air Force |
| USAF | United States Air Force |
| USS | United Space Starship |
| UW | Unpainted wheels |

## V
| | |
|---|---|
| VW | Volkswagen |

## W
| | |
|---|---|
| W | West |
| WB | Window box, or White base |
| WW | WhizzWheels (Corgi), or wide wheels (general) |

## Y
| | |
|---|---|
| YB | Yellow box, or Yellow base |
| YMCA | Young Men's Christian Association |

---

# 'Modern Diecast' information, contacts, collector clubs, etc.

**CORGI CLASSICS**
**United Kingdom**
Corgi Collector Club (Susan Pownall)
c/o Corgi Classics Ltd, Meridian East, Meridian
Business Park, Leicester, LE19 1RL. E-mail:
susie@collectorclubs.org.uk. Tel: 0870 607 1204.
**Australia**
Corgi Collector Club, Hobbyco Ltd., PO Box Q99,
Queen Victoria Building Post Office, Sydney, NSW
2000.
**New Zealand**
Corgi Collector Club New Zealand, PO Box 63064,
Papatoetoe South, Auckland, New Zealand.

**USA**
Corgi Collector Club, c/o Corgi Classics Inc., Suite
205, 430W. Erie Street, Chicgao IL60610.
**Canada**
Corgi Collector Club, 4461, Highway No.7,
Unionville, Ontario, L3R 1M1.

**LLEDO DAYS-GONE and VANGUARDS**
Lledo Days-Gone Collectors Club
Ray Dowding, PO Box 5959, Halesowen, West
Midlands, B63 3TS. Tel: 0121 550 5959
E-mail: admin@lledocollectorsclub.com
Club website: www.lledocollectorsclub.com

**EXCLUSIVE FIRST EDITIONS**
Gilbow (Holdings) Limited, 32 Woodhall Road,
Enfield, EN3 4LG

**OXFORD DIE-CAST**
PO Box 519, Berkhamstead, Herts., HP4 1 YR.
Tel: 01442 879996 Fax: 01442 877703
Website: www.oxforddiecast.co.uk

---

# Official Company Acknowledgements

The names 'CORGI TOYS', 'CARS OF THE '50s', 'CORGITRONICS', 'CORGIMATICS', 'HUSKY', 'JUNIORS' and 'ROCKETS' are all acknowledged as
trademarks of Corgi Classics Ltd. 'BRITAINS' is acknowledged as the trademark of Britains Ltd.
The name 'TRI-ANG' is acknowledged as a trademark of Hornby Hobbies Ltd., Margate, Kent.
The names 'MATCHBOX', 'MODELS of YESTERYEAR', 'DINKY TOYS' and 'SUPERFAST' are acknowledged as trademarks of Mattel Inc. USA.
The name 'MECCANO' is acknowledged as the trademark of MECCANO S.N., 73, rue Henri Barbusse, 92586 Clichy Cedex, France

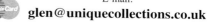

# Dinky Toys

22c Delivery Van
(no advertising)
1934 - 35

28c Delivery Van
'The Manchester Guardian'
Type 1, 1934 - 35

28d Delivery Van
'Oxo'
Type 1, 1934 - 35

28e Delivery Van
'Ensign Cameras'
Type 1, 1934 - 35

28e Delivery Van
'Firestone Tyres'
Type 1, 1934 - 35

28f Delivery Van
'Palethorpe's Sausages'
Type 1, 1934 - 35

28g Delivery Van
'Kodak Film'
Type 1, 1934 - 35

28b Delivery Van
'Pickfords Removals'
Type 1, 1934 - 35

28n Delivery Van
'Meccano'
Type 1, 1934 - 35

28L Delivery Van
'Crawford's Biscuits'
Type 1, 1934 - 35

28m Delivery Van
'Wakefield Castrol'
Type 1, 1934 - 35

28h Delivery Van
'Sharp's Toffee'
Type 1, 1934 - 35

# Dinky Toys

22f  Army Tank
1933 - 40

22e  Farm Tractor
and Trade Box 'A966B'
1933 - 40

22g  Streamlined Tourer
1935 - 41

24h  Sports Tourer Two-Seater
1934 - 40

31 'Holland Coachcraft' Van
1935 - 36

24a  Ambulance
1934 - 40

24e  Super Streamlined Saloon
1934 - 40

22b  Sports Coupé
1933 - 35

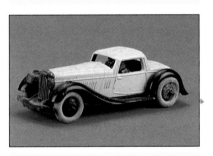

36b  Bentley Two-seat Sports Coupé
with Driver and Footman
1937 - 41

23a  Racing Car
1935 - 41

23a  Racing Car
1935 - 41

23s  Streamlined Racing Car
1938 - 40

# SPECIAL AUCTION SERVICES

## ESTABLISHED 1991

Collecting or selling? We provide professional and sound advice for both large and small accumulations and collections (including a pick up service) and hold regular auctions of Diecasts, Toys, Trains, Models, Figures, Dolls and Teddy Bears

# Dinky Toys

**Models shown above sold by Bonhams, Montpelier Street, London SW7.** Pictures reproduced by their kind permission.

**Models shown below sold by Christie's of South Kensington, London**. Pictures reproduced by their kind permission.

# Dinky Toys

23b  Hotchkiss Racing Cars
1946 - 48

30b  Rolls-Royce
1946 - 50

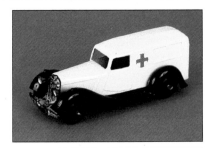

30f  Ambulance
1946 - 48

36f  British Salmson
Four-seater Sports Car
1947 - 50

38f  Jaguar SS100 Sports Car
1947 - 50

39c  Lincoln Zephyr Coupé
1947 - 50

39cu  Lincoln Zephyr Coupé
US issue  1950 - 52

39eu  Chrysler Royal Sedan
US issue  1950 - 52

39eu  Chrysler Royal Sedan
US issue  1950 - 52

101  Sunbeam Alpine Sports
1957 - 60

102  M.G. Midget Sports
1957 - 60

105  Triumph TR2 Sports
1957 - 60

**Models sold by Vectis Auctions Ltd, Thornaby, Stockton-on-Tees**.  Pictures reproduced by their kind permission.

145 Singer Vogue
1962 - 67

157 Jaguar XK120 Coupé
1954 - 62

A collection of
25d Petrol Tank Wagons
1934 - 50

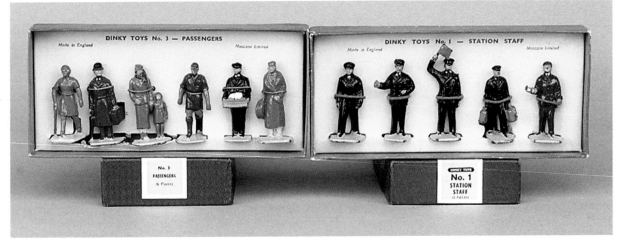

No.3 Passengers Set and No.1 Station Staff, 1954 - 56

**Models shown below sold by Christie's of South Kensington, London.** Pictures reproduced by their kind permission.

502 Foden Flat Truck (1st cab), 1947 - 54

289 'Thollembeek' Routemaster Bus, 1979

**Models sold by Vectis Auctions Ltd, Thornaby, Stockton-on-Tees**. Pictures reproduced by their kind permission.

961 Swiss Postal Bus (Vega Major Coach) 'PTT', 1973 - 77

Dublo Dinky models: 070 AEC Mercury Tanker, 073 Land Rover and Horse Trailer, 069 Massey-Harris Tractor and 076 Lansing Bagnall Tractor and Trailer, 1959 - 64

# Dinky Toys

944 'Corn Products' promotional model, 1963 - 64

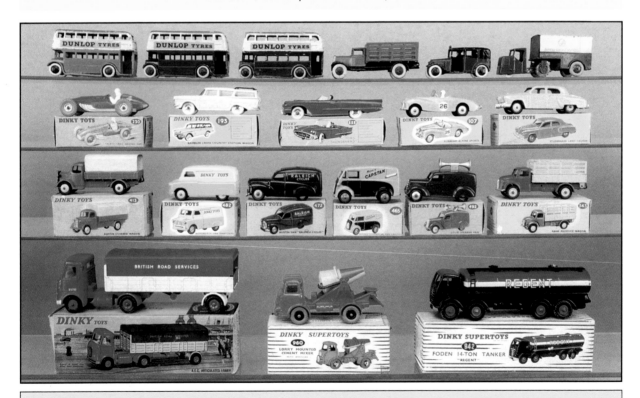

**Models sold by Vectis Auctions Ltd, Thornaby, Stockton-on-Tees.** Pictures reproduced by their kind permission.

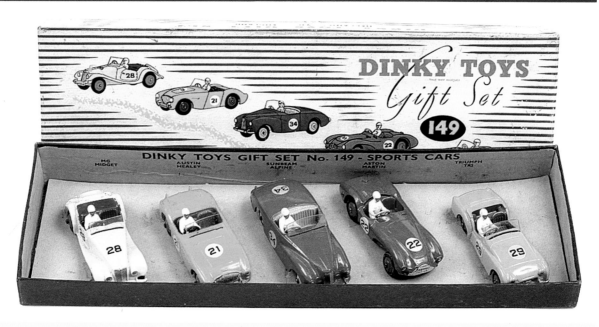

149 Sports Cars Gift Set, 1958 - 61

409 Bedford Articulated Lorry, 1956 - 63

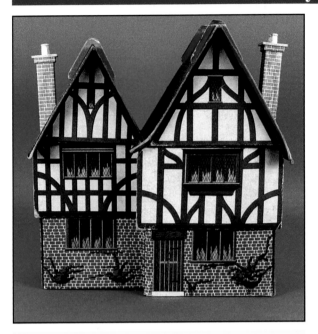

'Dolly Varden' Doll's House
1935 - 40

Trade Box of 29a 'Marmite' Motor Buses
1934 - 38

**Models sold by Vectis Auctions Ltd, Thornaby, Stockton-on-Tees.**   Pictures reproduced by their kind permission.

# French Dinky Toys

22a Sports Roadster
1933 - 37

22b Sports Coupé
1934 - 37

22d Sports Coupé
1934 - 37

32b Hotchkiss Racing Car
1950 - 51

24h Two-seat Sports Car
1936 - 37

24f Sportsman's Coupé
1940 - 48

24N Citroën 11BL
1958

24T Citroën 2cv
1955 - 59

24S Simca 8 Sport
1952 - 54

24U Simca 9 Aronde Elysée
1958 - 59

24UT Simca 9 Aronde Elysée Taxi
1956 - 58

24ZT Simca Ariane Taxi
1959

23H Talbot-Lago Racing Cars
with Trade Box, 1953 - 54

24Z Simca Vedette Versailles
1959

24V Buick Roadmaster
1956 - 59

25BV Peugeot Post Van, 1954 - 59

No.10 Assorted Figures Set, 1934 - 40

29E Isobloc Autocar, 1950 - 55

29E Isobloc Autocar, 1950 - 55

29D Somua-Panhard Paris Bus, 1952 - 54

**Models shown below sold by Vectis Auctions Ltd, Thornaby, Stockton-on-Tees.** Pictures reproduced by their kind permission.

1406 Renault 4L Sinpar
'Michel Tanguy', 1968 - 71

524 Renault Dauphine
with Trade Pack of six, 1959 - 60

14 Triporteur
1935 - 39

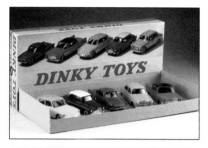

503 Touring Cars Gift Set
1963 - 64

1404 Citroën ID19
'Radio Tele Luxembourg' 1968 - 69

561 Citroën 'H' Van 'Baroclem'
(promotional), 1964

**Models shown above sold by Christie's of South Kensington, London.**
Pictures reproduced by their kind permission.

**Models shown below sold by Collectoys, Bourges, France.** Pictures reproduced by their kind permission.

1435E Citroën Présidentielle
in special presentation box, 1971

25-O Ford Milk Lorry 'Nestlé'
1950

588 Berliet Beer Lorry
'Kronenbourg', 1964 - 70

510 Peugeot 204
Spanish production, 1977 - 78

559 Ford Taunus 17M
Spanish production, 1968 - 69

560E Citroën 2cv Azam Van
Spanish production, 1968 - 70

# Britains

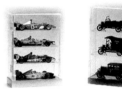

Above: Zebra Toys Double Deck Bus and
RAC Motor Cycle Patrol
Right: Chad Valley Humber Super Snipe

**Charbens**

Fire Engine with
Wheeled
Escape Ladder

All photos on this page:
Vectis Auctions Ltd.

The following history and listings of Benbros and Zebra models have been provided by Robert Newson.
Benbros was started in the late 1940s by brothers Jack and Nathan Benenson, at Walthamstow in north-east London. They first called themselves 'Benson Bros.' and made diecast toys and lead figures (some of which are marked 'Benson'). The name Benbros was adopted in 1951. One of their best known die-cast toys was a miniature coronation coach, copied from the Moko-Lesney coach. Their range of large die-cast toys was expanded during the 1950s with re-issues of

various Timpo Toys, for which Benbros had acquired the dies. The miniature 'T.V. Series' was introduced in late 1954, packed in individual boxes which resembled a 1950s television set. By 1956 there were 24 models in the T.V. Series, and soon after this the packaging was changed to red and yellow 'Mighty Midget' boxes. The Mighty Midgets were available up to 1965.
The Zebra Series was introduced in the 1960s in an attempt to update the range with better features and more accurate models. However, toy production was discontinued when Benbros was taken over in 1965.

## Benbros 'T.V. Series' and 'Mighty Midgets'

| Ref | Model and details | MPR |
|---|---|---|

Most models came in a wide range of colours, so these have not been listed, but full details of colours and other variations are given in the illustrated booklet 'Benbros T.V. Series & Mighty Midgets' by Robert Newson.

1  **Horse Drawn Hay Cart**
With man and raves.
Later models marked 'BENBROS' ......... **£30-40**
2  **Horse Drawn Log Cart**
With man and 'log'.
'Made in England' under horse .............. **£30-40**
3  **A.A. Motorcycle and Sidecar**
With rider and separate windscreen.
'Made in England' under sidecar ............ **£50-60**
4  **Stage Coach (with four horses)**
'KANSAS STAGE' cast in, separate driver
on some, 'BENBROS' on later models... **£60-75**
5  **Horse Drawn Gipsy Caravan**
No maker's name on model ................ **£100-150**
6  **Horse Drawn Milk Cart**
Milkman and horse, two separate or cast-in
churns, 'BENBROS' on later models ... **£80-100**
7  **Three-wheeled Electric Milk Trolley**
Milkman, 'EXPRESS DAIRY' cast in.. **£80-100**
8  **Foden Tractor and Log Trailer**
With log (wood dowel) ........................... **£50-60**
9  **Dennis Fire Escape**
Separate wheeled escape ladder ............. **£30-40**

10  **Crawler Bulldozer**
with rubber tracks.................................... **£20-30**
11  **Crawler Tractor with Hay Rake**
Rubber tracks. Same basic casting as
no. 10. No maker's name on model ....... **£20-30**
12  **Army Scout Car**
Separate or cast-in driver ....................... **£20-30**
13  **Austin Champ**
Separate or cast-in driver ....................... **£20-30**
14  **Centurion Tank**
with rubber tracks.................................... **£20-30**
15  **Vespa Scooter**  With rider ..................... **£60-70**

16  **Streamlined Express Loco**
('TV Series' only). 4 concealed wheels .. **£20-35**
16  **Chevrolet Nomad Station Wagon**
('Mighty Midget' only).
Most models have silver painted flash.... **£20-35**

17  **Crawler Tractor with Disc Harrow**
Rubber tracks. Same tractor as no. 11.
No maker's name on model .................... **£20-30**
18  **Hudson Tourer**  Chassis as no. 16......... **£20-30**
19  **Crawler Tractor and Trailer**
Rubber tracks. Tractor as nos. 11 and 17.
No maker's name on model .................... **£20-30**

20  **Foden 8-wheel Flat Lorry**
Early models in two-tone colours .......... **£70-90**

21  **Foden 8-wheel Open Lorry**
Early models in two-tone colours .......... **£70-90**
22  **ERF Petrol Tanker**
Similar to Matchbox 11a. No adverts or
with 'Esso' transfer on one side ............. **£70-90**
23  **AEC Box Van**
No transfers. Open rear end .................... **£50-60**
23  **Bedford Box Van**
Without adverts or with
'Dunlop' transfers. Open rear end.......... **£50-60**
24  **Field Gun.**  Solid wheels. No maker's
name on model. Firing mechanism......... **£15-25**
25  **Spyker**
Similar to Charbens no. 2. Both models
are marked with the maker's name ......... **£20-30**
26  **1904 Vauxhall 5 hp**
Same chassis as no.25 ............................. **£20-30**
27  **1906 Rolls-Royce**
Same chassis as no.25 ............................. **£20-30**
28  **Foden 8-wheel Flat Lorry with Chains**
'Chains' cast with the body; wheels may
be unpainted metal or Black plastic........ **£70-90**
29  **RAC Motorcycle and Sidecar**
Blue rider, separate windscreen and sidecar.
'Made in England' under sidecar,
'RAC' cast on front ................................. **£40-50**
30  **AEC Army Box Van**
Same casting as no. 23 in Military Green;
wheels may be painted or unpainted....... **£50-60**
30  **Bedford Army Box Van**
Same casting as no. 23 in Military Green
paint with red/yellow squadron transfer;
wheels unpainted ..................................... **£50-60**
31  **AEC Covered Lorry**
Cast metal 'canvas' tilt, riveted in
place, unpainted wheels........................... **£50-60**
31  **Bedford Covered Lorry**
Cast 'canvas' tilt, riveted in place,
unpainted wheels ..................................... **£50-60**
32  **AEC Compressor Lorry** (usually
Yellow). Unpainted metal wheels .......... **£50-60**
32  **Bedford Compressor Lorry**
Usually Yellow, unpainted metal wheels **£50-60**
33  **AEC Crane Lorry**
No hook cast in ....................................... **£50-60**
33  **Bedford Crane Lorry**. No hook,
plastic or unpainted metal wheels .......... **£50-60**
34  **A.A. Land Rover**
'AA ROAD SERVICE' cast in, open rear
end. Wheels may be painted or not......... **£50-60**
35  **Army Land Rover**
Military-Green body and wheels (usually),
open rear end, red/yellow squadron
transfer on some .............................. **£50-60**

36  **Royal Mail Land Rover**
Red body and wheels (usually), open rear,
'ROYAL MAIL E-II-R' cast in .............. **£60-80**

37  **Wolseley Six-Eighty Police Car**
Black body, unpainted wheels,
loud-hailers cast into roof. A little smaller
than Budgie no. 5 .................................... **£50-60**

38  **Daimler Ambulance**
Similar to Matchbox 14b.
Off-White (civilian) and
Dark Green (military) versions .............. **£50-60**

39  **Bedford Milk Float**
Similar to Matchbox 29a.
Orange or Red body, White crates.
Wheels: White metal or Black plastic..... **£50-60**

40  **American Ford Convertible**
Early issues: Lt. Blue or Red body with
press-fit base, unpainted wheels.... **£50-60**
Later issues: Blue, Green or Silver body
with rivetted base, Black plastic wheels . **£50-60**

41  **Army Hudson Tourer**
No. 18 in Military-Green, squadron transfer
on some, unpainted MW or BPW .......... **£50-60**

42  **Army Dispatch Motorcycle and Sidecar**
Castings as nos. 3 and 29, 'Made in England'
and 'AA' or 'RAC' cast on sidecar ........ **£50-60**

43-48  **Bedford Articulated vehicles**
Early issue tractor units have unpainted
metal wheels. Later wheels are Black plastic.
43  **Bedford Articulated Box Van**
'Dunlop' transfers on some .................... **£50-60**
44  **Bedford Articulated Crane Lorry**
With Silver or Black plastic wheels........ **£50-60**
**NB**  The box for this model is marked
'Articulated Low Loader' and has an
illustration showing such a vehicle carrying
a load of wooden planks. The illustrated
version was not put into production.
45  **Bedford Articulated Timber Lorry**
With 'log' (wood dowel); unpainted metal
wheels or Black or Silver plastic wheels **£50-60**
46  **Bedford Articulated Petrol Tanker**
Without adverts, or with 'Esso' transfer
on one side only ...................................... **£50-60**
47  **Bedford Articulated Dropside Lorry**
Box description: 'Articulated Waggon'.
Metal or Black plastic wheels................. **£50-60**
48  **Bedford Articulated Lorry with Chains**
'Chains' are cast with the model. Silver
trim on some, Black plastic wheels........ **£50-60**
49  **Karrier Bantam Bottle Lorry**
Similar to Matchbox 37a. 'Drink Coca-Cola'
transfers. No maker's name, BPW.... **£300-400**
50  **RAC Land Rover**
Blue body, 'RAC ROAD SERVICE'
cast in, open rear ......................................NGPP

# Benbros Zebra Toys

**Zebra Toys** were introduced in the early 1960s and were manufactured along with the existing production of large scale Benbros vehicles. Zebra Toys were packaged in distinctive black and white striped boxes. Most of the models had jewelled headlights and some also had windows and plastic interiors. The AA and RAC Mini Vans apparently had not been introduced when toy production by Benbros came to an end in 1965. They do not appear on a trade price list dated January 1965 but a small number of these models (probably a trial run) were sold off with the remaining toy stocks and are now in the hands of collectors.

In the following list, numbers in brackets are those shown on Zebra boxes. The other numbers are cast on the models themselves. There seems to be no connection between the two numbering systems! These models are rare in today's market.

| Ref | Model and details | MPR |
|-----|-------------------|-----|
| 100 (16) | **Foden Concrete Mixer** Red cab and chassis, Beige or Yellow barrel, 70 mm... | £125-150 |
| 101 (36) | **Scammell Scarab Articulated Van 'BRITISH RAILWAYS'** Maroon cab and trailer, Pale Orange or Mustard-Yellow tilt, 105 mm... | £100-125 |
| 103 (10) | **Jaguar 'E'-type** Met. Light Green, Met. Light Blue or Metallic Lt. Brown, 90 mm... | £250-300 |
| 104 (30) | **Routemaster Bus** Red, *'Fina Petrol goes a long way'* adverts, 111 mm... | £110-140 |
| 106 (34) | **Heinkel Bubble Car** Red or Blue body, 100 mm... | £110-140 |
| 107 (27) | **Daimler Ambulance** Cream body, 101 mm... | £100-125 |

| Ref | Model and details | MPR |
|-----|-------------------|-----|
| --- | **(20) Bedford Cattle Transporter** Red cab / chassis, Light Brown body, 101 mm... | £100-125 |
| --- | **Lansing Bagnall Rapide 2000** Fork Lift Truck, Red body, 89 mm. | £70-90 |
| --- | **Field Gun** 'BENBROS' cast in, 102 mm... | £15-20 |
| **AUSTIN MINI VANS** | | |
| --- (60) | **Austin Mini Van 'AA'** Yellow, 'AA PATROL SERVICE', opening side and rear doors... | £150-200 |
| --- -- | **Austin Mini Van 'RAC'** Blue, opening side and rear doors... | £150-200 |

| Ref | Model and details | MPR |
|-----|-------------------|-----|
| **MOTOR CYCLES (Triumph)** | | |
| --- (1) | **Police Patrol Motorcycle** 'Silver plated' finish, plastic rider, 'ENT 303' cast in, 84 mm... | £45-55 |
| --- | **Rally Motorcycle** Rally version of previous model... | £45-55 |
| --- (3) | **Army Despatch Motorcycle** Army version of previous model... | £45-55 |
| --- (4) | **Telegraph Boy Motorcycle** Telegraph version of previous... | £45-55 |
| --- (52) | **'RAC' Triumph Motorcycle and Sidecar** Black bike, White fairing... | £200-250 |
| --- (6) | **'A.A.' Triumph Motorcycle and Sidecar** Black bike, Yellow sidecar / fairing... | £200-250 |

# 'Qualitoys' and other Benbros model vehicles

This list includes all the other vehicles in the Benbros range, mostly large scale items. Many carried the name 'Qualitoy' as well as 'Benbros', and most were individually boxed. Dating of these models is quite difficult, since there were few contemporary advertisements, and the only catalogues known are trade price lists for 1964 and 1965. The Timpo re-issues were probably no earlier than 1952, and the various motorcycles were introduced in late 1955.

**Coronation Coach with 8 horses**
'ER' cast on doors, 'MADE IN ENGLAND' on drawbar. Later boxes marked 'Zebra Toys', 116 mm... **£30-40**

**State Landau with 4 horses**
Two separate footmen. 'MADE IN ENGLAND' under coach, 105mm.. **£30-40**

**Father Christmas Sleigh**
With four reindeer. Metallic green or metallic blue. 110 mm... **£80-90**

**Covered Wagon with 4 Bullocks**
Re-issue of a model by L. Brooks (Toys) Ltd. (1958). Hollow-cast lead bullocks (diecast on the Brooks model). 'MADE IN ENGLAND' lengthwise under, cloth canopy, Green wagon, Yellow wheels, cowboy. 186 mm... **£80-90**

**Covered Wagon with 4 Horses**
Same wagon as above. Canopy plain or with 'BUFFALO BILL'S COVERED WAGON' or 'CALGARY STAMPEDE COVERED WAGON' printed. Red or Green wagon (Yellow shaft) or Metallic Green or Metallic Blue (Red shaft). Yellow wheels, two barrels, metal or plastic cowboy holding whip. 186 mm... **£80-90**

**Rickshaw with two Passengers**
Pulled by Ostrich or Zulu. Shown in the Joplin book* as Crescent, but believed to be Benbros. 150 mm... **£125-175**

**Roman Chariot with two horses**
With figure. Metallic Green or Yellow with Red wheels. About 135 mm... **£60-80**

**Horse Drawn Farm Cart and man**
Re-issue of Timpo model. Light Green or Yellow cart, Brown horse... **£60-80**

**Horse Drawn Water Wagon**
Re-issue of Timpo model. Light Green wagon, Brown horse. **£80-100**

**Horse Drawn Log Wagon with Log**
Yellow with Red wheels, or Red with Yellow wheels, or Orange with Red wheels, Brown horse. 225 mm... **£80-100**

**Stephenson's Rocket Loco and Tender**
Metallic Brown, Gold or Silver 'plated' loco. Tender Met. Green, Met. Blue, Orange or Red. Boxed, 105 mm... **£35-45**

**Caterpillar Tractor**
Copy of Lesney model. Red or Yellow or Met. Blue, rubber tracks, 97mm. **£30-40**

**Caterpillar Bulldozer**
Copy of early Lesney model. Red tractor with Black blade, or metallic Blue with Red or Yellow blade. Rubber tracks. 118 mm... **£30-40**

**Caterpillar Excavator with driver**
Orange (Green shovel) or Metallic Blue (Red shovel), rubber tracks, Red or Green driver, 138 mm... **£30-40**

**Ferguson Tractor with driver**
No name on model. Yellow or Red with unpainted wheels, Metallic Green or Yellow with Red wheels, Orange with Black or Blue wheels. Driver Green, Brown, Blue, Metallic Blue or Grey. 73 mm... **£100-150**

**Ferguson Tractor with Cab and Shovel**
No name on model. Red, Yellow or dark Green, unpainted wheels, Green or Brown driver. 100 mm... **£100-150**

**Ferguson Tractor and Log Trailer**
With driver and log. Tractor details as above. Red trailer (179mm) with Yellow wheels... **£100-150**

**Ferguson Tractor with Roller**
With driver. No name on model. Former Timpo horse-drawn roller plus drawbar. Tractor as above, Yellow trailer with Red rollers. Trailer 109 mm... **£100-150**

**Ferguson Tractor with Harrow**
With driver. No name on model. Former Timpo horse-drawn harrow + drawbar. Tractor as above, Red or Yellow trailer, approx. 110 mm... **£100-150**

**Euclid Dumper Lorry**
Copy of Dinky 965. Met. Blue cab and chassis, Yellow or Orange tipper. 145mm. Boxed... **£220-260**

**Muir Hill Dumper with Driver**
Orange (Green tipper, Blue wheels), Yellow (Red or Orange tipper, Blue wheels), Metallic Green (Orange tipper, Blue wheels), or Red with Yellow tipper, Black wheels, 105 mm... **£50-60**

**A101 Army Land Rover and Field Gun**
Open Land Rover has two figures cast, separate windscreen, metal wheels with rubber tyres. Field gun marked 'BENBROS', solid rubber wheels. Matt Dark Green. 111 / 102 mm. **£125-175**

**A102 Lorry with Anti-Aircraft Gun**
Dark Green, Silver gun. 117mm. **£125-175**

**A103 Lorry with Radar Scanner**
Dark Green, Silver radar dish... **£125-175**

**A104 Lorry with Searchlight**
Dark Green. 117 mm... **£125-175**

**A105 Armoured Car and Field Gun**
Dark Green or Brownish-Green. Field gun same as A101. 96 / 102 mm... **£50-75**

**A106 Army AEC Lorry with Tilt**
'SUNDERLAND' cast doors. Dark Green or Brownish-Green, Green cloth tilt. 132 mm... **£125-150**

**A107 Army Closed Land Rover**
Casting as A101. Matt Dark Green, Black roof. Opening side and rear doors. 111 mm... **£50-75**

**A110  Army Articulated Low-Loader
and Field Gun**
Matt Dark Green Low-loader as no. 221,
Field Gun as no. A101 but with
metal hubs and rubber tyres ............ **£30-40**

**220  AEC Flat Lorry with chains**
'SUNDERLAND' cast on cab sides.
Red cab and chassis, light Green,
Blue, Beige or Metallic Green body.
130 mm. **£150-175**

**221  Articulated Low Loader**
Re-issue of Timpo model. Red or Green
cab with Red, Yellow or metallic Green
trailer. No name on model.166mm . **£25-30**

**223  Land Rover 'Royal Mail'**
Red (Black roof). 'ROYAL MAIL E-II-R'
cast on sides. Opening doors, 2 figures
cast inside. 111mm ...................... **£150-175**

**224  Articulated Tanker**
Re-issue of Timpo model, no maker's
name on model, 146mm.  Red or Orange
cab, Green or metallic Green or Yellow
trailer, 'MOTOR OIL ESSO PETROL'
transfer ................................... **£75-85**
Green cab, Red trailer,
'SHELL PETROL' label.................. **£75-85**
Light Green cab, Red trailer,
'UNITED DAIRIES' transfer.......... **£75-85**

**225  AEC Dropside Lorry**
'SUNDERLAND' cast on cab sides.
Red cab and chassis, light Green or
Blue body ..................................... **£120-140**

**226  Petrol Tanker**
Re-issue of Timpo model. Red cab and
chassis with Red or Yellow tank, light
Green cab / chassis with Yellow tank.
'Motor Oil Esso Petrol' or 'Fina Petrol
Goes a Long Way' transfer.
No name on model. 117 mm....... **£120-140**

**227  AEC Flat Lorry**
Re-issue of Timpo model.
'SUNDERLAND' cast on cab sides.
Red cab and chassis, light Green,
Blue or Cream body. .................. **£100-150**

**228  AEC Lorry with Tilt**
As no.225 with plain cloth tilt.
132 mm **£300-400**

---  **Forward Control Box Van**
'PICKFORDS REMOVALS' labels
Timpo re-issue, no maker's name.
99 mm. Green cab and chassis
with Light Green or Red body .... **£140-170**
Red cab, chassis and body, plain..... **£30-40**

---  **Forward Control Box Van**
'CHIVERS JELLIES' transfers
Red cab / chassis, Green body .... **£140-170**

---  **Articulated Box Van
'LYONS TEA'** transfers.
Timpo re-issue, no maker's name.
145 mm. Red or Green cab with
Green, Red or Cream trailer........ **£140-170**

---  **Articulated Box Van
'UNITED DAIRIES'** transfers.
Red cab with Green trailer .......... **£140-170**

---  **Articulated Box Van
'BISHOP & SONS DEPOSITORIES
LTD'** Light Green cab with
Red or Orange trailer................... **£140-170**

**A.A. Land Rover**
Casting as A107 and 223. 'AA ROAD
SERVICE' cast on sides and roof sign.
Opening side and rear doors,
two figures inside. Yellow with
Black roof or all Yellow. ............. **£125-150**

**310  Ruston-Bucyrus 10-RB Crane**
Maroon / Yellow body, Dark Green
chassis and jib, rubber tracks.
'BENBROS' cast underneath.......... **£70-80**

**311  Ruston-Bucyrus 10-RB Excavator**
Casting and colours As 310 model . **£70-80**

**AEC Lorry and Ruston-Bucyrus Crane**
'SUNDERLAND' cast on cab sides.
Red cab and chassis, Yellow body.
Crane as no. 310 model............... **£125-150**

**AEC Lorry with Ruston-Bucyrus Excavator**
'SUNDERLAND' cast on cab sides.
Red cab and chassis, Yellow body.
Excavator as no.311 model ......... **£125-150**

**A.A. Motorcycle Patrol**
Black cycle, AA badge cast on Yellow
sidecar and windscreen, 'TTC147' cast
on no. plates. 84 mm.
(i) Fixed forks, windscreen (plastic
glazing), Khaki metal rider ........ **£100-150**
(ii) Steering forks, curved cast
windscreen frame in place
of glazing, plastic rider............... **£100-150**

**RAC Motorcycle Patrol**
Black cycle, RAC badge cast on Blue
sidecar and windscreen. 'TTC147' cast
on no. plates. Steerable front forks,
windscreen with curved frame,
plastic rider. 84 mm..................... **£100-150**

**Solo Motorcycle with Rider**
Fixed forks, 'TTC147' cast on no. plates.
84 mm.
(i) **Police Patrol** - Maroon,
Black metal rider ............................ **£45-55**
(ii) **Telegraph Boy** - Red cycle and
metal rider ................................... **£45-55**
(iii) **Army Despatch Rider** -
Khaki cycle and metal rider ........... **£45-55**
(iv) **Rally Rider** -
Green, Blue metal rider................... **£45-55**

**Solo Motorcycle with Rider**
'Silver plated' cycles  are later versions
of those above, with steerable forks,
'TTC147' cast on no. plates and
plastic riders in four versions:
Police Patrol, Telegraph Boy, Army
Despatch Rider and Rally. 84 mm .. **£45-55**

**Motorcycle and Sidecar
'Express Window Service'**
Black / Cream, figure dressed in
Blue with flat cap ........................ **£175-200**

**Benbros Salesman's Sample Set**. Seven mostly
chrome vehicles, plain red box ... **£300-400**

* Reference: 'The Great Book of Hollow-Cast
Figures' by Norman Joplin (New Cavendish Books).

Benbros and Zebra models of 'AA' Patrol vehicles   PHOTO: VECTIS AUCTIONS LTD.

# Britains Ltd.

## Britains Vehicles, Guns and Novelties, 1880 - 1916

### BRITAINS VEHICLES, GUNS and NOVELTIES, 1880 - 1916

by James Opie

Although Britains is famous for manufacturing toy soldiers, it is not so widely known that they had produced toy vehicles before they made their first soldier. In one of their catalogues pre-dating toy soldier production, there are large and small Road Rollers, and probably manufactured even before these are a much larger and cruder Road Roller and Steam Crane, mostly built of tinplate (uncatalogued), and a Rotary Railway Express (uncatalogued), which was a lead die-cast floor toy rather than a toy train. All came boxed.

Dating in all probability from 1890 or earlier, the die-cast Road Rollers can lay claim to be the earliest attributable catalogued British die-cast toys.

| | |
|---|---|
| The London Road Roller c.1890 to 1895 | £2,500-4,000 |
| The Miniature Road Roller c.1890 to1916 | £750-1,000 |
| The Rotary Railway Express c.1891 to 1894 | £3,000-5,000 |

The next group of models, die-cast from lead alloy with steel and wire pins, springs, axles and ammunition, were the early guns and vehicles to accompany toy soldier production from 1895 to 1916. In fact, the first Britains spring gun was incorporated in a model soldier with a hollow rifle barrel and a steel spring set just behind the breech, so that a protruding piece of wire could be flicked through.

Set 28 included a three part mountain gun which loaded onto mules, set 39 was a Royal Horse Artillery set with a field gun and limber, and set 79 had the same gun as set 28, slightly modified with a wire towing eye to join to a small limber pulled by eight sailors. Set 144 used the same gun as set 39 with a modified limber as a Royal Field Artillery set. Sets 145 and 146 included a die-cast lead four wheel general purpose wagon. Sets 125 and 126 were Royal Horse Artillery sets made in a smaller size with a gun and limber, the gun from which, slightly modified without its towing hole, was also used in sets 148 and 149, and in small size second grade displays 04, 05 amd 06. Perhaps the most famous gun of all, the 4.7 inch Naval Gun, was at first sold without a catalogue number. This was the gun used by H.G. Wells in his book 'Little Wars'. The field gun from set 39 was also available separately in an un-numbered box entitled 'Royal Artillery Gun'.

In 1906, Britains introduced a horse-drawn four wheel general service waggon, which was used in sets 145 and 146. In 1914, Britains produced their first civilian vehicle which was part of their standard scale figure range, the Boy Scout Trek Cart, two of which were included in both set 180 and in set 181. This would probably have been predated by the Coster's Barrow, which is almost the right scale, but produced as part of the novelty range
As the majority of these guns and vehicles came as part of sets, I will give both the price of the boxed sets and the price of the individual guns and vehicles when found separately.

| | |
|---|---|
| Set 28 Mountain Artillery (oval base men), 1895-1908 | £350-500 |
| Set 28 Mountain Artillery (square base men), 1908-1916 | £250-350 |
| Mountain Artillery Gun (eight spoke wheels), 1895-1916 | £30-50 |
| Set 39 Royal Horse Artillery (shafted limber), 1896-1906 | £1,500-2,000 |
| Gun with bucket seats and Shafted Limber, 1896-1906 | £250-400 |
| Set 39 Royal Horse Artillery (centre pole limber), 1906-1916 | £800-1,000 |
| Gun and Centre Pole Limber, 1906-1916 | £80-100 |

| | |
|---|---|
| Royal Artillery Gun (boxed, no catalogue number), 1896-1916 | £120-150 |
| 4.7 inch Naval Gun (boxed, no catalogue number), 1896-1916 | £80-100 |
| Set 79 Royal Navy Landing Party (oval base men), 1897-1916 | £600-800 |
| Landing Party Gun and Limber, 1897-1916 | £100-150 |
| Set 125 Royal Horse Artillery, full dress, small size, 1902-1916 | £600-800 |
| Set 126 Royal Horse Artillery, field dress, small size, 1902-1916 | £600-800 |
| Small size Gun and Limber, grey finish (from set 125), 1902-1916 | £100-150 |
| Small size Gun and Limber, khaki (from set 126), 1902-1916 | £100-150 |
| Set 144 Royal Field Artillery, bucket seats, 1906-1916 | £1,500-2,000 |
| Gun with bucket seats and Centre Pole Limber, 1906-1916 | £300-400 |
| Set 145 Royal Army Medical Corps Four Horse Ambulance Waggon, 1906-1916 | £400-500 |
| Set 146 Army Service Corps Two Horse Waggon, 1906-1916 | £300-400 |
| Four wheel General Service Waggon, 1906-1916 | £60-90 |
| Set 148 Royal Lancaster Regiment Game Set, with gun, 1907-1916 | £6,000-7,000 |
| Set 149 American Soldiers Game Set, with gun, 1907-1916 | £6,000-7,000 |
| Set 04 British Army Encampment, small size, 1910-1916 | £400-500 |
| Set 05 British Army Encampment, small size, 1910-1916 | £500-600 |
| Set 06 British Army Encampment, small size, 1910-1916 | £600-700 |
| Small size Gun, without towing hole, 1907-1916 | £80-100 |
| Set 180, Boy Scout Display with two trek carts, 1914-1916 | £800-1,000 |
| Set 181, large Boy Scout Display with two trek carts, 1914-1916 | £3,000-4,000 |
| Trek Cart with Boy Scout, 1914-1916 | £150-200 |

### Novelties, 1900 - 1916

Probably from around 1900 or even before, Britains produced cast alloy novelty toys. Exact dates of production are unknown. Those listed below (unboxed except where specified) were in the 1915 catalogue, but had no catalogue number quoted. The catalogue also stated 'Miscellaneous castings. Jockeys, Bicycles, Warships, Yachts, etc., in several qualities and sizes for Race Games, &c.'

| | |
|---|---|
| Tea Pot, gilt, 1900-1916 | £20-30 |
| Coffee Pot, gilt, 1900-1916 | £20-30 |
| Kettle, gilt or black, 1900-1916 | £20-30 |
| Rocking Chair, 1900-1916 | £30-40 |
| Tea and Coffee Set, gilt, boxed, 1900-1916 | £200-300 |
| Saucepan, black, with lid, bright metal, 1900-1916 | £30-40 |
| Boiler with Lid, copper, gilt or black, 1900-1916 | £20-30 |
| Coal Vase with Tongs, copper, gilt or black, 1900-1916 | £25-40 |
| Watering Pot, red, 1900-1916 | £20-30 |
| Kettle on Stand, gilt, 1900-1916 | £35-50 |
| Large boxed Kitchen Set with kettles, 1900-1916 | £300-500 |
| Small boxed Kitchen Set with kettle, 1900-1916 | £200-300 |
| Baby's Chair, 1900-1916 | £40-60 |
| Push Chair, 1900-1916 | £35-50 |
| Caster's Barrow, blue or gold, 1900-1916 | £40-60 |
| Kitchen Steps, 1900-1916 | £30-40 |
| Football Association Cup, silver or gilt, 1904-1916 | £750-1,000 |

An illustration from the January 1951 Britains Ltd. catalogue.

Illustration of Mechanical Unit driving No. 127F "Fordson Major" Tractor.

Illustration of Mechanical Unit driving No. 128F "Fordson Major" Tractor.

MANUFACTURED BY WBritain IN LONDON ENGLAND

TRADE  REGD. No 459993.  MARK

# Britains Motor Vehicles

## BRITAINS MOTOR VEHICLES
by Mike Richardson

Most people are aware of the military vehicles made by Britains both before the War and after in 1/32 scale to go with their soldiers, but not so many are acquainted with the contemporary civilian models. Some of these models are only colour variations of the military versions, for example the 59F 'Four-wheeled Lorry with Driver' in the farm series is the same as 1335 'Lorry, Army, Four-wheeled type' but painted in a smart duotone colour scheme instead of khaki. Other models are only available in the civilian type, usually for the good reason that the army could not possibly have a use for a militarised version. A good example of this would be 1656 'John Cobb's Railton Wonder Car' (or 'Railton Mobil Special' as we know it!).

Britains are our oldest toy company which is still in business having been started in 1860 although the first of the famous soldiers did not appear until 1890. This still means over a hundred years continuous toy manufacture, surely a record. The motor lorry models appeared in late 1932 and were based on the Albion army lorries of the time with the familiar 'square' cab design which was to be a hallmark of the Britains lorries until the end of the decade. The range of 4, 6 and 10-wheel farm lorries are still illustrated in the 1940 catalogue. After the War the cab was brought up to date by a change to a more rounded Fordson type, not nearly so attractive.

The military ambulance was also used in civilian versions, a cream 'Corporation' and a blue 'Volunteer Corps' as alternative liveries to the khaki army one. The rarest version of this model is the red and black 'Royal Mail' van which was sold for a short time towards the end of the production run.

There are three civilian cars, a 'Two-seater Coupé' and two 'Sports Model Open Tourers' in the pre-war production. The coupé and the open sports car without driver and passenger do not have military equivalents, but when the open sports car has people in it then it is either a 'Mobile Police Car with 2 Officers' (finished in green with black wings), or a 'Staff Car with 2 Officers' as the military offering. The occupants of the car are legless and their lower regions are covered with a tartan rug - how nice for them on cold days! After the War there was a one-piece casting version of the staff car and police car without the separate grilles of the pre-war models and these were rather plain by comparison.

The final group of models consists of the superb record cars 'Bluebird' and 'Railton Special'. These came out in the late 1930s and each is over 6 inches long. The Bluebird was produced in three versions; a) with fully detailed removable chassis, b) without this part, and c) a slightly smaller one (just over 5 inches), without underside detail. The Railton Mobil Special always had the removable chassis and was available painted silver for 1s.6d. or chrome plated for 2s.6d.

After the War two new farm tractor models appeared, a couple of Fordson Majors produced with the active co-operation of the Ford Motor Company. These are excellent models both finished in the correct shade of dark blue and with the name 'Fordson' applied to the front and sides of the radiator. One version has standard wheels but the other (rarer) one had the spiked or 'spud' wheels used on heavy ground.

All these models are to the same scale as the soldiers (1/32), but there is also a similar range in '00' gauge (1/76 scale) to go with model railways. The smaller models date mainly from the post-war era although a sports car and a fastback saloon were seen pre-war. The small scale trucks have a Fordson cab similar to the later large scale farm and army lorries.

The large scale pre-war models are very collectable and prices are consequently very high for rare items in excellent condition and with original lovely boxes. Some few years ago a batch of replicas of the coupé were made here in England so exercise care when buying this model. Spare parts are, or have been available for most of these toys to enable repairs to be carried out.

# Britains Motor Vehicles (pre-war issues)

The models were constructed of a lead based alloy and the main body parts were hollow cast. However, parts such as wings and running boards were die-cast individually by hand. The Market Price Range figures refer to boxed models in excellent condition. Pre-war lorry models have a 'square nose' bonnet shape.

## Civilian Vehicles

**59 F  Four-wheeled Tipping Lorry with Driver**
Square nose, back and doors open, rubber tyres, 6" ................ **£400-500**

**60 F  Six-wheeled Tipping Lorry with Driver**
Two-tone Blue square nose body, White cab roof,
back and doors open, White rubber tyres, 6" ........................... **£150-200**

**61 F  Ten-wheeled Lorry with Driver**
Square nose, back and doors open, rubber tyres ...................... **£200-250**

**90 F  Builders Lorry**
As 59 F plus builders name on side.
*'DAVIS ESTATES LTD BUILDERS OF HOMES'* ............. **£4,000-5,000**

**91F and 92F Builders Lorry**
As 60F and 61F plus builders name on side. ...................... **£4,000-5,000**

**1398  Sports Model Open Tourer**
Cream body, Black chassis and wheels,
White rubber tyres, 4.25" ............................................ **£750-1,000**

**1399  Two-Seater Coupé** (fitted bumpers)
Cream body, Tan roof, wings and running-boards,
Black hubs, White tyres, 4.5". (Also in other colours) ....... **£1,000-1,250**

**1413  Mobile Police Car with two Officers**
2-piece casting, Green body, Black wings, White tyres, 4.75".
(Also in other colours) ................................................. **£600-700**

**1470  The Royal Household Set**
Coronation State Coach, King George VI plus the Queen
with twelve attendants ................................................. **£300-500**

**1513  Volunteer Corps 'AMBULANCE' with Driver,**
**Wounded Man and Stretcher**
Blue body, Red/White cross, White tyres............................ **£1,000-1,250**

**1514  Corporation Type Motor 'AMBULANCE' with**
**Driver, Wounded Man and Stretcher**
Cream body, Red/White cross, White tyres ......................... **£900-1,100**

**1552  'ROYAL MAIL' Van with Driver**
Post-Office Red body, Black bonnet,
'GR' plus crown design, White tyres ................................ **£1,600-2,000**

**---  1924 Wembley Exhibition Locomotive**
Bronze finished diecast locomotive on plinth with '1924 Wembley
Exhibition', '240 tons - largest locomotive in the world' ............. NGPP

**2024  Light Goods Van with Driver**
Various colours, 'BRITAINS LTD' logo ................................ **£600-800**

**2045  Clockwork Van** (c1938)
Various colours, driver, opening rear doors.
In Red box with Dark Yellow picture label.......................... **£900-1,200**

## Military Vehicles

Early issues of lorry and truck models in the ranges 1333 - 1433 and 1641 - 1643 had 'square' fronts, (post-war issues had 'rounded' fronts).

**1321  Armoured Car with Gun**
Military Green, solid metal wheels ......................................... **£100-125**

**1333  Lorry, Army, Caterpillar Type with Driver**
Military Green finish, rubber tyres, 6" ................................... **£150-200**

**1334  Four-wheeled Tipper Lorry with Driver** ............................ **£150-200**

**1335  Lorry, Army, Six-wheeled Type with Driver**
Military Green finish, rubber tyres, 6" ................................... **£150-200**

**1392  Autogiro**
Military Green, RAF roundels, pilot, three rotor blades .......... **£750-950**

**1432  Tender, Army, Covered, Ten-wheeled (with Driver)**
Military Green finish, White rubber tyres, 6" ......................... **£150-200**

**1433  Tender, Army, Covered, Ten-wheeled Caterpillar Type**
**(with Driver)** Military Green finish, White rubber tyres, 6" . **£150-200**

**1448  Staff Car**
Military Green car with 2 Staff Officers,
White rubber tyres, 4" .................................................... **£350-450**

**1641  Underslung Heavy Duty Lorry (18 wheels) with Driver**
Military Green finish, 10" ................................................ **£350-450**

**1641  Underslung Heavy Duty Lorry (18 wheels) with Driver**
with 1749 Mounted Barrage Balloon Winch......................... **£900-1,100**

**1642  Underslung Heavy Duty Lorry (18 wheels) with Driver**
with Mounted Searchlight, Military Green finish, 10" ......... **£350-450**

**1643  Underslung Heavy Duty Lorry (18 wheels) with Driver**
with Mounted Anti-Aircraft Gun (small) ............................ **£350-450**

**1643  Underslung Heavy Duty Lorry (18 wheels) with Driver**
with Mounted Anti-Aircraft Gun (large) ............................ **£600-800**

# Britains Military Vehicles and Guns (post-war issues)

## Military vehicles

Post-war issues of lorry and truck models in the ranges 1334 - 1433 and 1641 - 1643 had 'rounded' cabs, (pre-war issues had 'square' cabs).

**1334**    **Four-wheeled Army Lorry with Tipping Body**
('rounded' cab) with Driver, 6" long........................................**£150-200**

**1335**    **Six-wheeled Army Lorry with Tipping Body**
('rounded' cab) with Driver, 6" long........................................**£150-200**

**1433**    **Covered Army Tender**
('rounded' cab) Caterpillar type with Driver, 6".................**£150-200**

**1448**    **Army Staff Car**
1st issue: White tyres, with General (red/kakhi cap)
and Driver, 4" long..............................................................**£350-450**
2nd issue: Black tyres, General (all-kahki cap) and Driver..**£350-450**

**1512**    **RAMC Army Ambulance**
3rd version, split windscreen, driver, stretcher, patient.........**£200-250**

**1791**    **Royal Corps of Signals Motor Cycle Dispatch Rider**
sold unboxed............................................................................**£25-35**

**1791-DB Royal Corps of Signals Motor Cycle Dispatch Riders**
Four motorcycles with revolving wheels in display box ..........NGPP

**1832**    **Lorry and Gun Set.**
10 wheel Lorry and 2 pdr. anti-aircraft gun, driver, box ........**£150-200**

**1876**    **Bren Gun Carrier with Driver, Gunner and 2nd Guard**
Carden-Vickers type suspension cast-in, separate gun, 3½"...**£75-125**

**1877**    **Beetle Lorry and Driver** ..........................................**£65-75**

**1879**    **'OO' gauge Lorry with Trailer and Hydrogen Cylinders**
Military Green, solid wheels, red cylinders ..............................NGPP

**1897**    **RAMC Motor Ambulance Set** (18 pieces)
With Driver, Orderlies, Nurses, Stretcher and Wounded ..........NGPP

**2048**    **Military Set**
1877, 2041 and 2026 Gun ....................................................**£150-175**

**2150**    **Centurion Tank**
Military Green ......................................................................**£300-400**
Matt Green............................................................................**£175-200**
Dark green finish, US star to turret ........................................**£80-100**

**2154**    **Centurion Tank**
Sand colour finish. Box has illustrated label.........................**£225-275**

**2156**    **Centurion Tank**
Desert warfare finish ............................................................**£400-500**

**2175**    **Centurion Tank.** Self propelled 155mm gun, Matt Olive ..**£150-200**

## Guns and equipment

**1201**    **Gun of the Royal Artillery**
with shells, to fire with or without Amorce cap. 5.75" long ....... NGPP

**1263**    **Gun of the Royal Artillery**
with shells, to fire with or without Amorce cap. 3.75" long ....... NGPP

**1264**    **4.7 inch Naval Gun (mounted for field operations),**
with shells, to fire with or without Amorce cap. 7.75" long ....... NGPP

**1292**    **Gun of the Royal Artillery**
with shells, to fire with or without Amorce cap. 4.75" long ....... NGPP

**2026**    **25-pounder Gun Howitzer**
with shells, to fire with or without Amorce cap. 4" long ........... NGPP

**1639**    **Army Range Finder** (for all classes of Artillery)
a tripod mounted rangefinder with Operator .............................. NGPP

**1640**    **Searchlight**
with full movements, uses 3 volt torch battery. 2.5" high .......... NGPP

**1715**    **25-pounder (40 mm.) Light Anti-Aircraft Gun**
'firing a metal shell with great accuracy'. Base 2" in diameter .. NGPP

**1717**    Mobile Unit 25-pounder
Light A.A. Gun (1715) on 4-wheel screw-jack chassis, 4.5" ...... NGPP

**1718**    **Searchlight**
1640 on mobile screw-jack chassis, uses 3v battery. 4.5" long... NGPP

**1726**    **Howitzer Limber** (Lead). In Red box, Yellow label ................**£50-60**

**1728**    **Predictor, with Operator**
Aircraft position predictor on a stand, for A.A defence ............. NGPP

**1729**    **Height Finder, with Operator**
tripod mounted instrument for use with Predictor...................... NGPP

**1731**    **Spotting Chair (Swivelling)**
'with Man to lie down' (Service Dress, Shrapnel Helmet)......... NGPP

**1749**    **Balloon and Winch** (1939-).
Silver balloon, mooring ropes, box.........................................**£750-950**

**1757**    **Barrage Balloon Unit**
1641 Lorry + 1640 Barrage Balloon and Winch ...................**£200-300**

**2052DB Anti-Aircraft Unit** (15 pieces)
with usual personnel, 2 x 1728, 1 x 1729, 1 x (1639),
1 x 1731, 1 x 1640, Mobile A.A. Gun (1717) ........................... NGPP

**?**    **18 inch Heavy Howitzer.**
3 sprung shells, 6 lead shells, instructions, red box...............**£150-200**

**2107**    **18 inch Howitzer,**
1960s, wheeled, 11 plastic shells, plus loader, box ..............**£150-175**

Britains No.1448 Army Staff Car with Officer and Driver     Photo: Vectis Auctions Ltd.

## Motor-driven farm vehicles

| | | |
|---|---|---|
| 59F | 19?? | **Farm Tipping Lorry with Driver,** Light Green or Blue, round nose, 4 wheels, 6" long .. **£200-250** |
| 127F | 19?? | **Fordson 'MAJOR' Tractor with Driver,** fitted with spade-end wheels ...................................... **£200-250** |
| | | In prototype Green, unboxed ................................ **£400-500** |
| 128F | 19?? | **Fordson 'MAJOR' Tractor with Driver,** with rubber-tyred wheels ........................................... **£175-225** |
| 129 F | 1955 | **Timber Trailer with real log** Adjustable body. 8" ............................................... NGPP |
| 130 F | 1955 | **Trailer with Racks (Tipping Hay Cart)** Two wheels, body tips, tailboard drops. 4.5" .................. NGPP |
| 135 F | 1955 | **Disc Harrow** 2.5" ('Can be coupled in pairs to make tandem harrows, or to 136 F to make combination roller-harrow') .......... **£40-50** |
| 136 F | 1955 | **Roller** 2.25". (See 135 F) .................................................. **£40-50** |
| 137 F | 1955 | **Clockwork Set** Fordson Major Tractor with Driver, Mechanical Trailer (2041) + Tipping Hay Cart (130 F). 13.25" .... **£400-500** |
| 138 F | 1955 | **Four-Farrow Tractor Plough** (3-position adjustment of front wheel-arms possible) .... **£70-90** |
| 139 F | 1955 | **Clockwork Set** (Fordson Major Tractor with Driver and Mechanical Trailer (2041). 8.5" .............. **£225-275** |
| 171F | 19?? | **Fordson Power Major Tractor and Trailer** Blue/Orange Tractor, spiked wheels, red/black driver, Orange/Green Trailer, 2 racks, implements ..................................... **£500-600** |
| ? | ? | **Fordson Power Major Tractor.** Blue body, Orange wheels, an example given 'With the compliments of the Ford Motor Co Ltd'. On wooden plinth ...................................... **£300-400** |

The following were all supplied in cellophane fronted landscape boxes.
NB Some of the same model numbers were used twice for different models.

| | | |
|---|---|---|
| 8715 | ? | **Fordson E27N Tractor.** Henry Ford figure and display stand, boxed .................. **£75-85** |
| 9324 | ? | **County 1884 Tractor.** Black/white with electric motor in box ...................... **£125-150** |
| 9515 | 1980-85 | **Volvo BM Valmet 805 Tractor,** red/black .................... **£35-45** |
| 9517 | 1980-85 | **Massey-Ferguson MF2680 Double Rear wheeled Tractor,** red/white ......................................... **£45-55** |
| 9518 | 1980-85 | **Renault TX145-14 Turbo Tractor,** orange/black/white .... **£30-40** |
| 9520 | 1965-70 | **Fordson Major Tractor with Driver,** cast metal wheels, plastic outset lights ........................ **£100-125** |
| 9520 | 1980-85 | **Massey-Ferguson MF2680 Tractor,** red/white ............ **£40-50** |
| 9521 | ? | **County 1884 Tractor.** Yellow/grey, no power, driver, box ............................. **£125-150** |
| 9522 | 1970-80 | **Massey-Ferguson 595 Tractor** with safety cab, red body, silver cab ............................................... **£40-60** |
| 9522 | 1980-85 | **Renault Double Rear Wheeled Tractor,** orange/white .... **£40-45** |
| 9523 | 1980-85 | **Ford TW20 Tractor,** blue/white ............................... **£35-45** |
| 9524 | 1970-80 | **Ford 6600 Tractor,** blue/white, blue driver ................. **£60-70** |
| 9525 | 1980-85 | **Mercedes-Benz Tractor,** yellow/black ...................... **£35-45** |
| 9525 | ? | **Fordson Super Major** ........................................... **£125-150** |
| 9525 | ? | **Fordson New Major Tractor.** Bright blue, plastic rear hubs ................................. **£150-175** |
| 9526 | 1965-70 | **Ford Super Major '5000' Tractor** with spade end wheels, dark blue ............................ **£100-125** |
| 9526 | 1970-80 | **Deutz DX 110 Tractor,** green/black ......................... **£40-50** |
| 9527 | 1965-70 | **Ford Super Major '5000' Tractor** with rubber tyres, dark blue ................................... **£100-125** |
| 9527 | 1970-80 | **Fiat Half-Track Tractor,** red/black, beige driver ......... **£45-55** |
| 9528 | 1970-80 | **Fiat Tractor,** red/black ......................................... **£30-40** |
| 9529 | 1965-70 | **Massey-Ferguson 135 Tractor** with safety cab, red/white ...................................... **£65-75** |
| 9529 | 1970-80 | **Massey-Ferguson Tractor with Cab,** dark blue/white . **£60-70** |
| 9529 | 1980-85 | **Massey-Ferguson MF2680 Double Rear Wheeled Tractor,** red/grey ......................................... **£45-55** |
| 9530 | 1980-85 | **Deutz Eight Wheeled Tractor,** green/black ................ **£35-45** |

| | | |
|---|---|---|
| 9568 | ? | **Animal Transporter.** Farm Cart with cow, box ........ **£150-175** |
| 9569 | 1970-80 | **Unimog Tractor/Lorry,** green/yellow .......................... **£30-40** |
| 9570 | 1970-80 | **Massey-Ferguson 760 Combine Harvester,** red with driver .................................................. **£100-130** |
| 9571 | 1970-80 | **Farm Land-Rover, 'BRITAINS FARM'** ..................... **£30-35** |
| 9572 | 1970-80 | **Massey-Ferguson 595 Tractor** with Front Loader, yellow with red front loader ................................. **£100-130** |
| 9575 | 1980-85 | **'New Holland' Combine Harvester,** yellow ........... **£25-35** |
| 9576 | 1970-80 | **Farm Land-Rover,** blue with cream canopy ................ **£25-35** |
| 9580 | 1980-85 | **Magirus Deutz Iveco Animal Transporter,** dark blue cab, red/grey back .............................. **£25-35** |
| 9581 | 1980-85 | **Unimog Breakdown Truck,** white/orange/red ............ **£15-25** |
| 9582 | 1980-85 | **Magirus Deutz Iveco Flatbed Transporter,** white cab, grey back ........................................... **£25-35** |
| 9583 | 1980-85 | **Magirus Deutz Iveco Tipper Truck,** yellow/black ..... **£20-30** |
| 9581 | 1980-85 | **Unimog Breakdown Truck 'Recovery Service'** ......... **£20-30** |
| 9584 | 1970-80 | **Ford Tractor and Front Loader** .............................. **£45-55** |
| 9584 | 1980-85 | **Ford Tractor** with front loader .................................. **£40-50** |
| 9585 | 1980-85 | **Fiat Tractor and Vacuum Tanker** ........................... **£40-50** |
| 9586 | 1980-85 | **Volvo Tractor and Trailer** ..................................... **£45-55** |
| 9587 | 1980-85 | **Massey-Ferguson Tractor and Rear Dump** ............. **£45-55** |
| 9588 | 1980-85 | **Ford Tractor and Rotary Manure Spreader** ............. **£45-55** |
| 9589 | 1980-85 | **Deutz Tractor and Implements Set** ........................ **£100-125** |
| 9591 | 1970-80 | **Massey-Ferguson 595 Tractor and 2 Wheeled Trailer,** red/white tractor with green/yellow trailer ................... **£65-75** |
| 9591 | 1980-85 | **Fiat Tractor and Implements Set** ........................... **£100-125** |
| 9595 | 1970-80 | **Massey-Ferguson 595 Tractor** and Front Loader, red/white ............................................................ **£60-70** |
| 9596 | 1965-70 | **Ford Super Major '5000' Tractor Set,** Ford Tractor plus nine implements ........................... **£100-150** |
| 9596 | 1980-85 | **Deutz Tractor and Manure Spreader** ...................... **£45-55** |
| 9597 | 1970-80 | **Massey-Ferguson 595 Tractor and 8 Wheeled Trailer,** red/white ............................................................ **£65-75** |
| 9597 | 1980-85 | **Ford Tractor and 8 wheeled trailer** ....................... **£50-60** |
| 9597 | 1980-85 | **Mercedes-Benz Tractor with Tipper Hopper** ........... **£40-50** |
| 9598 | 1980-85 | **Massey-Ferguson MF2680 Tractor and Trailer** ....... **£45-55** |
| 9599 | 1980-85 | **Farm Tractor and Implements Set** ........................ **£100-125** |
| 9630 | 1965-70 | **Ford Super Major '5000' Tractor** with cab and Shawnee-Poole Rear Dump Set ........................... **£85-95** |
| 9670 | 1965-70 | **Dumper,** red with yellow wheels and blue driver ........ **£20-25** |
| 9676 | c1968 | **LWB Land Rover,** Sage green, driver, early sleeve box .......................... **£400-500** |

## Horse-drawn farm vehicles

| | | |
|---|---|---|
| 4 F | 1955 | **Tumbrel Cart with Farm Hand & Horse** with removable Hay Racks & Backboard. 7.25" ........ **£100-150** |
| 5 F | 1955 | **Farm Waggon with Farm Hand** plus two Horses, removable Backboard. 9.25" .......... **£100-150** |
| 6 F | 1955 | **General Purpose Plough** with Farm Hand & two Horses. 10.75" ..................... **£100-150** |
| 8 F | 1955 | **Farm Rake with Driver & Horse** with lever operated Rake. 5.75" .............................. **£200-300** |
| 9 F | 1955 | **Farm Roller with Farm Hand & Horse** 5" long ............................................................ **£100-150** |
| 12 F | 1955 | **Timber Waggon with Farm Hand & two Horses** with real log load. 11.75" .................................... **£170-200** |
| 20 F | 1955 | **Farmers' Gig with Horse & Farmer** Backboard drops. (Reins not supplied). 5.25" .......... **£125-150** |
| 40 F | 1955 | **Farm Cart & Horse** 5" long ............................................................. **£75-95** |
| 45 F | 1955 | **Milk Float & Horse** (Churns No.588 were recommended but not supplied with this model). 5" long ...................................... **£100-150** |
| 126 F | 1955 | **Horse Drawn Farm Cart** 5" long ............................................................. **£75-95** |
| 131 F | 1955 | **Horse Drawn Milk Float** with Milkman & two Churns. 5" ............................ **£100-150** |
| 142 F | 1955 | **Single Horse General Purpose Plough** with Ploughman. 10.25" ...................................... **£100-150** |

## 'Clockwork' series

| | | |
|---|---|---|
| 2041 | **Clockwork Unit (2-wheeled trailer)** | |
| | 'Will last 1 1/2 minutes when fully wound and capable of driving any other vehicle 20-30 feet'......................... | **£45-55** |
| 2045 | **Clockwork Van** | |
| | Finished in various colours with 'BRITAINS LTD' logo....... | **£500-700** |

## 'Motor & Road' series (civilian vehicles)

| | | |
|---|---|---|
| 1428 | **Road Signs Set** | |
| | Fifteen road signs and a Policeman...................................... | **£300-350** |
| 2024 | **Light Goods Van with Driver** | |
| | various colours, opening doors, 'Britains Ltd' logos, 6" long ... | NGPP |
| Set No 641 | **Civilian Motorcycle and Sidecar.** | |
| | Red Sidecar, Dark Brown motorcyclist, White/Red lady on pillion, child with yellow/Green hat in sidecar.............................. | **£900-1,100** |
| Set No. 641 | As above, but Grey Sidecar, Brown Motorcyclist, Yellow/Black lady, child in Red. ......................................... | **£700-900** |
| 653 | **Civilian Motorcycle/Rider.** | |
| | Red Motorcycle with Dark Grey Rider............................. | **£400-500** |
| | **Post-War U.S. Milk Tanker Lorry** | |
| | 'Milk - America's Health Kick'. Special issue - Yellow, Silver Tank, White hubs.................. | **£200-250** |
| 9610 | **Land Rover 'Police'**, boxed ............................................................ | **£30-40** |

## Autogiro and Record Cars (1:43 scale)

| | | |
|---|---|---|
| 1392 | **Autogiro** | |
| | Blue body, (other colours are known) including Military Green with pilot and three detachable rotor blades.................. | **£750-950** |
| ? | **Bluebird Record Car**, 1938. | |
| | (Napier-Campbell) Malcolm Campbell's car, lift-off body, detailed engine, White tyres.............................. | **£125-150** |
| 1656 | **Napier Railton**, 1938, John Cobb's car, '350.20 mph World Land Speed Record'. Painted ....................................... | **£150-200** |
| 1658 | **Napier Railton**, As 1656, but chromium-plated........................... | NGPP |

## Petrol pumps, etc.

Each of the pumps 1v - 7v has a cast delivery nozzle attached by a flexible hose to the rotating top arm.

| | | |
|---|---|---|
| 1v | 'SHELL' ................................................................................. | **£65-75** |
| 2v | 'B.P.'..................................................................................... | **£65-75** |
| 3v | 'ESSO' .................................................................................. | **£65-75** |
| 4v | 'MOBILGAS' ......................................................................... | **£65-75** |
| 5v | 'NATIONAL BENZOLE'........................................................ | **£65-75** |
| 6v | 'FINA'................................................................................... | **£65-75** |
| 7v | **'DOMINION' Petrol Pumps.** 3 pumps on plinth ................ | **£200-250** |
| 9v | **'CASTROL' Oil Cabinet,** sliding front / 3 pumps. 1.75" high. ..................................... | NGPP |
| 101v | **Stand with Three Pumps** 'SHELL', 'B.P.' and 'NATIONAL BENZOLE' pumps a base plus oil cabinet and operator.................................... | **£100-150** |
| 102v | **Stand with Three Pumps** 'ESSO', 'MOBILGAS' and 'FINA' pumps a base plus oil cabinet and operator.............. | **£175-225** |
| 103v | **Stand with Three Pumps** 'SHELL', 'ESSO' and 'MOBILGAS' pumps a base plus oil cabinet and operator.... | **£200-250** |
| ? | **'Regent' Petrol Pump.** Apparently never issued........................... | NPP |
| ? | **Petrol Pump Attendant and 'POWER' Pump.** Cream/Red overalls, 'Power' Pump.............................................. | **£80-90** |
| ? | **Petrol Pump Attendant and 'SHELL' Pump.** Brown/Green overalls, 'Shell' Pump ........................................ | **£80-90** |
| ? | **Rare 'Fina' Petrol Pumps Set.** Three 'Fina' Pumps on plinth, boxed.................................... | **£500-750** |
| 9689 | **Garage Set.** 'Shell', 'BP' and 'National' on plinth, boxed ........................ | **£300-400** |

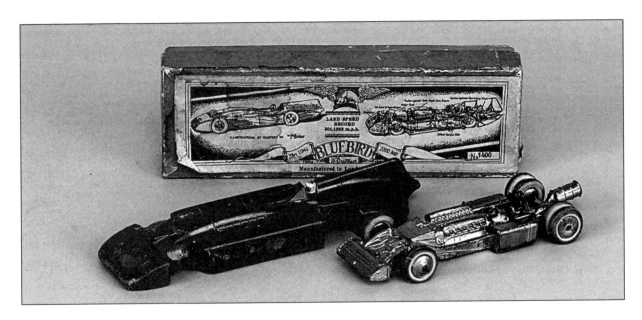

Britains Bluebird Record Car 1938       Photo: Vectis Auctions Ltd.

## 'CIRCUS' SERIES

**'Mammoth Circus Roundabout'**
Six horses (Black, Brown, White) plus riders, Green, Red and
Yellow Carousel canopy. Lead and card construction.
Circa 1910.................................................................**£2,000-3,000**

**Set No. 1444 Mammoth Circus Display.**
In special box (pre-war only). Blue Circus Ring, Clowns,
Ringmaster, rare Cowboy with Lasso, Liberty horse,
Elephants and Circus Performers ...............................**£4,000-5,000**

**'The Flying Trapeze' Set (No. 1141)**
High wire act with balancing clown and suspended girl
trapeze artiste, twirling paper parasol, wire
and card winder, marbled patterned box. 1936-39 .................**£1,500-2,500**

**354B and 359B.** 4 clowns in red, with elephant and hoop..................**£45 each**

**448B Lion Tamer.** Plus lion and tub ........................................**£50-60**

**447B Boxing Clown**......................................................................**£50-75**

**447B Boxing Kangaroo**..............................................................**£50-75**

**450B Performing Elephant.** no details........................................**£100-150**

**Elephant Ride Set.**
Brown elephant (rubber trunk, red blanket on back),
2 children, keeper, howdah, box.......................................**£150-200**

## RAILWAY ITEMS

**Set No. 1R Railway Station Staff Set** (post war only).
21 items tied to card including Man with Pipe, Lady with
Umbrella, Guard, Military Policeman, Station Master and
Timetable, 3 Porters/barrows/luggage, box ..............**£900-1,100**

**Set No. 158 Complete Railway Station.**
24 items tied in original box .......................................**£700-800**

**Set No. 333 Railway Station Staff.**
6 figures- Porters with trunks etc. in box .....................**£600-700**

**Set No. 1256 O Gauge Railway Set.**
17 items items tied to card, boxed................................**£500-600**

## MISCELLANEOUS SETS

**Set 4 Miniature Household.**
12 Pots and Pans etc. tied in box..................................**£600-800**

**Set MB 20 Miniature Garden Set.**
In box .............................................................................**£200-250**

**Set 16G Miniature Gardening Series.**
Flower beds/flowers etc, plus listing.............................**£300-400**

**Set MG 26 Miniature Garden Set.**
Large quantity of items, boxed..................................**£1,500-1,750**

**Set 38F Farm Set** (small edition). 12 farm animals etc. in box..........**£100-125**

**Set 134F Model Farm Set.**
Post War, 2 Fordson Tractors, plus log trailer,
hay wagon and other farm equipment .....................**£2,500-3,000**

**Set 145 Royal Army Medical Corps.**
Horse Drawn Ambulance, 1906. Collar harness, four horses,
2 riders, wagon and 2 men ..........................................**£500-750**

**Set No. 433 Round-Wing Royal Air Force Monoplane.**
Red, with Pilot and RAF roundels, boxed............................**£9,000-11,000**

**Set 1288 Royal Marines Band**
1933 version, Drum Major and 20 men .......................**£400-600**

**Set 1316 Salvation Army Band and Escort Set.**
Fifteen piece band in blue uniforms with
Bandmaster, Standard Bearer, Four Females and
four Officers...........................................................**£5,000-6,000**

**Set 1317 Salvation Army Band.**
23 Bandsmen (red uniforms) + Bandmaster (Blue uniform)..**£1,500-1,750**

**Set 1475 Historical Series Set.**
18 Beefeaters etc., strung in box ................................**£100-125**

**Set 1477 Queen Elizabeth Set**
Queen and George VI, 1953 Coronation Coach, Horses,
Royal Household, Marching Horseguards etc.........................**£1,500-2,000**

**Set 1495 Painter's Set.**
3 White/Black men with one red ladder. Tied in box .................**£400-450**

**Set No. 1654 Snow White and the Seven Dwarfs.**
Names of Dwarfs on backing card and pictures
of Dwarfs on box lid......................................................**£1,400-1,600**

**1968 Ex-Factory Prototype Sample.**
Un-issued Farm Series , blue tractor, three figures,
four animals, box .........................................................**£1,500-1,750**

**1939 'Lambeth Walk' Dancing Couple.**
Man in Brown bowler hat and suit with Green shirt,
Girl in Yellow jacket and Purple skirt.......................**£1,000-1,200**

**2034 Prairie Schooner with Pioneer Driver and Wife, Covered.**
Green/red wagon, white tin cover, four horses,
all strung on card in box ..............................................**£250-350**

**2073 'R.A.F. On the March' Set.**
7 Airmen/Rifles plus Officer/Sword, box.....................**£100-120**

**Set 5819 Coronation Set presented at**
**Britains Centenary Dinner in 1993.**
One of limited edition of 85, original box with menu. (QE II) ....**£200-250**

**9402 State Landau**
with instructions, Queen, Prince Philip, 6 grey horses,
3 drivers, 2 footmen, traces, figures tied in box...........**£100-150**

**'Nestle's Home Farm'.**
Variant of Home Farm Set 1F. Contents are the same but with
the 'Nestle's World Cow' substituted for the standard cow.
This is the only set known to exist................................**£1,750-2,000**

**Trade Box 222.**
One dozen 'Nestles' 'Map of the World' cows ...........**£700-800**

**Set 3/228 Bahamas Police Band.**
25 piece band, boxed................................................**£3,000-4,000**

**Set 2186 Bahamas Police Band.**
1959/60 only, Band Master and 25 men................**£2,500-3,000**

**Rare Britains & C.F. Eckhardt CIV Army Service Supply Column.**
Four-horse collar harness. Supply wagon with ASC tilt and
8 ASC crates, 4 drivers, 9 escort at the trail,
1 officer, oval bases, unboxed ...................................**£2,000-2,500**

## MISCELLANEOUS FIGURES, etc.

**Felix the Cat.**
Black/white cat on hind legs .......................................**£200-300**

**587 Village Idiot.**
Dark Blue Smock, Brown Trousers (other colours seen).............**£175-200**

**Army Service Supply Column.**
2 Four-Horse Wagons, 13 soldiers ..........................**£2,000-2,500**

**London Road Roller c.1800's.**
Red/Green/Gold, wood box .......................................**£2,000-3,000**

**'Everton' Football Team.**
Tied to card in box......................................................**£900-1,100**

**'Liverpool' Football Team.**
With Players, Referee, Linesman, Goal Post,
Corner Flags - boxed ...............................................**£1,000-1,250**

**Set 809 Cricketer.**
Circa 1910, cricket whites / red cap, moveable arms...................**£175-225**

**A Cricketer.**
In Whites, Blue cap ......................................................**£150-250**

**1934 Pro. Cococubs Series 'Jonathan'**
Boy eating Cadbury's chocolate .................................**£175-225**

**The FA Cup.** Very rare - shown in pre-WW 1 Britains Catalogues..**£750-1,000**

# Britains 'Lilliput' series

1:76 scale models manufactured under license by Horton (Toys and Games) Ltd., Reno Works, Middlesborough, England.

| | | |
|---|---|---|
| LV 601 | **Open Sports Car**, 2.25" long. All Red, Red/Black, Cream/Red, All Yellow, Pale Green or Dark Green. Maroon or Black seats | **£60-75** |
| LV 602 | **Saloon Car**, 2.25" long. Light Blue, Dark Blue, Mid-Blue, Pale Green or Dark Green | **£60-75** |
| LV 603 | **Articulated Lorry**, Light Brown/Green, Dark Brown/Green or all Cream ....4" long | **£60-70** |
| LV 604 | **Fordson Tractor with Driver** ............1.5" long | **£35-45** |
| LV 605 | **Milk Float and Horse** with Milkman. 2.25" long | **£45-55** |
| LV 606 | **Tumbrel Cart and Horse** with Hay Racks and Carter........2.75" long | **£45-55** |
| LV 607 | **Austin 3-ton Covered Military Truck** | **£45-55** |
| LV 608 | **Austin 3-ton Farm Truck**, Brown / Red, Brown / Yellow or Brown / Green | **£45-55** |
| LV 609 | **Austin Military Champ** | **£65-75** |
| LV 610 | **Centurion Tank** | **£35-45** |
| LV 611 | **Self-propelled 25-pounder Gun** | **£25-35** |
| LV 612 | **Humber 1-1/2 ton Military Truck** | **£35-45** |
| LV 613 | **Humber 1-1/2 ton Military Truck** .....Covered version | **£35-45** |
| LV 614 | **Farm Trailer** | **£15-25** |
| LV 615 | **Saracen Armoured Vehicle** | **£15-25** |
| LV 616 | **1½ ton Truck** | **£35-45** |
| LV 617 | **Civilian Ambulance**. Cream body with 'AMBULANCE' on sides, 'BRITAINS' on rubber tyres, Red plastic hubs | **£100-125** |
| LV 618 | **Army Ambulance** | **£40-50** |
| LV 619 | **'ROYAL MAIL' Van** | NGPP |
| LV 620 | **Bedford 3 ton High-sided Truck**, Dark Blue/Yellow, Red/Mid-Blue or Green/Red, all with Red hubs | **£40-50 each** |

**LV/SA Civilian Vehicles Set**. Eight vehicles on card in box .............. **£250-300**

**Set No. L/11 Railway Personnel and Vehicles Display**.
 6 various vehicles and 32 other items, with display card in box. .................. **£750-1,000**

**Lilliput Military Vehicles Set**.
 Fordson Ambulance and 1.5 ton Truck, Bedford 3 ton truck, Austin Champ and two Saracen Armoured vehicles .................. **£200-250**

**Lilliput Boxed Vehicles Set**.
 Contains LV/SA Fordson Tractor, Tumbrel Cart, Cart Horse and Carter, Milk Float and Man, Lorry, Car and Sports Car, box. .................. **£150-200**

**Petite Set D- Day Landings**.
 10 Allied figures plus map, boxed .................. **£50-75**

**Petite Set Gun and Limber, R.H.A.**
 6 Horse team and 3 riders, boxed .................. **£25-35**

**Petite Series No. 8926 Thornycroft AA Gun Truck**
 with service detachment, gun, 4 figures/papers, boxed ............... **£80-100**

# Britains 'Racing Colours of Famous Owners'

| Ref. / Owner / horse colour / Jockey's colours | MPR |
|---|---|
| **RC1 H.M. The King** Brown .. Black cap, Purple silks with Gold hoop | **£200-250** |
| **RC2 Lord Astor** Grey ..... Pink cap, Grey/Blue silks with diagonal Pink stripe | **£200-250** |
| **RC3 Lord Derby** Brown .. White cap, Black silks | **£200-250** |
| **RC6 Lord Roseberry** Grey ..... Pink cap, Green silks with Pink hoops | **£200-250** |
| **RC12 Mr J.V. Rank** Grey ..... Dark Blue cap, Yellow silks with Blue squares | **£150-200** |
| **RC63 The Aga Khan** Brown .. Brown cap, Green silks with Brown hoops | **£150-200** |

| Ref. / Owner / horse colour / Jockey's colours | MPR |
|---|---|
| **RC64 Dorothy Paget** Brown .. Yellow cap/Blue bands, Blue silks/Yellow hoops | **£200-250** |
| **RC67 Mr H.J. Joel** Brown .. Red cap, Black silks | **£150-200** |
| **RC82 Princess Elizabeth** Brown .. Black cap, Red /Black hoops | **£175-225** |
| **RC83 Winston S. Churchill** Brown .. Brown cap, Pink/Brown silks | **£200-250** |
| **RC142 Duke of Norfolk** Brown .. Red cap with Blue quartering, Blue silks | **£200-250** |
| **RC144 Msr. M. Boussac** Brown .. Grey cap, Orange silks | **£150-200** |

**Salesman's Sample Card of Jockeys** in racing colours and horses ......NGPP

# Britains Catalogues

**1905 Catalogue (1972 Copy Edition)**.
 Oblong format (21cm x 16.5cm). Monochrome Reprint Edition, 19 pages,Originally signed by Dennis Britain .................. **£30-40**

**1949 Export Edition Catalogue**.
 USA - 34 pages in the 1930's style .................. **£80-120**

**1952 'Clockwork Series' Supplement**.
 Lists all vehicles and sets with clockwork .................. **£70-80**

**1952 Britains 'Lilliput' 'World of Models' Catalogue**.
 20cm x 15cm. 11 pages .................. **£80-90**

**1952 'SP Fort Range Series' Supplement**.
 Folding single sheet with the Fort range .................. **£40-50**

**1953 Coronation Souvenir Supplement**.
 Colour and monochrome booklet .................. **£60-70**

**1953 'Pots and Pans' Supplement**.
 2 page colour illustrated leaflet .................. **£50-60**

**1955 Pocket Edition - 110th Edition**.
 128 pages, black/white, buff covers .................. **£65-75**

**1957 'New Lines' Catalogue** (Oblong).
 28 pages with Centurian Tank on cover .................. **£70-80**

**1958 Britains 'Herald' Catalogue**.
 Monochrome illustrated 3 page catalogue .................. **£75-100**

**1958 'New Lines' Supplement**.
 20 pages, 'New Additions', cameo photograph of William Britain (1828 -1906) on cover .................. **£80-90**

**1959 'Crown' and 'New Crown' Range**.
 Oblong (20 x 15cm), 16 pages booklet .................. **£50-60**

**1961 Catalogue, Price List, Order Form**.
 84 pages (landscape), some colour pages .................. **£80-120**

**1962 Catalogue**.
 Large landscape format. 88 black/white pages, colour cover ........ **£100-140**

**1963 Catalogue**
 Large landscape format. 72 pages + Price List and Order Form ..... **£80-120**

**1964 Catalogue**.
 Large landscape format. 64 pages + Price List and Order Form ..... **£80-120**

**1973 Trade Catalogue**.
 24 pages in full colour showing the range of products .................. **£30-45**

**Herald Miniatures Ltd. 1957 Catalogue**.
 Plus 'New Lines 1957' leaflet .................. **£250-300**

**Britains Herald Catalogue 1959**.
 '1st combined catalogue by the new Co'. .................. **£200-250**

# Britains Motor Cycles 1965 - 1975

Most have plastic saddles, plated engines and 'jewelled' headlights, and are packed in display boxes.

9640  **Two Go-Karts**, yellow/black or red/black ...................................... NGPP
9650  **Speedway Set.** Four differently coloured Speedway bikes....... **£100-125**
9666  **Motor Cycle Boxed Set** with 3 different motor cycles............. **£80-100**
9695  **BMW with Policeman**, white with black/white rider.................. **£70-90**
9696  **BMW with Civilian**, blue with white/blue rider........................... **£70-90**
9671  **Racing Norton**, yellow with red/green rider.............................. **£70-90**
9674  **Chopper Trike**, yellow/gold/black.......................................... NGPP
9677  **Long Fork Chopper**, red  with blue rider ................................... NGPP
9679  **German Army Motor Cycle**, khaki................................................ **£70-90**
9680  **'Chopper' Motor Cycle**, black with pink rder ............................ NGPP
9681  **German Army B.M.W. Combination**, khaki, two blue riders .... **£70-90**
9682  **U.S. Army Motor Cycle**, black with khaki rider.......................... **£70-90**
9683  **Drag Motor Cycle**, gold with grey rider...................................... NGPP
9684  **Speedway Motor Cycles**, silver with black riders....................... NGPP
9685  **Lambretta Scooter**, red/white scooter, blue and red riders....... **£80-100**
       White/blue scooter, orange/brown rider, blue passenger .......... **£100-125**
9687  **Honda**. Red/White/Silver bike, Black/Blue/White rider............. **£70-90**
9688  **BMW**, Silver bike, Black rider, '8', Blue helmet........................ **£70-90**
       Black bike, Brown rider, Grey soft hat ..................................... **£70-90**

9689  **Harley-Davidson**, red/white 'Buzz' with red/blue/yellow rider ... **£70-90**
       Red/Silver bike with 'Buzz' on panniers, Tan/Blue/White rider ... **£70-90**
9690  **Triumph Thunderbird 650cc**, red with blue/brown/red rider ..... **£70-90**
       Green bike, black seat............................................................... **£70-90**
       Metallic blue bike, black seat.................................................... **£80-100**
9691  **Gieves Challenger with Rider**, green with blue/brown rider ...... **£70-90**
       Green bike, yellow/nlack rider.................................................... **£70-90**
9692  **Harley-Davidson Electra Glide**. White bike, black seat.
       brown/grey Rider 'U.S.Sheriff' on panniers .................................. **£70-90**
9693  **Honda Benly 125cc**, red with black/blue/yellow rider .............. **£80-100**
9694  **B.M.W. 600cc**, Black/silver with black/blue rider ..................... **£80-100**
9696  **Triumph Speed Twin with Rider**, yellow/blue with black rider. **£70-90**
       Maroon/blue, black rider ............................................................ **£70-90**
9697  **Triumph Thunderbird Police Patrol** , white with black or
       dark blue police rider, loudhailer .............................................. **£70-90**
9698  **Dispatch Rider on Triumph Motor Cycle**,
       black bike, black/green rider ...................................................... **£70-90**
       Green/chrome bike, military green rider with armbands .............. **£70-90**
9698/2 **MV-Augusta Motor Cycle**,
       red '7', green/yellow or white/blue rider ..................................... NGPP
9699  **BMW Racing Combination**, red/yellow with two black riders.... NGPP

---

## BRITAINS SELECTED AUCTION RESULTS 2005 — 2007

**CHRISTIE'S, South Kensington**
**59F Four Wheel Farm Tipping Lorry**.
    Square-nose version in original box........................................... **£576**
**59F Four Wheel Farm Tipping Lorry**.
    Round-nosed post war version - boxed...................................... **£264**
**90F Builder's Lorry. 'DAVIS ESTATES'**.
    In original box ...................................................................... **£4,800**
**127F Tractor**. With driver and rubber tyres .................................. **£288**
**1400 Bluebird Record Car**.
    Blue with White tyres in original box......................................... **£120**
**1413 Mobile Police Car**. In Green in original box ......................... **£720**
**1513 Volunteer Ambulance**. In Dark Blue in original box ..................... **£1,320**
**1514 Corporation Motor Ambulance**.
    In White in original box ........................................................ **£1,080**
**2024 Goods Delivery Van. 'Britains Ltd'**. Pale Green, boxed................. **£840**
**Rare 'Fina' Petrol Pumps Set**.
    Three 'Fina' Pumps on plinth, boxed.......................................... **£900**
**Set No. 9689 Garage Set**.
    'Shell', 'BP' and 'National' on plinth, boxed ............................... **£360**
**Set No. 1441 Flying Trapeze**.
    Yellow/White/Red clown with Blue umbrella on trapeze,
    Gold/Blue lady trapeze artist in original box............................ **£1,080**

**DREWATT-NEATE AUCTIONS**, Clifton, Bristol.
**127F Fordson Major Tractor**. Spud wheels, VGC boxed ......................... **£330**
**1512 Army Ambulance**.
    Khaki with Red Cross roundels, stretcher, E, boxed ..................... **£90**

**Bluebird Record Car**. Blue body, GC, boxed ............................................. **£230**
**1659 Railton Wonder Car**. Lift off body, GC, boxed ............................... **£130**
**1877 Military Beetle Lorry**.
    Khaki and Canvas, driver, E, boxed......................................................... **£60**

**LACY, SCOTT & KNIGHT Auctions**. Bury St Edmunds, Suffolk
**BNM = Box Near Mint,  BVG = Box Very Good, UB = Unboxed**
**20F Farmer's Gig**. Green/Red, G in G box ............................................**£110**
**2048 Clockwork Set**.
    Beetle Lorry, driver, clockwork trailer, 25 pdr Howitzer,
    key, box with yellow label, M, BNM ....................................... **£185**
**Lilliput LV 17 Civilian Ambulance**,
    Cream, Red hubs, VG /UB................................................................ **£50**

**WALLIS & WALLIS**. Lewes, Sussex
**12F Timber Carriage**.
    Leaf Green, 2 horses, carter, original log, boxed, VGC  ..................... **£170**
**1433 Covered Tender**.
    Caterpillar Type, later style cab with driver, Boxed, VGC.................. **£120**
**2150 Centurion Tank**.
    Matt Olive Green, VGC-M, Box some age wear ................................. **£200**
**Fordson Major E27N**.
    Dark Blue/Orange, wound by starting handle, GC, unboxed ............... **£140**

The Chad Valley company (makers of board games and wooden toys) produced tinplate toy vehicles from 1932 incorporating the year of manufacture in the registration number on the number plates.

Their first 'Wee-Kin' diecast toy vehicles were produced around 1949 and had 'CV 1949' as the registration number. They were fitted with a key-wound clockwork motor and were designed more as toys than models having generic titles like 'Open Lorry' or 'Fire Engine'. The cars issued between 1951 and 1954 as Rootes Group promotionals are much better attempts at models and were sold at Rootes Group garages as well as normal toy shops. The tractors produced

from 1952 are particularly fine and well detailed models. The years shown below indicate the periods in which Chad Valley offered them for sale though not all the toys were available for the whole of the period and some were still in the shops well after production ceased in 1956.

(This introduction to Chad Valley was written by Sue Richardson who also provided the basic listing. Additional listing information came from the Cecil Gibson archives and John G. Butler of Berkhampstead, Herts.).

## Diecast clockwork toys and model vehicles

| | | | |
|---|---|---|---|
| 220 | 1949-53 | **Razor Edge Saloon**. Various colours, no. plates 'CV 1949', approximate. scale 1:43 | **£140-180** |
| 221 | 1949-53 | **Traffic Control Car**. Casting as 220 plus loudspeaker, 'CV 1949' | **£100-150** |
| 222 | 1949-53 | **'POLICE' Car**. As 220 plus loudspeaker | **£100-150** |
| 223 | 1949-53 | **Track Racer**. 'CV 1949' on number plates | **£100-150** |
| 224 | 1949-53 | **Double Decker Bus**. Red, 'CV 1949', 1:76 | **£200-250** |
| 225 | 1949-53 | **Open Lorry**. Various colours, 'CV 1949' | **£100-150** |
| 226 | 1949-53 | **Low-Loader**. Green / Red, 'CV 1949', 3 cases | **£100-150** |
| 227 | 1949-53 | **Timber Wagon**. 'CV 1949' | **£100-150** |
| 228 | 1949-53 | **Cable Layer**. Red cab, Green body, 'CV 1949' | **£100-130** |
| 229 | 1949-53 | **Breakdown Lorry**. 'CV 1949' | **£100-130** |
| 230 | 1949-53 | **Milk Float**. 'CV 1949', eight milk churns | **£150-180** |
| 231 | 1949-53 | **Fire Engine**. Red body, 'CV 1949' | **£100-130** |
| 232 | 1949-53 | **Tower Repair Wagon**. All-Green, 'CV 1949' | **£125-175** |
| 233 | 1949-53 | **Milk Tanker**. Blue / White, 'CV 1949' | **£150-175** |
| 234 | 1949-53 | **Petrol Tanker**. 'CV 1949' | **£150-175** |
| 239 | 1949-53 | **Dust Cart**. Tinplate sliding panels, 'CV 1949' | **£140-180** |
| --- | 1951-54 | **Guy Van**. Dark Blue / Cream, tinplate doors, *'Lyons Ice Cream Cadby Hall London W11'* | **£300-500** |
| --- | 1951-54 | **Guy Van**. Red body, Blue hubs, tinplate doors, Red *'CHAD VALLEY'* logo | **£300-500** |
| --- | 1951-54 | **Guy Van**. Green body, tinplate doors, Yellow *'Guy Motors Ltd, Commercial Vehicle Manufacturers'* | **£500-750** |

## Other issues (with or without motor)

| | | | |
|---|---|---|---|
| --- | 1950-55 | **Hillman Minx Saloon** | **£100-125** |
| --- | 1950-55 | **Humber Super Snipe**, blue / grey body | **£90-120** |
| --- | 1950-55 | **Guy Truck** | **£80-120** |
| --- | 1950-55 | **Sunbeam Racer** | **£100-125** |
| --- | 1950-55 | **Humber Hawk** | **£100-125** |
| --- | 1950-55 | **Rolls-Royce Razor Edge Saloon** | **£100-125** |
| --- | 1950-55 | **Routemaster London Bus** | **£125-150** |
| --- | 1950-55 | **Commer Avenger Coach** | **£100-125** |
| --- | 1950-55 | **Guy Truck 'LYONS ICE CREAM'** | **£350-500** |
| --- | 1950-55 | **Sunbeam-Talbot Saloon**, metallic pale brown | **£100-125** |
| --- | 1950-55 | **Guy Milk Tanker**, blue /cream, 'MILK' | **£200-300** |
| --- | 1950-55 | **Guy Cable Lorry** | **£100-150** |
| --- | 1950-55 | **Guy Petrol Tanker 'REGENT PETROL'** | **£300-400** |
| --- | 1950-55 | **Guy 'FIRE' Engine** | **£300-400** |
| --- | 1950-55 | **Guy Container Lorry** | **£100-150** |
| | 1950-55 | **Guy Refuse Lorry** | **£100-150** |

## Chad Valley model Tractors

| | | |
|---|---|---|
| 1952 | **Fordson Major E27N** Dark Blue body, Orange wheels, rubber tyres (2 types of tread on rear), steering, towbar with pin, clockwork wound by starting handle. Scale 1:16. Illustrated box or plain box with small label | **£300-400** |
| 1955 | **Fordson Major E27N** Red and Yellow with driver, clockwork, scale 1:43, boxed. Made under licence by 'Raybro & Sturdy Products S.A.', Johannesburg, South Africa, (model marked 'Chad Valley GB') | **£200-300** |
| 1954 | **Fordson Major DDN** Mid-Blue body, Orange wheels, rubber tyres, working steering, lifting bonnet, towbar/pin, hydraulic lift at rear (detachable centre arm), clockwork wound through rear hub. Scale 1:16. Illustrated box or plain box with small label | **£300-400** |
| | *Static version:* s previous model but without clockwork operation. Illustrated box or plain box plus small label. The word 'working' is deleted from all sides of box | **£200-300** |
| | *Chrome version:* Static version in chrome plate, wooden plinth with some. Ploughing trophy or Ford presentation model? | **£250-400** |
| 1955 | **Ford Dexta** Mid-Blue, Orange wheels, radiator panels and 'Fordson Dexta', not steerable, rubber tyres, hook, 1:16. Illustrated box | **£400-600** |
| 1955 | **Ferguson** Green, Red wheels, 'Ferguson' on sides, steering, hook, 1:16. Illustrated box inscribed 'Ferguson'. Promotional | **£500-700** |
| | Grey body, Grey wheels, hydraulic lift at rear | **£600-800** |
| 1950-55 | **Massey Ferguson Tractor**, with or without motor | **£400-600** |
| 1950-55 | **Fordson Major Tractor**, Red or Blue, motor in some Bright Yellow/Orange, Red wheels, key, boxed | **£400-600** **£1,750-2,250** |

## Rootes Group promotional models (scale 1:43)

| | | | |
|---|---|---|---|
| 236 | 1949-53 | **The Hillman Minx** Grey or Metallic Dark Blue body | **£100-140** |
| 237 | 1949-53 | **The Humber Super Snipe** Metallic Dark Green or Red body | **£100-140** |
| 238 | 1949-53 | **The Sunbeam-Talbot** Light Blue or Metallic Dark Green. Base has wording 'A Rootes Group Product' plus usual CV marks | **£140-180** |
| 240 | 1949-53 | **Commer Avenger Coach** Blue, Red or Green body, (1:76 scale) | **£200-250** |
| 242 | 1949-53 | **The Commer Hands** (6-wheel artic.) Red body with 'Commer Hands' sticker | **£250-300** |
| 507 | 1951-54 | **The Humber Hawk** Met. Dark Blue, Met. Dark Green, or mid-Green | **£100-140** |

Chad Valley 231 Fire Engine and 232 Tower Wagon  PHOTO: VECTIS AUCTIONS LTD.

The following history and listings have been researched by Robert Newson. The firm of Charbens & Co. was started around 1928 by Charles and Benjamin Reid and was based at Hornsey Road, Holloway, London N7. They made hollow-cast lead figures, and a few lead vehicles were also produced in the 1930s. After the war zinc die-casting was introduced, and some items exist in both lead and zinc versions (the latter from new dies). Zinc castings by Charbens very often have metal failure as a result of contamination from the lead that was still used extensively in the factory.

The 'Old Crocks' series of miniatures was introduced in 1955. After 1967 all vehicle models were deleted from the catalogue except for a few items included in sets with plastic figures. Production of figures was discontinued in 1973. Model numbers were allocated around 1954, so items which had already been withdrawn are not numbered. Dates of issue have been taken from catalogues or adverts, but inevitably are incomplete. Most pre-war items have 'RD' cast in, most post-war items have 'CHARBENS' cast underneath. Most were boxed.

| Model and details | MPR | Model and details | MPR | Model and details | MPR |
|---|---|---|---|---|---|

## Pre-war issues (part hollow-cast, part diecast construction)

**Motorcycle Policeman.**
Solid cast machine with green petrol tank . **£40-60**

**Police Motor Cycle and Sidecar.**
Solid cast machine, rider and passenger in black / white uniforms, black sidecar .... **£40-60**

**Soap Box Racer.**
Solid cast brown base, four red wheels (six spokes), Cub Scout pushing, Cub Scout rider + another ...................... **£400-600**

**Goat Cart with Girl.**
Blue or red cart and girl, brown or white goat, yellow 6-spoke wheels .......... **£90-120**

**Road Workers Set.**
Horse Roller (green / orange / brown), orange and black tar boiler truck with 6-spoke wheels, plus 4 workmen, a nightwatchman, hut, brazier, 'Road up' sign, pipe, 2 barriers .............. **£250-350**

**Gypsy Caravan.**
Blue / white caravan with white horse, yellow wheels (smaller at front) plus orange / black seated Gypsy woman with baby, standing man, washing + line, cooking pot ................ **£750-1,000**

**The Farm Wagon.**
Green / yellow 4 wheel wagon with two hay racks, brown carthorse, cream / black carter figure. In red card box with cream label. ............................. **£125-150**

**Horse-Drawn Baker's Wagon.**
Red with yellow wheels, 'T. SMITH' on roof ................................ **£600-800**

**Tumbril Cart** (two wheels). Green / yellow cart. 2 hay racks, brown horse, cream / black carter, cream card box...... **£100-125**

**Coster Cart with Donkey.** Green / yellow cart, solid sides, grey donkey, costermonger figure (see 24 below)....... **£100-125**

**Organ Grinder's Cart** (two wheels) Brown / yellow organ, grey donkey, red monkey with mug, brown / green organ-grinder .......................................... **£150-175**

**Governess's Cart** (two wheels). Yellow / black, cream / red or brown / black cart, 2 children, donkey, zoo-keeper figure .... **£100-125**

**Horse-Drawn Milk Float** (two wheels). Yellow / red cart with 'PURE MILK' cast in. Brown horse, milkman figure (see 25)..... **£80-100**

**Horse-Drawn Milk Float** (four wheels) Orange / white body with 'UNITED DAIRIES', 'PASTEURISED MILK' and 'CREAM' logo. 8-spoke wheels with rubber tyres, brown horse, white / blue milkman with bottle .......... **£400-600**

**Electric Milk Handcart.**
Dark Blue, with 'MILK' logo and Milkman, two crates of milk ................. **£200-300**

**Bread Handcart.**
Blue/white, 'HOVIS' logo, delivery-man, bread basket..................... **£200-300**

**Horse-Drawn Cape Cart** (two wheels).
Enclosed dark blue body and roof, brown horse, mid-blue figure .................. **£80-100**

**Horse-Drawn Tree Wagon** (four wheels).
Yellow / red log carrier, 12-spoke wheels, 4 horses, 2 white figures + poles............ **£200-300**

**Horse-Drawn Dairy Float** (four wheels).
Mid-blue, 'EXPRESS DAIRY', 'PURE MILK', 'BUTTER & EGGS', white shafts, brown horse, 8-spoke wheels, rubber tyres, white / blue milkman holding bottle ...... **£250-350**

**Horse-Drawn Coal Cart** (four wheels).
Black cart, coalman and sack, white/orange horse, 12-spoke wheels, 6 spare sacks .............. **£250-350**

**Horse Drawn Tar Wagon.**
White Horse, Black Wagon - boxed....... **£400-500**

**Horse-Drawn Railway Wagon** (four wheels)
Grey / red open wagon, driver, 'London Midland Scottish Railway' cast in, white horse ........................................ **£400-600**

**Horse-Drawn Grass Cutter.**
Yellow / red cutter, brown driver and horse (see also 3) ................................... **£100-125**

**Horse-Drawn Roller.** Green / yellow roller, brown driver and horse (see also 2) ....... **£100-125**

**Horse-Drawn Delivery Van.**
Blue / white, 'HOVIS', four wheels, brown horse, driver................................ **£400-600**

**Coffee Stall** (four wheels).
Orange / yellow stall, silver chimney, brown / white horse, tea urn and crockery ............................. **£150-175**

**Gamekeeper with Dog**
Gamekeeper with cap and shotgun, brown/white dog with bird in mouth...... **£100-125**

**Flower Seller**
Seated female figure with bunch of flowers, separate casting of basket of flowers ..... **£100-125**

**Jack's Band**
Nine assorted musicians plus conductor, boxed set .............................. **£400-600**

**Hay Cart**
Yellow/green cart, grey/black or brown horse, yellow / brown figure, boxed....... **£100-125**

**Walking Barrow Boy.**
A clockwork toy.
Green / blue / red / yellow. Boxed ......... **£150-175**

**Circus Clown Set.**
Clowns on Stilts, Clown on Unicycle, Clown climbing Ladder, Clown standing, Policeman clown ......... **£150-200**

**Circus Single Figures**
Liberty Horses, Performing Elephants, Seal with Balls, Strongman, Boxing Midgets, Acrobats, Parrot, Dog, Ringmaster ...each: **£15-20**

**Performing Animals Set**
2 elephants with tubs, ringmaster and seal with ball on nose ............................ **£400-500**

**'Mimic Series' Circus Set** - boxed.
Includes Clowns, Performers, etc........ **£900-1,100**
**Trapeze Artists Set.**
Two Artists on Wire - unboxed .............. **£300-400**

## Pre-war Motor Vehicles (all lead)

**6 Petrol Tanker**. Red, blue, yellow .......... **£300-400**
**524 Fire Engine**. Cast-in driver, separate ladder, rubber tyres................... **£200-300**

**525 Car and Caravan**. Six-light saloon car (red, green or yellow); yellow/orange Caravan copied from Dinky Toys 30g ... **£300-400**
**526 Motor Van**. No details ..................... **£150-250**

**728 Ambulance**. Man cast on rear step. Green or brown...................................... **£200-300**
**864 Racing Car.**
Pale blue, green or yellow ...................... **£75-100**

**865 Breakdown Lorry**. No details......... **£120-150**
**--- Bentley Ambulance.**
Copy of Dinky Toys 24a in off-white .... **£120-150**

**--- 1935 Bluebird Record Car.**
Blue body, White tyres, Union flag........ **£300-400**
**--- Armoured Car**. Six wheels, brown...... **£80-100**

**--- Caterpillar Tractor.**
Copy of Tootsietoy but larger.
'MIMIC TOY' cast underneath .............. **£150-250**
**--- Tank**. Copy of Tootsietoy. 'MIMIC TOY' cast underneath. Very dark blue ..... **£80-100**

**--- Mack Stake Lorry.**
Copy of Tootsietoy. Green and red......... **£100-125**
**--- Mack Lorry with AA Gun.**
Copy of Tootsietoy. Light brown, black and silver..................................... **£150-200**

**--- Mack Searchlight Lorry.**
Copy of Tootsietoy.
Light brown and black........................... **£150-200**
**--- Mack Barrage Balloon Set.**
No details. Johillco made a similar set... **£300-400**

- **46-49 Packard Saloon.**
'JAVELIN' cast under. Red or green ...... **£40-60**

- **46-49 Petrol Tanker.** Different from
pre-war tanker. Red, Green or Blue ........ **£40-60**

- **46-49 Station Wagon.** Tan with dark brown
bonnet and wings, spare wheel at rear .... **£40-60**

- **1959 British Paratrooper and Motorcycle.**
Military-green cycle/rider (red beret).. **£150-200**

1 **4?-60 Horse-Drawn Log Wagon.**
Yellow, red wheels, with man, 2 tandem
horses, wooden log, cream card box.. **£125-150**

2 **4?-67 Horse-Drawn Roller.**
Yellow with green or red roller, with
horse and man (seated)........................ **£125-150**

3 **4?-67 Horse-drawn Grass Cutter.**
Yellow, red wheels, unpainted cutter,
with horse and man (seated)................ **£125-150**

4 **4?-67 Horse-drawn Two-wheel Farm
Wagon with Raves.** Green wagon,
yellow shafts and wheels..................... **£125-150**

5 **4?-67 Horse-drawn Four-wheel Farm
Wagon with Raves.** Green wagon,
yellow shafts and wheels..................... **£125-150**

6 **4?-67 Tractor with Driver.**
Red or orange with metal wheels........ **£125-150**
Blue with rubber wheels...................... **£125-150**

7 **4?-62 Horse-drawn Van with Man.**
Blue with cream upper, metal wheels, labels:
'HOVIS BREAD' or 'PURE MILK' .. **£300-400**
Orange with light brown upper, rubber
wheels,'HOVIS BREAD' labels ........ **£300-400**

8 **4?-62 Tipper Lorry.** Various colours.... **£40-60**

9 **4?-62 Motor Coach.** Various colours. **£150-200**

10 to 14 **Light Vans.** Two castings known. The
first was a small boxy van with no rear
windows. The second (from the early 1950s)
was larger and more rounded, resembling a
Ford E83W, with two rear windows.

10 **4?-60 Royal Mail Van.** Red, 2nd casting
with black bonnet, 'ROYAL MAIL',
'G-VI-R' paper labels......................... **£100-125**

11 **4?-62 'AMBULANCE'.**
Cream, Red Cross (paper labels) ....... **£100-125**

12 **4?-62 'Carter Paterson' Van.** Dark green,
'CARTER PATERSON' paper labels.. **£100-125**

13 **4?-60 'Police' Van.** Dark blue,
'POLICE GR' paper labels ................ **£100-125**

14 **4?-62 Post Office Telephones Van.**
Green, 'POST OFFICE TELEPHONES'
on paper labels.................................... **£100-125**

15 **4?-62 Fire Engine and Wheeled Escape.**
Red or orange-red, unpainted
ladders, three firemen and hose.......... **£100-125**

16 **4?-67 Covered Wagon with Four Horses
and Driver.** Green or red wagon, yellow
wheels, cloth canopy, metal shaft and
horses. Red box, full-colour label.... **£100-125**
Orange wagon, plastic shaft / horses... **£100-125**

17 **4?-67 Tractor and Log Trailer with Driver.**
Tractor as No.6, Trailer as No.1
but drawbar in place of shafts ............ **£150-200**

18 **4?-62 Tractor and Grass Cutter with
two Drivers.** Tractor as No.6,
Trailer modified from No.3 ................ **£150-200**

19 **4?-67 Tractor and Reaper with two
Drivers.** Tractor as No.6, green Reaper (yellow
or red metal blades) or light blue Reaper
(red plastic blades), or all plastic ........ **£150-200**

20 **54-67 Mobile Crane.** Red body, green
chassis, unpainted or yellow jib.............. **£50-75**
Orange body, lt.blue chassis, yellow jib . **£50-75**

21 **54-67 Muir-Hill Dumper with Driver.**
Beige or orange with green or
yellow dumper.................................... **£40-60**
Red with yellow plastic dumper............. **£40-60**

22 **54-67 Travelling Zoo.** Elephant towing
two cages with two lions, two polar bears,
man. Red chassis, unpainted cages, yellow
roofs, metal or plastic animals ........... **£125-150**
With orange chassis, light blue cages,
yellow roofs........................................ **£100-125**

23 **55-58 Water Pistol.** no details................. **£5-10**

24 **54-55 Costermonger's Cart.**
Dark green cart, red or yellow wheels,
donkey, man and basket ......................... **£40-60**

25 **55-? Horse-drawn Milk Cart.**
Yellow with red wheels, 'PURE MILK'
labels. With man and churn................. **£125-150**

26 **54-62 Armoured Car.** Green or beige,
metal or rubber wheels .......................... **£40-60**

27 **55-67 Large Tractor.** Cast in two halves.
Red with yellow wheels or
orange with light blue wheels ............. **£200-300**

28 **54-67 Diesel Road Roller.** Green or pale
green, red wheels, unpainted flywheel.. **£80-100**

29 **54-62 Mincer.** Toy kitchen equipment .... **£5-10**

30 **55 Scammell Mechanical Horse
and Trailer.** Blue with 'LNER' labels,
or dark brown cab with beige trailer
and 'GWR' labels ................................ **£80-100**

31 **55-62 Articulated Low-loader
with Cable Drum.**
Red or green cab, yellow trailer........... **£80-100**

32 **55-62 Alfa-Romeo Racing Car.**
Hollow-cast lead, red, rubber wheels..... **£50-75**

33 **55-62 Cooper-Bristol Racing Car.**
Hollow-cast lead, green, rubber wheels.. **£50-75**

34 **55-62 Ferrari Racing Car.**
Hollow-cast lead, blue body,
yellow nose, rubber wheels................... **£50-75**

35 **54-67 Horse-drawn Log Wagon.**
As No.1 but single horse ...................... **£50-75**

36 **4?-55 3-wheel Pedestrian Electric Van.**
Dark blue, 'PURE MILK' or 'EXPRESS
DAIRIES' printed on sides; milkman,
crate / bottles .................................... **£160-200**
Orange, 'HOVIS' on sides, man,
tray of loaves .................................... **£160-200**

36 **57-62 Maudslay Horse Box.** Dark red,
'HORSE TRANSPORT' printed on sides,
with horse and driver.......................... **£160-200**
'NEWMARKET HORSEBOX'
Green/Red body ................................. **£160-200**

36 **1967 Steam Roller Large scale.**
Green body, red 12-spoke wheels,
unpainted roller, black chimney,
card box ............................................. **£300-400**

37 **60-62 Articulated Low-loader with
Rocket Missile.** Dark green cab / trailer,
orange / black missile launcher.
No makers name.................................. **£90-120**

38 **55-60 'Shoot and Save' Money Box**
Savings bank, with gun to fire
coin into bank .................................... **£90-120**

39 **1955 Telephone Kiosk** Red kiosk with
opening door, unpainted phone .............. **£15-20**

40 **4?-55 Fire Engine with Ladder and
Firemen.** Different from No.15. Red
body, unpainted 2-part ladder................ **£90-120**

41 **1955 Fireplace.** Dolls house item .......... **£5-10**

445 **1955 'Auto Race Set'** 'Andover series'.
Made only for the Flare Import Corporation,
230 Fifth Ave., New York. Contains 3 (Dinky
style) racing cars, 6 mechanics, man with
chequered flag. 43mm scale, hollow-cast.
Card box has Formula I race scene
on colour label.................................... **£300-400**

519 **1950 'The Hiker's Camp Set'.** Green
metal tent ('The Hikery'), male hiker resting,
male hiker walking with backpack and stick,
female hiker walking with backpack and
stick, female hiker reading a book, 2 plates,
2 cups. Brown card box with b/w picture
label on lid....................................... **£750-1,000**

--- **19?? 'Big Show' Circus Set** - boxed.
US issue with Clowns, etc.............. **£900-1,100**

--- **Large scale Wolf.**
Walking wolf figure ............................. **£40-60**

--- **Trade Pack with Six** Scammell
Articulated Dropside Lorries.............. **£300-350**

--- **Farm Hay Wagon.** Green/Red with
2 Racks, horse, 2 land girls, boxed .... **£200-250**

--- **Walking Barrow Boy.** Clockwork.
Man in long green coat pushing
two wheeled blue/yellow handcart
with orange trunk ............................... **£100-150**

4301 **Tractor and Driver.** Bright Red/Yellow,
metal hubs, Brown driver.................... **£100-125**

--- **Musical Trio Set.** With Pianist,
Piano, Cellist and Violinist, 7 pieces... **£200-300**

--- **'Performing Elephant' Set.** Ringmaster
with whip, elephant with tub, boxed... **£250-350**
--- **Circus Clown.** Clown in top hat and
tails climbing ladder in green............. **£250-350**

609 **Acrobat.**
Doing handstand on a chair................. **£100-150**

612 **'Fairy on Horse'.** Equestrienne in
orange dress, white horse .................. **£100-150**

**'OLD CROCKS' series**

1 **1904 Darracq.** Dark Blue, Red or
Orange, open 2-seater................................ £10-25
2 **1904 Spyker.** Yellow 4-seater open car.. £10-25
3 **1914 'Old Bill' Bus.** 2-piece casting, or
single casting + separate top deck,
Red or Orange .......................................... £10-25
4 **1907 Ford Model T**
2-piece casting, tin chassis, Dark Blue ... £10-25
Single casting, no separate chassis,
Dark Blue .................................................. £10-25
5 **1907 Vauxhall.**
Green open 2-seater................................... £10-25
6 **1906 De Dion Bouton.**
Light Green or Violet open 2-seater........ £10-25
7 **1898 Panhard.**
Light Green or Brown 2-seater ............... £10-25
8 **1906 Rolls-Royce Silver Ghost.**
Silver 4-seater open car........................... £10-25
9 **1903 Standard 6hp.**
Dark Red or Maroon with Beige roof..... £10-25
10 **1902 Wolseley.**
Light Blue 4-seater open car ................... £10-25
11 **1908 Packard Runabout.**
Light Green open 2-seater........................ £10-25
12 **1905 Vauxhall Hansom Cab.**
Orange/Beige............................................. £10-25

13 **1900 Straker Flat Steam Lorry.**
Light Green, packing case...................... £10-25
**1900 Straker Lowside Steam Lorry.**
Light Blue, three barrels.......................... £10-25
14 **Stephenson's 'Rocket' Locomotive.**
Yellow / Black ......................................... £10-25
15 **Tender for 'Rocket'**, colours as 14........ £10-25
16 **1909 Albion.**
Dark or Light Blue open truck............... £10-25
17 **1912 Rover.**
Orange 2-seater open sports ................... £10-25
18 **1911 Mercedes-Benz.**
Dark Green open 2-seater......................... £10-25
19 **Bedford Horse-Box.**
Brown, 'HORSE TRANSPORT' cast
on sides, 'H.G. IVORY' on tailgate.......... £15-25
20 **1910 Lanchester.**
Light Blue 4-seater sports ...................... £10-25
21 **1922 Morris Cowley.**
Beige 2-seater open ................................. £10-25
22 **1900 Daimler.** Maroon 2-seater ............ £10-25
23 **1904 Autocar.**
Dark Blue, open 3-wheeler .................... £10-25
24 **1870/80 Grenville Steam Carriage.**
Green or Light Green .............................. £10-25
25 **1905 Napier.**
Violet or Purple 2-seater racer ............... £10-25

26 **Fire Engine and Escape.**
Red or Orange ......................................... £10-25
27 **Articulated Breakdown Lorry.**
Dark Green cab, Light Blue trailer,
Orange crane ........................................... £10-25
28 **Mercer Runabout.**
Dark Blue or Green 2-seater sports......... £10-25

**MILITARY MODELS**
30 **Searchlight on 4-wheel Trailer.**
Green and Silver...................................... £10-25
31 **Twin Bofors Gun on Trailer.**
Green and Silver...................................... £10-25
32 **Radar Scanner on Trailer.**
Green and Silver...................................... £10-25
33 **Field Gun on Trailer.**
Green and Silver...................................... £10-25
34 **Rocket Gun on Trailer.**
Green and Silver...................................... £10-25
35 **Armoured Car.** Green ........................... £10-25

**'MINIATURE LORRIES'**
Listed in 1960 catalogue but not issued.
40 **Articulated Tanker** .............................NPP
41 **Articulated Lorry** ...............................NPP
42 **Six-wheeled Lorry** .............................NPP
43 **Six-wheeled Tanker** ...........................NPP

Charbens No. 36, '3-wheel Pedestrian Electric Vehicle'. PHOTO: VECTIS AUCTIONS LTD.

# Salco Series

**Mickey's Fire Brigade**
Red fire engine with unpainted ladder,
5 painted Mickey Mouse figures.
All card picture box........................... £750-1,000

**Mickey and Minnies' Piano**
Cream piano with operating handle,
Mickey and Minnie Mouse figures.
Black/Blue/Yellow/White all
card picture box................................... £200-300

**Mickey and Minnies' Barrel Organ**
Red organ with Yellow wheels,
Mickey and Minnie Mouse figures.
All card picture box............................. £200-300

**Milk Cart with Pluto and Donald Duck**
(no details).......................................... £200-300

**'Mickey and Minnie on the River'**
Green boat, 2 seats,
Mickey and Minnie figures .............. £750-1,000

**'Mickey and Donald's Garden' Set**
Blue wheelbarrow, spade, rake.
Boxed.............................................. £750-1,000

**Donald Duck's Dairy**
A cart with Donald and Pluto.
Yellow / red / blue / white.................. £300-450

**Horse-drawn Brewer's Dray**
Light Blue dray with Yellow detachable
brewery sign marked
'TOY TOWN BREWERS',
six unpainted barrels, black bowler-hatted
driver and brown horse........................ £300-400

**Window Cleaner** (boxed)
'Toyland Series'. Green/brown cleaner, red
bike, yellow sidecar, ladder, bucket .... £300-400

Corgi Toys sales material. Above: various counter-top and window display items.
Below: a huge replica of a Corgi Toys box.    PHOTOS: VECTIS AUCTIONS LTD.

# Corgi Toys

Corgi Toys were launched in 1956 by the Mettoy Company which had itself been founded in Northampton by Phillip Ullmann in 1933. The 'Mettoy' name was derived from the first three letters of 'Metal' plus 'toy' - the company's main product range being composed of lithographed metal toys. In 1948 Mettoy produced their first cast metal toys and called them 'Castoys'. The Castoys models contained a clockwork motor and when the first Corgi Toys models were introduced they also contained a mechanism. This, plus the introduction of window glazing, gave Corgi a competitive edge against their great rivals, Dinky Toys.

Corgi Toys were named after the Welsh breed of dogs and this logo will be found on virtually all the Corgi packaging. The models were produced in Swansea by Mettoy Playcraft Ltd., hence baseplates are marked 'Made in Gt. Britain'.

The development of the Corgi Toys product range was largely instigated by Howard Fairbairn, a Mettoy Company Director. Prior to his director appointment, he had been Head of Development at the Birmingham Aluminium Casting Co. and had considerable diecasting experience. The first truly Corgi Toys product was No.200 Ford Consul in 1956.

Corgi have always been famed for their model innovations. This was especially true when they were able to promote their models as 'The Ones With Windows'. Additionally, greater realism was achieved over time with, for example, better detailing of their wheel hubs.

Corgi introduced various model ranges which have stood the test of time. Today, virtually all the Corgi models produced in the 1950s and 1960s are highly sought after. In particular, model such as the range of 'Monte Carlo' Minis, the Gift Sets, Farm Tractors and the 'Chipperfield's Circus' subjects are very collectable. In addition, television and film related models such

Corgi Toys shop display card
Photo: Vectis Auctions

as 'Batman', 'James Bond' and similar items fetch very high prices at auction.

In 1983, the Mettoy company went into receivership and Corgi Toys became the subject of a management buy-out. From this time, the emphasis changed from the mass-production of toy vehicles to mainly the development of authentic limited edition models aimed at adult collectors - the 'Corgi Classics' range. Regrettably these items fall outside the scope of this publication. However, collectors requiring information on Corgi Classics are recommended to join the Corgi Collectors Club.

The Editor wishes to thank all who have contributed to the greatly revised listings.

## Market Price Range
**Please note that the prices shown refer to pristine models and boxes.
Items failing to match this standard will sell for less. Note also that boxes
must still contain all their original additional contents.**

# Corgi Toys Identification

Often referred to as 'the ones with windows', Corgi Toys were the first manufacturer to produce models with that refinement. Some of their first models also had a mechanical motor. Spring suspension was introduced from 1959 and in 1960 the first die-cast model to have an opening bonnet. The first models were based on real cars of the period. Similarly, with the launch of the 'Corgi Major Toys' in 1959, models of real commercial vehicles were available and competed with the Dinky 'Supertoys' range.

In the 1960s Corgi produced many successful film and TV-related models. Probably the best remembered was the 'James Bond' Aston Martin which sold in huge quantities in the autumn of 1965. Indeed, such is the popularity of the model that various versions have been marketed over the last forty years and are still available to the present day!

Corgi introduced many new features in the 1960s such as: jewelled headlights, opening bonnet revealing detailed engine, opening boot revealing spare, self-centering steering, ruby rear lights, etc. One particularly attractive model was the Midland Red Motorway Express Coach. The detailed interior even incorporated a toilet! Needless to say good examples of this model are highly sought after by bus collectors. Similarly the 'Chipperfields Circus' collection of models were beautifully produced and are highly prized today.

Innovations were frequent and imaginative in the 1960s. 'Golden Jacks' for instance, a built-in jacking system which enabled models to have 'Take-Off' wheels. And 'Trans-O-Lites' whereby light rays were captured and fed through prisms to illuminate the headlights. 'WhizzWheels' and the slightly larger scale of 1:42 were introduced in the 1970s.

A market strategy favoured by Corgi was the launching of a replica model car simultaneously with the real car. To date simultaneous launches have occurred with Austin Metro, Ford Escort, Triumph Acclaim, Ford Sierra and the MG Maestro 1600, which is a unique record. Corgi were the first die-cast manufacturers to introduce the dimensions of light, sound and movement into their models by using the micro-chip in their 'Corgitronic' range. The models 'come alive', for example by just pushing down on the rear axle or, in the case of the Road Repair Unit, by pressing the workman to activate the pneumatic drill sound. Others (like the Sonic Corgi Truck) can be operated from a remote control handset.

**Mechanical**. Some early Corgi Toys were produced in either the normal form or with a friction type flywheel motor. Exceptions were the sports cars and trucks which could not be converted to take the flywheel. The mechanisms were not robust and were phased out in 1959.

**Boxes**. July 1956 - Blue box, January 1959 - Yellow/Blue box (Two-tone cars were first to use them) December 1966 - Window box (2 square window ends) May 1973 - Angled window box (one square window end, coloured lines around box) 1980 - Yellow window box, 1987 New style Corgi logo box.

**Box contents**. Model boxes often contain much more than just the basic model. Prices shown in the Catalogue assume that not only is the model in pristine condition, but that it is accompanied by all the original additional contents. These can include: extra card packing, inner card or polystyrene trays, pictorial stands, plastic protectors, transit card protection intended for removal by the retailer, instruction and information leaflets, catalogues, consumables (such as unopened packets of rockets, decals, etc.). This particularly applies to some Novelty and Film/TV models, e.g., Nos. 268, 277, 497, 511, 1123, 1139, 1144 and Gift Sets 3, 10, 20 and 21. A further example relates to the early 'Blue box' models each of which should contain a concertina catalogue leaflet plus a 'Join the Corgi Club' leaflet. If original items are missing, e.g., the plastic dome protector included with 511 Chipperfields Poodle Truck or card protectors with other models, it will affect the price that a model will achieve.

Whilst every effort has been made to describe models and, where known, their accompanying contents, any further information would be welcomed.

Corgi Toys advertising sign.
This illuminated plastic and metal sign is fitted with chains for hanging. The yellow background
has the wording 'Naturally' in red and 'Corgi Toys' in blue.
PHOTO: VECTIS AUCTIONS LTD.

# Mettoy Diecast Toys – The 'Castoys' series

Castoys were produced by the Mettoy Company between 1948 and 1958 and were instigated by a request from Marks and Spencers for a robust, long lasting toy. The models were made of zinc alloy and were initially advertised as 'Heavy Cast Mechanical Toys'.

Generally, they had windows, a clockwork motor and brake, plus black rubber tyres on cast hubs. Of the original issues, only two models, No. 840, the 'Eight Wheel Lorry' and 870 'Delivery Van' remained in production after 1951 and these were packaged in attractive Yellow/

Red boxes which displayed a picture of the model inside. The later issues of the Delivery Van with their various attractive body designs are now rare and sought after items.

The following listing contains all the information available at present. The Editor would welcome any additional information on body colours and variations.

| Model and details | MPR |
| --- | --- |

## Large scale models 1:35

**---** **Milk Handcart**
19??
With 'MILK' logo and Milkman ...... **£150-175**

**718** **Luxury Observation Coach**
1956-58
Metallic Blue and Gold body with Silver raised roof section and base, Red door with Brown plastic male passenger. Destination board shows 'PRIVATE' and registration 'MTY 718' ...................................... **£250-350**
Metallic Brown and Pink body with Silver raised roof section and radiator, with Green female passenger............ **£200-300**

**810** **Limousine**
1948-51
Cream, Red or Green body, Red interior, 'MTY 810', clockwork ...... **£100-200**

**820** **Streamline Bus**
1948-51
Cream, Green or Red body, clockwork mechanism, Red pressed tin seating, solid rubber wheels, unpainted chassis. Registration No 'MTY 820'............. **£100-200**
As previous model but with opening door, registration No. 'MTY 720'..... **£100-200**

| Model and details | MPR |
| --- | --- |

Presented in Yellow/Red endflap boxes each displaying an excellent picture of the model contained within.

**830** **Racing Car**
1948-51
Light Green, 6, long approx, 'METTOY' cast in base, tinplate hollow printed wheels with motor and brake............ **£100-200**

**840** **8 Wheel Lorry**
1948-58
Metallic Blue cab with Grey rear body, Silver radiator and hubs.................... **£100-200**

**850** **Fire Engine**
1948-51
Red body, Silver ladder and crank.... **£100-200**
Red body, Silver extending ladder, no crank............................................ **£100-200**

**860** **Tractor**
1948-51
No models seen but shown in 1951 catalogue with Yellow/Red body ...NGPP

**863** **Ferguson TE20 Tractor and Trailer**
19??
Red/Blue tractor, Yellow trailer, Red hubs, painted plastic driver ...... **£200-300**

| Model and details | MPR |
| --- | --- |

**870** **Delivery Van** (plain, without advertising)
1948-51
Dark Blue, Cream, Green or Red ..... **£200-300**

**870** **Delivery Vans** (with advertising or logo)
**'EXPRESS DELIVERY'**
1952-55
Yellow or Blue body with Red logo and design on sides, clockwork........ **£600-800**
**'POST OFFICE TELEPHONES'**
1955-58
Green body, White logo, Royal crest in Gold, Silver two part extending ladder............................................ **£300-500**
**'ROYAL MAIL'**
1955-58
Red body, Silver trim, Yellow logo and Royal crest, 'MTY 870' ............. **£300-500**
**'AMBULANCE'**
1955-58
Cream body, Blue logo on sides....... **£200-300**
**'BOAC'**
1956-58
Blue body, Silver trim, White *Fly By BOAC* on roof.......... **£400-600**

## Small scale models 1:45

no ref. 1955-57 **Karrier Bantam Soft Drinks Van**
Dark red body, number plate 'CWS 300', spun huns, logo on rear:
'CWS SOFT DRINKS - THIRST COME - THIRST SERVED'................. **£1,500-2,000**

## Special 1:18 scale issue for Marks and Spencer

no ref. 1958 **'VANWALL' Racing Car**
Diecast body, perspex screen, driver, 'VANWALL' transfers, 'push and go' motor in some. 'Vanwall the famous British Grand Prix Winner' cast in base.
Green body, racing number '7' or '18', no Mettoy logo on base..........**£300-350**
French Blue body, racing number '20', no Mettoy logo on base..........**£300-350**
Red body, racing number '7'..............................................................**£300-350**
Cream body, racing number unknown...................................................**£300-350**

## 'Miniature Numbers' series

A range of models (produced between 1951 and 1954) based on just two vehicles - the Standard Vanguard and a Rolls-Royce. They came in attractive window boxes and featured a clockwork motor plus brake, adjustable steering (controlled by moving the central fog lamp) and moulded grey plastic wheels. Both diecast and plastic bodies have been observed. This listing has been taken from the 1951 Mettoy Catalogue and the Editor would welcome any additional information.

**502** 1951 **Standard Vanguard Saloon**
Shown with Green body in catalogue, (2 7/8" inches long) .. **£60-90**

**505** 1951 **Rolls-Royce Saloon**
Red or Blue body, 3"................. **£60-90**

**510** 1951 **Standard Vanguard Police Car**
Black with White 'POLICE' logo on doors; roof siren and bell ...... **£60-90**

**511** 1951 **Standard Vanguard Taxi**
Shown in 1951 catalogue with Yellow body and Red roof rack . **£60-90**

**512** 1951 **Standard Vanguard Fire Chief**
Red, White 'FIRE CHIEF' on doors; single Silver ladder on roof........ **£60-90**

**Larger versions:**

**602** 1951 **Standard Vanguard Saloon**
Blue body shown in catalogue (larger version of 502, 4¼")....... **£60-90**

**603** 1951 **Standard Vanguard Saloon**
As 602 but with automatic 'to and fro' bump feature............ **£60-90**

**605** 1951 **Rolls-Royce Saloon**
Yellow body shown in catalogue (larger version of 505, 4½")....... **£60-90**

**606** 1951 **Rolls-Royce Saloon**
As 605 but with automatic 'to and fro' bump feature............ **£60-90**

Corgi Toys 218 Aston-Martin DB4, 206 Hillman Husky,
214s Ford Thunderbird and 211s Studebaker Golden Hawk.

PHOTOS: CHRISTIE'S SOUTH KENSINGTON

| Model and details | MPR |
|---|---|

**150** 1957-61 **Vanwall Racing Car**
- Green body, Yellow seat, large or small 'Vanwall', flat hubs, RNs '1', '3' or '7', clear or Blue screen. 'Made in Gt Britain' or 'British Made' and large 'CORGI TOYS VANWALL' cast along base. Blue box with leaflet............................**£90-110**
- Mid-Green body, Silver seat, small 'Vanwall', clear screen. 'Made in Great Britain' cast along base. 'CORGI TOYS VANWALL' small across base. Flat hubs. RN '3'.......................**£90-110**
- Vermillion Red body, Silver or Yellow seat, small or large 'Vanwall', Blue or clear screen. RN '1', '3' or '7'. 'CORGI TOYS VANWALL' cast small across or large along base. Flat or spoked hubs. Blue/Yellow box.........**£125-175**

**150S** 1961-65 **Vanwall Racing Car** (with 'suspension')
- Vermillion Red body, Blue/White bonnet design plus Black RN '25', White driver, Silver seat, small 'Vanwall', 'Made in Gt. Britain' cast along the base. '150S CORGI TOYS VANWALL' across base....................**£90-110**
- Same but with Crimson body .........**£125-175**
- Promotional: 'Vandervell Products' finish..................NGPP

**150** 1972-74 **Surtees TS9 Formula 1**
- Metallic Purple or Metallic Blue body, 'BROOKE BOND OXO' logo, 8-spoke WhizzWheels.........................**£40-50**
- Metallic Turquoise body, cast 8-stud WhizzWheels .......................................**£30-40**
- 1975-76 Blue/Yellow body, DUCKHAMS', (in GS 29 only) ...............GSP

**151** 1958-61 **Lotus XI Le Mans Racing Car**
- Blue body, Red or Maroon seats, clear or Blue-tinted windscreen, RN '1', or '3'....................................**£200-250**
- Silver body, Red seats, RN '3'. Blue tinted screen............................**£120-150**
- Red body, Beige seats, RN '1'. Blue tinted screen............................**£200-250**

**151A** 1961-65 **Lotus XI Le Mans Racing Car**
- Blue body, Red seats, Red/White bonnet stripe, White driver, Black RN '7'..................................**£100-125**
- Blue body, no bonnet stripe, Red seats, White driver, Black racing number '7'...............**£100-125**
- Lemon body, RN '3', driver............**£130-160**

**151** 1974-76 **Yardley Mclaren M19A**
- White body, 'YARDLEY', RN '55', 8-spoke or stud WhizzWheels ............**£40-50**
- With Blue stripe on White helmet, WhizzWheels, (GS30 only) ....................GSP

**152** 1958-61 **B.R.M. Racing Car**
- Light or Dark Green body, Yellow seat, no driver, RNs '1', '3' or '7'. Blue box with leaflet............................**£90-110**
- 1961-65 Turquoise body, Union Jack on bonnet, RN's '1', '3' or '7'. Blue/Yellow box, no leaflet ...............**£90-110**

**152S** 1961-65 **B.R.M. Racing Car** (with 'suspension')
- Turquoise body, Union Jack on bonnet, White driver, RNs '1', '3' or '7', Blue/Yellow box, no leaflet ...........**£140-160**

**152** 1974-75 **Ferrari 312 B2**
- Red body, 'Ferrari/Shell' logo, RN '5', White driver, Orange/Blue helmet, 8-spoke or 8-stud cast hubs.................**£30-35**

**153** 1960-61 **Bluebird Record Car**
- Blue body, UK and US flags on nose, metal hubs..............................**£100-130**

**153A** 1961-65 **Bluebird Record Car**
- Blue body, UK and US flags on nose, plastic hubs ..........................**£100-130**
- Blue body with two Union Jacks on nose, plastic hubs .......................**£100-130**

**153** 1972-74 **Team Surtees TS 9B**
- Red body, Blue or Blue/White driver (Rob Walker), RN '26', 8-spoke hubs .**£40-50**
- Red body, 'NORRIS', (GS 30 only)..........GSP

**154** 1963-72 **Ferrari Formula 1**
- Red body, Ferrari bonnet badge, White driver, RN'36'. Plain blue/yellow card box ..................**£60-80**
- **Trade Pack of six 154 Ferrari Cars**...................... **£300-350**

**154** 1974-79 **'JOHN PLAYER SPECIAL' Lotus** (Drivers Emerson Fittipaldi or Ronnie Petersen).
- Black body, Gold trim, RN '1' or '4', 'JPS' logo, Black/Red helmet, 8-stud hubs, 'Fittipaldi' on box...........**£40-50**
- 'JPS' logo, Black or Blue helmet, 'Petersen' on box..............................**£40-50**
- 'JPS TEXACO' logo, Red helmet .......**£40-50**
- 'JPS TEXACO', Black helmet, 12-spoke hubs, (GS32 only) ....................GSP
- 'JPS SHELL' logo, Black/Red helmet, (GS30 only)......................................GSP
- Marks & Spencers issue: No 'Corgi' on base, 'TEXACO' logo, Orange (?) helmet .....................GSP

**155** 1964-69 **Lotus Climax Racing Car**
- British Racing Green body, Yellow stripe on bonnet, White driver, Blue helmet, RN '1' ...........................**£40-50**

**155** 1974-76 **'SHADOW' Formula 1**
- Black, 'UOP', driver (Jackie Collins) White/Maroon helmet, RN '17'..........**£40-50**

**156** 1967-68 **Cooper-Maserati**
- Dark Blue body, RN '7', White driver, Blue helmet...................**£40-50**

**156** 1974-76 **Graham Hill's Shadow**
- White/Red, RN'12', 'EMBASSY RACING'............................**£40-50**
- Special issue model: Presentation box has outer sleeve with 'Graham Hill OBE, Honoured Guest of the National Sporting Club Café Royal - Monday 24th November 1975', plus the menu for the day ......................................**£300-450**

**158** 1969-73 **Lotus Climax Racing Car**
- Orange and White body, Blue driver, White helmet, Black RN '8' and bonnet stripe..................................**£40-50**

**158** 1975-78 **Elf Tyrell Ford F1**
- Blue body, RN '1', 'ELF', Jackie Stewart driving........................**£40-50**

**159** 1969-72 **Cooper-Maserati**
- Yellow and White body, Black bonnet stripe, Blue driver, White helmet, cast wheels, Yellow number '3' ..........**£40-50**

**159** 1974-76 **Indianapolis Racing Car**
- Red, RN '20', Patrick Eagle driving....**£30-35**

**160** 1975-78 **'HESKETH' 308 F1**
- White body, Black helmet, 4-spoke or 8-stud hubs........................**£30-35**
- Yellow body, 'CORGI TEAM' logo, Orange driver (James Hunt), Black helmet, Blue belts, (GS26 only) .....GSP
- Marks & Spencers issue: White body and driver, 'CORGI' on some, Orange helmet ...............GSP

**161** 1971-73 **Santa Pod 'COMMUTER'**
- Red 'Dragster' body, Chrome engine, RN '2', WhizzWheels.........................**£25-30**

**161** 1977-78 **'ELF-TYRRELL' P34**
- Blue and Yellow body, 'ELF' logo, Red or Blue helmet, 8-stud hubs, Yellow RN '4'....................................**£25-30**

**162** 1978-79 **'ELF-TYRRELL' P34**
- Blue / White, 'FIRST NATIONAL BANK' logo, Red or Orange helmet ... **£25-30**
- Marks & Spencers issue: As previous model but no 'Corgi' on base, 8-stud hubs.......................GSP

**162** 1971-72 **'QUARTERMASTER' Dragster**
- Green / White, driver, plastic hubs ...... **£50-60**

**163** 1971-73 **Santa Pod Dragster 'GLOWORM'**
- White, Blue trim, Red chassis, driver .. **£30-35**

**164** 1972-73 **Ison Bros Dragster 'WILD HONEY'**
- Yellow/Black, Green glass, WW ......... **£40-50**

**165** 1972-74 **Adams Brothers 'DRAG-STAR'**
- Red/Yellow, 4 x V-8 engines, WW ...... **£30-35**

**166** 1971-74 **Ford Mustang 'ORGAN GRINDER'**
- Yellow/Green body, RN '39', driver.... **£30-35**

**167** 1973-74 **USA Racing Buggy**
- White/Red, RN '7', driver, US flag ..... **£40-50**

**169** 1974-77 **'STARFIGHTER' Dragster**
- Blue/Silver/Red body, 'FIRESTONE'.. **£30-35**

**170** 1974-77 **John Woolfe's Dragster**
- 'RADIO LUXEMBOURG', '208'......... **£35-45**

**190** 1974-77 **'JOHN PLAYER' Lotus**
- 1:18 scale, Black/Gold, RN '1', driver, removable wheels, tools included in box...............................**£40-50**

**191** 1975-80 **'TEXACO MARLBORO' F1 Mclaren.** 1:18 scale
- White/Red, RN '5', removable wheels, tools included in box...............**£40-50**

**200** 1956-61 **Ford Consul** (This was the first 'Corgi Toys' model). Flat spun hubs, no suspension, leaflet with early issues.
- Cream body ...........................**£125-150**
- Dark or Pale Green body ................**£125-150**
- Tan or Dark Tan body ....................**£125-150**
- Blue body ..................................**£125-150**
- Light Greyish-Brown body .............**£125-150**
- Bright Green body .........................**£125-150**

**200M** 1956-59 **Ford Consul** (with flywheel motor) Flat spun hubs, no suspension, leaflet with early issues.
- Blue body ..................................**£130-160**
- Dark Green ...............................**£130-160**
- Bright Green...............................**£130-160**
- Two-tone Green............................**£130-160**
- Green/Cream ...............................**£130-160**
- Silver/Cream ...............................**£130-160**
- Pale Grey over Green......................**£130-160**

**200** 1976-78 **BLMC Mini 1000**
• Metallic Blue body, Silver roof,
  Red or White interior ......................... **£20-25**
**200A** 1978-83 **BLMC Mini 1000**
• Met. Blue or Silver body, White or Red
  interior, Union Jack stripe on roof,
  WhizzWheels ...................................... **£25-35**

**201** 1956-61 **Austin Cambridge**
  Flat spun hubs, no suspension,
  leaflet with early issues.
• Pale Blue body ................................. **£125-150**
• Turquoise body ................................ **£125-150**
• Light Grey body ............................... **£125-150**
• Mid-Grey body ................................. **£125-150**
• Green/Cream .................................... **£125-150**
• Two-tone Green ................................ **£125-150**
• Silver over Metallic Green.............. **£150-175**

**201M** 1956-59 **Austin Cambridge**
          **(with flywheel motor)**
  Flat spun hubs, leaflet with early issues.
• Cream body ...................................... **£130-160**
• Red body .......................................... **£130-160**
• Slate Grey body ............................... **£130-160**
• Medium Grey body ........................... **£130-160**
• Silver or Metallic Blue ................... **£130-160**
• Burnt Orange body.......................... **£250-300**

**201** 1970-72 **The Saint's Volvo**
• White, White 'Saint' logo on red label,
  WhizzWheels, driver,
  Red/Yellow 'window' box .............. **£140-160**

**201** 1979-82 **BLMC Mini 1000**
• Silver, 'TEAM CORGI'/'8' on some.. **£15-25**
• Same model but with Orange body ..... **£15-25**
• Dk. Blue, without 'TEAM CORGI'..... **£15-25**
• Dark Blue, 'ESSO' and
  'MICHELIN' labels ............................ **£15-25**

**202** 1956-61 **Morris Cowley**
  Flat spun hubs, no suspension,
  leaflet with early issues.
• Bright Green body............................ **£125-150**
• Grey body ........................................ **£125-150**
• Blue body ......................................... **£125-150**
• Grey/Blue body ................................ **£125-150**
• Blue/Cream body ............................. **£125-150**
• Pale Green/Blue body ...................... **£125-150**
• White/Blue body .............................. **£125-150**

**202M** 1956-59 **Morris Cowley**
          **(with flywheel motor)**
  Flat spun hubs, leaflet with early issues.
• Pale Green body ............................... **£130-160**
• Mid-Green body ............................... **£130-160**
• Dark Green body .............................. **£130-160**
• Off-White body ................................ **£130-160**

**202** 1970-72 **Renault 16TS**
• Blue/Silver, Yellow interior, WW ........ **£25-30**

**203** 1970-72 **De Tomaso Mangusta**
• Met. Dk. Green, Gold stripes, RN '1'.. **£25-35**

**203** 1956-61 **Vauxhall Velox**
  Flat spun hubs, leaflet with early issues.
• Red body .......................................... **£125-150**
• Cream body ...................................... **£125-150**
• Yellow body ..................................... **£125-150**
• Yellow/Red body .............................. **£125-150**

**203M** 1956-59 **Vauxhall Velox**
          **(with flywheel motor)**
  Flat spun hubs, leaflet with early issues.
• Red body .......................................... **£200-250**
• Orange body ..................................... **£250-300**

**203** 1971-72 **De Tomaso Mangusta**
• Green/Gold, White interior, WW........ **£30-40**
• Green body, White interior,
  Silver base, WhizzWheels.................. **£30-40**

**204** 1956-61 **Rover 90**
  Flat spun hubs, leaflet with early issues.
• Cream or Off-White body ............... **£140-160**
• Light or Dark Grey body, flat hubs. **£140-160**
• Mid or Dark Green body, flat hubs.. **£140-160**
• Metallic Green body, flat hubs....... **£140-160**
• Met. Red lower body, Cream upper. **£140-160**
• Metallic Cerise over Grey body....... **£140-160**

**204M** 1956-59 **Rover 90 (with flywheel motor)**
  Flat spun hubs, leaflet with early issues.
• Bright Mid-Green or Dark Green .... **£150-175**
• Grey body ........................................ **£150-175**
• Metallic Green body ........................ **£200-250**

**204** 1972-73 **Morris Mini-Minor**
  All have WhizzWheels.
• Dark Blue body, Lemon interior ......... **£75-85**
• Deep Blue body, Lemon interior..... **£200-250**
• Met. Blue body, Lemon interior....... **£100-125**
• All-Orange body, Lemon interior .... **£100-125**
• Orange body, Black roof ................. **£120-150**

**205** 1956-62 **Riley Pathfinder**
  Flat spun hubs, leaflet with early issues.
• Red body .......................................... **£130-160**
• Blue body ......................................... **£130-160**
**205M** 1956-59 **Riley Pathfinder**
          **(with flywheel motor)**
  Flat spun hubs, leaflet with early issues.
• Red body .......................................... **£200-250**
• Mid Blue body ................................. **£200-250**
• Navy Blue body ............................... **£200-250**

**206** 1956-59 **Hillman Husky Estate**
  Flat spun hubs, leaflet with early issues.
• Tan or Greyish Light-Brown body... **£100-125**
• Metallic Blue and Silver body ........ **£130-170**
**206M** 1956-59 **Hillman Husky Estate**
          **(with flywheel motor)**
  Flat spun hubs, leaflet with early issues.
• Cream body ...................................... **£150-175**
• Mid-Blue body ................................. **£150-175**
• Dark Blue body ................................ **£150-175**
• Grey body ........................................ **£150-175**
• Turquoise body................................ **£250-300**

**207** 1957-62 **Standard Vanguard III**
  Flat spun hubs, leaflet with early issues.
• Off-White body (Red roof top)........ **£150-175**
• Grey body (Red roof)...................... **£120-140**
• Red over Green body ....................... **£120-140**
**207M** 1957-59 **Standard Vanguard III**
          **(with flywheel motor)**
  Flat spun hubs, leaflet with early issues.
• Primrose Yellow body ..................... **£190-230**
• Pale Green body, Red roof pillars.... **£145-175**

**208** 1957-60 **Jaguar 2.4 litre**
  Flat spun hubs, leaflet with early issues.
• White body...................................... **£120-150**
**208M** 1957-60 **Jaguar 2.4 litre**
          **(with flywheel motor)**
  Flat spun hubs, leaflet with early issues.
• Metallic Dark Blue body................. **£150-175**
**208S** 1960-63 **Jaguar 2.4 litre**
          **(with spring suspension)**
• Flat spun hubs, Lemon body........... **£120-150**
• Flat spun hubs, Pale Lemon body.... **£120-150**

**210** 1957-60 **Citroën DS19**
  Flat spun hubs, leaflet with early issues.
• Yellow body, Red roof, Grey
  or Silver baseplate............................ **£120-160**
• Met. Dark Green body, Black roof .. **£120-160**
• As previous but with bulge in base to
  take flywheel motor. Note that a
  '210M' was not produced ................ **£120-160**

**210S** 1960-65 **Citroën DS19 (with suspension)**
• Red body, Lemon interior,
  Grey base......................................... **£130-160**

**211** 1958-60 **Studebaker Golden Hawk**
  Flat spun hubs, leaflet with early issues.
• Blue body, Gold rear wing flashes... **£120-150**
• White body, Gold rear wing flashes **£120-150**
**211M** 1958-59 **Studebaker Golden Hawk**
          **(with flywheel motor)**
  Flat spun hubs, leaflet with early issues.
• White/Gold body............................. **£140-170**
**211 S** 1960-65 **Studebaker Golden Hawk**
          **(with spring suspension)**
• Gold ('plated') body, Red interior,
  White flash, shaped hubs ................ **£100-125**
• Gold (painted) body, shaped hubs.... **£100-125**

**212** 1958  **Road Racer**  Not released,
              one example known to exist.......NPP

**214** 1959-65 **Ford Thunderbird Hardtop**
  Flat spun hubs, leaflet with early issues.
• Pale Green (Cream hardtop),
  '1959' rear no. plate ........................ **£100-120**
• Same but blank rear plate................ **£100-120**
• Grey body (Red top),
  '1959' no. plate ............................... **£100-120**
**214M** 1959-60 **Ford Thunderbird Hardtop**
          **(with flywheel motor)**
  Flat spun hubs, leaflet with early issues.
• Pink (Black top),
  '1959' rear no. plate ........................ **£200-250**
• Pale Green body, Cream hardtop ..... **£170-200**
**214S** 1962-64 **Ford Thunderbird Hardtop**
          **(with spring suspension)**
• Shaped spun hubs, Metallic
  Grey/Red body, Lemon interior ....... **£100-120**
• Black/Red body, Lemon interior...... **£100-120**

**215** 1959-62 **Thunderbird Open Sports**
• Flat spun hubs, White body,
  Blue interior .................................... **£100-120**
• Blue body, Silver interior................ **£100-120**
**215S** 1962-64 **Thunderbird Open Sports**
          **(with spring suspension)**
• Red body, Yellow interior / driver ... **£125-150**

**216** 1959-62 **Austin A40**
  Flat spun hubs, leaflet with early issues.
• Two-tone Blue body........................ **£100-120**
• Red body, Black roof ...................... **£100-120**
**216M** 1959-60 **Austin A40 (with flywheel motor)**
  Flat spun hubs, leaflet with early issues.
• Red body, Black roof ...................... **£175-200**
• All-Red body................................... **£130-160**

**217** 1960-63 **Fiat 1800 Saloon**
• Light Blue (Lemon interior),
  smooth or shaped hubs...................... **£60-70**
• Two-tone Blue (Lemon interior),
  smooth or shaped hubs...................... **£80-90**
• Light Tan body, Lemon interior .......... **£60-70**
• Mustard Yellow body,
  Bright Yellow interior .................... **£100-120**

**218** 1960-62 **Aston Martin DB4**
• Red body (bonnet vent on some),
  flat or shaped hubs ............................ **£80-100**
• 1961-62 Red body, Red interior,
  cast 'spoked' hubs ............................. **£80-100**
• Primrose Yellow body with bonnet vent,
  Red interior, flat spun hubs............... **£80-100**
• Same model, but with cast
  'criss-cross' wheels ......................... **£140-170**

**219** 1959-63 **Plymouth Suburban Sports**
• Cream with Fawn roof, Red interior,
  smooth flat hubs ............................... **£80-100**

**220** 1960-65 **Chevrolet Impala**
  All have spun hubs.
• Metallic Red body, Red or
  Lemon interior, leaflet....................... **£70-80**
• Same, but Powder Blue body.............. **£70-80**
• Pink body, Lemon interior .............. **£150-175**
• Sky Blue body, Red interior .............. **£80-90**

**221** 1960-63 **Chevrolet Impala Cab**
- Yellow body, *'NEW YORK TAXI'*, Red interior, smooth/shaped spun hubs, roof box ......................**£90-110**

**221** 1960-63 **Chevrolet Impala State Patrol**
     See 'Emergency Vehicles' section.

**222** 1959-65 **Renault Floride**
- Dark Red body; Red, White or Yellow interior, flat or shaped hubs ..... **£60-70**
- Light Olive, Red interior, flat hubs...... **£70-80**
- Maroon body, Red, White or Yellow interior, flat or shaped hubs ..... **£60-70**
- Metallic Blue body, Red interior, flat or shaped hubs .............. **£60-70**

**224** 1961-65 **Bentley Continental**
    Opening boot with removable spare, special lights.
- Cream over Metallic Apple Green, Red interior ..................... **£120-140**
- Black over Silver body, Red int....... **£120-140**
- Two-tone Green or Gold body ........ **£120-140**
- Metallic Green and White body...... **£120-140**
- Cherry Red body, Lemon interior .... **£120-140**

**225** 1961-65 **Austin 7 (Mini) Saloon**
- Red body, Yellow interior, spun hubs .. **£75-85**
- Primrose-Yellow body, Red interior, flat hubs..................... **£500-600**
- Mid-Blue body, Red interior, shaped hubs................................ **£400-500**
- _Danish promotional:_ 'JENSEN'S', Red body, Lemon interior, flat spun hubs ... **£1,000-1,200**

**226** 1960-68 **Morris Mini Minor**
- Pale Blue body, Cream or Yellow interior, flat or shaped hubs .......... **£80-100**
- Pale Blue, Red interior, spun hubs... **£200-300**
- Red body, flat or shaped hubs ......... **£100-120**
- Metallic Maroon, Lemon interior, detailed cast hubs ............................ **£120-140**
- Yellow body ........................ **£200-250**
- _Danish promotional:_ 'JENSEN'S', Pale Blue body, Red interior, flat spun hubs ... **£1,200-1,400**
- Deep Blue body, (only in Gift Set 11) ......GSP
**NB** The Light Blue version of 226 was also used for a short time by a US games manufacturer in a table-top racing game. This model has a large drive-pin hole in the base and 'EAST AFRICAN RALLY' stickers on the bonnet, RN '3'. Not separately boxed.......................**£200-300**

**227** 1962-65 **Mini Cooper Rally**
- Bright Blue body, White roof and bonnet, Yellow interior, spun hubs, Union Jack and chequered bonnet flags, racing numbers '1', '3' or '7' .. **£200-300**
- Same but Bright Blue body and bonnet, White roof ......................... **£200-300**
- Primrose Yellow body, Red interior, White roof and bonnet with flags and RNs '1', '3' or '7'..................... **£200-300**
- Primrose Yellow body and bonnet, flags, RN '1'................... **£200-300**
- Green body, White roof. Not seen ...........NPP

**228** 1962-65 **Volvo P-1800**
- Beige body, Red interior, spun hubs .... **£65-75**
- Red body, Lemon interior, spun hubs **£80-100**
- Pink or Dark Pink body, Lemon int..... **£55-65**

**229** 1961-66 **Chevrolet Corvair**
- Mid-Blue body, Bright Yellow interior, spun hubs................................. **£60-70**
- Pale Blue body, Lemon or Red interior, shaped hubs ........................ **£60-70**
- Gold body, (in 'Golden Guinea' set).........GSP

**230** 1962-64 **Mercedes-Benz 220 SE**
    Shaped spun hubs, spare wheel in boot.
- Cream (Red interior) ........................... **£70-80**
- Metallic Red body, Lemon interior...... **£70-80**
- Black body, Lemon interior ............ **£70-80**
- Dark Blue body, Lemon interior .......... **£70-80**

**231** 1961-65 **Triumph Herald**
- Gold top / bottom, White in centre, Red interior, smooth flat hubs.......... **£100-130**
- Mid-Blue top / bottom, White centre, Red interior, shaped hubs.................... **£70-80**
- All Pale Blue (details, please!) ..............NGPP

**232** 1961-63 **Fiat 2100**
- Pale Pink with Mauve roof, Lemon interior, spun hubs .................. **£60-70**

**233** 1962-72 **Heinkel Trojan**
    Spun hubs or detailed cast hubs.
- Red body, Lemon interior ................... **£75-80**
- Dark Blue body, Lemon interior.......... **£75-80**
- Lilac body, Lemon interior ............. **£100-125**
- Orange body, Lemon interior.......... **£100-125**
- Pink body, Lemon interior ............. **£100-125**
- Metallic Blue body, spun hubs.......... **£100-125**
- Fawn body, spun hubs...................... **£100-125**
- Turquoise body, spun hubs.............. **£100-125**
**NB** This was the first Corgi model to have 'By Special Request' flash on the box.

**234** 1961-65 **Ford Consul Classic**
- Beige body, Pink roof, Lemon int........ **£70-80**
- Gold body.............................. **£70-80**

**235** 1962-66 **Oldsmobile Super 88**
    All with spun hubs.
- Black body, White side flash .............. **£85-95**
- Metallic Steel Blue, White side flash, Red interior ..................................... **£85-95**
- Light Blue body, Red interior, White side flash................................... **£85-95**

**236** 1964-68 **'CORGI' Motor School**
    (Austin A60)
- Light Blue body, two figures, 'Highway Code' leaflet, r/h drive .......**£90-110**
- _Export issue:_ Dark Blue, left-hand drive, leaflet ... **£125-150**

**238** 1964-68 **Jaguar Mk10**
    All issues have spun hubs, luggage in boot. Blue/Yellow box with leaflet.
- Pale Blue body, Red interior ............ **£100-120**
- Mid-Green body, Red interior .......... **£100-120**
- Deep Blue body, Red interior ......... **£150-175**
- Kingfisher Blue body, Lemon int. ... **£100-120**
- Sea-Green body, Red interior ......... **£200-300**
- Metallic Blue-Grey body, Red int.... **£125-150**
- Metallic Deep Blue body, Red or Lemon interior..................... **£125-150**
- Metallic Sea-Green body, Red int. ... **£175-200**
- Metallic Cerise body, Lemon int...... **£120-140**
- Metallic Silver body, Red interior.... **£175-200**
- Metallic Green body, Red interior ....**£115-135**

**239** 1963-68 **VW 1500 Karmann Ghia**
    Spare wheel/suitcase in boot, spun hubs.
- Cream body (Red interior).................... **£80-90**
- Red body (Yellow interior) .................. **£80-90**
- Gold body, Red or Yellow interior..... **£90-100**
- Red body, White or Yellow interior ..... **£80-90**
- Plum body, Red interior .................... **£90-100**
- Orange body, Yellow interior .......... **£130-160**

**240** 1963-64 **Fiat 600 Jolly**
    Spun hubs, two figures.
- Metallic Light Blue, Silver/Red top, Red interior ..................................... **£150-200**
- Met. Dark Blue body, Red interior .. **£120-140**
- Blue body, Red interior .................... **£120-140**
- Yellow body, Red interior ............... **£140-170**

**241** 1963-69 **Chrysler Ghia L64**
    All have shaped spun hubs or detailed cast hubs and a Corgi dog on the rear shelf.
- Met. Blue/White body, Cream int........ **£70-80**
- Metallic Green body, Cream interior ... **£70-80**
- Metallic Gold body ............................. **£70-80**
- Metallic Silver Blue body, Red int. ..... **£70-80**
- Metallic Copper................................... **£70-80**
- Lime Green, Yellow interior ........... **£100-125**

**242** 1965-66 **Ghia Fiat 600**
- Orange-Yellow body, Red interior, two figures in swim gear, windscreen but no canopy................ **£250-350**

**245** 1964-68 **Buick Riviera**
Model has 'Trans-O-Lites' and towbar.
- Metallic Gold body, Red interior, spoked hubs.......................................... **£70-80**
- Same, but with cast hubs .................. **£110-130**
- Metallic Steel body (Red interior)........ **£70-80**
- Metallic Greenish Blue body .............. **£70-80**
- Pale Blue body, spun or cast hubs ....... **£70-80**

**246** 1965-68 **Chrysler Imperial Convertible**
Shaped spun or detailed cast hubs.
All issues should include driver and passenger, golf trolley in boot, Blue/Yellow box with inner packing.
- Metallic Deep Red body, Pale Blue or Green interior ..................................... **£80-100**
- Metallic Turquoise body, Green int. .. **£80-100**
- Metallic Blue body, Pale Blue int. ....**£110-130**
- Met. Kingfisher Blue, Green int. ..... **£200-250**

**247** 1964-69 **Mercedes-Benz 600 Pullman**
- Metallic Maroon body, Cream interior, windscreen wipers, instruction sheet ... **£80-90**
- Metallic Red body, Cream interior, spun hubs............................................. **£80-90**

**248** 1965-67 **Chevrolet Impala**
- Brown body, Cream roof/interior, shaped spun hubs ................................ **£45-55**

**249** 1965-69 **Morris Mini-Cooper DeLuxe**
- Black body, Red roof, Lemon interior, 'wicker' panels, spun or cast hubs ... **£160-190**

**251** 1963-66 **Hillman Imp**
Model has spun hubs and luggage.
- Metallic Blue body, Yellow interior..... **£85-95**
- Metallic Bronze body, White side stripe and interior.......... **£100-125**
- Danish promotional: 'JENSEN'S', Light Blue body, Yellow interior, logo ................. **£1,000-1,200**

**252** 1963-66 **Rover 2000**
Spun hubs; leaflet in box.
- Metallic Light Blue or Steel Blue body, Red interior.............................**£90-110**
- Metallic Maroon body, Red or Yellow interior..................... **£230-280**

**253** 1964-68 **Mercedes-Benz 220 SE**
- Metallic Maroon body, luggage, spare wheel........................................ **£80-100**
- Met. Blue, luggage, spare wheel........ **£80-100**

**255** 1964-68 **Motor School A60**
- Dark Blue body, l/h drive, 5 language leaflet, (USA issue of 236). ........ **£125-145**

**256** 1965-68 **Volkswagen 1200 Rally**
- Orange body, RN '18', 'EAST AFRICAN RALLY', steering wheel on roof, rhinoceros figure ............................. **£250-300**

**258** 1965-70 **The Saint's Volvo P1800**
See 'Novelty, Film and TV-related' section.

**259** 1966-69 **Citroën 'Le Dandy'**
- Metallic Dark Red, Yellow interior, wire wheels ................................... **£125-150**
- Met. Blue body, White roof / boot... **£125-150**

**260** 1969-? **Renault 16 TS**
- Metallic Red, Yellow int., cast hubs .... **£35-45**

**261** 1965-69 **James Bond's Aston-Martin**
See 'Novelty, Film and TV-related' section.

**262** 1967-69 **Lincoln Continental Executive Limousine**
Box should also contain a picture strip for use with the on-board 'TV set'.
- Metallic Gold/Black body ............... **£120-140**
- Light Blue/Tan body ....................... **£125-150**

**263** 1966-69 **Rambler Marlin Sports**
- Red body, Black roof White interior, spun or cast hubs................................ **£60-70**
- White body, Blue roof, (in Gift Set 10) ....GSP

**264** 1966-69 **Oldsmobile Toronado**
- Met. Medium or Dark Blue body, smooth or cast spoked hubs, Cream interior .... **£50-60**

**269** 1977-83 **James Bond Lotus Esprit**
**270** 1968-78 **James Bond Aston-Martin**
**271** 1978-92 **James Bond Aston-Martin**
See 'Novelty, Film and TV-related' section.

**272** 1969-69 **Ghia Mangusta De Tomaso**
- Blue/White body, Gold stripes........... **£80-100**
- Orange-Red body .............................. **£80-100**

**272** 1981-83 **James Bond Citroën 2cv**
See 'Novelty, Film and TV-related' section.

**273** 1970-? **Rolls-Royce Silver Shadow**
With 'Golden Jacks', 'Take-Off wheels', and a spare wheel.
- Metallic Silver/Blue ........................... **£75-95**
- Pearlescent White over Grey, Blue int. **£65-85**

**273** 1982-83 **Honda Ballade 'BSM' Driving School Car**
- Yellow body with Red side stripes ...... **£25-35**

**274** 1970-72 **Bentley 'T' Series**
- Bright Pink body, Cream interior, special lights, WhizzWheels ................ **£40-50**

**275** 1968-70 **Rover 2000 TC**
With 'Golden Jacks', 'Take-Off wheels', and a spare wheel.
- Metallic Olive Green body, Brown or Red interior, Amber roof panel ........... **£75-85**
- Same but with White interior............. **£90-120**
- White body, Maroon interior, Amber roof panel ........................... **£120-150**
- Metallic Maroon body....................... **£90-120**
- Gold plated version .......................... **£150-250**

**275** 1981-84 **Mini Metro**
- Blue, Purple or Red body, Yellow int. . **£10-15**
- Gold body...................................... **£45-50**
- **'Royal Wedding' Metro**
Mauve body, Silver 'Charles & Diana' crest, special Mauve box..................... **£20-25**

**276** 1968-72 **Oldsmobile Toronado**
With 'Golden Jacks', 'Take-Off wheels'.
- Metallic Blue or Red body.................. **£50-70**
- Metallic Gold body, Cream interior ..... **£45-65**
- Metallic Green body, Cream interior ... **£45-65**
- Metallic Brown body, Cream interior .. **£45-65**

**276** 1982-83 **Triumph Acclaim**
- Metallic Blue, or Cream body, steering control.................................... **£7-10**

**277** 1982- **Triumph Acclaim 'BSM' Driving School Car**
- Yellow body, Black 'wheel' steering control on roof................................... **£15-20**

**278** 1982-? **Triumph Acclaim 'CORGI MOTOR SCHOOL' Car**
- Yellow body, with steering control ...... **£25-35**

**279** 1980-? **Rolls-Royce Corniche**
- Metallic Dark Red body, opening doors/bonnet/boot.................. **£20-25**

**280** 1970-78 **Rolls-Royce Silver Shadow**
- Metallic Silver upper body, Blue lower body, Brown interior, WhizzWheels.... **£35-40**
- Met. Blue body, Brown interior, WW .. **£35-40**

**281** 1971-72 **Rover 2000 TC**
- Metallic Red body, Yellow interior, Amber or clear roof, WhizzWheels ..... **£60-75**
- Purple body, Amber roof................. **£100-125**

**281** 1982- **'DATAPOST' Metro**
- Blue/White body, RN '77', adverts. ...... **£9-12**

**282** 1971-74 **Mini Cooper Rally**
- White/Black/Yellow, number '177', special lights, WhizzWheels ............... **£55-65**

**283** 1971-74 **DAF 'City' Car**
- Red/Black body, White interior, WW .. **£15-20**

**284** 1970-76 **Citroën SM**
- Green body, Pale Blue interior, spoked wheels .................................. **£40-45**
- Metallic Cerise, Pale Blue interior, spoked wheels .................................. **£40-45**

**285** 1975-81 **Mercedes-Benz 240 D**
- Silver, Blue, Bronze or Beige (all Metallic), WhizzWheels ............... **£25-35**

**286** 1975-79 **Jaguar XJC V-12**
- Blue/Black, Red/Black, Red, Pearl, Blue or Orange (all Metallic), WW ..... **£25-35**

**287** 1975-78 **Citroën Dyane**
- Metallic Green, duck decal, WW......... **£25-35**
- Same but Metallic Yellow/Black ......... **£25-35**
- Metallic Bronze, duck decal, WW....... **£25-35**

**288** 1975-79 **Minissima**
- Beige/Black/Yellow body ................... **£25-35**

**289** 1976-80 **VW Polo 'DBP'** (German issue)
- Yellow/White body, l/h drive, WW...... **£55-75**
**289** 1977-81 **Volkswagen Polo**
- Lime Green or Orange body ............... **£25-35**
**289** 1977-81 **VW Polo 'ADAC'** (German issue)
- As previous model but Yellow body.... **£55-75**

**290** 1976-77 **Kojak Buick**
See 'Novelty, Film and TV-related' section.

**290** 1977-82 **Starsky & Hutch Ford Torino**
See 'Novelty, Film and TV-related' section.

**291** 1977-80 **AMC Pacer**
- Metallic Red, opening doors / hatch .... **£20-25**

**291** 1982-? **Mercedes Benz 240 Rally**
- Muddy Cream body, RN '5', 'EAST AFRICAN RALLY' or 'E.A.R.' logos ... **£20-25**

**293** 1977-80 **Renault 5 TS**
- Orange, Silver or Silver/Blue, WW ..... **£20-25**
- French issue:
Light Blue body, Dark Blue roof, 'SOS MEDICINS'............................. **£80-100**

**294** 1980-84 **Renault 5 TS Alpine**
- Black body with White stripe ............. **£10-15**

**298** 1982-83 **Magnum P.I. Ferrari 308GTS**
See 'Novelty, Film and TV-related' section.

**299** 1982-? **Ford Sierra 2.3 Ghia**
- Metallic Light Brown/Black stripe, Dark Brown or Grey interior, Brown or Dark Grey base.
In special two-tone blue 'Ford' box..... **£20-25**
- Met. Lt. Brown, Met. Blue, Red or Yellow. Packed in White/Red 'Ford' box or normal Black/Yellow/Red box . **£15-20**

Corgi Toys 249 Mini-Cooper with De-luxe Wickerwork.    PHOTOS: VECTIS AUCTIONS LTD.

Corgi Toys 339 Mini-Cooper 'S' 'Monte-Carlo Rally 1967'.    PHOTOS: VECTIS AUCTIONS LTD.

A selection of Corgi Toys Racing Cars.    PHOTOS: VECTIS AUCTIONS LTD.

Corgi Toys 319 Lotus Elan S2 Hardtop.    PHOTOS: VECTIS AUCTIONS LTD.

**300** 1956-65 **Austin Healey 100-4**
Flat spun hubs, leaflet with early issues.
• Red with Cream interior ................. **£175-200**
• Cream with Red interior ................. **£175-200**
• Blue body with Cream interior ........ **£175-200**

**300** 1970-70 **Chevrolet Corvette Stingray**
• With 'Golden Jacks' / 'Take-Off Wheels',
and luggage. 'Plated' Bright Green,
Dark Red or Green body ..................... **£85-95**
• Metallic Red body, Black bonnet ..... **£65-75**
• Metallic Green body, Black bonnet ..... **£65-75**
**NB** Models without box header cards
contained instructions.

**300** 1979-82 **Ferrari 'DAYTONA'**
• Green, multicoloured flash, RN '5' ..... **£25-35**

**301** 1956-61 **Triumph TR2**
All have flat spun hubs.
• Cream body, Red seats ..................... **£150-200**
• Red body with Cream seats ............. **£150-200**
• Deep Green body with Cream seats. **£150-200**

**301** 1970-73 **Iso Grifo 7 litre**
• Met. Blue body, Black bonnet, White
interior, Silver or Black roll-bar, WW . **£30-35**

**301** 1979-82 **Lotus Elite Racing Car**
• Yellow/Red, RN '7', *'FERODO'* ......... **£20-25**

**302** 1957-65 **MG 'MGA'**
• Red (shades exist), Cream seats,
smooth or chrome spun hubs ........... **£200-240**
• Cream with Red seats ..................... **£200-240**
• Mid or Dark Metallic Green body,
Cream or Yellow seats, smooth or
shaped spun hubs ........................... **£200-240**
**302** 1969-72 **Hillman Hunter Rally**
• Blue body, White roof, Matt-Black
bonnet, RN '75', equipment,
kangaroo, 'Golden Jacks', transfers,
toolbox, leaflet, instructions ............. **£110-140**

**302** 1979-82 **VW Polo**
• Met. Brown/Red, RN '4', adverts ........ **£20-25**

**303** 1958-60 **Mercedes-Benz 300 SL**
**(Open Roadster)**
• Off-White body, Blue seats,
smooth hubs, Blue box .................... **£125-150**
• Blue body, White seats,
smooth hubs, Blue box .................... **£100-125**
• Cream body, Blue seats,
smooth hubs, Blue box .................... **£100-125**
**NB** If in rare plain overprinted box, add .... **£20-30**

**303 S** 1961-63 **Mercedes-Benz 300 SL**
**(Open Sports) (with Suspension)**
• Off-White body, Yellow interior,
Red bonnet stripe, flat spun hubs,
RNs '1' to '12' ............................... **£100-125**
• Off-White body, Light Blue interior,
Red bonnet stripe, flat spun hubs..... **£175-200**
• Mid-Blue body, Yellow interior,
Red bonnet stripe, RNs '1' to '12'... **£150-175**
**NB** 'Open Sports' models were housed
in 303S 'Open Roadster' boxes.

**303S2 Mercedes-Benz 300 SL**
1963-64 **(Open Sports with Driver)**
**(with Suspension)**
• With driver dressed in Grey suit, White
shirt and Red bow-tie. White body,
Yellow interior, Red bonnet stripe,
RNs '1' to '12', shaped spun hubs... **£100-130**
• Blue body, Yellow int., Red bonnet stripe,
RNs '1' to '12', shaped spun hubs... **£100-130**
• Chrome plated body, Lemon/Brown
interior, Red bonnet stripe, spoked
or cast hubs, RNs '1' to '12'.......... **£175-200**

**303** 1970-72 **Roger Clark's Ford Capri**
• White body, Black bonnet, RN '73',
decal sheet, WhizzWheels ............... **£70-80**
• As previous model but with Red spot
hubs. Yellow/Red box with:
'9 transfers for you to apply!'............**£90-110**

**304** 1959-61 **Mercedes-Benz 300 SL Hardtop**
• Yellow body, Red hardtop,
spun hubs, no suspension................. **£100-125**
• Yellow body / top, flat spun hubs .... **£300-400**

**304 S** 1961-63 **Mercedes-Benz 300 SL Hardtop**
**(with Suspension)**
• Chrome body, Red hardtop, stripe,
smooth or shaped hubs, '3' or '7' .... **£100-130**
• White body, Red hardtop,
RN '7', shaped hubs........................ **£300-400**

**304** 1971-72 **Chevrolet Camaro SS350**
• Dk. Blue body, White bonnet band,
interior and detachable roof,
special lights......................... **£40-50**

**305** 1960-63 **Triumph TR3**
• Metallic Olive Green or Cream body,
Red seats, smooth or shaped hubs ... **£150-175**

**305 S** 1962-63 **Triumph TR3**
**(with spring suspension)**
• Light Green, shaped spun hubs........ **£175-225**
• Cream body, shaped spun hubs........ **£175-225**

**305** 1972-73 **Mini Marcos GT 850**
• White body, Blue/White stripes,
Red interior, RN '7', WhizzWheels.... **£30-35**

**306** 1971-73 **Morris Marina 1.8 Coupé**
• Met. Red body, Cream interior, WW ... **£45-55**
• Met. Lime Green, Cream int., WW .... **£40-45**

**306** 1980-81 **Fiat X1/9S**
• Metallic Blue body with Red/Yellow bands,
racing number '3' or '6' ...................... **£15-20**

**307** 1962-64 **Jaguar 'E' type**
• Metallic Grey body with Red removable
hard-top, Brown interior, spun hubs,
box has inner packing ...................... **£100-125**
• Plum to Red body and top,
inner packing .................................. **£100-125**
**307** 1981-82 **Renault Turbo**
• Yellow/Red body,
*'CIBIE'*, RN '8', adverts ...................... **£10-15**

**308** 1972-76 **Mini Cooper 'S'**
**'MONTE CARLO'**
• Yellow body, '177', two spare wheels
on roof-rack, WW, (339 update) ...... **£100-125**
• Gold-plated body.
Only 144 thought to exist ......... **£1,000-1,500**

**308** 1982-82 **BMW M1**
• Yellow / Black, '25', 'TEAM BMW' .. **£10-15**

**309** 1962-65 **Aston-Martin DB4 Competition**
• Turquoise/White body, Lemon interior,
UK flags on bonnet, spun hubs,
RN '1', '3' or '7'............................. **£125-150**
• Variation with spoked hubs............. **£125-150**

**309** 1982- **VW 'TURBO'**
• White / Orange, RN '14', Red decals.. **£10-15**

**310** 1963-67 **Chevrolet Corvette Stingray**
• Met. Cerise, Lemon int., shaped hubs . **£70-80**
• Metallic Silver body, Lemon int.,
'wire' wheels .................................. **£70-80**
• Metallic Bronze body,
Lemon interior, 'wire' wheels ......... **£100-125**
**310** 1982- **'PORSCHE' 924 Turbo**
• Black/Gold, *'GOODYEAR'* ................. **£10-15**

**311** 1970-72 **Ford Capri V6 3-litre**
• Orange body, Gold wheels with
Red WW hubs, Black interior............. **£80-90**
• Fluorescent Orange, WhizzWheels...... **£50-60**
• Fluorescent Orange, Red WW hubs..... **£70-90**
• Red body / WW hubs, Black bonnet ... **£70-90**

**312** 1964-68 **'E' type Jaguar**
• Silver (vacuum plated) body,
RN '2', driver, spoked hubs............... **£80-100**

**312** 1971-74 **Marcos Mantis**
• Met. Red, White int., spoked hubs....... **£30-40**
**312** 1983- **Ford Capri 'S'**
• White, '6', hinged parcel shelf, ads. .... **£10-15**

**313** 1970-73 **Ford Cortina GXL**
• Metallic Blue body, Black roof,
Black and White interior,
Graham Hill figure, WW ................. **£80-100**
• Bronze body, Black roof, White int. .. **£80-100**
• Yellow body, Black roof ................. **£175-200**
• Metallic Pale Green body,
Black roof, White interior ................. **£80-90**
• Promotional: Tan body, Black roof,
Red interior, left-hand drive,
'CORTINA' number plate ............... **£250-350**

**314** 1965-72 **Ferrari Berlinetta 250 LM**
• Red body, RN '4', wire wheels............ **£60-70**
**314** 1976-79 **Fiat X1-9**
• Metallic Lime Green/Black body ....... **£25-35**
• Silver/Black body................................ **£25-35**
**314** 1982- **Supercat Jaguar XJS-HE**
• Black body, Red or Tan interior.......... **£10-15**

**315** 1964-66 **Simca 1000 Sports**
• Plated Silver, Red interior, RN '8',
Red/White/Blue racing stripes ......... **£70-80**
• Metallic Blue body, RN '8',
Red/White/Blue stripes ................... **£120-140**
**315** 1976-79 **Lotus Elite**
• Red or Yellow with White seats ......... **£20-25**

**316** 1963-66 **NSU Sport Prinz**
• Metallic Red body, Yellow seats,
spun hubs........................................ **£50-60**
**316** 1971-73 **Ford GT 70**
• Metallic Lime Green body,
Black engine cover, White interior,
RN '32', (unapplied) decal sheet ........ **£30-40**

**317** 1964-65 **Mini Cooper 'S'**
**'MONTE CARLO 1964'**
• Red body, White roof, Yellow interior,
RN '37', roof spotlight.
(*Paddy Hopkirk*)............................... **£200-250**
• Red body, Pink roof variation ......... **£250-300**

**318** 1965-66 **Mini Cooper 'S'**
**'MONTE CARLO 1965'**
• Red body, White roof, 'AJB 44B',
racing number '52',
no roof spotlight.............................. **£175-200**

**318** 1965-67 **Lotus Elan S2 Open Top**
• Metallic Steel Blue, RN '6' or '8', driver,
*'I'VE GOT A TIGER IN MY TANK'*,
'tiger' decal, logo on boot lid,
Blue/Yellow box, unapplied decals...**£115-135**
• White body, Black interior, same
'tiger' decal, spun hubs, unapplied
decal sheet (RN '7'), figure ............. **£500-600**

**318** 1965-68 **Lotus Elan S2 Open Top**
• Dark Green body, Yellow stripe with
Black or Red interior (Gift Set 37) ..........GSP
• White body, Black interior (GS40),
'tiger' label, unapplied decals ......... **£250-300**
• Met. Copper body, decals sheet ....... **£200-250**
• Yellow body, Green stripe,
Black interior, spun hubs ................. **£150-200**

**318** 1981-? **Jaguar XJS**
- Blue/Cream body with Red line.......... **£15-20**
- 1983-? Black/Red/White body,
RN '4', 'MOTUL', *'JAGUAR'* .......... **£15-20**

**319** 1967-69 **Lotus Elan S2 Hardtop
(with racing numbers)**
- Yellow body (Green top),
shaped hubs...................................... **£100-125**
- Blue body (White top),
shaped hubs...................................... **£100-125**
- Red body, White top, cast hubs.............. **£75-85**
- Red body, Red top, cast hubs................. **£75-85**
- Blue body, White top, cast hubs ......... **£75-85**
- Green and Yellow lift-off body .......... **£75-85**
- Red body with White top, WW........... **£75-85**
- **NB** 1967-69 boxed issues should include
a sheet of self-adhesive racing
numbers '1' to '12'.

**319** 1973-74 **Lamborghini P400GT**
- Metallic Silver body,
Purple/Yellow stripes, RN '7', WW .... **£25-30**
**319** 1978-81 **Jaguar XJS**
- Met. Red body, Black roof................... **£15-20**

**320** 1965-67 **Ford Mustang Fastback 2+2**
- Opening doors, suspension, Corgi dog,
sliding windows. Silver (Red interior),
detailed cast hubs ............................**£90-110**
- Metallic Deep Blue (Cream interior),
detailed cast hubs ............................**£90-110**
- Metallic Deep Blue (Cream interior),
spoked hubs......................................**£90-110**
- Light Green body (Cream interior),
spoked hubs......................................**£90-110**
- Metallic Purple body, Cream interior,
spoked hubs......................................**£90-110**
- Metallic Deep Yellow body, Black
bonnet and interior, cast hubs .......... **£500-750**

**320** 1978-81 **The Saint's Jaguar XJS**
See 'Novelty, Film and TV-related' section.

**321** 1965-66 **Mini Cooper 'S'
'MONTE CARLO 1965'**
- *(Timo Makinen).* Red body, White roof
without spotlight, 'AJB 44B' on
bonnet, RN '52'................................. **£200-250**
- Same, but in 317 picture box with
'No. 321' and
'MONTE CARLO WINNER' flash. **£350-450**
- Red body, White roof with spotlight,
RN '52', in 321 regular box......... **£200-250**
**321** 1966-67 **Mini Cooper 'S'
'MONTE CARLO 1966'**
- Red body, White roof with RN '2' and
*'TIMO MAKINEN'* and *'PAUL EASTER'*
signatures, no spotlight. White sticker on
box reads: '1966 MONTE CARLO
RALLY AUTOGRAPHED
MINI-COOPER 'S' in red lettering. **£250-350**
- Same but in 321 pictorial box with
'RALLY' text printed in Red panel. **£350-450**

**321** 1978-81 **Porsche 924 Saloon**
- Metallic Green body with hook .......... **£40-45**
- Red body ......................................... **£20-25**
- Met. Light Brown body, Red interior .. **£60-70**
**322** 1967-67 **Rover 2000 'MONTE CARLO'**
- Met. Maroon body, White roof, Red
int., '136', rally plaques, leaflet....... **£250-300**
- Same model but with Green interior......NGPP
- Model boxed in rare 252 box with
'322' labels over the box ends ......... **£300-350**
- 1967
**'INTERNATIONAL RALLY FINISH'**
White body, Black bonnet, Red interior,
White/Orange label on doors with
Black RN '21', cast hubs. 322 box with
Red 'ROVER 2000 INTERNATIONAL
RALLY FINISH' and box flash.
Paint shade differences are known... **£400-500**

**323** 1965-66 **Citroën DS19
'MONTE CARLO 1965'**
- Pale Blue with White roof,
Lemon interior, rally plaques and
no. '75', suspension ........................ **£225-275**

**323** 1974-78 **Ferrari Daytona 365 GTB/4**
- White/Red/Blue body, RN '81'........... **£10-15**

**324** 1966-69 **Marcos Volvo 1800 GT
(with driver)**
- White, Green stripes, Cream int......... **£80-100**
- Blue body, White stripes/bonnet,
Blue interior ................................... **£100-125**
- **NB** Boxed models should include an
unused decal sheet with RNs '4' and '8'.

**324** 1973-75 **Ferrari Daytona Le Mans**
- Yellow, RN '33', *'A. BAMFORD'*....... **£25-35**

**325** 1965-69 **Ford Mustang Competition**
- White body, double Red stripe on
bonnet, roof and boot. Blue interior,
spun hubs or 'wire' wheels or
cast 'alloy' wheels.............................. **£70-80**
- White body, double Red stripe on
bonnet, roof and boot plus Red side
stripe, cast 'alloy' wheels................. **£200-300**
- **NB** An unused sheet of four racing numbers
should be enclosed with this model.

**325** 1981- **Chevrolet Caprice**
- Met. Light Green or Dark Green ......... **£20-25**
- Metallic Silver over Dark Blue
(US export)......................................... **£70-80**

**327** 1967-69 **MGB GT**
- Dark Red body, Blue or Yellow
interior, spoked wheels,
Brown suitcase, leaflet .................... **£125-150**

**327** 1980-81 **Chevrolet Caprice Taxi**
- Yellow, *'THINK TWA'* ........................ **£15-20**

**328** 1966-67 **Hillman Imp
'MONTE CARLO 1966'**
- Metallic Dark Blue/White,
'FRW 306 C', rally plaques and
no. '107', spun hubs........................ **£175-200**
- **NB** If 'HILLMAN IMP 328' Yellow/Red
advertising card is with model, expect
price to be **20%** higher.

**329** 1973-76 **Ford Mustang Rally Car
(391 special)**
- Metallic Green, White roof, RN '69'... **£25-30**
**329** 1980-82 **Opel Senator**
- Dark Blue or Bronze, opening doors ... **£15-18**
- Silver body ........................................ **£25-30**

**330** 1967-69 **Porsche Carrera 6**
- White body, Red bonnet and doors,
RN '60', cast hubs, Blue engine cover **£60-80**
- White body, Dark Blue bonnet and
doors, RN '60', cast hubs,
Orange engine cover ........................**£110-130**

**331** 1974-76 **Ford Capri GT Rally**
- White body, Black bonnet and interior,
Red roof stripe, Red/Black
'TEXACO' logo, RN '5'................. **£200-250**

**332** 1967-69 **Lancia Fulvia Zagato**
- Metallic Green, Metallic Blue,
or Orange body, cast hubs.................. **£60-70**
- Yellow body, Black bonnet ............. **£100-125**

**333** 1966 **Austin Mini Cooper 'S'
'SUN - RAC Rally'**
Leaflet in Blue/Yellow box.
- Red body, White roof (without
spotlight), RN '21' and *'SUN RAC
INTERNATIONAL RALLY'* decals,
225 box with White label: '1966
RAC INTERNATIONAL RALLY'
in Blue. *(Tony Fall / Mike Wood)* .... **£275-325**
- Same model but with Morris grille.. **£500-800**

**334** 1968-70 **Mini Cooper 'Magnifique'**
- Metallic Dark Blue or Green, jewelled
lights, sunshine roof, Cream int. ...... **£125-150**

**334** 1981- **Ford Escort 1.3 GL**
- Blue, Green or Yellow body ............... **£12-15**
- Red body with 'AVIS' logo on roof..... **£25-35**

**335** 1968-70 **Jaguar 4.2 litre 'E' type**
- Met. Dark Red body, Black int., spoked
wheels, wing flap bubble pack......... **£100-125**
- Metallic Blue, Black interior,
wing flap bubble pack..................... **£100-125**
- Orange body, Black roof,
wing flap bubble pack...........................NGPP

**336** 1967-69 **James Bond Toyota 2000GI**
See 'Novelty, Film and TV-related' section.

**337** 1967-69 **Chevrolet Stock Car** *'STINGRAY'*
- Yellow body, Red interior, RN '13'..... **£45-60**

**338** 1968-71 **Chevrolet SS 350 Camaro**
- Metallic Lime Green/Black (Red
interior), Gold/Black or Bronze/Black,
'Golden Jacks'.................................. **£45-60**
**338** 1980-83 **Rover 3500**
- Metallic Blue, Red/Black or
Bronze/Brown ................................. **£20-35**

**339** 1967-71 **Mini Cooper 'S'
'MONTE CARLO 1967'**
- (i) Red body, White roof, RN '177',
2 spare wheels on roof-rack, Austin
grille, cast hubs, in 227 box with
White flash label with:
'1967 MONTE-CARLO WINNER B.M.C.
MINI-COOPER 'S' in Red lettering,
Red '339' flash on box end............. **£250-350**
- (ii) As (i) but shaped spun hubs,
slight Silver detail .......................... **£250-350**
- (iii) As (i) but with Morris grille........... **£250-350**
- (iv) As (i) but in 339 picture box with
'winners' text in Red lettering on box
front. Special leaflet ....................... **£125-150**
- (v) As (i) but in 339 box with the
'winners' text in Red panel ............. **£125-150**

**340** 1967-69 **Sunbeam Imp
'MONTE CARLO 1967'**
- (i) Metallic Blue, RN '77', spun or
cast hubs, flashed 328 box with '1967
MONTE CARLO SUNBEAM IMP
WINNER PRODUCTION CARS UP
TO 1000cc' in Blue capitals
plus model no. '340' ..................... **£200-300**
- (ii) As (i) but in 340 pictorial box with
'winner' text printed in Red on box
front plus cast detailed hubs............. **£200-300**
- (iii) As (i) but Metallic Dark Blue body,
cast detailed hubs, 'winner' text in
Red panel on box front................... **£250-350**
- (iv) As (i) but in plain box with no
'winner' flash .................................. **£60-80**

**340** 1981-84 **Rover 'TRIPLEX'**
- White/Red/Blue, RN '1'..................... **£15-20**

**341** 1968-70 **Mini Marcos GT 850**
- Metallic Maroon body (Cream seats),
'Golden Jacks' and 'Take-off' wheels . **£60-70**

**341** 1981-82 **Chevrolet Caprice**
- Red/White/Blue body, RN '43',
  *'STP'*, White tyres.............................. **£10-15**

**342** 1970-72 **Lamborghini P400 Miura**
- Red body, White interior, Black plastic
  fighting bull figure, WW. 1st type box:
  Blue/Yellow with 'Revised specification'
  label for 'Take-off' wheels................... **£85-95**
- 2nd type box: Red/Yellow box with
  'Revised specification' label ............... **£50-60**
  Lime Green, Red int., bull figure......... **£50-60**

**342** 1980-82 **'The Professionals' Ford Capri**
  See 'Novelty, Film and TV-related' section.

**343** 1969-73 **Pontiac Firebird**
- Met. Silver/Black, Red seats, Gold/Red
  'Take-Off wheels', 'Golden Jacks' ...... **£35-45**
- With Red-hub WhizzWheels................ **£50-60**

**343** 1980-81 **Ford Capri 3 litre**
- Yellow or Silver body, Black designs .. **£30-35**

**344** 1969-73 **Ferrari Dino Sports**
- Yellow with Black doors ('23'), WW .. **£40-50**
- Red with White doors ('30'), WW ...... **£40-50**
- With Red-hub WhizzWheels................ **£50-60**

**345** 1969-? **MGC GT 'Competition'**
- Yellow body, Black bonnet/tailgate/interior,
  spoked wheels, Black suitcase. 'MGB GT'
  on box overprinted 'NEW MGC'.
  Self-adhesive numbers enclosed ...... **£120-140**
- Orange body, Black interior, spoked
  wheels. In early Car Transporter Gift
  Sets 41 and 48 only ....................................GSP

**345** 1981-82 **Honda Prelude**
- Metallic Blue body, sunshine roof ....... **£10-15**
- Cream/Green body, sunshine roof........ **£10-15**
- Metallic Yellow body, sunshine roof ... **£10-15**

**346** 1982-84 **Citroën 2cv**
- Yellow/Black body .............................. **£10-15**
- Burgundy/Black body .......................... **£10-15**
- Red/White body .................................. **£10-15**
- Grey/Red body .................................... **£10-15**
- German promotional:
  Yellow, Black roof, 'REISGOLD' ... **£100-120**

**347** 1969-74 **Chevrolet Astro Experimental**
- Met. Dark Blue body, Red-hub WW ... **£40-50**
- Metallic Green body, Red-hub WW ... **£40-50**
- As previous but with plain WW ......... **£30-40**

**348** 1968-69 **Ford Mustang 'Pop Art'**
- Blue body and interior, Red/Orange
  'Flower-Power' labels, RN '20'.
  Not shown in catalogues ............... **£100-150**
- Light Blue body without labels........... **£60-70**

**348** 1980-81 **'Vegas' Ford Thunderbird**
  See 'Novelty, Film and TV-related' section.

**349** 1967-67 **'POP ART' Morris Mini**
  Red body, Lemon interior,
  4 psychedelic labels, *'MOSTEST'*
  logo, few only made........... **£2,250-2,750**
- Pre-production model:
  Blue body, Red int., cast hubs.... **£1,750-2,250**

**370** 1982-? **Ford Cobra Mustang**
- White/Black/Red/Blue, *'MUSTANG'*,
  with or without tailgate stripe ............. **£10-15**
- White, Red int., Blue/Red design ......... **£10-15**

**371** 1970-73 **Porsche Carrera 6**
- White/Red, RN '60', plated blue
  engine cover, WWs, (330 update)........ **£30-40**

**372** 1970-72 **Lancia Fulvia Zagato**
- Orange body, Black bonnet,
  Black interior, WhizzWeels................ **£35-45**

**373** 1981- **Peugeot 505**
- Red body, Silver or Black lining.......... **£10-15**

**374** 1970-76 **Jaguar 'E' type 4.2 litre**
- Red or Yellow, WW, (335 update) ....... **£55-65**

**374** 1973- **Jaguar 'E' type 5.3 litre**
- Yellow or Metallic Yellow body,
  'New' on box label............................... **£55-65**

**375** 1970-72 **Toyota 2000 GT**
- Metallic translucent 'candy' Blue body,
  White interior, WW,
  (modified 336), leaflet ......................... **£50-60**
- Met. Purple body, White int., WW ...... **£45-55**

**376** 1970-72 **Chevrolet Corvette Stock Car**
- Silver body, racing number '13',
  *'GO-GO-GO'*, WW, (337 update) ......... **£40-50**
- Met. Blue body, Red int., '13', WW.... **£40-50**

**377** 1970-72 **Marcos 3 litre**
- Yellow body, Black bonnet stripe and
  interior, WW, (324 conversion)............ **£40-50**
- White body, Grey sunroof, WW .......... **£50-60**
- Metallic Blue-Green body, Black
  interior, bonnet decal, WhizzWheels ... **£50-60**

**378** 1970-72 **MGC GT**
- Red body, Black bonnet, interior and
  suitcase, WhizzWheels, (345 update) .. **£80-90**
- Orange, (this version only in Set 20)........GSP

**378** 1982- **Ferrari 308 GTS**
- Red or Black, pop-up headlights.......... **£20-30**

**380** 1970-74 **Alfa Romeo P33**
- White, Gold rollbar, Red seats, WW ... **£25-30**

**380** 1983- **'BASF' BMW M1**
- Red/White, RN '80', aerofoil ............... **£7-10**

**381** 1970-76 **VW Beach Buggy**
- Met. Red/White, Blue/White,
  Orange/White or Red/White,
  2 Maroon surfboards, WW.................. **£15-20**

**381** 1983-? **'ELF' Renault Turbo**
- Red/White/Blue, RN '5', *'FACOM'* .... **£10-15**
- Blue/White, number '13', *'ELF'* ......... **£10-15**

**382** 1970-75 **Porsche Targa 911S**
- Metallic Silver-Blue body, Black roof
  with Gold stripe, Black interior, WW .. **£30-40**
- Same but with Red interior .................. **£35-45**
- Metallic Olive-Green body, Black roof
  with or without Gold stripe, WW ........ **£30-40**

**382** 1983-? **Lotus Elite 22**
- Metallic Blue body, 'Elite 22'.............. **£10-15**

**383** 1970-76 **VW 1200 'Flower Power'**
- Red with psychedelic Grenadine and
  Green daisy labels on bonnet / doors ... **£40-50**
- Red body, Green base,
  White interior, no flower decals........... **£25-35**

**383** 1970-73 **Volkswagen 1200 'ADAC'**
- .... See 'Emergency Vehicles' section
- **Volkswagen 1200 'PTT'**
  Yellow/Black body, Red int., Swiss..... **£70-90**

**383** 1977-78 **Volkswagen 1200 Rally**
- Blue, '5', chequered roof and sides .... **£10-15**

**384** 1978- **Volkswagen 1200 Rally**
- Blue body, RN '5', chequered stripes .. **£35-45**
- Same model but with *'CALEDONIAN
  AUTOMINOLOGISTS'* logo ............ **£100-125**
- Blue body, Cream interior, WW,
  '40th Anniversary 1938 - 1978'....... **£160-190**

**384** 1970-73 **Adams Brothers Probe**
- Red body, Silver base, WhizzWheels .. **£30-40**
- Metallic Gold body, WhizzWheels ..... **£30-40**
- Green body, White interior ................. **£30-40**

**384** 1983-84 **Renault 11 GTL**
- Dark Cream body, (export issue)......... **£25-30**
- Maroon or Metallic Mauve body ........ **£25-30**

**385** 1970-76 **Porsche 917**
- Metallic Blue or Red body, RN '3',
  cast or WhizzWheels, with leaflet ....... **£30-40**

**386** 1971-74 **Bertone Barchetta**
- Yellow/Black 'RUNABOUT', WW .... **£20-25**

**387** 1970-73 **Corvette Stingray Coupé**
- Metallic Blue body, Black bonnet,
  roof emblem, WhizzWheels................ **£35-45**
- Metallic Pink body, Black bonnet,
  Black interior...................................... **£35-45**

**388** 1970-74 **Mercedes-Benz C111**
- Orange/Black body, WhizzWheels ...... **£20-25**

**389** 1971-74 **Reliant Bond 'BUG' 700 ES**
- Orange body, 'BUG' labels,
  Cream interior, WW ............................ **£35-45**
- Lime Green body, WhizzWheels ......... **£65-75**

**391** 1972-72 **James Bond Ford Mustang**
  See 'Novelty, Film and TV-related' section.

**392** 1973-76 **Bertone Shake Buggy**
- Pink and Green body, detailed engine,
  flag, WhiaaWheels .............................. **£25-30**
- Yellow body, Black or Green interior .. **£25-30**

**393** 1972-79 **Mercedes-Benz 350 SL**
- White body, Pale Blue interior,
  chrome spoked wheels ........................ **£25-30**
- Metallic Blue or Dark Blue body,
  chrome disc wheels ............................. **£25-30**
- Metallic Green body, Brown interior ... **£65-75**

**394** 1972-77 **Datsun 240 Z 'Safari Rally'**
- 'East African Safari Rally' finish:
  Red body, RN '11', *'CASTROL'* and
  *'JAPAN'* logos ................................... **£30-35**

**395** 1972-73 **Fire Bug**
- Orange body, Whizzwheels, Red/Black
  or Pink/Black stripe, Yellow ladder
  (381 Beach Buggy) ............................. **£20-30**

**396** 1973-76 **Datsun 240 Z 'US Rally'**
- 'US Rally' finish:
  Red/White body, RN '46', *'JOHN
  MORTON'* and *'DATSUN'* logos......... **£30-40**

**397** 1974-76 **Porsche-Audi 917-10**
- White/Red body, 'L&M', RN '6',
  *'CORGI'*, driver ................................. **£25-30**

**400** 1974-75 **Volkswagen 1300
            'CORGI MOTOR SCHOOL'**
- Met. Red, roof steering wheel, cones **£80-100**
- Metallic Blue body............................ **£40-50**
- Metallic Blue body,
  'CORGI FAHR SCHULE',
  (German) ...................................... **£100-120**

**401** 1975-77 **Volkswagen 1300**
- As C400 but with 24 'bollards' and
  diorama for driving practice................ **£45-55**

**406** 1957-62 **Land Rover '109 WB'**
- Yellow body, Black roof,
  smooth hubs, thin tyres ...................... **£70-90**
- Met. Dark Blue body, Cream roof,
  smooth or shaped hubs,
  thin or thick tyres .............................. **£60-70**
- Green body with Tan tinplate cover,
  smooth hubs, thin or thick tyres.......... **£60-70**
- 'ETENDARD' variant:
  As previous issue but with 'ETENDARD'
  decals, plus Red/White/Green roundels
  on front wings ...................................NGPP

**406s** 1963 **Land Rover '109 WB'**
- Yellow body, Red seats,
  shaped hubs, suspension ..................... **£60-70**

**411** 1976-79 **Mercedes Benz 240 D**
- Orange/Black or Cream,
  *'TAXI'* on roof ................................ **£10-15**

- German issue: Black body, Red
  'TAXI' roof sign, 'TAXI' on doors ....... **£35-45**

**415** 1976-78 **Mazda Camper**
- Red body with drop-down tailboard,
  White caravan ...................................... **£25-30**

**416** 19?? **Land Rover**
- Belgian issue:
  Yellow body, Grey plastic canopy ... **£600-700**

**418** 1960-65 **Austin FX4 'TAXI'**
- Black, flat or shaped hubs, no driver ... **£50-60**
- Black, flat or shaped hubs,
  'younger' driver figure ......................... **£40-50**
- Black body, flat or shaped hubs,
  'older' driver figure ............................. **£35-45**
- Maroon body, Lemon interior, Grey
  base, Orange/Yellow window box ......**£80-110**

**419** 1978-79 **AMC Jeep CJ-5**
- Metallic Green body with White plastic
  top, or Metallic Dark Green body........ **£25-35**

**420** 1962-66 **Ford Thames 'Airborne' Caravan**
- Two-tone Green, Brown interior...... **£100-140**
- Blue/Cream, Red interior ................ **£175-200**
- Blue/Green, Brown interior ............ **£100-140**
- Two-tone Lilac, Beige interior ......... **£100-140**

**421** 1977-80 **Land Rover Safari**
- Orange body, Black roof rack with
  ladder, spare wheel............................... **£20-25**
- Red body, White roof rack with ladder,
  'FOREST FIRE WARDEN' logo.......... **£20-25**
- **Land Rover Workman's Bus**
  Yellow/Red body, no rack or ladder ......NGPP

**424** 1961-65 **Ford Zephyr Estate**
- Pale Blue body, Dark Blue bonnet and
  side flash, Lemon interior, luggage,
  flat or shaped spun hubs ................... **£80-100**

**425** 1978- **London Taxi** (FX4)
- Black body, 'TAXI', WW .................... **£10-15**
- Maroon body, Red interior, WW........ **£80-100**

**430** 1962-64 **Ford Bermuda 'TAXI'**
  (Ford Thunderbird)
- White body, Yellow / Red canopy ... **£100-130**
- White body,
  Lime Green / Red canopy ................ **£100-130**
- White body, Blue and Red canopy .. **£100-130**
- Metallic Blue body, Red canopy ...... **£200-300**

**436** 1963-65 **Citroën ID19 'SAFARI'**
- Yellow body, driver and passenger,
  detailed interior, roof luggage,
  'Wild Life Reservation' logo ........... **£100-125**

**438** 1963-77 **Land Rover 109 WB**
  Model has plastic canopy.
  Earlier issues have metal towhooks
  (plastic later), suspension.
- Dark Green body Grey or Tan canopy,
  Lemon interior, shaped hubs............ **£100-125**
- Dark Green body Cream canopy,
  Lemon interior, spun hubs ............... **£175-200**
- Dk. Brown body, Lt. Brown canopy,
  Red interior, shaped hubs................. **£100-125**
- Metallic Green body, Olive-Green
  canopy, Yellow interior, shaped hubs... **£60-80**
- Metallic Green body, Olive-Green
  canopy, Chrome hubs.......................... **£60-80**
- Metallic Green body, Olive-Green
  canopy, WhizzWheels ......................... **£60-70**
- Red body, Brown tilt, Red interior,
  shaped hubs........................................ **£60-70**
- 'LEPRA' variant:
  Metallic Green body, Tan canopy with
  'LEPRA' logo, Yellow interior,
  shaped hubs, Silver steering wheel .. **£500-750**
- Red body, Blue canopy, (in Gift Set 19)...GSP
- Promotional: with
  '10 MILLIONTH CORGI
  LAND ROVER' label ...........................NGPP

**440** 1966-69 **Ford Consul Cortina Super Estate**
- Metallic Dark Blue with Brown side
  panels, Cream interior, plastic golfer,
  caddie and trolley ............................ **£225-275**

**440** 1979- **Mazda Custom Pick-Up**
- Orange/Yellow/Red, US flag .............. **£20-30**
- Metallic Blue and Silver .................... **£20-30**

**441** 1979-83 **'GOLDEN EAGLE' Jeep**
- Brown/Tan or Gold/White,
  spare wheel on some ........................... **£15-20**

**443** 1963-65 **Plymouth Suburban USA Mail**
- Blue/White body, Red interior,
  'ADDRESS YOUR
  MAIL CAREFULLY' ....................... **£125-150**

**445** 1963-66 **Plymouth Suburban
  Sports Station Wagon**
- Pale Blue or Eggshell Blue body,
  Red roof, Lemon interior,
  Silver stripe, spun hubs.....................**£90-110**
- Beige body, Tan roof........................... **£55-65**

**447** 1983-? **'RENEGADE' 4x4 Jeep**
- Yellow, RN '5' (As 448 but without
  hood). Gift Set 36 model .........................GSP

**448** 1983-? **'RENEGADE' 4x4 Jeep**
- Yellow body, Red hood, RN '5'............. **£8-10**

**450** 1983-? **Peugeot Taxi** (French issue)
- Beige with Blue label, '739:33:33' ..... **£30-35**

**451** 19?? **Ford Sierra Taxi**
- Cream body ...........................................NGPP

**457** 1981-83 **Talbot Matra Rancho**
- Red/Black or Green/Black, tilt seats.... **£10-15**

**457** 1984-? **Talbot Matra Rancho**
- Orange/Black or White/Blue body,
  Brown seats ......................................... **£20-25**

**475** 19?? **Citroën Safari**
  See Novelty, Film and TV-related section.

**480** 1965-66 **Chevrolet Impala Taxi**
- Yellow body, Red roof, spun hubs ... **£100-125**
- Same but detailed cast wheels ......... **£100-125**

**485** 1965-69 **Mini Countryman with Surfer**
- Sea-Green body, Lemon interior,
  2 surfboards on roof-rack,
  male figure, special leaflet .............. **£200-250**
- Same but with unpainted grille ........ **£200-250**

**491** 1966-69 **Ford Consul Cortina Estate**
  All have Brown/Cream side/rear panels.
- Metallic Red, Metallic Blue or
  Metallic Dark Grey ...........................**£90-110**
  **NB** No golf equipment issued with
  this model (see 440).

**497** 1966-69 **'The Man From UNCLE' Car**
  See 'Novelty, Film and TV-related' section.

**507** 1969 **Chrysler Bermuda Taxi**
  Shown in catalogue but not issued............NPP

**2894** 19??-?? **VW Polo 'Deutsche Bundespost'**
- No details................................ **£40-50**

**2895** 19??-?? **VW Polo 'PTT'**
- No details................................ **£40-50**

# Corgi Toys 'Cars of the '50s' series

| | | | |
|---|---|---|---|
| **C801** | | **1957 Ford Thunderbird** | |
| | 82 | White/Tan, Cream/Orange or Cream/Black ............................... | **£15-25** |
| **C802** | | **Mercedes 300 SL** | |
| | 82 | Burgundy or Silver, suspension.. | **£15-25** |
| | 82 | Red body, no suspension ............ | **£15-25** |
| **C803** | | **1952 Jaguar XK120 Sports** | |
| | 83 | Red body/Black hood ................ | **£15-25** |
| **C803/1** | | **1952 Jaguar XK120 Rally** | |
| | 83 | Cream body, RN '56' ................ | **£15-25** |
| | 83 | White body, rally number '56' ... | **£15-25** |
| **C804** | | **Jaguar 'Coupé des Alpes'** | |
| | 83 | Cream/Grey, RN '56' or '414', some have rear wheel 'spats'...... | **£15-25** |
| **C805** | | **1956 Mercedes 300SC** | |
| | 83 | Black body, Tan hood................. | **£15-25** |
| | 84 | Maroon body .......................... | **£15-25** |
| | 86 | Beige body and hood................. | **£15-25** |
| | 87 | Grey, Black hood, (export)......... | **£15-25** |
| **C806** | | **1956 Mercedes 300SL** | |
| | 83 | Black body, Grey/Black hood .... | **£15-25** |
| | 86 | Black/Green body, Beige seats... | **£15-25** |

| | | | |
|---|---|---|---|
| | 86 | Red, (Cream int.), (export)......... | **£15-25** |
| | 86 | Blue body .............................. | **£15-25** |
| **C810** | | **1957 Ford Thunderbird** | |
| | 83 | White body .............................. | **£15-25** |
| | 84 | Pink body................................ | **£15-25** |
| | 87 | Red body................................. | **£15-25** |
| | ? | Cream body, Orange roof........... | **£15-25** |
| | ? | Black/White, Red/White int. ...... | **£15-25** |
| **C811** | | **1954 Mercedes SL** | |
| | 84 | Silver body .............................. | **£15-25** |
| | 86 | Red body................................. | **£15-25** |
| | 87 | Grey body, export model........... | **£15-25** |
| **C812** | | **1953 MG TF** | |
| | 85 | Green/Tan seats ........................ | **£15-25** |
| **C813** | | **1955 MG TF** | |
| | 85 | Red/Black ............................... | **£15-25** |
| | 87 | Cream/Red, export model ......... | **£15-25** |
| **C814** | | **1952 Rolls-Royce Silver Dawn** | |
| | 85 | Red/Black ............................... | **£15-25** |
| | 86 | White/Beige............................. | **£15-25** |
| | 86 | Silver/Black, export model......... | **£15-25** |

| | | | |
|---|---|---|---|
| **C815** | | **1954 Bentley 'R' type** | |
| | 85 | Black or Cream body ................ | **£15-25** |
| | 86 | Dark Blue and Light Blue body . | **£15-25** |
| | 86 | Cream/Brown, export model...... | **£15-25** |
| | ? | White body, Black roof ............. | **£15-25** |
| **C816** | | **1956 Jaguar XK120** | |
| | 85 | Red body, Black tonneau, '56' ... | **£15-25** |
| | ? | Red body, Cream hardtop.......... | **£15-25** |
| **C819** | | **1949 Jaguar XK120** | |
| | 85 | White body, Black hood, '7' ...... | **£15-25** |
| **C825** | | **1957 Chevrolet Bel Air** | |
| | 85 | Red body, White roof and flash . | **£15-25** |
| | 87 | Black/White, export model ........ | **£15-25** |
| **C869** | | **MG TF Racing Car** | |
| | 86 | Royal Blue body, Beige seats, RN '113' ................................. | **£15-25** |
| **C870** | | **Jaguar XK120** | |
| | 86 | Green body, Yellow seats, RN '6', export model ................. | **£15-25** |

# 'Corgi Classics' Cars (original mid-1960s issues)

**ORIGINAL ISSUES.** A factory fire ended production in 1969 of this original series of 'Classics'. Boxes are of two types: one with separate lid with coloured line-drawings printed on it and containing a separate picture of the model; and type two which has the model attached to a sliding-drawer style base in an outer box with half-flaps (similar printing to 1st type). Early issues have reference numbers '901' onwards which were changed to '9001' etc. just before release.

| | | | |
|---|---|---|---|
| 9001 | 1964-69 | **1927 3-litre Bentley** | |
| | | British Racing Green, RN '3', detachable hood, driver . | **£50-65** |
| 9002 | 1964-68 | **1927 3-litre Bentley** | |
| | | Red body, civilian driver, no RN, detachable hood........ | **£50-65** |
| 9004 | 1967-69 | **'WORLD OF WOOSTER' Bentley** | |
| | | As previous model but in Green or Red and with Jeeves and Wooster figures ......................... | **£125-175** |
| 9011 | 1964-68 | **1915 Model 'T' Ford** | |
| | | Black body, driver, passenger, brass radiator................. | **£50-65** |
| 9012 | 1965-68 | **Model 'T' Ford** | |
| | | Yellow/Black body, Black or Yellow wheels................. | **£50-65** |
| 9013 | 1964-69 | **1915 Model 'T' Ford** | |
| | | Blue/Black body, detachable hood, spare wheel, driver cranks.................. | **£50-65** |
| 9014 | 1967 | **1915 'LYONS TEA' Van** | |
| | | Appeared in 1967/68 catalogue but was not issued............ | NPP |

| | | | |
|---|---|---|---|
| 9021 | 1964-69 | **1910 38 hp Daimler** | |
| | | Red body, driver and 3 passengers, folded hood ........... | **£50-65** |
| 9022 | 1966 | **1910 38 hp Daimler** | |
| | | Appeared in the 1966 catalogue but not issued ................. | NPP |
| 9031 | 1965-68 | **1910 Renault 12/16** | |
| | | Lavender/Black body with carriage lamps ..................... | **£50-65** |
| 9032 | 1965-69 | **1910 Renault 12/16** | |
| | | Same model but Primrose Yellow and Black body ......... | **£50-65** |
| 9041 | 1966-70 | **1912 Rolls-Royce Silver Ghost** | |
| | | Silver and Black body, carriage lamps, spoked wheels.. | **£50-65** |
| | | Maroon body, Silver roof and bonnet ............................ | **£75-85** |

**RE-INTRODUCED ISSUES.** Four of the 'Classics' were **re-introduced in 1985** when original tools were discovered. They have new numbers, 'SPECIAL EDITION' on their baseplates and are packed in Grey/Red boxes which do not contain a picture of the model. 13,500 of each colour were made.

| | | | |
|---|---|---|---|
| C860 (9041) | | **1912 Rolls-Royce Silver Ghost** | |
| | | Silver, Black or Ruby Red body ..................................... | **£20-25** |
| C861 (9002) | | **1927 3-litre Bentley open top** | |
| | | British Racing Green, Black or Ruby Red body .......... | **£20-25** |
| C862 (9031) | | **1910 Renault 12/16** | |
| | | Yellow, Pale Blue, Cream or Brown body ..................... | **£20-25** |
| C863 (9012) | | **1915 Model 'T' Ford** | |
| | | Black, Red or Blue body ................................................ | **£20-25** |

# Corgi Toys Duo Packs

These packs combine standard models with (mainly) similar 'Junior' models. Launched early in 1982 in France with the name 'Les Plus de Corgi', the packs later became available in the UK in Woolworths as 'Little and Large; the Little One Free'.

**See also 'Novelty, Film and TV-related' section for additional details.**

No.53 **Triple Pack** (1982), **'Stunt Bikes':** 171 Street Bike, 172 Police Bike, 173 Café Racer ................................... NGPP

**'Les Plus de Corgi' Duo Pack range:**

| | | |
|---|---|---|
| 1352 | Renault 5 (307) Metro (C275).......... | **£15-25** |
| 1353 | Austin Metro .................................... | **£15-25** |
| 1354 | Texaco Lotus (C154) Junior 53 ...... | **£15-25** |
| 1355 | Talbot Matra Rancho (457)............. | **£15-25** |
| 1356 | Fiat XI/9 (306) ................................ | **£15-25** |

| | | |
|---|---|---|
| 1357 | Golden Eagle Jeep (C441) ................ | **£15-25** |
| 1358 | Citroën 2cv..................................... | **£15-25** |
| 1359 | Ford Escort (334), Junior 105.......... | **£15-25** |

**F.W. Woolworth's 'Little & Large' Promotional Duo Pack selection:**

| | | |
|---|---|---|
| 1352 | Renault 5 (307) Metro (C275).......... | **£15-25** |
| 1353 | Austin Metro .................................... | **£15-25** |
| 1355 | Talbot Matra Rancho (457)............... | **£15-25** |
| 1356 | Fiat XI/9 (306) ................................ | **£15-25** |
| 1359 | Ford Escort (334), Junior 105.......... | **£15-25** |
| 1363 | Buck Rogers (607)........................... | **£50-60** |
| 1364 | Space Shuttle 'NASA' (648)............. | **£20-30** |
| 1365 | 469 Routemaster Bus, E71 Taxi ...... | **£20-30** |
| 1371 | Volkswagen Turbo (309).................. | **£15-25** |

**Other Duo Packs** (most available in UK).

| | | |
|---|---|---|
| 1364 | Space Shuttle 'NASA' (648)............. | **£20-30** |
| 1365 | 469 Routemaster Bus, E71 Taxi ....... | **£15-25** |

| | | |
|---|---|---|
| 1372 | Jaguar XJS (319)............................... | **£15-25** |
| 1373 | Ford Capri (312) Junior 61 .............. | **£15-25** |
| 1378 | Porsche 924, Yellow ........................ | **£15-25** |
| 1380 | Mercedes 240D, Metallic Grey ........ | **£15-25** |
| 1381 | Ferrari 308GTS, Red ....................... | **£15-25** |
| 1382 | Ford Mustang (320).......................... | **£15-25** |
| 1383 | Mack Fire Pumper ........................... | **£15-25** |
| 1384 | Ford Thunderbird, Cream/Orange .... | **£15-25** |
| | Ford Thunderbird, Cream/Black....... | **£15-25** |
| 1385 | Austin Metro 'DATAPOST' .............. | **£15-25** |
| 1389 | Ford Sierra (299) Junior 129 ........... | **£15-25** |
| 1390 | Porsche 924, Black ........................... | **£15-25** |
| 1393 | 447 Jeep and E182 Jeep.................... | **£15-25** |
| 1394 | 448 Jeep and E183 Jeep.................... | **£15-25** |
| 1395 | 495 Mazda, E184 Range Rover......... | **£15-25** |
| 1396 | Space Shuttle................................... | **£15-25** |
| 1397 | BMW M1 'BASF' (380).................... | **£15-25** |
| 1401 | Lotus Elite and E10 TR7 ................. | **£15-25** |
| 1402 | 1133 Tipper plus E85 Skip Truck .... | **£15-25** |
| 1403 | Mercedes Tanker, E185 Van ............ | **£15-25** |
| 1405 | Jaguar ............................................. | **£15-25** |

# The UKs No.1 magazine for model collectors

**NEWSTAND PRICE**

# £3.30

per issue

**YOUR DISCOUNTED PRICE**

# £2.74

per issue

**SAVINGS PER ISSUE**

# 56p

## This price is based on a years subscription for £32.95

## Subscribe today & save!

uk only

# Priority Order Form

❑ I enclose a cheque for £32.95 made payable to Diecast Collector

❑ Please debit my credit/debit card with £32.95 ❑ Visa ❑ Mastercard ❑ Switch

❑ I would like to subscribe to Diecast Collector and pay £3 for 3 issues followed by £8.25 per quarter *Please note, this is a direct debit offer only

Title: ..........................................................................

Initial: ..........................................................................

Surname: ..........................................................................

Address: ..........................................................................

..........................................................................

..........................................................................

..........................................................................

Postcode: ..........................................................................

Tel No: ..........................................................................

Email: ..........................................................................

Code: DCRAM2

*Warners Group Publications plc will automatically provide you relevant direct mail and/or telephone information. If you do not want to receive this information please tick here [ ]*
*Warners Group Publications plc may also email you with information about relevant products and services. If you do want to receive email please tick box [ ]*
*Warners Group Publications plc will occasionally allow selected third parties to contact you about their products and services. Please indicate your preferences below.*
*Please tick here if you do not want to receive relevant direct mail and/or telephone information from third parties [ ]*
*Please tick here if you do want to receive relevant email from selected third parties [ ]*

## Instructions to your Bank or Building Society to pay by Direct Debit.

Please fill in the whole form including official use box using a ball point pen and send it to:

**Diecast Collector Subscriptions, Warners Group Publications plc, Freepost PE211, West Street, Bourne, Lincolnshire, PE10 9BR**

FOR WARNERS GROUP PUBLICATIONS PLC OFFICIAL USE ONLY This is not part of the instruction to you Bank or Building Society.

Telephone ____________________

**Name(s) of Account Holder(s)**

____________________

**Bank/Building Society account number**

____________________

**Branch Sort Code**

DIRECT Debit

____________________

**Name and full postal address of your Bank or Building Society**

To: The Manager ____________________

Bank ____________________

Address ____________________

____________________

**Reference Number** Banks and Building Societies may not accept Direct Debit Instructions for some types of account

____________________

**Originator's Identification Number** 9 4 2 2 4 0

**Instruction to your Bank or Building Society**
Please pay Warners Group Publications Direct Debits from the account detailed in this instruction subject to the safeguards assured by the Direct Debit Guarantee. I understand that this instruction may remain with Warners Group Publications Plc and, if so, details will be passed electronically to my Bank/Building Society.

Signature ____________ Date ____________

Please complete and return form to:

**Diecast Collector, Subscriptions, FREEPOST PE211, Bourne, PE10 9BR**

| Model and details | MPR | Model and details | MPR | Model and details | MPR |
|---|---|---|---|---|---|

**Market prices shown here are for guidance only. They refer ONLY to mint models in pristine boxes that are complete with <u>all</u> of their original contents. WW = WhizzWheels, MPR = Market Price Range.**

**100** 1957-65 **Dropside Trailer**
• Cream/Red or Yellow body, drawbar . **£50-60**

**101** 1958-63 **Platform Trailer**
• Grey/Yellow or Silver/Blue or
Silver/Lemon body ............................ **£60-70**

**109** 1968-69 **'PENNYBURN' Trailer**
• Blue body, Yellow chassis,
accessories, leaflet ......................... **£40-50**

**403** 1956-60 **Bedford 12 cwt Van**
**'DAILY EXPRESS'**
• Dark Blue. Blue box with leaflet ... **£150-175**
• Same model but Deep Blue body... **£150-175**

**403M** 1956-60 **Bedford 12 cwt Van**
**'KLG PLUGS'**
**(with flywheel motor)**
• Bright Red body, leaflet in box ...... **£150-175**

**403** 1974-79 **Thwaites Skip Dumper**
• Yellow/Green tipping body, driver,
WhizzWheels..................................... **£30-40**

**404** 1956-62 **Bedford Dormobile**
Smooth or ribbed roof, smooth or shaped
hubs. Early issues have divided
windscreen. Blue box with leaflet.
• Cream (Blue roof on some)........... **£120-140**
• Turquoise ...................................... **£120-140**
• Blue ............................................. **£120-140**
• Red or Metallic Red ...................... **£120-140**
• Yellow body, Pale Blue roof........... **£300-350**
• Yellow lower half, Blue upper half **£300-350**
• All-Yellow body, with suspension.. **£100-150**

**404M** 1956-60 **Bedford Dormobile**
**(with flywheel motor)**
Blue box also contains leaflet.
• Red or Metallic Red ....................... **£130-160**
• Turquoise body............................. **£130-160**
• Blue body..................................... **£130-160**

**405** **Bedford Van 'AFS'**
See 'Emergency Vehicles' section.

**405** 1981-? **Ford Transit Milk Float**
**'DAIRY CREST'**
• 'MILK MARKETING BOARD' on
each side and 'MILK' on rear ........... **£20-30**

**405** 1982-? **Ford Transit Milk Float**
• Blue/White, 'LOTTA BOTTLE'........ **£10-15**

**406** 1971-75 **Mercedes-Benz Unimog**
• Yellow/Green body, Blue interior...... **£25-35**
• Yellow/Red body with Blue interior .. **£25-35**
• Blue/Red body with Blue interior .... **£25-35**

**407** 1957-62 **Smiths Karrier Bantam**
• *'HOME SERVICES HYGIENIC
MOBILE SHOP'*, Pale Blue body,
Red logo, smooth hubs.................. **£125-150**

**408** 1957-59 **Bedford 'AA' Service Van**
• Yellow/Black, divided windscreen,
smooth hubs, Blue box, leaflet....... **£125-150**
• As previous but Blue/Yellow box .... **£125-150**
• 1959-63 Same, but shaped hubs,
Blue/Yellow box, no leaflet........... **£120-140**
• Same, but single windscreen,
ridged roof, spun hubs .................. **£100-125**

**409** 1959-65 **Forward Control Jeep**
• Light Blue body, Red grille,
smooth or shaped hubs ...................... **£80-90**

**409** 1976-77 **Unimog Dumper**
• White/Red or Blue/Yellow body,
suspension, hook.............................. **£20-30**

**409** 1981-? **'ALLIS CHALMERS' Forklift**
• Yellow body, pallets/load/driver......... **£15-20**

**411** 1958-62 **Karrier Bantam Van**
**'LUCOZADE'**
• Yellow body, Grey shutter,
smooth hubs, Blue box .................. **£130-160**
• Shaped hubs, Blue/Yellow box ...... **£120-140**

**413** 1960-64 **Smiths Karrier Bantam**
**Mobile Butchers**
• White/Blue van, spun hubs,
*'FAMILY BUTCHERS'*, meaty decals.
Blue box with leaflet ..................... **£125-150**
• Same model but with suspension ... **£125-150**

**413** 1976-78 **Mazda Motorway Maintenance**
• Yellow/Black body, figure, road signs,
bollards, decal sheet enclosed,
(modified 478/493)............................ **£25-35**

**416** 1959-61 **R.A.C. Land Rover**
• Blue body, *'RADIO RESCUE'* on cab
roof sign, metal canopy, smooth
hubs, Blue/Yellow box .................. **£150-175**
• Blue body, no cab roof sign, *'RADIO
RESCUE'* on canopy, shaped hubs . **£160-200**
• Belgian issue:
Yellow body, Green metal canopy,
'TS RADIO' decals on doors ... **£1,000-1,250**

**416s** 1962-64 **R.A.C. Land Rover**
**(with suspension)**
• Blue body, Lemon interior, suspension,
*'RADIO RESCUE'* on plastic canopy. **£75-95**
• Belgian issue:
Yellow body, Grey plastic canopy,
'TS RADIO' decals on doors ... **£1,000-1,250**

**417** 1960-62 **Land Rover**
**'BREAKDOWN SERVICE'**
• Red body, Yellow tinplate canopy,
spun hubs..........................................**£90-110**

**417s** 1963-65 **Land Rover**
**'BREAKDOWN SERVICE'**
**(with suspension)**
• Red body, Yellow tinplate canopy,
shaped hubs ................................. **£160-190**

**421** 1960-63 **Bedford 12 cwt Van**
**'EVENING STANDARD'**
• Black body, Silver ridged roof, smooth
hubs, undivided windscreen .......... **£150-175**
• Black lower body,
Silver upper and roof.....................**£110-130**
• Medium Blue body,
'AVRO BODE' logo ....................... **£250-300**

**422** 1960-62 **Bedford 12 cwt Van**
**'CORGI TOYS'**
• Yellow body, Blue roof,
smooth or shaped hubs ................. **£300-400**
• reversed colours: Blue body,
Yellow roof, smooth hubs ............. **£600-800**
• variation: Blue lower half with
Yellow upper body and roof.......... **£600-800**

**424** 1977-79 **Security Van**
• Black/Yellow/White, *'SECURITY'* .... **£10-15**

**426** 1962-64 **'CHIPPERFIELDS CIRCUS'**
**Mobile Booking Office**
• Karrier Bantam in red and blue, with
clown and circus posters, spun hubs.
Blue/yellow card box.................... **£300-400**
• Same model but with shaped hubs. **£250-300**

**426** 1978-81 **Chevrolet Booking Office**
**Van 'PINDER'**
• Yellow/Red/Blue body, 'PINDER JEAN
RICHARD', WW, two loudspeakers.. **£35-45**
**NB** The 'clown's face' poster may be at the
front or the rear on the n/s of the model.

**428** 1963-66 **Karrier Ice-Cream Van**
**'MR SOFTEE'**
• Blue/White body, detailed chassis,
salesman swivels .......................... **£200-250**

**431** 1964-66 **Volkswagen Pick-Up**
• Yellow body, Red or Olive-Green
canopy, Red 'VW' emblem ............... **£60-70**
• Met. Gold body, Red 'VW' emblem,
Red canopy and int., spun hubs...... **£250-350**

**431, 432, 433** **Chevrolet Vans**
('VANATIC', 'VANTASTIC' and
'VANISHING POINT').
See 'Novelty' section.

**433** 1962-64 **Volkswagen Delivery Van**
• Red/White body, Red or Yellow int. .. **£60-70**
• Dutch promotional issue:
'VROOM & DREESMANN',
Grey body, spun hubs .................... **£200-300**

**434** 1962 **Volkswagen Kombi**
• Metallic Pale Grey over Green body,
Red interior, spun hubs .................... **£65-75**
1963-66 Two-tone Green,
Red or Yellow interior ...................... **£60-70**

**435** 1962-63 **Karrier Bantam Van**
• Blue/White/Yellow,
*'DRIVE SAFELY ON MILK'* ......... **£100-120**

**437** 1979-80 **Chevrolet Van 'COCA-COLA'**
• Red body, White logo, tinted roof
windows, crates ................................ **£20-25**

**440** 1979-80 **Mazda Custom Pick-up**
• Yellow body, Red roof...................... **£15-20**

**441** 1963-67 **Volkswagen Van**
**'CHOCOLATE TOBLERONE'**
• Blue body, Lemon interior,
'Trans-o-lite' headlamps................. **£80-100**

**443** 1963-66 **Plymouth Suburban US Mail**
• Blue/White body, *'ADDRESS YOUR
MAIL CAREFULLY'*......................... **£65-75**

**447** 1965-66 **'WALLS ICE CREAM' Van**
• Blue/Cream Ford Thames van,
salesman, boy, spare transfers.
Blue/Yellow card box, inner base,
correct folded leaflet,
unapplied decal sheet.................... **£600-800**

**450** 1964-67 **Austin Mini Van**
- Green body with unpainted grille, Red interior.......................................... **£55-65**
- Green body, painted grille, Red interior. .................................... **£130-160**
- Promotional: Metallic Green body, Grey base, Red interior, White *'FDR1.2009/17'* logo. In original 450 box with club slip. Dutch promotional?........ **£300-400**

**452** 1956-63 **Commer Dropside Lorry**
- Red and Cream body, (raised ridge on some cab roofs), smooth or shaped hubs ....................................... **£80-100**
- Blue body, Cream back ................... **£80-100**

**453** 1956-60 **Commer Refrigerated Van 'WALLS ICE CREAM'**
- Dark Blue cab, Cream back, smooth roof, flat spun hubs............ **£175-200**
- Light Blue cab, Cream back, cast roof, flat spun hubs ................. **£125-150**

**454** 1957-63 **Commer Platform Lorry**
- Met. Blue cab and chassis, Silver-Grey platform, flat hubs, leaflet ............. **£120-140**
- Yellow cab / chassis, Silver platform............................... **£120-140**

**455** 1957-60 **Karrier Bantam 2-ton**
- Blue, Red or Grey body, Red platform, smooth hubs ............ **£120-140**
- Early Mettoy issue: Red body with *'C.W.S. SOFT DRINKS'* logo on rear..................... **£120-140**

**456** 1960-63 **ERF 44G Dropside Lorry**
- Yellow cab and chassis, Metallic Blue back, smooth/shaped hubs ......... **£70-80**
**457** 1957-65 **ERF 44G Platform Lorry**
- Two-tone Blue or Yellow/Blue body, smooth hubs................................... **£80-100**
**458** 1958-66 **E.R.F. Earth Dumper**
- Red / Yellow, 'ERF' cast-in, smooth or shaped hubs .................... **£80-100**
**459** 1958-60 **ERF 44G Van 'MOORHOUSES LEMON CHEESE'**
- Yellow/Red ..................................... **£150-200**

**459** 1973-78 **Raygu Rascal Roller**
- Yellow/Green body, *'Road Roller'*..... **£20-30**

**460** 1959-61 **E.R.F. Neville Cement Tipper 'TUNNEL CEMENT'**
- Lemon cab/chassis, Silver base, metal filler caps .................................. **£40-50**
- As previous version, but with Red plastic filler caps ........................ **£70-80**

**462** 1970-? **Commer Van 'CO-OP'**
- White/Blue body, Blue/Yellow box.. **£80-100**
**462** 1971-? **Commer Van 'HAMMONDS'**
- Green/Blue/White promotional model, cast hubs. In un-numbered Corgi box with '462' handwritten .................. **£200-300**

**465** 1963-66 **Commer Pick-Up Truck**
- Red/Yellow, Yellow/Red or Green/Grey, 'Trans-O-Lites'.............. **£50-60**

**466** 19?? **Commer Milk Float**
- White cab, chassis and load; Blue rear roof and sides.................... **£80-100**
- Promotional issue: As previous model but with 'CO-OP' labels. Plain card box ........ **£80-100**

**470** 1965-72 **Forward Control Jeep**
- Blue/Grey, Mustard Yellow, Pale Green or Light Blue body, detachable canopy ............................. **£35-40**

**471** 1965-66 **Karrier Bantam Snack Bar**
- Blue/White, 'JOE'S DINER', figure, opening hatch..................... **£140-170**
- Belgian issue: Blue/White, 'PATATES FRITES'... **£200-250**

**474** 1965-68 **Musical 'WALLS ICE CREAM' Van**
- Ford Thames van in Blue/Cream, musical movement (must function for top price), diorama but no figures. Blue/Yellow card box with correct folded leaflet, fresh decal sheet...... **£700-900**

**477** 1966-68 **Land Rover Breakdown**
- Red, Yellow tilt, spare wheel on some, hook, WhizzWheels ................. **£40-50**

**478** 1965-68 **Jeep Tower Wagon (Forward Control)**
- Green, Yellow and Silver, figure ........ **£40-50**

**479** 1968-71 **Commer Mobile Camera Van**
- Blue/White body, shaped hubs, *'SAMUELSON FILM COMPANY LTD'*, camera and operator ...................... **£150-175**
- Same model but with cast hubs...... **£150-175**

**483** 1968-72 **Dodge Tipper Truck**
- White cab, Blue tipper, *'KEW FARGO'*, cast hubs .................. **£60-70**

**484** 1967-69 **Dodge Livestock Transporter**
- Beige/Green body, *'KEW FARGO'*, with five pigs...................................... **£35-45**

**486** 1967-69 **'KENNEL CLUB' Truck**
- White/Orange Chevrolet Impala with 'Vari-View' dachshund picture, four dogs, cast hubs.........................**£110-140**

**493** 1975-78 **Mazda B 1600 Pick-Up**
- Blue/White or Silver/Blue body......... **£20-25**

**494** 1967-72 **Bedford Tipper**
- Red cab/chassis, Yellow tipper........... **£60-70**
- Red cab/chassis, Silver tipper............**£90-110**
- Yellow cab/chassis, Blue tipper......**£110-130**
- Blue cab/chassis, Yellow tipper....... **£130-150**

**508** **Commer Minibus 'Holiday Camp Special'**
- White/Orange, Green luggage, spun hubs, leaflet................................. **£80-90**

## MAJOR PACKS

**1100** 1958-63 **Bedford 'S' Carrimore (Low-loader)**
- Yellow cab, Metallic Blue low-loader trailer, smooth or shaped hubs........ **£140-170**
- Red cab, Metallic Blue low-loader trailer, winch.................................. **£140-170**

**1100** 1971-73 **Mack Truck 'TRANS-CONTINENTAL'**
- Orange cab, Black/Orange/Silver trailer ....................................... **£40-50**
- Orange/Metallic Lime Green............. **£70-80**

**1101** 1957-62 **Bedford 'S' Carrimore Car Transporter**
- Blue cab, Yellow transporter body, *'CORGI CAR TRANSPORTER'*..... **£140-170**
- Red cab, Blue transporter body, smooth hubs.................................... **£140-170**
- Yellow cab and transporter body, Silver ramps.................................... **£300-400**

**1101** 1976-81 **Mobile Crane**
- Yellow/Blue, *'Warner & Swasey'* ...... **£25-30**

**1102** 1958-62 **'EUCLID' TC-12 Bulldozer**
- Yellow body, Pale Grey tracks. Box has inner lining ...................... **£120-140**
- Same model but with Black tracks. **£120-140**
- Pale Lime-Green body.................... **£120-140**
**1102** 1974-76 **Crane Freuhauf (Berliet Dumper)**
- Yellow cab, Orange dumper body, *'Road Maker Construction'* logo ....... **£30-35**

**1103** 1960-65 **'EUCLID' Crawler Tractor**
- Yellow or Pale Lime-Green body, Pale Grey tracks............................. **£150-175**
- Same model but with Black tracks. **£150-175**

**1104** 1958-63 **Bedford 'S' Carrimore Machinery Carrier**
- Red cab, Silver trailer, smooth hubs, operable winch .............................. **£140-170**
- Same but with Blue cab.................. **£140-170**

**1104** 1974-77 **Bedford 'TK' type Horse Transporter**
- Green or Metallic Green, *'NEWMARKET'*, 4 horses and boy .... **£50-60**

**1105** 1962-66 **Bedford 'TK' type 'Corgi Car Transporter'**
- Red cab, Blue/White trailer, collapsible decks............................ **£175-225**

**1105** 1976-80 **Berliet Racehorse Transporter**
- Brown/White, *'NATIONAL RACING STABLES'*, four horses ..................... **£40-50**

**1106** 1972-77 **Mack Container Truck 'ACL'**
- Yellow/Black/White body, two Red containers .............................. **£40-50**
- Promotional issue for the '3M' company.................... **£120-140**

**1107** 1963-66 **'EUCLID' with Dozer with Driver**
- Yellow body, Black or Grey tracks **£150-200**
- Red body.................................... **£150-200**
- Lime-Green body........................... **£80-100**
**1107** 1978-79 **Berliet Container Lorry 'UNITED STATES LINES'**
- Blue cab, White chassis, two Grey containers........................ **£30-40**

**1108** 1982 **Ford Truck 'MICHELIN'**
- Blue/White artic. body, 2 containers .. **£40-50**

**1109** 1979 **Ford Truck 'MICHELIN'**
- Blue/Yellow body, 2 containers.......... **£40-50**

**1110** 1959-64 **Bedford 'S' Tanker 'MOBILGAS'**
- Red/White articulated body, detachable cab, Lemon interior...... **£150-200**
- Same but with shaped spun hubs ... **£150-200**

**1110** 1965-67 **Bedford 'S' Tanker 'SHELL BENZEEN'**
- Blue/White articulated tanker, Dutch model ........................... **£1,800-2,200**

**1110** 1976-80 **'JCB' Crawler Loader**
- Yellow/White body, Red bucket, Black tracks, driver............................ **£30-35**

**1110** 1976-80 **'JCB' Crawler**
- Yellow and White body, driver........... **£30-40**
- Light Blue/Orange with Light Blue chassis ............................. **£30-40**
- Yellow body, Light Blue cab, Red bucket...................................... **£30-40**
- Red body, Light Blue cab and bucket **£30-40**
- Orange body, *'BLOCK CONSTRUCTION'* ............. **£30-40**

**1113** 1981-86 **'HYSTER' Handler**
- Yellow or Black/White main body, *'US Lines'*, hoist .......................... **£100-125**
- 1986-87 Yellow or Black/White main body, *'SEALINK'*, container, export model .................................. **£100-125**
- 1986-87 White/Dark Blue/Yellow, *'MICHELIN'*, container ................. **£100-125**

**1116** 1979-? **Refuse Lorry (Shelvoke and Drewry Revopak)**
- Orange/Silver or Red/Silver body ...... **£20-30**
- 1988 Blue cab, White tipper, *'BOROUGH COUNCIL'* ..................... **£5-10**

**1117** 1980-85 **'FAUN' Street-sweeper**
- Orange and Yellow or All-Yellow, with operator........................................ **£20-30**

**1119** 1983 **Mercedes Load Lugger**
- Yellow/Red body, *'CORGI'* .............. **£15-20**

**1121** 1983 **Ford Tipper (Corgimatic)**
- Orange/Beige body, *'CORGI'* ........... **£15-20**

**1126** 1961-65 **Racing Car Transporter 'ECURIE ECOSSE'**
- Metallic Dark Blue body, logo in Yellow lettering ................ **£200-250**
- later version: logo in Orange lettering................. **£130-160**
- with logo in White lettering .......... **£130-160**
- with logo and raised ridges in Light Blue................................. **£130-160**
- Metallic Light Blue body with logo in Red lettering ....................... **£130-160**

**1128** 1963-76 **'PRIESTMAN' Cub Shovel**
- Red/Yellow body, driver................ **£100-125**

**1129** 1962-65 **Bedford 'S' Tanker 'MILK'**
- Blue/White articulated body, detachable cab .............................. **£200-250**

**1130** 19??-?? **Euclid TC12 Twin Crawler Tractor**
- Lime Green body, Black tracks ...... **£100-125**

**1131** 1963-66 **Bedford 'TK' Carrimore Machinery Low Loader**
- Blue cab, Silver trailer, Yellow detachable rear axle unit, spun hubs................. **£120-140**
- Same, but Black detachable rear axle unit..................................... **£80-100**

**1132** 1963-65 **Bedford 'TK' Carrimore**
- Yellow cab and ramp, Red low loader trailer, spare wheels, no winch ....... **£200-250**

**1137** 1966-69 **Ford Articulated Truck 'EXPRESS SERVICES'**
- Blue/Silver/Red body, 'H' series tilt-cab ........................... **£100-120**

**1138** 1966-69 **Ford Articulated Transporter 'CORGI CARS'**
- Red body, Silver tilt cab, two-tone Blue trailer...................... **£145-175**

**1140** 1965-67 **Bedford 'TK' Petrol Tanker 'MOBILGAS'**
- Red/Silver/White artic. body, tilting cab, box includes inner packing, leaflet. **£125-175**

**1141** 1965-67 **Bedford 'TK' Milk Tanker 'MILK'**
- Blue/White artic. body, tilting cab . **£175-225**

**1142** 1967-74 **Holmes Wrecker Truck**
- White/Red/Gold, 2 mechanics........ **£100-125**

**1144** 19??-?? **Berliet Wrecker Truck**
- Red/White/Blue, Gold booms/hooks, striped window box ........................... **£50-70**

**1145** 1969-76 **Unimog Goose Dumper**
- Yellow/Red body, *'406'*..................... **£50-60**

**1146** 1970-73 **Scammell Carrimore Mk.V**
- Orange/White/Blue Tri-deck Transporter articulated transporter with three collapsible decks................... **£125-150**

**1147** 1969-72 **Scammell Truck**
- Yellow/White, *'FERRYMASTERS INTERNATIONAL HAULIERS'* ..... **£130-160**

**1148** 1969-72 **Scammell Carrimore Mk.IV**
- Red/White car transporter body with Yellow chucks...........................**£90-110**

**1150** 1971-77 **Mercedes (Unimog 406) Snowplough**
- Green/Black, 2 Red flags, Orange/Silver plough.......................... **£30-35**
- Yellow cab and back, Red chassis, Silver plough ...................................... **£30-35**

**1151** 1970 **'Co-operative Society'** See 'Gift Sets'.

**1151** 19?? **Mack Tanker 'EXXON'**
- Red/White body, striped window box **£60-70**

**1152** 1971-76 **Mack Tanker 'ESSO'**
- White/Red/Blue, Gloster Saro Tanker **£40-50**
- Same model but 'EXXON' logo ........ **£70-80**

**1152** 1983- **'BARRATT' Tipper**
- Green/White body, tipper section tips .. **£5-10**

**1153** 1973-74 **'PRIESTMAN' Crane**
- Red/Orange body, *'Higrab'*.............. **£60-70**

**1153** 1983-84 **'WIMPEY' Tipper** (Scania)
- Green/Silver body (later Yellow) ......... **£5-10**

**1154** 1974-76 **Priestman Crane Truck**
- Yellow/Red body, Silver boom, hook **£45-55**

**1154** 1979 **Giant Tower Crane 'BLOCK CONSTRUCTION'**
- Orange/Yellow crane, White body ..... **£55-65**

**1155** 1975-79 **'Skyscraper' Tower Crane**
- Yellow/Red body, Black tracks .......... **£35-40**

**1156** 1977-79 **Volvo Concrete Mixer**
- Yellow/Red/Orange body, *'RAPIER'*. **£30-35**
- 1980 Orange/White body, *'BLOCK CONSTRUCTION'*.............. **£30-35**

**1157** 1976-81 **Ford Tanker 'ESSO'**
- White/Red articulated body................ **£25-35**

**1158** 1976 **Ford Tanker 'EXXON'**
- White/Black artic. body, US issue...... **£50-60**

**1159** 1976-79 **Ford Car Transporter**
- Metallic Blue/White artic. body ......... **£60-70**
- Metallic Green articulated body ......... **£60-70**

**1160** 1976-78 **Ford Tanker 'GULF'**
- White/Orange articulated body .......... **£30-40**

**1161** 1976-78 **Ford Tanker 'ARAL'**
- Blue/White/Black, German export ..... **£60-80**

**1169** 1982 **Ford Tanker 'GUINNESS'**
- Red/Cream/Black articulated body .... **£60-80**

**1170** 1982 **Ford Car Transporter**
- Red/White/Yellow articulated body ... **£50-60**

See also 'Corgi Commercial Vehicles' (for other breakdown recovery vehicles, etc.), and the 'Corgi Gift Sets' section.

| Model and details | MPR |
|---|---|

**209**   1958-61   **Riley Pathfinder 'POLICE' Car**
- Black and Silver body, bell ............ **£100-150**

**213**   1959-61   **Jaguar Fire Chief's Car**
- Red body, bell, Grey aerial,
roof sign, smooth spun hubs .......... **£150-200**

**213s**   1961-62   **Jaguar Fire Chief's Car**
      **(with suspension)**
- As 213 model but shaped hubs ....... **£150-200**
- Deep Cherry Red, Lemon interior,
spun hubs.................................... **£500-600**

**223**   1959-61   **Chevrolet Impala 'State Patrol'**
- Black body, Silver stripe, Lemon interior,
Grey aerial. Box also contains
internal packing ........................... **£120-140**

**237**   1962-66   **Oldsmobile Sheriff's Car**
- Black body, White roof, 'COUNTY
SHERIFF', clear or Blue light.
Box also contains internal packing ..... **£80-90**

**260**   1979-81   **Buick 'POLICE' Car**
- Metallic Blue/White, 'CITY OF
METROPOLIS', two light bars .......... **£30-40**

**284**   1982-83   **Mercedes-Benz 240 D**
- Red body, 'NOTRUF 112', flashing
lights, German export model.............. **£20-25**

**293**   1977-80   **Renault 5 TS**
- Metallic Orange or
Two-tone Blue body, WW.................. **£15-25**
    1980-81
- French issue: Two-tone Blue,
roof light, 'S.O.S. MEDICINS'.......... **£25-35**

**295**   1982-83   **Renault 5 TS Fire Chief**
- Red/White 'SAPEURS POMPIERS',
French export................................. **£15-20**

**297**   1982-86   **Ford Escort 'Panda' Car**
- Light or Dark Blue, White doors,
Blue warning lights, 'POLICE'.......... **£15-20**

**326**   1980-81   **Chevrolet Caprice**
      **'POLICE' Car**
- Black/White body, suspension ............ **£20-30**

**332**   1980-81   **Opel Doctors Car**
- German issue:
White/Red, 'NOTARTZ' .................... **£30-40**

**339**   1980      **Rover 3500 'POLICE' Car**
- White and Red body............................ **£20-25**

**373**   1970-76   **VW 1200 Police Car**
- Green and White body, Red interior,
'POLIZEI', Blue roof light, WW....... **£70-80**
- White body, Red interior, Silver base,
Blue roof light, 'POLIZEI'.............. **£90-120**
- Black/White/Blue, 'POLITIE'.......... **£90-120**
- White body, Red int., Blue roof light,
Black 'POLICE' on White decal...... **£40-50**
- Same, but White 'POLICE' lettering
on Blue decal................................. **£40-50**
- White body, Black hatch/bonnet stripes,
Red interior, 2 figures, 'POLICE'....... **£40-50**

**383**   1970-73   **VW 1200 'ADAC'**
- Yellow body, Black roof with '1341',
'ADAC STRASSENWACHT' logos .. **£75-85**

**386**   1987      **Mercedes 'POLIZEI'**
- Green/White body, two Blue warning
lights, German export model.............. **£30-40**

**395**   1972-73   **Fire Bug**
- Orange body, Whizzwheels, Red/Black
or Pink/Black stripe, Yellow ladder
(381 Beach Buggy) ............................ **£20-30**

**402**   1972-77   **Ford Cortina GXL Police Car**
- White/Red body, 'POLICE' labels,
(updated 313)................................ **£55-65**
- White/Red body, 'POLIZEI',
German issue ................................ **£75-85**

**405**   1956-60   **Bedford Fire Tender 'A.F.S.'**
- Bright or Dark Green 'Utilicon' body,
divided windscreen, Silver or Black
ladder, smooth or shaped hubs.
Blue box with leaflet ...................... **£150-180**

**405M** 1956-59   **Bedford (Utilicon) Fire Tender**
- Red body, divided windscreen, Silver or
Black ladder, 'FIRE DEPT', smooth or
shaped hubs, friction motor.
Blue box with leaflet ...................... **£120-150**

**405**   1978-80   **Chevrolet Ambulance**
- White/Orange, patient on stretcher
and two attendants ........................ **£20-25**

**406**   1980-81   **Mercedes Bonna**
      **'AMBULANCE'**
- White body, Red/Black design, opening
doors, stretcher, ambulancemen .......... **£15-20**
- German issue: Cream body,
'KRANKENWAGEN'........................ **£30-40**
- Danish issue: Red/White, 'FALCK'... **£30-40**
- Swedish issue:
White/Red/Black body, 'SDL 951' ..... **£30-40**

**407**   1980      **Mercedes Bonna**
      **'AMBULANCE'**
- White body, Red/Black design, opening
doors, stretcher, ambulancemen .......... **£15-20**

**408**   1957-59   **Bedford 'AA' Service Van**
- Yellow/Black, divided windscreen,
smooth hubs, Blue box, leaflet........ **£140-160**
- 1958-59   Yellow/Black, undivided
windscreen, smooth or shaped hubs,
Blue box, leaflet ............................. **£100-125**
- 1959-63   Yellow/Black, undivided
windscreen, shaped hubs,
Blue/Yellow box, no leaflet................**£90-110**
- late issue: Yellow/Black, single
windscreen, ridged roof, flat hubs......**£90-110**

**412**   1957-60   **Bedford 'AMBULANCE'**
- Cream 'Utilicon' body, divided screen,
smooth hubs. Blue box with leaflet **£140-160**
- As previous model but with
one-piece windscreen ..................... **£160-190**
- Factory error: A few examples of
412 were issued with
'HOME SERVICES' front labels..........NGPP

**412**   1976-79   **Mercedes Police Car**
- White/Black body, 'POLICE' logo,
Blue roof lamp............................... **£30-35**
- Green/White body, 'POLIZEI' logo,
Blue roof lamp, German issue ........... **£35-45**

**414**   1975-77   **Jaguar XJ12-C**
- White/Blue body, 'COASTGUARD'.. **£10-15**

**416**   1959-61   **R.A.C. Land Rover**
- Blue body, 'RADIO RESCUE' on cab
roof sign, metal canopy,
smooth hubs, Blue/Yellow box ....... **£140-160**
- Blue body, no cab roof sign, 'RADIO
RESCUE' on canopy, shaped hubs . **£150-190**

- Belgian issue:
Yellow body and metal canopy, 'TS'
decals on sides, 'RADIO' on roof... **£250-300**

**416s** 1962-64   **R.A.C. Land Rover**
- Blue body, Lemon interior, suspension,
'RADIO RESCUE' on plastic canopy **£65-75**
- Belgian issue:
Yellow body, Grey plastic canopy,
'TS RADIO' decals on doors .......... **£250-300**

**416**   1977-79   **Buick Police Car**
- Blue body or Metallic Blue body,
'POLICE', two policemen ................. **£25-30**

**419**   1960-65   **Ford Zephyr Motorway Car**
- White or Cream, smooth or shaped
hubs, 'POLICE', large or
small roof light ............................. **£100-125**
- Export issues: with 'POLITIE' or
'RIJKS POLITIE' logo (Dutch)...... **£150-200**

**421**   1977-79   **Land Rover Station Wagon**
- Red body, White roof-rack,
'FOREST WARDEN'........................ **£20-25**

**422**   1977-80   **'RIOT POLICE' Wagon**
- Red/White body, water cannon,
White number '6' .............................. **£15-20**

**423**   1960-62   **Bedford 12cwt. Tender**
- Red body, Black ladder, undivided
windscreen, smooth or
shaped hubs, 'FIRE DEPT.' ........... **£140-160**
- Red body, unpainted ladder,
undivided screen, shaped hubs........ **£125-150**

**424**   1976-79   **'SECURITY' Van**
- Black/Yellow/White body,
mesh windows, WW ......................... **£10-15**

**428**   1978-80   **Renault 'POLICE' Car**
- Black/White body, (export isssue) ...... **£55-65**

**429**   1978-80   **'POLICE' Jaguar XJ12-C**
- White/Red/Blue body, aerial, lights .... **£25-35**

**430**   1978-80   **Porsche 924 'POLICE'**
- Black/White body, warning light ........ **£15-20**

**430**   1978-80   **Porsche 924 Police Car**
- German issue:
White/Green 'POLIZEI'.................... **£40-50**
- French issue:
White/Black, 'POLICE' ................... **£40-50**

**437**   1962-65   **Cadillac Superior Ambulance**
- Cream over Red body, 'AMBULANCE'
on side windows, Amber roof light..... **£80-90**
- 1965-68   Light Blue over White body,
'AMBULANCE' on sides, Red cross
on bonnet, Red roof light .............. **£100-125**
- Met. Red over Met. Silver body ..... **£100-125**

**439**   1963-65   **Chevrolet Impala**
- Red body, 'FIRE CHIEF', White stripe,
Lemon interior, aerial, Yellow roof
light, firemen, with White painted
door labels with 'FIRE DEPT'........ **£140-170**
- White rectangular label on front
doors 'FIRE DEPT'........................ **£80-100**
- with round Red label on front
doors 'FIRE DEPT'........................ **£80-100**

**448**   1964-69   **Austin 'POLICE' Mini Van**
- Dark Blue body, Red interior, shaped
or cast hubs, aerial, policeman and
dog, pictorial stand and internal
support packaging ......................... **£250-300**

**461** 1972-79 **'Police' Vigilant Range Rover**
- White/Blue, warning lights, policemen, 8 'POLICE' emergency signs plus bollards .............................. **£25-35**
- White/Red, 'LANGZAAM', policemen, emergency signs, Dutch model .......... **£50-60**

**463** 1964-66 **Commer 'AMBULANCE'**
- Cream or White body, Red interior, Blue tinted windows and roof light. **£120-140**

**464** 1967-68 **Commer 'POLICE' Van**
- Dark Blue body, 'COUNTY POLICE', window bars, clear roof light, leaflet ........................................ **£100-125**
- Same, but Metallic Light Blue, with Blue roof light ........................... **£100-125**
- Dark Blue, window bars, Red roof light, 'CITY POLICE', leaflet ........ **£175-200**
  Dark Blue, 'open' windows, Blue roof light, White 'POLICE' cast into sides, with instructions ................ **£90-110**
- Deep Green body, 'POLICE', export model, opaque rear/side windows ... **£400-500**
- German issue: Metallic Green body, 'POLIZEI' .... **£150-175**
- French issue: Metallic Blue body, 'SECOURS'.... **£150-175**
- Dutch issue: Metallic Blue body, window bars, 'RIJKSPOLITIE'............................. **£150-175**

**477** 1966-67 **Land Rover Breakdown**
- Red body, Yellow canopy with spotlight and 'BREAKDOWN SERVICE' logo, rubber (or later plastic) 'tyre' crank, shaped or cast hubs .......................... **£45-55**
- Same, but with large or small Silver crank, WW ................................ **£35-40**

**481** 1965-69 **Chevrolet Police Car**
- White/Black body, 'POLICE PATROL', Red roof lights, two policemen ....... **£100-125**

**482** 1966-69 **Chevrolet Impala**
- Red over White body, Chrome stripe, bonnet logo, Blue light, Grey aerial, rectangular 'FIRE CHIEF' label on front doors, detailed cast or shaped spun hubs.................................................. **£75-95**
- With round label on front doors 'FIRE CHIEF' ..................................... **£75-95**

**482** 1974-77 **Vigilant Range Rover**
- Red and White body with 'AMBULANCE' logo .......................... **£25-30**
- White body with Blue side stripe and 'AMBULANCE' logo, stretcher and two ambulancemen.............................. **£25-30**

**483** 1979 **Belgian Police Range Rover**
- White body, Red stripes, warning lights, policemen, emergency signs .... **£75-85**

**484** 1978-80 **AMC Pacer 'RESCUE'**
- White/Orange/Black body, '35'.......... **£10-15**
- Same but with 'SECOURS' logo ........ **£40-50**

**489** 1980 **Volkswagen Polo**
- German issue: White/Green, 'POLIZEI'.................... **£50-55**
- German issue: 'ADAC' ...................... **£50-55**

**490** 1967-69 **Volkswagen Breakdown**
- Unpainted fittings, Chrome tools, Red 'VW' emblem, Red/Yellow stripe label, two spare wheels. Avocado body, shaped hubs, 'BREAKDOWN SERVICE' labels, spun or cast hubs...................**£90-110**
- 1968-72 Same, but with 'RACING CLUB' labels (in GS 12)........GSP

**492** 1966-70 **VW 1200 Car**
- Green body, White roof, White 'POLIZEI' on bonnet, No '18' logo.... **£80-95**
- White body with Black 'POLIZEI' on doors and bonnet, (Germany) .... **£200-250**

**492** 1966-69 **VW European Police Car**
- Dark Green body, White roof and wings, Red 'POLIZEI', Blue lamp. Box should contain 'True Scale Steering' Red/Yellow cardboard roof fitting.........................................**£90-110**
- Dutch model: All-White body, Light Brown interior, driver, crest on doors, 'POLITIE', Blue lamp ............... **£175-225**
- Swiss model: All-White body, Light Brown interior, driver, crest on doors, 'POLITZIE', Blue lamp ................. **£175-225**

**506** 1968-69 **Sunbeam Imp 'Panda' Car**
- White body, Black bonnet and roof, Blue roof light ...................................... **£80-90**
- White body, Black roof, 'luminous' door panels, Blue roof light ................ **£80-90**
- Light Blue body, White roof, 'luminous' door panels, Blue roof light ............... **£80-90**

**509** 1970-75 **Porsche 911s Targa 'POLICE' Car**
- White/Red body, Black roof................ **£55-65**
- White/Red body, 'POLIZEI', siren, warning lights...................................... **£55-65**
- 'RIJKSPOLITIE' export issue .........**£110-130**

**513** 19?? **Citroën Safari 'ALPINE RESCUE'**
- White/Red car, skis and sled on roof-rack, skier, St Bernard dog, Blue/Yellow 'window' box ...............**£90-110**

**700** 1974-79 **Motorway Ambulance**
- White/Red, 'ACCIDENT'................... **£15-20**

**702** 1975-79 **'ACCIDENT' Breakdown Truck**
- Red/Black, single bumper, hook ......... **£10-15**

**703** 1976-78 **Hi-Speed Fire Engine**
- Red body, Yellow ladder .................... **£10-15**

**911** 1976-80 **Air-Sea Rescue Helicopter**
- Blue/Yellow body, Black 'flick-spin' rotor, 'N 428'.......... **£15-20**

**921** 1975-81 **Hughes OH-6A Helicopter**
- White/Red, 'POLICE', 'RESCUE', warning lights .................................... **£15-20**

**921/1** 1975-80 **'POLIZEI' Helicopter**
- White/Blue, 'POLIZEI', Black 'flick-spin' rotor, German issue .......... **£25-30**

**921/2** 1975-80 **'POLITIE' Helicopter**
- White/Blue, 'POLITIE', Black 'flick-spin' rotor, Dutch issue ... **£25-30**

**921/4** 1975-80 **'ADAC' Helicopter**
- Yellow body, 'D-HFFM', Black 'flick-spin' rotor ...................... **£25-30**

**921/6** 1975-80 **Swiss Red Cross Helicopter**
- Red helicopter body, Black blades, 'flick-spin' rotor ................................. **£25-30**

**922** 1975-78 **Casualty Helicopter**
- Sikorsky Skycrane in Red and White . **£25-30**

**923** 1975-78 **Casualty Helicopter**
- Army Sikorsky Skycrane with Olive/Yellow body ............................. **£25-30**

**924** 1977-81 **Air-Sea Rescue Helicopter**
- Orange/Yellow/Black, 'RESCUE' ...... **£25-30**

**927** 1978-79 **Surf Rescue Helicopter**
- Blue/White body, 'SURF RESCUE'... **£25-30**

**931** 1979-80 **Jet Ranger Helicopter**
- White/Red, 'POLICE RESCUE', 'flick-spin' rotor ................................. **£25-30**

**1001** 1980-82 **HCB Angus Firestreak**
- Red body, Yellow ladder, 2 firemen plus equipment................... **£60-70**

**1103** 1976-81 **Chubb Pathfinder**
- Red/Silver, 'AIRPORT CRASH TRUCK', operable pump and siren, orange logo ........................................ **£60-70**
- Same model but non-working siren, Brick-Red logo ........................ **£50-60**
- Red/Silver, 'NEW YORK AIRPORT' logo .......... **£80-90**

**1118** 1981-83 **Chubb Pathfinder**
- Red body, 'AIRPORT FIRE SERVICE', operable water pump ........................... **£60-70**

**1126** 1977-81 **Dennis Fire Engine 'SIMON SNORKEL'**
- Red/White/Yellow, turntable, ladder, 6 firemen ................................ **£55-65**

**1127** 1964-74 **Bedford Fire Engine 'SIMON SNORKEL'**
- Red/Yellow/Silver, turntable, ladder, 6 fireman ............................. **£100-125**

**1140** 1982 **Ford Transit Wrecker**
- White/Red, '24 Hour Service', operable winch, hook, ...................... **£15-20**
- As previous but logo changed to 'RELAY' ........................... **£15-20**
- 1982 Export model: Red/Yellow, 'ABSCHLEPPDEENST'.................... **£15-20**

**1142** 1967-74 **'HOLMES WRECKER'**
- Red/White/Blue, Grey or Gold twin booms, ladder, 2 spare wheels...........**£90-110**

**1143** 1968-80 **'AMERICAN LA FRANCE'**
- Articulated Fire Engine in Red/White/Yellow, shaped spun or detailed cast wheels, 4-part extending ladder, 5 firemen, plain early box ..... **£90-120**
- As previous model but in later striped window box .......................... **£80-100**

**1144** 1975-78 **Berliet Wrecker Recovery**
- Red/White/Gold body, with Gold or Grey hoists................... **£60-70**

**2029** 1980-83 **Mack Fire Engine**
- Red body, warning light, detachable ladder, 'HAMMOND FIRE DEPT' .... **£15-25**

| Model and details | MPR | Model and details | MPR | Model and details | MPR |
|---|---|---|---|---|---|

**50** 1959-66 'Massey-Ferguson 65' Tractor
- Bright Red bonnet, seat and metal hubs,
  Pale Grey chassis,
  Black plastic steering wheel............ **£160-200**
- Bright Red bonnet, bare metal seat,
  Red metal hubs,
  Grey plastic steering wheel ............. **£100-125**
- Dark Red bonnet, Silver metal
  steering wheel and seat,
  Fawn engine, Red plastic hubs........ **£140-160**

**NB** A variation with Copper metal
  seat is known to exist ............................NGPP

**50** 1974-77 'Massey-Ferguson 50B' Tractor
- Yellow/Black/Red body, windows ...... **£60-80**

**51** 1959-64 'Massey-Ferguson' Tipper Trailer
- Red chassis, Yellow or Grey body,
  Red metal or plastic wheels ............... **£40-45**

**53** 1960-66 'Massey-Ferguson 65'
  Tractor with Shovel
- Bright Red bonnet without decals, Grey
  plastic steering wheel, Silver metal
  seat/shovel, fawn engine, fawn rams
  with Black decals, Red metal hubs . **£120-150**
- As previous model, but Bright
  Red bonnet has thin Black outline
  decals, Red plastic hubs .................. **£100-125**
- Same but Bright Red bonnet has
  thin Black outline decals, bare metal
  rams / shovel, Red plastic hubs....... **£100-125**
- Red bonnet with White/Black decals,
  Silver metal steering wheel, Fawn engine
  and rams, Fawn bucket with Silver
  interior, Red plastic hubs................. **£150-180**

**54** 1974-?? 'Massey-Ferguson 50B'
  Tractor with Shovel
- Yellow and Red body and shovel........ **£60-80**

**54** 1962-64 'Fordson Power Major' Tractor
  (Roadless Half-Tracks)
- Blue body, Orange rollers and wheels,
  Black rubber tracks, lights in
  radiator grille. Plain 'early' box ...... **£250-300**
- Same but with Grey rubber tracks, lights
  at sides of grille, in picture box ...... **£250-300**

**55** 1961-63 'Fordson Power Major' Tractor
- Blue/Grey/Red body, Orange metal
  hubs, Silver seat/steering wheel ...... **£400-500**
- Blue/Grey/Red body, Dull Orange plastic
  hubs, Silver seat/steering wheel ...... **£150-200**

**55** 1977-?? 'David Brown 1412' Tractor
- Black/Red/White body ........................ **£60-80**

**56** 1961-63 Four-Furrow Plough
- Red/Brown/Yellow body ..................... **£30-35**

**56** 1977-?? Farm Tipper Trailer
- Red/Yellow or Red/White body
  with drop-down tailboard ................... **£10-15**

**57** 1963-66 'Massey Ferguson 65'
  Tractor with Fork
- Red/Silver/Cream body, Red hubs,
  driver, steering wheel ...................... **£160-180**
- Same model but with Orange hubs . **£125-150**

**58** 1965-72 Beast Carrier
- Red/Cream/Blue body, four calves ..... **£45-55**

**60** 1964-71 'Fordson Power Major' Tractor
- Blue body / steering wheel, bare metal
  seat, driver, Red plastic hubs........... **£150-200**

**61** 1964-71 Four-Furrow Plough
- Blue/Silver body................................. **£30-35**

**62** 1965-72 Ford Tipper Trailer
- Red/Yellow body, two raves................ **£20-25**

**64** 1965-69 Forward Control Jeep
- Red body, Yellow/White working
  conveyor, farmhand figure ................ **£80-100**

**66** 1966-72 'Massey-Ferguson 165' Tractor
- Red/Blue/White, engine sound........ **£120-140**

**67** 1967-72 'Ford Super Major' Tractor
- Blue/White/Silver body,
  'FORD 5000', instructions.............. **£100-150**
- Blue with Grey plastic hubs,
  Pale Blue mudguards, driver........... **£100-150**

**69** 1967-72 'Massey-Ferguson 165'
  Tractor and Shovel
- Red/Blue body, Silver shovel, driver**£350-400**

**71** 1967-72 Fordson Disc Harrow
- Yellow/Red/Silver body ...................... **£30-35**

**72** 1971-73 'Ford 5000'
  Tractor and Towbar
- As Corgi 67 but with frame,
  bucket and pipes............................. **£200-250**

**73** 1970-73 'Massey-Ferguson'
  Tractor and Saw
- As Corgi 66 + Yellow rotating saw. **£185-225**

**74** 1969-72 'Ford 5000' Tractor and Scoop
- As Corgi 67 + Yellow/Silver scoop. **£250-300**

**100** 1957-61 Dropside Trailer
- Yellow/Red/Grey body........................ **£40-50**

**101** 1958-61 Platform Trailer
- Yellow/Grey or Blue/Grey body ......... **£40-50**

**102** 1958-59 Rice's Pony Trailer
- Red body, Brown chassis, wire
  drawbar, smooth hubs, plastic pony .... **£70-80**
- Red body, Silver chassis, wire drawbar,
  smooth hubs, plastic pony .................. **£60-70**
- 1959-65 Red body, Black chassis, wire or
  cast drawbar, smooth or shaped hubs.. **£60-70**
- Red body, Silver chassis, wire or cast
  drawbar, smooth or shaped hubs......... **£60-70**
- Cream body, Red chassis, wire or cast
  drawbar, smooth or shaped hubs......... **£60-70**
- 1961-68 Tan/Cream body, Silver chassis,
  cast drawbar, shaped hubs................... **£60-70**

**112** 1969-72 Rice Beaufort Horse-Box
- Blue/White horse-box with
  mare and foal....................................... **£25-30**

**484** 1967-69 Dodge Livestock Transporter
- Beige/Green/Graphite Grey body, spun
  hubs, 'KEW FARGO', 5 pigs.
  Blue/Yellow card box .......................... **£70-80**
- Later issue with cast hubs.
  Blue/Yellow window box.................... **£70-80**

## Major Packs
## (and large farming models)

**1111** 1959-60 'Massey-Ferguson'
  Combine Harvester
- Red/Yellow, Yellow metal wheels,
  metal tines, card box has
  internal packing ............................... **£100-150**

**1111** 1960-61 'Massey-Ferguson 780'
  Combine Harvester
- Red/Yellow, Yellow metal wheels,
  plastic tines, card box has
  internal packing ............................... **£100-150**
- 1961-64 Red/Yellow, Red plastic wheels,
  Yellow plastic tines, card box has
  internal packing ............................... **£175-225**

**1112** 1977-78 'David Brown' Tractor
  and Combine Harvester
- Corgi 55 Tractor with Red/White/Black
  combine harvester ........................... **£150-175**

# Aircraft models

| Model and details | MPR |
|---|---|
| **650** 1973-80 **'BOAC' Concorde** | |
| • White/Blue with Gold tail design, all-card box with 'BRITISH AIRWAYS', box has inner packing | **£70-80** |
| • White/Blue with Red/White/Blue tail, display stand, 'G-BBDG' | **£50-60** |
| • Version with White stripes on tail | **£15-25** |
| • Version with crown design on tail | **£15-25** |
| **651** 1973-81 **'AIR FRANCE' Concorde** | |
| • White/Blue with Gold tail design, all-card box | **£70-80** |
| • White body, Red/White/Blue tail, display stand | **£40-50** |
| **652** 1973-81 **'JAPAN AIRLINES' Concorde** | |
| • White/Red/Blue/Black, all-card box, inner packing | **£150-200** |
| **653** 1973-81 **'AIR CANADA' Concorde** | |
| • White/Red/Blue/Black, all-card box, inner packing | **£150-200** |
| **1119** 1960-62 **HDL Hovercraft 'SR-N1'** | |
| • Blue/Grey/White body, Yellow rudders and wheels (Major Pack) | **£100-130** |
| **1301** 1973-77 **Piper Cherokee Arrow** | |
| • Yellow/Black with White wings, or White/Blue, 'N 286 4 A' | **£35-45** |

| Model and details | MPR |
|---|---|
| **1302** 1973-77 **Piper Navajo** | |
| • Red/White, 'N 9219 Y' | **£35-45** |
| • Yellow/White, 'N 9219 Y' | **£35-45** |
| **1303** 1973-77 **Lockheed F104A Starfighter** | |
| • Silver body | **£60-70** |
| • Camouflage with Black crosses | **£60-70** |
| **1304** 1973-77 **Mig-21 PF** | |
| • Blue or Silver, number '57', Red stars, retractable undercarriage | **£35-40** |
| **1305** 1973-?? **Grumman F-11a Tiger** | |
| • Blue 'NAVY', or Silver with US stars | **£60-70** |
| **1306** 1973-77 **North American P51-D Mustang** | |
| • Silver or Camouflage, Black props, US stars, moveable controls | **£35-40** |
| **1307** 1973-77 **Saab 35 X Draken** | |
| • Silver or Camouflage, retractable undercarriage, Swedish markings | **£35-45** |
| **1308** 1973-77 **BAC (or SEPCAT) Jaguar** | |
| • Silver or Camouflage, retractable wheels, moveable control surfaces | **£35-45** |
| **1309** 1973-77 **'BOAC' Concorde** | |
| • Dark Blue/White, retractable wheels | **£45-55** |
| **1310** 1973-77 **'AIR FRANCE' 'BOEING 707B'** | |
| • White/Blue body, Silver wings, retractable wheels | **£55-65** |

| Model and details | MPR |
|---|---|
| **1311** 1973-77 **Messerschmitt ME410** | |
| • All Silver body, Black Iron Crosses on wings and fuselage | **£35-45** |
| **1312** 1973-77 **Boeing 727 'TWA'** | |
| • White body, Silver wings, retractable wheels | **£35-45** |
| **1313** 1973-77 **Japanese Zero-Sen A6M5** | |
| • Green or Silver with Red circles, retractable wheels | **£35-45** |
| **1315** 1973-77 **'PAN-AM' Boeing 747** | |
| • White body, Silver wings, hinged nose, retractable wheels, 'AIR CANADA' | **£35-45** |
| **1315/1** **'BRITISH AIRWAYS' Jumbo Boeing 747** | |
| • White/Silver, Blue logo, hinged nose, retractable wheels | **£55-65** |
| **1316** 1973-77 **McDonnell Douglas F-4c5** | |
| • Phantom II in Silver or Camouflage with retractable undercarriage | **£35-45** |
| **1320** 1978-80 **'BRITISH AIRWAYS' VC-10** | |
| • White/Silver with Red tail, Blue logo, retractable wheels | **£35-45** |
| **1325** 1978-80 **'SWISSAIR' DC-10** | |
| • White/Silver with Red stripe and tail, retractable wheels | **£35-45** |

# Military and R.A.F. models

| Model and details | MPR |
|---|---|
| **350** 1958-62 **Thunderbird Missile** | |
| • Blue, Green or Silver missile with Red tip, Air Force Blue loading trolley | **£65-75** |
| **351** 1958-62 **RAF Land Rover** | |
| • Blue body, RAF roundel, spare wheel, windows, flat spun hubs | **£90-110** |
| • Same model but with suspension, flat spun hubs | **£90-110** |
| **352** 1958-62 **RAF Vanguard Staff Car** | |
| • Blue bodied Standard Vanguard with RAF roundel | **£80-100** |
| **353** 1959-61 **Decca Radar Scanner** | |
| • Blue/Orange, scanner rotates | **£35-45** |
| **354** 1964-66 **Commer Military Ambulance** | |
| • Military Green body, Red Interior, Red cross, driver, Blue glazing | **£125-150** |
| **355** 1964-65 **Commer Van 'US MILITARY POLICE'** | |
| • Red interior, driver, Blue roof light, leaflet in box | **£125-150** |
| **356** 1964-66 **VW Personnel Carrier** | |
| • Military Green, Red interior, driver, Blue roof light, 'US Personnel' | **£125-150** |
| **357** 1964-66 **Land Rover** | |
| • Military Green, Lemon interior, driver, White star, 'Weapons Carrier' | **£240-280** |
| **358** 1964-68 **Oldsmobile Staff Car** | |
| • Red interior, White star, 'HQ STAFF', driver, 3 passengers, aerial | **£125-150** |
| **359** 1964-66 **Commer Army 'FIELD KITCHEN'** | |
| • Blue interior, US star on roof, driver/attendant, 'US ARMY' | **£125-150** |
| **414** 1961-63 **Bedford Dormobile Military Ambulance** | |
| • Olive drab body, Red crosses, smooth hubs | **£100-125** |
| • Same model but with shaped hubs and suspension | **£100-125** |
| **500** 1963-64 **US Army Land Rover** | |
| • Rare version of model 357 | **£200-250** |
| **900** 1974-78 **German Tiger MkI Tank** | |
| • Brown/Green, rubber tracks, fires shells (12 supplied) aerial, '144' | **£30-40** |
| **901** 1974-78 **Centurion Mk.I Tank** | |
| • Rubber tracks, fires shells (12 supplied), aerial, Union Jacks | **£30-40** |

| Model and details | MPR |
|---|---|
| **902** 1974-80 **American M60 A1 Tank** | |
| • Rubber tracks, fires shells (12 supplied) | **£30-40** |
| **903** 1974-80 **British Chieftain Tank** | |
| • Fires shells (12 supplied), rubber tracks | **£30-40** |
| **904** 1974-78 **German King-Tiger Tank** | |
| • 'B 34', rubber tracks, fires shells, (12 supplied) Black crosses | **£30-40** |
| **905** 1975-76 **Russian SU100 Tank Destroyer** | |
| • Grey, Red Star, fires shells (12 supplied), rubber tracks | **£30-40** |
| **906** 1975-76 **Saladin Armoured Car** | |
| • Rubber tracks, fires shells (12 supplied), elevating gun | **£30-40** |
| **907** 1976-80 **German Rocket Launcher** | |
| • Steel Blue/Red, half-track, detachable limber, fires rockets (12) | **£30-40** |
| **908** 1977-80 **French AMX Recovery Tank** | |
| • Crane, lifting dozer blade, equipment, 3 figures | **£40-50** |
| **909** 1977-80 **Tractor Gun and Trailer** | |
| • Sand-coloured British gun and trailer, fires shells (12 supplied) | **£40-50** |
| **920** 1975-78 **Bell Army Helicopter** | |
| • Military-Green with Army markings, Black or Green rotor | **£15-20** |
| **922** 1975-78 **Casualty Helicopter** | |
| • Red/White/Yellow Sikorsky helicopter, number '3', Red crosses | **£15-20** |
| **923** 1975-78 **Sikorsky Sky Crane** | |
| • Military-Green, Red cross, 'ARMY' | **£15-20** |

## MAJOR PACKS
## (Military models)

| Model and details | MPR |
|---|---|
| **1106** 1959-61 **Karrier Decca Radar Van** | |
| • Cream body, 4 Orange bands, rotating scanner, aerials, box has interior packing | **£125-175** |
| • Same, but with 5 Orange bands | **£100-125** |

| Model and details | MPR |
|---|---|
| **1108** 1958-60 **Bristol Bloodhound Guided Missile and Launching Ramp** | |
| • Green ramp, Yellow/Red/White Guided Missile, RAF markings | **£125-150** |
| **1109** 1959-61 **Bristol Bloodhound Guided Missile and Loading Trolley** | |
| • Green ramp, Yellow/Red/White Guided Missile, RAF markings | **£125-150** |
| **1112** 1959-62 **Corporal Guided Missile on Launching Ramp** | |
| • Military-Green mechanical base, White missile, Red rubber nose cone, instruction sheet in box | **£200-250** |
| • 1960-62 Same but with separately boxed 1408 Percussion Head and instructions | **£200-250** |
| **1113** 1959-62 **Corporal Guided Missile Erector Vehicle** | |
| • With lifting mechanism and Missile, spare wheel, leaflet | **£250-350** |
| **1115** 1958-61 **Bristol Ferranti Bloodhound** | |
| • Yellow/Red/White Guided Missile with RAF markings | **£65-75** |
| **1116** 1959-61 **Bloodhound Launching Ramp** | |
| • Launching ramp for 1115. Rotates, has lifting mechanism | **£55-65** |
| **1117** 1959-61 **Bloodhound Loading Trolley** | |
| • For use with 1115. Military-Green, spare wheel, drawbar pivots | **£55-65** |
| **1118** 1959-64 **International Tow Truck** | |
| • Military-Green with British markings (US markings on box picture) | **£125-150** |
| • Dutch issue: Silver grille and sidelights | **£125-150** |
| • US Army issues | **£125-150** |
| **1124** 1960-61 **Launching Ramp for Corporal Guided Missile** | |
| • Military-Green, operable mechanisms, in plain 'Temporary Pack' box | **£100-125** |
| **1133** 1965-66 **Troop Transporter** | |
| • International six wheeled truck, 'US 7811332', hook | **£175-200** |
| **1134** 1965-66 **'US ARMY' Fuel Tanker** | |
| • Olive Bedford 'S' Type Artic., US Army star, 'NO SMOKING' | **£225-275** |
| **1135** 1965-?? **Heavy Equipment Transporter** | |
| • Bedford Carrimore, Military Green, US Army star, driver, Red interior | **£225-275** |

# Novelty, Film and TV-related models

| Model and details | MPR |
|---|---|

**107** 1967-70 **Batboat on Trailer**
- Black boat (tinplate fin cover) with Batman and Robin figures, gold trailer (suspension, cast wheels). Blue/yellow pictorial box also contains black accessory towing hook for attachment to Batmobile ................ **£125-150**
- 1974-81 Black boat (plastic fin), Batman and Robin figures, gold trailer (no suspension, WW), striped window box .......................**£90-110**

**201** 1970-72 **The Saint's Volvo**
- White body, White 'Saint' logo on red label, WhizzWheels, driver, Red/Yellow 'window' box ............... **£150-200**

**258** 1965-68 **The Saint's Volvo P1800**
- White body, Black 'Saint' logo (transfer), Red interior, driver, spun hubs, Blue/Yellow card box ...................... **£200-250**
- 1968-70 White body, White 'Saint' logo on Red label, Red interior, driver, cast hubs, Blue/Yellow card box ..... **£200-250**
  1968-70 As previous version but white 'Saint' logo on blue label ............NGPP
- 1970-71 White body, White logo on Red label, Yellow interior, WW ...... **£135-155**

**259** 1979-80 **Penguinmobile**
- White car with 'Penguin' and Red/Yellow parasol, Black/Yellow 'window' box .. **£35-40**

**260** 1979-81 **Superman Police Car**
- Blue/White body, *'CITY of METROPOLIS'*, Black/Yellow pictorial window box.... **£60-70**

**261** 1965-69 **James Bond's Aston-Martin**
(From the film *'Goldfinger'*)
- Bright Gold body (metal roof), Red interior, wire wheels. With James Bond at the wheel, passenger seat ejector (with bandit figure). Accessories: envelope with 'secret instructions', spare bandit figure, self-adhesive '007' badge, (plus 'Model Car Makers to James Bond' Corgi Catalogue in earlier boxes). Blue/Yellow picture box has inner pictorial stand....................... **£300-350**
- variant: Same model but the opening roof component is made of plastic........NGPP

**261** 1979-81 **Spiderbuggy**
- Red/Blue jeep body with crane, Spiderman and Green Goblin figures. Black/Yellow pictorial window box.. **£75-100**

**262** 1967-69 **Lincoln Continental Executive Limousine**
- Metallic Gold/Black body, with picture strip for onboard 'TV set' ... **£125-150**
- Light Blue/Tan body, with picture strip for onboard 'TV set'............... **£150-175**

**262** 1979-80 **Captain Marvel's Porsche**
- White with flames and stars, driver, Black/Yellow 'window' box............... **£35-40**

**263** 1979-81 **Captain America's Jetmobile**
- White/Red/Blue body, Red wheels, Black/Yellow 'window' box............... **£25-30**

**264** 1979-82 **Incredible Hulk Truck**
- Bronze Hulk in Red cage on Mazda pick-up, Black/Yellow 'window' box . **£60-70**

- Same model but Hulk in Grey cage.... **£70-80**
**NB** Dark Bronze Hulk is rare – add **£10** to price.

**265** 1979-82 **Supermobile**
- Blue/Red/Silver body, Superman at the controls, moving 'fists' . Black/Yellow pictorial 'window' box has 10 spare rockets and an instruction leaflet ........ **£40-50**

**266** 1968-72 **Chitty Chitty Bang Bang**
- Chrome, Brown and Red body, Red/Yellow retractable 'wings', figures of Caractacus Potts, Truly Scrumptious, a boy and a girl. Pictorial Blue/Yellow 'window' box comes in two sizes .................. **£350-400**
- 1992 25th Anniversary replica: model on 'mahogany' display stand. Direct mail offer from Corgi............... **£60-70**

**266** 1979-83 **Spider Bike**
- Red/Blue motorcycle, Spiderman rider, Black wheels, Black or Red handlebars forks, Black or Blue seat and fairing, amber or clear windshield, rocket launchers. Box also contains 10 spare rockets on sprue.
  Box 1: Black/Yellow pictorial 'window' box with header card ........... **£100-125**
  Box 2: Black/Yellow 'window' box without header card ........................ **£100-125**
  Box 3: Black/Red/Yellow striped 'window' box without header card.. **£100-125**

**266** 1980-82 **Spider Bike**
- Same model but White wheels........ **£100-125**

**267** 1966-67 **Batmobile**
- (i): Gloss Black body, Red 'Bat' logo on doors and gold cast hubs, Batman and Robin figures, 'pulsating flame', sealed secret instructions concealed in box base. 12 spare rockets (Red or Yellow) attached to sprue, self-adhesive 'Batman' badge. Pictorial card box with diorama, earliest versions had 'features' leaflet within............ **£400-500**
- (ii): As previous model but with Matt Black body............................. **£500-600**
- 1967-72 As (i) but with towing hook cast into base. Blue/Yellow 'window' box (some in earlier card boxes)..... **£225-275**
- 1967-72 (iv): As (i) but cast Silver wheels. Black/Blue/Yellow 'window' box................................. **£225-275**
- 1973 (v): As (iv) but with Red WhizzWheels (with Chrome hubs) and without pulsating 'flame' effect. Blue/Yellow 'window' box with missiles and instructions ................. **£300-400**
- 1974-77 (vi): As (v) but with Black WhizzWheels and without pulsating 'flame' effect. Copyright information cast in base, Dark Blue/Yellow 'window' box (header card on some), spare rockets, no instruction sheet .. **£150-175**
- 1977-79 (vii): As (vi) casting but wider WhizzWheels, no Robin figure. Black/Red/Yellow 'window' box .... **£150-175**
- 1979-80 (viii): Gloss Black, Gold slasher blade and tow hook, aerial, Batman and Robin figures, wide WW, striped 'window' box..... **£150-175**

**268** 1978-80 **Batman's Batbike**
- Black/Red rocket-firing motorcycle with Red or Grey Batman figure. Black and Yellow 'window' box (header card on some), spare rockets............ **£80-100**
- 1980-83 As previous versions but in Black/Red/Yellow striped 'window' box....................................... **£50-70**

**268** 1967-72 **The Green Hornet's 'Black Beauty'**
- Black body, Green interior, driver and Green Hornet figures, transfer on roof, spun hubs. Fires missiles from front, radar spinners from rear. Four of each, plus 'secret instructions' are in Blue/Yellow pictorial card box which should also include a greaseproof paper roof decal protector and inner pictorial card .................. **£200-250**
- Same but with cast detailed hubs.... **£400-500**

**269** 1977-83 **James Bond Lotus Esprit**
(From film *'The Spy Who Loved Me'*)
- White body, Black windows, operable fins and rocket mechanism. . Early Black/Yellow pictorial 'window' box with plain base must contain instruction sheet and 10 spare rockets attached to sprue .. **£125-165**
- Later pictorial 'window' box has instructions printed on base, 10 spare rockets............................. **£100-130**
- 1977 10 gold-plated versions of 269 were presented to VIPs at the film's launch. These models had special mountings and boxes................. **£1,000-1,500**
- Pre-production model: Demonstration model in a case. Red/Yellow/Blue/Green ........... **£1,000-1,400**

**270** 1968-76 **James Bond's Aston-Martin DB5**
- Silver body (slightly larger than 261). Features as 261, plus revolving number plates and extending tyre slashers. Box must contain inner pictorial stand, James Bond leaflet, sealed 'secret instructions' packet, unused '007' lapel badge (different from 261), set of unapplied no. plates and bandit figure. Variations include Gold or Silver coloured bumpers, metal or plastic spoked rear wheels.
  Box 1: Pictorial wing-flap box. Model sits on card platform under vac-formed bubble (fragile, few made) ......................... **£300-400**
  Box 2: Blue/Yellow 'window' box (some with card 'upstand' till 1973, few made)............................. **£400-600**
  Box 3: Black/Blue/Yellow striped 'window' box (1973-76)................. **£200-250**
- 1977-78 As previous version but with fixed number plates, 'solid' chrome WW, no tyre-slashers, Striped window box (no 'secret instructions'), ejectable passenger lodged in box inner......... **£100-130**

**271** 1978-81 **James Bond Aston-Martin**
- Silver body (1:36 scale), Red interior, Gold radiator/bumpers, WhizzWheels ('spoked' detail or 'alloy racing'). Early Black/Yellow boxes had '1:36' printed on window tag, plus header card ........ **£70-80**
- Later Black/Yellow boxes did not have the window tag ..................................... **£50-60**
- Final issues had Black/Red/Yellow striped window boxes or Purple boxes .......... **£50-60**

- 1990 'MODELAUTO' promotional:
  Silver, Red interior, 2 figures, Blue logo
  'National Motor Museum Holland'. **£180-220**
- 1991-92 Reissue of C271 in clear plastic
  display box with plastic '007' badge .. **£20-30**

271/1 1992 Silver body (1:36 scale),
  small 4-spoked wheels .............. **£70-90**
271/2 1993 Re-run of 271/1 ......................... **£70-90**

272 1981-83 **James Bond Citroën 2cv**
  (From film *'For Your Eyes Only'*)
- Yellow body, opening bonnet, WW.
  Box (1): Black/Red/Yellow 'window'
  box with pictorial header card............ **£30-40**
  Box (2): Black/Red/Yellow 'compact'
  box with pictorial top flap.................. **£30-40**
- 1981 Gold plated version:
  (12 only produced). 'Strada Jewellry'
  Certificate should be present..... **£2,000-3,000**

277 1968-72 **'MONKEES' Monkeemobile**
- Red body, White roof, Yellow logo, cast
  detailed wheels. Figures of Mike,
  Mickey, Davy and Pete plus red
  plastic 'Monkees' guitar.
  Blue/Yellow 'window' box ............. **£250-300**
- Same, but no 'Monkees' guitar ....... **£250-300**
- In Blue/Yellow 'window' box with
  clip-in cardboard header as used for
  shop display purposes .................... **£800-900**
NB Pre-production model with
  plastic engine exists.

278 1981 **Dan Dare's Car**
- Red/Yellow space vehicle.
  Planned but not produced......................NPP

290 1976-77 **Kojak's Buick**
- Bronze body (various shades), 4-spoke
  or disc type wheel hubs, 'gunfire' sound,
  self-adhesive 'Lieutenant' badge,
  figures of Kojak (no hat) and Crocker
  (blue jacket). Black/Yellow
  pictorial 'window' box .................... **£150-175**
- Same but disc type wheel hubs ....... **£100-125**
- 1977-80 Same but Kojak figure has a
  hat and Crocker has a Black jacket.
  'New' tag on some boxes ................... **£60-75**

292 1977-82 **Starsky & Hutch Ford Torino**
- Red/White body, figures of Starsky,
  Hutch, and a suspect. Black/Yellow
  pictorial 'window' box .................... **£100-150**
- 1986 Reissued as export
  model (20,000 units) ......................... **£10-15**

298 1982-83 **Magnum P.I. Ferrari 308GTS**
- Red Ferrari with 4-spoke or disc wheels.
  Black/Red/Yellow pictorial
  'window' box..................................... **£20-30**

320 1978-81 **The Saint's Jaguar XJS**
- White body, standard or 'dished'
  WhizzWheels. Black/Yellow 'window'
  box (yellow or black inner)................ **£50-60**

336 1967-69 **James Bond's Toyota 2000 GT**
  (From film *'You Only Live Twice'*)
- White body, Red aerial, 2 figures, rocket
  launchers in boot. Diorama box must
  have card reinforcements to protect aerial,
  8 spare rockets on sprue, sealed envelope
  marked 'Secret Instructions' which also
  contains self-adhesive '007' badge . **£250-300**

342 1980-82 **'The Professionals' Ford Capri**
- Metallic Silver body, dished or disc hubs,
  figures of Cowley, Bodie and Doyle.
  Pictorial 'window' box .................... **£125-150**
- Same but with chrome wheel hubs . **£150-175**
- Matt Silver body, Dk. Red interior.. **£125-150**

348 1980-81 **'Vegas' Thunderbird**
- Red body with Dan Tanner figure
  Black/Yellow pictorial 'window' box . **£60-80**

391 1972-72 **James Bond Mustang Mach I**
  (From film *'Diamonds Are Forever'*)
- Red body, Black bonnet, White interior
  and base, WW (2 types known).
- Red/Yellow 'window' box has
  '007' Red sticker ............................. **£175-200**
- Same model but with 'CORGI
  TOYS' shop display stand............... **£300-400**

**CHEVROLET VANS**
423 1978-78 **'ROUGH RIDER'**
- Yellow van, motorcycle labels ............ **£20-25**
431 1978-79 **'VANATIC'**
- White van, polychromatic side labels . **£15-20**
432 1978-79 **'VANTASTIC'**
- Black van, Yellow/Red design ........... **£15-20**
433 1978 **'VANISHING POINT'**
- Chevrolet van shown in 1978
  catalogue but not issued ..........................NPP
434 1978-80 **'CHARLIE'S ANGELS' Van**
- Pink Chevrolet Custom van, Yellow or
  Brown interior, 4-spoke wheels.
  Black/Yellow pictorial 'window' box . **£60-75**
- 2nd issue with solid disc wheels ........ **£50-60**
435 1979-80 **'SUPERMAN' Van**
- Metallic Silver Chevrolet 'SuperVan'.
  Black/Yellow pictorial 'window' box
  (printing variations seen).................... **£35-45**
436 1979-80 **'SPIDERVAN'**
- Blue Chevrolet van, 'Spiderman' design,
  4-spoke wheels.
  Black/Yellow pictorial 'window' box . **£80-90**
- 2nd issue with solid disc wheels ........ **£50-60**
437 1979-80 **'COCA COLA'**
- Red Chevrolet van, White design,
  tinted roof windows, crates ................. **£30-35**
NB Various other labels were designed for
  the Chevrolet 'Van' series. Some prototype
  labels were printed but not officially used.
  Some of these may have found their way on
  to repainted van castings - they are NOT
  official Corgi issues. Logos include:
  'Apache Patrol', 'Light Vantastic',
  'Vanilla Treat', 'Cosmos', 'Columbia',
  'Aquarius', 'Centaur', 'Colorama',
  'Rocket Van', 'Centaur', plus four other
  unlettered 'psychedelic' designs.

436 1963-65 **Citroën 'WILDLIFE SAFARI'**
- Yellow Citroën ID19, driver and passenger,
  detailed interior, roof luggage,
  'Wild Life Reservation' logo............. **£70-80**

447 1965-66 **'Walls Ice Cream' Van**
- Ford Thames van in Blue/Cream,
  salesman, boy, spare transfers.
  Blue and Yellow card box,
  inner base, leaflet ........................... **£200-300**
448 1964-69 **Austin Police Mini Van**
- Dark Blue body, Red interior, shaped or
  cast hubs, aerial, White 'POLICE' logo,
  policeman and dog, pictorial stand and
  internal support packaging..............**£115-130**

450 1968-71 **Lunar Bug**
- Red, White, Blue. Blue/Yellow window
  box includes inner packing ................. **£60-70**
472 1964-66 **'VOTE FOR CORGI'**
- Corgi 438 Land Rover in Green/Yellow,
  Red interior, two figures,
  Blue/Yellow card box ..................... **£100-120**

474 1965-68 **Musical 'Walls Ice Cream' Van**
- Ford Thames van in Blue/Cream,
  musical movement (must function),
  diorama but no figures. Blue/Yellow
  card box with packing ring and
  packing piece, plus
  unused sticker sheet......................... **£300-400**

475 1964-65 **'Olympic Winter Sport'**
- White/Yellow Citroën Safari, '1964',
  roof-rack, skier, skis.
  Diorama 'By Special Request' box ....**£90-110**

475 1965-68 **'CORGI SKI CLUB'**
- Citroën Safari with Off-White body,
  Red roof-rack, 4 Yellow skis and 2 poles,
  bonnet transfer, Brown dashboard/rear
  seats, Green front seats....................**£110-130**
- White body, Yellow Roof-rack, 4 Red
  skis and 2 poles, Green dashboard/rear
  seats, Brown front seats ..................**£110-130**

479 1967-71 **Mobile Camera Van**
- Blue/White Commer van, spun hubs,
  camera/operator, 'Samuelson Film
  Services', equipment case ............. **£100-125**
- Same model but detailed cast hubs ..... **£80-90**

486 1967-69 **'KENNEL CLUB' Truck**
- White/Orange Chevrolet Impala
  with 'Vari-View' dachshund picture,
  four plastic dogs ................................ **£50-60**

487 1965-69 **'CHIPPERFIELDS'**
  **Parade Vehicle**
- 472 Land Rover in Red/Blue, *'CIRCUS
  IS HERE'* label, chimpanzee, clown,
  Blue/yellow card box ..................... **£175-200**

497 1966-66 **'The Man From UNCLE's**
  **'Thrush Buster'**
- Oldsmobile (235) with White body,
  cast wheels, cast spotlights, 'UNCLE'
  logo, gun sound, figures of Napoleon
  Solo and Ilya Kuriakin. Blue/Yellow
  pictorial card box (which must include
  internal packaging, roof packing,
  and 3-D 'Waverley' ring) ............... **£500-600**
- Same but Metallic Purplish-Blue
  body, cast or plastic spotlights ....... **£175-250**

499 1967-69 **'1968 Winter Olympics'**
- White/Blue Citroën, 'Grenoble
  Olympiade', Red or Yellow roof rack,
  Yellow or Red skis/poles, male
  tobogganist, female skier. Blue/Yellow
  'window' box, instruction sheet ...... **£200-250**

503 1964-70 **'CHIPPERFIELDS'**
  **Giraffe Transporter**
- Red/Blue Bedford 'TK',
  cast or spun wheels, 2 giraffes.
  Blue/Yellow card box ..................... **£100-150**
- 1970-71 As previous model but
  larger 'stepped' front wheels........... **£130-170**
- Window box variation .................... **£200-300**

510 1970-73 **Team Manager's Car**
- Red Citroën, *'Tour De France'*,
  figures, spare wheels, *'Paramount'* .... **£70-80**

511 1970-71 **'CHIPPERFIELDS'**
  **Poodle Truck**
- Blue/Red Chevrolet Impala Pick-Up,
  *'PERFORMING POODLES'* labels,
  cast wheels, trainer (Mary Chipperfield),
  4 White and 2 Black poodles. Blue
  and Yellow 'window' box (should
  include a plastic dome over dogs)... **£250-300**

513 1970-72 **Citroën Safari 'Alpine Rescue'**
- White/Red car, Yellow roof-rack,
  St Bernard, sled, skis, male figure.
  Blue/Yellow 'window' box ............. **£200-250**

607 1963-68 **'CHIPPERFIELDS'**
  **Elephant Cage**
- A Corgi Kit with Brown plastic cage
  and elephant mouldings, instruction
  leaflet. Blue/Yellow card box............. **£50-75**

**647** 1980-83 **Buck Rogers Starfighter**
- White/Blue, Yellow retractable wings, Wilma Dearing and Tweaky figures, Black/Yellow pictorial 'window' box, 10 spare rockets ................................... **£40-45**

**648** 1981-82 **NASA Space Shuttle**
- White/Black body, 'USA Satellite', opening hatch ...................................... **£20-25**

**649** 1979-82 **James Bond Space Shuttle**
(From the film *'Moonraker'*)
- White body (C468 casting), separate satellite (early versions retained by nylon strap). Larger pictorial Black/Yellow box ............................... **£50-75**

**681** 1972 **Stunt Bike**
- Gold body, Blue and Yellow rider, Red trolley, 'window' box, (19,000)....... **£125-150**

**700** 1974-80 **Motorway Service Ambulance**
- White/Red futuristic vehicle, WW ........ **£8-12**

**701** 1974-80 **Inter-City Mini-Bus**
- Orange body, Yellow labels, WW ......... **£8-12**

**801** 1969-69 **Noddy's Car**
- Yellow/Red car with dickey-seat, cast hubs, chrome bumpers. Figures of Noddy, Big-Ears, and black-faced Golly. Pictorial Blue/Yellow 'window' box ....... **£1,000-1,500**
- As previous model but Golly has Light Tan face ...................... **£750-1,000**
- As previous model but Golly has Grey face .................................. **£350-500**
- 1969-73 As previous model but with Master Tubby (light or dark brown) instead of Golly ................. **£200-300**

**802** 1969-72 **Popeye's Paddle-Wagon**
- Yellow/White body, Red wings, Blue paddle covers, White or Yellow rear wheels, anchors, moving figures of Popeye, Olive Oyl, Swee'Pea, Bluto and Wimpey. Blue/Yellow pictorial 'window' box ................... **£300-350**

**803** 1969-72 **The Beatles Submarine**
- Yellow/White, psychedelic design, hatches (Yellow rear, White front) open to show John, Paul, George and Ringo, pictorial window box with Blue-Green inner lining . **£250-300**
- 1970-71 With two Red hatch covers ............ **£250-300**
- With one red hatch and one white hatch ............................. **£400-500**
- Pre-production issue: Gold plated, periscope attached to sprue. Only eight issued ................. **£600-750**

**804** 1975-78 **Noddy's Car**
- Red/Yellow car, no dickey-seat, no rear bumper. Figure of Noddy only. Dark Blue/Yellow pictorial 'window' box.................................. **£150-175**

**805** 1970-71 **Hardy Boys Rolls-Royce**
- 9041 Silver Ghost casting in Red, Blue and Yellow, plated wheels. Bubble-pack of five Hardy Boys figures also within the Blue/Yellow 'window' also.......................... **£150-175**

**806** 1970-72 **Lunar Bug**
- Red/White/Blue, *'Lunar Bug'*, windows, drop-down ramps ............... **£65-75**

**807** 1971-73 **Dougal's Magic Roundabout Car** (based on 510 Citroën)
- Yellow/Red, with Brian, Dougal and Dylan. Yellow/Blue 'window' box with decal sheet .............................. **£175-225**
- 1973-74 Same but in Black/Yellow 'window' box, with decal sheet....... **£130-160**

**808** 1971-73 **Basil Brush's Car**
- Red/Yellow car with hand-painted Basil figure, 'Laugh tapes' and soundbox are in separate printed box within pictorial Blue/Yellow 'window' box................................. **£175-200**

**809** 1973-73 **Dick Dastardly's Car**
- Blue/Red/Yellow racing car with Dick and Muttley figures. Dark Blue/Yellow 'window' box .... **£150-175**

**811** 1972-74 **James Bond Moon Buggy**
- Blue/White body, Yellow WhizzWheels, Red scanner. Roof opening mechanism should be working. Blue/Yellow pictorial window box...................... **£200-250**

**H851** 1972-74 **Magic Roundabout Train**
- Red/Blue, Mr Rusty and Basil in the locomotive (engine sound), Rosalie and Paul in the carriage and Dougal in the van. Blue/Yellow pictorial 'window' box with Blue nylon tow-rope ........ **£200-300**

**H852** 1972-74 **Magic Roundabout Carousel**
- Red/Yellow/Blue working roundabout with Swiss musical movement playing the TV theme. Dylan, Paul, Rosalie, Florence and Basil figures. Blue/Yellow pictorial card box ....... **£350-400**

**H853** 1972-74 **Magic Roundabout Playground**
- Contains a modified H852, H851 (with the figures), plus Zebedee, Dylan, four kids, see-saw, park bench, 3 Blue and 3 Orange shrubs and 2 flowers. Operating carousel and track. Theme music plays when Dylan is wound up ................... **£1,000-1,250**

**H859** 1972-74 **Mr McHenry's Trike**
- Red/Yellow trike and trailer, Mr McHenry and pop-up Zebedee figures, Blue and Yellow pictorial 'window' box with blue towing cord and instruction sheet ............... **£150-175**

**H860-H868**
1972-74 **Magic Roundabout figures**
Packed in individual clear plastic tubs:
- 860 Dougal, • 861 Florence, • 862 Zebedee,
- 863 Mr Rusty, • 864 Brian the Snail,
- 865 Basil, • 866 Ermintrude the Cow,
- 868 Dylan the Rabbit ................ Each: **£25-35**

**925** 1976-81 **Batcopter**
- Black body, Red 'Bat' rotors, Batman figure, operable winch ........... **£65-75**

**926** 1978-80 **Stromberg Helicopter**
(From *'The Spy Who Loved Me'*)
- Black body/rotors, ten spare rockets. Black/Yellow 'window' box............... **£60-70**

**927** 1978-80 **Chopper Squad Helicopter**
- White/metallic Blue Jet Ranger helicopter, operating winch. Black/Yellow pictorial 'window' box . **£35-45**

**928** 1981-82 **Spidercopter**
- Blue/Red body, 'spider legs'. Black/Yellow pictorial 'window' box . **£40-50**

**929** 1979-80 **'DAILY PLANET' Jetcopter**
- Red/White body, rocket launchers, Black/Yellow pictorial 'window' box contains 10 spare rockets .................... **£60-90**

**930** 1972-80 **'Drax' Helicopter**
(From the film *'Moonraker'*)
- White body, 'Drax' logo, ten spare rockets. Black/Yellow 'window' box............... **£60-70**

**9004** 1967-69 **'The World of Wooster' Bentley**
- Green 9002 Bentley with figures of Jeeves and Wooster, plated wheels. Bubble-packed in display base........... **£70-90**

## MAJOR MODELS

**1121** 1960-62 **'CHIPPERFIELDS' Crane Truck**
- Red body, Raised Blue log and wheels, operable grey tinplate jib and hook, instruction leaflet. Blue/Yellow lidded box with packing............................ **£125-150**
- 1963-69 Red body, raised Blue logo and wheels, operable chrome tinplate jib / hook, leaflet. Blue/Yellow card box with end flaps .......................... **£125-150**

**1123** 1961-62 **'CHIPPERFIELDS' Circus Cage**
- Red body, Yellow chassis, smooth hubs, red diecast end and middle sliding doors, 2 plastic lions (in stapled bags), animal name decals, instructions. Blue/Yellow lidded box with packing.................. **£100-125**
- 1963-68 Red body, Yellow chassis, smooth or spun hubs, Blue plastic end and middle sliding doors, 4 animals (lions, tigers or polar bears in stapled bags), animal name decals. Blue/Yellow card box with end flaps .................... **£75-100**

**1130** 1962-70 **'CHIPPERFIELDS' Horse Transporter**
- Bedford TK truck, Red/Blue, Green or Red 'horse-head' design at rear, cast or spun hubs, 6 Brown or Grey horses, Blue/Yellow card box with card packing around horses.................... **£175-225**
- 1970-72 As previous model but with larger 'truck' wheels............... **£150-175**

**1139** 1968-72 **'CHIPPERFIELDS' Menagerie Transporter**
- Scammell Handyman MkIII, Blue/Red cab, Blue trailer with 3 plastic cages, 2 lions, 2 tigers and 2 bears. Blue and Yellow pictorial 'window' box with packing to hold animals, plus spare self-adhesive securing tape for animals....................................... **£250-300**

**1144** 1969-72 **'CHIPPERFIELDS' Crane and Cage with Rhino**
- Red/Blue Scammell Handyman MkIII, 'COME TO THE CIRCUS' on n/s, silver jib/hook, stepped 'truck' front wheels on some, Grey rhinoceros in plastic cage. Blue/Yellow 'window' box with pre-formed blister-pack around animals ............................... **£300-400**

**1163** 1978-82 **Human Cannon Truck**
- Red and Blue body, *'MARVO'* figure . **£30-40**

**1164** 1980-83 **Berliet 'DOLPHINARIUM'**
- Yellow cab, Blue trailer, Clear plastic tank, two dolphins, girl trainer. Black/Yellow 'window' box with header card on some........................ **£100-150**
- Yellow cab, Yellow trailer, 'window' box with header card on some ........ **£100-150**

74

# Marks & Spencer issues

In 1978 a special series of models and sets were produced for sale through selected M & S stores. They were packed in attractive non-standard boxes and had unique liveries. They were issued in small quantities.

## SINGLE MODELS

| | | | |
|---|---|---|---|
| 8800 | 79 | **Custom Van**  No details | **£25-35** |
| 8801 | 79 | **Spindrift Helicopter** | |
| | | Black body with Yellow chassis, | |
| | | floats and rotor blades | **£25-35** |
| 8802 | 79 | **Massey Ferguson Tractor** | |
| | | Red/Black body with White | |
| | | arms and Red shovel | **£40-50** |
| 8803 | 79 | **Buick 'FIRE CHIEF' Car** | |
| | | Red body with 'City Fire | |
| | | Department' logo on bonnet | **£50-75** |

## SMALL SETS

| | | | |
|---|---|---|---|
| 8000 | 78 | **F1 Racing Set** | |
| | | 162 'ELF' Tyrrell (Dark Blue) | |
| | | and 160 Hesketh F1 (White) | **£75-100** |
| 8001 | 78 | **Wings Flying Team** | |
| | | 301 Lotus Elite (Green), Nipper | |
| | | aircraft (White), Grey trailer | **£100-150** |
| 8002 | 78 | **Motorway Police Patrol** | |
| | | C429 'POLICE' Jaguar (Green) | |
| | | and 160 Hesketh F1 X1-9 | **£60-80** |
| 8003 | 79 | **Spindrift Power Boat Team** | |
| | | 301 Ferrari Daytona (Yellow) | |
| | | and Yellow power boat on trailer | **£60-80** |

## MEDIUM SETS

| | | | |
|---|---|---|---|
| 8100 | 78 | **Racing Team** | |
| | | C421 Land Rover (White with | |
| | | 'FORMULA' logo), 338 Rover, | |
| | | and 301 Lotus on trailer | **£150-200** |
| 8101 | 78 | **Wings Flying School** | |
| | | C421 Land Rover (Grey with | |
| | | 'WINGS' logo) Grey helicopter, | |
| | | Nipper aircraft on Grey trailer | **£150-200** |
| 8102 | 78 | **Motorway Breakdown** | |
| | | C429 'POLICE' Jaguar, | |
| | | 293 Renault 5 (Yellow) plus | |
| | | Berliet Wrecker with 'RESCUE | |
| | | BREAKDOWN SERVICES' | **£100-150** |
| 8103 | 79 | **Spindrift Power Boat Team** | |
| | | Includes Spindrift 301 Ferrari, | |
| | | Helicopter and Dinghy | **£150-200** |

## LARGE SETS

| | | | |
|---|---|---|---|
| 8400 | 78 | **GP 'FORMULA 1 RACING TEAM'** | |
| | | 160 Hesketh (White), 162 'ELF' Tyrrell | |
| | | (Dark Blue), Fiat X1-9 (Blue) | |
| | | and Land Rover (White) | **£200-250** |
| 8401 | 78 | **Wings Flying Club** | |
| | | Land Rover, Helicopter, Tipsy Nipper | |
| | | aircraft on trailer, Lotus Elite | **£200-250** |
| 8402 | 78 | **Motorway Rescue** | |
| | | 'POLICE' Jaguar, Berliet Wrecker, | |
| | | Renault 5 and Fiat X1-9 | **£200-250** |
| 8403 | 79 | **Spindrift Power Boat Team** | |
| | | Ferrari Daytona (Yellow), Yellow | |
| | | power boat on trailer, Yellow/Black | |
| | | helicopter, plus MF Tractor and | |
| | | 'RESCUE' dinghy | **£200-250** |

# Trophy Models

The models were specially produced in 1961 to be sold by Marks & Spencer. The set consisted of five vacuum-plated 'gold' models taken from the existing Corgi product range, each mounted on a detachable black moulded base with a gold name label. The models were packaged in white boxes with red/grey design plus 'St Michael Trophy Models' in red. They did not sell well at the time of issue but are keenly sought after by present day collectors. All have Gold vacuum-plated body and Red wheels and radiator grille.

| | | | |
|---|---|---|---|
| 150 S | 61 | **Vanwall Racing Car** | **£100-200** |

| | | | |
|---|---|---|---|
| 152 | 61 | **BRM Racing Car** | **£100-200** |
| 300 | 61 | **Austin-Healey Sports Car** | **£100-200** |
| 301 | 61 | **Triumph TR2 Sports Car** | **£100-200** |
| 302 | 61 | **MG 'MGA' Sports Car** | **£100-200** |

# Duo Packs
## (Film and TV-related models)

| | | | |
|---|---|---|---|
| 1360 | 82 | **Batmobile** | |
| | | 267 plus a Corgi juniors version, | |
| | | Black/Red/Yellow 'window' box | **£125-150** |
| 1361 | 7? | **James Bond Aston-Martin** | |
| | | 271 plus a Corgi Juniors version, | |
| | | Black/Red/Yellow 'window' box | **£100-125** |
| 1362 | 7? | **James Bond Lotus Esprit** | |
| | | 269 plus a Corgi Juniors version, | |
| | | Black/Red/Yellow 'window' box | **£100-125** |
| 1363 | 82 | **Buck Rogers Set** | |
| | | 647 and a smaller version, | |
| | | Black/Yellow pictorial 'window' box | **£40-50** |
| 1376 | 82 | **Starsky & Hutch Ford Torino** | |
| | | 292 plus a Corgi Juniors version, | |
| | | Black/Yellow pictorial 'window' box | **£50-70** |
| 1372 | ?? | **'Magnum PI' Ferrari** (298) | **£80-100** |

# The 'Exploration' Range

A range of fantasy toys introduced in 1980.

| | | |
|---|---|---|
| D2022 | **'SCANOTRON'**, Green/Black | **£10-15** |
| D2023 | **'ROCKETRON'**, Blue/Yellow | **£10-15** |
| D2024 | **'LASERTRON'**, Orange/Black | **£10-15** |
| D2025 | **'MAGNETRON'**, Red/Black | **£10-15** |

# 'The Muppets Show'

| | | | |
|---|---|---|---|
| D2030 | 79 | **Kermit's Car** | |
| | | Yellow car with a famous Green | |
| | | frog, bubble-packed | **£40-45** |
| | 80 | Same model but in Red/Yellow | |
| | | pictorial 'window' box | **£35-40** |
| D2031 | 79 | **Fozzie Bear's Truck** | |
| | | Red/Brown/White truck, Silver or | |
| | | Black hooter, bubble-packed | **£35-40** |
| | 80 | Same model but in Red/Yellow | |
| | | pictorial 'window' box | **£30-35** |
| D2032 | 79 | **Miss Piggy's Sport Coupé** | |
| | | Pink sports car, Red or Pink dress, | |
| | | bubble-packed | **£40-45** |
| | 80 | Same model but in Red/Yellow | |
| | | pictorial 'window' box | **£35-40** |
| D2033 | 79 | **Animal's Percussionmobile** | |
| | | Red traction-engine, Yellow or Red | |
| | | wheels, Yellow or Black chimney, | |
| | | Yellow or Silver cymbal. | |
| | | Bubble-packed | **£35-40** |
| | 80 | Same model but in Red/Yellow | |
| | | pictorial 'window' box | **£30-35** |

# Qualitoys

A range of sturdy toys made up from the same basic parts. First issued in 1969, they were aimed at the pre-school age group. They were publicized as being from the 'makers of Corgi Toys' and did not form part of the Corgi range as such. Though difficult to find, they have little collectable value at the present time.

| | |
|---|---|
| Q701 | **Pick Up Truck** |
| Q702 | **Side Tipper** |
| Q703 | **Breakdown Truck** |
| Q704 | **Tower Wagon** |
| Q705 | **Horse Box** |
| Q706 | **Giraffe Transporter** |
| Q707 | **Fire Engine** |
| Q708 | **Pick Up Trailer** |

# Corgitronics, Corgimatics

These models are generally of plastic construction and feature a device called 'Battery-operated Micro-Chip Action'.

| | | | |
|---|---|---|---|
| 1001 | 82 | **HCB Angus Firestreak** | |
| | | Red/Yellow/White, 'RESCUE', | |
| | | electronic siren, on/off switch | **£60-70** |
| 1002 | 81 | **Sonic Corgi Truck Set** | |
| | | Yellow/White/Black/Red, | |
| | | remote control, | |
| | | SHELL SUPER OIL', 'BP OIL' | **£25-30** |
| 1002 | 81 | **'YORKIE' Truck Set** | |
| | | White/Yellow/Blue/Orange, | |
| | | remote control, | |
| | | 'MILK CHOCOLATE YORKIE' | **£25-30** |
| 1003 | 81 | **Ford Road Hog** | |
| | | Black, Yellow/White twirls, | |
| | | 2-tone horn, press-down start | **£15-20** |
| 1004 | 81 | **'Beep Beep Bus'** | |
| | | Red, 'BTA WELCOME TO BRITAIN', | |
| | | 2-tone horn, press-down start | **£20-25** |
| | 83 | Red body with | |
| | | 'WELCOME TO HAMLEYS' | **£20-25** |
| 1005 | 82 | **Police Land Rover** | |
| | | White/Red/Blue, 'POLICE', | |
| | | electronic siren, press-down start | **£15-20** |
| 1006 | 82 | **'RADIO WEST' Roadshow** | |
| | | 'Your Local Radio 605', AM radio, | |
| | | advertised but not issued | **NPP** |
| 1006 | 82 | **'RADIO LUXEMBOURG'** | |
| | | Red/White, 'RTL 208', | |
| | | AM radio, 3 loudspeakers | **£25-30** |
| 1007 | 82 | **Road Repair Unit** | |
| | | **Land Rover and Trailer** | |
| | | Yellow/Red/Silver, 'ROADWORKS', | |
| | | press start, road drill and sound | **£25-35** |
| 1008 | 82 | **Fire Chief's Car** | |
| | | Red/White/Yellow/Silver, | |
| | | 'FIRE DEPARTMENT', | |
| | | press-down start, siren | **£15-20** |
| 1009 | 83 | **MG Maestro 1600** | |
| | | Yellow/Black, press start, | |
| | | working front and rear lights | **£15-20** |
| | | Red/Black body. Sold in | |
| | | Austin-Rover Group box | **£20-25** |
| 1024 | 83 | **'Beep Beep Bus'** | |
| | | Red, 'BTA', supplied exclusively | |
| | | to Mothercare shops | **£20-25** |
| 1121 | 83 | **Ford Transit Tipper Lorry** | |
| | | Orange/Black, flashing light and | |
| | | working tipper | **£20-25** |

# Miscellaneous Corgi models

| | | | |
|---|---|---|---|
| 171 | 82 | **Street Bike** | |
| | | Red, Silver and Black body, | |
| | | multicoloured swirl | **£5-10** |
| 172 | 82 | **'POLICE' Bike** | |
| | | White/Black/Silver body | **£5-10** |
| 173 | 82 | **Cafe Racer** | |
| | | Silver and Black RN '26', | |
| | | '750 cc Class' | **£5-10** |
| 391 | 72 | **'FIREBUG'** | |
| | | Orange body, Yellow ladder, | |
| | | 'FIREBUG', WhizzWheels | **£15-25** |
| 450 | 68 | **Lunar Bug** | |
| | | Red, White, Blue. Blue/Yellow | |
| | | window box, inner packing | **£60-70** |
| 806 | 70 | **Lunar Bug** | |
| | | Red/White/Blue, 'Lunar Bug', | |
| | | windows, drop-down ramps | **£65-75** |
| 1104 | 65 | **Dolphin Boat on Trailer** | |
| | | Blue/White boat, Red trailer | **£50-75** |

## Identification of Routemaster Double-Decker Bus models

### 1ST CASTING, 1964 - 1975
### MODEL No. 468 ONLY – CLOSED TOP MODEL

Length 114 mm, die-cast body comprised of two separate castings which make up the lower and upper decks. The castings are separated by a white plastic joint.

The baseplate is die-cast, painted grey and stamped 'Corgi Toys', 'LONDON TRANSPORT', 'ROUTEMASTER', 'MADE IN ENGLAND' plus the Patent No. 904525. The early issues had turned metal wheels with rubber tyres. These lasted until 1973 when cast metal wheels were introduced with plastic tyres and in 1974/75 WhizzWheels were seen.

Early issues also had jewelled headlights which were replaced in 1973 by the cast-in type painted silver. The decals are of the transfer printed variety and there is a board at the front only. The model has spring suspension, windows, a metal platform handrail and a driver and clippie. The interior seats are white or cream.

### 2ND CASTING, 1975 ONWARDS
### CLOSED TOP AND OPEN TOP MODELS

MODEL Nos: C460, C463, C464, C467, C469, C470, C471, C473, C475, C476, C477, C479, C480, 1004 and all the numbers allocated to the 'Specials'.
  Length 123 mm, die-cast body comprised of two separate castings which make up the lower and upper decks. The castings are separated by a cream plastic joint for normal issues and very often by a coloured joint for 'Specials'. Until Model No. 480 was issued as an AEC Renown in 1983 the plastic baseplates were stamped 'CORGI', 'LONDON TRANSPORT', 'ROUTEMASTER' and 'MADE IN ENGLAND'. However 'LONDON TRANSPORT' and 'ROUTEMASTER' were removed from this time onwards.

The logos were originally stick-on labels followed by tampo printing in the mid-eighties. The seats were normally white or cream but other colours are used for the 'Specials' (eg. Red in the 'BRITISH DIE-CAST MODEL TOYS CATALOGUE' Special). The model has silver painted cast-in headlights, spring suspension, windows, a metal platform handrail but apart from the very early issues does not have a driver or clippie.
The wheels are of the WhizzWheel type. The early issues were of a close fitting type e.g. 'BTA', 'SWAN & EDGAR', 'DISNEYLAND'. However by the time the model was issued they had become protruding. The wheel hubs are either chrome (earlier models) or painted with plastic tyres.

## Routemaster Buses, 1964-1975, (1st casting)

| | | | |
|---|---|---|---|
| 468 | 64 | 'NATURALLY CORGI',<br>Red, London Transport, *'CORGI CLASSICS'* adverts. | **£60-70** |
| 468 | 64 | 'NATURALLY CORGI', (Australian),<br>Green/Cream/Brown,<br>'NEW SOUTH WALES GOVERNMENT TRANSPORT',<br>*'CORGI CLASSICS'* adverts. | **£1,000-1,250** |
| 468 | 66 | 'RED ROSE COFFEE', (Canadian promotional),<br>Red body, driver and clippie, 1st type box | **£1,000-1,250** |
| 468 | 67 | 'OUTSPAN ORANGES', (Australian issue)<br>'NEW SOUTH WALES GOVERNMENT TRANSPORT',<br>Green/Cream/Brown body | **£1,000-1,250** |
| 468 | 67 | 'OUTSPAN ORANGES', Red, London Transport, '10',<br>(diecast or WhizzWheels) | **£60-70** |
| 468 | 68 | 'GAMAGES', Red, London Transport, '10' | **£200-250** |
| 468 | 69 | 'CHURCH'S SHOES', Red, London Transport,<br>'10', Union Jacks | **£200-250** |
| 468 | 70 | 'MADAME TUSSAUDS', Red, London Transport, '10' | **£100-175** |
| 468 | 75 | 'THE DESIGN CENTRE', Red, London Transport, '10' | **£80-100** |
| 468 | ? | 'cokerchu', '2d', Red, London Transport, promo | **£200-300** |

469 Routemaster Bus (2nd casting),
'Mettoy Welcomes Swiss Buyers to Corgi Factory'

## Routemaster Buses, 1975 – 1983, (2nd casting)

| | | | |
|---|---|---|---|
| C467 | 77 | 'SELFRIDGES', Red, London Transport, '12'.<br>Box 1 – standard;<br>Box 2 – 'SELFRIDGES' own | **£20-25** |
| C469 | 75 | 'BTA WELCOME TO BRITAIN',<br>Red, London Transport, '11', driver, clippie | **£15-20** |
| C469 | 76 | 'THE DESIGN CENTRE',<br>Red, LT, '11', driver, clippie,<br>*'Visit The Design Centre'* in black or red | **£125-150** |
| C469 | 77 | 'CADBURYS DOUBLE DECKER',<br>Orange, on-pack offer, special box | **£12-18** |
| C469 | 77 | 'METTOY Welcomes Swiss Buyers to Swansea' | **£300-400** |
| C469 | 79 | 'SELFRIDGES', Red, London Transport, '12'.<br>Re-issue of C467 (see above) | **£20-25** |
| C469 | 79 | 'LEEDS PERMANENT' BUILDING SOCIETY',<br>'LEEDS', '22' | **£15-20** |
| C469 | 79 | 'SWAN & EDGAR', Red, London Transport, '11' | **£25-35** |
| C469 | 79 | 'HAMLEYS', Red, London Transport, '11' | **£15-20** |
| C469 | 80 | 'HAMLEYS', Five clowns advert., '6' | **£10-15** |
| C469 | 78 | 'BTA', Red, London Transport, ('7', '11' or '12') | **£10-15** |
| C469 | 82 | 'BLACKPOOL ILLUMINATIONS',<br>Cream/Green, '21' | **£30-40** |
| C469 | 83 | 'CORGI COLLECTORS VISIT' | **£300-400** |
| C469 | 83 | 'GAMLEYS', Red, *'Toyshop Of The South'* | **£10-15** |
| C469 | 83 | 'EAGLE STAR', White/Black, '1 Threadneedle Street' | **£10-15** |
| C469 | 83 | 'REDGATES', Cream/Brown (Red seats) '25' | **£30-40** |
| C469 | 83 | 'L.T. GOLDEN JUBILEE',<br>Red/White/Silver, 21, *'1933-1983* ', (1,000) | **£30-40** |
| C469 | 83 | 'BLACKPOOL PLEASURE BEACH',<br>Cream/Green, Blackpool Transport, '23',<br>*'Britain's No.1 Tourist Attraction'* | **£35-45** |
| C469 | 83 | As previous model but open top | **£50-55** |
| C469 | 83 | 'NORBROOK MOTORS', Dark Blue (White seats), '57' | **£12-18** |
| C469 | 83 | As previous model but Red version | **£12-18** |
| C469 | 83 | 'DION DION', Dark Blue, *'Saves You More'* | **£10-15** |
| | | S. African issue: incorrect label *'Saves You Money'* | **£15-20** |
| C469 | 83 | 'THORNTONS', Brown/Cream, route '14' | **£10-15** |
| C469 | 83 | 'MANCHESTER LIONS',<br>Cream, '105BN Manchester' | **£15-20** |
| C469 | 84 | 'NEW CORGI COMPANY',<br>Red, '29th March 84',<br>*'South Wales - De Cymru*, (2,000) | **£15-20** |
| C469 | 84 | 'BRITISH MEAT', Red | **£10-15** |
| C469 | ? | 'COBHAM BUS MUSEUM' | **£25-35** |
| C470 | 77 | 'DISNEYLAND', Yellow open top | **£10-15** |
| C471 | 77 | 'SEE MORE LONDON', Silver, '25',<br>*'The Queen's Silver Jubilee London Celebrations 1977'* | **£10-15** |
| C471 | 77 | 'WOOLWORTHS', Silver, '25',<br>*'Woolworths Welcome The World'*,<br>*'Queens Silver Jubilee 1977'* | **£20-30** |
| C523 | 86 | 'BRITISH DIECAST MODEL<br>TOYS CATALOGUE', Red | **£10-15** |
| C638 | 89 | 'Great Book of CORGI', Yellow/Blue, '1956-1983'.<br>Originally only available with book | **£25-35** |

# Corgi Toys Accessories

| Item and details | MPR |
|---|---|

## Corgi Kits
| | | | |
|---|---|---|---|
| 601 | 61-68 | **Batley 'LEOFRIC' Garage** .... | **£20-25** |
| 602 | 61-66 | **'A.A.' and 'RAC'** | |
| | | Telephone Boxes..................... | **£50-60** |
| 603 | 61-66 | **Silverstone Pits**..................... | **£30-40** |
| 604 | 61-66 | **Silverstone Press Box**............ | **£50-60** |
| 605 | 63-67 | **Silverstone Club House and** | |
| | | Timekeepers Box.................. | **£60-70** |
| 606 | 61-66 | **Lamp Standards** (2)................ | **£5-10** |
| 607 | 63-67 | **Circus Elephant and Cage** ..... | **£45-55** |
| 608 | 63-66 | **'SHELL' Filling Station**......... | **£35-45** |
| 609 | 63-66 | **'SHELL' Filling Station** | |
| | | Forecourt Accessories........... | **£25-35** |
| 610 | 63-66 | **Metropolitan Police Box and** | |
| | | Public Telephone Kiosk........ | **£60-70** |
| 611 | 63-66 | **Motel Chalet**.......................... | **£25-35** |

## Self-adhesive accessories
| | | | |
|---|---|---|---|
| 1460 | 1959 | **'A' Pack** (66 items) including | |
| | | Tax Discs, Number Plates, 'GB' | |
| | | and 'Running-In' labels, etc...... | **£10-15** |
| 1461 | 1959 | **'B' Pack** (36 items) including | |
| | | White-wall tyre trim, | |
| | | 'Styla Sportsdiscs', | |
| | | Number Plates, etc.................. | **£10-15** |
| 1462 | 1959 | **'C' Pack** (69 items) including | |
| | | Number Plates, Commercial and | |
| | | Road Fund Licences (A, B and C), | |
| | | 20 and 30mph Speed Limit and | |
| | | Trailer Plates, etc .................... | **£10-15** |
| 1463 | 1959 | **'D' Pack** (100 items) including | |
| | | Number Plates, 'Corps | |
| | | Diplomatique' and 'L' Plates, | |
| | | Touring Pennants, etc.............. | **£10-15** |
| 1464 | 1961 | **'E' Pack** (86 items) including | |
| | | Assorted Badges, 'Take-Off Wheels', | |
| | | Trade and Licence Plates, etc .. | **£10-15** |

## Spare wheels
for 'Take-off Wheels' models; bubble-packed on card.
| | | | |
|---|---|---|---|
| 1341 | 1970 | for **344 Ferrari Dino Sport**. | |
| | | Shown in 1969 catalogue but model | |
| | | issued with WhizzWheels........ | **£10-15** |
| 1342 | 1968 | for **300 Chevrolet Corvette**..... | **£10-15** |
| 1351 | 1968 | for **275 Rover 2000 TC**........... | **£10-15** |
| 1352 | 1968 | for **276 Oldsmobile Toronado**. | **£10-15** |
| | | for **338 Chevrolet Camaro**...... | **£10-15** |
| | | for **343 Pontiac Firebird** | |
| | | Shown in 1969 catalogue but | |
| | | model issued without | |
| | | 'Take-off Wheels' .................... | **£10-15** |
| 1353 | 1970 | for **342 Lamborghini P400** ..... | **£10-15** |
| | | for **302 Hillman Hunter Rally** | **£10-15** |
| 1354 | 1970 | **273 Rolls Silver Shadow** ........ | **£10-15** |
| 1361 | 1968 | **341 Mini Marcos GT 850**. (The | |
| | | first 'Take-Off Wheels' model). | **£10-15** |

## Figures
| | | | |
|---|---|---|---|
| 1501 | 63-69 | **Racing Drivers and** | |
| | | **Pit Mechanics** (6) .................. | **£10-15** |
| 1502 | 63-69 | **Silverstone Spectators** (6)...... | **£10-15** |
| 1503 | 63-69 | **Race Track Officials** (6)......... | **£10-15** |
| 1504 | 63-69 | **Press Officials** (6) .................. | **£10-15** |
| 1505 | 63-69 | **Garage Attendants** (6) ........... | **£10-15** |

## Corgi 'Cargoes'
Bubble-packed on card.
| | | | |
|---|---|---|---|
| 1485 | 1960 | **Lorry Load - Planks** .............. | **£10-15** |
| 1486 | 1960 | **Lorry Load - Bricks** .............. | **£10-15** |
| 1487 | 1960 | **Lorry Load - Milk Churns** .... | **£10-15** |
| 1488 | 1960 | **Lorry Load - Cement** ............ | **£10-15** |
| 1490 | 1960 | **Skip and 3 Churns** ................ | **£10-15** |

## Spare tyre packs
| | | | |
|---|---|---|---|
| 1449 | 70-71 | New Standard 15 mm .............. | **£10-15** |
| 1450 | 58-70 | Standard 15 mm....................... | **£10-15** |
| 1451 | 61-70 | Utility Vehicles 17 mm ........... | **£10-15** |
| 1452 | 61-70 | Major Models 19 mm .............. | **£10-15** |
| 1453 | 65-70 | Mini Cars 13 mm..................... | **£10-15** |
| 1454 | 67-70 | Tractor wheels (Rear) 33 mm. | **£10-15** |
| 1455 | 67-70 | Tractor wheels (Front) 19 mm.. | **£10-15** |
| 1456 | 67-70 | Racing wheels (Rear) 16 mm ... | **£10-15** |
| 1457 | 67-70 | Racing wheels (Front) 14 mm .. | **£10-15** |
| 1458 | 67-70 | Commercial (Large) 24 mm ..... | **£10-15** |
| 1459 | 67-70 | Commercial (Medium) 19 mm . | **£10-15** |

## Miscellaneous
| | | | |
|---|---|---|---|
| 1401 | 58-60 | Service Ramp (operable) ......... | **£15-20** |
| 1445 | 1962 | Red bulb for 437 Ambulance........ | **£2-3** |
| 1441 | 1963 | Red bulb for 464 Police Van ...... | **£2-3** |
| 1443 | 1967 | Red flashing bulb, 437 Amb....... | **£2-3** |
| 1444 | 1967 | Blue flashing bulb, 464 Police ..... | **£2-3** |
| 1445 | 1967 | Bulb for 'TV' in 262 Lincoln ...... | **£2-3** |
| 1446 | 1970 | Tyres for 1150 Snowplough......... | **£2-3** |
| 1480 | 1959 | Nose cone, Corporal Missile ..... | **£2-3** |
| 1497 | 1967 | **James Bond Spares** | |
| | | 2 Bandits + lapel badge (261) .. | **£15-25** |
| 1498 | 1967 | **James Bond Spares** | |
| | | Missiles for 336 Toyota ........... | **£10-15** |
| 1499 | 1967 | **Green Hornet Spares** | |
| | | Missiles & scanners (268) ........ | **£10-15** |
| ? | 1960s | **Corgi Club Badge** | |
| | | Gold Corgi dog, Red backing... | **£20-25** |
| ? | 62-64 | **'SHELL' Filling Station and** | |
| | | **Garage**. Blue/Red/White, single | |
| | | floor, plastic 'SHELL' logo... | **£300-400** |
| ? | 62-64 | **'CENTRAL PARK GARAGE'** | |
| | | Blue/Yellow/Red/White, three | |
| | | floors, 'SKYPARK' logo ...... | **£300-400** |
| 24205 | 1967 | **Batmobile Accessory Pack** | |
| | | (sprue of missiles).................... | **£25-35** |

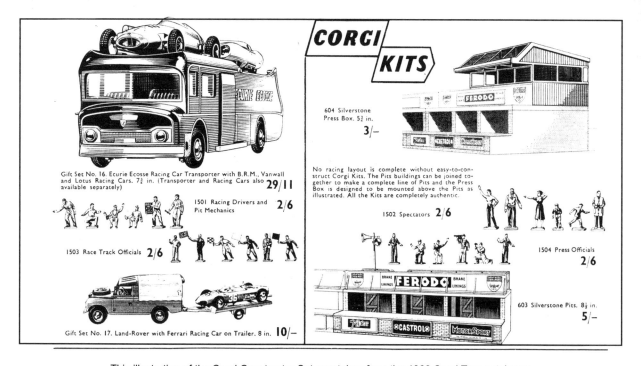

Gift Set No. 16. Ecurie Ecosse Racing Car Transporter with B.R.M., Vanwall and Lotus Racing Cars. 7½ in. (Transporter and Racing Cars also available separately) **29/11**

1501 Racing Drivers and Pit Mechanics **2/6**

1503 Race Track Officials **2/6**

Gift Set No. 17. Land-Rover with Ferrari Racing Car on Trailer. 8 in. **10/-**

**CORGI KITS**

604 Silverstone Press Box. 5¾ in. **3/-**

No racing layout is complete without easy-to-construct Corgi Kits. The Pits buildings can be joined together to make a complete line of Pits and the Press Box is designed to be mounted above the Pits as illustrated. All the Kits are completely authentic.

1502 Spectators **2/6**

1504 Press Officials **2/6**

603 Silverstone Pits. 8½ in. **5/-**

This illustration of the Corgi Constructor Set was taken from the 1966 Corgi Toys catalogue.

# Gift Sets

Original internal packaging for securing models and accessories must all be present before sets can be considered complete and therefore to achieve the best price. See Corgi Toys model identification page.

| Ref | Year(s) | Set details | MPR |
|---|---|---|---|

**1** 1957-62 **Transporter and 4 Cars**
- 1101 Blue/Yellow Bedford Carrimore Transporter plus 201 Austin Cambridge, 208 Jaguar 24, 301 Triumph TR2 (or 300 Austin-Healey) and 302 MGA, plus two Yellow/Black 'Corgi Toys' dummy boxes ...................................... **£700-900**

**1a** 1957-62 **Transporter and 4 Cars**
- 1101 Red/Two-tone Blue Transporter, 200 Ford Consul, 201 Austin Cambridge, 204 Rover 90, 205 Riley, 2 Yellow 'Corgi Toys' dummy boxes ...... **£400-500**

**1b** 1959-62 **Transporter and 4 Cars**
- 1101 Red/Two-tone Blue Transporter, 214 Thunderbird Hardtop, 215 Thunderbird Convertible, 219 Plymouth Suburban, 220 Chevrolet Impala. (US set)........... **£400-500**

**1c** 1961-62 **Transporter and 4 Cars**
- 1101 Red/Two-tone Blue Transporter, 210s Citroën (or 217 Fiat 1800), 219 Plymouth Suburban, 226 Mini, 305 Triumph TR3. (US issue set) ...... **£400-500**

**1** 1966-72 **Farm Set**
- Ford 5000 Tractor + 58 Beast Carrier, pictorial stand......................... **£100-120**

**1** 1983 **Ford Sierra Set**
- Ford Sierra 299 with Blue body, Blue/Cream Caravan ................................ **£20-30**

**2** 1958-68 **Land Rover and Pony Trailer**
- 438 Land Rover (Green, Beige tin tilt) and 102 Rice Pony Trailer (Red/Black)..... **£175-225**
- Same set but All Red Land Rover...... **£175-225**
- Lt. Brown Land Rover (Apricot plastic tilt), Lt. Brown/Cream trailer .............. **£175-225**

**2** 1971-73 **Unimog Dumper and Shovel**
- 1128 Mercedes Tipper and 1145 Unimog Goose. Yellow/Blue 'window' box ........ **£60-70**

**2** 1980-81 **Construction Set**
- 54 Tractor, 440 Mazda, tool-box and cement mixer ............................ **£30-35**
  1980-80 French export:
- 1110 and 1156 plus cement mixer.......... **£30-40**

**3** 1959-63 **Thunderbird Missile Set**
- 350 Thunderbird Missile and 351 Land Rover. Blue/Yellow card box .............. **£175-220**

**3** 1967-69 **Batmobile and Batboat**
- 1st issue: 267 Batmobile with 'Bat' wheels, plus 107 Batboat, in plain Blue 1st issue 'window' box with inner tray and 4 figures, instruction sheet ......... **£500-700**
- 2nd issue: 267 Batmobile with Red wheels (without 'Bat' design), plus 107 Batboat. Yellow/Blue 'window' box should also have unopened instruction pack ....... **£900-1,100**
  1980
- 3rd issue: 267 Batmobile (plain cast wheels), and 107 Batboat (WW), two figures. Striped 'window' box should also contain instructions in unopened packet ......... **£200-300**

**4** 1958-60 **Bristol Ferranti Bloodhound Guided Missile Set**
- Contains: 351, 1115, 1116, 1117. Blue/Yellow card box ........................ **£250-350**

**4** 1974-75 **Country Farm Set**
- Models 50 and 62 plus hay load, boy and girl. Striped 'window' box .... **£100-125**

**5** 1959-60 **Racing Car Set**
- 150 (Red), 151 (Blue), 152 (Green). Smooth hubs. Yellow/Blue lift-off lid box, vac-formed inner ........................ **£200-300**
  1960-61
- 150 (Red), 151 (Blue with Red bonnet stripe), 152 (Green). Flat or cast spoked wheels. Yellow/Blue box, polystyrene tray...... **£300-350**

**5s** 1962-63 **Racing Car Set**
- 150s (Red), 151a (Blue), 152s (Turquoise). Yellow/Blue box with 'Gift Set 5s' stickers, inner polystyrene tray .......... **£400-500**

**5** 1967-72 **Agricultural Set**
- 484 Livestock Transporter and pigs, 438 Land Rover (no hood) 62, 69, 71, accessories 1490 skip and churns, 4 calves, farmhand and dog, 6 sacks. Box has inner pictorial stand.............. **£500-750**

**5** 1976-77 **Country Farm Set**
- As Farm Set 4, but minus boy, girl and hay load................................. **£100-150**

**6** 1959-60 **'Rocket Age' Set**
- Contains: 350, 351, 352, 353, 1106, 1108, 1117 ......................... **£3,000-4,000**

**6** 1967-69 **Cooper-Maserati Set**
- Contains 490 VW Breakdown Truck plus 156 Maserati on trailer. 'Window'/flap box .............................. **£150-175**

**7** 1959-64 **Tractor and Trailer Set**
- 50 Massey-Ferguson 65 Tractor and 51 Trailer. Yellow/Blue card box ........ **£300-400**

**7** 1968-76 **'DAKTARI' Set**
- 438 Land Rover in Green with Black Zebra stripes, spun or cast hubs. 5 figures: Paula, Dr Marsh Tracy with chimp Judy on his lap, a Tiger on the bonnet, and Clarence The Short-Sighted Lion (with spectacles!). Yellow/Blue 'window' box.................. **£175-225**
- With WhizzWheels. Striped box ........ **£100-125**

**8** 1959-62 **Combine Harvester, Tractor and Trailer Set**
- Contains 1111, 50 and 51. Tractor has Copper seat, Red metal hubs ........ **£250-300**

**8** 1968-74 **'Lions of Longleat' Set**
- Land Rover with shaped hubs, keeper, 3 lions, plastic den, 3 joints of meat. Yellow/Blue 'window' box with header card and inner packing ........... **£175-225**
- Same but WW. Striped 'window' box. **£100-125**

**9** 1959-62 **Corporal Guided Missile Set**
- Contains: 1112, 1113, 1118 ................. **£300-400**

**9** 1968-72 **Tractor, Trailer and Shovel Set**
- Contains 66 Ferguson 165 Tractor with 69 Shovel and 62 Tipper Trailer with detachable raves. Yellow/Blue all-card box with inner pictorial stand.............. **£200-250**

**9** 1979-82 **'RNLI' Rescue Set**
- Land Rover and Dinghy on trailer. White, Blue, Red, Black. Striped 'window' box **£75-95**

**9** 19?? **3 Racing Minis Set**
- Yellow, White and Blue, numbers/stripes and adverts, special 'Hamleys' box........ **£90-110**

**10** 1968-69 **Marlin Rambler Set**
- Blue/White 319 with Trailer, 2 canoes (1 with figure). Yellow/Blue box, inner packing, pictorial tray ................ **£200-250**

**10** 1973-78 **Tank Transporter Set**
- Contains 901 Centurion Mk.I Tank and 1100 Mack articulated transporter. Picture card box.................................. **£100-120**

**10** 1982 **Jeep Set**
- Red 441 plus motorcycle on trailer......... **£20-25**

**10** 1985 **Sierra and Caravan Set**
- C299 Sierra + Pale Brown caravan........ **£25-35**

**11** 1960-64 **ERF Dropside and Trailer**
- 456 and 101 with cement and planks load. Yellow/Blue picture box, inner card stand .................................. **£125-175**
- As above but with WhizzWheels ........... **£90-110**

**11** 1971-72 **London Transport Set**
- Contains 418 Taxi, 468 'OUTSPAN' Bus, 226 Mini (Deep Blue), policeman on stand, Striped 'window' box with inner tray.................................... **£140-160**
- 1980-82. C425 Taxi with C469 Bus 'B.T.A.' and policeman figure................ **£35-45**

**12** 1961-64 **'Chipperfields Circus' Set**
- 1121 Crane Truck 'CHIPPERFIELDS' and 1123 Circus Cage, plus instructions. Yellow/Blue all-card picture box ........ **£250-350**

**12** 1968-71 **Grand Prix Racing Set**
- 155, 156 and 330 with 490 VW tender, 3 mechanics, 16 bollards and hay bales. Yellow/Blue 'window' box also contains cones in bag, instructions, 'Mr Retailer' card and inner polystyrene tray .......... **£350-450**
- 1971-72. 158, 159 and 330 (or 371) with 490 Volkswagen tender, 3 mechanics, 16 bollards and hay bales. The artwork on the box and the vac-formed base are different from previous issue ........ **£250-350**

**12** 1981- **Glider and Trailer Set**
- 345 with Trailer and Glider.................... **£50-60**

**13** 1964-66 **Fordson Tractor and Plough Set**
- Contains 60 Fordson Power Major Tractor and 61 Four Furrow Plough in Blue, Orange plastic front and rear hubs. Yellow/Blue box with inner tray ......... **£300-400**

**13** 1968-72 **Renault 16 Film Unit**
- White/Black, 'TOUR DE FRANCE', 'PARAMOUNT', cameraman, cyclist. Yellow/Blue box with inner tray plus plain orange card backdrop ................. **£250-350**

**13** 1981-82 **Tour de France 'RALEIGH' Team Car**
- 373 Peugeot, White body, Red/Yellow 'RALEIGH' / 'TOTAL' logos, racing cycles, Manager with loudhailer ......... **£150-175**

**14** 1961-64 **Tower Wagon Set**
- 409 Jeep, Yellow cradle, lamp standard, electrician. Yellow/Blue card box ....... **£100-120**

**14** 1969-73 **Giant 'DAKTARI' Set**
- Gift Set and items plus 503 and 484 transporters (spun hubs), large and small elephants. Blue/Yellow window box with pictorial header card, inner tray ......... **£250-350**
- Version with WhizzWheels. Striped 'window' box with pictorial header card and inner tray............................... **£150-200**

**15** 1963-64 **Silverstone Set**
- 150s, 151a, 152s, 215s, 304s, 309, 417s, 3 buildings, plain box (no picture).................... **£1,500-2,500**
  1964-66
- 150s, 154, 152s, 215s, 304s, 309, 417s, 3 buildings, layout on box............. **£1,500-2,500**

**15** 1968-77 **Land Rover and Horsebox Set**
- Contains 438, 112, spun hubs, mare and foal. Yellow/Blue box contains inner polystyrene tray ............................. **£100-125**
- Version with WhizzWheels. Striped 'window' box has inner card packing ..... **£55-75**

**15** 1986 **'TARMAC' Motorway Set**
- 'Motorway Maintenance' Green/Black 1128 Mercedes Tipper, Mazda Pickup and a compressor..................................... **£20-30**

**16** 1961-65 **'ECURIE ECOSSE' Set**
- 1126 Transporter with 3 individually boxed racing cars in all-card lift-off lid box with instruction leaflet and internal packing. Metallic Dark Blue 1126 Transporter (with Orange lettering), 150 Vanwall (Red, '25'), 151 Lotus XI (Blue, RN '3'), 152 BRM (Turquoise, RN '3')................ **£400-500**

- Met. Dk. Blue 1126 Transporter (with Yellow lettering), 150s Vanwall, 151a Lotus XI (Blue, '7'), 152s BRM ......... **£400-500**
- 1965. Met. Light Blue 1126 Transporter (with Red Lettering), 150s Vanwall, 152s BRM, 154 Ferrari (RN '36') ...... **£350-400**
- Met. Dk. Blue 1126 Transporter (with Light Blue lettering and ridges), 150s Vanwall, 152s BRM, 154 Ferrari ........ **£300-350**

**17** 1963-67 **Ferrari Racing Set**
- 438 Land Rover in Red with Green top, Red 154 Ferrari F1 on Yellow trailer. Yellow/Blue box has inner tray .......... **£225-275**

**17** 1977-80 **Military Set**
- Contains 904, 906, 920 ........................... **£40-50**

**18/1** 19?? **3 Mini Racers Set**
- *CHELSEA', 'PARK LANE'* and *'PICADILLY'* logos ................................. **£20-30**

**18/2** 19?? **Mini Special Editions Set**
- with *'RED HOT', 'RITZ'* and *'JET BLACK'* logos ................................. **£20-30**
  NB  C18/1 and C18/2 were sold (in long 'window' boxes) exclusively by Woolworths.

**18** 1961-63 **Ford Tractor and Plough Set**
- 55 Fordson Power Major Tractor and 56 Four Furrow Plough in Blue/Red/Yellow. Drab Orange hubs. Yellow/Blue box with inner tray .................................. **£200-250**

**18** 1975-80 **Emergency Gift Set**
- Contains 402, 481, C921 ........................ **£60-70**

**19** 1962-68 **'CHIPPERFIELDS' Cage Set**
- 1st issue: 438 Land Rover (metal tilt) and 607 Elephant and cage on trailer. Blue/Yellow picture box has inner card tray + additional packing............. **£250-300**
- 2nd issue: As before but 438 Land Rover has a plastic tilt......................... **£175-225**

**19** 19?? **'RNLI' Set**
- 438 Land Rover plus Orange dinghy on trailer with *'Mumbles Lifeboat'* logo .... **£60-70**

**19** 1972-77 **Land Rover and Nipper Aircraft**
- 438 Land-Rover (Blue/Orange, tinplate tilt) + trailer. Blue/Orange/Yellow plane *'23'* or Blue/Orange/White plane *'23'*. Yellow/Blue 'window' box..................... **£60-70**

**19** 1973-77 **'CORGI FLYING CLUB'**
- As previous set but Land-Rover has a plastic tilt......................... **£45-60**

**19** 1979-82 **Emergency Gift Set**
- C339 and C921. Striped 'window' box... **£40-60**

**19** 1980-82 **Emergency Gift Set**
- C339 and C931 in Red/White. Striped 'window' box ............................. **£40-60**

**20** 1961-64 **'Golden Guinea' Set**
- Gold-plated 224 Bentley Continental, 234 Ford Consul, 229 Chevrolet Corvair, Catalogue, 2 Accessory Packs. Inner card tray with lower card packing, outer Dark Green sleeve with window ......... **£400-500**

**20** 1970-73 **Tri-Deck Transporter Set**
      (Scammell Handyman Mk.III)
- 1st issue contains 1146 Transporter with six 'WhizzWheels' cars: 210 'Saint's' Volvo, 311 Ford Capri, 342 Pontiac, 372 Lancia, 377 Marcos, 378 MGC GT (Red body). Instruction sheet, 'Mr Retailer' transit card protector......................................... **£600-700**
  NB  GS 20 may be found with widely differing contents as Corgi used up excess stock in this Set.
- Harrods set: Late issue set with: 1146 Transporter, 382 Porsche Targa (Silver Blue), 313 Ford Cortina GXL (Bronze/Black), 201 Volvo (Orange 'Saint' label), 334 Mini (Orange) and 377 Marcos (Silver Green). Box also has instruction sheet and 'Mr Retailer' transit card protector ..... **£600-700**

**20** 1978-80 **Emergency Gift Set**
- C429, C482, C921. Box has inner tray ... **£35-45**

**21** 1962-66 **ERF Dropside and Trailer**
- 456 and 101 with milk churns and self-adhesive accessories. Yellow/Blue box with inner card stand ................... **£225-275**

**21** 1969-71 **'Chipperfields' Circus Set**
- Contains 1144 Crane and Cage, and 1139 Menagerie Transporter. Yellow/Blue window box with internal packaging and 'Mr Dealer' box protector card ..... **£1,600-1,900**

**21** 1980-82 **Superman Set**
- Contains 260, 265 and 925, plus inner tray and plastic rockets on sprue......... **£100-125**

**22** 1962-65 **Farming Set**
- Contains 1111 M-F Combine Harvester, 406 Land-Rover and Trailer, 51 Tipping Trailer, 101 Platform Trailer, 53 M-F 65 Tractor with Shovel, 1487 Milk Churns, 1490 Skip and 3 churns, plus models in Gift Set 18. Lift-off all-card picture box with inner polystyrene tray............ **£2,000-2,500**

**22** 1980-82 **James Bond Set**
- 269 Lotus Esprit, 271 Aston-Martin DB5 and 649 Space Shuttle + rockets, 2 spare bandit figures. Box has inner tray ......... **£350-450**

**23** 1962-66 **'CHIPPERFIELDS' Set**
- 1st issue: 1121 Crane Truck, 2 x 1123 Animal Cages (2 lions, 2 polar bears), plus Gift Set 19 and 426 Booking Office. All-card lift-off lid picture box with inner polystyrene tray.......................... **£400-600**
      1964
- 2nd issue: as 1st issue but 503 'TK Giraffe Truck' replaces 426 Booking Office, inner polystyrene tray......................... **£300-400**

**23** 1980-82 **Spiderman Set**
- 261 Spiderbuggy, 266 Spiderbike, 928 Spidercopter with figures, missiles on sprue. In striped 'window' box ...... **£150-200**

**24** 1963-68 **Commer Constructor Set**
- 2 cab/chassis units, 4 interchangeable bodies plus milkman and accessories. Yellow/Blue picture box with lift-off lid and inner polystyrene tray.............. **£100-130**

**24** 1976-78 **Mercedes and Caravan**
- 285 in Metallic Blue plus 490 Caravan in White. Striped 'window' box .............. **£30-40**
- 1979. 285 in Met. Brown plus 490 Caravan in Bronze. Striped 'window' box ........... **£30-40**

**25** 1963-66 **BP or Shell Garage Set**
- 224, 225, 229, 234 and 419 all in Blue/Yellow boxes plus: 601 Batley Garage, 602 'AA' and 'RAC' Boxes, 606 Lamp Standards (2), 608 Filling Station, 609 accessories, 1505 Figures. Plain card box with or without layout picture....... **£1,000-1,500**

**25** 1969-71 **Racing Car and Tender**
- 159 and VW Tender, 2 sets of decals in stapled bags. Blue/Yellow window box, inner plastic tray......................... **£120-140**

**25** 1980-81 **Talbot Rancho Set**
- 457 plus two motorcycles on trailer........ **£25-30**

**26** 1971-76 **Beach Buggy Set**
- 381 plus Red Sailing Boat with Blue sail. Orange/Yellow 'window' box.......... **£40-50**

**26** 1981-83 **Corgi Racing Set**
- 457 Talbot Matra Rancho, 160 Hesketh (Yellow), 'Corgi Racing Team' trailer..... **£35-45**

**27** 1963-72 **Priestman Shovel on Machinery Carrier**
- 1128 and 1131 (Bedford). Blue/Yellow box with inner tray ........ **£175-225**

**28** 1963-65 **Transporter and 4 Cars**
- 1105 Bedford TK Transporter with 222 Renault Floride, 230 Mercedes-Benz, 232 Fiat, 234 Ford Classic, 2 dummy 'Corgi Toys' boxes, instructions. Pictorial box, internal card packing .... **£400-500**

**28** 1975-78 **Mazda B1600 Dinghy Set**
- 493 Mazda + dinghy and trailer. Striped 'window' box ............................. **£35-40**

**29** 1963-65 **Massey-Ferguson Set**
- Contains 50 Massey-Ferguson Tractor with driver and 51 Tipper Trailer - Cream/Yellow, Red plastic rear hubs. Yellow/Blue all-card box with inner tray ................. **£250-300**

**29** 1981-82 **'CORGI' Pony Club**
- Contains 441 Jeep, 112 trailer, girl on pony, 3 jumps, 3 hay bales. Striped 'window' box ............................. **£55-65**

**29** 1975-76 **'DUCKHAMS' FI Racing Set**
- Surtees Racing Set with 323 Ferrari Daytona and 150 Ferrari in Blue/Yellow *'DUCKHAMS RACING TEAM'* livery. Striped 'window' box ............................. **£35-40**

**30** 1973-73 **Grand Prix Gift Set**
- 'Kit' versions of 151 Yardley (1501), 154 JPS (1504), 152 Surtees (1502) plus 153 Surtees (1503)? in unique Norris livery. Picture 'window' box. Mail order only ................. **£100-120**

**30** 1979-80 **Circus Gift Set**
- Land Rover and Trailer ........................ **£60-75**

**31** 1964-68 **Buick Riviera Boat Set**
- 245 Buick, Red boat trailer, and Dolphin Cabin Cruiser towing lady water-skier. Pictorial sleeve box with internal packing display tray around models.... **£250-350**

**31** 1976-80 **Safari Land Rover Set**
- C341 Land Rover with animal trailer, Warden and Lion. Box has inner polystyrene tray ..................................... **£35-45**

**32** 1965-68 **Tractor, Shovel and Trailer Set**
- 54 Massey-Ferguson 65 Tractor, 69 Shovel, 62 Tipping Trailer with detachable raves - Red/Cream/Yellow. Yellow/Blue picture box with inner pictorial stand............. **£250-300**

**32** 1976-79 **Lotus Racing Set**
- C301 Lotus Elite, and C154 JPS Lotus on trailer ................................. **£100-125**
- 1979-83. C301 Lotus Elite, and C154 Texaco Lotus on trailer ................ **£35-45**

**33** 1965-68 **Tractor and Beast Carrier**
- Contains 55 and 58 ........................ **£200-250**
- 1968-72. Contains 67 and 58 .............. **£80-100**

**33** 1980-82 **'DLRG' Rescue Set**
- White/Red 421 Land Rover and boat on trailer ....................................... **£50-70**

**34** 1976-79 **Tractor & Tipping Trailer**
- Contains 55 and 56 ........................ **£55-65**

**35** 1964-68 **London Traffic Set**
- 418 Taxi with 468 *'Corgi Toys'* or *'Outspan'* Bus, policeman on stand. Yellow/Blue box, inner tray .......... **£175-200**

**35** 1978-79 **'CHOPPER SQUAD' Surf Boat**
- Contains 927, 419, trailer, rescue boat.... **£30-40**

**36** 1967-70 **Marlin Rambler Set**
- Contains 263 and Boat ........................... **£45-65**

**36** 1967-71 **Oldsmobile Toronado Set**
- 276 (Greenish-Blue), Chrome trailer, Yellow/Blue 'SWORDFISH' boat, 3 figures. Yellow/Blue box................. **£200-300**

**36** 1983 **Off-Road Set**
- 447 (Dark Blue/Cream, RN '5') plus power-boat on trailer ............................... **£25-35**

**36** 1976-78 **Tarzan Set**
- Light Green 421 Land Rover and trailer, paler Green 'zebra' stripes, Tarzan, Jane, Cheetah (chimp), boy, dinghy with hunter, elephant, snake, vines, etc. Yellow/Blue 'window' box with inner pictorial backing display ............ **£250-350**

**37** 1966-69 **'Lotus Racing Team'**
- 490 VW Breakdown Truck, Red trailer with cars 318, 319, 155, plus 2 sets of spare racing numbers ('5' and '9' or '4' and '8'), a 1966 illustrated checklist, a sealed pack of cones, set of bollards and a spare Lotus chassis unit. Yellow/Blue 'window' box has inner polystyrene tray ............ **£400-500**

**37** 1979-80 **Fiat X-19 Set**
- Fiat X-19 and Boat 'Carlsberg'.............. **£30-40**

**38** 1977-78 **Mini 1000 Camping Set**
- Cream Mini with 2 figures, tent, barbecue, in inner display stand .............**£90-110**

**38** 1965-67 **'1965 Monte Carlo Rally'**
- 318 Mini Cooper 'S', 322 Rover 2000, and 326 Citroën DS19. Monte Carlo Rally emblem on each bonnet. Yellow/Blue all-card box contains pictorial stand and inner card packing .................. **£1,000-1,250**

**38** 1980- **Jaguar XJS Set**
- 319 with Powerboat on Trailer................ **£20-30**

**40** 1966-69 **'The Avengers' Set**
- John Steed's Bentley (Green body, Red wire wheels), Emma Peel's Lotus Elan (Black/White body), Steed and Emma Peel figures, 3 Black umbrellas. Yellow/Blue picture box with inner pictorial stand . **£500-600**
- With Red/Black Bentley with Silver wire wheels..................... **£350-450**

**40** 1976-82 **'Batman' Gift Set**
- Contains modified 107 Trailer plus 267 Batmobile (WW) and 925 Helicopter. 12 missiles on a sprue. Striped box also has inner tray with card packing ......... **£500-600**

**41** 1966-68 **Carrimore Car Transporter with Ford Tilt Cab**
- 1138 Transporter (Red/Two-tone Blue), 252 Rover 2000 (Metallic Plum), 251 Hillman Imp (Metallic Bronze), 440 Ford Cortina Estate (Metallic Blue), 226 Morris Mini-Minor (Light Blue), 321 Austin Mini Cooper 'S' (Red, RN '2', '1966 Monte Carlo Rally', with roof signatures), 249 Morris Mini Cooper DeLuxe (Black/Red, 'wickerwork' panels). Pictorial lift-off lid box with inner polystyrene tray. Only sold by mail order ...................... **£750-850**

**41** 1969-69 **Carrimore Car Transporter with Scammell Cab**
- 1148 Transporter (Red/Two-tone Blue), 226 Morris Mini-Minor (Metallic Maroon), 345 MGC GT (Orange in earliest sets, Yellow/Black later), 340 Sunbeam Imp (1967 Monte Carlo, Metallic Blue, RN '77'), 258 Saint's Volvo P1800 (White with Orange label), 249 Morris Mini Cooper DeLuxe (Black/Red with 'wickerwork' panels), 339 Mini Cooper 'S' ('1967 Monte Carlo Rally', RN '177'), plus sealed bag of cones and leaflet. Pictorial lift-off lid box with inner polystyrene tray. Only sold by mail order .............. **£750-850**

**41** 1977-81 **Silver Jubilee Set**
- The State Landau, HRH Queen Elizabeth and Prince Phillip (+ a Corgi!)................ **£15-20**

**42** 1978-79 **Agricultural Set**
- Contains 55 David Brown Tractor plus 56 Trailer, Silo and Elevator .............. **£100-125**

**43** 1979-80 **Silo and Conveyor Set**
- 'CORGI HARVESTING COMPANY Ltd' **£40-50**

**44** 1978-80 **Metropolitan Police Set**
- 421 Land Rover, 112 Horsebox, Policeman on horse. Striped 'window' box .............. **£40-50**

**44** 1978-80 **Mounted Police Set**
- French issue, Policeman on horse .......... **£50-75**

**45** 1966 **'All Winners' Set**
- 261 James Bond's Aston-Martin, 310 Chevrolet Stingray, 324 Marcos Volvo, 325 Ford Mustang Competition, 314 Ferrari Berlinetta. Yellow/Blue 'window' box.................. **£350-450**

**45** 1978-79 **Royal Canadian Police Set**
- Land Rover (421), Trailer (102), 'Mountie' on horse ........................ **£125-150**

**46** 1966-69 **'All Winners' Set**
- 264 Oldsmobile Toronado (Metallic Blue), 307 Jaguar 'E'-type (Chrome finish, RN '2', driver), 314 Ferrari Berlinetta (Red, RN '4'), 337 Chevrolet Stingray (Yellow, RN '13'), 327 MGB GT (Red/Black, suitcase). Box should contain unopened bag of cones and decal sheets..................... **£400-500**

**46** 1982 **Super Karts Set**
- Red Kart, Purple Kart, with Silver/Red driver in each..............................NGPP

**47** 1966-71 **Ford 5000 Tractor and Conveyor Set**
- Contains 67, trailer with conveyor belt, figure and accessories. Box has inner display card................. **£200-250**

**47** 1978-80 **Pony Club Set**
- 421 Land Rover and Horsebox in Metallic Bronze, girl on pony figure....... **£35-40**

**48** 1967-68 **Carrimore Car Transporter with Ford Tilt Cab**
- 1138 Transporter (Orange/Silver/Two-tone Blue) with 252 Rover 2000 (Metallic Plum), 251 Hillman Imp (Metallic Maroon), 440 Ford Cortina Estate (Metallic Blue), 249 Morris Mini Cooper DeLuxe (with wickerwork' panels), 226 Morris Mini-Minor (Metallic Maroon), 321 Mini Cooper 'S' ('1966 Monte Carlo Rally'), Red/White, RN '2'. Blue/Yellow 'window' box with inner polystyrene packing .......... **£600-800**
- 1968 'SUN/RAC' variation: As previous set but 321 Mini Cooper is replaced by 333 SUN/RAC Rally Mini. 251 Hillman Imp is changed to Metallic Gold with White stripe and the 226 Austin 7 Mini is now Metallic Blue with RN '21'....................................... **£700-900**

**48** 1969 **Carrimore Car Transporter with Scammell Cab**
- 1148 Transporter (Red/White) with 345 MGB (Orange), 340 Sunbeam Imp (1967 Monte Carlo, Metallic Blue, '77'), 258 Saint's Volvo P1800 (White with Orange label), 249 Morris Mini Cooper DeLuxe (with 'wickerwork' panels), 339 Mini Cooper 'S' ('1967 Monte Carlo Rally', RN '177'), 226 Morris Mini-Minor (Metallic Maroon), plus sealed bag of cones and leaflet. Blue/Yellow 'window' box, inner polystyrene packing .......... **£500-750**

**48** 1978-80 **'PINDER' Circus Set**
- Contains C426, C1163, C30, ringmaster, artistes, animals, seating, and cardboard cut-out 'Jean Richard Pinder' 'Big-Top' circus tent. Striped 'window' box ....... **£125-150**

**49** 1978-80 **'CORGI FLYING CLUB'**
- Metallic Green/White Jeep (419) with Blue/White Tipsy Nipper Aircraft.......... **£50-60**

**51** 19?? **'100 Years of the Car' Set**
- 3 Mercedes: C805 (White), C806 (Black), C811 (Red), Originally for Germany ...... **£20-25**

**?** 1978-80 **'The Jaguar Collection'**
- C804 (Cream), C816 (Red), C318 (Mobil Green/White). ('UNIPART' stores)................................ **£30-35**

**53** 19??-?? **Land Rover and Thunderbirds Missile Set**
- Models as listed.................................. **£500-750**

**54** 1978-80 **Swiss Rega Set**
- Bonna Ambulance and Helicopter .......... **£30-35**

**55** 1978-80 **Norway Emergency Set**
- Police Car, Breakdown Truck, Ford Transit Ambulance, 'UTRYKKNINGUSSETT'..................... **£20-30**

**56** 1978-80 **Swedish Set**
- Ford 'POLIS', Bonna Ambulance........... **£12-18**

**57** 1978-80 **Swedish Set**
- Contains Volvo and Caravan .................. **£12-18**

**57** 1978-80 **Volvo 740 and Caravan**
- Red Volvo, White/Red/Blue Caravan. Swedish export ..................................... **£15-20**

**61** 1978-80 **Swiss 'FEUERWEHR' Set**
- 1120 Dennis Fire Engine, Sierra 'POLITZEI', Escort Van 'NOTRUF' ...... **£30-35**

**64** 1965-69 **FC Jeep 150 and Conveyor Belt**
- Jeep (409) Yellow/White Conveyor .... **£100-130**

**65** 1978-80 **Norway Set**
- Ford Transit Ambulance plus Helicopter **£20-30**

**67** 1978-80 **Cyclists Sets**
- Sold in France, 2 Cars, 2 Bicycles. Three sets: 67/1, 67/2, 67/3.......Each set: **£20-30**

**70** 1978-80 **Danish 'FALCK' Set**
- Bonna Ambulance and Ford Breakdown Truck .......................... **£20-30**

**72** 1978-80 **Norway Set**
- With C542 plus Helicopter 'LN OSH' .... **£20-30**

**1151** 1970 **Scammell 'Co-op' Set**
- Blue/White 1147, 466 and 462. Promo in brown box........................... **£400-500**

**?** 1967 **Monte Carlo Game** (Scandinavian set)
- Fernel Developments game with two Lavender 226 Minis, '1967 Rallye Monte Carlo' bonnet labels, RNs '1' and '4', plastic/paper winding roads, cards, dice shakers, Blue/White/Red box ............. **£350-450**

**?** 1980 **Construction Site Set**
- Contains 54 with 440 (Mazda Pick-Up) . **£30-35**

**US EXPORT SETS** — made exclusively for FAO Schwarz of America.

**FAO-012**
c1966 **'BEST IN SHOW' Animal Gift Set**
- Contains GS2 Land-Rover with Rice's Pony Trailer, 484 Dodge Kew Fargo and 486 Chevrolet Impala 'Kennel Club'. Blue/Yellow individual card boxes, Blue/Yellow presentation box ....... **£1,500-2,000**

**FAO-804**
c1968 **'CIRCUS' Set**
- Contains GS7 'Daktari' Set, 470 Forward Control Jeep, 1123 'Chipperfields' Circus Animal Cage and GS19 'Chipperfields Circus' Land-Rover and Elephant Cage on Trailer. Blue/Yellow individual boxes, Blue/Yellow presentation box ....... **£1,750-2,250**

**?** 1995 **'The Italian Job'**
- Produced by TMC Marketing for Rover MG to celebrate shipment of real Minis. Finished in Red, White and Blue with 'Longbridge Channel Tunnel Crossing 1965' decal on roof. 1:36 scale, on wooden plinth and in presentation box. Only 100 sets issued............................ **£200-300**

Husky models were introduced by Mettoy Playcraft in 1965 to compete with the Matchbox 1-75 range. These small-scale models have plenty of detail and action-features and the range includes cars, commercials, military and Film/TV specials.

The models have either a plastic or die-cast chassis together with various types of regular wheels and WhizzWheels. Models could only be obtained from 'Woolworths' stores and were only sold in blister packs. Production under the 'Husky' trade name ceased in 1969 and the range was reissued in 1970 as 'Corgi Juniors'. To facilitate this change, 'HUSKY' was removed from the baseplates which were then re-engraved 'CORGI JUNIORS'.

The models were mostly fitted with 'WhizzWheels' to enable them to be used on the 'Rocket Track' and to compete against the new Matchbox 'Superfast' range. Corgi Juniors were blister packed on blue/white card for the 'regular' issues and red/white card for the 'specials'. Each pack incorporated a 'Collectors Card' picture of the real vehicle and these could be cut out and pasted into a special collectors album.

**The Market Price Range shown for 'Husky' and 'Corgi Juniors' refers only to mint condition models in unopened blister packs (and later in pristine boxes).**

## 'Husky' models  1965 - 1969

| Model and details | | MPR |
|---|---|---|
| **1** | 65-69 **Jaguar Mk.10** | |
| | All have Yellow interior. | |
| 1-a1 | 65-66 (small), Met. Blue, GPW | **£20-25** |
| 1-a2 | 1966 (small), Red body, GPW | **£50-60** |
| 1-b1 | 1967 Light Metallic Blue, GPW | **£20-25** |
| 1-b2 | 1967 Blue body, GPW | **£25-30** |
| 1-b3 | 1968 Light Met. Blue body, tyres | **£25-30** |
| 1-b4 | 1968 Cream body, tyres | **£45-55** |
| 1-b5 | 1969 Dark Blue body, tyres | **£25-30** |
| 1-b6 | 1969 Dark Maroon body, tyres | **£30-35** |
| **2** | 65-69 **Citroën Safari with Boat** | |
| 2-a1 | 65-66 (small casting) Pale Yellow body, Tan boat, GPW | **£20-25** |
| 2-b1 | 1967 Metallic Green body, Brown boat, GPW | **£50-60** |
| 2-b2 | 1967 Metallic Gold body, Blue boat, GPW | **£40-45** |
| 2-b3 | 68-69 Met. Gold, Blue boat, tyres | **£20-25** |
| 3-a1 | 65-67 **Mercedes 220** Pale Blue, GPW | **£15-20** |
| 3-bt | 67-68 **Volkswagen Police Car** White/Black doors, smooth hubs with tyres | **£25-30** |
| 3-b2 | 1969 With detailed hubs / tyres | **£25-30** |
| **4** | 65-69 **Jaguar Fire Chief** | |
| 4-a1 | 65-66 (small casting), Red body, chrome siren, 'Fire', GPW | **£25-30** |
| 4-bl | 1967 as previous model | **£25-30** |
| 4-b2 | 68-69 Same but with tyres | **£30-35** |
| 5-a1 | 1965 **Lancia Flaminia**, Red, GPW | **£45-55** |
| 5-a2 | 65-66 Blue, GPW | **£15-20** |
| 5-b1 | 67-69 **Willys Jeep**, Metallic Green, Grey windshield | **£15-20** |
| 5-b2 | 67-69 With Yellow windshield. | **£25-30** |
| 6-a1 | 65-67 **Citroën Safari Ambulance**, White, Red cross, GPW | **£20-25** |
| 6-b1 | 68-69 **Ferrari Berlinetta** Red body, tyres | **£25-30** |
| 6-b2 | 68-69 Maroon body, tyres | **£25-30** |
| 7-a1 | 65-66 **Buick Electra** Orange-Red, GPW | **£15-20** |
| 7-b1 | 1967 **Duple Vista 25 Coach** Green/White, GPW | **£30-35** |
| 7-b2 | 68-69 Same but with tyres | **£20-25** |
| 8-a1 | 65-66 **Ford Thunderbird** (open) Pink, Black open body, GPW | **£30-35** |
| 8-b1 | 1967 **Ford Thunderbird Hardtop** Yellow, Blue top, GPW | **£45-55** |
| 8-c1 | 67-69 **Tipping Farm Trailer** Yellow, Red back, tyres | **£10-15** |
| 9-a1 | 65-67 **Buick 'Police' Patrol** Dark Blue, GPW | **£20-25** |
| 9-b1 | 68-69 **Cadillac Eldorado** Light Blue, tyres | **£20-25** |
| 10-a1 | 65-67 **Guy Warrior Coal Truck** Red, GPW | **£15-20** |
| 10-a2 | 68-69 Same model | **£15-20** |
| 11-a1 | 65-67 **Forward Control Land Rover** Green body (shades), metal or plastic base, rear corner windows, GPW | **£15-20** |
| 11-a2 | 68-69 Same, but Metallic Green, no corner windows, GPW | **£15-20** |
| 12-a1 | 65-66 **Volkswagen Tower Wagon** Yellow/Red, GPW | **£20-25** |

| Model and details | | MPR |
|---|---|---|
| 12-b1 | 1967 **Ford Tower Wagon** Yellow, Red tower, GPW | **£30-35** |
| 12-b2 | 1967 White, Red tower, GPW | **£30-35** |
| 12-b3 | 68-69 White, Red tower, tyres | **£20-25** |
| 13-a1 | 65-66 **Guy Warrior Sand Truck** Yellow, GPW | **£15-20** |
| 13-a2 | 67-68 Blue, GPW | **£15-20** |
| 13-a3 | 1969 Blue, tyres | **£20-25** |
| 14-a1 | 65-66 **Guy Warrior Tanker 'Shell'** Yellow, round tank, GPW | **£20-25** |
| 14-b1 | 1967 Same, but square tank | **£20-25** |
| 14-b2 | 1967 **Guy Warrior Tanker 'Esso'** White, square tank, GPW | **£20-25** |
| 14-b3 | 68-69 Same, but with tyres | **£20-25** |
| 15-a1 | 65-66 **VW Pick Up**, Turquoise, GPW. | **£15-20** |
| 15-b1 | 67-68 **Studebaker Wagonaire TV Car** Yellow body, GPW | **£20-25** |
| 15-b2 | 1968 Metallic Blue body, GPW | **£25-30** |
| 15-b3 | 1969 Metallic Blue body, tyres | **£25-30** |
| 16-a1 | 65-66 **Dump Truck/Dozer** Yellow, Red back, GPW | **£15-20** |
| 16-a2 | 1966 **Dump Truck/Dozer** Red, Grey back, GPW | **£20-25** |
| **17** | 65-69 **Guy Warrior 'Milk' Tanker** | |
| 17-a1 | 65-66 White, round tank, GPW | **£20-25** |
| 17-b1 | 1967 White, square tank, GPW | **£20-25** |
| 17-b2 | 1968 Cream, round tank, GPW | **£20-25** |
| 17-b3 | 1969 Cream, round tank, tyres | **£20-25** |
| 18-a1 | 65-66 **Plated Jaguar** (small casting) Chrome, GPW | **£20-25** |
| 18-bi | 67-68 Same, but larger casting | **£20-25** |
| 18-b2 | 1969 Larger casting, tyres | **£30-35** |
| 19-a1 | 1966 **Commer Walk Thro' Van** Red body, GPW | **£40-45** |
| 19-a2 | 66-67 Green body, GPW | **£25-30** |
| 19-b1 | 68-69 **Speedboat on Trailer** Gold trailer, Red, White and Blue boat, tyres | **£15-20** |
| 20-a1 | 65-66 **Ford Thames Van** Red, Yellow ladder, GPW | **£20-25** |
| 20-b1 | 1967 **VW 1300 with Luggage** Tan body, tyres | **£35-45** |
| 20-b2 | 67-69 With Blue body | **£20-25** |
| 21-a1 | 66-67 **Forward Control Military Land Rover**, GPW | **£15-20** |
| 21-b1 | 68-69 **Jaguar 'E'-type 2+2** Maroon body, tyres | **£20-25** |
| 22-a1 | 65-66 **Citroën Safari Military Ambulance**, GPW | **£20-25** |
| 22-b1 | 67-68 **Aston-Martin DB6** Metallic Gold body, GPW | **£25-30** |
| 22-b2 | 68-69 **Aston-Martin DB6** Purple body, tyres | **£30-35** |
| 23-a1 | 66-67 **Guy Army Tanker**, GPW | **£15-20** |
| 23-b1 | 1968 **Loadmaster Shovel** Orange body, BPW | **£25-30** |
| 23-b2 | 68-69 Yellow body, BPW | **£15-20** |
| 24-a1 | 66-67 **Ford Zephyr Estate** Blue body, GPW | **£20-25** |
| 24-a2 | 68-69 **Ford Zephyr Estate** Red, GPW | **£25-30** |
| 25-a1 | 66-67 **SD Refuse Van**, Blue, GPW | **£15-20** |
| 25-a2 | 1968 Red body, GPW | **£40-50** |
| 25-a3 | 68-69 Red body, tyres | **£40-45** |

| Model and details | | MPR |
|---|---|---|
| 26-a1 | 66-67 **Sunbeam Alpine** Metallic Bronze body, Blue hard top, GPW | **£25-30** |
| 26-a2 | 1967 Same, but Red body, GPW | **£45-55** |
| 26-a3 | 68-69 Red body, Blue top, tyres | **£50-55** |
| 27-a1 | 66-67 **Bedford Skip Lorry** Maroon body, GPW | **£20-25** |
| 27-a2 | 1967 **Bedford Skip Lorry** Dark Green body, GPW | **£50-60** |
| 27-a3 | 1967 Orange body, GPW | **£20-25** |
| 27-a4 | 68-69 Orange body, tyres | **£20-25** |
| 28-a1 | 66-67 **Ford Breakdown Truck** Blue, metal jib, GPW | **£15-20** |
| 28-a2 | 68-69 Blue, Gold jib, tyres | **£20-25** |
| 29-a1 | 66-67 **ERF Cement Mixer**, Yellow, Red barrel, GPW | **£15-20** |
| 29-a2 | 68-69 Yellow, Red barrel, tyres | **£20-25** |
| 30-a1 | 66-67 **Studebaker Wagonaire Ambulance**, White, Red Cross, stretcher, GPW | **£25-30** |
| 30-a2 | 68-69 Same, but with tyres | **£25-30** |
| 30-a3 | 1969 **Studebaker Wagonaire** Pale Green body, tyres | **£35-40** |
| 31-a1 | 66-67 **Oldsmobile Starfire Coupé** Olive Green body, GPW | **£15-20** |
| 31-a2 | 68-69 Same but with tyres | **£20-25** |
| 32-a1 | 66-67 **Volkswagen Luggage Elevator** White body, Yellow conveyor, GPW | **£25-30** |
| 32-a2 | 1967 With Blue conveyor, GPW | **£35-45** |
| 32-a3 | 68-69 Red, Blue conveyor, GPW | **£35-40** |
| 33-a1 | 1967 **Farm Trailer and Calves** Olive Green, tyres | **£10-15** |
| 33-a2 | 68-69 Turquoise, tyres | **£10-15** |
| 34-a1 | 1967 **Tractor** Red, Red exhaust, tyres | **£30-40** |
| 34-a2 | 68-69 Red, Black exhaust, tyres | **£20-25** |
| 35-a1 | 1967 **Ford Camper** Yellow, GPW | **£20-25** |
| 35-a2 | 1967 Metallic Blue, GPW | **£30-40** |
| 35-a3 | 68-69 Metallic Blue, tyres | **£25-30** |
| 36-a1 | 1967 **Simon Snorkel Fire Engine** Red, GPW | **£20-25** |
| 36-a2 | 68-69 Red, with tyres | **£20-25** |
| 37-a1 | 68-69 **NSU Ro80** Metallic Blue, tyres | **£25-30** |
| 38-a1 | 1968 **Rices Beaufort Single Horse Box** Turquoise, tyres | **£10-15** |
| 38-a2 | 1969 Metallic Green body, tyres | **£20-25** |
| 39-a1 | 1969 **Jaguar XJ6 4.2** Yellow, Red interior, tyres | **£45-55** |
| 40-a1 | 1969 **Ford Transit Caravan** Red body, tyres | **£25-35** |
| 40-a2 | 1969 Lime green body, tyres | **£25-35** |
| 41-a1 | ? **Porsche Carrera 6** In catalogue but not issued | **NPP** |
| 42-a | 1969 **Euclid Truck** Yellow body, Red dumper | **£40-45** |
| 43-a | ? **Massey-Ferguson 3003** | **£40-45** |

**See also following section and 'Corgi Rockets'**

## Husky Film and TV-related models, 1967 - 1969

**1001-a1** 1967 **James Bond Aston Martin DB6**
Silver, Red interior,
2 ejector figures, GPW ............. **£180-200**
**1001-a2** 68-69 **James Bond Aston Martin DB6**
Same but with tyres ................... **£180-200**
**1002-a1** 67-69 **Batmobile**
Black, Batman and Robin
figures, tow hook, GPW ........... **£150-160**

**1003-a1** 67-69 **Batboat**
Black boat, Red fin, Batman
and Robin figures, GPW........... **£150-160**
**1004-a1** 68-69 **Monkeemobile**
Red, White roof, 4 figures,
'Monkees' on doors, tyres ........ **£160-180**

**1005-a1** 68-69 **Man From UNCLE Car**
Blue, 3 Missiles on sprue,
2 figures, tyres .......................... **£160-175**

**1006-a1** 1969 **Chitty Chitty Bang Bang**
Chrome, Dark Grey base, Red wings,
Yellow fins, 4 figures, tyres....... **£140-180**

## Husky and Corgi Juniors Gift Sets 1968 - 1970

**3001** 68-69 **4 Garage Set**,
Contains 23, 27, 29, or 9, 30 or 36 .... **£75-100**
**3002** 68-69 **Batmobile Set**
1002 Batmobile and 1003 Batboat
on trailer .................................. **£250-300**
**3002** 1970 **'Club Racing' Set**
Juniors set of 8 racing cars including
Mini Cooper 'S' in Metallic Mauve,
Ford Capri, Morgan, etc.................. **£150-250**
**3003** 68-69 **Car Transporter Set**
2002 Husky Car Transporter plus
16, 26, 6-2, 21-2, 22-2, 26 .............. **£125-175**

**3004** 68-69 **4 Garage Set**,
Contains 23-2, 29 ............................... **£60-80**

**3004** 19?? **James Bond 'OHMSS' Set**
Contains 1004, 1001, 1011, 1012 plus
un-numbered VW Beetle in Red with
Black No'5' on White circle on
sides. (Film 'On Her Majesty's
Secret Service') ....................... **£5,000-6,000**
**3005** 68-69 **Holiday Time / Leisure Time**
Contains 2-2, 5-2, 7-2, 15-2, 19-2,
20-2, 21-2, 35-1........................... **£150-200**

**3006** 68-69 **Service Station**,
Contains 14-c, 22-2, 28...................... **£60-80**

**3007** 68-69 **'HUSKY MULTIPARK'**
In 1968 catalogue but not issued ..............NPP

**3008** 68-69 **Crime Busters Set (Husky set)**
Contains 1001, 1002, 1005.... **£400-600**
1970 **Corgi Juniors** 3008 set.......... **£400-600**

**3011** 19?? **Road Construction Set**
Gift Set containing seven models .... **£120-140**

# Corgi Juniors 1970 – 1972

The models in this list were each accompanied by a colourful Picture Card,
the lack of which could adversely affect the model's potential price.

| Model and details | MPR |
|---|---|
| **1**-a1 1970 **Reliant TW9 Pick Up** | |
| Beige body, Black WW ........ **£20-25** | |
| **1**-a2 70-72 Orange body, Black WW ........ **£15-20** | |
| **2**-a1 1970 **Citroën Safari with** (white) **Boat** | |
| Blue body, tyres...................... **£30-40** | |
| **2**-a2 1970 With Black WhizzWheels ...... **£20-25** | |
| **2**-a3 71-72 Yellow body, BWW ............. **£20-25** | |
| **2**-a4 71-72 Purple body, BWW ............. **£20-25** | |
| **3**-a1 1970 **Volkswagen 1300 Police Car** | |
| White body, tyres................... **£30-35** | |
| **3**-a2 1970 With Black WhizzWheels ...... **£20-25** | |
| **3**-a3/4 71-72 With chrome WhizzWheels ..... **£20-25** | |
| **4**-a1 70-72 **Zeteor 5511 Tractor** | |
| Orange, Red base, BPW.......... **£10-15** | |
| **5**-a1 1970 **Willys Jeep** | |
| Tan body, Brown int., tyres..... **£15-20** | |
| **5**-a2 1970 With Black WhizzWheels ....... **£10-15** | |
| **5**-a3 1971 With chrome WhizzWheels ..... **£10-15** | |
| **5**-a4 1970 Orange, Brown int., BWW ..... **£10-15** | |
| **5**-a5 1971 Same, chrome Whizzwheels ... **£10-15** | |
| **5**-a6 71-72 Red body, Yellow int., CWW.. **£10-15** | |
| **6**-a1 1970 **De Tomaso Mangusta** | |
| Lime Green, BWW ................. **£10-15** | |
| **6**-a2 1970 Metallic Purple, Black WW .... **£10-15** | |
| **6**-a3 71-72 Metallic Purple, CWW........... **£10-15** | |
| **7**-a1 1970 **Duple Vista 25 Coach** | |
| Red body/White roof, tyres.... **£20-25** | |
| **7**-a2 1970 Yellow/White, Black WW ...... **£12-15** | |
| **7**-a3 71-72 Purple/White, chrome WW ... **£12-15** | |
| **7**-a4 71-72 Orange/White, chrome WW ... **£12-15** | |
| **8**-a1 1970 **Tipping Farm Trailer** | |
| Blue, Orange back, tyres........ **£10-15** | |
| **9**-a1 1970 **Cadillac Eldorado** | |
| Met. Green, Red int., tyres..... **£25-30** | |
| **9**-a2 1970 With Black WhizzWheels ...... **£15-20** | |
| **9**-a3 1970 White/Black, BWW ............... **£15-20** | |
| **9**-a4 1971 White/Black, chrome WW ...... **£15-20** | |
| **9**-b1 71-72 **Vigilant Range Rover** | |
| White body, chrome WW....... **£12-15** | |
| **10**-a1 1970 **Guy Warrior Coal Truck** | |
| Orange body, tyres ............... **£15-20** | |
| **10**-b1 71-72 **Ford GT7O**, Orange, CWW .. **£20-25** | |
| **11**-af 1970 **Austin Healey Sprite Le Mans** | |
| Red body, Blue interior, Grey base, | |
| '50', sticker pack, Black WW .. **£30-35** | |
| **11**-a2 1971 Yellow int., chrome WW........ **£30-35** | |
| **11**-a3 71-72 Red body, Yellow interior, | |
| Black base, CWW................... **£30-35** | |
| **12**-a1 1970 **Reliant-Ogle Scimitar GTE** | |
| White body, Black WW ......... **£20-25** | |
| **12**-a2 1970 Metallic Blue, chrome WW ... **£20-25** | |
| **12**-a3 71-72 Matt Blue, chrome WW ........ **£20-25** | |

| Model and details | MPR |
|---|---|
| **13**-a1 1970 **Guy Warrior Sand Truck** | |
| Blue body, tyres..................... **£20-30** | |
| **13**-a2 71-72 Red body, chrome WW........... **£12-15** | |
| **14**-a1 1970 **Guy Warrior Tanker 'ESSO'** | |
| (square tank), White, tyres.... **£25-35** | |
| **14**-a2 71-72 White, chrome WW ............... **£15-20** | |
| **15**-a1 1970 **Studebaker Wagonaire TV Car** | |
| Metallic Turquoise , tyres ..... **£35-40** | |
| **15**-a2 1970 Yellow body, Black WW ........ **£25-30** | |
| **15**-a3 1970 Met. Lime Green, BWW ........ **£25-30** | |
| **15**-a4 71-72 Met. Lime Green, CWW........ **£25-30** | |
| **16**-a 70-72 **Land Rover Pick Up** | |
| Metallic Green body, tyres ..... **£20-25** | |
| **17**-af 1970 **Volkswagen 1300 Beetle** | |
| Met. Blue, 'flower' decals....... **£45-50** | |
| **17**-a2 70-72 Metallic Green body............... **£20-25** | |
| **19**-a1 1970 **Speedboat on Trailer** | |
| Blue trailer, Red,White and | |
| Blue boat, tyres..................... **£20-30** | |
| **19**-a2 1970 With Black WhizzWheels ...... **£20-30** | |
| **19**-a3 71-72 With chrome WhizzWheels .... **£10-15** | |
| **20**-a1 1967 **Volkswagen 1300 with Luggage** | |
| Mustard Yellow body, tyres .... **£30-40** | |
| **20**-a2 67-69 Red body, Black WW.............. **£20-25** | |
| **21**-a1 71-72 **BVRT Vita-Min Mini Cooper S** | |
| Metallic Purple, CWW........... **£30-40** | |
| **22**-a1 1970 **Aston-Martin DB6** | |
| Purple body, tyres................... **£50-60** | |
| **22**-a2 1970 Metallic Olive body, tyres...... **£45-50** | |
| **22**-b1 71-72 **Formula 1 GP Racing Car** | |
| Yellow body, WW ................. **£15-20** | |
| **23**-a1 70-72 **Loadmaster Shovel** | |
| Yellow body, BPW.................. **£10-12** | |
| **24**-a1 71-72 **Aston-Martin DBS** | |
| Green body, chrome WW........ **£30-40** | |
| **25**-a1 70-72 **SD Refuse Van** | |
| Orange / chrome, tyres........... **£15-20** | |
| **26**-a1 71-72 **ERF Fire Engine Water Tender** | |
| Red body, chrome WW .......... **£12-15** | |
| **27**-a1 1970 **Bedford Skip Lorry** | |
| Orange, Silver skip, tyres....... **£20-25** | |
| **28**-a1 1970 **Ford Breakdown Truck** | |
| Blue body, tyres..................... **£20-25** | |
| **28**-a2/3 1970 Blue or Turquoise, BWW ...... **£15-20** | |
| **29**-a1 71-72 **Simon Snorkel Fire Engine** | |
| Red body, chrome WW .......... **£12-15** | |
| **30**-a1 1970 **Studebaker Wagonaire** | |
| **Ambulance**, White body, | |
| removable stretcher, tyres ...... **£25-30** | |
| **30**-a2 1970 With Black WhizzWheels ...... **£20-25** | |
| **30**-a3 1970 With non-removable stretcher, | |
| Black WhizzWheels................ **£15-20** | |

| Model and details | MPR |
|---|---|
| **30**-a4/5 71-72 Fixed stretcher, small CWW .. **£15-20** | |
| **31**-a1 70-71 **Land Rover Breakdown** | |
| Purple body ............................. **£15-20** | |
| **31**-a2 1972 Red body ................................ **£12-15** | |
| **32**-a1 70-71 **Lotus Europa**, | |
| Met. Green, CWW .................. **£20-30** | |
| **32**-a2 1972 Green body, CWW ................. **£15-20** | |
| **33**-a1 1970 **Farm Trailer and Calves** | |
| Orange, tyres .......................... **£10-15** | |
| **33**-b1 70-72 **Jaguar 'E'-type Series 2** | |
| Yellow, CWW ........................ **£20-30** | |
| **34**-a1 70-72 **B.M. Volvo 400 Tractor** | |
| Red, Yellow wheels, tyres ...... **£15-20** | |
| **35**-a1 1970 **Ford Camper** | |
| Turquoise, tyres...................... **£30-35** | |
| **35**-a2 70-2 Same, but Black WW ............. **£25-30** | |
| **35**-a3 70-2 Red, Cream back, BWW......... **£20-25** | |
| **36**-a1 1970 **Simon Snorkel Fire Engine** | |
| Red body, tyres....................... **£20-25** | |
| **37**-a1 1970 **NSU Ro80** | |
| Metallic Blue body, tyres ....... **£25-30** | |
| **37**-a2 1970 Metallic Mauve body, | |
| Black WhizzWheels ............... **£15-20** | |
| **37**-a3 1970 Purple body, Black WW ......... **£15-20** | |
| **37**-a4 71-72 Purple body, CWW ............... **£15-20** | |
| **37**-a5 71-72 Metallic Copper body, CWW.. **£15-20** | |
| **38**-a1 1970 **Rices Beaufort Single Horse Box** | |
| Metallic Green body, tyres ..... **£20-30** | |
| **38**-a2 1970 Red body, tyres....................... **£20-30** | |
| **38**-a3 1970 Red body, Black WW ............. **£20-25** | |
| **38**-a4 71-72 Metallic Copper, CWW........... **£20-25** | |
| **39**-a1 1970 **Jaguar XJ6 4.2** | |
| Yellow, Red interior, tyres...... **£35-40** | |
| **39**-a2 1970 Silver, Red interior, BWW ..... **£25-35** | |
| **39**-a3 71-72 Silver, Red interior, CWW...... **£25-30** | |
| **39**-a4 71-72 Met. Red, Yellow int., CWW.. **£25-30** | |
| **39**-a5 71-72 Red body, Yellow int., CWW.. **£25-30** | |
| **40**-a1 1970 **Ford Transit Caravan** | |
| Yellow body, Blue interior, | |
| Silver rear door, tyres............. **£25-30** | |
| **40**-a2 1970 Yellow, Cream int., BWW ...... **£20-25** | |
| **40**-a3 1970 Blue body, Cream int., BWW . **£20-25** | |
| **40**-a4 71-72 Blue body, Cream int., CWW.. **£20-25** | |
| **40**-a5 71-72 Metallic Pale Blue body, | |
| Cream interior, CWW ............. **£15-20** | |
| **40**-a6 1972 Metallic Pale Blue body, Cream | |
| int., Black plastic base, CWW **£15-20** | |
| **41**-a1 1970 **Porsche Carrera 6** | |
| White body, clear canopy, | |
| RN '19', tyres......................... **£25-35** | |
| **41**-a2 1970 Blue tinted canopy, BWW ...... **£20-25** | |
| **41**-a3 71-72 Blue tinted canopy, CWW...... **£15-20** | |

## Husky/Juniors Major Models

42-a1 1970 **Euclid Dumper**
Yellow cab, Red back, Dark
Grey base, Black wheels ......... **£15-20**
42-a2 1970 Red cab, Yellow back,
unpainted base, CWW............ **£10-15**
42-a3 71-72 Yellow cab, Red back,
Dark Grey base, BWW .......... **£10-15**
42-a4 71-72 Blue cab, Silver back,
Dark Grey base, CWW .......... **£10-15**
42-a5 71-72 Blue Cab, Yellow back,
Dark Grey base, CWW .......... **£10-15**
43-a1 1970 **Massey Ferguson Tractor Shovel**
Yellow body, Red int., BPW .. **£12-15**
43-a2 71-72 Yellow body, Red shovel
and interior, BPW.................... **£10-15**
44-a1 70-72 **Raygo Rascal Road Roller**
Blue / Orange, BPW .............. **£10-12**
45-a1 1970 **Mercedes 280SL**
Met. Silver, Red int., tyres ...... **£30-35**
45-a2 1970 Metallic Blue body,
Red interior, Black WW.......... **£20-25**
45-a3 1970 Yellow body, Red interior,
unpainted base, BWW............. **£15-20**
45-a4 1970 Yellow body, Red interior,
White base, BWW................... **£15-20**
45-a5 1970 Red body, Cream int., BWW .. **£25-30**
45-a6 71-72 Red body, Cream int., CWW .. **£25-30**
45-a7 71-72 Blue body, Cream interior,
unpainted base, CWW............. **£20-25**
46-a1 1970 **Jensen Interceptor**
Maroon body, Yellow interior,
unpainted base, tyres .............. **£35-40**
46-a2 1970 Maroon body, Black WW ..... **£25-30**
46-a3 1971 Orange body, CWW............. **£25-30**
46-a4 1972 Metallic Green body, CWW.... **£25-30**
47-a1 71-72 **Scammell Concrete Mixer**
White / Red, CWW ................ **£10-15**
48-a1 71-72 **ERF Tipper Truck**
Red cab, Silver back, unpainted
or Grey base, CWW................ **£15-20**
48-a1 71-72 Blue cab, Orange back ......... **£15-20**
48-a1 71-72 Blue cab, Yellow back............ **£15-20**
49-a1 71-72 **Pininfarina Modulo**
Yellow, Red stripe, CWW ....... **£15-20**
50-a1 71-72 **Ferrari 512s**
Metallic Red, CWW............... **£15-20**
51-a1 71-72 **Porsche 917**
Gold, RN '23', CWW .............. **£15-20**
52-a1 71-72 **Adams Probe 16**
Metallic Pink, CWW .............. **£15-20**
54-a1 71-72 **Ford Container Wagon**
Red, Yellow skip, CWW ......... **£15-20**

55-a1 70-72 **Daimler Fleetline Bus**
Red, 'Uniflo', CWW.............. **£15-20**
56-a1 70-72 **Ford Capri Fire Chief**
Red/White, 'Fire' decal
on door, White int., CWW ...... **£25-30**
56-a2 70-72 With 'Fire Chief' decal ...... **£25-30**
56-a3 70-72 All-Red, 'Fire Chief' on door,
Yellow interior, CWW ........... **£25-30**
57-a1 70-72 **Caddy Hot Rodder**
Metallic Blue, 'Caddy Hot Roddy'
on doors, sticker pack, CWW . **£12-15**
57-a2 70-72 Metallic Pink body, CWW...... **£12-15**
58-a1 71-72 **G.P. Beach Buggy**
Met. Red, Cream int., CWW... **£10-12**
58-a2 71-72 Same, but Yellow interior....... **£10-12**
59-a1 71-72 **The Futura**, Orange, Black
base, sheet of stickers, CWW . **£15-20**
60-a1 71-72 **VW Double Trouble Hot Rod**
Metallic Pink, CWW.............. **£15-20**
61-a1 70-72 **Mercury Cougar Police Car** . **£15-20**
62-a1 1970 **Volvo P1800**
Red, Yellow int., CWW ......... **£35-40**
62-a2 71-72 Red, Blue interior, CWW....... **£25-30**
62-a3 1972 Red, Cream interior, CWW..... **£45-50**
63-a1 70-72 **Ford Escort Monte Carlo
Rally Car**, Met. Blue, RN '32',
Red int., stickers sheet, CWW **£40-50**
63-a2 1972 With Yellow interior, CWW..... **£50-60**
63-a3 1972 With Cream interior, CWW..... **£50-60**
64-a1 71-72 **Morgan Plus 8**
Yellow, CWW ........................ **£25-35**
64-a2 71-72 Red, RN '20', CWW.............. **£25-35**
65-a1 71-72 **Bertone Carabo**
Met. Purple, White int, CWW **£12-15**
65-a2 71-72 Orange interior, CWW ........... **£10-12**
67-a1 71-72 **Ford Capri 'Hot Pants' Dragster**
Yellow body, CWW ............... **£35-40**
70-a1 71-72 **US Racing Buggy**, Blue........ **£15-20**
71-a1 71-72 **Marcos XP**, Orange, CWW ... **£15-20**
72-a1 71-72 **Mercedes-Benz C111**, Red.... **£15-20**
73-a1 71-72 **Pininfarina Alfa Romeo P33**
Blue body, chrome WW ......... **£15-20**
74-a1 71-72 **Bertone Barchetta**, Orange ... **£15-20**
75-a1 71-72 **Superstock Car**
Silver, Union Jack, stickers..... **£20-25**
76-a1 71-72 **Chevrolet Astro**, Met. Red..... **£15-20**
77-a1 71-72 **Bizzarrini Manta**, CWW........ **£15-20**
78-a1 71-72 **Old MacDonald's Truck** ....... **£30-40**
1017 71-72 **Holmes Wrecker and
Towing Cradle**, Yellow cab,
Red back, 'Auto Rescue'.... **£100-120**

2001 68-69 **'HUSKY' Multi Garage**
A set of four garages (no cars),
'Husky' on base..................... **£20-30**
70-75 Corgi Juniors issue as previous
model but with 'CORGI' logo,
'Juniors' on base..................... **£10-15**
2002 67-69 **'HUSKY' Car Transporter**
Hoynor MkII, White/Blue/Orange,
cab, 'Husky' on base .............. **£30-40**
70-72 Corgi Juniors issue as previous
model but with 'CORGI' logo,
'Juniors' on base..................... **£25-35**
2003a 68-69 **Machinery Low-Loader**
Red/Blue/Yellow, cab, drop-down
ramp, 'Husky' base ................ **£25-35**
2003b 70-73 Corgi Juniors issue as previous
model with metal wheels or
WW, 'Juniors' on base ........... **£25-35**
2004a 68-69 **Removals Delivery Van**
Red or Blue cab, plated box,
'HUSKY REMOVALS', metal
wheels, 'Husky' on base ......... **£45-55**
2004b 70-72 Corgi Juniors issue:
'CORGI REMOVALS',
WW, 'Juniors' base ................ **£30-35**
2006 70-79 **Mack 'ESSO' Tanker**
White body and tank,
WW, 'Juniors' on base ........... **£30-35**

## Husky Accessories

1561/2 68-69 **Traffic Signs**........................... **£20-30**
1571 68-69 **Pedestrians** ........................... **£10-15**
1572 68-69 **Workmen**............................... **£10-15**
1573 68-69 **Garage Personnel** ................. **£10-15**
1574 68-69 **Public Servants**..................... **£10-15**
1580 68-69 **Husky Collector Case**
storage for 48 models ............ **£15-25**
1585 68-69 **Husky Traveller Case**,
opens to form Service Station
(this item never seen).................**NPP**
2001 68-69 **'HUSKY' Multi Garage**,
A set of four garages, (no
cars), 'Husky' on base ........... **£25-35**
70-75 As previous but with 'CORGI'
logo, 'Juniors' on base ........... **£10-15**
--- 1970s **USA Dealer Display Unit**.
A wooden revolving unit with
lighting, brown/black,
'Collect Husky Models'...... **£200-300**

# Corgi Juniors Film and TV-related models, 1970 - 1972

1001-a1 1970 **James Bond Aston-Martin DB6**
Silver, Red interior, 2 ejector figures,
Grey plastic wheels .................... **£150-175**
1001-a2 1970 **James Bond Aston-Martin DB6**
Silver, Red interior, 2 ejector figures,
Black WhizzWheels................. **£150-175**
1001-a3 71-72 **James Bond Aston-Martin DB6**
Silver, Red interior, 2 ejector figures,
chrome WhizzWheels ................. **£150-175**

1002-a1 1970 **Batmobile**
Black, Batman and Robin figures, tow
hook, GPW, 'Corgi Junior' base . **£125-150**
1002-a2 1970 **Batmobile**
Black, Batman and Robin figures,
tow hook, Black WhizzWheels... **£125-150**
1002-a3 71-72 **Batmobile**
Black, Batman and Robin figures,
tow hook, chrome WhizzWheels **£125-150**
1003-a1 1970 **Batboat**
Black boat, Red fin, Batman and Robin
figures, GPW, 'Junior' base ........ **£125-150**
1003-a2 1970 **Batboat**
Black boat, Red fin, Batman and Robin
figures, Black WhizzWheels....... **£125-150**

1003-a3 71-72 **Batboat**
Black boat, Red fin, Batman and Robin
figures, chrome WhizzWheels .... **£125-150**

1004-a1 1970 **Monkeemobile**
Red, White roof, 4 figures, 'Monkees'
on doors, tyres, 'Junior' base ...... **£125-150**
1004-a2 1970 **Monkeemobile**
Red, White roof,4 figures, 'Monkees'
on doors, tyres, 'Junior' base ...... **£125-150**
1004-a3 1971 **Monkeemobile**
Red, White roof, 4 figures, 'Monkees'
on doors, tyres, Black WW ........ **£125-150**

1005-a1 1970 **Man From U.N.C.L.E. Car**
Blue, 3 missiles on sprue, 2 figures,
tyres, 'Junior' label on base ........ **£125-150**

1006-a1 1970 **Chitty Chitty Bang Bang**
Chrome body, 4 figures, tyres ..... **£125-150**
1006-a2 1971 **Chitty Chitty Bang Bang**
Chrome body, 4 figures, BWW... **£125-150**

1007-a1 71-72 **Ironsides Police Van**
Blue, 'San Francisco' logo, Ironside
in back, chrome WhizzWheels.... **£125-150**

1008-a1 71-72 **Popeye's Paddle Wagon**
Yellow, Blue, Popeye with Olive and
Swee' Pea, chrome WW............. **£125-150**

1010-a1 1972 **James Bond Volkswagen**
Orange, Green stripe / 'Corgi Toys'
on roof, RN '5', Yellow interior,
chrome WhizzWheels ................ **£700-900**
1011-a1 71-72 **James Bond Bobsleigh**
Yellow, '007' decal, Grey plastic bumper,
George Lazenby figure, BWW ... **£400-600**
1012-a1 71-72 **S.P.E.C.T.R.E. Bobsleigh**
Orange, 'Boars Head' decal,
Grey plastic bumper, Blofleld figure,
Black WhizzWheels ................... **£700-900**
1013-a1 71-72 **Tom's Go Cart**
Yellow, Tom figure, chrome WW ... **£50-60**
1014-a1 71-72 **Jerry's Banger**
Red, Jerry figure, CWW .............. **£50-60**

# Husky and Corgi Juniors Catalogues and listings

**HUSKY CATALOGUES**
**Leaflet (single fold)** Mettoy Playcraft (Sales) Ltd
1966.
  Red, illustrating No.1 Jaguar Mk.10 on
cover and Nos.1-29 inside. '1/9 each' ...... **£20-25**
**Leaflet (Belgian issue)**
  Mettoy Playcraft (Sales) Ltd 1966.
As previous leaflet but Nos.1-32 shown,
printed in French ...................................... **£20-25**

**Booklet (10 pages)** Mettoy Playcraft (Sales) Ltd
1966. Front/rear covers feature a row of garages and
cars. 1002 Batmobile and 1001 JB's Aston-
Martin featured, plus Nos.1-36 ................... **NGPP**
**Catalogue (24 pages)** no ref.  1967.
  Cover shows boy with Husky vehicles and sets.
Good pictures of all the rare models and Gift
Sets plus accessories and models 1-41 ..... **£30-40**

**CORGI JUNIORS CATALOGUES**
**Catalogue (16 pages)** Mettoy Playcraft 1970.
  Blue cover with 10 models featured. Fine
pictures of all the rare early models including
GS 3004 Bond 'O.H.M.S.S.' Set etc. ....... **£30-40**
**Corgi Juniors Collectors Album** no ref. 1970.
  28 pages. To hold cards cut from Corgi Junior
bubble packs. Has details of featured models
below space for card. Centre two pages have
'Corgi Toys' adverts plus articles, etc....... **£10-15**

## Corgi Juniors Twin-Packs

Corgi Juniors bubble-packed in pairs from 1977 approximately.

| | | |
|---|---|---|
| 2501 London Bus and Taxi .......................... **£20-30** | 2512 Space Shuttle + Star Ship 'Liberator' . **£40-50** | 2524 Custom Van Twin ............................... **£25-35** |
| 2502 Land Rover Breakdown / Jaguar XJS. **£30-40** | 2513 Fire Tender and Ambulance ............... **£20-30** | 2525 Triumph TR7 + Dinghy on Trailer...... **£40-50** |
| 2503 Land Rover and Horse Box................. **£20-30** | 2514 Building Set ....................................... **£25-35** | 2526 Dumper Truck + Shovel Loader ........ **£25-35** |
| 2504 Land Rover Breakdown plus | 2515 Citroën and Speedboat ....................... **£25-35** | 2527 'Kojak' and Police Helicopter............ **£50-60** |
|     AMC Pace Car............................ **£30-40** | 2516 Tractor and Tipping Trailer ................ **£25-35** | 2528 Starsky and Hutch Twin Pack ........... **£50-60** |
| 2505 'DAILY PLANET' Van + Helicopter.. **£20-30** | 2518 Mercedes and Caravan ....................... **£25-35** | 2529 James Bond Lotus and Helicopter .. **£100-150** |
| 2506 Supermobile and Superman Van ........ **£50-60** | 2519 Batmobile and Batboat.................... **£150-200** | 2530 Rescue Range Rover and Helicopter .. **£30-40** |
| 2507 Tom's Cart and Jerry's Banger........... **£20-30** | 2520 Rescue Set ......................................... **£30-40** | 2506 AMF 'Ski-daddler' |
| 2508 Popeye's Tugboat plus | 2521 James Bond Lotus plus |     Snowmobile and trailer .................. **£100-150** |
|     Olive Oyl's Aeroplane........................ **£20-30** |     Aston-Martin DB5........................ **£150-200** | 2538 Buck Rogers Starfighter and |
| 2510 F1 and F5000 Racing Cars................. **£30-40** | 2522 Army Attack Set.................................. **£30-40** |     NASA Columbia Shuttle ................... **£40-50** |
| 2511 Sting Helicopter and Scout Car.......... **£20-30** | 2523 Police Car and Helicopter .................. **£25-35** | |

## Corgi Juniors 1975 – 1983

Market Price Range - scarcer items as shown, otherwise
under £15.  These models are fitted with WhizzWheels.

| Model and details | MPR | Model and details | MPR | Model and details | MPR |
|---|---|---|---|---|---|
| E2 80-81 **Blake's Seven Liberator** ...... **£75-100** | | E60 77-79 **James Bond Lotus Esprit** | | 133 82-83 **Buick Regal 'POLICE'** | |
| E3 77-81 **Stromberg's Helicopter** ......... **£25-35** | |        1: with side & rear wings.... **£100-125** | |       Car, 'Magnum PI'................ **£25-35** | |
| E6 79-80 **'Daily Planet' Helicopter** ....... **£15-20** | |        2: without wings; some have | | 134 82-83 **Barney's Buggy**, Red/Orange, | |
| E11 79-85 **Supermobile**........................... **£20-30** | |         'TURBO' side design ...... **£100-125** | |       (The Flintstones').................... **£25-35** | |
| E17-2 79-81 **Metropolis 'POLICE' Car** .. **£25-35** | | E64 80-82 **'The Professionals'** | | E148 83-84 **USS Enterprise** ...................... **£15-20** | |
| E19 80-82 **Pink Panther Motorcycle** .... **£15-20** | |       Ford Capri ........................... **£15-20** | | E149 83 **Klingon Warship** .................... **£15-20** | |
| E20-2 79-81 **Penguinmobile** .................... **£20-30** | | E67-2 80-83 **Popeye's Tugboat** ............... **£15-20** | | E151 83 **Wilma's Coupé** ...................... **£25-35** | |
| E21 77-80 **Charlie's Angels Van** ............. **£15-20** | | E68 77-79 **Kojak's Buick Regal** ............. **£20-25** | | 198 83 **James Bond Citroën 2cv** ....... **£50-75** | |
| E23 79-81 **Batbike** ................................... **£75-100** | | E69 76-80 **Batmobile** .............................. **£75-100** | | E2009 ? **James Bond 'Aerocar'** ('The | |
| E24 79-80 **'SHAZAM' Thunderbolt** ....... **£40-50** | | E72-2 79-83 **Jaguar XJS**, Blue or Red........... **NGPP** | |       Man With the Golden Gun'). | |
| E25 79-80 **'Capt. America' Porsche**........ **£40-50** | |       **Jaguar XJS**, Red with White | |      NB: Not a licensed product........... **£160-190** | |
| E32 70-74 **The Saint's Jaguar XJS** ........ **£65-85** | |       'MOTOR SHOW' logo ..... **£20-30** | | | |
| E33 79-80 **'Wonderwoman's Car**........... **£30-40** | | E73 80 **'DRAX' Helicopter**................ **£20-25** | | | |
| E38 80-83 **Jerry's Banger**....................... **£15-20** | | E75 77-80 **Spidercopter** ........................ **£20-30** | | | |
| E40-2 79-81 **J. Bond's Aston-Martin** ..... **£100-125** | | E78 76-81 **Batcopter**............................. **£60-70** | | **GERMAN ISSUES:** | |
| E41 79-81 **J. Bond Space Shuttle** ........... **£50-75** | | E79-2 80-83 **Olive Oyl's Aeroplane**........... **£15-20** | | E119 83 **'FLUGHAFEN-FEURWEHR'** | |
| E44-2 79-80 **Starship Liberator** .............. **£50-75** | | E80 79-80 **'MARVEL COMICS' Van**.... **£20-30** | |       Fire Engine ....................... **£15-20** | |
| E45 77-81 **Starsky & Hutch Ford Torino** **£15-20** | | E82-2 81-82 **Yogi Bear's Jeep** .................. **£20-30** | | 120 ? **Leyland Van, 'Eiszeit'**............ **£15-20** | |
| E49-2 81-83 **Woody Woodpecker's Car** .. **£15-20** | | E84-2 80-83 **Bugs Bunny Vehicle** ............. **£15-20** | | 120 83 **Ice Cream Van,** | |
| E50 79-80 **'Daily Planet' (Leyland) Van,** | | 99 79-81 **Jokermobile** ......................... **£30-40** | |       'FRESHLICHE'................. **£15-20** | |
|        Red or Silver........................ **£15-20** | | 100 81-83 **Hulk Cycle** ........................... **£30-40** | | 121 83 **Chevrolet Van,** | |
| E52-2 82-83 **Scooby Doo's Vehicle** ........... **£20-25** | | E115 81-83 **James Bond 2cv Citroën** ....... **£40-50** | |       'TECHNISCHER' .............. **£15-20** | |
| E56 79-80 **Chevrolet 'SPIDERVAN'** ....... **£20-25** | | 128 82-83 **Fred's Flyer** ......................... **£25-35** | | 126 82-83 **Ford Transit Breakdown,** | |
| E57-2 79-80 **Spiderbike** ........................... **£20-25** | | 131 82-83 **Ferrari 308, 'Magnum PI'** .... **£25-35** | |       'ABSCHIEPPDIENST' ........ **£15-20** | |
| E59-1 80-83 **Tom's Cart** ........................... **£15-20** | | | | 127 82-83 **'ADAC' Car** .......................... **£20-25** | |

## Corgi Juniors Sets

| | | |
|---|---|---|
| 2601 **Batman Triple-Pack** ..................... **£150-200** | E3030 **James Bond 'The Spy Who Loved Me'** | E3100 **Construction Gift Set** (7 items)...... **£75-100** |
| E2001 **Multi Garage Complex.** 4-garages.. **£30-35** |     **Gift Set**, 76-77. (E3, E60, | E3101 **Fire Gift Set** (6 items) .................... **£75-100** |
| E3001 **Multi Garage and three cars** .......... **£45-55** |     'Jaws' Van, Mercedes, Speedboat). **£250-350** | E3103 **Emergency Gift Set** (6 items)........ **£75-100** |
| E3005 **Leisure Time Set** .......................... **£100-125** | E3040 **Superman 'Metropolis' Set**............ **£75-100** | E3105 **Transporter Gift Set** |
| E3009 **Service Station and three cars**....... **£80-100** | E3071 **'Growlers' Speed Set.** Ford GT70, |     (Mercedes Transporter + 4 cars) ..... **£75-100** |
| E3013 **Emergency Rescue Set** |     Ferrari 312s, Marcos XP, CanAm, | 3107 **'Sports Cars'.** Five pieces in set....... **£30-40** |
|     Rescue Station + 3 models ................ **£70-85** |     Jaguar 'E'-type, Porsche 917 ......... **£100-150** | E3108 **'Scoobie & His Friends' Set**, |
| E3109 **Agricultural Set.** 2 Tractors, | E3080 **Batman Gift Set**, 1980-82 |     5 items ............................................ **£75-100** |
|     Land-Rover, 3 Trailers, 2 Huts..........**£90-110** |     (E20, E23, E69, E78, E99)........... **£300-400** | E3114 **'Superheroes' Gift Set** |
| 3019/1 **James Bond 'Octopussy' Set**, | E3081 **Superman Gift Set** |     (Batman / Superman vehicles) ...... **£100-125** |
|     1983-84 ........................................ **£100-125** |     (E6, E11, E17, E47, E50) ............. **£125-150** | E3116 **'Crimefighters' Gift Set** |
| E3021 **Crimefighters Gift Set** | E3082 **James Bond 'Goldfinger' Gift Set**, |     (Starsky & Hutch, James Bond |
|     (E45, E60, E68, E69, E75, E78) .... **£400-600** |     1980-82, (E40, E41, E60, E73, |     and Buck Rogers vehicles)............ **£125-150** |
| E3023 **Mercedes Transporter** plus 4 cars. **£75-100** |     + 'Jaws' van) ................................ **£400-500** | E3184 **'Data Post' Set** Contains 6 items...... **£40-50** |
| E3024 **Construction Gift Set** (6 vehicles) . **£75-100** | E3084 **Cartoon Characters Set** | |
| E3026 **Emergency Gift Set** (6 vehicles) .... **£75-100** |     (E19, E38, E58, E67, E79)........... **£100-125** | |

**FORD D SERIES TRUCK (1970-75)**

| | | |
|---|---|---|
| 2002 | Car Transporter, White cab, Blue lower, Red deck | £20-25 |
| | Red cab, White deck | £40-50 |
| 2003 | Low Loader, Blue | £20-25 |
| 2004 | 'CORGI' Removals Van, Red cab | £40-50 |
| | Light Blue cab | £40-50 |
| 2007 | Low Loader, Red cab, Blue trailer with Orange Junior digger load | £25-35 |
| 2012 | Military Low Loader + US vehicle | NGPP |

**FORD D SERIES SETS (1970-76)**

| | | |
|---|---|---|
| 3003 | Car Transporter Set, White or Red cab, 5 Juniors | £40-50 |
| 3011 | Low Loader Set, Red cab, 6 Juniors | £50-60 |
| 3024 | Low Loader Set, Blue cab, Yellow trailer (1976), 6 Juniors | £50-60 |
| 3025 | Car Transporter Set, Yellow cab, Orange deck (1976), 5 Juniors | £30-35 |

**MACK TRUCKS (issued 1971-75)**

| | | |
|---|---|---|
| 2006 | 'ESSO' Tanker, White | £10-15 |
| 2010 | 'EXXON' Tanker, White | £20-25 |
| 2011 | 'US' Army Tanker, Military Green | £20-25 |
| 2027 | 'RYDER RENTALS', Yellow cab + box trailer | £10-15 |

**MERCEDES TRACTOR UNITS, CAR TRANSPORTER (issued 1976)**

| | | |
|---|---|---|
| 2014/15 | White cab and deck, Blue chassis | £20-25 |
| 2015 | White cab, Yellow deck, Red chassis | £20-25 |
| NB. | Transporter Sets 3023, 3015, 3105 | £30-35 |

**MERCEDES TANKERS (1983-84)**

| | | |
|---|---|---|
| 1130 | 'CORGI CHEMCO', Red or White | £10-15 |
| 1130 | 'SHELL' Yellow or White cab | £10-15 |
| 1166 | 'GUINNESS' | £10-15 |
| 1167 | 'DUCKHAMS' | £10-15 |
| 1167 | '7 UP' | £20-30 |

**MERCEDES BOX TRAILERS (1978-85)**

| | | |
|---|---|---|
| 1111 | 'SAFEWAY' | £15-20 |
| 1129 | 'ASG SPEDITION' | £10-15 |
| 1129 | 'CORGI' Black or White cab | £10-15 |
| 1131 | 'CHRISTIAN SALVESON' | £10-15 |
| 1137 | 'SOUKS SUPERMARKET' (Saudi issue) | £25-30 |
| 1139 | 'HALLS FOOD' | £10-15 |
| 1144 | 'ROYAL MAIL PARCELS' | £10-15 |
| 1145 | 'YORKIE' | £10-15 |
| 1146 | 'DUNLOP' | £10-15 |

| | | |
|---|---|---|
| 1166 | 'ARIA DAIRY' | £10-15 |
| 1175 | 'INTERNATIONAL' | £60-70 |
| 1175 | 'TI RALEIGH' | £10-15 |
| 1176 | 'ZANUSSI' | £10-15 |
| 1177 | 'WEETABIX' | £10-15 |
| 1178 | 'MAYNARDS' | £10-15 |
| 1202 | 'PICKFORDS HOMESPEED' | £60-70 |
| 2028 | 'GERVALS DANONE' | £10-15 |
| 2020 | 'BIRDS EYE' | £10-15 |
| --- | 'B. H. S.' | £20-30 |
| --- | 'CARTERS Lemonade' | £25-35 |

**MERCEDES SETS**

| | | |
|---|---|---|
| 1200 | 'DUCKHAMS' & 'GUINNESS' Tanker plus 3 Scammells | £40-50 |
| 1403 | 'CORGI CHEMCO', plus Junior Van | £25-30 |
| 3128 | 'DUCKHAMS' & 'YORKIE', plus 10 Juniors | £40-50 |

**RECOMMENDED READING**
'CORGI SUPER JUNIOR and SUPERHAULER GUIDE'. Full details plus pictures compiled by Andy and Pat Browning, 3 Waterside Terrace, Ninn Lane, Great Chart, Ashford, Kent, TN23 3DD.

# Corgi Rockets

This model range was issued between 1970 and 1972 to compete against Mattel 'Hot Wheels' and similar products. The models had 'WhizzWheels' and featured a special 'Tune-Up' system which increased the play value and speed of the virtually frictionless wheels. They were very robust, being advertised as 'four times stronger' than most other diecast racers. To begin with, seven Corgi Juniors were adapted as Rockets and five of those received a vacuum metallised finish. A range of accessories was also issued in the form of 'Speed Circuits' etc, and each car was provided with a special 'Golden Tune-Up Key' which released the base. The bubble-packed models are difficult to find in top condition and prices reflect their scarcity.

| | | | |
|---|---|---|---|
| D 901 | 1970-72 | **Aston-Martin DB-6** Met. Deep Gold, Green interior | £60-70 |
| D 902 | 1970-72 | **Jaguar XJ-6** Metallic Green, Cream interior | £80-90 |
| D 903 | 1970-72 | **Mercedes-Benz 280 SL** Met. Orange body, White interior | £60-70 |
| D 904 | 1970-72 | **Porsche Carrera 6** Orange-Yellow body, Black '19' | £60-70 |
| D 905 | 1970-72 | **'The Saint's Volvo P1800** White body, Blue/White 'Saint' label on bonnet | £80-90 |
| D 906 | 1970-72 | **Jensen Interceptor** Metallic Red, Yellow interior | £60-70 |
| | | Pink / Cream body | £80-90 |
| D 907 | 1970-72 | **Cadillac Eldorado** Metallic Copper, White interior | £60-70 |
| D 908 | 1970-72 | **Chevrolet Astro** Metallic Red/Black body | £40-50 |
| D 909 | 1970-72 | **Mercedes-Benz C111** Red or Blue, White interior | £40-50 |
| D 910 | 1970-72 | **Beach Buggy** Orange body, Black interior | £30-40 |
| D 911 | 1970-72 | **Marcos XP** Gold body, Chrome interior | £30-40 |
| ? | 1970-72 | **Ford Capri** Purple body | £40-50 |
| D 913 | 1970-72 | **Aston-Martin DBS** Metallic Blue, Yellow interior | £70-90 |
| D 916 | 1970-72 | **Carabo Bertone** Met. Green/Blue, Orange interior | £20-30 |
| D 917 | 1970-72 | **Pininfarina Alfa-Romeo** Metallic Purple/White | £20-30 |
| D 918 | 1970-72 | **Bitzzarini Manta** Metallic Dark Blue, White interior | £20-30 |

| | | | |
|---|---|---|---|
| D 919 | 1970-72 | **'Todd Sweeney' Stock Car** Red/Purple/Yellow/Black, '531' | £75-100 |
| D 920 | 1970-72 | **'Derek Fiske' Stock Car** White/Red, Silver bonnet, Red logo, RN '304' | £75-100 |
| D 921 | 1970-72 | **Morgan Open Sports** Metallic Red body, Black seats | £60-75 |
| D 922 | 1970-72 | **Rally Ford Capri** Yellow, Orange/Black stripe, '8' | £75-100 |
| | | Green, Black bonnet, (GS 2 model) | £60-75 |
| D 923 | 1970-72 | **'James Bond' Ford Escort** White, Pale Blue stripes, '7', 'JAMES BOND', White '007' and 'SPECIAL AGENT' logos (from film 'On Her Majesty's Secret Service') | £500-700 |
| D 924 | 1970-72 | **Mercury Cougar XR7** Red body, Black roof, Yellow int. | £30-40 |
| D 924 | | **'James Bond'** issue: Red/Black with Yellow side flash, interior and skis on roof rack (from film 'On Her Majesty's Secret Service') | £500-700 |
| D 925 | 1970-72 | **'James Bond' Ford Capri** White body, Black/White check design, 2 bonnet stripes, RN '6', (film 'On Her Majesty's Secret Service') | £500-700 |
| D 926 | 1970-72 | **Jaguar 'Control Car'** Metallic Brown body, Red roof blade, Blue/White figures | £200-250 |
| D 927 | 1970-72 | **Ford Escort Rally** White, Red '18', 'DAILY MIRROR' labels on doors, '1970 Mexico World Cup Rally Winner' | £300-400 |
| D 928 | 1970-72 | **Mercedes 280 SL 'SPECTRE'** Black body with Red 'SPECTRE' logo, plus boar's head design | £250-300 |

| | | | |
|---|---|---|---|
| D 930 | 1970-72 | **Bertone Barchetta** Met. Green over White, Red int. | £40-50 |
| D 931 | 1970-72 | **'Old MacDonald's Truck'** Yellow cab, Brown rear | £75-100 |
| D 933 | 1970-72 | **'Holmes Wrecker'** White or Blue cab, White back, 'AUTO RESCUE' | £125-150 |
| D 937 | 1970-72 | **Mercury Cougar** Met. Dark Green body, Yellow int. | £20-30 |

## Rockets Gift Sets

| | | | |
|---|---|---|---|
| D 975 | 1970 | **Super Stock Gift Set 1,** D 905, D 919, Trailer, 3 figures | £250-350 |
| D 976 | 1970 | **Super Stock Gift Set 2,** D 922, D 920, Trailer, 3 figures | £250-350 |
| D 977 | 1970 | **Super Stock Gift Set 3,** D 926, D 919, D 920, 5 figures | £300-400 |
| D 978 | | **'OHMSS' Gift Set,** Models of cars in the James Bond film 'On Her Majesty's Secret Service': D 923 and D 925 (as driven in the ice-racing scene), D 924 (as driven by 'Tracey'), D 928 (as driven by the Chief of 'SPECTRE') | £5,000-6,000 |
| | | **NB** Male skier has red metal base, red/yellow skis, yellow poles. | |

## Rockets Catalogues

| | | |
|---|---|---|
| 1969 | **8-page booklet**, listing the first 7 issues, Green model on cover | £20-25 |
| 1970 | **16-page booklet**, most issues, good pictures of rare models, sets, etc. | £30-35 |

## Rockets accessories (Introduced in 1970. All NGPP)

| | | | | | |
|---|---|---|---|---|---|
| D 2051 | **Action Speedset**, One car, 'Autostart', 12 ft of track | | | D 1938 | **Super Crossover** |
| D 2052 | **Super Autobatics Speedset,** One car, 'Autostart', 16 ft of track plus 'leaps' etc | 2 cars, 'Autostart', 32' of track plus 'leaps' etc | D 2071 | D 1945 | **Adaptors** (3) |
| D 2053 | **Clover Leaf Special Speedset,** A car, 'Autostart', track, 'clover-leaf leaps' etc | **Jetspeed Circuit,** One car, 'Superbooster', 16 ft of track + 'leaps' etc | D 2074 | D 1963 | **Track** (16ft) |
| D 2058 | **Race-Abatic Speedset,** | **Triple-Leap Speed Circuit,** One car, 19 ft, 6 in of track | D 2075 | D 1970 | **Super Booster** |
| | | **Grand Canyon Circuit,** One car, 12 ft of track | D 2079 | D 1971 | **Hairpin Tunnel** |
| | | **World Champion Speedset,** Two cars, 2 x 16 ft of track, two Boosters | D 1928 | D 1976 | **Quickfire Start** |
| | | **Rocketlube Tune-up Kit** | D 1931 | D 1977 | **Lap Counter** |
| | | **Superleap** | D 1934 | D 1978 | **Pitstop** |
| | | **Autofinish** | D 1935 | D 1979 | **Spacehanger Bend** |
| | | **Connections** (3) | D 1936 | | |
| | | **Space Leap** | D 1937 | | |
| | | **Autostart** | | | |

# Catalogues (UK Editions)

Information taken from the Cecil Gibson Archives and this Catalogue compiler's own collection of reference material. Note: 'Concertina' leaflets were issued with models sold in the early Blue boxes.

| Year | Publication details | MPR |
|---|---|---|

**1956** **Concertina leaflet** No ref. Blue cover, famous Corgi dog, shows first 14 models, no prices ................... **£25-30**

**1956** **Concertina leaflet** No ref. Blue cover with Red/Gold Corgi dog. Depicts first 14 models; shows prices of both normal and mechanical models ...................... **£25-30**

**1957** **Concertina leaflet 50/157/K1**. Blue cover with Red/Gold Corgi dog. Depicts ten models and lists mechanical models in red ..... **£25-30**

**1957** **Concertina leaflet 40/257/K1**. As previous item, but no mechanical models ...... **£25-30**

**1957** **Concertina leaflet 40/257/K2**. As previous leaflet but with the addition of 208 ..... **£25-30**

**1957** **Concertina leaflet 50/557/K3**. As 40/257/K2 plus 100,150, 408, 454, 'WOW! CORGI TOYS' logo .............. **£25-30**

**1957** **Catalogue Leaflet 20/657/C2**. Unfolded size (11" x 8 3/4"). Cover shows 1st type blue box for 208 Jaguar ........ **£25-30**

**1957** **Concertina leaflet 100/1057/K3**. Blue cover showing 100, 150, 207, 208, 302, 405, 408, 453, 455 ................. **£25-30**

**1957** **Concertina leaflet 50/1057/K4**. Blue cover, 'WOW! CORGI TOYS' logo. First 'MAJOR' toy (1101) within ....... **£25-30**

**1957** **Concertina leaflet 50/1157/K4**. Cover shows 102, 210, 406, 407, 412, 1101, 'WOW! CORGI TOYS' logo ..... **£25-30**

**1957** **Four-fold leaflet 25/257/C1/UK**. 'Blue box' 208 Jaguar on cover, 15 model pictures inside ..................... **£25-35**

**1957** **Four-fold leaflet 25/257/C2/UK**. As previous item but 24 model pictures.. **£25-35**

**1957** **Four-fold leaflet 50/1057/C3/UK**. Shows GS 1 Bedford Transporter and six cars on Blue/Yellow cover ........ **£25-35**

**1957** **Four-fold leaflet 25/1157/C4/UK**. As previous leaflet plus 101 and 102.. **£25-35**

**1958** **Catalogue Leaflet 15/158/C4**. Unfolded size (1' x 11"). 1101 Transporter on cover. **£20-25**

**1958** **Catalogue Leaflet 10/258/C5**. Unfolded size (1' x 11"). 1101 Transporter on cover. **£20-25**

**1958** **Catalogue Leaflet 40/258/C5**. Same . **£20-25**

**1958** **Concertina leaflet 52/258/K5**. Cover shows GS 1 and 2, 101, 211, 302, 457, 459, 1100, 1401, 1450........ **£20-25**

**1958** **Box Insert 52/258/K5**. 1401 Corgi Service Ramp on cover .... **£15-20**

**1958** **Concertina leaflet 52/258/K6**. 350 'Thunderbird' Missile on cover. .... **£15-20**

**1958** **Concertina leaflet 52/258/K6**. Cover has GS 1 and 2, 101, 211, 302, 457, 459, 1100, 1401, 1450, + 350, 351 ...... **£20-25**

**1958** **Concertina leaflet 300/658/K7**. Shows GS 3, 151, 209, 458, 'NEW CORGI TOYS' logo + prices .. **£20-25**

**1958** **Box Insert 3.350/658/K7**. 1401 Corgi Service Ramp on cover .... **£15-20**

**1958** **Four-fold leaflet** No ref. Shows GS 1 Bedford Transporter and 6 cars on Blue/Yellow cover, plus 211. No prices or car listing ....................... **£25-35**

**1958** **Box Insert 5/658/K7**. 458 E.R.F. Truck and 209 Police Car on cover ...... **£15-20**

**1958** **Catalogue 650/858/C8**. First 'book' catalogue. Cover depicts boy playing with Bloodhound Missile + other vehicles . **£40-50**

**1958** **Box Insert 10/658/K7**. 458 E.R.F. Truck and 209 Police Car on cover ............. **£15-20**

**1958** **16 page Catalogue 40/1058/C8**. Boy and large collection on cover ...... **£20-25**

**1958** **Box Insert 120/1058/K8**. 458 E.R.F Truck and 209 Police Car on cover..... **£15-20**

**1959** **Four-fold leaflet** No ref. Blue cover with 'THE ROCKET AGE WITH CORGI TOYS' (issued with Rocket Age models) ....... **£20-30**

**1959** **Interim leaflet** No ref. September 1959. Lists 152, 50 Tractor, 350 Thunderbird, new Ford TT van and accessories ....... **£20-30**

**1959** **16 page Catalogue UK 9/59**. M-F Tractor No. 50 and BRM No. 152 on cover. Farming + 'MAJOR' issues...... **£35-45**

**1959** **20 page Catalogue** No ref. Racing Car and Tractor design on cover ...... **£30-35**

**1959** **Single page leaflet** No ref. Features Renault Floride plus 'STRAIGHT FROM THE MOTOR SHOW' logo. .......... **£20-30**

**1959** **Two fold leaflet** No ref. 'AUTHENTIC ROCKET AGE MODELS' models..... **£20-30**

**1960** **Interim leaflet** No ref. Depicts M1 Motorway scene .............. **£20-30**

**1960** **20 page Catalogue** No reference number, otherwise as next item........... **£25-35**

**1960** **20 page Catalogue UK 9/60**. Cover has motorway bridge scene and Corgi models. First 'CHIPPERFIELDS' issues.......... **£30-40**

**1960** **Interim Leaflet** No ref. 1119 Hovercraft, etc. on cover ........... **£20-25**

**1961** **24 page Catalogue** No reference number, otherwise as next item............ **£30-40**

**1961** **24 page Catalogue UK 9/61**. Racetrack scene on cover. Listings/pictures include new Sports Cars, Express Coach and Kits.. **£30-40**

**1961** **Price List** No ref. Single double-sided sheet (size as catalogue), 'Revised price list as from August 1961'. 'UK' on back ......... **£1-2**

**1961** **Interim leaflet** No ref. 231 Triumph Herald, etc. on cover ..... **£20-25**

**1962** **Two-fold Checklist** No ref. Front depicts Blue/Yellow 'CORGI TOYS' + 7 models. Red/Grey interior plus first check list. **£20-30**

**1962** **Interim leaflet** No ref. 224 Bentley plus 304s Mercedes on cover ............. **£20-25**

**1963** **32 page Catalogue C/100/62**. Cover depicts schoolboy (in red cap and blazer) crossing road with Corgi dog. No date shown .. **£40-50**

**1963** **32 page Catalogue** No ref. Same cover as C/100/62 but boy's cap and blazer are Blue. '1963-64' shown on cover ........ **£30-40**

**1963** **40 page Catalogue** As previous item, but expanded to 40 pages......... **£30-40**

**1964** **Interim Leaflet - Playcraft Toys Ltd 1964**. 251 Hillman Imp, etc. on cover ............NGPP

**1964** **40 page Catalogue - Playcraft Toys Ltd 1964**. '1965', 'CORGI TOYS', 'CORGI CLASSICS'. First Routemaster listed **£25-35**

**1964** **Two-fold Checklist - Playcraft Toys Ltd 1964**. Leaflet featuring 241 Ghia ..... **£25-35**

**1965** **Interim Leaflet - Playcraft Toys Ltd 1965**. 155 Lotus Climax Racing Car, etc. ..... **£20-25**

**1965** **40 page Catalogue** No reference number or text, otherwise as next item ............ **£25-35**

**1965** **40 page Catalogue - Playcraft Toys Ltd 1965**. 261 JB's Aston Martin DB5 on cover. Rallye Monte Carlo issues. 'Price 3d'. **£25-35**

**1965** **Two-fold Checklist - Mettoy Playcraft (Sales) Ltd 1965**. Leaflet with 6 model cars from 6 nations on cover. ............ **£20-25**

**1966** **48 page Catalogue C2017/9/66**. Features 'BATMAN' and 'THE AVENGERS' etc. Includes price list. 190 x 78mm., '4d'. **£25-35**

**1966** **Leaflet C2038/66**. 'MODEL CAR MAKERS TO JAMES BOND'.......... **£20-25**

**1966** **Four-fold Checklist C2039/4/66**. Leaflet similar to previous with 'MODEL CAR MAKERS TO JAMES BOND'. 1127 Simon Snorkel featured............. **£20-25**

**1967** **Three-fold Checklist - Mettoy Playcraft (Sales) 1967**. Front shows 'NEW' in five languages + 1142 Holmes Wrecker .... **£20-25**

**1967** **48 page Catalogue C/2017/7/67**. Lincoln Continental (262 ) on both covers. 'Price 6d'. Unissued 9022 Daimler and 9014 'Lyons Tea' shown .................... **£30-35**

**1967** **Interim Leaflet** No ref. 1142 'Holmes' Wrecker on cover ....... **£20-25**

**1968** **48 page Catalogue C2017/9/68**. Cover has 268 'Chitty Chitty Bang Bang'. 'Take-off Wheels' issues listed............................ **£30-35**

**1969** **Seven-fold Checklist - Mettoy Playcraft (Sales) Ltd 1969**. Unfolds to 2'6" x 8 3/4". 'Concorde' model on cover + 302 Hillman Hunter. Listings include 'Corgi Comics', 'CHIPPERFIELDS' and Set No.48..... **£30-35**

**1970** **48 page Catalogue - The Mettoy Co Ltd 1970**. 388 Mercedes-Benz C111 on cover, first 'WhizzWheels' models listed ...... **£30-35**

**1971** **Two-fold Checklist - 1970 Mettoy Co Ltd**. 6 WhizzWheels models on the cover. The final 'Take-Off Wheels' issues listed .. **£15-20**

**1972** **48 page Catalogue C2017 Petty 7/71/LOI7b**. Cover shows 1972 Car models. 'CORGI COMICS' inside ..... **£20-25**

**1972** **48 page Catalogue C2017 Petty 7/71/LOI7B (2nd)**. Cars across both covers ..................... **£20-25**

**1972** **4-page Brochure (A4)** No ref. 'Corgi Juniors with WhizzWheels' 'Juniors Extra' section of TV models. **£10-15**

**1973** **40 page Catalogue 1973 Mettoy Co Ltd**. F1 Racing Cars featured on the cover. **£10-15**

**1974** **40 page Catalogue C2107**. 'Corgi '74' on cover ...................... **£10-15**

**1974** **40 page Catalogue C2111**. Same....... **£10-15**

**1974** **40 page Catalogue 1974 Mettoy Co Ltd**. 'John Player' Lotus on cover ............. **£10-15**

**1975** **Catalogue Leaflet** No ref. Unfolded size 2' x 8½'. 'Corgi 75' on cover ........ **£10-15**

**1975** **Three-fold leaflet - 1975 Mettoy Co Ltd**. Helicopters, Noddy's Car, etc on the cover. Numbers given 'C' prefix........... **£10-15**

**1976** **Three-fold leaflet - 1976 Mettoy Co Ltd**. 'KOJAK' on first page. Roadmaking and Public Services listings................. **£10-15**

**1977** **48 page Catalogue C2210**. Silver Jubilee Coach on cover. Large section listing Corgi 'Juniors'... **£10-15**

**1977** **48 page Catalogue C2211**. 'Corgi 77' on cover ...................... **£10-15**

**1977** **32 page Catalogue C2222**. 'Corgi 77' on cover ...................... **£10-15**

**1978** **48 page Catalogue The Mettoy Co Ltd**. James Bond's Lotus on cover, 'JEAN RICHARD PINDER' models within .. **£10-15**

**1979** **48 page Catalogue C2250**. James Bond's Space Shuttle on the cover. 'SUPERMAN' and 'THE MUPPETS' listed inside .... **£10-15**

**1980** **48 page Catalogue C2270**. C339 Rover 'Police' and C1001 HCB ANGUS on cover. Foreign 'POLICE' issues listed........... **£10-15**

**1980** **48 page Catalogue C2275**. 'RESCUE' Vehicle plus '1980/81' on cover......... **£10-15**

**1980** **32 page Catalogue C2282**. As previous, but no Juniors included.. **£10-15**

**1980** **32 page Catalogue C2283**. Same ...... **£10-15**

**1981** **32 page Catalogue C2285**. 'CORGI' container on cover ............... **£10-15**

**1981** **32 page Catalogue C2290**. Same. **£10-15**

**1981** **32 page Catalogue C2292**. Same ...... **£10-15**

**1982** **32 page Catalogue C2337**. C802 Mercedes on cover, 'Corgitronics' within .......... **£10-15**

**1983** **36 page Catalogue - Mettoy Co PLC**. Boxed models on cover, new Mercedes and Scania trucks inside..................... **£10-15**

**1984** **32 page Catalogue** No ref. 'CORGI '84' and boxed models on cover. The last catalogue with the Corgi Dog emblem . **£5-10**

**1985** **48 page Catalogue** No ref. Cover shows new 'CORGI' trade name logo. The new 'CLASSICS' Commercials listed.......... **£5-10**

## Trade Catalogues

Catalogues for trade purposes have been produced for some years and occasionally are offered for sale to collectors. No information is available on catalogues issued before 1980 but those from the 1980-90 decade tend to be in the **£5** to **£15** range.

## Newsletters and Club Magazines

Mettoy Corgi Newsletters.................................................................................................**£5-6**
Corgi Club Magazines   1950s ...............................................................................**£20-25**
                        1960s ...............................................................................**£15-18**

# Catalogues, Leaflets and Box Inserts  (Overseas Editions)

## IDENTIFICATION of OVERSEAS CATALOGUES

The overseas editions are comprised of specially amended U.K. editions and there are many versions. They may be identified by:

- All the text being in the relevant language.
- A special reference number (but not always), e.g. 52/258/K5 AUSTRALIA.
- An adapted checklist/pricelist in the language/currency of the country concerned.
- The name of the country either on the cover, on page two, or on the checklist.
- Some complete catalogues were issued with all the text being in the language concerned, e.g. French, German, etc.
- Normally overseas editions, unlike U.K. editions, do not display the catalogue price on the cover. The exception to this rule being those issued with all the text in the language concerned.

As stated above, the overseas editions are basically the same as the U.K. editions. Similarly the catalogues, leaflets and box inserts issued in any one particular year were the same for all overseas countries. The only differences being the reference numbers, the type of language and currency shown. The following listing of overseas editions correspond with the country by country listings and will assist collectors identify the various editions. The reference codes shown, e.g. '52/258/K5' are common to all countries with a country reference being added as required, e.g. '52/258/K5 EAST AFRICA'. The '258' part refers to the month and year of issue, i.e. Feb. 1958.

## TYPES of CATALOGUES LISTED

**Box Inserts** - These were inserted in the early blue box issues circa 1957-1959. They have a single fold and contain a checklist with prices in the local currency, plus a few pictures of the latest models.
**Catalogue Leaflets** - These are large, full colour leaflets, usually listing the full range available, together with pictures plus a checklist with prices.
**Catalogues** - These may contain 16, 20, 32, 40 or 48 pages and are full colour booklets containing the complete current range.
**Interim Leaflets** - Usually a double folded leaflet issued to supplement the main catalogues. These contain six pages, plus a checklist of the latest issues.

The information contained in these listings has been obtained from Corgi archive material. Whilst many issues have been listed, we believe others exist and we would welcome any such information.

Overseas catalogues were produced in much smaller numbers than were the U.K. editions. Consequently as they seldom appear for sale, it is not possible to give their individual market prices. For guidance purposes however, some have been known to sell for prices in excess of **£100**. As a result the extremely rare issues such as British East Africa, West Africa, Malta, Hong Kong, etc. may be expected to attract a premium.

## African issues

**English text - local currency**

**BRITISH EAST AFRICA**
1959 **16 page Catalogue '8/59'.**
'British East Africa 8/59' on cover,
along with a tractor and racing car ...... **£70-80**
1960 **20 page Catalogue '9/60'.**
'British East Africa 9/60' on cover ..... **£50-60**
62/63 **Interim Leaflet** (no ref.).
'British East Africa' on checklist ......... **£25-35**
61/62 **Interim Leaflet** (no ref.).
'British East Africa' on top of page 2 .. **£25-35**

**EAST AFRICA**
1958 **Box Insert '52/258/K5 East Africa'.**
'East Africa' on checklist ..................... **£25-35**
1965 **Interim Leaflet** (no ref.). 'East Africa'
plus 'Mettoy 1965' on checklist........... **£20-25**
64/65 **40 page Catalogue** (no ref.).
'East Africa 8/64' on checklist............. **£35-45**

**KENYA, UGANDA & TANGANYIKA**
1958 **Catalogue Leaflet '15/158/C3 KUT'.**
'Kenya, Uganda and Tanganyika'........ **£30-35**
1958 **Box Insert**
**'3.350/658/K7/KEN.-UG.-TAN'** ...... **£30-35**

**RHODESIA**
**Early Distributors**: Coombe & Dewar Pty Ltd.
P.O. Box 1572, Bulawayo and P.O. Box 663,
Salisbury.
61/62 **Interim Leaflet** (no ref.).
'Rhodesia' top of page two ................. **£25-35**
62/3 **Interim Leaflet** (no ref.).
'Rhodesia' on checklist ........................ **£25-35**
1962 **32 page Catalogue 'C/100/62'.**
'Rhodesia 1/63' on checklist.
Red suited boy on cover...................... **£50-60**
1964 **Interim Leaflet** (no ref.). 'Rhodesia'
plus 'Playcraft 1964' on checklist........ **£20-30**
1965 **Interim Leaflet** (no ref.). 'Rhodesia' +
'Mettoy 1965' on checklist ................. **£20-30**

**RHODESIA, ZAMBIA & MALAWI**
65/66 **40 page Catalogue** (no ref.).
'Rhodesia/Zambia/Malawi 8/65' on
checklist, + '1965' on cover................ **£50-60**

**SOUTH AFRICA & RHODESIA**
1958 **Box Insert '52/258/K5 South**
**Africa/Rhodesia'** on checklist............ **£25-35**
1958 **Box Insert '52/258/K6**
**South Africa/Rhodesia'.**
'South Africa/Rhodesia' on checklist... **£25-35**

**SOUTH AFRICA**
1958 **Box Insert '10/658/K7/S. Africa'.**
'S. Africa' on checklist page ............... **£25-35**
58/59 **16 page Catalogue '40/1058/C8/S. Africa'.**
'S. Africa' on back .............................. **£50-60**
61/62 **Interim Leaflet** (no ref.).
'South Africa' on page two ................. **£25-35**
62/63 **Interim Leaflet** (no ref.).
'South Africa' on checklist................... **£25-35**
1964 **Interim Leaflet** (no ref.). 'S. Africa' and
'Playcraft Toys Ltd. 1964' checklist .... **£25-35**
1965 **Interim Leaflet** (no ref.). 'South Africa'
plus 'Mettoy 1965' on checklist........... **£25-35**
1966 **48 page Catalogue 'C/2017/9/66'.**
'South Africa' on checklist and cover.. **£30-40**
1967 **Interim Leaflet** (no ref.). 'South Africa'
on cover, plus 'Mettoy, etc. 1967' on
last page................................................ **£25-35**
1971 **2-fold checklist '© 1970 Mettoy Co Ltd'.**
'Corgi Toys with WhizzWheels' plus
'Australia', 'S.Africa' and 'USA' on cover.
Checklist prices in all 3 currencies ...... **£15-20**

**NB** As listed under CANADA, a catalogue was issued in 1970 with a combined CANADA and SOUTH AFRICAN checklist.

## Australia

**Address of Corgi Club in 1959**: The Secretary, Corgi Model Club (Australian Section), P.O. Box 1607, M. Melbourne C1.

1957 **Catalogue Leaflet '20/657/C2/AUS'.**
Checklist dated 1.6.57. Cover shows
early 'Blue Box' with model 208......... **£25-35**
1958 **Box Insert '52/258/K5/Australia'.**
Cover shows model 350....................... **£25-35**
1958 **Box Insert '52/258/K6/Australia'.**
1401 Service Ramp on cover .............. **£25-35**
1958 **Box Insert '10/658/K7/Aus'.**
Cover shows models 209 & 458.......... **£25-35**
1959 **16 page Catalogue** (no ref.).
'Australia 8/59' on cover .................... **£70-80**
61/62 **Leaflet** (no ref.).
'Australia' on top of page two ............. **£25-35**
62/63 **Leaflet** (no ref.). 'Australia' checklist . **£25-35**
1967 **Leaflet** (no ref.). 'Australia' on cover . **£20-25**
1971 **2-fold Checklist '© 1970 Mettoy Co Ltd'.**
'Corgi Toys with WhizzWheels' plus
'Australia', 'S.Africa' and 'USA' on cover.
Checklist prices in all 3 currencies ...... **£10-15**

## Austria

**German Text. 'Kontrolliste fur den sammler'**
1957 **Leaflet '20/657/C2/A'.**
'Austria' on checklist ........................... **£30-35**
61/62 **Interim Leaflet** (no ref.).
'Austria' on top of page two ............... **£20-25**
1964 **Interim Leaflet** (no ref.).
'Austria' on checklist ........................... **£20-25**
64/65 **40 page Catalogue** (no ref.).
'Austria 9/64' on checklist.................. **£35-45**
1965 **Interim Leaflet** (no ref.).
'Austria' on checklist ........................... **£20-25**

## Belgium

**Early distribution**:
Joets Eisenmann, S.A.,
111/113 Rui Masui, Bruxelles, Teleph: (02)
15.48.50.
**1958 Belgian Corgi Club**:
M. Le Secretaire du Club Corgi,
Jouets Eisenmann,
20 BD M. Lemonnier, Bruxelles.

**English Text - French Checklist:**

'Liste de Contrôlle pour le Collectionneur'
1958 **Box Insert '52/258/K6/Belgium'.**
'Belgium' on checklist .......................... **£30-35**
1958 **Box Insert '5/658/K7/Belg.'.**
'Belg' on checklist ............................... **£30-35**
1967 **Leaflet** (no ref.). 'Belgium' on cover .. **£20-25**

**English Text - Flemish Checklist:**

'Kontroleer zo de Verzameling'
1966 **48 page Catalogue 'C/2017/9/66'.**
'Belgium' on cover and on checklist ... **£35-45**
1967 **Leaflet** (no ref.).
'Belgium (Flemish)' on cover ............. **£20-25**

**English Text - separate French and Flemish checklists:**

61/62 **Interim Leaflet** (no ref.).
'Belgium' on top of page two ............. **£20-25**
62/63 **Interim Leaflet** (no ref.).
'Belgium' on checklist ........................ **£20-25**
63/64 **40 page Catalogue** (no ref.).
'Belgium 8/63' on checklist ................ **£40-50**
64 **Interim Leaflet** (no ref.). 'Belgium' and
'Playcraft 1964' on checklist .............. **£20-25**
65 **Interim Leaflet** (no ref.). 'Belgium'
and 'Mettoy 1965' on checklist .......... **£20-25**
1967 **Leaflet** (no ref.). 'Belgium' on cover .. **£20-25**
67/68 **48 page Catalogue 'C2017/7/67'.**
'Belgium (French) 1967' on checklist . **£35-45**
67/68 **48 page Catalogue 'C2017/7/67'.**
'Belgium 8/67' on Flemish checklist and
'Belgium (French) 8/67' on
French checklist ................................. **£35-45**
1974 **40 page Catalogue** (no ref.).
'C2103 Belgium' on Flemish checklist
plus '2107' on French checklist .......... **£15-25**

**English Text - French/Flemish combined checklist:**

1957 **Catalogue Leaflet '20/657/C2/B'.**
'Belgium' on checklist ........................ **£25-35**
1958 **Catalogue Leaflet '20/258/C5/B'.**
'Belgium' on checklist ........................ **£25-35**

**French Text - French checklist:**

1958 **Box Insert '120/1058/K8/Belg'.**
No. 458 E.R.F. on cover ...................... **£25-35**
1960 **20 page Catalogue** (no ref.).
'Belgium 9/60' and 'Frs.3.' on cover... **£40-50**
1961 **24 page Catalogue** (no ref.).
'Belgium 9/61' and 'Frs.3.' on cover... **£40-50**
65/66 **40 page Catalogue** (no ref.).
'Belgium 8/65' on checklist ................ **£30-40**

## Canada

**English text - local currency**
1958 **Catalogue Leaflet '40/258/C5/CA'.**
'Canada' on checklist .......................... **£30-35**
1958 **Box Insert '52/258/K5/Canada'.**
'Canada' on checklist .......................... **£30-35**
1958 **Box Insert '52/258/K6/Canada'.**
'Canada' on checklist .......................... **£30-35**
1958 **Box Insert '5/658/K7/CAN'.**
'CAN' on checklist .............................. **£30-35**
1960 **20 page Catalogue 'Canada 9/60'.**
'Canada 9/60' on cover ....................... **£40-50**
60/61 **Interim Leaflet 'Canada'.**
'Canada' on checklist .......................... **£30-35**
61/62 **24 page Catalogue 'Canada 9/61'.**
'Canada 9/61' on cover ....................... **£60-70**
61/62 **Interim Leaflet 'Canada'.**
'Canada' on checklist .......................... **£30-35**
1963 **32 page Catalogue 'C/100/62'.**
'Canada 1/63' on cover ....................... **£50-60**
1964 **Interim Leaflet 'Canada'.** 'Canada' and
'Playcraft Toys Ltd. 1964' checklist .... **£30-35**

1965 **Interim Leaflet 'Canada'.** 'Canada' and
'Mettoy etc. 1965' on checklist........... **£30-35**
64/65 **40 page Catalogue 'Canada 9/64'.**
'Canada 9/64' on checklist plus
'1965' on cover .................................. **£40-50**
65/66 **40 page Catalogue 'Canada 8/65'.**
'Canada 8/65' on checklist plus
'1966' on cover .................................. **£40-50**
1966 **48 page Catalogue 'C2017/9/60'.**
'Canada' on cover and checklist .......... **£40-50**
1967 **Interim Leaflet 'Canada'.** 'Canada' on
cover plus 'Mettoy 1967' on last page. **£25-35**
1969 **7-fold Leaflet 'Canada'.** Concorde
featured on cover; '8/69' on checklist . **£50-60**

**French Text Issue**
1966 **48 page Catalogue 'C/2017/9/66'.**
'Canadian (French)' on cover ............. **£50-60**
**Combined Canadian and South African checklist**
1970 **48 page Catalogue** (no ref.).
'Canada, South Africa' on checklist. 'The
Mettoy Co. Ltd. 1970' on rear cover ... **£50-60**

## Denmark

**All the text in Danish**
1960 **20 page Catalogue** (no ref.).
'Denmark 9/60' and '25 re' on cover... **£40-50**
1961/62 **24 page Catalogue** (no ref.).
'Denmark 9/61' and '25 re' on cover... **£40-50**
1977 **48 page Catalogue 'C2214'.**
'Katalog' and 'Corgi 77' on cover ...... **£10-15**

**English text - Danish checklist.**
'Samlerers Kontrolliste'
60/61 **Interim Leaflet** (no ref.). 'Denmark'.. **£20-25**
61/62 **Interim Leaflet** (no ref.).
'Denmark' on page two........................ **£20-25**
63/64 **40 page Catalogue** (no ref.). '1963-64' on
cover, 'Denmark 8/63' on checklist ..... **£50-60**
1964 **Interim Leaflet** (no ref.). 'Denmark'
and 'Playcraft 1964' on checklist......... **£20-25**
64/65 **40 page Catalogue** (no ref.). '1965' on
cover, 'Denmark 9/64' on checklist ..... **£40-50**
65/66 **40 page Catalogue** (no ref.). 'Denmark 8/65'
on checklist plus '1966' on cover ........ **£30-40**
1966 **48 page Catalogue 'C2017/9/66'.**
'Denmark' on cover and checklist ....... **£30-40**
1974 **40 page Catalogue 'C2105 1974'.**
Danish checklist, 'Corgi 74' on cover . **£10-15**
80/81 **48 page Catalogue 'C2271'.**
Checklist + '1980/81' on cover........... **£10-15**
81/82 **30 page Catalogue 'C2292'.**
Checklist + '1981-82' on cover .......... **£10-15**

## Eire

1958 **Box Insert '52/258/K6/EIRE'.**
'Eire' on checklist .............................. **£20-25**
1958 **Box Insert '5/658/K7/EIRE'.**
'Eire' on checklist .............................. **£20-25**
60/61 **Interim Leaflet** (no ref.)
'Eire' on checklist .............................. **£20-25**
62/63 **Interim Leaflet** (no ref.)
'Eire' on checklist .............................. **£15-20**
64/65 **Interim Leaflet** (no ref.). 'Eire' plus
'Playcraft 1964' on checklist .............. **£15-20**

## Finland

**English Text - local currency**
63/64 **40 page Catalogue** (no ref.). 'Finland 8/63'
on checklist plus '1963-64' on cover... **£30-40**
1965 **Interim Leaflet** (no ref.). 'Finland 6/65'
and 'Mettoy 1965' on checklist .......... **£15-20**

## France

**English Text - French checklist**
61/62 **Interim Leaflet** (no ref.).
'France' on page two........................... **£30-40**
62/63 **Interim Leaflet** (no ref.).
'France' on checklist ........................... **£30-40**
63/64 **40 page Catalogue** (no ref.).
'France 8/63' on checklist plus
'1963-64' on cover ............................. **£60-70**
64/65 **Interim Leaflet** (no ref.). 'France' and
'Playcraft 1964' on checklist .............. **£30-40**
1965 **Interim Leaflet** (no ref.). 'France' and
'Mettoy 1965' on checklist ................. **£30-40**

**French Text and checklist .**
'Liste de Controle pour le Collectioneur'.
1965 **40 page Catalogue** (no ref.). 'France 8/65'
on checklist plus 'Playcraft Toys Ltd.
1965' on rear cover ............................ **£50-60**
1968 **48 page Catalogue 'C2017/8/67'.**
French text - '1968' on cover.............. **£30-40**
1969 **48 page Catalogue 'C2017/9/68'.**
French text - '1969' on cover.............. **£20-30**
1973 **40 page Catalogue** (no ref.).
French text - '1973' on cover.............. **£15-20**
1974 **40 page Catalogue 'C2107 1974'.**
French text - '1974' on cover.............. **£15-20**
1975 **Catalogue Leaflet** (no ref.).
French text - 'Corgi '75' on cover ....... **£10-15**
1977 **16 page Catalogue** (no ref.).
French text plus 'Corgi '77' on cover.. **£20-30**
80/81 **48 page Catalogue 'C2275'.**
French text plus '1980/81' on cover
(includes Juniors) ............................... **£20-25**
80/81 **32 page Catalogue 'C2282'.**
French text plus '1980/81' on cover .... **£15-20**
81/82 **32 page Catalogue 'C2290'.** French text
plus '1981 Mettoy' on rear cover........ **£15-20**

## Holland

**Agent for Holland:**
N.V.S/O, Herengracht 25, Amsterdam.

**Dutch Text throughout**
1959 **20 page Catalogue** (no ref.).
'Holland 8/59' plus 'FL.O.10'
on cover plus Dutch text ..................... **£70-80**
1961 **24 page Catalogue** (no ref.).
'Holland 9/61' plus 'F.O.10' on cover
plus Dutch text ................................... **£50-60**

**French Text - Dutch checklist.**
'Kontroleer zo de Verzameling'.
80/81 **48 page Catalogue 'C2281'.**
'1980 Mettoy' on rear cover ............... **£20-30**
81/82 **30 page Catalogue 'C2291'.**
French text, Dutch checklist, plus
'1981 Mettoy' on rear cover ............... **£20-30**

**English Text with French and Dutch checklists**
1974 **40 page Catalogue** (no ref.).
'C2107 1974' on French checklist.
'C2103 1974' on Dutch checklist ........ **£20-30**

**English text - Dutch checklist**
1957 **Catalogue Leaflet '20/657C2/NL'.**
'Holland' on checklist ......................... **£20-30**
1958 **Catalogue Leaflet '15/158/C4/H'.**
'Holland' on checklist ......................... **£25-30**
1958 **Box Insert '52/258/K5/HOLLAND'.**
'Holland' on checklist ......................... **£25-30**
1958 **Box Insert '52/258/K6/HOLLAND'.**
'Holland' on checklist ......................... **£25-30**
1958 **Box Insert '5/658/K7/HOL.'.**
'HOL' on checklist .............................. **£25-30**
60/61 **Interim Leaflet** (no ref.).
'Holland' on checklist ......................... **£25-30**
61/62 **Interim Leaflet** (no ref.).
'Holland' top of page two ................... **£25-30**

62/63 **Interim Leaflet** (no ref.).
'Holland' on checklist.......................... **£25-30**
63/64 **40 page Catalogue** (no ref.).
'Holland 8/63' on checklist................. **£60-80**
1964 **Interim Leaflet** (no ref.).
'Holland' on checklist.......................... **£25-30**
64/65 **40 page Catalogue** (no ref.).
'Holland 9/64' on checklist................. **£25-30**
1965 **Interim Leaflet** (no ref.).
'Holland' on checklist.......................... **£25-30**
1966 **48 page Catalogue 'C2017/9/66'**.
'Holland' on cover and checklist ......... **£40-50**
1967 **Interim Leaflet** (no ref.).
'Holland' on cover ............................... **£20-25**
67/68 **48 page Catalogue 'C2017/7/67'**.
'Holland 8/67' on checklist................. **£50-60**
1969 **48 page Catalogue 'C2017/9/68'**.
'Holland 10/68' on checklist............... **£30-40**
1974 **40 page Catalogue 'C2211 1974'**.
Dutch text in checklist........................ **£20-25**
1974 **40 page Catalogue** (no ref.).
C2107 on French checklist plus
C2103 on Dutch checklist................... **£20-25**

## Hong Kong

1961 **Catalogue** (no ref.).
24 pages, 'Hong Kong 9/61' on cover . **£70-80**
61/62 **Interim Leaflet** (no ref.).
'Hong Kong' on page two..................... **£20-25**
1963 **Catalogue 'C/100/62'**. 24 pages,
'Hong Kong 3/63' on checklist............ **£60-80**
1963 **Interim Leaflet** (no ref.).
'Hong Kong' on checklist..................... **£20-25**
1964 **Interim Leaflet** (no ref.).
'Hong Kong' on checklist..................... **£20-25**
65/66 **40 pages** (no ref.).
'Hong Kong 8/65' on checklist............ **£60-80**
1966 **Catalogue 'C2017/9/66'**. 48 pages,
'Hong Kong' on cover and checklist ... **£60-80**

## Italy

**1963 Concessionaria per l'Italia: Ditta 'Guimar'**
**via Disciplini 7, Milano (303). 'Distinta di**
**Controllo per i Collezzionisti'.**
1958 **Box Insert '52/258/K5 ITALY'**.
'Italy' on checklist.............................. **£25-35**
1958 **Box Insert '52/258/K6 ITALY'**.
'Italy' on checklist.............................. **£25-35**
1958 **Box Insert '5/658/K7 ITALY'**.
'Italy' on checklist.............................. **£25-35**
1959 **Catalogue** (no ref.).
20 pages, 'Italy 8/59' on cover .......... **£50-75**
60/61 **Interim Leaflet** (no ref.).
'Italy' on checklist.............................. **£20-25**
1961 **Catalogue** (no ref.).
24 pages, 'Italy 9/61' on cover .......... **£40-50**
61/62 **Interim Leaflet** (no ref.).
'Italy' on page two.............................. **£20-25**
62/63 **Interim Leaflet** (no ref.).
'Italy' on checklist.............................. **£20-25**
63/64 **Catalogue** (no ref.).
40 pages, 'Italy 8/63' on checklist ..... **£70-80**
1964 **Interim Leaflet** (no ref.).
'Italy' on checklist.............................. **£20-25**
64/65 **Catalogue** (no ref.).
40 pages, 'Italy 9/64' on checklist ..... **£30-40**
1965 **Interim Leaflet** (no ref.).
'Italy' on checklist.............................. **£20-25**
1967 **Catalogue** (no ref.). 'Italy' on cover.
'ATTENDETE OGNIMESE LE
NOVITA 'CORGI'............................... **£20-25**

**1974 Concessionaria per l'Italia:**
**Toyuro s.n.c., Via S. Vittore 45, Milano (20123).**
1974 **Catalogue 'C2112 1974'**. 40 pages,
'Italia' reference on checklist.............. **£15-20**
80/81 **Catalogue 'C2278'**.
48 pages, Italian text throughout.......... **£10-15**
81/82 **Catalogue 'C2293'**. 32 pages,
Italian text throughout......................... **£10-15**

## Japan

1968 **Folded Leaflet**................................... **£40-50**
1973 **Catalogue** (no ref.).
40 pages, Japanese text throughout...... **£20-30**

## Malta

1964 **Leaflet** (no ref.). 'Malta' on checklist . **£25-35**
64/65 **Catalogue** (no ref.).
40 pages, 'Malta 8/64' on checklist ..... **£50-60**
1965 **Leaflet** (no ref.). 'Malta' in checklist .. **£25-35**

## New Zealand

64/65 **Catalogue** (no ref.). 40 pages,
'New Zealand 8/64' on checklist ......... **£50-60**
1965 **Leaflet** (no ref.).
'New Zealand' on checklist ................ **£25-30**
65/66 **Catalogue** (no ref.). 40 pages,
'New Zealand 8/65' on checklist ......... **£50-60**

## Norway

**'Se dem alle 1 den nye Katalogen, Samlers**
**Liste'. English Text - Norwegian checklist**
61/62 **Leaflet** (no ref.). 'Norway' on page 2 . **£25-35**
62/63 **Leaflet** (no ref.). 'Norway' checklist... **£25-35**
1964 **Leaflet** (no ref.). 'Norway' checklist.... **£20-25**
64/65 **Catalogue** (no ref.). 40 pages,
'Norway 9/64' on checklist................. **£30-40**
1965 **Leaflet** (no ref.). 'Norway' checklist.... **£20-25**
1966 **Catalogue** (no ref.). 40 pages,
'Norway 8/65' on checklist................. **£30-40**
1966 **Catalogue 'C2017/9/66'**. 48 pages,
'Norway' on cover and checklist ......... **£35-45**
67/68 **Catalogue 'C2017/7/67'**. 48 pages,
'Norway 8/67' on checklist................. **£35-45**
1970 **Catalogue** (no ref.). 48 pages,
'Norway' on checklist......................... **£25-30**
1974 **Catalogue 'C2113'**. 40 pages,
Norwegian checklist............................ **£15-20**
80/81 **Catalogue 'C2272'**. 48 pages,
Norwegian checklist............................ **£10-15**
1975 **Catalogue Leaflet** (no ref.). Norwegian
text throughout, plus '1975 Mettoy'.... **£10-15**

## Portugal

**'Lista de controle para o colecionador'.**
**English Text - Portuguese checklist.**
1957 **Catalogue Leaflet '25/257/C2/P'**.
'Portugal' on checklist ........................ **£25-35**
1960 **Leaflet** (no ref.). 'Portugal' checklist .. **£20-25**
61/62 **Leaflet** (no ref.). 'Portugal' on page 2. **£20-25**
62/63 **Leaflet** (no ref.). 'Portugal' checklist .. **£20-25**
63/64 **Catalogue** (no ref.). 40 pages,
'Portugal 8/63' on checklist ................ **£35-45**
1964 **Leaflet** (no ref.). 'Portugal' checklist .. **£20-25**
67/68 **Catalogue 'C2017/7/67'**. 48 pages,
'Portugal 8/67' on checklist ................ **£35-45**

## Singapore / Malaya

1958 **Box Insert '52/258/K5**
**SINGAPORE/MALAYA'**,
'Singapore/Malaya' on checklist.......... **£25-35**
1958 **Catalogue Leaflet '10/258/C5/SM'**.
'Singapore/Malaya' on checklist.......... **£25-35**
1958 **Box Insert '3.350/658/K7 SING.-MAL'**.
'Sing.-Mal' on checklist...................... **£25-35**
1960 **Catalogue** (no ref.). 20 pages,
'Singapore Malaya 9/60' on cover....... **£70-80**
1960 **Leaflet** (no ref.).
'Singapore/Malaya' on checklist.......... **£25-35**
1961 **Catalogue** (no ref.). 24 pages,
'Singapore/Malaya 9/61' on checklist . **£60-70**

62/63 **Leaflet** (no ref.).
'Singapore/Malaya' on checklist.......... **£25-30**
62/63 **Catalogue 'C/100/62'**. 32 pages,
'Singapore/Malaya 2/63' on checklist . **£50-60**
1965 **Leaflet** (no ref.).
'Singapore/Malaya' on checklist.......... **£20-25**

## Spain

**Spanish Text and checklist. 'Lista de**
**Coleccionistas'.**
1961 **Checklist**.
24 pages, 'Spanish 9/61' on cover ....... **£30-40**
**English Text - Spanish checklist.**
**'Lista de Precios para Coleccionistas'**
1962 **Checklist 'C/100/62'**.
'Spanish' on checklist .......................... **£25-30**
80/81 **Checklist 'C2273'**.
Spanish text in checklist ...................... **£10-15**

## Sweden

**'Kontrollista för Samlaren'.**

**English text - Swedish checklist**
1958 **Box Insert '52/258/K5/SWEDEN'**.
'Sweden' on checklist .......................... **£25-35**
1958 **Box Insert '52/258/K6/SWEDEN'**.
'Sweden' on checklist .......................... **£25-35**
1958 **Box Insert '5/658/K7/SWEDEN'**.
'Sweden' on checklist .......................... **£25-35**
1959 **Catalogue** (no ref.).
16 pages, 'Sweden 8/59' on cover ....... **£40-50**
60/61 **Leaflet** (no ref.). 'Sweden' checklist ... **£20-25**
1961 **Catalogue** (no ref.).
24 pages, 'Sweden 9/61' on cover ....... **£40-50**
61/62 **Leaflet** (no ref.). 'Sweden' on page 2.. **£20-25**
62/63 **Leaflet** (no ref.). 'Sweden' checklist ... **£20-25**
63/64 **Catalogue** (no ref.).
40 pages, 'Sweden 8/63' on checklist .. **£50-60**
64/65 **Catalogue** (no ref.).
40 pages, 'Sweden 9/64' on checklist.. **£40-50**
1965 **Leaflet** (no ref.). 'Sweden' checklist ... **£20-25**
1966 **Catalogue** (no ref.).
40 pages, 'Sweden 6/65' on checklist.. **£35-45**
1966 **Catalogue 'C2017/9/66'**. 40 pages,
'Sweden' on cover and checklist .......... **£35-45**
1967 **Leaflet** (no ref.). 'Sweden' on cover ... **£20-25**
1974 **Catalogue 'C2106 1974'**.
40 pages, Swedish text on checklist .... **£15-20**
1975 **Leaflet** (no ref.). All Swedish text....... **£10-15**
80/81 **Catalogue 'C2277'**.
48 pages, Swedish text throughout ...... **£10-15**

**Swedish text - Norwegian checklist**
81/82 **Catalogue 'C2287'**. 32 pages,
Swedish text + Norwegian checklist.... **£10-15**

## Switzerland

**English Text - English/Swiss checklist**
1957 **Catalogue Leaflet '20/657/C2/CH'**.
'Switzerland' on checklist .................... **£70-80**
1958 **Box Insert '52/258/K5/Switzerland'**.
Reference on checklist ......................... **£25-35**
1958 **Box Insert '52/258/K6/Switzerland'**.
Reference on checklist ......................... **£25-35**
1958 **Box Insert '5/658/K7/SWITZ'**.
Reference on checklist ......................... **£25-35**
1958 **Catalogue '25/1058/C8/SWITZ'**.
16 pages, 'Switz' on checklist.
New issues in French ........................... **£70-80**
1958 **Catalogue Leaflet '5/658/C5/CH'**.
'Switzerland' on checklist.................... **£25-35**
1960/61 **Leaflet** (no ref.).
'Switzerland' on checklist.................... **£25-30**
1961 **Catalogue** (no ref.). 24 pages,
'Switzerland 9/61' on cover ................ **£40-50**
61/62 **Leaflet** (no ref.). 'Switzerland' on p.2. **£20-25**
62/63 **Catalogue 'C100/62'**. 32 pages,
'Switzerland 1/63' on checklist............ **£40-50**

62/63 **Leaflet** (no ref.).
'Switzerland' on checklist.................... £20-25
1964 **Leaflet** (no ref.).
'Switzerland' on checklist.................... £20-25
64/65 **Catalogue** (no ref.).
40 pages, 'Switzerland' on checklist.... £25-35
1965 **Leaflet** (no ref.).
'Switzerland' on checklist.................... £20-25
1966 **Catalogue** (no ref.). 40 pages,
'Switzerland 8/65' on checklist........... £30-40
1966 **Catalogue 'C/2017/9/66'**. 48 pages,
'Switzerland' on cover and checklist ... £30-40
1967 **Leaflet** (no ref.).
'Switzerland' on cover ........................ £20-25
1969 **Catalogue 'C2017/9/68'**. 48 pages,
'Switzerland 10/68' on checklist.......... £30-40

## USA

**1958 Sole Distributor for U.S.A.: Reeves International Incorp., 1107 Broadway, New York 10, N.Y.**
1958 **Catalogue Leaflet '20/458/C5/U.S.A.'**.
'U.S.A.' on checklist............................ £30-40

1958 **Box Insert '20/658/K7/U.S.A.'**.
'U.S.A.' on checklist ........................... £30-40
1959 **Catalogue 'USA 8/59'**. 16 pages, pictures
of tractor and racing car on cover........ £70-80
1961 **Catalogue 'USA 9/61'**.
24 pages, 'U.S.A. 9/61' on cover......... £50-60
1961/62 **Leaflet**. 'U.S.A.' on page two........ £25-30
1962/63 **Catalogue 'C/100/62'**.
32 pages, Cover shows boy in red with
corgi dog. 'U.S.A. 5/63' on checklist .. £70-80
1962/63 **Leaflet 'USA 8/65'**.
'USA' on checklist ............................. £25-30
1964 **2-fold Checklist** (no ref.).
Ghia L 6.4 featured on cover.
'USA' and '© Playcraft Toys 1964'..... £25-30
1964/65 **Catalogue** (no ref.). 40 pages,
Green 9001 Bentley and Ghia L6.4 on
cover. 'USA 8/64' on checklist ........... £55-65
1965/66 **Catalogue** (no ref.).
40 pages, 'U.S.A. 8/65' on checklist ... £55-65
1967 **Leaflet** (no ref.). 'U.S.A.' on cover ..... £20-25
1968/69 **Catalogue 'C2017/9/68'**.
48 pages, Chitty-Chitty-Bang-Bang on
cover. 'USA 10/68' on checklist .......... £30-40

1971 **2-fold Checklist '© 1970 Mettoy Co Ltd'**.
'Corgi Toys with WhizzWheels' plus
'Australia', 'S.Africa' and 'USA' on cover.
Checklist prices in all three currencies £25-30

## International issues 1981-85

The catalogue listings are printed in English, French and German.
**Catalogue 'C2293'** was issued as a miniature booklet.

## 1965 Corgi Club address

**Canada**: Kleinberg Agencies 1085 St Alexander St., Montreal, Quebec, Canada.
**South Africa**: PO Box 6024, Johannesburg,
U..S.A.: ...........1107 Broadway, New York 10, N.Y.

Thrills and spills on the 1966 Corgi Toys catalogue cover.

# Shop display and 'point-of-sale' items

| Year | Item details | MPR |
|---|---|---|

**1950s Carded 3-D display stand.**
Red, yellow, blue black 'CORGI TOYS'
plus 'NEW' in various languages ......... **£250-300**

**57-59 Display stand, wooden.** Ten cream
'corrugated' hardboard shelves, pale blue
display background with yellow and blue
plastic 'CORGI TOYS' sign screwed to
top of display, (30 x 29 x 12 inches) .... **£200-300**

**57-59 Display card/sign.** Tin/cardboard,
yellow/blue with gold 'dog' logo, 'Wow!
Corgi Toys-The Ones with Windows'... **£100-150**

**57-59 Display card/sign** As previous item
but with 'New Corgi Major Toys
- The Ones With Windows'.................. **£100-150**

**57-59 Wooden display unit.** Two shelf
stand with Blue backing logo 'CORGI TOYS',
'THE ONES WITH WINDOWS', 'MODEL
PERFECTION' and 'NEW' plus the early
gold Corgi dog on red background ...... **£200-300**

**57-59 Counter display unit.** Cardboard, single
model display card with Dark Blue inner
display area, 'new - CORGI TOYS'....... **£75-125**

**57-59 Counter display unit**
Cardboard, 2 tiers with 'New - CORGI
MAJOR TOYS' in yellow/blue ........... **£200-300**

**57-59 Counter display unit.** Cardboard,
2 tier unit, 'COLLECT CORGI TOYS'
and 'New MODELS EVERY MONTH'
logos in yellow/blue............................. **£200-300**

**57-59 Counter display unit**
Cardboard, Renault Floride (222) pictorial
display card with '1959 MOTOR SHOW'
and 'EARLS COURT' logos................. **£300-400**

**57-59 Counter display unit (cardboard)**
Citroën (475) pictorial display card with
'new - THE CITROEN' and 'OLYMPIC
WINTER SPORTS' logos..................... **£200-300**

**1959 Display unit**
Shows picture of GS8 'Combine Harvester
Set'. 'At work in the field' logo........... **£150-200**

**57-67 Metal display stand**
Tiered stand 75cm x 30cm x 45cm high,
three 'CORGI TOYS' and Black logos, +
3 early gold Corgi dog emblems.......... **£175-225**

**1960 Counter display box.** Stand for GS1
Bedford Carrimore (1101) and 4 cars... **£300-400**

**1960 Window display sign**
Yellow background with 'Naturally Corgi
Toys' in Red and Blue, illuminated. 27"
long x 8" high. (Belgian market?) ........ **£500-700**

**60-61 Window sticker**
'NEW MODELS EVERY MONTH'........ **£30-40**

**1960s Metal display stand** has
'Corgi Display C2034' on the back ...... **£100-150**

**66-69 Window sticker**
Advertising new releases ......................... **£20-30**

**60-69 Oblong window sign.** Glass or plastic
with 'CORGI TOYS' and 'PRECISION
DIE-CAST SCALE MODELS' logos
plus gold Corgi 'dog'
logo in blue/yellow/red design............. **£200-300**

**1960s Tinplate stand.** 5 Grey tiers topped by
'CORGI TOYS'/Gold dog header ........ **£200-300**

**60-69 Glass display sign**
Square sign, gold corgi dog on Red panel
within Blue lined glass surround .......... **£150-200**

**1961 Moulded Corgi Dog.** on hind feet holding
a 'CORGI CHRISTMAS CARD'......... **£200-300**

**68-83 Metal display stand.** Tiered stand
75 cm x 3.5 cm c 45 cm high, with three
'CORGI TOYS' Black/Yellow logos, plus
3 White/Red late Corgi dog emblems... **£150-200**

**71-73 Oblong sign.** Plastic, with 'CORGI' and
'TESTED BY THE CORGI TECHNOCRATS'
plus white Corgi 'dog' logo on red square,
yellow background plus three
'Technocrats' faces................................ **£100-150**

**63-65 Display stand, rotary, C2001/2**
For self-selection, 7 tray unit,
large 'CORGI TOYS' header sign ........ **£200-300**

**63-65 Display stand, rotary, C2003.**
Self-selection, 4 columns, 4 compartments
(45 x 30 in.), large 'CORGI TOYS'
header boards ....................................... **£200-300**

**63-65 Display stand, rotary, C2004**
Self-selection, 4 column,
72 compartments (72 x 30 in.).............. **£200-300**

**63-65 Display stand, rotary, C2005**
Self-selection, 2 column,
36 compartments (72 x 30 in.).............. **£150-200**

**63-65 Display stand, rotary, C2006**
Self-selection, 2 column,
36 compartments (55 x 30 in.).............. **£100-150**

**63-65 Display stand, plastic, C2007**
Large moulded plastic counter display to
house up to 50 models, large black header
display board with 'NATURALLY CORGI
TOYS' on yellow/blue background,
and 'JOIN THE CORGI MODEL CLUB'
on display front ..................................... **£200-300**

**1960s Electric Display stand, revolving, C2008**
Glass fronted, to house 100-120 models with
light and dark simulated wood panels with four
'CORGI' logos, (38 x 24 x 24 in.)........ **£400-600**

**57-66 Showcase, glass, C2009**
3 glass shelves, 3 'CORGI TOYS' logos
(black/blue) plus gold Corgi 'dog' logo
on red background, (20x15x9 in.) ........ **£200-300**

**1970s Corgi Juniors unit, E9051.** Yellow plastic
(21.75 x 21.75 in.), for 48 models, 'LOOK
FOR WHIZZWHEELS MODELS'...... **£100-150**

**1975 Army diorama.** Plastic, for tanks.. **£175-225**

**1976 Kojak's Buick.** Card counter-top .. **£100-125**

**1979 'Corgi Toys' display unit.** Metal,
approx. 3' x 2' with 4 shelves / racks ... **£250-300**

**? Shop display card.** 'Mr SOFTEE Ice
Cream free with this Corgi Toy' .......... **£300-400**

**? Shop display stand**
'New! Chrysler Imperial'...................... **£150-200**

**? Shop Display Stand** with 'New! The Bentley
Continental'. Brown and Cream fold out
cardboard counter display unit.............. **£400-500**

**? 'Corgi Toys' Hanging Tin Sign.** 'Corgi' Dog
and 'Corgi Kits' (52cm x 20cm).......... **£400-500**

**1979 'CORGI TOYS' Metal Stand.**
Approx. 3ft x 2ft with 4 shelves/racks . **£250-300**

**Magic Roundabout display stand.**
Cardboard............................................ **£400-500**

## CORGI TOYS WINDOW POSTERS
**485 Mini Countryman with Surfer.**
'New This Month', 245mm x 200mm .... **£100-150**

**428 Karrier Bantam Ice Cream Van.**
'Mister Softee' 'New This Month',
245mm x 200mm ................................. **£100-150**

**Citroën Safari 'Wildlife Preservation'.**
'New This Month' 245mm x 200mm...... **£100-150**

**428 Karrier Bantam Ice Cream Van.** 'Mister
Softee'. 'Each box end worth 6d For any
Mister Softee Van', 270mm x 140mm ..... **£100-150**

**270 Aston-Martin DB5.** 'James Bond' - 'Now
with Revolving Number Plates and
Tyre Slashers', 400mm x 120mm............. **£200-250**

**261 Aston-Martin DB5.** 'James Bond' and
'Goldfinger', 300mm x 200mm ............... **£200-250**

We would welcome more information please.

| Ref. | Model | on or after page |
|---|---|---|
| 50 | Massey-Ferguson Tractor | 70 |
| 51 | M-F Trailer | 70 |
| 53 | MF Tractor Shovel | 70 |
| 54 | MF Tractor Shovel | 70 |
| 54 | Fordson Half-Track | 70 |
| 55 | Fordson Major Tractor | 70 |
| 55 | David Brown Tractor | 70 |
| 56 | Four-Furrow Plough | 70 |
| 56 | Farm Tipper Trailer | 70 |
| 57 | Massey-Ferguson Tractor | 70 |
| C57 | Volvo and Caravan | 72 |
| 58 | Beast Carrier | 70 |
| 60 | Fordson Power Major | 70 |
| 61 | Four-Furrow Plough | 70 |
| 62 | Tipper Trailer | 70 |
| 64 | Conveyor on Jeep | 70 |
| 66 | Massey Ferguson 165 | 70 |
| 67 | Ford Super Major | 70 |
| 69 | MF Tractor & Shovel | 70 |
| 71 | Fordson Disc Harrow | 70 |
| 72 | Tractor and Towbar | 70 |
| 73 | MF Tractor & Saw | 70 |
| 74 | Tractor & Scoop | 70 |
| 100 | Dropside Trailer | 65 |
| 101 | Platform Trailer | 65 |
| 102 | Pony Trailer | 70 |
| 107 | Batboat on Trailer | 72 |
| 109 | Pennyburn Trailer | 65 |
| 112 | Horse Box | 70 |
| 150 | Vanwall | 53 |
| 150 | Surtees TS9 | 53 |
| 151 | Lotus XI | 53 |
| C151 | McLaren 'Yardley' | 53 |
| 152 | BRM Racing Car | 53 |
| C152 | Ferrari 312-B2 | 53 |
| 153 | Bluebird Record Car | 53 |
| 153 | Team Surtees | 53 |
| 154 | Ferrari Formula 1 | 53 |
| C154 | Lotus 'JPS' | 53 |
| C154 | 'Texaco Special' | 53 |
| 155 | Lotus Climax | 53 |
| C155 | Shadow F1 | 53 |
| 156 | Cooper-Maserati | 53 |
| C156 | Shadow F1 (G. Hill) | 53 |
| 158 | Lotus Climax | 53 |
| C158 | Tyrell-Ford 'Elf' | 53 |
| 159 | Cooper-Maserati | 53 |
| C159 | Indianapolis Car | 53 |
| 160 | Hesketh Racing Car | 53 |
| 161 | Santa Pod 'Commuter' | 53 |
| 161 | Elf-Tyrell Project 34 | 53 |
| 162 | Quartermaster Dragster | 53 |
| C163 | Santa Pod Dragster | 53 |
| 164 | Ison 'Wild Honey' | 53 |
| 165 | Adams Brothers Dragster | 53 |
| 166 | Ford Mustang | 53 |
| C167 | USA Racing Buggy | 53 |
| C169 | Starfighter Jet Dragster | 53 |
| C170 | John Woolfe's Dragster | 53 |
| C171 | Street Bike | 75 |
| C172 | Police Bike | 75 |
| C173 | Cafe Racer | 75 |
| 190 | Lotus 'John Player' | 53 |
| 191 | McLaren 'Texaco Marlboro' | 53 |

| Ref. | Model | on or after page |
|---|---|---|
| 200 | Ford Consul | 53 |
| 201 | 'The Saint's Volvo | 53 |
| 201 | Austin Cambridge | 53 |
| 202 | Morris Cowley | 53 |
| 203 | Vauxhall Velox | 53 |
| 203 | De Tomaso Mangusta | 53 |
| 204 | Rover 90 | 53 |
| 204 | Morris Mini-Minor | 53 |
| 205 | Riley Pathfinder | 53 |
| 206 | Hillman Husky | 55 |
| 207 | Standard Vanguard III | 55 |
| 208 | Jaguar 24 litre | 55 |
| 209 | Riley Police Car | 68 |
| 210 | Citroën DS19 | 55 |
| 211 | Studebaker Golden Hawk | 55 |
| 213 | Jaguar Fire Service | 68 |
| 214 | Ford Thunderbird | 55 |
| 215 | Thunderbird Sports | 55 |
| 216 | Austin A40 | 55 |
| 217 | Fiat 1800 | 55 |
| 218 | Aston Martin DB4 | 55 |
| 219 | Plymouth Suburban | 55 |
| 220 | Chevrolet Impala | 55 |
| 221 | Chevrolet Cab | 55 |
| 222 | Renault Floride | 55 |
| 223 | Chevrolet 'Police' | 68 |
| 224 | Bentley Continental | 55 |
| 225 | Austin 7 Saloon | 55 |
| 226 | Morris Mini-Minor | 55 |
| 227 | Mini-Cooper Rally | 55 |
| 228 | Volvo P-1800 | 55 |
| 229 | Chevrolet Corvair | 55 |
| 230 | Mercedes-Benz 220SE | 55 |
| 231 | Triumph Herald | 55 |
| 232 | Fiat 2100 | 55 |
| 233 | Heinkel Trojan | 55 |
| 234 | Ford Classic | 55 |
| 235 | Oldsmobile Super 88 | 55 |
| 236 | Motor School Austin A60 | 55 |
| 237 | Oldsmobile 'Sheriff' | 55 |
| 238 | Jaguar Mk10 | 55 |
| 239 | VW Karmann Ghia | 55 |
| 240 | Fiat 600 Jolly | 55 |
| 241 | Chrysler Ghia L64 | 55 |
| 242 | Fiat 600 Jolly | 55 |
| 245 | Buick Riviera | 55 |
| 246 | Chrysler Imperial | 55 |
| 247 | Mercedes-Benz Pullman | 55 |
| 248 | Chevrolet Impala | 55 |
| 249 | Morris Mini-Cooper | 55 |
| 251 | Hillman Imp | 55 |
| 252 | Rover 2000 | 55 |
| 253 | Mercedes-Benz 220 SE | 55 |
| 255 | Motor School Austin A60 | 55 |
| 256 | VW Safari Rally | 55 |
| 258 | The Saint's Volvo | 55 |
| 259 | Citroën 'Le Dandy' | 55 |
| C259 | Penguinmobile | 55 |
| 260 | Renault R16 TS | 55 |
| 260 | Buick Police Car | 68 |
| C260 | Superman Police Car | 72 |
| 261 | James Bond's Aston Martin | 72 |
| C261 | Spiderbuggy | 72 |
| 262 | Lincoln Continental | 55 |
| C262 | Cpt. Marvel's Porsche | 72 |
| 263 | Marlin Rambler | 55 |

| Ref. | Model | on or after page |
|---|---|---|
| C263 | Capt.America Jetmobile | 72 |
| 264 | Oldsmobile Toronado | 55 |
| C264 | Incredible Hulk Van | 72 |
| C265 | Supermobile | 72 |
| 266 | Chitty Bang Bang | 72 |
| C266 | Spider Bike | 72 |
| C267 | Batmobile | 72 |
| 268 | 'Green Hornet' | 72 |
| C268 | Batman's Bat Bike | 72 |
| 269 | James Bond's Lotus | 72 |
| 270 | James Bond's Aston Martin | 72 |
| 271 | Ghia De Tomaso Mangusta | 55 |
| C271 | James Bond's Aston Martin | 72 |
| C272 | James Bond's Citroën 2cv | 72 |
| 273 | Rolls-Royce Silver Shadow | 55 |
| 274 | Bentley 'T' Series | 55 |
| 275 | Rover 2000 TC | 55 |
| C275 | Mini Metro | 55 |
| C275 | Royal Wedding Metro | 55 |
| 276 | Oldsmobile Toronado | 55 |
| C276 | Triumph Acclaim | 55 |
| 277 | 'Monkeemobile' | 72 |
| C277 | Triumph School Car | 55 |
| C278 | Dan Dare Car | 72 |
| C279 | Rolls-Royce Corniche | 55 |
| C279/3 | Rolls-Royce | 55 |
| C280 | Rolls-Royce Shadow | 55 |
| 281 | Rover 2000 TC | 55 |
| C281 | Metro 'Datapost' | 55 |
| 282 | Mini-Cooper Rally | 55 |
| 283 | DAF 'City' Car | 55 |
| C284 | Citroën SM | 55 |
| C285 | Mercedes-Benz 240D | 55 |
| C286 | Jaguar XJC V-12 | 55 |
| C287 | Citroën Dyane | 55 |
| C288 | Minissima | 55 |
| 289 | VW Polo 'DBP' | 55 |
| 289 | VW Polo | 55 |
| | | |
| 290 | Kojak's Buick | 72 |
| 291 | AMC Pacer | 55 |
| C291 | Mercedes 240 Rally | 55 |
| C292 | 'Starsky & Hutch' | 72 |
| 293 | Renault 'Medicins' | 55 |
| 293 | Renault 'Pompiers' | 55 |
| C294 | Renault Alpine | 55 |
| 297 | Ford Escort 'Police' | 68 |
| 298 | Magnum PI Ferrari | 55 |
| 299 | Ford Sierra | 55 |
| 300 | Austin-Healey 100-4 | 55 |
| 300 | Corvette Stingray | 55 |
| C300 | Ferrari Daytona | 55 |
| 301 | Triumph TR2 | 55 |
| 301 | Iso Grifo | 55 |
| C301 | Lotus Elite | 55 |
| 302 | MG 'MGA' | 55 |
| 302 | Hillman Hunter Rally | 55 |
| C302 | Volkswagen Polo | 55 |
| 303 | Mercedes-Benz 300SL | 55 |
| 303 | Roger Clark's Capri | 57 |
| 304 | Mercedes-Benz 300SL | 57 |
| 304 | Chevrolet Camaro | 57 |
| 305 | Triumph TR3 | 57 |
| 305 | Mini Marcos GT | 57 |
| 306 | Morris Marina | 57 |
| C306 | Fiat X1-9 S | 57 |

| Ref. | Model | on or after page |
|---|---|---|
| 307 | Jaguar 'E'-type | 57 |
| 307 | Renault Turbo | 57 |
| C308 | Mini-Cooper S | 57 |
| C308 | BMW M1 | 57 |
| 309 | Aston Martin DB4 | 57 |
| C309 | Volkswagen Turbo | 57 |
| 310 | Chevrolet Stingray | 57 |
| 310 | Porsche 924 Turbo | 57 |
| 311 | Ford Capri V6 | 57 |
| C312 | Ford Capri S | 57 |
| 312 | Jaguar 'E'-type | 57 |
| 312 | Marcos Mantis | 57 |
| 313 | Ford Cortina GXL | 57 |
| 314 | Ferrari Berlinetta | 57 |
| C314 | Fiat X1-9 | 57 |
| C314 | Supercat Jaguar | 57 |
| 315 | Simca 1000 Sports | 57 |
| C315 | Lotus Elite | 57 |
| 316 | NSU Sport Prinz | 57 |
| 316 | Ford GT 70 | 57 |
| 317 | Mini-Cooper 'Monte Carlo' | 57 |
| 318 | Mini-Cooper 'Monte Carlo' | 57 |
| 318 | Jaguar XJS | 57 |
| 318 | Lotus Elan | 57 |
| 318 | Lotus Elan S2 | 57 |
| 319 | Lotus Elan S2 | 57 |
| 319 | Jaguar XJS | 57 |
| 319 | Lamborghini P400GT | 57 |
| 320 | Ford Mustang Fastback | 57 |
| C320 | The Saint's Jaguar | 72 |
| 321 | Porsche 924 Saloon | 57 |
| 321 | Mini-Cooper 'Monte Carlo' | 57 |
| 322 | Rover 'Monte Carlo' | 57 |
| 323 | Citroën 'Monte Carlo' | 57 |
| 323 | Ferrari Daytona | 57 |
| 324 | Marcos Volvo 1800 | 57 |
| 324 | Ferrari Daytona LM | 57 |
| 325 | Chevrolet Caprice | 57 |
| 325 | Mustang Competition | 57 |
| C326 | Chevrolet Police Car | 57 |
| 327 | MGB GT | 57 |
| C327 | Chevrolet Caprice Taxi | 57 |
| 328 | Hillman 'Monte Carlo' | 57 |
| 329 | Opel Senator | 57 |
| 329 | Ford Mustang | 57 |
| 330 | Porsche Carrera 6 | 57 |
| 331 | Ford Capri 'Texaco' | 57 |
| 332 | Lancia Fulvia Sports | 58 |
| 333 | Mini-Cooper 'Sun/RAC' | 58 |
| 334 | Mini-Cooper 'Magnifique' | 58 |
| C334 | Ford Escort 1.3 GL | 58 |
| 300 | Jaguar 'E'-type 42 | 58 |
| 300 | James Bond's Toyota | 72 |
| 337 | Chevrolet Stock Car | 58 |
| 338 | Chevrolet Camaro | 58 |
| C338 | Rover 3500 | 58 |
| 339 | Mini-Cooper '67 Monte Carlo' | 58 |
| C339 | Rover Police Car | 58 |
| 340 | Sunbeam 'Monte Carlo' | 58 |
| C340 | Rover 'Triplex' | 58 |
| 341 | Mini Marcos GT | 58 |

## Bonham's Auctions

Montpelier Galleries, Montpelier Street, London SW7 1HH
Tel: 0044 (0) 20 7393 3900
E-mail: leigh.gotch@bonhams.com
Website: www.bonhams.com/toys
**Note that** the auction prices shown do not include premium or tax.
Abbreviations: **M** = Mint, **E** = Excellent, **G** = Good,
**VG** = Very Good, **F** = Fair, **P** = Poor

**CORGI TOYS models**
**22a Sports Tourer. 'Hornby Series'**, Red/Cream, Blue wheels, Good ...... **£280**
**1107 Euclid TC-12 Tractor with Dozer Blade**. Yellow, E, box G ............. **£456**

## Christie's South Kensington

South Kensington, London.
+44 (0)20 7752 3274
**Auction Prices shown include the buyer's premium.**
Abbreviations: **M** = Mint, **E** = Excellent, **G** = Good,
**VG** = Very Good, **F** = Fair, **P** = Poor

**Gift Set 15 Silverstone Racing Layout**.
As per Catalogue - E-M in VG 2nd issue box with picture on lid .... **£1,920**
**Gold-plated James Bond Lotus Esprit** in Gold Presentation Display Box.
(Only 10 models produced for the world premiere of 'The Spy Who
Loved Me'). With brass plaque 'Presented by the Mettoy Co. Ltd.
7th July 1977', and instruction card. VG overall ............................... **£5,400**

## Collectoys

Hotel Frank Hornby, Place George Sand, 18000 Bourges, France.
E-Mail: contact@collectoys.fr    Website: www.collectoys.fr

**Model** condition shown in CAPITALS,
i.e., 'A - D' with 'A' being the top grade.
**Box** condition is shown in Lower Case,
i.e. 'a - d' with 'a' being the top grade ('o.' = unboxed)

**P416 Land Rover** (Belgian Issue). Yellow body,
plastic Grey canopy, M in E box ......................................................... **£740**
**1110 Bedford 'S' Tanker** - Dutch issue for Royal Dutch Shell Company.
'SHELL' logo, 'Benzeen - Tuleen- Xyleen' on tank, plus literature
issued with model. **NB** Catalogue currently wrongly shows
the model as having a 'TK' cab.......................................................... **£2,260**

## Dreweatt-Neate Auctions

Apsley Road Saleroom, St Johns Place, Apsley Road,
Clifton, Bristol BS8 2ST.

**902 Foden Flat Truck**. 2nd type, Orange/Green, VGC, boxed ................... **£210**
**1109 Bloodhound Rocket**. As per Catalogue, VGC, boxed ........................ **£160**
**1126 Ecurie Ecosse**. Dark Blue, Orange lettering, E, boxed .................... **£170**
**1140 Bedford 'TK' Tanker 'Mobilgas'**, Excellent, boxed ......................... **£140**
**Gift Set 6 Racing Car Set**. VW Breakdown Lorry etc, VGC, boxed ........ **£115**
**Gift Set 40 The Avengers**. As per Catalogue, Red Bentley etc.,
VGC, boxed .................................................................................... **£240**

## Lacy, Scott & Knight

The Auction Centre, 10 Risbygate Street,
Bury St Edmunds, Suffolk, IP33 3AA
E-mail: fineart@lsk.co.uk    Web: www.lsk.co.uk
Abbreviations: **M** = Mint, **NM** = Near Mint, **E** = Excellent,
**VG** = Very Good, **G** = Good, **B** = Boxed, **BP** = Bubble Pack,
**WB** = Window box, **CD** = Cast detailed, **CF** = Camouflage.

**50 Massey-Ferguson 65**. 1st type, Red bonnet and metal wheels,
M in NM box ................................................................................. **£150**
**73 Massey-Ferguson 165 Tractor with Saw**. M in VG box...................... **£175**
**215S Ford Thunderbird**. Mint boxed ...................................................... **£120**
**300 Austin-Healey**. M in NM blue box (leaflet)......................................... **£120**
**454 Commer Lorry**. NM in VG box ........................................................ **£100**

**492 European Police Car**. Dark Green, White roof/wings, 'Polizei',
with true scale steering roof fitting, leaflet and 'cone' protector,
Mint in Near Mint box ..................................................................... **£105**
**H852 Magic Roundabout Carousel**. M in NM box ................................. **£330**
**H853 Magic Roundabout**. Complete NM in NM box ................................ **£780**
**G.S. 47 Ford Tractor/Conveyor**. M in VG box ....................................... **£155**

## Special Auction Services

Kennetholme, Midgeham,
Reading, Berkshire.
Tel: 0118 971 2949  www.invaluable.com

**267 Batmobile**. With instructions / badge / 9 rockets. Model E,
box G-VG (one tear)........................................................................ **£240**
**268 Green Hornet's Black Beauty**. VG-E in VG-E box ........... **£200**
**290 Kojak's Buick**. With hat, E-M in E box................................. **£70**
**292 Ford Torino**. E-M in VG-E box ........................................... **£100**
**302 Hillman Hunter Rally**. Model and Box E (No kangaroo) .. **£100**
**309 Aston-Martin Competition**. Model E in VG box .............. **£120**
**336 Toyota 2000GT**. As Catalogue, VG in VG box .................. **£220**
**448 Austin Police Van**. E, lacks inner card, box G..................... **£110**
**475 Citroën Safari - Ski Club**. Complete, E in E box ............. **£110**
**485 BMC Mini Countryman**. Model and box E......................... **£240**
**497 'Man from Uncle' 'Thrushbuster'**.
Metallic Blue with 'Waverley' ring, E in G box ................. **£190**
**1113 Corporal Guided Missile Vehicle**.
VG-E nosecone perished, G-VG box ..................................... **£140**
**1008 Popeye's Paddle Wagon**. Juniors issue - E in VG pack ..... **£130**

## Vectis Auctions Ltd.

Fleck Way, Thornaby,
Stockton -on-Tees TS17 9JZ
Abbreviations: M = Mint, NM = Near Mint, EP = Excellent Plus,
E = Excellent, GP = Good Plus, G = Good, F = Fair

**CORGI TOYS CARS**
**227 Morris Mini 'Competition'**. Primrose/White, E in E blue/yellow box **£220**
**227 Morris Mini 'Competition'**. Blue/White, GP in G box ...................... **£160**
**238 Jaguar Mk. X**. Deep Blue, Red Interior, spun hubs,
Mint in EP blue/yellow box, leaflet........................................................... **£190**
**304 Mercedes-Benz 300 SL Hardtop Roadster**. Yellow including hood,
flat spun hubs, M in GP blue/yellow box........................................... **£300**
**304S Mercedes-Benz 300SL Hardtop**. White, Red hard-top,
racing No. '3', EP in E blue/yellow box ........................................... **£220**
**307 Jaguar E-type**. Graphite Grey, brown interior,
M in E blue/yellow box with shop sticker............................................ **£150**
**307 Jaguar E-Type**. Plum Red, E in E blue/yellow box .......................... **£120**
**313 Ford Cortina GXL**. Tan body, Black roof, Red interior,
WhizzWheels E, complete with figure, in excellent box...................... **£320**
**317 Mini Cooper 'S' 'Rally Monte-Carlo'**. Red with White roof,
lemon interior, spun hubs, No. '37', NM in GP box............................ **£240**
**318 Lotus Elan 'Tiger in Tank'**. White, black interior,
EP in G blue/yellow box.................................................................. **£150**
**320 Ford Mustang Fastback**. Deep Blue, Cream interior,
wire wheels, NM in E....................................................................... **£110**
**321 Mini Cooper 'S' 'Monte Carlo'**. First Catalogue listing,
GP in G box, correct folded leaflet.................................................... **£160**
**321 Mini Cooper 'S' 'Monte Carlo'**. With roof signatures,
M in NM box with flash................................................................... **£300**
**323 Citroën DS19 'Monte Carlo'**. Details as 11th Edition,
E in E blue/yellow box, leaflet .......................................................... **£220**
**328 Hillman Imp 'Monte Carlo'**. Details as per 11th Edition,
NM in G-GP box, folded leaflet ....................................................... **£150**
**331 Ford Capri GT Rally**. White body, Black bonnet/interior. Red roof
stripe, Red/Black 'TEXACO' labels, racing number '5', EP............... **£280**
**333 Mini Cooper 'RAC' Rally**. Red, M in E Blue/yellow box with
correct folded leaflet ........................................................................ **£240**
**334 Mini Cooper 'Magnifique'**. Blue, Cream interior, cast hubs,
M in NM box, folded leaflet.............................................................. **£140**
**355 Commer 'Military Police'**. Green, red interior, blue glass,
NM in GP box, folded leaflet ............................................................ **£140**

**339 Mini Cooper 'S' 'Monte Carlo'**. Red, cast hubs, '1967 Monte-Carlo winner' on box, RN '177', E in EP blue/yellow picture box, correct folded leaflet.........................................................................**£200**

**349 'Pop Art' Morris Mini**. Blue/yellow carded box, Red body, lemon interior, 'MOSTEST' logo, Near Mint in M box with collectors leaflet..............................................................................**£2,300**

## CORGI TOYS COMMERCIALS

**404 Bedford Dormobile**. Cream, flat spun hubs, M in G blue box............**£140**
**404 Bedford Dormobile**. Yellow, Pale Blue roof, spun hubs, NM in GP box.........................................................................................**£360**
**406 Land Rover**. Yellow/Black, spun hubs, E in G-GP box......................**£150**
**408 Bedford Van 'AA'**. Yellow/Black, E in GP rare yellow/blue box ........**£150**
**416 Land Rover 'RAC'**. Blue with roof sign, EP in G - GP box..................**£150**
**420 Ford Thames 'Airborne' Caravan**. Lilac/Pale Mauve body, spun hubs, EP in GP blue and yellow box..............................................**£120**
**420 Ford Thames 'Airborne' Caravan**. Green/Cream body, spun hubs, M in E box..............................................................................**£140**
**420 Ford Thames 'Airborne' Caravan**. Blue/White, spun hubs, M in EP box.............................................................................................**£220**
**422 Bedford Van 'Corgi Toys'**. Blue/Yellow, NM in GP blue/yellow box **£600**
**440 Ford Consul Cortina Super Estate**. Blue, Cream interior, complete with golfer, caddy boy, trolley and bag, overall NM in EP box ..........**£260**
**447 Ford Thames 'Walls' Van**. Pale Blue, Cream, spun hubs, Mint Boxed, folded leafllet.............................................................................**£850**
**448 BMC Mini Van 'Police'**. As per Catalogue, with dog, Mint Boxed ....**£340**
**474 Ford Thames 'Walls' Van**. As Catalogue, EP in G blue/yellow box, correct folded leaflet, unapplied decal street..........................................**£340**
**491 Ford Consul Cortina Estate**. Grey, 'woody' sides, Cream interior, M in E box.................................................................................**£110**
**503 Giraffe Transporter**. Model as Catalogue, M in EP box ..................**£120**
**1110 Bedford 'S' type Tanker 'Mobilgas'**. EP in GP box .......................**£150**

## CORGI TOYS MISCELLANEOUS

**356 VW 'US Personnel'**. Green, Red interior, M in GP box.....................**£140**
**359 Field Kitchen**. Military Green, Blue interior, NM in GP box.............**£160**
**468 Routemaster Bus**. 'New South Wales Government Transport', Outspan' side decals, M in E box with leaflet..........................................**£1,300**
**1111 MF Combine Harvester**. Red/Yellow, red plastic hubs, NM-M in G box..............................................................................................**£140**

## CORGI TOYS NOVELTY ITEMS

**266 'Chitty Chitty Bang Bang'**. As per catalogue, M in EP window box **£440**
**267 Batmobile (i)**. Gloss Black, red bat hubs, NM in M box, Excellent inner stand, complete...........................................................**£660**
**267 Batmobile (ii)**. Matt Black, red bat hubs, NM in GP box ...................**£400**
**267 Batmobile (v)**. Red WhizzWheels, G in G striped box ........................**£280**
**268 'The Green Hornet'**. Spun hubs variation. Model details as per catalogue. NM in M inner stand, E picture box ............................**£320**
**277 The 'Monkeemobile'**. As per catalogue, E in GP box.........................**£150**
**391 James Bond's Mustang Mach 1**. E+ including window box/flash......**£180**
**497 'The Man from Uncle'**. Blue, Waverley ring, M inGP box .................**£140**
**802 Popeye's Paddle Wagon**. Mint in E pictorial window box .................**£300**
**803 'The Beatles' Submarine**. Yellow, Red hatches, E in G window box..**£190**
**804 Noddy's Car**. As Catalogue, Near Mint in E window box ..................**£240**
**805 'The Hardy Boys' Rolls-Royce**. Excellent in Good Plus window box **£140**
**811 Moon Buggy**. Model EP in GP window box .....................................**£150**

## CORGI TOYS GIFT SETS

**GS 1 Transporter Set**. Yellow/Blue1101 Bedford 'S' type. Models as per 11th Edition listings. All G - E in G window box GP outer box ...........................................**£750**
**GS 1 Transporter Set**. Red/Blue 1101 Bedford 'S' type. Models as per the 11th Edition. All G - NM. The tray is E and the outer box lid Fair .........................**£360**
**GS 3 'Batman' 1st issue Set**. Batmobile and Batboat both M, tray EP, blue/yellow outer window box is Excellent. ...........................................**£800**
**GS 5 Racing Cars Set** (1960-61). Models as per 11th Edition are EP-M. The tray is E and the blue/yellow box is G.............................................**£260**
**GS 5s Racing Cars Set**. Good outer box. Models as listed in 11th Edition. Mint. The model display stand is Fair..................................................**£180**
**GS 9 Tractor Trailer and Shovel Set**. Models as listed in 11th Edition. NM. The display stand and outer box are excellent............................**£170**
**GS 12 Grand Prix Set, complete with 'Mr Retailer' transit card**. Models listed as per 11th Edition are E - M, window box is E ............**£540**
**GS 12 1st Circus Set**. Models as per11th Edition, GP - E, box lid Fair.....**£280**
**GS13 Tour de France**. Overall Mint, Tray and inner stand Near Mint, blue/yellow window box and pictorial stand E ....................................**£340**
**GS 15 Silverstone Set** 1964-66. Set as listed in 11th Edition..................**£2,000**

**GS16 Racing Car Set**. Outer box Good but grubby. 150s, 151a,152 and 1126 Metallic Dark blue body, Light Blue lettering GP-E, Box E .......**£380**
**GS17 Ferrari Set**. 437 Land Rover and 155 Ferrari NM - M. Good Plus blue picture box, inner stand EP.............................................**£170**
**GS 19 'Chipperfields Circus' 2nd issue**. 438 Land Rover has plastic tilt. Other details as per Catalogue. Condition GP, tray E, box GP............**£140**
**GS 20 Transporter Set**. Details as Catalogue, E-M, tray NM, G blue/yellow box ..............................................................................**£420**
**GS 21 Chipperfields Circus**. Contains 1144 Crane Truck and 1139 Menagerie Trailer, Excellent model and box ..........................**£2,050**
**GS 22 Farming Set**. Lid and inner tray G - GP. All items generally Good Plus - Near Mint ................................................................................**£750**
**GS 22 'James Bond' Set**. Outer striped box G. All 3 pieces E - M complete with accessories.....................................**£320**
**GS23 Chipperfields Circus 1st. issue**. As per Catalogue, contents G - E, inner tray GP, outer lift-off lid G - GP.............................................**£320**
**GS23 Chipperfields Circus 2nd. issue**. As per Catalogue, contents NM-M, tray/card are EP and the outer box is GP.................**£580**
**GS 27 Priestman Shovel**. As per 11th Edition - NM in box with E lid. .....**£140**
**GS 28 Transporter Set**. All pieces GP - E, outer box is Good.....................**£680**
**GS 31 Buick Riviera**. As Catalogue, overall condition is NM to M, pictorial stand is EP and outer box is GP-E.........................................**£420**
**GS 33 Tractor and Beast Carrier**. Models as listed in the 11th Edition plus tractor driver, 4 animals and plastic net. M in GP picture box ....**£260**
**GS 37 'Lotus Racing Team'**. All items E - M, outer blue/yellow box G with all accessories..................................**£340**
**GS 38 'Monte-Carlo Rally'**. All items EP-NM, inner pictorial stand GP, outer picture box Good...................................................................**£640**
**GS 40 'The Avengers Set'**. With rare Red/Black Bentley, models EP - M, stand and outer box E.....................................................**£500**
**GS 41 Transporter Set with 'Monte Carlo' Mini**. All items Good Plus - Excellent, box Good...............................................**£340**
**GS 41 Transporter Set**, 1966-68 issue. Models listed as per 11th Edition are all E -M. The inner tray and base are GP-E. The outer lift-off picture lid is NM .................................................**£900**
**GS 48 Transporter Set** (1969). Models include 'Monte-Carlo' Sunbeam Imp and Mini cars. All GP - NM, outer window box Fair....................**£420**

# Wallis & Wallis

West Street Auction Galleries, Lewes, Sussex, BN7 2NJ.
Telephone: 01273 480208, E-mail: auctions@wallisand wallis.co.uk
Abbreviations: **M** = Mint, **GC** = Good Condition, **QGC** = Quite Good
Condition, **VGC** = Very Good Condition, **BMW** = Box has minor wear.

## CORGI TOYS MODELS

**150 Vanwall Racing Car**. Green/Cream seats, VGC, Boxed, minor wear....**£75**
**154 Ferrari Racing Car**. Red, No. '36', spun wheels, VGC-M, BMW .......**£75**
**258 Volvo P1800**. White, Black 'Saint' logo, Mint. Box with minor wear..**£190**
**302 Hillman Hunter Rally**. Model/contents VGC, window box VGC.........**£95**
**359 Army Field Kitchen**. As per Catalogue - Boxed, Mint.......................**£110**
**373 VW 1200 Beetle**. WW, Dark Green/White, 'POLIZEI', M, Box has minor wear........................................................................................**£70**
**391 Ford Mustang**. Red, Black bonnet centre, Mint, Boxed, some wear ...**£120**
**441 Volkswagen Van**. 'Toblerone', Boxed, minor wear, vehicle VGC ......**£80**
**471 Smith's Canteen**. 'Joe's Diner', Mint, box with minor wear, leaflet ...**£160**
**509 Porsche Targa**. WW, Dutch, White/fluorescent orange 'RIJKSPOLITIE', M, BMW.....................**£110**
**805 Hardy Boys Rolls-Royce**. As per catalogue, contents VGC, box has minor wear .............................................................................**£170**
**1111 MF Combine Harvester**. Red/Yellow, Boxed, VGC (minor chips) ...**£100**
**1140 'Mobilgas' Tanker**. As per Catalogue, VGC, box has minor wear......**£170**
**1141 Milk Tanker**. Blue/White, VGC, Mint, Box has minor wear ...........**£150**
**GS 13 Tour de France**. As per Catalogue, Mint, box has minor wear. .......**£160**
**GS 31 Riviera Set**. As per Catalogue, VGC-M, box has minor wear .........**£210**
**GS 35 Traffic Set**. As per Catalogue, contents Mint, box has minor wear..**£190**
**GS 46 'All Winners' Set**. As per Catalogue, box complete, models Mint ..**£500**

# Crescent Toys

The Crescent Toy Company was founded in July 1922 by Henry G. Eagles and Arthur A. Schneider in a workshop 30 feet square at the rear of a private house at 67 De Beauvoir Crescent, Kingsland Road, London N1.

They manufactured model soldiers, cowboys, kitchen sets, etc. from lead alloy. These were hollow castings, hand painted, packed one dozen to a box, and sold to wholesalers at six shillings per dozen boxes. The small firm prospered and eventually opened up a factory in Tottenham. With the second World War came a ban on metal toys and production was changed to munitions. After the War the firm resumed making metal hollow-cast toys and in addition marketed the diecast products of a firm called DCMT (Die Casting Machine Tools Ltd).

As a consequence early post-war models had 'DCMT' cast into the underside of the body. In 1948 the firm opened a modern factory on a four-acre site at Cymcarn, a Welsh mining village near Newport, Monmouth (now Gwent) and two years later transferred all production there, maintaining only an office in

London. From this time Crescent toys made their own diecast products without 'DCMT' on them. Hence it is possible to find the same models with or without 'DCMT' cast in. Die Casting Machine Tools went their own way and from 1950 produced models under the name of 'Lone Star'.

Crescent Toys will be best remembered for their excellent ranges of military models and farm equipment but probably most of all for their superb reproductions of the racing cars of the 1950s.

The post-war model listings printed here were extracted from a unique collection of original trade catalogues (1947-80) most kindly provided by Mr. J. D. Schneider, the former Managing Director of Crescent Toys Ltd. All of the original research and actual compiling of the lists was undertaken by Ray Strutt.

The Editor would also like to thank Les Perry of Rochdale for additional information.

| Model and details | | | MPR |
|---|---|---|---|

## EARLY POST-WAR MODELS
(various colours)

| | | | |
|---|---|---|---|
| 223 | 1948 | **Racing Car** | £40-60 |
| 422 | 1949 | **Sports Car** | £40-60 |
| 423 | 1949 | **Oil Lorry** | £40-60 |
| 424 | 1949 | **Truck Lorry** | £40-60 |
| 425 | 1949 | **Saloon Car** | £40-60 |
| 800 | 47-49 | **Jaguar** | £40-60 |
| 802 | 47-49 | **Locomotive** | £40-60 |
| 803 | 47-48 | **Locomotive**, Silver | £40-60 |
| 804 | 48-49 | **Police Car**, Black | £40-60 |
| | 48-50 | **Deep Sea Diver**, in diving suit, with equipment, boxed | £250-325 |
| 1221 | 1949 | **Fire Engine**, Red body | £40-60 |
| 1225 | 1949 | **Dog Display Set** | £200-250 |
| --- | --- | **Garages**, retailing at 1/-, 1/6, 2/6 and 4/-. Complete with Modern Pumps, Motor Cars and Garage Attendants, 'CRESCENT GARAGES' logo | £200-300 |
| FC330 | --- | **Domestic Iron and Stand** | £20-30 |
| --- | --- | **Zulu-drawn Rickshaw.** Red/Green rickshaw, 'Zulu' with wheel attached to foot, colonial couple in tropical dress and pith helmets in rickshaw | £125-175 |
| --- | --- | **Milk Bar Set** | £300-400 |
| --- | --- | **Barber Shop Set** | £300-400 |

## FARM EQUIPMENT
(various colours)

| | | | |
|---|---|---|---|
| 1802 | 49-60 | **Tractor and Hayrake** | £300-400 |
| 1803 | 67-74 | **Dexta Tractor and Trailer** | £300-400 |
| 1804 | 50-59 | **Tractor and Disc Harrow** | £300-400 |
| 1805 | 50-61 | **Tractor** | £200-300 |
| 1806 | 50-60 | **Hayrake** | £10-15 |
| 1807 | 1950 | **Disc Harrow** | £10-15 |
| 1808 | 50-56 | **Platform Trailer** | £10-15 |
| 1809 | 50-56 | **Ricklift Trailer** | £10-15 |
| 1809 | 62-80 | **Dexta Tractor** | £150-200 |
| 1810 | 50-80 | **Box Trailer / Farm Trailer**, (No.148 1968-74) | £15-20 |
| 1811 | 50-67 | **Animal Trailer / Cattle Trailer**, (No.148 1968-71) | £10-15 |
| 1811 | 75-81 | **Dexta Tractor and Trailer** | £150-200 |
| 1813 | 1950 | **Timber Wagon** (Horse Drawn) | £75-95 |
| 1814 | 50-60 | **Plough Trailer**, (No.150 1968-71) | £20-30 |
| 1815 | 1950 | **Hayloader** | £20-30 |
| 1816 | 1950 | **Roller Harrow** | £20-30 |
| 1817 | 50-56 | **Timber Trailer** | £20-30 |
| 1818 | 54-60 | **Tipping Farm Wagon** | £20-30 |
| 1819 | 54-55 | **Large Farm Wagon** | £30-40 |

## DIECAST ACTION TOYS
(various colours)

| | | | |
|---|---|---|---|
| 1219 | 54-59 | **'Milking Time' Set.** 2 Milkmaids, 2 cows, calf. Card box, picture on lid | £125-175 |
| 1222 | 54-59 | **Builders & Decorators Truck** Red handcart, unpainted ladder and bucket, beige figure on green base. Grey card box with drawing of set | £125-175 |
| 1268 | 54-59 | **Mobile Space Rocket** | NGPP |
| 1269 | 54-59 | **Mobile Crane** | £80-100 |
| 1272 | 54-59 | **Scammell Scarab and Box Trailer** | £100-150 |
| 1274 | 54-59 | **Scammell Scarab and Low Loader** | £100-150 |
| 1276 | 55-59 | **Scammell Scarab and Oil Tanker 'ESSO'** | £150-200 |
| 2700 | 56-60 | **Western Stage Coach** | £80-90 |
| 2705 | 1955 | **Western Stage Coach** | £80-90 |
| - | | **Scammell Scarab Set,** Mechanical Horse, Box Trailer and Low Loader | £100-150 |

## MILITARY MODELS
(All in military colours)

| | | | |
|---|---|---|---|
| 155 | 60-68 | **'Long Tom' Artillery Gun** | £20-35 |
| 235 | 1946 | **Cannon**, operable | £20-25 |
| F 355 | 1938 | **Tank and Cannon Set** | £100-125 |
| 650 | 54-59 | **Military Set:** two 696 British Tanks, one 698 Scout Car, one 699 Russian Tank | £150-200 |
| NN656/2 | | | |
| | 38-40 | **Field Gun and Gunner** | £40-50 |
| NN692 | | | |
| | 38-40 | **Deep Sea Diver**, with equipment | £300-350 |
| NN693 | | | |
| | 38-40 | **A.R.P. Searchlight Unit**, 3 personnel, boxed | £150-175 |
| NN694 | | | |
| | 38-40 | **A.R.P. Rangefinder Unit**, 2 personnel, boxed | £150-175 |
| 695 | 38-40 | **A.R.P. First Aid Post:** a tent, two stretcher bearers and patient, Red Cross nurse | £150-175 |
| F 695 | 1946 | **Howitzer**, unpainted, with spring and plunger, 'CRESCENT' cast-in | £10-20 |
| 696 | 54-59 | **British Tank** | £40-50 |
| 698 | 54-59 | **Scout Car** | £30-40 |
| 699 | 54-56 | **Russian Tank** | £40-50 |
| NN700 | | | |
| | 38-40 | **Royal Engineers Field Set:** Engineers (2 standing, 2 kneeling), telegraph pole, transmitter, aerial. Box has colour picture of set on lid | £150-200 |
| 701 | - | **GPO Telephone Engineers Set:** 4 men, telegraph pole, hut, cart, accessories. Box has colour picture of set on lid | £150-200 |
| 702 | - | **Sound Locator Unit,** operator figure, boxed | £60-80 |
| K 703 | 38-40 | **Field Wireless Unit** with two Soldiers | £120-150 |
| K 704 | 38-40 | **R.A.M.C. Stretcher Party,** 2 Soldiers and Patient | £125-150 |
| 1248 | 1957 | **Field Gun** | £5-10 |
| 1249 | 58-79 | **18-lb Quick-Firing Gun** | £10-15 |
| 1250 | 58-80 | **25-pdr Light Artillery Gun** | £10-15 |
| 1251 | 58-80 | **5.5" Medium Heavy Howitzer** | £10-15 |
| 1260 | 76-79 | **Supply Truck** | £40-60 |
| 1263 | 62-80 | **Saladin Armoured Car** | £50-60 |
| 1264 | 75-80 | **Scorpion Tank** | £12-16 |
| 1265 | 77-80 | **M109 Self-Propelled Gun** | £12-15 |
| 1266 | 78-79 | **Recovery Vehicle** | £12-15 |
| 1267 | 58-63 | **'Corporal' Rocket and Lorry** | £125-150 |
| 1270 | 58-60 | **Heavy Rescue Crane** | £50-60 |
| 1271 | 58-60 | **Long Range Mobile Gun** | £100-125 |
| 1271 | 76-80 | **Artillery Force** | £20-30 |
| 2154 | 62-74 | **Saladin Armoured Patrol** (No.1270 1975-80) | £60-75 |

## HISTORICAL MODELS
(in regal colours)

| | | | |
|---|---|---|---|
| 1300 | 75-76 | **Royal State Coach** | £20-30 |
| 1301 | 77-79 | **Royal State Coach**, (Commemorative box) | £20-30 |
| 1302 | 77 | **Royal State Coach / Figures** | £20-30 |
| 1450 | 56-60 | **Medieval Catapult** | £20-30 |
| 1953 | 54-60 | **Coronation State Coach** | £100-125 |

**Miniature 'WILD WEST' Transport**
(various colours)

| | | | |
|---|---|---|---|
| 906 | 1956 | **Stage Coach** | £30-40 |
| 907 | 1956 | **Covered Wagon** | £30-40 |

Crescent Toys.

Above: BRM and Vanwall Racing Cars.

Right: An early model of a Dodgem Car.

Below: Ferrari, Gordini and Mercedes-Benz
Racing Cars.

PHOTOS:
VECTIS AUCTIONS LTD.

## G.P. RACING and SPORTS CARS

| | | | |
|---|---|---|---|
| 1284 | 56-60 | **Mercedes-Benz**, all-enveloping silver body, racing number '12' | **£90-120** |
| 1285 | 56-60 | **B.R.M. Mk.II**, mid green, '7' | **£90-120** |
| 1286 | 56-60 | **Ferrari**, orange-red | **£90-120** |
| 1287 | 56-60 | **Connaught**, dark green, racing number '8' | **£90-120** |
| 1288 | 56-60 | **Cooper-Bristol**, light blue, racing number '2' | **£90-120** |
| 1289 | 56-60 | **Gordini**, French blue, racing number '14' | **£90-120** |
| 1290 | 56-60 | **Maserati**, cherry red, racing number '3' | **£90-120** |
| 1291 | 57-60 | **Aston-Martin DB3s**, white/light blue | **£100-150** |
| 1292 | 57-60 | **Jaguar 'D' type**, dk. green | **£100-150** |
| 1293 | 58-60 | **Vanwall**, dark green, racing number '10' | **£150-200** |
| 6300 | 1957 | **Racing Cars Set**, 1284 - 1289 in display box | **NGPP** |
| | 58-60 | Same, but 1290 replaces 1284 | **NGPP** |

## LONG VEHICLES (various colours)

| | | | |
|---|---|---|---|
| 1350 | 75-80 | **Container Truck** | **£20-25** |
| 1351 | 75-80 | **Petrol Tanker** | **£20-25** |
| 1352 | 75-80 | **Girder Carrying Truck** | **£20-25** |
| 1353 | 75-80 | **Flat Platform Truck** | **£20-25** |

### 'TRUKKERS' (various colours)

| | | | |
|---|---|---|---|
| 1360 | 76-81 | **Cement Mixer** | **£5-20** |
| 1361 | 76-81 | **Covered Truck** | **£5-20** |
| 1362 | 76-81 | **Tipper Truck** | **£5-20** |
| 1363 | 76-81 | **Recovery Vehicle** | **£5-20** |
| 1364 | 76-81 | **Super Karrier** | **£5-20** |

## CRESCENT SHIPS

**SHIP MODEL IDENTIFICATION.** Crescent Ships are of rather crude manufacture and have virtually no identifying features. Only the HMS 'Vanguard' and the 'H' or 'I' Class Destroyer are known to have *CRESCENT* cast in. A few of the early models had a little paper 'Crescent' half-moon label. Ship models were packed in cream cardboard boxes of varying quality.

### BATTLESHIPS
**HMS 'King George V'**. Grey hollow-cast, with main armament only, boxed ................. **£20-30**
Same but additional separately cast secondary armament ..................................... **£20-30**
**HMS 'Vanguard'**. Grey / black / white, solid, *CRESCENT* cast-in ....................... **£10-15**

| | | | |
|---|---|---|---|
| Q 3 | 1940 | **Battleship Set**. Battleship plus four Sailors | **£80-100** |
| S 3 | 1940 | **Warships Set**. Battleship and Destroyer, eight Sailors | **£100-200** |
| NN 691 | | **HMS 'Malaya'**. Grey hollow-cast, black funnels, boxed | **£90-120** |

### AIRCRAFT CARRIERS
- **HMS 'Victorious'** (boxed). Grey hollow cast body, separate unpainted aircraft . **£20-35**

NN 667 **HMS 'Eagle'**. Grey hollow-cast, Union Jack sticker on box, unpainted planes. **£20-35**

### OTHER WARSHIPS
**'H' or 'I' Class Destroyer**. Unpainted solid cast body, *CRESCENT*" cast into bow.......... **£20-30**
**'H' or 'I' Class Destroyer**. Same model plus three lead figures of naval personnel............ **£40-60**
**'V' and 'W' Class Destroyer**. Grey hollow-cast body........................................ **£5-8**
A 34 **Gunboat**. Grey hollow cast ................... **£5-8**
234 **Submarine**. Unpainted, conning tower and deck gun, 4"......... **£20-30**
C 310 **'County' Class Cruiser**, **'Cumberland'**, Grey hollow-cast...... **£10-20**
K 664 **'County' Class Cruiser**, Grey hollow-cast ................................. **£10-20**
K 665 **War Transport Ship**, Grey hollow-cast, boxed .................... **£20-30**

### PASSENGER SHIPS
--- **'Queen Mary'**. Black / white / red, hollow-cast body, boxed .................. **£50-75**
--- **'Dunnottar Castle'**. Mauve / white / red, hollow-cast, boxed ..................... **£50-75**
--- **'Athlone Castle'**. Mauve / white / red, hollow-cast, boxed ........................ **£50-75**

'Dunnottar Castle' and 'Athlone Castle' were part of the 'Union Castle' fleet and the models were sold in souvenir boxes, probably on board.

## CRESCENT AIRCRAFT

| | | | |
|---|---|---|---|
| O 2 | 1940 | **Spitfire Set.** Two Spitfires with two Pilots and two Mechanics | **£100-200** |
| Q 2 | 1940 | **Spitfire Set.** As O 2 but new ref. no. | **£100-200** |
| U 2 | 1940 | **Aircraft Set.** Five Aircraft plus three Pilots and six Groundcrew | **£200-300** |
| FC38 | 1946 | **Aeroplane**, Spitfire | **£25-35** |
| FC89 | 1946 | **Aeroplane**, Mosquito | **£25-35** |
| FC90 | 1946 | **Aeroplane**, Lightning, 3" x 2", US markings | **£25-35** |
| FC179 | 1946 | **Khaki Bomber** | **£15-20** |
| FC372 | 1946 | **Aeroplane**, Lightning, 4.75" x 3", US markings | **£25-35** |
| FC663 | 1946 | **North Sea Patrol.** Aeroplane with pilot and one other crew member | **£80-100** |

## MISCELLANEOUS models and sets

**'Dodgem' Car**, Blue version seen, other colours possible..................... **£100-200**
**'Tower Bridge'**, various colours.................. **£20-30**
**'Dial 999' Police and Robbers Set**. Contains black police car with loudhailer on roof and four semi-flat action figures (policeman running, policeman and dog, two fleeing villains, (one with swag). In card box with b/w label ............. **£200-300**
**Road and Car Set**. Racing Car, Mechanic, Garage sign, Petrol Pump etc. ......... **£100-125**

**'Dan Dare' Set**. With figures of Dan Dare, Miss Peabody, Dan Dare in spacesuit, 2 Treens (1 silver, 1 gold), rocket and launcher. Packed in card box ......................... **£400-500**
**Trade Box** for 6 x No.363 'Shell-BP' clip-on signs. Green/red/blue box with lid...... **£30-40**
**Gas Cooker**. White, boxed ..................... **£100-125**
**1225 'My Doggies' Set**. With printed card wall backdrop and instructions. Green/Red kennel, three dogs, two bones, 'Beware of the Dog' sign..... **£200-300**
**1201 Petrol Station**. With two 'Power' and one 'Fina' petrol pumps, air pump. Box folds out to reveal forecourt scene .. **£175-225**
**1823 Model Bridge**. Green bridge/ 2 flights of steps and 'Esso' adverts. ................. **£50-75**
**1236 Bridge Signal**. White gantry with 4 mechanically operated signals. ..... **£45-55**
**Miniature Train Set**. Blue locomotive with 4 open wagons ............................. **£60-80**
**Miniature Train Set**. Red locomotive with 3 green passenger coaches ................. **£60-80**
**Station Set**. Station Master, Porter and trolley, 2 lady passengers, negro porter and waiter, mechanic........................ **£125-175**
**521 Cowboy Set**. Comprising 5 cowboys on foot in various poses ..................... **£80-100**
**? Indian Set**. One mounted Indian and four on foot, various poses............... **£80-100**
**2214 Wild Animals Set**. Kangaroo, Lion, Polar Bear, Giraffe, Zebra, Gorilla, Horse, baby Elephant, baby Giraffe ......... **£120-160**
**Farm Set**. Cow, Goat, Sheep, Dog, Farmhand with Pitchfork............... **£140-170**
**Farm Display Set**. Red Tractor and Trailer, Cow, Goose, Donkey, Pony, Plough Horse, Calf, Bullock, Pig, Goat, Farmhand with Pitchfork, Girl, Driver..................... **£350-450**
**Hen Coop Set**. Green hen house, girl/bucket, two hens, cockerel, dish ................. **£130-160**
**Stage Coach Set**. Yellow Coach with red wheels, driver, 2 horses .............. **£100-150**
**Tricky Tractor**. Yellow tractor, green/black driver, clockwork action................. **£200-260**
**1450 Medieval Catapult**. Green metal catapult, brown plastic wheels ..........**£90-110**
**The Crescent Fortress**. Tinplate Castle with internal fold out section................. **£240-280**
**160/1 Tank Set**. Three camouflaged miniature tanks and an armoured car ............. **£250-300**
**Naval Set**. Warship with officer, rating with flags, rating with telescope............. **£60-75**
**Deep Sea Diver Set**. Diver in Grey diving suit, helmet, compressor and pump, bollards, three tools ................ **£125-150**
**North Sea Patrol**. Two Aeroplanes, one brown and one green with pilots..... **£100-140**
**Royal Horse Artillery Set**. 6 Horse team, 3 field drivers with whips, limber with 2 seated gunners, field gun with sprung breech ............................ **£200-250**
**RAF Set**. Two Officers, Pilot, Mechanic and two small aircraft............. **£100-150**
**2107 Farm Animals**. 12 Farm animals in pictorial box................................. **£100-130**

---

## CRESCENT TOYS SELECTED AUCTION RESULTS 2005 — 2007

### Vectis Auctions Ltd.
Fleck Way, Thornaby, Stockton -on-Tees TS17 9JZ
Abbreviations: M = Mint, NM = Near Mint, EP = Excellent Plus,
E = Excellent, GP = Good Plus, G = Good, F = Fair

**CRESCENT TOYS**
**Dexta Tractor/Trailer.** Tractor Blue, Trailer Red/Yellow, Red plastic hubs. **£80**
**Tower Bridge.** Gold body, E in E box ......... **£25**
**HMS 'Eagle' Aircraft Carrier.** Grey, twin black funnels, VG in F box .... **£110**

**691 HMS 'Malaya'.** Grey battleship, twin black funnels, gilt guns, E in VG box ............... **£130**
**693 ARP Unit.** Searchlight, two standing operators, spotter with binoculars, E in E box ......................... **£400**
**694 ARP Unit.** Range finder and operator, kneeling spotter with binoculars, E in VG box .................. **£280**
**703 Field Unit.** Two kneeling wireless operators, triangular aerial, E in VG box........................ **£240**
**700 Royal Engineers Set.** Two telephone engineers, telegraph pole, wire, E in VG box........................ **£400**

# Meccano
# Dinky Toys

## HISTORY OF DINKY TOYS

In 1931, Meccano Ltd introduced a series of railway station and trackside accessories to accompany their famous 'HORNBY' train sets. These 'Modelled Miniatures' were in sets numbered 1 – 22 and included railwaymen, station staff, passengers and trains. Set number 22 was comprised of six vehicles which were representative rather than replicas of actual vehicles. It was first advertised in the Meccano Magazine of December 1933.

At about this time 'Tootsie Toys' of America were introducing model vehicles into the United Kingdom and they were proving to be very popular. Consequently Meccano Ltd decided to widen their range of products and issue a comprehensive series of models to include vehicles, ships and aircraft.

'Modelled Miniatures' therefore became 'Meccano Dinky Toys' and set number 22 the first set of 'Dinky Cars'. The first 'Dinky Toys' advertisement appeared in the April 1934 edition of the Meccano Magazine. The first Dinky car produced after the change of name was 23a in April 1934. It was probably based on an early MG but was again generally representative rather than an accurate model. Set 22 cost 4/- and consisted of: 22a Sports Car, 22b Sports Coupé, 22c Motor Truck, 22d Delivery Van, 22e Tractor and 22f Tank and is today highly sought after.

The range of models produced grew quickly so that the Meccano Magazine of December 1935 was claiming that there were 200 varieties to choose from! Although the phrase 'Dinky Toys' became a household name,

the actual range was of course far greater and was not limited to cars; it even included dolls house furniture. Indeed, by the time the famous Binns Road factory in Liverpool finally closed its doors in November 1979 over 1,000 different designs had been produced. Pre-war models are rare today and fetch high prices, which reflects how difficult it is to find a model in really good condition. This is because so many 1930s models were made from an unstable alloy which has tended to crystallise and disintegrate. Fortunately the post-war models do not suffer from the same problem and much of today's collecting interest is centred around the delightful models produced in the fifties and sixties with Gift Sets being particularly sought after. Most Dinky Toys boxes were made by McCorquodale in Northern Ireland.

In 1987 the Dinky trade name was bought by Matchbox who were at the time part of the Universal International Co. of Hong Kong. They introduced the 'Dinky Collection' in 1988 with some very fine models in a constant scale of 1:43. On the 7th May 1992 it was announced in the 'New York Times' that 'Tyco Toys Inc.' had acquired by merger the 'Universal Matchbox Group' and with it the famous 'Dinky Toys' brand name.

In 1998, Mattel bought the Matchbox brand and in 1999 disclosed that all new car models will be classified as 'Dinky Toys', including those previously included in their Matchbox Models of Yesteryear range. At the beginning of 2001 however, both of those famous names have been all but buried in favour of Mattel's 'Hot Wheels' brand since most of their products have been aimed at the US toy market.

# Dinky Toys Model Identification

**Common Features.** There are several features common to various groups of models and to avoid unnecessary repetition in the listings they are shown below. Exceptions to these general indications are noted in the listings.

**'Dinky Toys', 'Meccano Ltd', or 'Meccano Dinky Toys'.**
These wordings are to be found cast or stamped on the base-plate or chassis or in the case of early models without a base they are cast into the model itself. Some very early models have 'HORNBY SERIES' cast-in (e.g, those in the 22 series).

**Wheel hubs.** Solid one-piece wheel/tyre castings were fitted to the 'Modelled Miniatures' and first pre-war 'Dinky Toys'. They had 'Hornby' or 'Meccano' cast onto their rims and were covered in a thin colour wash or silver-plated. This casting was soon replaced with more realistic cast hubs (having a smooth convex face) fitted with white (sometimes coloured) rubber tyres. Pre-war hubs may be black, coloured or sometimes silver-plated. Post-war hubs were of the 'ridged' type having a discernible ridge simulating a hub cap. They were painted and usually fitted with black rubber tyres.

**Supertoys hubs and tyres.** When Supertoys were introduced in 1947 the ridged type of hub was used on the Fodens with black 'herringbone pattern' tyres, and on the Guys with smooth black tyres. Fodens graduated to the use of 'fine radial-tread' tyres first in black, later in grey, then to black again but with a more chunky 'block' tread. Supertoys later acquired plastic hubs and plastic tyres.

**Hub materials.** Lead was used originally for a short time, the majority of models from the mid-1930s to the early 1960s having diecast mazak hubs. Small models like motor-cycles or the 35b Racer were fitted with solid one-piece wheel/tyre moulding (white or black rubber pre-war, black post-war). In 1958/9 aluminium hubs were introduced and some models (such as 131, 178, 179, 180, 181, 182 and 290 Bus) appeared fitted with either type. Plastic hubs replaced the diecast versions on racing cars numbered 230-235 while the Austin A30 and Fiat 600 were given solid one-piece wheel/tyre plastic injection mouldings. **Speedwheels** were introduced in the 1970s and some model can be found fitted with metal wheels or Speedwheels. The former are more collectable.

**Baseplates** are tinplate or diecast unless described otherwise. Plastic moulded baseplates are generally restricted to a few models made after 1970. **Model Numbers** appear on many Dinky Toys baseplates but not all. The **Model Name** however appears on virtually every post-war Dinky Toy. Pre-war models usually had neither (the 38 and 39 series are exceptions having the model name on their baseplates).

**Construction Materials.** All models assumed to be constructed at least in part of a diecast alloy. Some pre-war models were made of a lead alloy like the 22 and 28 series plus the few odd models such as 23 a Racing Car and 23m Thunderbolt. The Blaw-Knox Bulldozer was one of the very few produced (right at the end of its production) in plastic.

**Windows.** Pre-war and early post-war models had tinplate or celluloid windscreens. Moulded plastic windscreens appeared in the 1950s on open car models. The first Dinky to be fitted with all-round plastic window glazing was the Austin A105 Saloon. Some models in production at the time were fitted with glazing later and may therefore be found with or without it.

**Hooks** were not fitted to the first Supertoys Foden models (1947). Small hooks were fitted in early 1948, the usual (larger) hook appearing in mid-1948.

**Axles** were all 'crimped' pre-war and on these series of models post-war: 23, 25, 29, 30, 34, 35, 36, 37, 38, 39, 40 and 280. Otherwise models had rivet-ended axles until the advent of Speedwheels. Early Guy models had tinplate clips to retain the front axles. Pre-war axles are generally thinner than post-war at 0.062mm diameter while post-war axles are 0.078mm in diameter.

**Size of models** (where shown) is in millimetres and refers to the longest overall measurement (usually the length). In the case of pre-war models slight inaccuracies may occur from expansion of the casting as it ages in the course of time.

**The Scale of Dinky Toys** was originally 1:43 (with a few exceptions). Supertoys Foden and Guy vehicles (introduced in 1947) were in a scale of 1:48 while military models issued from 1953 were smaller at 1:60. Most aircraft models before 1965 were around 1:200 and ships 1:1800. In the late 1960s and early 1970s the 1:36 scale was introduced, mostly for cars.

**Dinky Numbering System.** The dual/triple reference numbers used on some Dinky Toys and Supertoys (for example 409 / 521 / 921 Bedford Articulated Lorry) refers to the basic model type and casting and not to model colours. The renumbering by Meccano was an administration process to re-catalogue production of existing lines and introduce new models. New colours on existing castings which arise at about the time of renumbering are therefore coincidental with it rather than a consequence of it.

**Identification of early post-war Dinky Toys cars.**
Note that pre-war wheel hubs may be smooth diecast or the rare chrome ('Tootsie-Toy' type) hubs which attract a premium.

**Post-war 30 Series**

| | |
|---|---|
| Circa 1946 | Open chassis with smooth black wheel hubs. |
| Circa 1948 | Plain chassis with ridged black wheel hubs. |

**36 Series**

| | |
|---|---|
| Circa 1946 | Moulded chassis; smooth black wheel hubs. |
| Circa 1948 | Moulded chassis; ridged black wheel hubs. |

**38 Series**

| | |
|---|---|
| Circa 1946 | With pre-war lacquered tinplate base secured by spread spigots (not rivets), silvered sidelights, smooth black hubs. |
| Circa 1946 | Solid steering wheels, smooth black hubs, silvered sidelights, black painted baseplate. |
| Circa 1947 | As above but with silver-edged windscreen. |
| Circa 1948-49 | Open or solid steering wheel, ridged hubs, black painted baseplate. |
| Circa 1950 | As above but with coloured wheel hubs. |

**39 Series**

| | |
|---|---|
| Circa 1946 | 'Gold' pre-war baseplate, smooth black wheel hubs, silver door handles and radiator cap. |
| Circa 1948 | Black painted baseplate, ridged black hubs. |
| Circa 1950 | As above but with coloured wheel hubs. |

**40 Series**
See the 40 Series listings for identification and illustrations.

## Box Types Introduction

A mint condition model car without its correct box is worth but a fraction of its mint boxed equivalent. Furthermore, as model boxes made from card do not survive as well as their die-cast contents, pristine box examples are scarce and becoming scarcer. The condition of a box is of paramount importance and attention is drawn to the section in the catalogue introduction, namely: 'Classifying the Condition of Models and Boxes'.

The following listing provides collectors with a working knowledge of the range of box types issued. In addition details are given of their dates of issue, their design and of the models which used them. See also the colour sections for examples of many types of boxes.

Whilst every care has been taken in preparing the listing, other variations may exist and information on them is welcomed. Similarly, with no 'dates of birth' available the dates of issues shown are approximate and again any further information is welcomed.

## Box Identification

### Model colour identification marks - colour spots

These are shown on the box lid end flap and take the form of a circular colour spot. This may be either a single colour or, in the case of the later two-tone car issues, a two-tone colour spot. Colour spots were used until the early 1960s.
NB The dual numbered 234/23H box displays the **Ferrari** model name against a blue panel which matches the main body colour.

### Dual numbered boxes 1953 - 1954

A new numbering system was introduced which resulted in models being issued displaying both the old and new reference numbers. The information was shown on the box end flaps as follows:
Old model number shown in red letters on either side of a larger white number set on a black oval background, e.g. 40J **161** 40J. Dual numbered boxes were only issued for a short period and may attract a premium. The numbers may be large or small.

### Pre-war issues

Apart from special issues such as 23m Thunderbolt Speed Car and 23p Gardner's M.G. Record Car, individual models were sold unboxed. They were usually packaged in half-dozen retailers trade packs (see the section on Trade Packs). Models were also sold in boxed sets (see the Gift Set Section).

**Post-war** After the second world war models continued to be sold unboxed from trade boxes until 1953/54 when the first individual boxes were introduced. The boxes have been catalogued into three types as follows:

    **Type 1**: Card boxes with tuck-in flaps
    **Type 2**: Display boxes -Blister packs, rigid plastic packs, vacuform packs and card window boxes.
    **Type 3**: Export Issue boxes.

## Type 1 1953 – 1975 All card box with tuck-in end flaps

**(i) 1953- 1954 Deep yellow box** with 'DINKY TOYS' in red plus the model's name and type in black. A white reference number on a black oval background is on the box end flaps but no reference number is shown on the box face. The model is pictured on the box sides but without a white shaded background. Colour spots shown on box-end flaps as applicable. Foreign language information is shown on one of the end flaps of the early issue boxes. Box in general use during the model renumbering period. Consequently, dual numbered boxes will be found. It would appear that only models 23f, g, h, j, k and n, and 40j were housed in individual boxes prior to renumbering. Please supply details of any other models housed in boxes displaying just their old reference number.

**(ii) 1955 - 1956 Same as (i)** but a white reference number on a black oval background is shown on the face of the box to the left of the model picture. Also as (i) but with a white reference number on a red oval background and placed either to the left or the right of the model picture. Box in general use for all issues.

**(iii) 1956 - 1960 Same as (ii)** but model pictures are displayed against a white shadow background. In some instances only one picture. had a shadow, e.g. 171 Hudson Commodore and in others both pictures were given a shadow; e.g. 152 Austin Devon. Box in general use for all issues. Later issues display 'WITH WINDOWS', caption in a red line features box.

**(iv) c1960 Deep yellow plain box** with no model picture, 'DINKY TOYS' and text in red; rarely used. Colour spots shown as applicable. We believe these boxes may have been used for mail-order or possibly export purposes. The Editor would welcome any new information. Known examples: 103, 108, l09, 163, 178 and 191.

**(v) 1959–1961 Plain lighter yellow box** with no model picture. It has two yellow and two red sides. 'DINKY TOYS' is shown in yellow on red sides. Colour spots shown as applicable. Models recorded: 105, 109, 131, 150, 157, 165, 169, 173. 174, 176, 178, 187, 189, 191, 192 and 230 to 235. The special issue 189 Triumph Heralds used this box.

**(vi) 1960 - 1966 Yellow box** with a separate red line features box placed to the right of the model picture. Colour spots still in use on early 1960s issues. Foreign language text on one box end flap and 'WITH WINDOWS' captions on box face. Models recorded: 105, 112, 113, 131, 144, 148, 155, 157, 164–167, 176–178, 181/2, 184, 186, 191-195, 197, 199, 230-235, 237, 239 and 449. Later issues without colour spots. Boxes used for some South African issues display both English and Afrikaans text.

**(vii) c.1962 – 1963 Lighter yellow box** similar to (v) but colour spots not in use. A scarce issue box which may attract a premium. Model recorded: 166.

**(viii) 1962 – 1963 Yellow box with a red end** features panel around the left side of the box. Recorded models: 113, 147 and 198.

**(ix) 1962 – 1963 (?) Yellow/red box** similar to previous items, but has yellow ends, yellow top and bottom panels and red side panels, the latter virtually filled with the text: *'DINKY TOYS'*. Colour spots not seen. See page vii of the colour section for an illustration of this box (containing 178 Plymouth Plaza).

**(x) 1963 – 1970 Yellow box** with a red end features panel around the right side. The panel is bisected by the model picture and is with or without a large or small white arrow design. Models recorded: 112-114. 120, 127-130, 133-139, 140-148, 198, 240-243, 268, 273 and 274. Some South African issues used this box, e.g. 141 Vauxhall Victor Estate Car. They display both English and Afrikaans text. The rare Triumph 2000 Saloon promotional issues will be found in this box. Some have an applied white label on the box face showing the colour of the model, e.g. Olive-Cactus.

**(xi) 1966 – 1969 Detailed full colour picture box** with pictorial scene on two sides with 'DINKY TOYS' in red letters. Recorded issues: 133, 136, 183, 212, 214, 225 plus Hong Kong issues 57/001-57/006.

**(xii) 1968 – 1974 White-fronted box** with a thin yellow band across the box face. A yellow laurel leaf design on a black background is a main box feature. The white face of the box may contain features information such as '1st AGAIN' and 'SPEEDWHEELS'. Variation exists with a semi-pictorial box face (probably an export special) e.g. 176 NSU R80. Models recorded: 157, 159 165/6, 169, 174/5, 179, 183, 192, 205 and 212. NB. A variation of this box exists with a large red 'DINKY TOYS' and number to the left of the picture and no yellow band across the face, e.g. 138 Hillman Imp.

## Type 2  1962 – 1980  Display boxes, Blister packs, Rigid plastic and Vacuform packs, Window boxes

**(i) 1962 – 1964 Blister Card Packs** used for racing cars nos. 205210. Red/yellow display card with chequered flag design.

**(ii) 1967 – 1971 Rigid plastic 'see-through' case** with lift-off lid. models displayed on a card base with a black 'roadway' surface. The base sides are yellow with 'DINKY TOYS' in red. Recorded issues: 110, 116, 127, 129, 131/2, 142, 152-154, 158, 161, 163/4, 168, 175, 187-189, 190, 208, 210, 213, 215, 216, 220/1 and 223/4.

**(iii) 1972 – 1976 Vacuform Packs**. Models displayed on a black base with a blue surface with 'DINKY TOYS' in red/white letters. The model is covered by a close fitting plastic cover. Known issues: 129, 131, 149, 168, 178 and 192 plus 1:25 issues 2214, 3162 and 2253.

**(iv) 1976 – 1979 Window Box** with 'see-through' cellophane front

and blue and red header card with a 'DINKY DIECAST TOYS' in yellow letters. Variations exist with a model picture on the header card e.g. 112 'Purdey's TR7'. Known issues: 113, 120, 122/3/4, 128. 180, 192, 207/8, 211, 221/2/3 and 226/7.

**(v) 1968 – 1969 Plastic see-through red box** made in a garage shape to house 'Mini Dinky' issues.

**(vi) 1979 Bubble Pack** 219 'Big Cat' Jaguar.

## Type 3   1966 – 1980   Export issue boxes

**(i) 1966 – 1980 An all yellow card and cellophane 'see-through' display box** with outward-folding ends. 'DINKY TOYS' and four diagonal stripes plus 'A MECCANO PRODUCT MADE IN ENGLAND' are in red on the box face. The box display base may be either yellow or have a black 'roadway' design.

Whilst generally used for export issues it was specifically used for the U.S. export series 'MARVELS IN MINIATURE - which appeared in red letters on the box front. Later issues listed the models on the base of the box.

A box variation exists with just 'DINKY' and 'A MECCANO PRODUCT' on the face of the box plus the model name and number. The base of the box is yellow. The box was issued with a card protection strip which stated: 'Mr DEALER PLEASE REMOVE THIS STRIP'. Models known to have been issued in this box include: 110-115, 120, 127/8, 133-138, l41/2. 151, 161, 170-172, 190, 192, 196, 215, 237, 240-243, 257/8, 57/006. **NB** We believe this box was probably used in the UK but would be grateful for confirmation.

**(ii) 1966 – 1968 All gold card and cellophane 'see-through' display box** with just 'DINKY' in gold letters set in a red panel on the box front plus red and black diagonal stripes. 'A MECCANO PRODUCT MADE IN ENGLAND' in black is also on the front of the box. Only used for a short time so models in these boxes often sell at a premium. The known issues are: 112, 113, 148, 193, 215, 238, 240-243, 340 and 448.

**(iii) 1979 – 1980 A flat yellow box with blue end flaps**. Used to house the Swiss promotional issue No. 223 Hesketh F1 Racing Car 'OLYMPUS CAMERAS'.
**Export issue**: 449 has been observed in an 'all gold' box.

## 40 Series issues distribution, renumbering and packing

Models in the 40 Series were initially sold unboxed from retailers' trade boxes of 6 models as follows:

| | | |
|---|---|---|
| i) | 1947-50 | Plain Brown card box with lift-off lid. On the end of the lid was a Yellow label displaying the quantity, the model's name and its reference number, e.g., '6  RILEY SALOON   40a'. |
| ii) | 1950-54 | All Yellow card box with lift-off lid. The contents were printed in Black on the end of the box lid. |
| iii) | 1954 | Models renumbered. When the 40 Series models were renumbered, the final all-Yellow card boxes for six displayed both the original number and its new number, for example: '158   RILEY SALOON   40a'. |
| iv) | 1954-60 | The renumbered models were individually boxed in the first type of Yellow end-flap boxes as follows:<br>a) Displaying the dual numbers for a short time, e.g., '40a  158  40a' on the end flap.<br>b) Displaying just the model's new number, e.g., '158' plus the correct colour spot for  the model. |

## Chassis types, 1934 – 1950

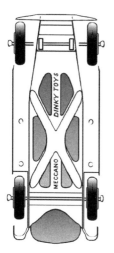
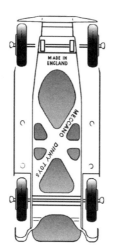
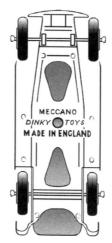
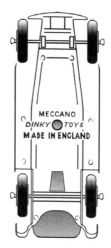
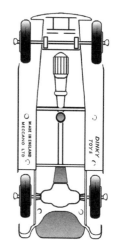

**1934 - 1935**
'Criss-cross' chassis
1st type
with or without
slot for spare wheel

**1935 - 1936**
'Criss-cross' chassis
2nd type
with or without
slot for spare wheel

**1936 - 1940**
Open chassis
with or without
slots for figures

**1946 - 1947**
Plain chassis, no
slots for figures,
hole for caravan
drawbar

**1948 - 1950**
'Moulded'
(detailed) chassis,
hole for caravan
drawbar

## 24 Series radiator grille types, 1934 – 1940

**1st type**
**1934 - 1938**
With diamond shape
in centre of bumper
No radiator badge
No over-riders

**2nd type**
**1934 - 1938**
No diamond shape in
centre of bumper
No radiator badge
No over-riders

**3rd type**
**1938 - 1940**
'Bentley' style
with radiator badge
and over-riders

The first and second type grilles will be found on the both the first and second type chassis.
The later third type grille will be found with the second type chassis.

# Dinky Toys Cars – Identification of wheel types

These drawings are provided for general guidance only. They are not all strictly to the same scale.

1935 - 1941.
Pair of smooth-hub diecast wheel hubs as fitted to all car models. Crimped axle ends.

1935 - 1941.
Smooth-hub diecast wheel hubs as fitted to 23a Racing Car. Note the 'arrow-head' or 'herring-bone' tyre treads.

1947 onwards.
Ridged-hub diecast wheel as on all early post-war issues. Rounded axle ends. Smooth tyres. French versions are often referred to as 'convex' and are sometimes plated.

1958
Treaded plastic wheel fitted to 160 Austin A30. Smooth (non-treaded) wheels were also fitted to this model.

c1958.
Treaded tyre design as fitted to 111 Triumph TR2.

c1959.
Spun aluminium hubs as fitted to many car models.

c1967.
16-spoke cast wheel as on 281 Fiat Pathé News car.

c1970.
No. 100 Lady Penelope's 'FAB 1' 2nd type wheel shown. 1st type has six raised studs in a 'starfish' pattern.

c1968.
Cast wheel used on No. 13 Ferrari in the 'Mini-Dinky' series.

c1972.
Detailed cast wheel as fitted to 252 Pontiac Parisienne Police Car.

**Market Price Range (MPR) for pre-1954 unboxed car models.**
Prior to 1954, virtually all the cars were sold unboxed from retailer's trade boxes of either 6, 4 or 3 models. Consequently, all pre-1954 issues (except for 23m and 23s) have been priced as being unboxed. Post-1954 models were all boxed and have been priced accordingly. As a consequence, models which have been renumbered will often be found to have two differing prices – one for the pre-1954 unboxed version and another for its boxed and renumbered successor.
See also the Trade Box section for details of individual boxes and packs that were used to supply shops.

| Model and details | MPR |
|---|---|

**22a** 1933-35 **Open Sports Car**
'Modelled Miniature' with 'HORNBY SERIES' cast into lead body, solid metal wheel/tyre castings (thinly painted in metallic blue, purple, green, yellow or red, or not painted at all) lead windscreen surround, tinplate radiator (grille may be same colour as body, or overpainted with the colour of the mudguards).
- Blue body, Yellow seats and mudguards.................................. **£400-600**
- Blue body, Red seats / mudguards.... **£400-600**
- Cream body, Red seats / mudguards. **£400-600**
- Cream body, Green seats and mudguards.................................. **£400-600**
- Cream body, Blue seats/mudguards.. **£400-600**
- Red body, Cream or Blue seats and mudguards.................................. **£400-600**
- Yellow body, Green seats and mudguards.................................. **£400-600**
- Orange-Brown body, Cream seats and mudguards ............ **£400-600**
- Green body, Yellow seats and mudguards.................................. **£400-600**

**22b** 1933-35 **Closed Sports Coupé**
'Modelled Miniature' with 'HORNBY SERIES' cast into lead body, solid metal wheel/tyre castings (coloured or plain, as 22a), tinplate radiator (painted in main body colour).
- Cream body, Red roof and mudguards......................... **£1,500-2,000**
- Cream, Green roof and mudguards......................... **£1,500-2,000**
- Red body, Blue roof/mudguards . **£1,500-2,000**
- Red body, Cream roof and mudguards......................... **£1,500-2,000**
- Blue body, Red roof/mudguards . **£1,500-2,000**
- Blue body, Yellow roof and mudguards......................... **£1,500-2,000**
- Yellow body, Green roof and mudguards......................... **£1,500-2,000**
- Orange body, Green roof and mudguards, Gold wash wheels ... **£1,500-2,000**

**22g** 1935-41 **Streamline Tourer**
Model has cast steering wheel and windscreen, smooth diecast hubs which may be painted as body colour or a contrasting colour. Some have chrome hubs.
Body colours:
- Green, Maroon, Red, Light or Dark Blue, Cream, Buff or Black..... **£300-400**
- Turquoise body, Blue hubs, White tyres......................... **£750-1,000**
South African issues:
Leaf Green with plated hubs............. **£250-350**

**22h** 1935-41 **Streamlined Saloon**
A saloon version of 22g (no steering wheel). Wheels may be painted as body colour or a contrasting colour.
- Red, Maroon, Blue or Cream........... **£300-400**

**23** 1934-35 **Racing Car** (1st casting)
Lead body, no racing number, no driver, 0, 2, 3 or 4 exhausts stubs (without pipe), coloured tyres on some.
- Cream or White body with either Blue, Cream, Green, Orange or Red top and nose flash..................... **£200-300**

- Yellow body with Blue upper body flash, 3 exhaust stubs ........................ **£200-300**

**23a** 1935-41 **Racing Car** (23 re-issued)
As 1st casting but diecast body, no driver, no number, Black or White tyres, 4 exhausts.
- White body and hubs, Blue top flash and circle on nose ............................ **£200-300**
- Cream body and hubs, Red top flash and circle on nose ............................ **£200-300**
- Blue body, White top flash and circle on nose .................................. **£200-300**
- Orange body, Green top flash and circle on nose .................................. **£200-300**
- Yellow body, Dark Blue flash and circle on nose .................................. **£200-300**
- Brown body, Cream top flash .......... **£200-300**
- Silver body, Green number '8'.......... **£200-300**

**23a** **Racing Car** (2nd casting)
With driver plus raised circles for racing numbers, 6 exhausts in fishtail.
*Colour type 1*:
With minor colour sidestripes and perhaps coloured tyres.
(Sometimes known as '**humbug**' version).
*Colour type 2*:
Broad nose flash, even width top rear flash. (Also known as '**humbug**' version).
*Colour type 3*:
Broad flash at cockpit and pointed ends top flash, cast circle on nose.
Variations:
- **Type 1**, Cream body, Red stripes, number '9'................................**£1,000-1,500**
- **Type 2**, Blue with White stripes / driver, RN '11' ...............................**£1,000-1,500**
- **Type 2**, Yellow body, Dark Blue top flash, racing number '7' or '1'................. **£200-300**
- **Type 2**, Blue body, White top flash, racing number '11', '4' or '5' .......... **£200-300**
- **Type 2**, Yellow with Blue stripes, racing number '7', silvered 'Tootsie Toy' type hubs............... **£1,000-1,500**
- **Type 2**, Orange with Green stripes, racing number '10', silvered 'Tootsie Toy' type hubs............... **£1,000-1,500**
- **Type 3**, White body, Blue nose/circle and top flash, racing number '2'...... **£200-300**
- **Type 3**, Cream body, Red nose/circle and top flash, racing number '3'....... **£200-300**
- **Type 3**, Red body, Cream nose and flash, no number, no transverse ribs. **£200-300**
- **Type 3**, White body, Green nose/circle and top flash, racing number '6'....... **£200-300**
- **Type 3**, Orange body, Green nose/circle and top flash, racing number '4'....... **£200-300**
- Casting variation with driver, raised racing number circle on nearside only, no detailed exhaust, Orange body, Green nose circle, Green RN '4' ...... **£150-175**
- Orange body, long Green upper body flash, 3 exhaust stubs, Green racing number '4' or '10'...................... **£150-175**
- Yellow body, long Dark Blue upper body flash, plated hubs .................... **£200-250**

**23a** 1946-52 **Racing Car** (3rd casting)
With transverse body ribs, no raised circle for racing numbers, and only issued in colour type 3, with or without racing numbers.
(Re-introduced in 1954 as 220).

- Red or Red/Green body, Silver nose circle, top flash and side circle (Red RN '4'), Red hubs ...................... **£50-75**
- Silver body, Red nose circle, top flash and side circle (Silver RN '4'), Red hubs ... **£50-75**
- Red body, Cream flashes, Black hubs .. **£50-75**

**23b** 1935-41 **Hotchkiss Racing Car**
- Blue body with Dark Blue, Red or Silver flash and number '2', '5' or '8' ........ **£300-400**
- Cream body, Red flash and RN '1'... **£300-400**
- Yellow body, Blue flash and RN '3'. **£300-400**
- Orange body, Green flash / RN '6'... **£300-400**
- Green body, Yellow flash / RN '5'... **£300-400**
- Turquoise body, Red flash / RN '4'.. **£300-400**
- Turquoise body, Blue flash/RN '4'... **£300-400**
1946-48
- Red with Silver flash and RN '5' ........ **£50-75**
- Silver with Red flash and RN '5' ........ **£50-75**

**23c** 1936-38 **Mercedes-Benz Racing Car**
- Red, Light Blue, Silver, Yellow or Light Green body with contrasting body flashes, with or without racing numbers '3', '4' or '5', driver cast-in, Black hubs, treaded tyres................. **£200-250**
- 1938-40 As previous model but with rivetted baseplate bearing information.......... **£150-200**
- 1946-50 ('Large Open Racing Car'). Re-issued 23c in Blue or Silver, with various racing numbers................. **£40-50**

**23d** 1936-38 **Auto-Union Racing Car**
Early pre-war issues without driver:
- Red, Turquoise, Pale Green, Yellow or Silver body, racing numbers on some, clipped-in tinplate base .................... **£300-500**
- Bottle-Green body........................... **£750-1,000**
- 1938-41 Later pre-war issue with driver, rivetted baseplate ................... **£250-350**
- 1946-50 Early post-war issue with driver: Red or Silver body, with or without racing number, Black or White tyres.. **£80-100**
- Later post-war issue without driver .... **£80-100**

**23e** 1936-38 **'Speed Of The Wind' Racing Car**
- Red, Blue, Light Blue, Green, Yellow or Silver body, plain clipped-in tinplate base, driver, with or without racing numbers '3' or '6', Black hubs and herringbone tyres. Lead fakes exist........................... **£50-75**
- 1938-41 With rivetted baseplate bearing information.............................. **£50-75**
- 1946-49 Red or Silver, rivetted informative baseplate, Red hubs, Grey tyres...................................... **£35-45**
- 1950-54 (Renumbered to 221) Silver body and hubs, plain base ......... **£35-45**

**23f** 1952-54 **Alfa-Romeo Racing Car**
- Red body, White racing number '8', Red diecast hubs, not boxed ................ **£85-95**
  1954 (Renumbered to 232)

**23g** 1952-54 **Cooper-Bristol Racing Car**
- Green body, White RN '6', Green ridged hubs, not boxed.............. **£85-95**
  1954 (Renumbered to 233)

**23h** 1953-54 **Ferrari Racing Car**
- Blue body, Yellow nose, RN '5' and ridged hubs, not boxed.................. **£85-95**
  1954 (Renumbered to 234)

**23j** 1953-54 **H.W.M. Racing Car**
- Light Green body, Yellow '7',
  Green ridged hubs, not boxed .............. **£85-95**
  1954      (Renumbered to 235)

**23k** 1953-54 **Talbot-Lago Racing Car**
- Blue body, Yellow RN '4',
  Blue diecast hubs, not boxed ............... **£85-95**
  1954      (Renumbered to 230)

**23m** 1938-41 **'Thunderbolt' Speed Car**
- Silver body, Black detailing, Union Jacks
  on tail, Silver baseplate. In original Blue
  box dated '2-38', code: 'A2247' ....... **£125-150**
- Red body, Silver detailing ................. **£300-400**

**23n** 1953-54 **Maserati Racing Car**
- Red, White flash and RN '9',
  Red diecast hubs, not boxed ................ **£85-95**
  1954      (Renumbered to 231)

**23p** 1939-40 **Gardner's MG Record Car**
- Dark Green, White flash and 'MG' logo,
  Union Jacks, 'MG Magnette' on lacquered
  unpainted tinplate baseplate,
  Yellow box, dated '9-39' ................. **£300-400**
- 1946-47  Dark Green body,
  Union Jacks, no flash, 'MG Record Car'
  on base, not boxed ........................... **£80-100**

**23s** 1938-40 **Streamlined Racing Car**
- Light Green body, Dark Green
  detailing, lead ........................... **£100-125**
- Light Blue body, Dark Blue or
  Silver detailing, lead ..................... **£100-125**
- Orange body, lead ........................... **£100-125**
- Light Green, Light Blue, Red or
  Orange body, mazak diecasting ......... **£75-100**
- 1948-54  Light, Mid or Dark Green
  body, Silver or Green flashes ............... **£50-65**
- Navy Blue body with Silver or
  Green flashes ........................... **£50-65**
- Silver body with Red, Green or
  Blue flashes ........................... **£50-65**
- Red body with Silver or Black flashes,
  Black base ........................... **£50-65**
  1954      (Renumbered to 222)

**24a** 1934-40 **Ambulance**
  See 'Emergency Vehicles' Section.

**24b** 1934-38 **Limousine**
  Types 1 or 2: criss-cross chassis.
  Types 1, 2 or 3: grille, no sidelights,
  no spare wheel, 3 side windows,
  3 'stacked' parallel horizontal bonnet
  louvres. Blue, Black or plated
  'Tootsie-Toy'type hubs.
- Body/chassis colours:
  Maroon/Dark Maroon, Maroon/Grey,
  Maroon/Black, Blue/Yellow,
  Dark Blue/Black, Yellow/Brown ...... **£300-500**
  1937-40    casting change:
- Same colours but no spare wheel slot,
  3 parallel bonnet louvres, open chassis,
  'Bentley' grille and bumper ............. **£200-400**

**24c** 1934-38 **Town Sedan**
  Types 1 or 2: criss-cross chassis.
  Types 1, 2 or 3: grille, spare wheel,
  no sidelights, separate windscreen/steering
  wheel casting, smooth Blue, Black or
  plated 'Tootsie-Toy'type hubs.
- Body/chassis colours:
  Green/Black, Green/Yellow,
  Pale Green/Red, Dark Blue/Dark Blue,
  Cream/Dark Blue, Cream/Black,
  Dark Blue/Black ........................... **£300-500**
  1937-40    casting change:
- Same colours but open chassis,
  no spare wheel slot, narrower
  boot, shorter door handles ................. **£200-400**

**24d** 1934-38 **Vogue Saloon**
  Types 1 or 2: criss-cross chassis.
  Types 1, 2 or 3: grille, with nearside spare
  wheel, no sidelights. Smooth Blue,
  Black or plated hubs with White tyres.
- Body/chassis colours:
  Blue/Dark Blue, Blue/Black, Blue/Maroon,
  Cream/Blue, Brown/Green, Pink/Green,
  Red/Grey, Green/Blue, Green/Black,
  Maroon/Black ........................... **£400-600**
  1937-40    casting change:
- Same colours but open chassis, higher
  'domed' roofline, no spare wheel ..... **£300-500**

**24e** 1934-38 **Super Streamlined Saloon**
  Types 1 or 2: criss-cross chassis.
  Types 1, 2 or 3: grille, no spare or sidelights,
  12 bonnet louvres. Smooth Blue, Black or
  plated 'Tootsie-Toy' type hubs.

- Body/chassis colours:
  Maroon/Black, Red/Maroon, Green/Maroon,
  Red/Black, Green/Blue, Red/Brown,
  All Maroon ........................... **£400-600**
  1937-40    casting change:
- As previous model but with
  13 bonnet louvres ........................... **£400-600**

**24f** 1934-38 **Sportsmans Coupé**
  Criss-cross chassis, with spare wheel,
  no sidelights, smooth hubs.
- Blue/Blue, Blue/Black, Yellow/Brown,
  Cream/Dark Blue, Tan/Brown .......... **£200-400**
- 1937-40   casting change:
  Open chassis, higher 'domed'
  roofline, no spare wheel ................... **£200-400**

**24g** 1934-38 **Sports Tourer Four-seater**
  Types 1 or 2: criss-cross chassis.
  Types 1, 2 or 3: grille, spare wheel hub
  cast-in, no sidelights, open tinplate
  windscreen, separate dashboard/steering
  wheel casting.  Blue or Black smooth hubs
  or plated 'Tootsie-Toy'type hubs.
- Body/chassis colours:
  Yellow/Black, Yellow/Blue, Yellow/Brown,
  Blue/Brown, Cream/Green, Cream/Brown,
  Black/Cream, Blue/Maroon ............. **£300-500**
- 1937-40   casting change:
  Open chassis, filled-in windscreen,
  cast impression of spare wheel ........ **£300-500**

**24h** 1934-38 **Sports Tourer Two-seater**
  Types 1 or 2: criss-cross chassis.
  Types 1, 2 or 3: grille, spare wheel hub
  cast-in, no sidelights, open tinplate
  windscreen, separate dashboard/steering
  wheel casting. Plated, Blue or
  Black smooth hubs.
- Body/chassis colours:
  Red/Red, Green/Dark Green, Yellow/Green,
  Yellow/Blue, Yellow/Black, Yellow/Brown,
  Black/Cream, Cream/Green, Red/Green,
  Blue/Brown, Yellow/Purple ............. **£400-600**
- 1937-40   casting change:
  Open chassis, filled-in windscreen,
  cast impression of spare wheel ........ **£400-600**

**25j** 1947-48 **Jeep**
- Red body, Black, Red or Blue hubs.... **£80-100**
- Green body, Black or Red hubs.......... **£80-100**
- Aqua or Sky Blue body,
  Black or Yellow hubs....................... **£100-150**

Dinky Toys

36b Bentley
2-seat Sports Coupé
with
Driver and Footman
1937-41

PHOTO: VECTIS AUCTIONS LTD.

**25y** 1952-54  **Universal Jeep**
- Red body, Blue hubs ............................ **£80-100**
- Red body, Red hubs ............................. **£80-100**
- Dark Green body, Mid-Green hubs .... **£80-100**
- Dark Green body, Maroon hubs ......... **£80-100**
  1954        (Renumbered to 405)

**27d** 1950-54  **Land Rover**.
  See 'Farm and Garden Models'.

**27f** 1950-54  **Estate Car**.
  See 'Farm and Garden Models'

**30a** 1935-40  **Chrysler 'Airflow' Saloon**
          (renumbered to 32)
  No chassis, separate bumper units, lead
  versions exist, smooth plain or silvered hubs.
- Turquoise, Maroon, Cream, Green,
  Purplish Blue, Red,
  (hubs may be any colour) ................. **£500-750**
- With 'Tootsie-Toy' type plated
  chrome hubs ..................................... **£300-400**
- 1946  Cream or Green body,
  smooth hubs, White tyres ................. **£250-300**
- 1946-48  Blue, Cream or Green body,
  ridged hubs usually Black................. **£200-250**
  South African issue:
- Turquoise body, Dark Blue hubs,
  White tyres ....................................... **£300-500**
- Dark Blue body, Dark Blue hubs,
  White tyres ....................................... **£300-500**

**30b** 1935-40  **Rolls-Royce**
  Open chassis, no sidelights, authentic radiator,
  smooth Black hubs or coloured hubs.
  **NB**: Models with coloured hubs
  attract a premium.
- 1935-40  Cream/Black, Red and Maroon,
  Blue/Black, Dark Blue/Black,
  Fawn/Black, Tan/Dark Brown,
  Red/Black, All Black ....................... **£500-600**
- Yellow/Brown, Red/Red, Grey/Grey,
  Green/Light Green,
  Pale Green/Black ............................. **£250-350**
- Turquoise/Dark Blue, Silvered hubs. **£500-750**
- Light Blue body,
  smooth Black wheel hubs ................. **£250-350**
- Fawn body, Black hubs,
  Black open chassis ............................ **£250-350**
- 1946  Fawn body, Black open
  chassis and smooth hubs .................. **£150-200**
- Fawn, Black open chassis,
  ridged Silver hubs ........................... **£200-250**
- 1946-50  Plain (closed) chassis,
  ridged hubs, Mid-Blue/Black,
  Violet-Blue/Black, Greyish-Brown/Black,
  Dark Blue/Black, Light Blue/Black,
  Fawn/Black ...................................... **£150-200**

**30c** 1935-40  **Daimler**
  Open chassis, no sidelights, authentic
  radiator, smooth hubs.
- 1935-40  Cream/Black, Blue/Black,
  Dark Blue/Black, Yellow/Black,
  Fawn/Black ...................................... **£300-400**
- Turquoise/Black, Fawn/Black,
  Light Green/Black............................. **£200-300**
- Pink/Maroon, Red/Red ..................... **£175-250**
- Two-tone Grey or two-tone Green.... **£300-500**
- 1940-41  Pale Tan body,
  Black chassis and hubs .................... **£200-250**
- 1945-46
  Beige body, smooth black hubs ........ **£300-400**
- Green or Fawn body,
  smooth or ridged hubs ...................... **£90-120**
- 1946-50  Plain (closed) chassis, ridged hubs.
  Dark Green/Black, Cream/Black,
  Fawn/Black, Beige/Black,
  Grey/Black, Light Green/Black ........ **£100-150**
- Mid-Green body, Pale Green hubs ... **£100-125**

**30d** 1935-38  **Vauxhall**
  Open chassis, no sidelights, spare wheel
  in wing, 'egg box' or 'shield' grille.
- Green/Black, Blue/Black, Grey/Black,
  Yellow/Black, Brown/Black ............. **£200-300**

- Yellow/Brown, Cream/Brown,
  Tan/Brown........................................ **£200-300**
- Two-tone Grey or two-tone Green.... **£300-400**
- 1938-40  Radiator change:
  As previous model but with 'shield'
  grille, Black or coloured chassis....... **£200-300**
- 1946  Dark Olive Green, open chassis,
  smooth Black hubs, White tyres ....... **£100-125**
- 1946-50  Plain (closed) chassis, no spare
  wheel, Green/Black, Dark Brown/Black,
  Maroon/Black, Yellow/Black, Grey/Black,
  Olive-Green/Black, Blue/Black ........ **£100-125**
- Hub variation:
  Dark Olive Green body, Black chassis,
  Silver ridged hubs, thick axles.......... **£200-250**

**30e** 1935-48  **Breakdown Car**
  See 'Commercial Vehicles' section.

**30f** 1936-41  **Ambulance**
  See 'Emergency Vehicles' section.

**30g** 1936-50  **Caravan**
  See 'Accessories (Pre-War)' section.

**32** 1934-35  **Chrysler 'Airflow' Saloon**
          (renumbered from 30a)
- Maroon (lead) body, no chassis,
  separate bumpers.............................. **£200-250**
- Same model, but diecast body ......... **£200-250**

**34a** 1935-40  **'Royal Air Mail' Service Car**
  See 'Commercial Vehicles and Vans' section.

**35a** 1936-40  **Saloon Car**
  Some versions may have spare wheel cover
  in a darker shade of the main colour.
- Mid-Blue, Dark Blue, Maroon, Grey,
  Yellow, Red, Turquoise, Black or
  White solid rubber wheels ................... **£65-75**
- 1946-48  Grey or Light Blue body
  (spare wheel cover not enhanced),
  Black rubber wheels............................. **£50-60**

**35az** 1939-40  **Fiat 2-seater Saloon**
- Red, Blue or Green, White rubber wheels,
  'Simca 5' cast inside. French issue..... **£80-100**

**35b** 1936-39  **Racer**
- Red, Silver, Yellow or Blue body, with or
  without driver, White solid rubber wheels,
  Red grille and steering wheel .............. **£65-75**

**35b** 1939-54  **Midget Racer**
- Silver body, Red grille, Brown driver,
  solid Black rubber wheels only ........... **£65-75**
- Same, but with Silver driver ................ **£65-75**
- Green body, Black tyres.................... **£150-175**
  1954        (Renumbered to 200)

**35c** 1936-40  **MG Sports Car**
- Red, Pale or Dark Green, Turquoise, Yellow,
  Dark Blue or Maroon, Silver detailing,
  White solid rubber wheels
  (Black later) ..................................... **£75-100**
- 1946-48  Red or Green body, Silver on
  grille only, Black rubber wheels only ... **£40-50**

**35d** 1938-40  **Austin 7 Car** (open tourer)
  Wire windscreen frame, Black or White
  rubber wheels, Silver radiator and steering
  wheel, hole for driver.
- Light Blue, Dark Blue, Turquoise, Grey,
  Lime Green, Maroon or Yellow, (Yellow
  may have Orange spare wheel cover)... **£50-60**
  1946-48  No wire windscreen frame,
  no hole for driver.
- Light Blue, Grey or Yellow body, Silver on
  grille only, Black rubber wheels only ... **£35-45**
- As previous model, but Fawn body ...... **£45-55**

**36a** 1937-41  **Armstrong-Siddeley Limousine**
          **with Driver and Footman**
  Detailed chassis with slots, tinplate figures,
  sidelights, Black smooth hubs.

- Red/Dark Red, Grey/Dark Grey,
  Maroon/Dark Maroon,
  all-Maroon ................................. **£1,000-1,500**
- 1946  Grey body, Black smooth
  wheel hubs, moulded chassis with
  or without slots, no figures .............. **£100-130**

**36a** 1947-50  **Armstrong-Siddeley**
  (no slots or figures), moulded chassis,
  ridged hubs (black or coloured),
  plated radiator.
- Mid-Blue/Black, Grey/Black, Maroon/Black,
  Red/Maroon, Mid-Brown/Black,
  Light Blue/Black, Powder Blue/Black,
  Saxe-Blue/Black, Olive-Green/Black,
  Turquoise/Black, Blue/Blue.............. **£175-200**

**36b** 1937-41  **Bentley 2 seat Sports Coupé**
          **with Driver and Footman**
  Detailed chassis with slots, tinplate figures,
  sidelights, smooth black hubs.
- Cream/Black, Yellow/Maroon,
  Grey/Grey .................................. **£1,000-1,500**
- 1946  Light Green or Saxe Blue body,
  smooth black hubs, moulded chassis
  (slots on some), no figures................ **£200-300**

**36b** 1947-50  **Bentley**
  Moulded chassis (no slots/figures),
  ridged hubs, plated radiator.
- Green/Black, Dark Blue/Black,
  Light Blue/Black, Grey/Black,
  Fawn/Black, Light Fawn/Black ........ **£175-200**

**36c** 1937-41  **Humber Vogue Saloon**
          **with Driver and Footman**
  Detailed chassis with slots, tinplate figures,
  sidelights, plated radiator.
- Green/Dark Green, Blue/Dark Blue, all
  Royal Blue, smooth Black hubs . **£1,100-1,400**
- 1946  Early post war issues with
  smooth Black hubs, moulded chassis
  with or without slots, no figures ....... **£100-150**

**36c** 1947-50  **Humber Vogue**
- Dark Brown/Black, Dark Blue/Black, Grey/Black,
  Maroon/Black, Mid-Green/Black,
  no slots or figures, ridged hubs......... **£120-150**
- Light Blue body, Black moulded chassis,
  ridged Black hubs, plated radiator.... **£150-200**

**36d** 1937-41  **Rover Streamlined Saloon**
          **with Driver and Footman**
  Detailed cast chassis with slots, tinplate
  driver and passenger, sidelights,
  Black smooth hubs.
- Light Green body,
  mid-Green wings, White tyres.... **£1,000-1,500**
- Red Green body, Maroon wings,
  White tyres ...................................... **£400-600**
- 1946  Early post war issues with
  smooth Black hubs and moulded
  chassis with or without slots............. **£150-200**

**36d** 1947-50  **Rover**
  No slots or figures, ridged hubs.
- Dark, Saxe, Mid or Bright Blue/Black,
  Light or Mid-Green/Black................. **£130-170**
- Green body with Light Green hubs .. **£200-250**
- Dark Blue body, Black wings,
  Light Blue hubs................................ **£300-350**
- Navy Blue body, Black wings/hubs.. **£300-350**

**36e** 1937-41  **British Salmson Two-seater**
          **Sports Car with Driver**
  Detailed chassis, hole in seat for driver,
  cast Red or Green driver, Black hubs,
  solid windscreen, sidelights, spare
  wheel on some.
- Royal Blue/Black, Blue/Dark Blue,
  Black/Red, Grey/Dark Grey,
  Silver/Black, Red/Maroon .......... **£1,000-1,500**
- 1946  **British Salmson**
  Early post war issues with smooth Black
  hubs, moulded chassis, no driver...... **£125-175**
- Rare Brown issues ........................... **£400-600**

**36e** 1947-50 **British Salmson Two-seater**
**Sports Car**
Moulded chassis, no hole in seat,
tinplate windscreen, ridged hubs.
- Red/Black, Light, Mid or Dark Green/Black,
Fawn/Black, Mid-Blue/Black, Grey/Black,
Sky-Blue/Black or Saxe-Blue/Black .. **£90-150**
- Red or Brown body............................ **£300-400**

**36f** 1937-41 **British Salmson Four-seater**
**Sports Car with Driver**
Detailed chassis, hole in seat for driver,
cast driver, sidelights, Black smooth hubs
and solid windscreen, cast-in spare wheel
at rear.
- Red/Maroon, Green/Dark Green,
Grey/mid-Grey,
Deep Blue/Black ........................ **£1,000-1,500**

**36f** 1947-50 **British Salmson Four-seater**
**Sports Car**
No hole or driver, tinplate windscreen,
ridged hubs. Black moulded chassis.
- Light or Mid-Green, Brown, Grey, Fawn,
Greenish-Grey, Light Grey or Red ... **£150-200**
**NB** Early Post War Issues 38 and 39 Series:
see the Model Identification section for details.

**38a** 1940-41 **Frazer Nash BMW Sports**
- Red body, smooth Black hubs,
Red or Maroon seats ........................ **£200-300**
- Light Green with Dark Green seats .. **£200-300**
- Dark Blue body and smooth hubs,
Fawn seats........................................ **£150-250**
- Light Grey body, Brown seats .......... **£150-250**
- 1946 Special issue:
Dark Blue body, Light Blue seats,
'Hornby Series' tinplate sheet base... **£150-250**
1947-50 Regular issues:
Black base, Black ridged hubs,
celluloid windscreen:
- Lt. or Dk. Blue (Fawn or Grey seats)... **£75-95**
- Grey (Fawn, Khaki or Blue seats) .... **£140-160**
- Grey (Red seats and hubs)................ **£140-160**
- Blue (Blue hubs) .............................. **£140-160**
- Light Grey (Blue seats, Black hubs). **£140-160**

- Blue with Putty seats ........................ **£140-160**
- 1950-55 As previous models but
made for export only........................ **£140-160**
1955 (Renumbered 100)

**38b** 1940-41 **Sunbeam Talbot Sports**
**NB** All 38b issues may be found with or
without silver edging to the windscreen.
- Red (Maroon tonneau), Red or Black
smooth hubs, lacquered metal base .. **£200-300**
1946
- Grey body, Fawn seats,
Black smooth hubs.......................... **£300-400**
- Green with Dark Green tonneau,
Black smooth hubs.......................... **£300-400**
1947-49
From 1947, most have Black
ridged hubs and Black tinplate baseplate.
Body/tonneau colours:
- Red/Maroon ..................................... **£120-140**
- Maroon/Grey.................................... **£120-140**
- Light Green/Green ........................... **£120-140**
- Brown/Blue ...................................... **£120-140**
- Green/Dark Yellow .......................... **£120-140**
- Lt.Grey (Grey or Dk. Blue tonneau) **£120-140**
- Dk.Grey (Grey or Lt. Blue tonneau) **£120-140**
- Yellow / matt Fawn, Yellow hubs..... **£200-300**
- Deep Yellow body and hubs with Dark
Green tonneau, Silver edged screen . **£200-300**
- Dk. Blue body, Light Grey tonneau.. **£120-140**
- Lt. Blue body, Dark Grey tonneau.... **£120-140**
- Mid-Blue body, Grey tonneau .......... **£120-140**
- Brown/Blue, Silver edged screen .... **£120-140**
- 1950 Late post war issues with coloured
hubs, e.g., Yellow body, Green tonneau,
Yellow hubs or Red body,
Maroon tonneau, Red hubs .............. **£100-150**
- Red body, Dark Green
tonneau, Red hubs............................ **£100-150**
- 1950-55 As previous models but
made for export only........................ **£120-160**
1955 (Renumbered 101)

**38c** 1946 **Lagonda Sports Coupé**
- Early post war issues with
smooth Black hubs........................... **£120-140**
1947-50
From 1947, most have ridged Black hubs.
- Green body, Black or
Dark Green seats ............................. **£120-140**
- Grey body, Fawn or Maroon seats.... **£120-140**
- Maroon body, Dark Blue or
Grey seats........................................ **£120-140**
- Light Grey body, Mid or
Dark Grey seats ............................... **£120-140**
- 1950-55 As previous models but
made for export only........................ **£120-140**
1950 Late post war issues with
coloured hubs, e.g., Green body
with Light Green hubs ..................... **£120-140**
1955 (Renumbered 102)

**38d** 1940-41 **Alvis Sports Tourer**
- Green body, Black seats and hubs,
lacquered base ................................. **£140-180**
- Maroon body, Red seats,
lacquered base ................................. **£140-180**
- 1946 Early post war issues........ **£120-160**
1947-50:
From 1947, all had a Black painted baseplate.
- Green/Dark Green............................ **£120-140**
- Green/Brown.................................... **£120-140**
- Green body, Black seats,
Black or Green hubs ........................ **£120-140**
- Maroon/Grey, Red hubs................... **£120-140**
- Maroon/Red ..................................... **£120-140**
- Light Blue/Dark Blue....................... **£120-140**
- Blue body, Grey seats and hubs........ **£120-140**
- Grey body, Blue seats and hubs........ **£120-140**
- 1950-55 As previous models but
made for export only......................... **£120-140**
1955 (Renumbered 103)

**38e** 1940 ? **Triumph Dolomite**
Planned and catalogued but not issued......NPP

**38e** 1946 **Armstrong Siddeley Coupé**
- Early post war issues with
Black smooth hubs...........................£100-150
1947-50 From 1947, all have a Black
painted baseplate. Body / interior colours:
- Grey/Deep Blue .............................£120-140
- Light Grey/Blue ..............................£120-140
- Light Grey/Green ...........................£120-140
- Light Green/Grey ...........................£120-140
- Grey/Dark Green..............................£120-140
- Bright Green/Grey ..........................£120-140
- Red/Maroon ....................................£120-140
- Cream/Blue .....................................£120-140
- Dark Green body and interior..........£120-140
- Royal Blue body, Dark Green int. ....£120-140
- Apple Green body, Dark Grey int.....£120-140
- 1950 Light Green body,
Apple Green hubs ...........................£250-300
- Light Green body, Grey interior,
Mid-Green hubs ..............................£250-300
- Light Grey body,
Dark Green interior, Grey hubs ........£250-300
- Grey body, Dk. Blue int., Red hubs..£250-300
- Grey body, Dark Blue interior,
Pale Blue hubs ................................£250-300
- Grey body, Dark Blue interior,
Mid-Blue hubs ................................£250-300
- 1950-55 As previous models but
made for export only.........................£250-300
1955 (Renumbered 104)

**38f** 1940-41 **Jaguar (SS100) Sports Car**
2 celluloid windscreens, clear lacquered
baseplate. Some windscreen edges have
silver detailing.
- Khaki/Blue, Blue/Grey, Light Blue/Grey,
Grey/Blue, Grey/Black, Red/Maroon,
Dark Brown/Black ............................£300-400
- 1946 Early post-war issues with Black
smooth hubs (later issues ridged) .....£120-150
1947-50 From 1947, all have a Black
painted baseplate.
- Light, Mid- or Dark Blue body,
Grey or Putty interior.......................£120-140
- Light Brown body, Blue interior.......£120-140
- Red body, Maroon interior...............£120-140
- Brownish-Grey body, Black interior.£120-140
- Grey body, Red interior, Red hubs ...£250-300
- 1950 Late post-war issues with coloured
hubs, e.g., Light Blue body, Putty interior
(Blue hubs) or Red body, Maroon
interior (Red hubs)...........................£250-350
- 1950-55 As previous models but
made for export only.........................£200-300
1955 (Renumbered 105)

**39a** 1939-41 **Packard Super 8 Tourer**
- Smooth hubs, Silver or lacquered
baseplate. Light Green, Grey, Black,
Yellow, Blue.....................................£300-400
- 1946 Early post-war issues with
Black smooth hubs...........................£100-125

- 1947-50 All have a Black painted
baseplate, ridged hubs.
Dark Brown, Green or Olive-Green .£100-125
- 1950 Late post-war issues with
coloured ridged hubs.....................£800-1,100

**39b** 1939-41 **Oldsmobile 6 Sedan**
- Black, Maroon, Yellow, Mid Blue, Light
or Mid-Grey or Green, Silver base...£150-200
- 1946 Early post-war issues with
smooth Black hubs...........................£100-150
1947-50 All have Black baseplate
(open at rear), ridged hubs.
- Grey, Brown, Green or Fawn body ..£100-125
- Cream body.....................................£120-140
- Violet-Blue ....................................£130-170
- 1947-50 US issue: Light Blue
body, Black hubs............................£800-1,100
- 1950 Late post-war issues with
coloured ridged hubs.....................£800-1,100
- 1952 Export issue: Beige body
and hubs, closed rear baseplate......£800-1,100

**39bu** 1950-52 **Oldsmobile Sedan** (US issue)
- Cream with Dark Blue wings,
Black baseplate ...........................£1,500-2,000
- Cream body, Tan wings, Black
baseplate (closed at rear),
Black hubs...................................£1,500-2,000
- Cream body, Tan wings,
Cream hubs..................................£1,500-2,000
- Tan body and hubs,
baseplate closed at rear ..............£1,000-1,200
- Light Blue body, Dark Blue
wings, Light Blue hubs..............£1,000-1,200

**39c** 1939-41 **Lincoln Zephyr Coupé**
- Lacquered baseplate, smooth Black hubs.
Grey/Black, Yellow Red or Green ....£150-175
- 1946 Early post-war issues with
smooth Black hubs...........................£100-150
- 1947-50 Black painted baseplate,
ridged hubs. Light Grey, Brown,
Maroon or Red body .........................£90-120
- 1950 Late post war issues with
coloured ridged hubs, e.g., Light 'Riley'
Green with darker Green hubs or
Red body with Red hubs or
Yellow with Green hubs .............£1,800-2,000

**39cu** 1950-52 **Lincoln Zephyr Coupé**
(US issues). All have Black painted
baseplate and ridged hubs.
- Red body and hubs,
Maroon wings .............................£3,000-4,000
- Cream body and hubs,
Brown wings ...............................£1,500-2,000
- Tan with Brown wings,
Black hubs...................................£1,500-2,000

**39d** 1939-41 **Buick Viceroy Saloon**
Lacquered baseplate, smooth Black hubs.
- Grey, Green, Maroon, Cream, Blue..£200-300

- 1946 Early post-war issues with
Black smooth hubs...........................£100-125
- Olive body, smooth hubs.................£100-125
1947-50 All have Black painted
baseplate, ridged hubs.
- Light or Dark Green, Maroon, Fawn, Blue,
Beige or Grey, matching hubs .........£120-140
- Mustard body, Mustard rhubs ..........£120-140
- Greyish-Brown body,
Light Brown ridged hubs .................£120-140
- Apple Green body and ridged hubs ..£120-140
- 1950 Late post-war issues with coloured
ridged hubs, e.g., Light 'Riley' Green body
with darker green hubs or Brown body
with Green or Yellow hubs ...........£800-1,100

**39e** 1939-41 **Chrysler Royal Sedan**
- Lacquered baseplate, smooth Black hubs.
Black, Green, Royal Blue or Grey....£100-150
- Yellow body, Black hubs ..............£800-1,100
- 1946 Early post-war issues with
smooth Black hubs...........................£100-125
1947-50 All have ridged hubs.
- Light Blue, Mid-Blue, Dark Blue, Light
Green, Mid-Green, Dark Green or Dark
Grey body, Black hubs and baseplate..£85-110
- As previous models but with
Silvered baseplate ...........................£250-350
- Cream body, Light Green hubs,
Black baseplate ...........................£1,000-1,500
- 1950 Late post-war issues with coloured
ridged hubs, e.g., Light 'Triumph 1800'
Blue with Blue hubs......................£800-1,100

**39eu** 1950-52 **Chrysler Royal Sedan**
(US issues). Black baseplate, Blued axles.
- Yellow with Red wings,
Yellow or Black hubs ..................£3,000-3,500
- Two-tone Green body,
Light Green hubs .........................£1,500-2,000

**39f** 1939-41 **Studebaker State Commander**
- Lacquered baseplate,
smooth Black wheel hubs.
Yellow, Green or Dark Grey body .£800-1,100
- 1946 Early post-war issues with
smooth Black hubs...........................£100-150
- 1946 Yellow, smooth Black hubs..£800-1,100
1947-50 From 1947, all have
Black baseplate, ridged hubs.
- Green, Olive or Maroon body...........£120-140
- Dk. or Lt. Grey body, Black hubs.....£120-140
- Dark Maroon body, Black hubs........£120-140
- Very Dark Blue body, Black hubs.....£120-140
- Tan body, Black ridged hubs ...........£120-140
- Mid-Blue body, Mid-Blue hubs........£600-800
- Dark Green body, Black hubs...........£120-140
- 1950 Late post-war issues with
coloured ridged hubs....................£800-1,100

## 40a and 158   RILEY SALOON

**40a**  1947-50   **Riley Saloon**
*1st baseplate*: Tinplate baseplate '40A' has
small lettering and the rear wheels are
retained by cast pillars. Not boxed.
• Light, Mid or Dk. Grey body,
  Black hubs .................................... **£100-125**
• Light Grey body, Tan hubs ............. **£100-125**
• Mid-Green body, Black hubs ............. **£80-100**
1950-53
*2nd baseplate*: with '40A' and large lettering.
Also with tow-hook aperture.
• Dark Blue or Mid-Blue body,
  Black hubs .................................... **£100-125**
• Grey body, Black hubs ..................... **£150-175**
• Dark Green body, Black hubs .......... **£100-125**
• Cream body, Black hubs .................. **£100-125**
1954 - 40a was renumbered to 158

**158**  1954-55   **Riley Saloon**
(renumbered from 40a)
158 baseplate has large lettering;
no tow-hook aperture.
• Cream body, Mid-Green hubs........... **£150-175**
• Mid-Green body, Green hubs ........... **£150-175**
• Light Green body and hubs .............. **£150-175**
• Light Green body, Mid-Green hubs.... **£150-175**
• Dark Blue body, Mid-Blue hubs ....... **£150-175**
• Light Grey body and hubs ............... **£150-175**

## 40b and 151   TRIUMPH 1800 SALOON

**40b**  1948-49   **Triumph 1800 Saloon**
Small baseplate lettering, rear axles held
by cast pillars (see diagram). Not boxed.
• Light, Mid or Dk. Grey body,
  Black hubs .................................... **£100-125**
• Light, Mid or Dark Grey body,
  Grey hubs ..................................... **£100-125**
• Mid-Blue body and hubs ................. **£100-125**
• Light Blue body, Blue or Fawn hubs **£100-125**
• Fawn body, Black or Fawn hubs ...... **£100-125**
• Black body, Black hubs ................... **£400-600**
1949-54
*2nd baseplate*: Small lettering on baseplate,
  rear axle held by baseplate tabs.
• Mid or Dark Blue body, Fawn hubs . **£100-125**
• Light Blue body and hubs................ **£100-125**
• Fawn body, Green hubs ................... **£100-125**
1954 - 40b was renumbered to 151

**151**  1954-60   **Triumph 1800 Saloon**
(renumbered from 40b)
151 baseplate has large lettering.
• Fawn body, Green hubs, Black base. **£125-150**
• Dark Blue, Light Blue hubs..............**£110-130**
• Light Blue body, Mid-Blue hubs .......**£110-130**
• Light Blue body, Fawn hubs.............**£110-130**
• Light Blue body, Grey hubs.............**£110-130**
• Mid-Blue body, Light Blue hubs .......**£110-130**

**40c**  1940   **Jowett Javelin**. Factory drawing
exists but model not issued......................NPP

## 40d and 152   AUSTIN (A40) DEVON

**40d**  1949-54   **Austin (A40) Devon**
Small baseplate lettering, rear axle held
by the baseplate. Not boxed.
• Maroon body and hubs ................. **£100-125**
• Red body, Maroon hubs .................. **£400-600**
• Light Grey-Green body and hubs ..... **£100-125**
• Light Grey-Green body, Beige hubs. **£100-125**
• Light Blue body, Mid-Blue hubs ...... **£100-125**
• Mid-Blue body, Light Blue hubs ...... **£100-125**
• Dark Green body, Cream hubs ........ **£100-125**
• Bright Blue body, Mid-Blue hubs.... **£125-150**
1954 - 40d was renumbered to 152

**152**  1954-59   **Austin (A40) Devon**
(renumbered from 40d)
Large baseplate lettering
(see example diagrams).
'DEVON' cast into underside of roof.
• Suede Green body and hubs ............ **£150-175**
• Dark Blue body, Mid-Blue hubs...... **£150-175**
• Tan body, Suede Green hubs ........... **£500-700**
• Maroon body, Red hubs.................. **£175-200**
• Red body, Maroon hubs................... **£175-200**
• Light Blue body and hubs................ **£400-500**
• Dark Blue body, Light Blue hubs ..... **£150-175**
• Light Green body, Mid-Green hubs.. **£150-175**
• Dark Green body with Fawn hubs.... **£150-175**
1956-59   *Two-tone issues*:
• Blue upper body and hubs,
  Yellow lower body .......................... **£200-300**
• Cerise lower body, Green upper
  body, Cream hubs .......................... **£200-300**

## 40e and 153   STANDARD VANGUARD

**40e**  1948-49   **Standard Vanguard**
*1st casting*: Open rear wheel arches,
small baseplate lettering, rear axle secured
by tinplate clip. Not boxed.
• Fawn body and hubs ........................ **£125-150**
• Fawn body, Red hubs...................... **£150-175**
• Cream body, Green hubs ................. **£750-1,000**
1949-50     *baseplate change*: Open rear
  wheel arches, small or large base lettering,
  rear axle held by baseplate tabs.
• Fawn body and hubs ....................... **£100-125**
• Mid-Blue body and hubs ................. **£100-125**
• Maroon body and hubs ................... **£100-125**
• Dark Blue body, Fawn hubs ............ **£500-600**
1950-54     *2nd casting*:
  Closed rear wheel arches.
• Light Blue body, Fawn hubs............. **£100-125**
• Fawn body with Fawn hubs ............. **£100-125**
• Maroon body, Fawn hubs ............... **£750-1,000**
1954 - 40e was renumbered to 153

**153**  1954-60   **Standard Vanguard**
(renumbered from 40e)
'VANGUARD' cast into underside of roof,
  large baseplate lettering.
• Mid-Blue body,
  Cream, Blue or Fawn hubs .............. **£100-150**
• Dark Blue body, Fawn hubs ............ **£200-250**
• Fawn body, Fawn hubs ................... **£100-150**
• Cream body, Cream hubs................. **£100-150**
• Maroon body, Fawn hubs ............... **£100-150**
• Maroon body, Maroon hubs.......... **£750-1,000**
**NB** The ridge which appears on the boot
  of some Vanguard models is the result
  of worn die replacement.

## 40f and 154   HILLMAN MINX

**40f**  1951-54   **Hillman Minx**
*1st baseplate*: Small baseplate lettering
  (see diagram). Not boxed.
• Tan body, Fawn hubs ...................... **£120-145**
• Mid-Green body, Light Green hubs.. **£120-145**
• Light Green body and hubs ............. **£120-145**
• Light Green body, Mid-Green hubs.. **£120-145**
• Dark Tan body, Green hubs ............ **£120-145**
• Dark Tan body, Cream hubs ........... **£120-145**
• Light Tan body, Cream hubs........... **£120-145**
• Dark Green body, Mid-Green hubs.. **£120-145**
1955 - 40f was renumbered to 154

**154**  1955-59   **Hillman Minx**
(renumbered from 40f)
'HILLMAN MINX' cast under roof.
*2nd baseplate*:
Large baseplate lettering (see diagram).
• Dk. Tan body, Cream or Green hubs.**£110-140**
• Pale Tan body, Blue or Yellow hubs..**£110-140**
• Light Green body and hubs ............. **£175-200**
• Dark Green body, Light Green hubs. **£175-200**
• Pale Green body, Light Green hubs.. **£175-225**

• Light Green body, Mid-Green hubs.. **£175-225**
*Two-tone issues*:
• Pale Blue lower body and hubs,
  Cerise upper body .......................... **£200-250**
• Lime Green lower body,
  Cream upper body and hubs ........... **£200-250**

## 40g and 159   MORRIS OXFORD

**40g**  1950-54   **Morris Oxford**
Small baseplate lettering. Not boxed.
• Fawn body, Grey hubs ...................... **£80-100**
• Grey body and hubs .......................... **£80-100**
• Green body, Light Green hubs........... **£80-100**
• Green body, Fawn hubs .................... **£80-100**
1954 - 40g was renumbered to 159

**159**  1954   **Morris Oxford**
(renumbered from 40g)
Small baseplate lettering, 'MORRIS
OXFORD' cast into underside of roof.
• Dark Green body and hubs ............... **£140-175**
• Green body, Light Green hubs.......... **£140-175**
• Beige body and hubs (Export issue). **£500-800**
• Blue body, Grey hubs ................... **£1,500-2,000**
• Fawn body, Grey or Stone hubs ...... **£120-140**
*Two-tone issues*:
• Green upper body and hubs,
  Cream lower body ........................... **£150-175**
• Cream upper body and hubs,
  Cerise lower body ........................... **£150-175**
• Turquoise upper body, Cream lower
  body, Turquoise-Green hubs ........... **£500-700**

## 40h and 254   AUSTIN (FX3) TAXI

**40h**  1952-54   **Austin (FX3) Taxi**
Diecast chassis with cast-in driver
and model number. Not boxed.
• All-Yellow body and hubs,
  Black chassis, interior and driver ..... **£100-125**
• All-Yellow body and hubs,
  Brown chassis, interior and driver.... **£150-250**
• Dark Blue body, Light Blue hubs,
  Black chassis, interior and driver ..... **£250-350**
• Mid-Blue body and hubs,
  Black chassis, interior and driver ..... **£400-600**
1954 - 40h was renumbered to 254

**254**  1956-59   **Austin (FX3) Taxi**
(renumbered from 40h)
• Blue body, Light Blue hubs ............. **£500-750**
• Black body, spun hubs,
  Grey chassis ('254'),
  Grey interior and driver ................... **£140-170**
*Two-tone issue*:
• Yellow upper body and hubs,
  Dark Green lower body,
  Black chassis ('254'),
  Black interior and driver.................. **£140-170**

## 40j and 161   AUSTIN (A40) SOMERSET

**40j**  1953-54   **Austin (A40) Somerset**
Large lettering on baseplate. Not boxed.
• Pale Blue body and hubs ................. **£100-125**
• Red body and hubs........................... **£100-125**
• Mid-Blue body and hubs ................. **£100-125**
• Dark Blue body, Mid-Blue hubs....... **£100-125**
1954 - 40j was renumbered to 161

**161**  1954   **Austin (A40) Somerset**
(renumbered from 40j)
Large baseplate lettering, 'AUSTIN
SOMERSET' cast into underside of roof.
• Pale Blue body,
  Mid or Dark Blue hubs ..................... **£80-100**
• Red body and hubs ........................... **£80-100**
1956-59   *Two-tone issues*:
• Red lower body and hubs,
  Yellow upper body .......................... **£200-250**
• Cream lower body and hubs,
  Black lower body ............................ **£200-250**

# 40 Series cars identification

See also the 'Dinky Toys Cars - Box Types' and 'Model Identification' information pages.
Please note that the illustrations on this page are not all to the same scale.

### 40b and 151 Triumph 1800 Saloon
Casting with rear axle pillars — 1948 - 50
Small lettering on baseplate, as illustrated — 1948 - 53
Large lettering on baseplate (not illustrated) — 1954 - 60
Two raised rails on baseplate, as illustrated — 1948 - 53
No raised rails on baseplate (not illustrated) — 1954 - 60

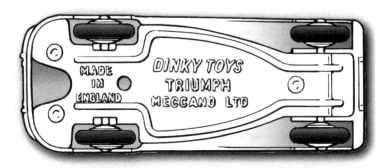

### 40e and 153 Standard Vanguard
Tinplate clip secures rear axle — 1948 - 49
Small lettering on baseplate — 1948 - 53
Baseplate has raised rails — 1948 - 53

Casting with open wheel arches
(no spats) — 1948 - 50

Baseplate tabs secure rear axle — 1949 - 60
Large lettering on baseplate — 1954 - 60
No raised rails on baseplate — 1954 - 60
Body casting includes rear wheel spats — 1951 - 60

### 40f and 154 Hillman Minx
1951 - 54 — Small lettering on baseplate, two raised rails on baseplate, rear axle secured by baseplate tabs.
1954 - 59 — Large lettering on baseplate, no raised rails on baseplate, rear axle secured by baseplate tabs.

**101  1957-60  Sunbeam Alpine** (touring finish)
- Maroon body, Cream interior,
  Cream diecast hubs, Grey driver ...... **£120-140**
- Same model, but with spun hubs ...... **£200-300**
- Light Turquoise body, Dark Blue interior,
  Mid-Blue diecast hubs, Grey driver . **£150-175**
- Same model, but with spun hubs ...... **£150-175**
- Light Blue body, Blue diecast hubs .. **£150-175**

**102  1957-60  MG Midget** (touring finish)
- Deep Yellow body, Red interior,
  Red diecast hubs, Grey driver .......... **£225-275**
- Pale Green body, Cream interior,
  Cream diecast hubs, Grey driver ...... **£250-350**
- Late issues with spun aluminium hubs,
  in plain or lighter yellow boxes ....... **£250-350**

**103  1957-60  Austin Healey 100** (touring finish)
- Red body, Grey interior,
  diecast hubs and driver .................... **£250-300**
- Cream body, Red interior and hubs,
  Grey driver ..................................... **£250-300**

**104  1957-60  Aston-Martin DB3S**
          (touring finish)
- Light Blue body, Dark Blue interior,
  Mid-Blue hubs, Grey driver............. **£150-200**
- Salmon-Pink body, Red interior
  and diecast hubs, Grey driver,
  Matt or Gloss baseplate ................... **£150-200**

**105  1957-60  Triumph TR2** (touring finish)
  Grey body, Red interior and hubs,
  Grey driver ..................................... **£250-300**
- Same, but with spun hubs and plastic
  steering wheel. 'Plain' printed or
  late lighter yellow box ..................... **£300-400**
- Lemon Yellow body, Pale Green interior,
  Mid-Green hubs, Grey driver .......... **£250-300**
- 1959-60  As before but with spun hubs,
  in 'plain' printed box with Yellow spot,
  or in late lighter Yellow box ........... **£350-450**

**106  1954-58  Austin A90 Atlantic**
          (Renumbered from 140a)
- Light Blue body,
  Cream interior, Cream hubs............. **£125-150**
- Light Blue body, Red interior,
  Red or Cream hubs .......................... **£125-150**
- Light Blue body, Dark Blue interior,
  Cream or Dark Blue hubs ................. **£125-150**
- Black body, Red interior and hubs,
  White tyres...................................... **£125-150**
- Pink body, Cream interior,
  Cream hubs, '106' on baseplate........ **£100-120**
  **NB**  Interiors may have a gloss or matt finish.

**107  1955-59  Sunbeam Alpine Sports**
          (competition finish)
- Pale Blue, Beige or Cream interior,
  Cream hubs, '26', racing driver........ **£125-150**
- Deep Pink body, Grey interior,
  Cream hubs, RN '34', racing driver . **£125-150**
  **NB**  See also 'Factory samples' listing
  at the end of this section.

**108  1955-59  MG Midget** (competition finish)
- Red body, Tan interior, Red hubs,
  RN '24', racing driver...................... **£150-200**
- Cream body, Red interior, Red hubs,
  RN '26' or '28', racing driver........... **£150-200**
  **NB**  The version of 108 issued in the
  US is numbered 129.

**109  1955-59  Austin-Healey 100**
          (competition finish)
- Cream body, Red interior and hubs,
  racing driver and no. '22' or '23'...... **£150-200**
- Yellow body, Blue interior and hubs,
  racing driver and no. '21' or '28'...... **£150-200**

**110  1956-59  Aston-Martin DB3S**
          (competition finish)
- Grey body, Blue interior and hubs,
  racing driver and number '20' .......... **£150-175**
- Mid-Green body, Red interior,
  Red ridged hubs, number '22' or '25'**£150-200**
- Light Green body, Red interior,
  Red ridged hubs, RN '22' or '25' ..... **£200-250**

**110  1966-67  Aston-Martin DB5**
- Metallic Red, Cream or Black interior,
  '110' on base, spoked wheels .......... **£100-120**
- 1967-71  Metallic Red or Blue,
  Cream or Black interior, plain base,
  spoked wheels ................................. **£100-120**
  **NB**  See also 'Factory samples'
  listing at the end of this section.

**111  1956-59  Triumph TR2 Sports Car**
          (competition finish)
- Salmon-Pink body, Blue interior and
  hubs, racing driver no. '29'........ **£200-250**
- Turquoise body, Red interior and hubs,
  racing driver and racing no. '25' ..... **£200-250**

**112  1961-66  Austin-Healey Sprite Mk.II**
- Red body, Cream int., spun hubs...... **£125-175**
  South African issues:
  (English / Afrikaans on box,
  all have spun hubs)
- Turquoise body, Cream interior ........ **£500-750**
- Light or Dark Blue, Cream interior .. **£500-750**
- Lilac (Pink) body, Cream interior..... **£500-750**

**113  1962-69  MG 'MGB' Sports Car**
- Cream body, Red interior,
  Grey plastic driver, spun hubs .......... **£100-125**
  South African issues:
  (English / Afrikaans on box,
  all have spun hubs)
- Mid-Blue body, Red interior.......... **£750-1,000**
- Red body, Cream interior.............. **£750-1,000**
- Ivory body ................................... **£750-1,000**

**114  1963-71  Triumph Spitfire**
  Sports car with Blue side driver (plastic),
  spun hubs, jewelled headlamps.
  1963-66
- Met. Silver-Grey body, Red interior . **£120-140**
- Red body, Cream interior................. **£120-140**
- 1966-70  Metallic Gold body, Red
  interior, 'Tiger In Tank' on bootlid ... **£120-140**
- 1966-70  Metallic Gold body,
  without bootlid logo, Red interior .... **£130-150**
- 1970-71  Metallic Purple body,
  Gold interior.................................... **£150-200**

**115  1965-69  Plymouth Fury Sports**
- White open body, Red interior, cast wheels,
  driver and passenger, 'window' box ..... **£70-80**

**116  1966-71  Volvo P 1800 S**
- Red body, White interior, wire wheels . **£60-75**
- Metallic Red, Light Blue interior,
  wire wheels ...................................... **£100-130**

**120  1962-67  Jaguar 'E' type**
- Red body, detachable Black or Grey
  hardtop plus optional Cream or Grey
  folded soft-top, spun hubs................. **£100-130**
- Metallic Blue and White, Black,
  Grey or Cream body, spun hubs ....... **£100-130**
- Metallic Light Blue and Black body,
  White interior, spun hubs................. **£700-900**

**122  1977-78  Volvo 265 DL Estate**
          (Some made in Italy by Polistil under license)
- Metallic Blue (Brown interior), or Cream
  with '265DL' wing badges, cast hubs... **£25-30**
- 1979-80  Orange version without
  '265 DL', Brown box ......................... **£35-40**
  **NB**  See also 'Factory samples'
  listing at the end of this section.

**123  1977-80  Princess 2200 HL**
- Metallic Bronze with black roof side
  panels, plastic wheels......................... **£30-35**

- All White body ................................... **£30-35**
- White body, with Blue roof OR Blue
  side panels......................................... **£30-35**

**124  1977-79  Rolls-Royce Phantom V**
- Metallic Light Blue, boot opens -
  bonnet does not (see 152) .................. **£35-45**

**127  1964-66  Rolls-Royce Silver Cloud Mk.3**
- Metallic Blue or Metallic Green body,
  White interior, spun hubs .................. **£65-75**
- 1966-69  Metallic Gold body,
  White interior, cast hubs ................... **£55-65**
- 1969-72  Metallic Red body,
  White interior, cast hubs ................... **£55-65**

**128  1964-67  Mercedes-Benz 600**
- Metallic Maroon body, White interior,
  spun hubs, three figures/luggage . **£45-55**
- 1967-75  Metallic Maroon body, White
  interior, Blue base, spun hubs or
  Speedwheels, driver only.................. **£30-40**
- 1975-79  Metallic Blue, White
  interior, driver, Speedwheels................ **£30-35**

**129  1954?  MG Midget** (US issue)
- Ivory body, Maroon or Red interior and
  tonneau, Red hubs, no driver or
  racing number (see 108).
  '129' on Yellow box...................... **£900-1,100**
- Red body, Tan interior and tonneau,
  Red hubs, no driver or RN (see 108),
  Yellow box with '129' ................. **£900-1,100**

**129  1965 -72  Volkswagen 1300 Sedan**
- Met. Blue body, White interior, spun
  hubs, registration plate 'K.HK 454'...... **£45-55**
- 1972-76  Metallic Bright Blue,
  White interior, Speedwheels ................ **£30-35**

**130  1964-66  Ford Consul Corsair**
- Red or Metallic Wine Red body,
  Off-White interior, spun hubs.............. **£65-75**
- 1966-69  Pale Blue, Metallic Dark Grey
  base, Off-White interior, spun hubs...... **£45-55**
  **NB**  Baseplates may have rounded or
  dimpled rivets.

**131  1956-61  Cadillac Eldorado**
- Yellow body, Cerise interior, Grey or
  Brown driver, Grey or Cream diecast
  hubs, packing also in box .................**£110-140**
- Salmon-Pink body, Grey interior, Grey
  driver, Beige diecast hubs,
  packing piece also in box..................**£110-140**
- 1962-63  As previous models but
  with spun hubs ................................ **£300-400**

**131  1968-70  Jaguar 'E'-type 2+2**
- White body, Light Blue or Red interior,
  Gold base, cast spoked wheels ...........**£90-110**
- 1970-75  Metallic Copper body,
  Blue interior, Gold base, cast spoked
  wheels or plastic wheels ..................... **£70-80**
- 1975-76  Metallic Purple body, Light
  Blue interior, cast spoked wheels ....... **£80-100**
- 1976-77  Bronze body, Speedwheels .. **£70-90**
- 1977-77  Metallic Red or Post Office
  Red body, Blue int., Speedwheels ...... **£80-100**

**132  1955-61  Packard Convertible**
- Light Green body, Red interior and
  hubs, Grey driver .............................**£110-140**
- Pale Tan body, Red interior and
  hubs, Grey driver .............................**£110-140**
- 1962-63  As previous models
  but with spun hubs ........................... **£130-160**

**132  1967-74  Ford 40 RV**
- Metallic Silver body, Red interior,
  spoked wheels ................................... **£30-40**
- Fluorescent Pink body, Yellow engine
  cover, White interior, spoked wheels.... **£35-45**

- Metallic Light Blue body,
  Red or Yellow interior............................ **£30-40**
**NB** Early models have red headlight recesses.

**133** 1955-60 **Cunningham C5R Road Racer**
- White body, Dark Blue stripes,
  Brown interior, RN '31', Blue hubs,
  Light Blue driver................................. **£65-75**
- Off-White body,
  Blue interior and driver........................ **£65-75**
- As previous models but with
  spun aluminium hubs......................... **£150-175**

**133** 1964-66 **Ford Cortina**
  (issued to replace 139)
- Metallic Gold/White body,
  Red interior, spun hubs ........................ **£70-85**
- 1966-68 Pale Lime body,
  Red interior, spun hubs ........................ **£75-90**

**134** 1964-68 **Triumph Vitesse**
- Metallic Aqua Blue body, White side
  stripe, Red interior, spun hubs ............. **£70-85**
- Metallic Aqua Blue body, White side
  stripe, Grey interior, spun hubs........... **£85-95**
Indian issues:
  Manufactured in India and fully licensed by
  Meccano. Sold as 'Dinky Toys' and not the
  later 'Nicky Toys'. Box marked 'Licenced
  Manufacturer & Registered User in India,
  S. Kumar & Co., Registered Proprietors of
  Trade Mark Meccano Ltd.' Model base also
  marked 'Licensee in India S. Kumar & Co.'.
  Variations:
- Green body, White flash,
  cast hubs, rubber tyres ...................... **£300-400**
- Red body, cast hubs, rubber tyres ..... **£300-400**

**135** 1963-69 **Triumph 2000 Saloon**
  Red interior, Grey base, spun hubs,
  wipers, luggage.
- Normal colours:
  Metallic Green with White roof or
  Metallic Blue with White roof............. **£70-90**
- Gift Set 118 colour:
  White body, Blue roof, Red interior,
  spun hubs, individually boxed ...........**£110-140**
Promotional colours:
  Each promotional issue was packed in a
  standard Yellow/Red card picture box.
- Black body, Cactus-Green or
  White roof ........................................ **£350-500**
- Blue Grey body, Black roof.............. **£350-500**
- Light Green body with Lilac roof..... **£350-500**
- Metallic Green with White roof........ **£350-500**
- Brown body, Light Green roof ......... **£350-500**
- British Racing Green, White roof..... **£350-500**
- Red or Cherry Red body,
  White roof, Blue interior.................. **£350-500**
- White body, Black roof, Blue int...... **£350-500**
- White body, Light Green roof,
  Blue interior .................................... **£350-500**
- White body, Light Grey roof,
  Blue interior .................................... **£350-500**
- White body, Wedgewood Blue roof,
  Blue interior .................................... **£350-500**
- Dk. Green body, Cactus-Green roof . **£350-500**
- Gunmetal body, Black roof,
  with 'Gunmetal/WD' label on box .. **£350-500**
- Dark Grey body, Sky-Blue roof........ **£350-500**

**136** 1964-65 **Vauxhall Viva**
- White-Grey body, Red int., spun hubs . **£60-75**
- 1965-68 Metallic Bright Blue body,
  Red interior, spun hubs ........................ **£55-65**
- 1969-73 Pale Metallic Blue body,
  Red interior, spun hubs ........................ **£50-65**

**137** 1963-66 **Plymouth Fury Convertible**
  All issues have spun hubs.
- Green body, Cream hood .................... **£70-85**
- Metallic Grey body, Cream hood ......... **£70-85**
- Pink body, Cream hood....................... **£70-85**

- Blue body, Cream hood ...................... **£70-85**

**138** 1963-66 **Hillman Imp**
  All issues have spun hubs and 'luggage'.
- Metallic Silver-Green body, Red or
  White interior, cast headlamps............. **£75-85**
- 1966-68 Metallic Red body,
  jewelled or plastic headlamps ............... **£70-90**
- 1968-73 Metallic mid-Blue body,
  Red interior, jewelled headlamps.......... **£70-90**
- Same but with Blue interior, in
  picture box with white background .. **£175-200**
- Late issue:
  Metallic Deep Blue body,
  Red interior, bare metal baseplate .... **£175-225**

**139** 1963-64 **Ford Consul Cortina**
- Pale Blue body, Off-White interior,
  spun hubs, cast headlamps................... **£65-75**
- 1964-65 Metallic Blue body,
  Fawn interior, spun hubs...................... **£65-75**
South African issues:
  (English / Afrikaans on box, spun hubs).
- Bright Green body, Fawn interior.. **£750-1,000**
- Dark Green body, Fawn interior .... **£800-1,100**

**139a** 1949-54 **Ford Fordor Sedan**
  All have small lettering on the black
  baseplates which may be gloss or matt.
- Yellow, Red, Green or Tan body,
  (all with matching hubs) .................. **£100-120**
- Green body, Yellow hubs ................ **£100-120**
- Brown body, Red hubs..................... **£100-120**
- Tan body, Maroon hubs ................... **£100-120**
- Red body, Maroon hubs ................... **£100-120**
**NB** Later issues have 'Ford Sedan' cast
into underside of roof.
1954        (Renumbered to 170)

**139am** 1950-54 **US Army Staff Car**
  See 'Military Vehicles' section.

**139b** 1950-54 **Hudson Commodore**
- Dark Blue body, Stone roof / hubs ... **£150-200**
- Dark Blue body, Tan roof and hubs .. **£100-150**
- Deep Cream body,
  Maroon roof and hubs...................... **£200-300**
- Royal Blue body,
  Pale Tan roof and hubs .................... **£200-300**
- Grey lower body, Light Blue roof (as
  151 (40b) Triumph Renown Blue).... **£200-300**
- Dark Blue body, Grey roof / hubs .... **£200-300**
1954        (Renumbered to 171)

**140a** 1951-53 **Austin A90 Atlantic**
- Mid-Blue body, Red interior,
  Cream hubs ..................................... **£300-400**
- Mid-Blue body and hubs,
  Dark Blue interior ....................... **£1,200-1,500**
- Mid-Blue body, Chocolate
  interior, Cream hubs................... **£1,000-1,250**
- Deep Blue body,
  Red interior and hubs.................. **£1,250-1,500**
- Red body,
  Maroon interior and hubs............ **£1,500-2,000**
- Light Blue body, Red interior,
  Cream hubs ..................................... **£250-350**
- Red body, Cream interior and hubs ...**£110-130**
- Light Blue body, Matt Red interior and
  hubs, Cream steering wheel..............**£110-130**
- Light Blue body, Gloss Red interior and
  hubs, Ivory steering wheel................**£110-130**
- Pink body, Cream interior and hubs ..**£110-130**
- Black body, Red interior and hubs ....**£110-130**
**NB** Interiors may have a gloss or matt finish.
1954        (Renumbered to 106)
**140b** 1951-54 **Rover 75 Saloon**
- Maroon body and hubs. Not boxed .. **£100-125**
- Maroon body, Red hubs. Not boxed . **£100-125**
- Cream body and hubs. Not boxed .... **£100-125**
- Cream body, Blue hubs.

- Supplied in dual-numbered box
  ('140b/156')................................. **£140-180**
- Red body, Maroon hubs. Supplied in
  dual-numbered box ('140b/156') **£1,000-1,250**
1954        (Renumbered to 156)

**140** 1963-69 **Morris 1100**
- Light Blue or Dark Blue, spun hubs..... **£60-70**
South African issues:
  (English / Afrikaans on box, spun hubs).
- White body, Blue roof, Red interior . **£500-700**
- Caramel body, Red interior.............. **£500-700**
- Sky Blue body, Red interior ............ **£500-700**

**141** 1963-67 **Vauxhall Victor Estate Car**
- Yellow body, Blue interior, spun hubs.. **£60-70**
1963        South African issues:
  (English / Afrikaans on box, spun hubs).
  Pink, Ivory or Yellow body,
  all with Blue interior......................... **£400-600**
- US promotional: Dark Red body, Blue
  interior, spun hubs.
  Paper labels with Yellow wording:
  'LIGHTNING FASTENERS LTD',
  'TECHNICAL SERVICES' ............. **£500-750**

**142** 1962-68 **Jaguar Mk.10**
- Metallic Light Blue or Mid-Blue,
  Red interior, spun aluminium hubs....... **£50-65**
1963        South African issues:
  (English / Afrikaans on box, spun hubs).
- Ivory body..................................... **£500-750**
- Green body with White roof............. **£500-750**
- Sky Blue body, Red interior,
  luggage, Cream base..................... **£800-1,100**
**NB** Gold, US export issue 'see-through'
window boxes. Model nos. 134, 138 and
142 housed in these boxes may attract a
premium of 50%.
See 'Cars - Box Types' for a complete listing.

**143** 1962-67 **Ford Capri**
- Turquoise body, White roof,
  Red interior, spun hubs ....................... **£60-70**

**144** 1963-67 **Volkswagen 1500**
- Off-White body, Red interior,
  luggage, spun hubs............................. **£65-75**
- Metallic Gold or Bronze body,
  Blue interior, luggage, spun hubs ......... **£65-75**
- Metallic Gold or Bronze body,
  Red interior, luggage, spun hubs ...... **£100-125**
1963        South African issues:
  (English / Afrikaans on box, spun hubs).
- Metallic Green body, spun hubs ....... **£500-750**
- Caramel body ................................. **£500-750**

**145** 1962-67 **Singer Vogue**
  All issues have spun hubs and Red interior.
- Metallic Light Green body................... **£75-85**
- Yellow body ............................... **£1,500-2,000**

**146** 1963-67 **Daimler 2.5 litre V8**
- Metallic Pale Green body,
  Red interior, spun hubs .................... **£100-120**
**147** 1962-69 **Cadillac '62**
- Metallic Green body,
  Red or White interior, spun hubs.......... **£60-75**

**148** 1962-65 **Ford Fairlane**
- (Non-metallic) Pea Green body,
  Cream interior, open or closed
  windows, spun hubs............................ **£75-85**
- Same model but with Red interior.... **£100-125**
1965-67
- Metallic Green body, Off-White interior,
  open windows. Standard card box.... **£200-300**
1963        South African issues:
  (English / Afrikaans on box, spun hubs).
- Bright Blue body, closed windows,
  White tyres ..................................... **£500-800**

- Dark Blue body, Light Grey interior,
  no base number, White tyres............. **£500-800**
- Heather Grey body, Light Grey interior,
  no base number, White tyres............. **£500-800**
- Dark Grey, Cream interior ................ **£500-800**
- US issue:
  Metallic Emerald Green body, spun hubs,
  Gold 'see-through' window box ....... **£300-400**

**149** 1971-75 **Citroën Dyane**
- Metallic Bronze body, Black roof and
  interior, Speedwheels ............................ **£30-35**
- 1971-75  Light Grey body,
  Dark Grey or Black roof........................ **£25-30**

**150** 1959-64 **Rolls-Royce Silver Wraith**
- Two-tone Grey body, suspension,
  spun hubs, Chromed metal bumpers..... **£55-65**
- Later issues with plastic bumpers......... **£60-85**
  **NB** The French version of 150 (French
  reference 551) was cast from English-made
  dies, was assembled in France, and has
  'Made in France' on the baseplate.

**151** 1954-59 **Triumph 1800 Saloon**
  (renumbered from 40b). See '40 Series' pages.

**151** 1965-69 **Vauxhall Victor 101**
  All issues have spun hubs.
- Pale Yellow body, Red interior ........... **£80-100**
- Metallic Red body, White interior ...... **£80-100**

**152** 1954-59 **Austin (A40) Devon**
  (renumbered from 40d). See '40 Series' pages.

**152** 1965-67 **Rolls-Royce Phantom V**
- Navy Blue body, Beige interior,
  chauffeur and two passengers,
  spun hubs or cast hubs ..................... **£100-125**
- 1967-77  Design change:
  Very Dark Blue body, White interior
  with Chauffeur but no passengers,
  Blue base, cast hubs............................. **£40-50**

**153** 1954-59 **Standard Vanguard**
  (renumbered from 40e). See '40e' listing.

**153** 1967-71 **Aston-Martin DB6**
  All issues have spoked wheels.
- Metallic Silver Blue body, Red int. ...... **£60-70**
- Metallic Turquoise body, White int. ... **£80-100**

**154** 1955 **Hillman Minx**
  (renumbered from 40f). See '40f' listing.

**154** 1966-69 **Ford Taunus 17M**
- Yellow body, White roof, Red interior,
  rounded spun hubs or cast wheels ........ **£40-50**

**155** 1961-66 **Ford Anglia 105E**
  All issues have spun hubs.
- Turquoise or Green body, Red int..... **£100-125**
- Turquoise body, Pale Blue interior ..... **£80-100**
- Very Pale Green body, Red interior.
  In mail-order box with correct spot .. **£350-450**
  **NB** Meccano issued a batch to Ford to
  mark the first Ford made on Merseyside
  on 8th March 1963. Some were fixed
  on plinths and given as souvenirs.
  1963  South African issues:

(English and Afrikaans on box, spun hubs).
- Caramel body, Red interior............... **£500-750**
- Off-White body, Red interior........... **£500-750**
- Light Blue body, Red interior........... **£500-750**

**156** 1954-56 **Rover 75** (renumbered from 140b)
- Red body, Maroon hubs.................. **£750-1,000**
- Green body, Cream hubs.................... **£200-250**
- Maroon body, Cream hubs................ **£130-150**
  1956-59  Two-tone issues:
- Light Green upper body, Mid-Green
  lower body and hubs, treaded tyres .. **£150-175**
- Dull two-tone Green body,
  Mid-Green hubs '156' to base ......... **£300-400**
- Light Green upper body, Turquoise
  lower body, Mid-Green hubs ........ **£750-1,000**
- Mid-Blue upper body, Cream lower
  body and hubs, treaded tyres .......... **£175-225**
- Dark Blue upper body,
  Cream lower body and hubs ............ **£250-350**
- Violet-Blue upper body,
  Cream lower body and hubs ............ **£400-600**

**156** 1968-71 **Saab 96**
- Metallic Red body, spun hubs............... **£65-75**
- Metallic Blue body, spun hubs ............ **£65-75**

**157** 1954-57 **Jaguar XK120**
- Yellow body, Light Yellow hubs....... **£175-200**
- Red body, Red diecast hubs.............. **£150-175**
- White body, Fawn hubs ................... **£125-150**
- Dark Sage Green body,
  Beige or Fawn hubs ........................ **£150-200**
  1957-59  Two-tone issues:
- Turquoise lower body,
  Cerise upper body, Red hubs ........... **£250-300**

- Sky-Blue lower body,
  Red upper body, Red hubs .............. **£250-300**
- Yellow lower body, Light Grey
  upper body and hubs ......................... **£250-300**
- 1959-62   Red body, spun hubs ........ **£250-300**
- Dark Sage Green body, spun hubs.... **£250-300**

**157**  1968-73   **BMW 2000 Tilux**
Box has inner pictorial stand.
- Blue/White, Red interior, cast hubs ...... **£55-65**
- Metallic Blue with Gold upper half.... **£90-120**
- Pale Blue body, Red interior,
  with spun hubs ........................................NGPP

**158**  1954-55   **Riley Saloon**
See '40' Series information.

**158**  1967-70   **Rolls-Royce Silver Shadow**
All issues have cast hubs.
- Metallic Red, White interior ................. **£45-55**
- 1970-73   Metallic Bright Blue,
  White interior .......................................... **£55-65**
- Metallic Light Blue, White interior ..... **£55-65**

**159**  1954   **Morris Oxford**
See '40' Series information.

**160**  1958-62   **Austin A30**
Smooth or treaded solid grey plastic wheels.
- Turquoise body ................................... **£90-120**
- Pale Beige body ................................. **£90-120**
**NB**   A version of the Austin A30 has been
reported with spun hubs, but is not confirmed.

**160**  1967-74   **Mercedes-Benz 250 SE**
- Met. Blue body, working stop-lights .... **£30-40**
- 1974   Metallic Blue body, White interior,
  bare metal baseplate, spun hubs,
  bubble-packed ..................................... **£100-125**

**161**  1954   **Austin (A40) Somerset**
See the '40j' listing.

**161**  1965-69   **Ford Mustang Fastback**
- White (Red seats), 'MUSTANG' decal
  badge on wings,
  chrome detailed wheels.......................... **£70-90**
- 1969-73   Yellow body, Blue seats,
  cast-in logo replaces decal ................... **£60-70**
- Orange body (no decal), Speedwheels . **£40-50**

**162**  1956-60   **Ford Zephyr Mk.I**
- Cream upper body, Dark Green lower
  body, Cream hubs ............................... **£80-100**
- Cream upper body, Lime Green lower
  body, Cream hubs ................................**£110-140**
- Two-tone Blue body, Grey hubs ....... **£100-125**
**NB**  Rear no. plate may be plain or Silver.

**162**  1966-70   **Triumph 1300**
- Light Blue body, Red interior,
  spun aluminium hubs ........................... **£65-75**

**163**  1956-60   **Bristol 450 Coupé**
- British Racing Green body, Light
  Green hubs, racing number '27' ....... **£120-140**

**163**  1966-70   **Volkswagen 1600 TL**
- Red or Dark Metallic Red,
  cast detailed hubs ................................. **£40-50**
- Metallic Blue body, Speedwheels......... **£60-70**

**164**  1957-60   **Vauxhall Cresta**
- Maroon lower body, Cream upper
  body, Cream hubs ............................... **£100-125**
- 1957-60   Green lower body,
  Grey upper body, Grey hubs............. **£100-125**
**NB**  Rear no. plate may be plain or Silver.

**164**  1966-71   **Ford Zodiac Mk.IV**
- Metallic Silver body, Red interior,
  Yellow or Black chassis, cast wheels ... **£50-60**
- Pale Met. Blue body, Yellow chassis,
  cast wheels ............................................ **£75-85**
- Metallic Copper body, Red interior,
  Yellow chassis, cast wheels,
  rigid plastic case.................................... **£50-60**

**165**  1959-60   **Humber Hawk**
- Black and Green lower body,
  Black roof, spun hubs ....................... **£125-150**
- Maroon lower body and roof,
  Cream upper body, spun hubs........... **£100-125**
**NB**  Both versions have been observed with
or without a front number plate casting.
- 1959-63   Black lower body, all Green
  upper body, spun hubs, with front number
  plate casting, in late issue lighter
  Yellow box with Green spot ............. **£200-250**

**165**  1969-76   **Ford Capri**
- Metallic Green body, Orange interior,
  Speedwheels.......................................... **£50-60**
- Metallic Purple body, Orange interior,
  Speedwheels.......................................... **£50-60**
- Met. Turquoise body, Yellow interior,
  Speedwheels.......................................... **£60-70**

**166**  1958-63   **Sunbeam Rapier**
- Yellow lower body, Deep Cream
  upper body, Beige hubs...................... **£80-100**
- Same but with spun hubs ................. **£100-125**
- Blue lower body, Turquoise upper
  body, Blue hubs.................................. **£100-125**
- Same but with spun hubs ................. **£100-125**

**166**  1967-70   **Renault R16**
- Metallic Blue, spun hubs ..................... **£40-50**

**167**  1958-63   **A.C. Aceca Sports Coupé**
- Grey body, Red roof, Red hubs ..........**£90-110**
- Cream body, Reddish-Maroon roof,
  Silver hubs ...........................................**£90-110**
- Deep Cream body, Dark Brown roof,
  Cream hubs ...........................................**£90-110**
__167 issues with spun hubs:__
- All Matt-Cream body.
  Lighter Yellow box, Cream spot....... **£300-350**
- Cream body, Maroon roof................ **£140-170**
- Cream body, Dk. Brown roof .......... **£140-170**
- Grey body, Red roof.
  In plain Red/Yellow box ................... **£140-170**

**168**  1959-63   **Singer Gazelle Saloon**
- Deep Brown lower, Cream upper
  body, spun aluminium hubs ................**£90-110**
- Dark Green lower, Grey upper
  body, spun aluminium hubs ................**£90-110**
- Black body, spun aluminium hubs..........NGPP

**168**  1968-70   **Ford Escort**
- Pale Blue or White, cast detailed hubs . **£45-55**
- 1970-74   Met. Red body, spun hubs.... **£65-75**
- 1974-75   Met. Blue, Speedwheels....... **£65-75**

**169**  1958-63   **Studebaker Golden Hawk**
- Tan body, Red rear side panel and hubs,
  White tyres, plain Yellow/Red box ......**£90-110**
- Same, but spun hubs, White tyres.... **£90-120**
- Light Green body, Cream rear side
  panel and hubs, White tyres...............**£90-120**

- Same, but with spun aluminium
  hubs, White tyres .............................. **£100-130**

**169** 1967-69 **Ford Corsair 2000 E**
- Silver body, Black textured roof.......... **£70-85**

**170** 1954-56 **Ford Fordor Sedan**
  (renumbered from 139a)
- Tan body, Red hubs........................... **£120-150**
- Yellow body, Red hubs .................... **£120-150**
- Green body, Red hubs...................... **£120-150**
- Red body, Red hubs ......................... **£120-150**
  1956-58 'Highline' versions:
- Red lower body, Cream upper body,
  Red hubs ............................................ **£350-450**
- Blue lower body, Pink upper body,
  Blue ridged hubs .............................. **£350-450**
  1958-59 'Lowline' versions:
- Red lower body, Cream upper body,
  Red ridged hubs ................................ **£200-250**
- Blue lower body, Pink upper body,
  Blue ridged hubs .............................. **£200-250**

**170m** 1954-54 **Ford US Army Staff Car**
  See 'Military Vehicles' section.

**170** 1964-70 **Lincoln Continental**
- Metallic Bronze body, White roof,
  Blue interior, cast wheels..................... **£75-85**
- Light Blue body, White roof,
  Mid-Blue interior, cast wheels.............. **£75-85**

**170** 1979 **Ford Granada Ghia**
  Not issued, but a Metallic Silver factory
  publicity sample was sold by Vectis Auctions
  in 1999 for £470.

**171** 1954-56 **Hudson Commodore Sedan**
  (renumbered from 139b)
- Dark Blue body,
  Pale Tan upper body and hubs .......... **£100-150**
- Royal Blue body,
  Pale Tan upper body and hubs .......... **£250-350**
- Light Blue body,
  Pale Tan upper body, Fawn hubs ...... **£400-600**
- Cream body,
  Chocolate upper body and hubs........ **£100-150**
- Cream body, Chocolate upper body,
  Red hubs, large lettering on base..... **£100-150**
  1956-58 'Highline' versions:
- Turquoise lower body,
  Red upper body, Red hubs ................ **£350-450**
- Blue lower body,
  Red upper body, Red hubs ................ **£350-450**
- Blue lower body,
  Chocolate upper body, Red hubs ..... **£350-450**
- Light Grey lower body with
  Mid-Blue upper body, Blue hubs ..... **£350-450**
  1958-59 'Lowline' versions:
- Turquoise lower body,
  Chocolate upper body, Red hubs ..... **£350-450**
- Light Grey lower body with
  Mid-Blue upper body, Blue hubs ..... **£350-450**

**171** 1965-68 **Austin 1800**
- Met. Blue body, Red int., spun hubs .... **£60-80**
- Light Blue body, Red int., spun hubs ... **£60-80**

**172** 1954-56 **Studebaker Land Cruiser**
- Light Green body, Mid-Green or
  Mid-Blue hubs ................................... **£90-110**
- Blue body, Fawn or Beige hubs....... **£130-160**
- Light Beige body, Cream hubs ......... **£250-350**
  1956-58 'Highline' versions:
- Beige lower body, Maroon upper
  body, Cream hubs............................. **£150-200**
- Beige lower body, Tan upper body,
  Cerise hubs ...................................... **£150-200**
  1958-59 'Lowline' versions:
- Cream lower body and hubs,
  Maroon upper body........................... **£150-200**
- Cream lower body and hubs,
  Light Tan upper body........................ **£150-200**

**172** 1965-69 **Fiat 2300 Station Wagon**
- Two-tone Blue body, Red interior,
  spun aluminim hubs .............................. **£60-80**

**173** 1958-62 **Nash Rambler Station Wagon**
- Turquoise body with Cerise flash, Grey
  hubs, no number on later baseplates....**£90-110**
- Pink body with Blue flash, Cream
  hubs, no number on later baseplates....**£90-110**
- As previous but with spun hubs, plain
  Yellow/Red box without picture ......... **£90-120**
- Beige body, Blue side flash,
  spun hubs, White tyres..................... **£200-300**

**173** 1969-72 **Pontiac Parisienne**
- Metallic Maroon body, Lemon interior,
  retractable aerials, cast wheels.......... **£80-100**
- Metallic Blue body............................. **£80-100**

**174** 1958-63 **Hudson Hornet**
- Red lower body, Cream roof and
  side flash, Beige hubs, White tyres......**£90-110**
- Yellow lower body, Dark Grey roof
  and flash, Cream hubs, White tyres.. **£100-125**
- Later issues with spun hubs ............. **£140-170**

**174** 1969-72 **Ford Mercury Cougar**
- Blue or Metallic Dark Blue body,
  cast hubs or Speedwheels ................... **£55-75**

**175** 1958-61 **Hillman Minx**
- Grey lower body, Mid-Blue upper
  body and hubs ................................... **£100-125**
- Grey lower body, Mid-Blue upper
  body,spun hubs................................. **£200-250**
- Pale Brown body, Green roof and
  boot, Beige hubs ............................... **£100-125**
- Pale Brown body, Green roof and
  boot, spun hubs ................................ **£200-250**

**175** 1969-73 **Cadillac Eldorado**
- Metallic Purple body, Black roof,
  Orange interior, cast or Speedwheels ... **£70-90**
- Metallic Sea-Green body, Black roof,
  Orange interior, cast or Speedwheels ... **£70-90**

**176** 1958-63 **Austin A105 Saloon**
  First Dinky Toys car to have full
  window glazing.
  Body sides have a contrasting panel line.
  Treaded tyres may be Black or White.
- 1958-59 Cream body, Navy Blue
  panel line, Cream hubs ......................**£90-110**
- Pale Grey body, Red line, Red hubs . **£130-160**
- 1959-63 Cream body, Dark Blue
  roof and panel line, Cream hubs....... **£100-125**
- Cream body, Mid-Blue roof and
  panel line, Cream hubs .................... **£150-175**
- Cream body, Mid-Blue roof and
  panel line, spun aluminium hubs ..... **£150-175**
- Cream body, Mid-Blue roof
  (but no panel line)............................ **£150-175**
- Pale Grey body, Red roof and panel
  line, Light Grey hubs ....................... **£150-175**
- Pale Grey body / roof, Red panel
  line, spun hubs ................................ **£125-175**

**176** 1969-74 **N.S.U. Ro80**
- Metallic Red body, spun hubs,
  luminous seats, working lights ............ **£40-50**
- Metallic Blue body............................. **£100-150**

**177** 1961-66 **Opel Kapitan**
- Light Greyish-Blue body,
  Red interior, spun hubs ....................... **£60-75**
  1963 South African issues:
  (English and Afrikaans on box, spun hubs).
- Mid or Dark Blue body
  with Red interior...................... **£1,000-1,200**
- Caramel body, Red interior........ **£1,000-1,200**
- Pale Yellow body, Red interior ... **£1,000-1,200**

**178** 1959-63 **Plymouth Plaza**
  All issues have spun hubs.
- Light Blue body, Dark Blue roof and
  side flash, Gloss Black baseplate.......**£110-140**
- Salmon Pink body, Light Green
  roof and side flash............................ **£150-190**
- Light Tan body, Light Green roof and
  side flash, matt-Black base .............. **£150-200**
- Light Blue body, White roof and flash,
  White treaded tyres,
  Lighter Yellow box ........................... **£175-225**
- Sky-Blue body, White roof and flash,
  late issue – no number on baseplate . **£300-400**

**178** 1975-79 **Mini Clubman**
- Bronze body, opening doors, jewelled
  headlights on some, Speedwheels......... **£40-50**
- Red body, Speedwheels .................... **£100-125**

**179** 1958-63 **Studebaker President**
- Light Blue body, Dark Blue flash,
  Cream hubs, White tyres..................... **£90-120**
- Yellow body, Blue flash and hubs,
  White tyres.......................................... **£90-120**
- Late issues with spun hubs ............... **£120-150**

**179** 1971-75 **Opel Commodore**
- Metallic Blue body, Black roof,
  Speedwheels.......................................... **£55-75**

**180** 1958-63 **Packard Clipper**
- Cerise upper body, Cream lower body
  and hubs, White tyres .......................... **£90-120**
- Orange lower body, Light Grey upper
  body and hubs, White tyres ............. **£100-125**
- Late issues with spun hubs ............. **£130-150**

**180** 1979-80 **Rover 3500**
- White body, plastic chassis and wheels.
  Made in Hong Kong, scale 1:35 .......... **£25-35**

**181** 1956-70 **Volkswagen Saloon**
  Cast hubs issues:
- Pale Grey body, Mid-Blue hubs .......... **£75-95**
- Blue-Grey body, Mid-Blue hubs .......... **£75-95**
- Dark Blue body, Mid-Blue hubs ....... **£120-140**
- RAF Blue body, Mid-Blue hubs ....... **£120-140**
- Lime Green body, Mid-Green hubs .. **£120-140**
  Spun hubs issues:
- Pale Grey body, spun hubs .............. **£75-100**
- Blue-Grey body, spun hubs............... **£75-100**
- Pale Blue body, spun hubs, unpainted
  or matt or gloss black baseplate......... **£75-100**
- RAF Blue body, spun hubs ............... **£75-100**
  Plastic hubs issue:
- Pale Blue body, Mid-Blue plastic
  hubs, Matt Black base..................... **£300-350**
  **NB** See also 'Factory samples' listing.
  South African issues:
  (English and Afrikaans text on box, spun hubs).
- Lime Green or Pale Yellow
  body, Red interior ..................... **£1,200-1,400**
- Pale Blue or Metallic Blue body,
  Red interior ............................... **£1,200-1,400**
- Grey body, Red interior ............. **£1,200-1,400**

**182** 1958-66 **Porsche 356a Coupé**
- Pale Blue body, Cream hubs............. **£100-120**
- Pale Blue body, Mid-Blue hubs ....... **£100-120**
- Pale Blue body, spun hubs............... **£100-120**
- Cerise body, Cream hubs ................. **£120-140**
- Cerise body, spun hubs ................... **£120-140**
- Cream, window glazing,
  Mid-Blue hubs ................................. **£120-140**
- Cream, glazing, Beige hubs ............. **£120-140**
- Cream body, glazing, spun hubs....... **£120-140**
- Red body and hubs, in standard
  Yellow box (no coloured spot) ......... **£120-140**
- Red body and hubs. In late issue
  lighter Yellow box with Red spot ..... **£250-350**

- Plum Red body, spun hubs.
  In lighter Yellow box ...................... **£250-350**

**183  1958-60  Fiat 600**
- Red body, smooth or treaded solid
  Grey plastic wheels............................... **£70-80**
- Pale Green body, smooth or treaded
  solid Grey plastic wheels...................... **£70-80**

**183  1966-74  Morris Mini Minor (Automatic)**
- Metallic Red body, matt or gloss Black
  roof, White interior, spun hubs. Box
  should contain 'Meccano Automatic
  Transmission' leaflet ........................... **£70-85**
- Metallic Red body, Black roof,
  White interior, Speedwheels ................ **£70-85**
- Metallic Bright Blue body,
  White interior, spun hubs.................. **£100-125**
- **NB** Late issues with 'Austin Cooper S'
  cast on boot (250 casting) exist .............NGPP
  Various registration numbers will also
  be found, e.g., 'UVR 576D',
  'MTB 21G', 'HTB 21H'.

**184  1961-65  Volvo 122 S**  (all with spun hubs)
- Red body, Off-White interior............... **£70-80**
- Dark Red body ................................. **£200-250**
- Off-White body, White interior ....... **£200-250**
  Cream body, Cream interior ............ **£200-250**
  1962   South African issues:
    (English and Afrikaans on box).
- Grey-Blue body, White interior ........ **£600-800**
- Sage Green, White interior .............. **£600-800**
- Pale Green, Fawn interior................ **£600-800**

**185  1961-63  Alfa Romeo 1900 Sprint**
- Yellow body, Red interior, spun hubs... **£70-90**
- Red body, Off-White int., spun hubs.... **£70-90**
**186  1961-67  Mercedes-Benz 220 SE**
  All issues have spun hubs.
- Lt. Blue body, Red or White interior.... **£50-65**
- Light Blue body, Yellow interior .......... **£60-75**
- RAF Blue body, Cream interior............ **£50-65**
  1963   South African issue:
    (English and Afrikaans text on box).
- Sky Blue or Grey body ..................... **£400-600**

**187  1959-64  VW Karmann Ghia Coupé**
- Red body, Black roof, spun hubs,
  White tyres, 'plain' box ....................**£110-130**
- Dark Green body, Cream roof,
  spun hubs, White tyres, 'plain' box ...**£110-130**
- Same issue in late issue picture box . **£100-150**

**187  1968-77  De Tomaso Mangusta 5000**
- Fluorescent Pink body, White panels
  front/rear, Black interior, cast wheels,
  racing number '7'................................ **£35-40**

**188  1968-74  Jensen FF**
- Yellow body, Black interior, cast wheels
  or Speedwheels. In rigid plastic case.... **£70-90**

**189  1959-64  Triumph Herald Saloon**
  All issues have spun hubs.
- Pale or Light Blue roof and sides
  with White centre ............................. **£75-85**
- Green roof / sides with White centre.... **£75-85**
  **Special issues**: (all in plain standard
    yellow box with colour spot)
- Alpine Mauve body ......................... **£500-750**
- Magenta body .................................. **£500-750**
- Red lower body and roof, White
  upper body, Red spot on box ............ **£500-750**
- Greyish-Green, Pale Whitish-Green
  roof, plain box, correct colour spot .. **£500-750**
- Pinkish-Brown body,
  Pale Grey roof.................................. **£500-750**
- Dark Grey body and roof, Pale Grey
  bonnet and boot, standard box ......... **£500-750**
- All Red, box with Red spot .............. **£500-750**

- Very Dark Blue lower body and
  roof, Pale Blue mid-section .............. **£500-750**
- Deep Grey and White body .............. **£500-750**
- Pale Lilac body, Bluish White roof,
  in box with Blue and White spot ..... **£500-750**
- Black and Pale Grey body .............. **£500-750**
- Monaco Blue body........................... **£500-750**
- Monaco Blue lower body and roof,
  Sebring White upper body ............... **£500-750**
- Powder Blue, blue spot on box........ **£500-750**
- Powder Blue/Sebring White,
  Light Blue spot on box .................... **£500-750**
- Lichfield Green body ...................... **£500-750**
- White body, White spot on box ....... **£500-750**

**189  1969-76  Lamborghini Marzal**
- Green/White or Red/White,
  cast detailed hubs............................ **£25-45**
- Yellow/White body, cast detailed hubs . **£40-45**
- 1976-78
- Metallic Blue/White, Speedwheels....... **£35-45**
- Dark Met. Green/White, Speedwheels . **£35-45**

**190  1970-74  Monteverdi 375 L**
- Metallic Maroon body, White interior,
  cast wheels or Speedwheels.
  In rigid plastic case ......................... **£35-45**
  **NB** See also 'Factory samples' listing.

**191  1959-64  Dodge Royal Sedan**
  All have spun hubs, White treaded tyres.
- Cream body with Tan rear flash ....... **£125-150**
- Cream body, Blue rear flash, lighter
  Yellow box, late issue –
  no number on base .......................... **£150-200**
- Pale Green body with Black flash .... **£125-150**
  **NB** Casting used for 258 'USA Police Car'.

**192  1959-64  De Soto Fireflite**
  All have spun hubs, White treaded tyres.
- Grey body, Red roof and side flash .. **£100-125**
- Turquoise body, Lt. Tan roof / flash . **£140-160**

**192  1970-80  Range Rover**
  Cast detailed hubs or Speedwheels.
- Met. Bronze body, Pale Blue interior ... **£25-35**
- Yellow body, Red interior ................... **£25-35**
- Black body, Red interior ..................... **£40-60**
- Met. Bronze body, Pale Grey interior... **£40-60**
  **NB** See also 'Factory samples' listing.

**193  1961-69  Rambler Station Wagon**
- Pale Yellow body, White roof,
  Red interior, Black plastic roof-rack,
  spun hubs, standard box ...................... **£70-80**
- Same model but with White interior.
  In Gold 'see-through' US export
  window-box ................................... **£150-175**
  1962   South African issues:
    (English / Afrikaans on box, spun hubs).
- Lilac body, Cream or Black roof,
  Red interior ................................. **£750-1,000**
- All-Lilac body, Red interior.......... **£750-1,000**
- Sage Green body, Red interior....... **£750-1,000**
- Pale Blue body, Cream roof,
  Red interior ................................. **£750-1,000**
- Dark Blue body, White roof,
  Red interior ................................. **£750-1,000**
- Light Greyish-Green body,
  Black roof, Red interior ................ **£750-1,000**
- All-Cream body, Red interior ........ **£750-1,000**

**194  1961-67  Bentley 'S' Coupé**
- Grey body, Red interior, Tan hood,
  Grey male driver, spun hubs,
  gloss black baseplate......................... **£100-125**
- Metallic Bronze body, Cream interior,
  Dark Blue hood, driver, spun hubs ... **£150-200**

**NB** Late issues of 194 have plated plastic parts.
  1962   South African issues:
    (English / Afrikaans on box, spun hubs).
- Lime Green body, Red interior,
  Black hood ................................ **£1,000-1,200**
- Cream body, Red interior,
  Dark Cream hood...................... **£1,000-1,200**

**195  1961-71  Jaguar 3.4 Mk.II**
  All have spun hubs.
- Maroon body, White interior ............... **£70-90**
- Cream body, Red interior..................... **£70-90**
- Light Grey body, Red interior.............. **£70-90**
  1962   South African issues:
    (English and Afrikaans on box, spun hubs).
- Light or Sky-Blue body,
  Cream or Red interior ...................... **£600-800**
- Red or Off-White body,
  Cream or Red interior ...................... **£600-800**

**196  1963-70  Holden Special Sedan**
  (First Dinky to have jewelled headlights).
  All have spun hubs.
- Metallic Gold body, White roof........... **£70-80**
- Turquoise body, White roof,
  Grey baseplate, Off-White interior ....... **£70-80**
- Turquoise body, White roof,
  Silver baseplate, Red interior............... **£70-80**
- Turquoise body, White roof,
  Dark Grey baseplate, Red interior ........ **£70-80**
  1966   South African issue:
    (English and Afrikaans on box, spun hubs).
- White body, Turquoise roof.............. **£600-800**

**197  1961-71  Morris Mini Traveller**
  All have spun hubs.
- Cream body, Lemon interior............. **£600-800**
- Cream body, Red interior................ **£90-110**
- Cream body, Pale Blue interior........ **£300-400**
- Dark Green body, Pale Blue interior  **£300-400**
- Dark Green body, Yellow interior..... **£500-700**

- Fluorescent Green body, Red interior,
  with or without front number plate... **£160-190**
- Fluorescent Pink body, Red interior . **£200-250**
  **NB** Unlike 199, there is no
  'colour change' label on the 197 box.
**198  1962-69  Rolls-Royce Phantom V**
  (First Dinky Toys model with metallic
  paint and opening windows).
- Metallic Cream lower body, Metallic Light
  Green upper body, Blue or Red interior,
  glossy baseplate, spun hubs, chauffeur. **£75-85**
- Metallic Cream upper body, Grey lower
  body, Red interior, glossy baseplate,
  chauffeur, spun hubs ........................... **£75-85**
- Two tone Grey body, Red interior,
  matt baseplate, chauffeur, spun hubs .... **£75-85**
  1963   South African issues:
    (English / Afrikaans on box, spun hubs).
- Dark Grey over Metallic Cream body,
  Red interior ............................... **£1,000-1,200**
- Sage Green or Two-Tone Grey .... **£1,000-1,200**
- Pale Grey body, Ivory roof,
  Red interior ............................... **£1,000-1,200**
- Pale Grey body, Grey roof,
  Red interior ............................... **£1,000-1,200**
- Lime Green body, Ivory roof,
  Red interior, spun hubs .............. **£1,000-1,200**
**199  1961-71  Austin 7 Countryman**
  All have spun hubs.
- Blue body, Yellow interior,
  Gloss Black base............................. **£130-160**
- Electric Blue, Powder Blue or
  Blue-Grey body with Red interior
  and 'wood' trim............................... **£80-100**
- Fluorescent Orange or Fluorescent
  Pink body, Red interior, Matt Black base.
  Box must bear a small oblong label
  stating:
  'COLOUR OF MODEL MAY DIFFER
  FROM ILLUSTRATION'................ **£250-300**

- Deep Grey body, Red interior,
  Brown 'woodwork' ............................ **£150-200**

**200** 1954-57 **Midget Racer**
  (renumbered from 35b)
- Silver body, Red grille, Brown driver,
  solid Black rubber wheels. ................... **£65-75**

**200** 1971-78 **Matra 630 Le Mans**
- Blue body, RN '5', '9' or '36',
  Speedwheels .................................... **£25-30**

**201** 1979-80 **Plymouth Stock Car**
- Blue body, racing number '34',
  wide plastic wheels ............................. **£35-45**

**202** 1971-75 **Fiat Abarth 2000**
- Fluorescent Red/White, Speedwheels... **£20-30**
**202/2** 1979-80 **Customised Land Rover**
- Yellow body, White crash guard. White
  or Black rails/aerials (344 casting) ....... **£25-35**

**203** 1979-80 **Customised Range Rover**
- Black body, Yellow/Red design,
  White plastic chassis/crash guard ........ **£25-30**

**204** 1971-74 **Ferrari 312 P**
- Metallic Red body and doors,
  Speedwheels, RN '60'.......................... **£30-35**
- Same, but with White doors ................. **£30-35**

**205** 1962-64 **Talbot Lago Racing Car**
  (renumbered from 230)
- Blue, body Red or Yellow plastic hubs,
  RN '4', boxed or blister-packed.
  ('230' on base) ................................. **£250-350**
**205** 1968-73 **Lotus Cortina Rally**
- White body, Blue interior, Red bonnet
  and side stripe, 'Monte Carlo' logo,
  RN '7', 2 aerials, cast hubs................... **£70-80**

**206** 1962-64 **Maserati Racing Car**
  (renumbered from 231)
- Red/White body, Red or Yellow plastic
  hubs, boxed or blister-packed.
  ('231' on base) ................................. **£250-350**
- late issue:
  Same but in lighter Yellow box ....... **£150-200**
**206** 1978-80 **Customised Corvette**
- Red/Yellow or White/Black, plastic
  chassis and wide wheels ...................... **£20-30**

**207** 1962-64 **Alfa-Romeo Racing Car**
  (renumbered from 232)
- Red body, Red plastic hubs, boxed
  or blister-packed, ('232' on base) ..... **£250-350**
- late issue:
  Same but in lighter Yellow box ....... **£150-200**
**207** 1977-80 **Triumph TR7 Rally**
- White/Red/Blue, RN '8',
  plastic chassis and wheels, 'Leyland'... **£25-35**

**208** 1962-64 **Cooper-Bristol Racing Car**
  (renumbered from 233)
- Dark Green, White flash, RN '6',
  Red plastic hubs, boxed or
  blister-packed, ('233' on base)......... **£250-350**
- late issue:
  Same, but in lighter Yellow box ....... **£150-200**
**208** 1971-75 **VW Porsche 914**
- Yellow body, Black interior,
  cast detailed hubs ............................. **£25-30**
- Promotional version in Yellow/Red
  promotional box ................................. **£70-80**
- 1976-80 Metallic Blue/Black body,
  Speedwheels..................................... **£25-30**

**209** 1962-64 **Ferrari Racing Car**
  (renumbered from 234)
- Blue, Yellow triangle, angled '5',
  Yellow plastic hubs, boxed or
  blister-packed, ('234' on base).......... **£300-400**
- late issue:
  Same but in lighter Yellow box ........ **£300-400**

**210** 1962-65 **Vanwall Racing Car**
  (renumbered from 239)
- Green, '239' on base, Yellow plastic
  hubs, boxed or blister-packed ........... **£250-350**
- Green body, Green plastic hubs........ **£250-350**

**210** 1971-73 **Alfa-Romeo 33 Tipo**
- Red body, Black doors, White interior,
  RN '36', cast wheels, leaflet in box ..... **£30-35**

**211** 1975 **Triumph TR7 Sports Car**
- Metallic Blue, Union Jack badge........ **£90-100**
- Yellow, Black bumpers and interior ... **£90-100**
- Yellow, Grey bumpers and interior..... **£90-100**
- Red body, Black bumpers and interior . **£50-60**
- Red body, Grey bumpers and interior... **£50-60**

**212** 1965-70 **Ford Cortina Rally**
- White body, Black bonnet, 'EAST
  AFRICAN SAFARI' and 'CASTROL'
  logos, Black or Red RN '8', spotlight,
  Red interior, spun hubs. Picture box... **£80-100**

**213** 1970-73 **Ford Capri Rally**
- Metallic Red body, Black bonnet, Yellow
  interior, RN '20', rigid plastic case ..... **£55-65**
- 1973-75 Bronze body, Black bonnet,
  spotlights, wing mirrors, Speedwheels,
  rigid plastic case................................ **£55-65**

**214** 1966-69 **Hillman Imp Rally**
- Dark Blue body, Red interior,
  'MONTE CARLO RALLY' logo, RN '35',
  spun hubs, picture box ......................... **£70-80**

**215** 1965-66 **Ford GT Racing Car**
- White body, Red interior,
  RN '7', spun hubs .............................. **£55-65**
- 1966-70
  Same, but with Silver spoked wheels ... **£35-45**
- 1970-74 Metallic Green body, Gold
  engine, Orange/Black stripe, Yellow
  interior, RN '7', Silver spoked wheels . **£45-55**
- Metallic Green body, Silver engine,
  Red or Black interior .......................... **£35-45**
- Metallic Green body, Dark Blue/White
  stripe, White interior .......................... **£35-45**
- Yellow or Metallic Blue,
  Silver or Gold wheels ......................... **£35-45**

**216** 1967-69 **Dino Ferrari**
- Red body, Light Blue interior.............. **£40-50**
- 1969-75 Metallic Blue/Black, Silver or
  brass spoked wheels or Speedwheels ... **£30-40**

**217** 1968-70 **Alfa Romeo Scarabeo OSI**
- Pink body, cast spoked wheels ............. **£30-35**
- 1969-74 Red, Orange or Green
  body, Speedwheels................................ **£25-30**

**218** 1969-73 **Lotus Europa**
- Yellow body, Blue panels/roof,
  chequered flags, Gold engine .............. **£35-45**
- 1973-75 Yellow/Black or Metallic Blue
  body, Silver engine, Speedwheels ........ **£30-35**
**219** 1977-79 **Leyland Jaguar XJ-5.3**
- White body, 'Leyland' decal.
  (Made in Hong Kong)............................ **£35-45**
**219** 1978-79 **'Big Cat' Jaguar**
- White/Red, Black 'Big Cat' decal,
  sold unboxed ....................................... **£35-45**

- Boxed version with 'Big Cat' logo ....... **£50-75**

**220** 1954-56 **Small Open Racing Car**
  (renumbered from 23a)
- Silver with Red hubs, RN '4'............... **£40-50**
- Red with Silver hubs, RN '4'............... **£40-50**

**220** 1970-73 **Ferrari P5**
- Metallic Red body,
  Yellow interior, cast hubs.................... **£25-30**
- 1973-75 Metallic Red body,
  Yellow interior, Speedwheels............... **£25-30**

**221** 1954-56 **'Speed Of The Wind' Racing Car**
  (renumbered from 23e)
- Silver body with plain baseplate........... **£40-45**

**221** 1969-76 **Corvette Stingray**
- Metallic Gold body,
  Silver or Gold spoked wheels ............... **£25-35**
- 1976-78 Red or White body,
  Black bonnet, Speedwheels .................. **£25-35**

**222** 1954-56 **Streamlined Racing Car**
  (renumbered from 22s)
- Silver body; Red, Blue or Green trim... **£60-70**

**222** 1978-80 **Hesketh 308 E**
- Dark Blue or Bronze, RN '2',
  cast-detailed or Speedwheels ............... **£20-30**
- Swiss promotional issue: Same but
  in 'OLYMPUS CAMERAS' box .......... **£50-75**

**223** 1970-75 **McLaren M8A Can-Am**
- White body, Metallic Blue engine
  cover, cast detailed wheels.................... **£25-35**
- 1976-78 Metallic Green body,
  Black engine cover, White interior,
  Speedwheels....................................... **£25-35**

**224** 1970-74 **Mercedes-Benz C111**
- White body, Blue interior, cast hubs..... **£25-35**
- Metallic Dark Red body,
  White interior, cast hubs ..................... **£25-35**

**225** 1971-76 **Lotus F1 Racing Car**
- Metallic Red body with number '7',
  inner pictorial box and stand ............... **£25-35**
- 1976-77 Lime-Green or Metallic
  Blue body with RN '7'......................... **£25-35**

**226** 1972-75 **Ferrari 312 B2**
- Red body with racing number '5'........ **£25-35**
- 1976-80 Bronze or Gold body, Black,
  White or Yellow rear wing, RN '5'....... **£25-35**

**227** 1975-77 **Beach Buggy**
- Yellow/Grey or Yellow/White body ..... **£25-35**
- Green/Grey or Pink/Black body .......... **£25-35**
  NB See also 'Factory samples' listing.

**228** 1970-72 **Super Sprinter**
- Blue/Silver or Blue/Orange body,
  Speedwheels........................................ **£25-35**

**230** 1954-60 **Talbot Lago Racing Car**
  (renumbered from 23k) (renumbered to 205)
  Blue body, Yellow RN '4',
  Blue diecast hubs ............................. **£150-175**
- 1960-62 Blue body, Yellow RN '4',
  spun aluminium hubs ........................ **£150-175**

**231** 1954-60 **Maserati Racing Car**
  (renumbered from 23n) (renumbered to 206)
- Red body, White flash / RN '9',
  Red diecast hubs ............................. **£150-175**
- Red body, White flash / '9',
  Yellow plastic hubs .......................... **£200-250**
- 1960-62 Red body, White flash
  and RN '9', spun hubs ...................... **£150-175**

**232** 1954-60 **Alfa-Romeo Racing Car**
(renumbered from 23f) (renumbered to 207)
- Red body, White RN '8',
Red diecast hubs ............................. **£175-200**
- Red body, White RN '8',
Red plastic hubs ............................. **£200-250**
1960-62 Red body,
White RN '8', spun hubs ................. **£150-175**

**233** 1954-60 **Cooper-Bristol Racing Car**
(renumbered from 23g) (renumbered to 208)
- Green body and cast hubs,
White flash, RN '6'.......................... **£100-120**
- 1960-62 Green body, White flash,
RN '6', spun hubs........................... **£145-165**
- Green body, White flash / '6',
Red plastic hubs ............................. **£200-300**

**234** 1954-60 **Ferrari Racing Car**
(renumbered from 23h) (renumbered to 209)
- Blue body, Yellow nose-cone,
cast hubs and RN '5'........................ **£150-200**
- 1960-62 Blue body, Yellow
nose-cone, RN '5', spun hubs........... **£200-250**
- 1962-62 Blue body, Yellow triangle
on nose, RN '5', spun hubs, boxed... **£350-450**
- Blue body, White triangle on nose,
RN '8', Blue plastic hubs ................. **£400-500**
- South African issue:
Red body, RN '36', dimpled base
rivets, spun hubs.
(English/Afrikaans on box).............. **£400-500**

**235** 1954-60 **H.W.M. Racing Car**
(renumbered from 23j)
- Pale Green body, Yellow RN '7',
Green cast hubs. .............................**£110-140**

**236** 1956-59 **Connaught Racing Car**
- Pale Green body, Red interior, Mid-Green
hubs, RN '32', White driver ............. **£100-120**

**237** 1957-60 **Mercedes-Benz Racing Car**
- Gloss White body, Red interior,
Red plastic hubs or spun hubs,
Red RN '30', Yellow driver.............. **£100-125**
- 1960-62 Matt White body, Red interior,
Red plastic hubs or spun hubs,
RN '30', Blue driver ...........................**£90-110**
- 1962-64 Matt White body,
plastic hubs, RN '30', Tan driver ........**£90-110**
- Late issue:
Matt White body, Red plastic hubs,
RN '30', Blue or Yellow driver.
Late issue Yellow window box ......... **£100-130**

**238** 1957-60 **Jaguar 'D' type**
- Turquoise body, Blue interior,
White driver, with or without RN '4',
Blue diecast hubs ............................. **£100-125**
NB Boxes for 238 that have a descriptive
adhesive label stating 'Le Mans 1955/56/57'
may attract a premium.
- 1960-62 Turquoise body, Blue interior,
White driver, RN '4', spun hubs ..... **£120-150**
- 1962-65
Turquoise body, Blue interior or
Turquoise interior, White or Yellow
driver, RN '4', Blue or Yellow plastic
hubs, in plain lighter Yellow box...... **£250-300**

**239** 1958-60 **Vanwall Racing Car**
- Green body, Green hubs, White or
Yellow driver, RN '25', '26' or '35',
'VANWALL' logo ............................. **£140-170**

- 1960-62 Green body, White driver,
RN '35' or '26', spun hubs ............... **£140-170**
- 1962-65 Green body, White or Tan
driver, RN '35', Yellow plastic hubs.
In lighter Yellow box ........................ **£200-250**
- Green body, Yellow driver,
RN '35', Yellow plastic hubs.
In lighter Yellow box ........................ **£200-250**
- Green body, Green plastic hubs........ **£200-250**

**240** 1963-70 **Cooper Racing Car**
- Blue body, White design, Black RN '20',
spun hubs, White driver
(Silver or Yellow helmet)....................... **£60-75**

**241** 1963-70 **Lotus Racing Car**
- Green body with number '7' or '36', spun
hubs, White driver, Silver helmet ......... **£60-75**
- Green body with racing number '24',
spun hubs, driver with Red helmet ....... **£60-75**
- South African issue:
Green body with RN '24', cast wheels,
White driver with Red helmet ......... **£400-600**

**242** 1963-71 **Ferrari Racing Car**
- Red body, RN '36', spun hubs,
driver, Silver helmet............................. **£60-75**

**243** 1963-71 **B.R.M. Racing Car**
- Green, Yellow cowl, RN '7',
spun hubs, Red helmet ........................ **£60-75**
- 1963-71 Metallic Green (shades exist),
Yellow cowl, number '7', spun hubs .... **£60-75**
NB Gold, US export issue 'see-through'
window boxes. Model nos. 237 - 243
housed in these boxes may attract
a premium of 50%.

**254** 1956-59 **Austin Taxi** (FX3)
See '40h' listing.

**260** 1971-72 **VW 'Deutsche Bundespost'**
- Yellow body (129 casting, 100mm),
German export model ...................... **£100-150**

**262** 1959-60 **Volkswagen 'PTT' Car**
All are Swiss Post export models.
- (181 casting, 90mm, fixed doors),
Yellow/Black, Yellow cast hubs ....... **£500-750**
- 1960-62 As previous issue but
with spun aluminium hubs............... **£500-750**
- 1962-66
Same, but with plastic hubs ............. **£500-750**
NOTE: 262 models listed above should
be in the correct French / German box
with 'Auto Suisse VW' and 'Schweizer
Postauto VW' on the end flap.
- 1966-68 129 casting (100mm):
Yellow/Black, opening doors,
spun hubs, hard plastic case............. **£150-200**
- 1968-72 Yellow/Black, opening
doors, plastic hubs........................... **£100-125**
- 1972-76 Yellow/Black, opening
doors, Speedwheels.......................... **£100-125**

**268** **Renault Dauphine Mini-cab**
See 'Public Transport' section.
**281** **'PATHE NEWS' Camera Car**
See 'Novelty, Film and TV' section.

**340** 1954-66 **Land Rover**
(renumbered from 27d)
- Mid-Green body, Light Brown interior,
Green cast hubs, Beige cast driver ....... **£75-85**
- 1966-69 Orange body, Green interior,
Red cast hubs, Beige cast driver....... **£300-350**
- Orange body, Deep Blue interior,
Red cast hubs, Beige cast driver.......... **£75-85**
- 1969-71 Dark Red body, Red cast hubs,
Yellow interior, Blue plastic driver....**£110-140**

- 1971 Red body, Yellow interior,
Blue plastic driver, Green or
Yellow plastic hubs.............................**£110-140**
- Orange body, Dark Green interior,
Blue plastic driver, Red plastic hubs .**£110-140**
- Orange body, Black interior, no driver
(as issued), Red plastic hubs.............**£110-140**
- Red body, Yellow interior and
plastic hubs, no driver (as issued)......**£110-140**

**341** 1954-66 **Land-Rover Trailer**
(renumbered from 27m)
- Orange body, Red hubs........................ **£20-30**
- Green body, Green hubs ...................... **£20-30**
- Red body, Black plastic hubs........... **£150-200**
- Olive-Drab body .............................. **£150-200**

**342** 1966-72 **Austin Mini-Moke**
- Metallic Green, Grey canopy with 1 or 2
windows, bubble-packed or boxed ....... **£45-55**
- 1972-75
Metallic Greenish-Blue, 1 canopy
window, bubble-packed or boxed ......... **£45-55**

**344** 1954-61 **Estate Car**
See 'Farm and Garden Models'.
**344** 1970-72 **Land Rover Pick-Up**
See 'Farm and Garden Models'.

**370** 1969-76 **Dragster Set**
- Yellow/Red, driver, 'FIREBALL',
'INCH-PINCHER', starter unit ........... **£40-50**

**405** 1954-66 **Universal Jeep**
(renumbered from 25y)
- Red body and cast hubs ..................... **£80-100**
- Green body and cast hubs.................. **£80-100**
- 1966-67 Red body, matt base,
red plastic hubs, supplied in late
lighter yellow box ........................... **£100-130**
- Same, but with gloss base................. **£100-130**
1963 South African issues:
(English / Afrikaans on box).
- Green body with Red hubs .............. **£400-600**
- Off-White body with Red hubs ........ **£400-600**

**448 / 449** **Chevrolet El Camino Pick-up**
See 'Commercial Vehicles' section.

**475** 1964-66 **Model 'T' Ford**
- Blue body, Yellow panels and wheels,
driver/female passenger ...................... **£45-55**

**476** 1967-69 **Morris Oxford** ('Bullnose')
- Yellow body, Blue chassis,
Fawn hood, driver .............................. **£45-55**

**516** 1965-66 **Mercedes-Benz 230 SL**
- Metallic Red, Cream roof, windows.
(French issue).................................... **£75-95**

**675** 1954-59 **Ford US Army Staff Car**
See 'Military Vehicles' section.

**Models 2162, 2214 and 2253**
are in a scale of 1:25. They were mounted
on a printed card base with a vacuform
display cover which is photo-sensitive and
vulnerable to yellowing.
**2162** 1973-76 **Ford Capri**
- Metallic Blue, Black roof,
Black or Blue interior ........................ **£90-120**
**2214** 1974-76 **Ford Capri Rally Car**
- Red, Black roof and bonnet, RN '12',
Black or Blue interior ...................... **£100-125**
**2253** 1974-76 **Ford Capri 'POLICE' Car**
- White/Orange, Blue light ................ **£100-125**

## Dinky Toys cars made by Meccano, Paris, France and sold in Britain    (see French Dinky Toys listings)

| | | | |
|---|---|---|---|
| 24kz | 1939-40 | **Peugeot Car**, Red or Blue, (rubber tyres for UK)...................... |
| 516 | | **Mercedes-Benz 230sl**, Bronze body, Cream interior................ |
| 518 | 1962-65 | **Renault 4L**, Brown or Grey body, steering, windows.............. |
| 524 | 1965-67 | **Panhard 24c** Dark Metallic Grey body .................................. |
| 532 | | **Lincoln Premiere**, Metallic Light Green body, Dk. Green roof |
| 530 | 1965-66 | **Citroën DS19**, Light Green body, Light Grey roof .................. |
| 535 | 1962-65 | **Citroën 2cv**, Blue body, steering, windows........................... |

| | | |
|---|---|---|
| 550 | 1962-65 | **Chrysler Saratoga**, Pink/White body, windows ..................... |
| 551 | 1959-64 | **Rolls-Royce Silver Wraith** |
| | | Same as UK issue 150 'Made in France' ............................ |
| 553 | 1962-65 | **Peugeot 404**, Green or White, windows .............................. |
| 555 | 1962-65 | **Ford Thunderbird**, White, driver, steering.......................... |

## Dinky Toys cars made in Hong Kong

Models **57-001 to 57-006** all have spun hubs, detailed end-flap picture boxes, and are in a scale of 1:42. Hong Kong made models were issued in tab-ended alternative pictorial card boxes or rare yellow 'see-through' cellophane window boxes.

| | | | | |
|---|---|---|---|---|
| 57-001 | 1965-67 | **Buick Riviera** ........................ | Light Blue body with Cream roof and Red interior, cast wheels.................... | **£140-180** |
| 57-002 | 1965-67 | **Chevrolet Corvair Monza** .... | Red body, Black roof, White interior, cast wheels.................................. | **£140-180** |
| 57-003 | 1965-67 | **Chevrolet Impala** ................ | Yellow body with White roof and Red interior, cast wheels......................... | **£140-180** |
| | | US / Canadian issue: | Yellow body with Yellow roof, cast wheels | **£140-180** |
| 57-004 | 1965-67 | **Oldsmobile Dynamic '88'** .... | White body, Blue roof, Red interior, cast wheels..................................... | **£180-220** |
| 57-005 | 1965-67 | **Ford Thunderbird** ................ | Blue body with Ivory roof, Red interior, cast wheels................................ | **£180-220** |
| 57-006 | 1965-67 | **Nash Rambler Classic** .......... | Light Green body with Silver roof trim, Cream interior, cast wheels ............... | **£180-220** |

## 'Mini-Dinky' models

Models 10 – 61 inclusive were made in a scale of 1:65.
Models 94 – 99 inclusive were made in a scale of 1:130.

Mini-Dinky models were issued in 1968 and were made in Hong Kong and Holland. Each model was sold with a free red plastic garage. The cars are fitted with Flexomatic Independent Suspension. Racing cars 60 and 61 were made by Best Box of Holland (now EFSI). The models listed are illustrated in the 1968 US issued 3-page fold-out leaflet which advertised them as 'Swinging Value' at 59 cents and 69 cents. Models 94-99 Construction Vehicles are illustrated in a US issued 'Mini-Dinky' fold-out launch leaflet '1'.

| | | |
|---|---|---|
| 10 | **Ford Corsair**, Yellow or Metallic Gold **£40-50** |
| 11 | **Jaguar 'E' type**, Red or Met. Maroon .. **£50-75** |
| 12 | **Corvette Stingray**, Blue or Metallic Dark Blue ................................. **£50-60** |
| 13 | **Ferrari 250 LM**, Red or Met. Maroon. **£40-50** |
| 14 | **Chevrolet Chevy II**, Yellow or Metallic Maroon ................................. **£40-50** |
| 15 | **Rolls-Royce Silver Shadow**, Blue ........ **£60-80** |
| 16 | **Ford Mustang**, White, Cream or Metallic Blue ...................................... **£40-50** |
| 17 | **Aston Martin DB6**, White .................. **£50-75** |
| 18 | **Mercedes Benz 230 SL**, White/Black.. **£40-50** |
| 19 | **MGB Roadster**, Blue ......................... **£50-75** |

| | | |
|---|---|---|
| 20 | **Cadillac Coupé de Ville**, Silver or White ................................. **£50-60** |
| 21 | **Fiat 2300 Station Wagon**, Blue or Yellow/White ..................... **£40-50** |
| 22 | **Oldsmobile Toronado**, Met. Pale Blue **£40-50** |
| 23 | **Rover 2000**, Blue ........................... **£40-50** |
| 24 | **Ferrari Superfast**, Red ................... **£40-50** |
| 25 | **Ford Zephyr 6**, Silver ..................... **£40-50** |
| 26 | **Mercedes 250 SE**, White or Bronze..... **£40-50** |
| 27 | **Buick Riviera**, Blue ........................ **£40-50** |
| 28 | **Ferrari F 1**, Red, '7'......................... **£40-50** |
| 29 | **Ford F 1**, White ............................. **£40-50** |
| 30 | **Volvo 1800s**, Blue .......................... **£40-50** |
| 31 | **VW 1600TC**, Blue or Metallic Green... **£40-50** |

| | | |
|---|---|---|
| 32 | **Vauxhall Cresta**, Silver or Dark Green **£40-50** |
| 33 | **Jaguar**, Red............................**£50-75** |
| 57 | **Chevrolet Corvair Monza**, Red/Black **£40-50** |
| 60 | **Cooper**, Blue '10'.........................**£50-75** |
| 61 | **Lotus Racing Car**, Green, '4'.........**£50-75** |
| 94 | **International Bulldozer**, Yellow............**£70-90** |
| 95 | **International Skid Shovel**, Yellow......**£100-150** |
| 96 | **Payloader Shovel**, White ................**£70-90** |
| 97 | **Euclid R40**, Yellow, 10 wheels .................**£70-90** |
| 98 | **Michigan Scraper**, Yellow ............**£100-125** |
| 99 | **Caterpillar Grader**, Orange..................**£70-90** |
| - | **'Mini-Dinky' 12-Car Collector Case**, with models ....................................... **£500-750** |

## 'Dinky Toys' issued by Airfix Products Ltd.

Issued by Airfix as 'DINKY TOYS'; made in France to 1:43 scale. Supplied in the last design of Red/Yellow/Blue 'Dinky Toys' window box with header card. They were all issued circa 1980 and all are in the Market Price Range of **£10-15**.

| | | |
|---|---|---|
| 500 | **Citroën 2cv** ......Red/Orange or Green body, 'duck' motif, open roof ..... |
| 500 | **Citroën 2cv** ......Red/Orange or Green body, 'duck' motif, closed roof... |
| 501 | **Fiat Strada** ......Blue or Metallic Bronze body, no decals ..................... |
| 502 | **BMW 530** ......Purple body with 'flame' decal on doors ...................... |
| 502 | **BMW 530** .......Metallic Green with Black 'cougar' decal .................. |
| 503 | **Alfetta GTV** ....Red or Yellow body, Green 'clover leaf' on bonnet ...... |

| | | |
|---|---|---|
| 504 | **Citroën Visa** ....Red body, no decals.................................... |
| 505 | **Peugeot 504** .....Blue body with 'flame' decal on doors ......... |
| 505 | **Peugeot 504** .....Greenish-Gold with Black 'cougar' decal on doors....... |
| 506 | **Alfa-Sud** ....Not seen......................................................NPP |
| 507 | **Renault 14** .....Not seen........................................................NPP |
| 508 | **Ford Fiesta** ......Not seen.................................................NPP |

## COUGAR Model Toys

Many of the 'Airfix Dinky Toys' appeared erratically in the early 1980s (in France, then in the UK), under the name 'Cougar Model Toys'. For information on this small range of 'budget' toys, please see the 'French Meccano Dinky Toys' chapter where they are listed at the end of the 'Cars' section.

## AIRFIX – matchbox sized miniatures made in Hong Kong

Although announced in 1980, only a few seem to have appeared in the UK. Market Price Range **£10-15**.

| | | |
|---|---|---|
| 101 | **'56 Corvette**........... White body with Red flash, bubble-packed................ |
| 103 | **Chevette**................. Yellow, 'Turbo' decal, Silver base, bubble-packed..... |
| 104 | **Honda Accord**....... Lilac body, Orange flash, Silver base, bubble-pack .. |
| 105 | **Toyota Celica** ...... Red body, '3', Silver base, Orange bubble-pack ....... |
| 106 | **Datsun 280Z**.......... Brown body, bubble-packed ........................ |
| 107 | **BMW Turbo** .......... Orange body, Black/Yellow flash, bubble-packed...... |
| 108 | **Alfa Romeo** .......... Purple body with Yellow flash, bubble-packed ....... |
| 110 | **Stepside Pick-up** ..... Blue and Brown body, bubble-packed............ |
| 110 | **Camper** ........ Yellow and Two-tone Brown body ......................... |
| 113 | **Pick-up** ................ Red and Black body, '4 x 4' decal ................... |
| 114 | **Firebird** ............... Black body ..................................... |
| 115 | **Camaro** ................. Red body with racing-number 'Z28' ............... |
| 116 | **'63 Corvette**........... Metallic Blue body.................................... |

| | | |
|---|---|---|
| 117 | **'71 Corvette**........... Yellow body with 'Vette' decal............................ |
| 119 | **Ford Van**................. Blue body with Orange flash ........................... |
| 120 | **Renegade Jeep** ....... Yellow/Green body, Silver base, Green packaging .... |
| 121 | **Chevy Blazer**......... Red body ................................................ |
| 122 | **Sun Van** .............. Orange body with 'Sun Van' decal, Blue packaging .. |
| 123 | **Yamaha 250 MX** ..... Blue body with 'Yamaha' decal ..................... |
| 124 | **Honda MT 250** ...... Orange body with 'Honda' decal ..................... |
| 125 | **Kawasaki Fll 250** ... Red body with 'Kawasaki' decal ..................... |
| 126 | **Suzuki TM 400** ...... Yellow/Black body with 'CCI' and 'Suzuki' decals ... |
| 129 | **T-Bird Convertible** Red and White body ................................... |
| 130 | **Chevy Convertible**. Metallic Blue and White body ......................... |

# Wooden prototypes, first castings and factory colour samples

These are unique items, produced as samples within the factory to aid the design and development process. Some were made for publicity and catalogue illustration purposes prior to actual volume production. Price guidance is usually not possible since they so rarely come to market in significant quantities. However, the sale in 2001 by Christie's of the Remy-Meeus Collection has enabled us to list the following:

## Pre-war items

**38a Frazer-Nash BMW**, Blue with Grey interior, Turquoise hubs ....**£400-500**
**38a Frazer-Nash BMW**, (first casting), Green with Dark Green
    seats, fabricated, painted tinplate baseplate .........................**£300-400**
**38d Alvis**, (first casting), Blue with Tan seats, 'ALVIS' in
    Indian ink on base ........................**£300-400**
**38e Armstrong-Siddeley Coupé**, (colour sample), plain Brown
    dashboard, production baseplate painted Khaki.................**£200-300**

**38f Jaguar Sports Car**, (wooden prototype),
    Dark Green body, 'JAGUAR' in Indian ink on base .....**£1,200-1,500**
**38f Jaguar Sports Car**, (1st casting), Green body, Grey seats.......**£800-1,000**

**39a Packard Sedan**, (wooden prototype),
    Dark Blue with Silver windows, 'PACKARD' on base.......**£600-800**
**39b Oldsmobile Six Sedan**, (wooden prototype), Dark Green with Silver
    windows, 'Oldsmobile Six Sedan' in Indian ink on base ....**£500-800**
**39c Lincoln Zephyr**, (wooden prototype of saloon version, not coupé),
    unpainted, with 'Lincoln Zephyr' in pencil on base ...........**£500-600**
**39d Buick Viceroy**, (wooden prototype), Maroon with Silver
    windows, 'BUICK' in pencil on base..................**£600-800**
**39e Chrysler Royal Sedan**, (wooden prototype), Red with Silver
    windows, 'CHRYSLER' in Indian ink on base.............**£1,400-1,700**
**39f Studebaker State Commander Coupé**, (wooden prototype),
    Yellow Ochre with Silver windows, 'STUDEBAKER' in
    Indian ink on base...........................**£1,500-1,750**
**39 Series Hupmobile**, (wooden prototype), Green with Silver
    windows, 'HUPMOBILE' in Indian ink on base.
    Not issued as a production model ..................**£1,200-1,500**
**39 Series Luxicab**, (wooden prototype), Black and Pale Yellow
    with Silver windows, 'LUXICAB' in pencil on rear spare wheel
    cover and '1st sample not approved' in pencil on base.
    Not issued as a production model ..................**£1,100-1,400**
**39 Series Luxicab**, (wooden prototype), Black and Canary Yellow
    with Silver windows, 'LUXICAB' in pencil on rear spare
    wheel cover. Not issued as a production model............**£1,100-1,400**

## Post-war paint colour samples

**38b Sunbeam-Talbot**, Red body, hubs and tonneau. Tie-on label stating:
    'Approved 22 Oct 1948', plus paint code details.................**£200-300**
**38e Armstrong-Siddeley Coupé**, Green body, Light Grey interior,
    Green hubs. Tie-on label stating:
    'Approved 22 Oct 1948', plus paint code details.................**£200-300**
**39b Oldsmobile Sedan**, Beige body, Fawn hubs. Tie-on label stating:
    '1 Oct 1948', plus paint code details....................**£300-500**
**39e Chrysler Royal Sedan**, Cream body, Light Green hubs.
    Tie-on label stating: '1 Oct 1948', plus paint code details ..**£300-500**
**40b Triumph 1800**, Black body, Silver hubs, rear window pillars.
    Two tie-on labels stating: '30/9/48', + paint code details....**£500-600**
**40d Austin Devon**, Red body, Maroon hubs. Tie-on label stamped:
    '6 Jan 1950', plus paint code details ....................**£400-600**
**40e Standard Vanguard**, Fawn body, Fawn hubs, axle clip,
    open rear wheel arches. Tie-on label stating:
    '18 Oct 1948', plus paint code details...................**£400-600**

## Other prototypes and designs

**We are also aware of the following (these were not in Christie's sale)**

107 Sunbeam Alpine in Maroon with Grey interior (unfinished casting)..NPP
107 Sunbeam Alpine in Light Blue with Cream interior (unfinished casting)..
110 Aston-Martin in Grey with Blue interior (unfinished casting) ............NPP
111 Triumph TR2 in Pink with Blue interior.................................NPP
122 Volvo 256DL Estate in White.........................................NPP
122 Volvo 256DL Estate in Red..........................................NPP
122 Volvo 256DL Estate in Green.........................................NPP
170 Ford Granada Ghia in Metallic Silver..................................NPP
181 Volkswagen Saloon in Pale Blue (with baseplate, 1970s)................NPP
181 Volkswagen Saloon in Pale Blue (with spun hubs, 1970s)................NPP
181 Volkswagen Saloon in Metallic Blue ..................................NPP
181 Volkswagen Saloon in Turquoise......................................NPP
190 Monteverdi 375L Metallic Gold (Copper), White interior, cast wheels.....
190 Monteverdi 375L in Metallic Black, Red interior, cast wheels..........NPP
211 Triumph TR7. Metallic Green body, Red, Grey or Green interior......NPP
227 Beach Buggy. Copper body, Grey hood, 'fire' design .........................NPP
507 Albion Tanker. Green, 'MILK MARKETING BOARD' ......**£2,000-2,500**
57-001 Buick Riviera with Slate Grey body (Hong Kong made model) ...NPP

**ALL WOODEN PROTOTYPES found in Liverpool Charity Shop and sold by Bonhams in 2004:**

**29h Duple Roadmaster Coach**, light blue/grey .....................................**£680**
**25y Universal Jeep**, dark green, tin windscreen .................................**£650**
**30w Hindle Smart Helecs**, maroon 'BR' logo on front...........................**£600**
**40g Morris Oxford**, cream/blue, '17/64 Morris' on base ...................**£2,000**
**132 Packard Convertible**, cream, red interior....................................**£880**
**472 Austin Van**, green, light green hubs .......................................**£720**
**480 series Bedford Van**, cream, green hubs .....................................**£850**
**Unreleased Austin Wagon** prototype, red cab, blue back ..................**£1,500**
**522 Big Bedford Lorry**, orange cab, green back ...............................**£1,500**
**Unreleased Leyland Fire Engine** prototype.....................................**£600**
**641 Army 1 ton Lorry**, military green, grey windows...........................**£600**
**673 Army Scout Car**, military green .............................................**£360**
**674 Army Champ**, military green ................................................**£300**

**A recent Vectis sale produced these prototype items:**

**Motorised Tram 'LYNDAS COMPOUND'**, Blue, Cream, Grey roof,
2" long, complete with photos of model on layout ....................................**£240**
**Wooden mock-up Tram** with plastic wheels, Cream and Red with
roof pole ........................................................................**£280**

(right) **Pre-war Dinky Toys wooden prototype**:
**39 Series Luxicab**
Black and Canary Yellow
with Silver windows,
'LUXICAB' in pencil on
rear spare wheel cover.
Not issued as a production model

Photograph: Christie's, South Kensington

## Commercial Vehicles Box Types Introduction

A mint condition commercial vehicle without its correct box is worth a fraction of the value of its boxed equivalent. Furthermore, as model boxes made from card do not survive as well as their die-cast contents, pristine box examples are scarce and becoming scarcer. The condition of a box is of paramount importance and attention is drawn to the section in the main catalogue introduction, namely: 'Classifying the Condition of Models and Boxes'.

The following listing provides collectors with a working knowledge of the range of box types issued. In addition details are given of their dates of issue, their design and of the models which used them. See also the colour sections for examples of many types of boxes.

Whilst every care has been taken in preparing the listing other variations no doubt exist and information on these is welcomed.

Similarly with no 'dates of birth' available the dates of issue shown are approximate and again any further information is welcomed.

## Commercial Vehicles Box Identification

(See also 'Dinky Toys Trade Boxes' section).

### Model Colour Identification Marks

These are shown on the box lid and label and take the form of either a circular colour spot or a capital letter, e.g. 'R' for red. A colour spot may be a single colour or in the case of the later two-tone colours models a two-tone colour spot.

### 'Lead-free' labels 'LF'

In the l950s the government introduced new regulations concerning the lead content of die-cast models. Consequently, to indicate that a model complied with the new regulations, a round white label with 'LF' in blue was added to box end labels for a short time. Alternatively, an 'LF' coloured ink stamp was used. (See example in the colour section.)

### Model Reference Numbers

These are always shown on the box lid and label.

### Dual numbered boxes c. l953 – 1954

A new numbering system was introduced which resulted in models being issued displaying both the old and new reference numbers. The information was shown in one of two ways:

(a) A black new number stamped alongside the old number

(b) A small old model number shown in red on either side of a larger black new number, e.g. 511 911 511". (See examples in the colour section). Dual numbered boxes (issued for a relatively short period) may attract a premium.

### Quality Control Box Markings. 1947 – 1957
#### (a) Factory Checkers' Marks

A quality control mark may be found on the base of the buff coloured boxes. This takes the form of a coloured ink stamp of a reference number within a circle, e.g. 'M42' or 'M19'. Stamped on the underside of the blue covered box lid may be found a similar ink stamp e.g. 'ZQ Z8'.
#### (b) Date Stamps

Ink stamped on the base of boxes or box lids may be found a purple date stamp relating to the date of the model's issue. Recorded examples include: 'GR950' on a (25x) orange coloured box; '10 KR 55' on a (933) blue/white stripe box; 'H656' on a (902) blue/white stripe box; 'KB956' on a (433) yellow covered box lid; '01057' on a (689) military blue/white box.

The Editor would welcome any further information on this subject.

### Pre-war issues 1933 – 1939

Apart from sets (see the Gift Sets listing) commercial vehicles were sold unboxed. They were usually packaged in half-dozen retailers trade packs such as Nos. 28/1, 28/2 and 28/3 Delivery Vans.

### Post-war Issues 1947 – 1979

In 1947 the first individual boxes were introduced to house the exciting new range of 'Supertoys' models. However, the small commercial vehicles continued to be sold unboxed from trade packs until 1953/54.

The boxes have been catalogued into four types as follows:

Type 1 1947-75 - Boxes with lift-off lids
Type 2 1953-75 - All card boxes with tuck-in end flaps
Type 3 1963-79 - Display boxes
Type 4 l964-64 - Export only boxes

---

### TYPE I    1947 - 69    BOXES WITH LIFT-OFF LIDS

#### A  1947-49

(A-a) Brown card box with wrap around all-white label with red lettering 'DINKY SUPERTOYS' and model number shown in black. Model shown as a black/white photographic illustration, e.g., 563 Heavy Tractor.

(A-b) Brown card box with separate labels on the box top and one box end. The half red and white box labels show 'DINKY SUPERTOYS' in red. Model number is white on a black oval background. In addition the main label displays an illustration of the model and whilst the main design of the label remains constant, the position of the model does vary as follows:

(i) Facing inwards on the right side of the label.
 Models recorded using this box: 25x, 501 (1st type), 521 and 563.

(ii) Facing outwards on the left side of the label.
Models recorded using this box: 502, 503, 511, 512, 513 (all 1st types). The small separate label attached to the right side of the box lid is white with red model information text. Some labels include a line drawing of the model eg. 503 and 513.

(iii) Buff plain card box with a single 'wrap round' red and white label which covers the box lid from end to end with 'DINKY SUPERTOYS' in red on the larger Foden type box, one end of the label contains information about the model in German, French and Spanish. In addition, the model number on the top and ends is now white on a circular black background. The model picture is facing inwards from the right and the models recorded in this box to date are: 504 Tanker 1st type and 531.

(iv) As previous issue but the model picture is facing outwards from the left. Models recorded: 511, 512, 521 and 533.

#### B  c.1950

(i) Green covered box with red and white wrap-around label. Models recorded in this box: 25x, 501, 502, 503, 504 (1st and 2nd types), 504 'MOBILGAS', 511, 512, 513 and 521. Model picture facing inwards from the right. 'DINKY SUPERTOYS' in red letters.
(ii) Orange card box with black printing, e.g., 25x Breakdown Lorry.
(iii) Orange card box with orange/white label, e.g., 25x Breakdown Lorry.

#### C  c.1951

(i) Pale or dark blue covered box with wrap-around red and white label. Model picture facing inwards from the right with 'DINKY SUPERTOYS' logo. Models recorded: 25x, 501, 502, 503, 504 (1st and 2nd types), 505, 511, 512, 513, 514 (all issues except 'Spratts'), 521, 531/931, 532/932 and 533/933.

(ii) Pale or dark blue box with wrap-around orange and white label with 'DINKY SUPERTOYS'. Model picture facing inwards from the right front. Beneath the model picture is a black factory code, e.g. on the 522 Big Bedford lorry issue the code is '50522'. Models recorded: 25x, 504 (1st / 2nd), 511, 514 'LYONS' and 'SLUMBERLAND', 531 and 571.

(iii) Same as C(ii) but with model picture facing outwards from the left. Models recorded: 502(1st), 503 (2nd) and 512.

(iv) Same as C(ii) but with model picture facing inwards from the right front but with 'DINKY TOYS'. Models recorded: 501(1st type), 504 Tanker (1st and 2nd types), 504 'MOBILGAS', 514 'WEETABIX', 514 'SLUMBERLAND', 514'SPRATTS', 521, 522, 564, 591/991, and 917.

(v) Same as C (iv) but with model picture facing outwards from the left front. Models recorded: 502, 503 (1st types), 512, 513 (1st types).

(vi) Same as C (iv) but with model picture facing inwards from the left front. Models 505 (1st type), 532 and 581 US issue.

#### D  c1953

(i) Blue and white striped box lid with dark blue bottom section. Box lid is white with dark blue parallel stripes. 'DINKY TOYS' logo is shown in red plus a colour picture of the model facing inwards from the right. The model number is on the left of the picture. Colour identification spots shown as appropriate on box ends. Models recorded:
409, 418, 430, 582, 511, 511/911, 512, 512/912, 513, 513/913, 521/921, 901/2/3 (2nd type). 911/12/13. 917, 921, 923 ('ketchup bottle'), 923 ('baked beans can'), 930, 931, 932/33, 941/42, 963, 980, 982, 991.

**NB** The 417 Leyland Comet Lorry yellow/green issue was housed in a box with a blue/yellow picture.

(ii) As D (i), but with 'DINKY SUPERTOYS' logo and with the model picture facing inwards from the right. Models recorded:
901/2/3, 905, 913, 918/9, 923, 930, 934/5/6, 942/3, 948, 954, 958, 960, 963/4, 966/7/8/9, 973, 977, 982/3/4, 986, 991, 994.
On the box side is a note stating the colour of the model which may vary from the one illustrated on the box front. This only happened when a model was issued for a short time and hence some of the rarest models were issued in this manner (e.g. 902 Foden Flat Truck in yellow/green livery was issued in box with red/green model picture; 913 Guy Flat Truck with tailboard in yellow/green livery issued in box with all-green model picture; 934 Leyland Octopus Wagon in blue and yellow livery was issued on the standard box with a yellow/green model picture but displaying a dark blue colour spot).
The Editor would welcome any further examples.

(iii) As D (ii), but with model picture facing outwards from the left. 'DINKY SUPERTOYS' logo. Model recorded No.982.

(iv) As D (ii), but with model picture facing inwards from the left. 'DINKY SUPERTOYS' logo. Model recorded No. 979.

(v) Plain blue and white striped box with no model picture on lid. A white end label 'DINKY SUPERTOYS' and the model details in blue letters. Models recorded: 920 and 923.

**E   Yellow covered box lid with blue bottom section.**
(i) c.1956 - 1959
On two of the box sides is a picture of the model set against a white shadow background. The top of the box lid has a 'DINKY TOYS' logo in red. Colour spots shown as appropriate. In addition white circular 'LF' (lead free) labels may be found. Models recorded: 408/9, 417, 419, 430/1/2/3, 437.
NB. The rare 408 Big Bedford Lorry in pink and cream livery was issued in this box but with the standard maroon and fawn model box picture.

(ii) Yellow covered box lid but with red side panels with pictorial scene with 'DINKY TOYS' logo in red. The box lid shows the model picture facing inwards from the right with a pictorial scene in an end panel on the left. Models recorded: 401, 408, 417, 419, 425, 430, 434, 448, 450, 925, 960, 964, 972 and 978.

(iii) Same as previous issue but with 'DINKY SUPERTOYS' logo. Models recorded: 908, 934, 935, 944, 958/9, 962, 964, 972 and 978.
NB. No. 935 Leyland Octopus with chains in the rare dark blue and grey livery was issued in the standard box with the green and grey version illustrated but with a dark blue spot displayed.

(iv) All yellow covered lid with a pictorial scene in the middle of the box lid top. 'DINKY SUPERTOYS' in red. Models recorded: 959, 987/8/9.

**F   'One off' box issues with lift-off lids.**

(i) Plain dark blue covered box with no picture. White label on box lid end with dark blue text. Model recorded: 982 Pullman Car Transporter in rare mid-blue livery with brownish-grey decks.

(ii) Orange covered box (c.1950) with white/orange wrap-around lid label. Models recorded: 25x Breakdown Truck and 14c Coventry Climax Fork Lift Truck.

### TYPE 2        1953 - 1975
### ALL CARD BOXES WITH  TUCK-IN END FLAPS

**A   1953 - 1964**
(i) Deep yellow box with 'DINKY TOYS' in red plus the model's name and type in black. A white reference number on a black or red oval background is on the box end flaps but no reference is shown on the box face. The model is pictured on the box sides with or without a white shadow background. Colour spots shown as applicable. Foreign language information is shown on one of the box end flaps. Box used for small and medium size models, e.g., 431/432. Box in general use during the model renumbering period. Consequently dual numbered boxes will be found.
Very few boxes were issued displaying just the old type of reference number. Recorded models to date: 25d, e, f, g and 30e. In addition, 29c Bus and 29e Coach have been identified. Please send details if you have any other examples. Later issues display 'WITH WINDOWS' captions.

(ii) Plain light yellow box with two red sides and no model picture. The 'DINKY TOYS' logo, the model type and its reference number are shown in yellow and white. Colour spots are shown as appropriate. Models recorded: 252, 413, 414 and 428 plus 070 and 071 Dublo Dinky.

(iii)   1963 - 1970
Yellow box with red end features panel around the front right side, with or without an upward pointing white arrow. Models recorded: 273, 274, 435.
(iv)   1966 - 1969
A detailed full colour picture box with 'DINKY TOYS' in red plus a pictorial scene on two sides. A yellow laurel leaf design on a black background incorporates the model number Models recorded: 280, 402, 407 'KENWOOD', 914, 923, 944/5, 959/60, 965, 970, 972 and 978.

(v)   1968 - 1974
White fronted box with a narrow yellow band across the face. The box front displays 'DINKY TOYS' in red plus the model number and type in black and white letters. A colour picture of the model is shown on two sides. Models recorded: 407, 438/9/40, 91, 917, 974, 978 and 980.

(vi)   1966 - 1970
Picture box used for large commercials with two full pictorial sides with 'DINKY TOYS' in red. The other sides are yellow and red. Models recorded: 434 'AUTO SERVICES', 914 and 945.

(vii)   1970 - 1975
Heavy card box used for heavy models e.g. 924 Centaur Dump Truck. Box has white face with a colour picture of model combined with a black band across the face and sides.

(viii)   Promotional Box Types
(a)   No. 274 'JOSEPH MASON PAINTS' Minivan. Dark red box with white letters plus an enclosed leaflet.
(b)   No. 491 Plain yellow box with red letters. 'JOBS DAIRY'.
(c)   No. 917 Mercedes-Benz LP1920 Truck with 'HENRY JOHNSON' logo. Plain white card box with no lettering
(d)   No. 940 Mercedes-Benz, 'FISONS', plain white box

### TYPE 3        1963 - 1979        DISPLAY BOXES

**A   1970 - 1976 Vacuform packs**
Models displayed on a black card plinth with a blue surface with 'DINKY TOYS' in red and white. The model is covered by a close-fitting see-through protective plastic cover. Known examples include:  407,416, 438/9, 915, 944, 945 'ESSO' and 'LUCAS' issues.

**B   1976 - 1979 Window boxes**
Cellophane fronted window boxes with a dark blue and red header card giving the model's name and 'DINKY DIECAST TOYS' in yellow and white letters. Known examples include: 275, 432, 440, 451, 940, 950 and 980.
C     1963 - 1966 Fold-back lid display box
224 Commer Convertible Truck and 975 Ruston Bucyrus Excavator which also had a coloured outer box display wrapper issued for a while.

### TYPE 4        1964 - 1966        EXPORT ONLY BOXES

**A   1964 - 1966**
An all-yellow card and cellophane 'see-through' display box.
'DINKY' plus the model type and number is shown across the box front in red letters plus 'A MECCANO PRODUCT MADE IN ENGLAND'. Box issued with a card protection strip. Known models include: 275, 434, 492, 914. A version of this box was used for the 944 'SHELL BP' tanker - see picture in the colour section, Also used for the U.S. Export Series: 'MARVELS IN MINIATURE' which is shown on the sides of the box front in red capital letters, e.g. 275, 434, 437, 448 and 965. Later issues display the range on the base of the box.

**B   c.1965**
Same as previous issue but all-gold box with two black and red diagonal stripes. A rare box type. Known issues include 434 and 989.

### INNER BOX LININGS and MODEL SUPPORTS

To be complete a box should contain all its original model supports. The following issues all had supports or linings. In some instances top and bottom linings were included (2).
14c, 400, 561, 581, 908(2), 924, 930(3), 958, 964, 965, 967, 968, 969(2), 972, 974, 976, 977(2), 979(2), 980, 982, 983(2), 984(2), 985(2), 986, 989(2).

123

## The 25 Series Lorries 1934 - 1950

**Type 1**: **(1934-36)**, 'open' chassis (usually black), tinplate radiator, no headlamps,
no front bumper, 'smooth' cast hubs (various colours) with large white tyres. 105 mm.

**Type 2**: **(1936-46)**, 'open' chassis (usually black), diecast radiator with headlamps but
no front bumper, 'smooth' cast hubs (various colours), with large white tyres. 105 mm.

**Type 3**: **(1947-48)**, 'closed' chassis (only in black), diecast radiator with headlamps but
no front bumper, 'smooth' or 'ridged' wheel hubs (only in black) ,with black tyres. 105 mm.

**Type 4**: **(1948-50)**, detailed moulded chassis (only in black), diecast radiator with headlamps and
with bumper, 'ridged' coloured wheel hubs with black tyres. 110 mm.

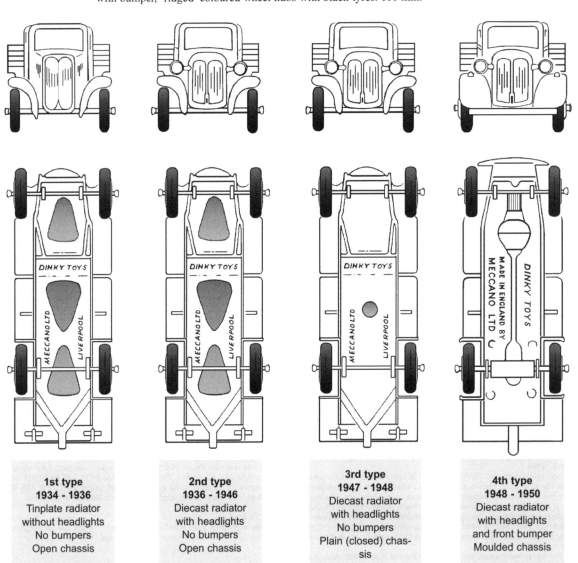

| **1st type** 1934 - 1936 | **2nd type** 1936 - 1946 | **3rd type** 1947 - 1948 | **4th type** 1948 - 1950 |
|---|---|---|---|
| Tinplate radiator without headlights No bumpers Open chassis | Diecast radiator with headlights No bumpers Open chassis | Diecast radiator with headlights No bumpers Plain (closed) chassis | Diecast radiator with headlights and front bumper Moulded chassis |

**25 Series Trucks 1934-50 Wheel types** The first pre-war issues have cast metal wheels followed by chrome (rare) or diecast hubs with large white tyres. The early post-war issues c.1946 have smooth hubs and large black tyres. **1947-48** issues have ridged black hubs with large black tyres. The last issues **c.1949-50** have coloured ridged hubs and attract a premium. Similarly early cast or chrome hubs also attract a premium.

# Guy cab types

**Guy 1st type cab 1947 - 1954**
Exposed radiator
No gusset at either
side of number plate

**Guy 2nd type cab 1954 - 1958**
Exposed radiator
With gusset at each
side of number plate

**Guy Warrior cab 1958 - 1964**
Radiator behind grille
Restyled front with
sidelights in wings

# Foden cab types

**1947 - 1952**
**Foden 'DG'**
(1st type) cab
Exposed radiator
Colour flashes on sides

**1952 - 1964**
**Foden 'FG'**
(2nd type) cab
Radiator behind grille
No colour flashes on sides

## Identification of
# Ford Transit Van
### castings
### (not illustrated)

**Type 1**: **(1966-74)**, has sliding driver's door, opening hinged side door, and twin rear doors.

**Type 2**: **(1974-78)**, non-sliding driver's door, one side-hinged door, one top-hinged rear door.

**Type 3**: **(1978-80)**, as Type 2 but with a slightly longer bonnet (18 mm.)

**Dinky Toys 505 Foden Flat Truck with Chains**
'DG' (1st type) cab
Exposed radiator
Colour flashes on sides

# Dinky Toys Commercial Vehicles

**Market Price Range (MPR) for pre-1954 unboxed commercial vehicle models:**
Prior to 1954, virtually all smaller, non-Supertoy commercial vehicle models were sold unboxed from retailer's trade boxes of either 6, 4 or 3 models. Consequently, all pre-1954 issues have been priced as being unboxed.

Post-1954 models were all boxed and have been priced accordingly. As a consequence, models which have been renumbered will be found to have two differing prices – one for the pre-1954 unboxed version and another for its boxed and renumbered successor. See also the Trade Box section for details of individual boxes and packs that were used to supply shops.

| Model and details | MPR |
|---|---|

**14a  B.E.V. Truck**
1948-54   (renumbered in 1954 to 400)
- Mid-Blue body with Blue hubs, Fawn driver, hook .............................. **£30-35**
- Grey body (with Blue, Grey or Red hubs), Fawn driver, hook............. **£30-35**

**14c  Coventry Climax Fork Lift**
1949-54   (renumbered in 1954 to 401)
- Orange, Brown or Dark Red body, Green forks, Fawn driver, 1 PP........... **£25-30**

**14z  Three-wheel Delivery Van**
- 1938-40  'Triporteur' with Green, Red, Grey, Blue or Yellow body, Black hubs, White tyres, driver is always a different colour from van, imported French model .........NGPP

## 22 Series

**22c  Motor Truck**
1933-35  Two-piece lead body with 'HORNBY SERIES' cast-in, tinplate radiator, diecast wheels that may be plain or may have an applied colour wash.
- Blue cab, Red truck body........... **£1,250-1,500**
- Blue cab, Cream or Yellow truck body, Blue wash wheels....................... **£1,250-1,500**
- Red cab, Green truck body ........ **£1,250-1,500**
- Red cab, Blue truck body........... **£1,250-1,500**
- Red cab, Cream truck body....... **£1,250-1,500**
- Yellow cab, Blue truck body...... **£1,250-1,500**

**22c  Motor Truck**
1935-40  Diecast one-piece body, open rear window.
- Orange-Red, Maroon, Green or Blue coloured diecast hubs...................... **£125-150**
- Dark Blue body, chrome hubs.......... **£125-150**
- Off-white body, Mid-Blue hubs....... **£125-150**
1945-47
- Red, Green or Brown body, open rear window, Black diecast hubs.......... **£60-70**
1948-50
- Red, Green or Brown body, closed rear window, Black diecast hubs.......... **£60-70**

**22d  Delivery Van**  (no advertising)
1933-33  Type 1, lead body, tinplate radiator, 'HORNBY SERIES' cast-in.
- Green cab, Blue van body, Blue wash wheels....................... **£2,500-3,000**
1933-34
- Orange/Blue body, plain metal wheels (no colour wash) ...................... **£2,500-3,000**
- Blue/Yellow body, Red wheels .. **£2,500-3,000**
- As previous models but with 'DINKY TOYS' cast-in.................... **£400-500**

**22d  Delivery Van 'MECCANO'**
- 1934  Type 1, Orange cab and chassis, Blue van with Red/Black 'Meccano Engineering For Boys'.............. **£3,000-5,000**

| Model and details | MPR |
|---|---|

- 1934-35  Type 1
Yellow body (lead), 'Meccano Engineering For Boys' in Red and Black. Model number was 22d until April 1935, then it was renumbered **28n** ........................... **£900-1,200**

## 25 Series

**25a  Wagon**
1934-36  Type 1, Black chassis.
- Maroon body.................................. **£300-400**
- Green body.................................... **£300-400**
- Red body ...................................... **£300-400**
- Blue body ..................................... **£300-400**
1936-40  Type 2, Black or Red chassis.
- Maroon body.................................. **£125-150**
- Green body.................................... **£125-150**
- Red body ...................................... **£125-150**
- Blue body ..................................... **£125-150**
1936-40  Type 2
- Blue body with Orange chassis........ **£150-200**
1947-48  Black chassis, Type 3
- Grey, Green, Red, Orange, Stone or Blue body.................................... **£70-80**
1948-50  Black chassis, Type 4
- Grey, Green, Light Blue, Orange, Cream or Red body ....................... **£70-80**

**25b  Covered Wagon**
1934-36   (plain, no advertising)
Type 1, Black chassis.
- Blue body, Cream tilt ...................... **£300-400**
1936-40  Type 2, Black chassis.
- Green body,
Green, Cream or Yellow tilt............. **£140-180**
- Cream body, Yellow tilt .................. **£140-180**
- Fawn body, Cream tilt..................... **£140-180**
1936-40  Type 2, Green chassis.
- Orange body, Cream tilt.................. **£150-200**

**25b  Covered Wagon 'CARTER PATERSON'**
1936-40  Type 2, Black chassis.
- Green body, Blue hubs, Green or Cream tilt, 'Express Carriers London'......... **£500-750**
- Green body, Blue hubs, 'Special Service To The Seaside'.... **£500-750**
- Variation with silvered hubs ........... **£500-750**

**25b  Covered Wagon 'MECCANO'**
1936-40  Type 2, Black chassis.
- Green body, Cream tilt, 'Engineering For Boys'................... **£300-400**
- Variation with silvered hubs ........... **£500-600**
- Orange body, Cream tilt, Green chassis, Blue hubs ............ **£2,000-2,500**

**25b  Covered Wagon 'HORNBY TRAINS'**
1936-40  Type 2, Black chassis,
- Fawn body, Cream tilt, Gold lettering .................................. **£300-400**

**25b  Covered Wagon**
1945-47  Type 3, Black chassis,
- Green/Green, Grey/Light or Dark Grey, Blue/Grey ...................... **£100-140**

| Model and details | MPR |
|---|---|

1947-50   Type 4, Black chassis,
- Green/Green, Grey/Grey, Cream/Red or Cream/Blue.............. **£100-140**
- Yellow body, Blue tilt, Black ridged hubs ........................... **£300-400**

**25c  Flat Truck**
1934-36  Type 1, Black chassis,
- Dark Blue body ............................... **£150-200**
1936-40  Type 2, Black chassis,
- Green or Stone body ...................... **£125-150**
1946  Type 2, Black chassis,
- Fawn, Green or Grey body, smooth hubs ................................... **£70-80**
1947-48  Type 3, Black chassis,
- Green, Blue, Stone or Grey body........ **£70-80**
1948-50  Type 4, Black chassis,
- Green, Blue, Orange or Stone body..... **£70-80**
**NB** Some pre-war (1934-40) Truck issues will be found with a '20 mph' disc on the rear.

**25d  Petrol Tank Wagon**
1934-35  Same chassis casting as other 25 series lorries but with hook removed. Type 1 with Black chassis.
- **(plain, unlettered)**
Red body, no advertising, open windows to back of cab.......... **£500-750**
- **'SHELL BP'** Red body .................. **£500-750**
- **'SHELL'** Red body, Blue hubs, 'SHELL LUBRICATING OIL' in Gold serif lettering ....................... **£500-750**
- **'ESSO'** Green body ....................... **£500-750**
- **'POWER'** Green body ................... **£500-750**
- **'PRATTS'** Green body ................... **£500-750**
- **'CASTROL'** Green body, Blue hubs ..................................... **£500-750**
- **'TEXACO'** Red body, Black hubs, White logo: 'PETROLEUM & PRODUCTS'..... **£500-750**

**25d  Petrol Tank Wagon**
1936-46  Type 2 with Black chassis.
- **'PETROL'** Red body, Black or White lettering . **£500-750**
- **'SHELL BP'** Red body, Blue or chrome hubs....... **£500-750**
- **'MOBILOIL'** Red body ................... **£500-750**
- **'TEXACO'** Red body.................... **£500-750**
- **'PETROL'** Green body ................... **£500-750**
- **'ESSO'** Green body, Black or Blue hubs........................ **£500-750**
- **'POWER'** Green body ................... **£500-750**
- **'CASTROL'** Green body, Black or Blue hubs ...... **£500-750**
- **'REDLINE GLICO'** Blue body, Red panel, Gold lettering ............................... **£500-750**
1945  **'POOL'** (Wartime)
- Type 2, White chassis. Grey body, Black hubs, Black lettering ................................ **£300-400**
1945-46  **'POOL'** (Wartime) Type 2.
- Grey or Khaki body, Black chassis. **£300-400**

- Dark Green body, Black chassis,
  Blue hubs, Gold logo ...................... **£300-400**
  1946-47 'PETROL'
  Type 3, Black chassis,
- Red body .................................... **£200-250**
- Orange body .................................. **£200-250**
- Mid-Green body ............................... **£200-250**
- Dark Green body .............................. **£200-250**
  1947-48 'PETROL'
  Type 4, Black chassis,
- Mid-Green body ............................... **£200-250**
- Dark Green body .............................. **£200-250**
- Orange body .................................. **£300-400**
  1948-50 'PETROL'
  Type 4, Black chassis,
- Red body **£150-200**
- Light Green body ............................. **£150-200**
- Mid-Green body ............................... **£150-200**
  1948-? 'PETROL'
  Type 4, Black chassis,
- Yellow body .................................. **£200-300**

**25e Tipping Wagon**
  1934-35 Type 1, Black chassis,
- Maroon/Yellow body ........................ **£150-200**
  1936-40 Type 2, Black chassis,
- Maroon/Yellow .............................. **£100-125**
- Brown/Turquoise ............................ **£100-125**
- Fawn/Fawn .................................. **£100-125**
  1946-46 Type 2, Black chassis,
- Grey, Green or Fawn ........................ **£70-80**
  1947-48 Type 3, Black chassis,
- Grey, Stone, Green or Yellow body ..... **£70-80**
  1948-50 Type 4, Black chassis,
- Grey, Stone or Brown body ................ **£70-80**
- Blue/Pink body .............................. **£70-80**
**NB** Some early post-war 25 series Trucks
exist with smooth hubs.

**25f Market Gardeners Lorry**
  1934-35 Type 1
- Green body, Black chassis .............. **£150-200**
- Yellow body, Green chassis ............ **£150-200**
  1936-40 Type 2
- Green body, Black chassis .............. **£70-80**
- Yellow body, Black chassis ............. **£70-80**
- Green body, Yellow chassis ........... **£150-200**
  1945-47 Type 3, Black chassis and hubs,
- Green, Grey, Stone or Yellow body ..... **£70-80**
  1947-50 Type 4, Black chassis and hubs,
- Green, Grey, Yellow or Red body ....... **£70-80**
- Orange body, Black hubs ............... **£140-160**
- Orange body, Green hubs ............... **£300-400**
- Green body, Black chassis,
  Yellow hubs ................................ **£70-80**

- Yellow body and hubs, Black chassis .. **£70-80**

**25g Trailer**    (renumbered in 1954 to 429)
  1935-40
  Cast-in hook, tinplate drawbar,
- Dark Blue body .............................. **£35-40**
- Green body ................................... **£35-40**
  1946-47 Cast-in hook, tinplate drawbar,
- Green, Grey, Stone,
  Pale Blue or Orange ...................... **£15-20**
  1947-48 Cast-in hook, wire drawbar,
- Green, Stone, Pale Blue or
  Orange body ................................ **£15-20**
  1948-49 Tinplate hook, wire drawbar,
- Green, Stone, Pale Blue or
  Orange body ................................ **£15-20**
  1950-54 Tinplate hook, wire drawbar,
- Green or Red body .......................... **£15-20**
**NB** Most 25g Trailers have a white 'T' on a
square black background, located at the rear.

**25m Bedford End Tipper**
  (renumbered in 1954 to 410).
  All 25m models were sold from trade
  packs of six.
- 1948-52 Dark Green cab and truck
  body, Black hubs, crank-handle
  operates tipper ............................. **£100-120**
  1948-54
- Orange cab and truck body,
  Black hubs .................................. **£100-120**
- Orange cab and truck body,
  Light Green hubs ........................... **£500-750**
- Cream cab / truck body, Red hubs ... **£500-750**
- Dark Green cab and truck body,
  Light Green hubs ........................... **£300-400**
- Red cab, Cream back, Red hubs ...... **£100-120**
- Yellow cab / hubs, Mid-Blue back... **£100-120**

**25p Aveling Barford Road Roller**
  1948-54    (renumbered in 1954 to 251)
- Mid or Pale Green body with
  driver and hook, Red wheels............... **£30-40**
- All-Orange body, Tan driver ........... **£150-200**

**25r Forward Control Lorry**
  1948-54    (renumbered in 1954 to 420)
- Orange body, Black hubs ................ **£100-150**
- Orange body, Green hubs................ **£100-150**
- Cream body, Black hubs ................ **£100-150**
- Cream body, Blue hubs.................. **£100-150**
- Cream body, Black hubs ................ **£100-150**

- Dark Brown body, Green hubs ........ **£100-150**
- Green body, Cream hubs.................. **£100-150**
- Green body, Red hubs ..................... **£100-150**
- Grey body, Red hubs........................ **£100-150**

**25s Six-wheeled Wagon**
  1937-40
- Reddish-Brown body, Cream,
  Brown or Grey tilt, holes in seat
  (but no figures)................................ **£100-125**
- Royal Blue body ............................ **£200-250**
  1945-48
- Brown (various shades), Green or
  Dark Blue body, Grey or Light Blue tilt,
  with or without holes for figures
  (but no figures)................................ **£100-125**
- Brick Red body, Grey tilt,
  Black hubs.................................... **£125-150**

**25t Flat Truck and Trailer**
  (25c Flat Truck, and matching 25g Trailer).
  1945-47 Type 3.
- Green, Blue, Orange or Stone .......... **£140-160**
  1947-50
- Type 4. Green or Orange................. **£120-140**

**25v Bedford Refuse Wagon**
  (renumbered in 1954 to 252).
  1948-54 (Trade box contains 4)
- Fawn body, Green opening shutters
  and rear door ..................................**£90-110**

**25w Bedford Truck** (renumbered in 1954 to 411)
  1948-54
- Light Green cab, truck body and hubs.
  (Shades of Pale Green exist)..............**£90-110**
- As previous model, but with 'straight
  across' Black front mudguards......... **£250-350**
- Dark Green cab, Light Green truck
  body, Light Green hubs.................... **£300-400**
- Light Green cab / body, Red hubs ... **£500-750**

**25x Commer Breakdown Lorry**
  (renumbered in 1954 to 430)
  1949-54 'DINKY SERVICE' logo.
  First issues in Trade Boxes of 4,
  then individually in Orange card boxes.
- Tan cab and chassis (various shades),
  Light Green back, Red hubs,
  Black logo .................................... **£125-150**
- Dark Grey cab, Violet Blue back,
  Red hubs, White logo...................... **£150-175**
- Dark Grey cab, Royal Blue back,
  Red hubs, White logo...................... **£135-165**

## 28 Series Delivery Vans
NB    After reaching '28y' in Meccano's numbering system, further issues in this series were numbered '280'.

**28a    Delivery Van 'HORNBY TRAINS'**
1934-34
- Type 1. Orange body,
  'Hornby Trains' logo ................. **£3,000-5,000**
  1934-35
- Type 1. Yellow body,
  'Hornby Trains British & Guaranteed'
  in Gold. Blue wash wheels ........ **£3,000-4,000**
  1935-36
- Type 2. With smooth cast hubs ....... **£400-500**

**28a    Delivery Van 'GOLDEN SHRED'**
Cream body, 'Golden Shred Marmalade'
on right hand side, 'Silver Shred
Marmalade' on left hand side.
- 1936-39  Type 2 ........................ **£3,000-4,000**
- 1939-41  Type 3 ........................... **£750-1,000**

**28b    Delivery Van 'PICKFORDS'**
Royal Blue, 'Pickfords Removals & Storage,
Over 100 Branches' in Gold.
1934-35
- Type 1, Purple wash wheels ....... **£4,000-5,000**
  1935-35
  Dark Blue. Dieast hubs, White tyres
- Type 1 ...................... **£4,000-5,000**
- Type 2 ...................... **£750-1,000**

**28b    Delivery Van 'SECCOTINE'**
Blue body, 'Seccotine Sticks
Everything' in Gold.
- 1935-39  Type 2 ................... **£750-1,000**
- 1939-41  Type 3 ............................. **£300-400**

**28c    Delivery Van
'MANCHESTER GUARDIAN'**
'The Manchester Guardian' in Gold.
1934-35   Type 1.
- Black/Red body,
  Yellow wash wheels ................. **£4,000-5,000**
  1935-39   Type 2.
- Red body, smooth cast hubs ............ **£400-500**
  1939-41   Type 3
- Red body ...................................... **£400-500**

**28d    Delivery Van 'OXO'**
Blue body, 'Beef In Brief' and
'Beef At Its Best' in Gold.
1934-35   Type 1.
- Green wash wheels ................... **£4,000-5,000**
  1935-39   Type 2.
- Smooth cast hubs ....................... **£750-1,000**
- 1939-41   Type 3 ............................. **£700-900**

**28e    Delivery Van 'ENSIGN CAMERAS'**
Orange body, 'ENSIGN CAMERAS'
(on n/s) and 'ENSIGN LUKOS FILMS'
(on o/s) in Gold.
1934-35
- Type 1, Blue wash wheels ......... **£4,000-5,000**

**28e    Delivery Van 'FIRESTONE TYRES'**
'Firestone Tyres' in Gold.
1934-35
- Type 1, White body .................... **£4,000-5,000**
  1935-39
- Type 2, Blue or White body ......... **£750-1,000**
  1939-41
- Type 3, Blue or White body ............. **£400-500**

**28f    Delivery Van 'PALETHORPES'**
Pale Grey-Blue body, Pink sausage decal,
'Palethorpes Royal Cambridge' on van sides,
'Palethorpes Model Factory' on rear
(Red and Navy Blue transfers).
1934-35
- Type 1, Blue wash wheels ......... **£4,000-5,000**
  1935-38
- Type 2, smooth cast hubs ............. **£750-1,000**

**28f    Delivery Van 'VIROL'**
Yellow body, 'Give Your Child A Virol
Constitution' in Black.
1938-39
- Type 2, Blue wash wheels ........... **£750-1,000**
  1939-41
- Type 3, smooth cast hubs ............. **£400-500**

**28g    Delivery Van 'KODAK'**
Yellow body,
'Use Kodak Film To Be Sure' in Red.
1934-35
- Type 1, Blue wash wheels ......... **£4,000-5,000**
  1935-39
- Type 2, smooth cast hubs ............ **£750-1,000**
  1939-41
- Type 3 ...................................... **£400-500**

**28h    Delivery Van 'SHARPS TOFFEES'**
'Sharps Toffee, Maidstone' in Gold.
1934-35
- Type 1, Black/Red body,
  Yellow wash wheels .................. **£1,500-2,000**
  1935-35
- Type 2, Red body, smooth cast hubs **£500-700**

**28h    Delivery Van 'DUNLOP'**
Red body, 'Dunlop Tyres' in Gold.
- 1935-39  Type 2 ........................... **£750-1,000**
- 1939-41  Type 3 .............................. **£400-500**

**28k    Delivery Van 'MARSH & BAXTER'**
Dark Green body,
'Marsh's Sausages' and pig logo in Gold.
1934-35
- Type 1, Purple wash wheels ....... **£4,000-5,000**
- Type 1, Green wash wheels ....... **£4,000-5,000**
  1935-39
- Type 2, smooth cast hubs ............. **£750-1,000**
  1939-41
- Type 3 ...................................... **£500-700**

**28L    Delivery Van 'CRAWFORDS'**
Red body, 'Crawfords Biscuits' in Gold.
1934-35
- Type 1, Yellow wash wheels ...... **£2,500-3,500**
- Type 1, Green wash wheels ....... **£2,500-3,500**

**28m    Delivery Van 'WAKEFIELD'S  CASTROL'**
Green body, 'Wakefield Castrol
Motor Oil' in Red.
1934-35
- Type 1, Yellow wash wheels ...... **£4,000-5,000**
  1935-39
- Type 2, smooth cast hubs ................ **£400-500**
  1939-41
- Type 3 ...................................... **£1,500-2,000**

**28n    Delivery Van 'MECCANO'**
Lemon Yellow body, 'Meccano Engineering
For Boys' in Red and Black.
1934-35
- Type 1. Renumbered from 22d .. **£4,000-5,000**
  1935-35
- Type 2, smooth cast hubs ................ **£400-500**

**28n    Delivery Van 'ATCO'**
Green body, 'Atco Lawn Mowers Sales and
Service' in Gold/Red.
- 1935-39  Type 2 ........................... **£750-1,000**
- 1939-41  Type 3 .............................. **£500-700**

**28p    Delivery Van 'CRAWFORDS'**
Red body, 'Crawfords Biscuits in Gold.
- 1935-39  Type 2 ........................... **£750-1,000**
- 1939-41  Type 3 ........................... **£750-1,000**

**28r    Delivery Van 'SWAN'**
Black body, 'Swan Pens' and logo in Gold.
- 1936-39  Type 2 ........................... **£750-1,000**
- 1939-41  Type 3 ........................... **£750-1,000**

**28s    Delivery Van 'FRYS'**
Brown or Cream body,
'Frys Chocolate' in Gold.
- 1936-39  Type 2 ........................... **£750-1,000**
- 1939-41  Type 3 .............................. **£300-400**

Rear view of

28p

'Crawford's'  Delivery Van
(1st type)

PHOTO: VECTIS AUCTIONS LTD.

**28t   Delivery Van 'OVALTINE'**
Red body,
'Drink Ovaltine For Health' in Gold/Black.
• 1936-39  Type 2 ........................ **£2,000-3,000**
• 1939-41  Type 3 ............................. **£400-500**

**28w   Delivery Van 'OSRAM'**
Yellow body, 'Osram Lamps - a G.E.C.
Product' in Gold/Black.
• 1936-39  Type 2 ........................... **£750-1,000**
• 1940-41  Type 3 ............................. **£500-700**

**28x   Delivery Van 'HOVIS'**
White body, 'Hovis For Tea' in Gold/Black.
• 1936-39  Type 2 ........................... **£750-1,000**
• 1939-41  Type 3 ............................. **£400-500**

**28y   Delivery Van 'EXIDE'**
Red body, 'Exide Batteries' and
'Drydex Batteries' in Gold/Black.
• 1936-39  Type 2 ............................. **£400-500**
• 1939-41  Type 3 ............................. **£400-500**

**NB   Further issues in this series were numbered
'280', as follows:**

**280   Delivery Van**  (plain, no advertising)
1945-47
• Red or Blue, Type 3, open windows.... **£50-60**
1948-54
• As previous model, but with
filled-in rear windows .......................... **£50-60**
• Green body, Type 3,
filled-in rear windows ...................... **£400-500**
• Olive ('Military') Green body, Type 3,
filled-in rear windows .......................... **£80-95**

**NB**  The 280 casting provided the basis
for 34c Loudspeaker Van.

**280a   Delivery Van 'VIYELLA'**
Blue body, 'Viyella Regd. for the Nursery'
in White and Black.
• 1937-39  Type 2 ........................ **£2,000-2,500**
• 1939-41  Type 3 ............................. **£700-950**

**280b   Delivery Van 'LYONS TEA'**
1937-39
• Dark Blue body, 'Lyons Tea Always
the Best' in Red and White.
Only issued as Type 2 ................... **£750-1,000**

**280b   Delivery Van 'HARTLEYS JAM'**
Cream body, 'Hartleys is Real Jam'
in Red/Green.
• 1939-39  Type 2 ........................... **£800-1,000**
• 1939-40  Type 3 ............................. **£400-500**

**280c   Delivery Van 'SHREDDED WHEAT'**
Cream body, Red stripe,
'Welwyn Garden City, Herts' in Black.
• 1937-39  Type 2 ........................... **£750-1,000**
• 1939-40  Type 3 ............................. **£400-500**

**280d   Delivery Van 'BISTO'**
1937-40
• Yellow body, 'Ah! Bisto' with logo,
Type 2        ........................... **£350-500**
1938-39
• Type 2, with large
'Bisto Kids' transfer ..................... **£750-1,000**
• Type 2, small Bisto Kids transfer,
with pie on table ............................ **£600-800**
1939-40
• Type 3, small Bisto Kids transfer
with pie on table ............................ **£400-500**
1940
• Yellow body, wording altered to
'Bisto' with logo ............................. **£400-500**

**280e   Delivery Van 'ECKO'**
1937-39
• Type 2, Dark Green body,
'ECKO Radio' in Gold.................... **£500-750**

**280e   Delivery Van
'YORKSHIRE EVENING POST'**
Cream body, 'Yorkshire Evening Post -
The Original Buff'.
• 1938-39  Type 2 ........................... **£750-1,000**
• 1939-39  Type 3 ............................. **£600-800**

**280f   Delivery Van 'MACKINTOSHS'**
Red body, Gold logo: 'Mackintosh's Toffee
- A Smile in Every Piece'.
• 1937-39  Type 2 ........................... **£750-1,000**
• 1939-40  Type 3 ............................. **£400-500**

**NB   Nos. 280g – 280m Delivery Vans were
made as promotional models.**
All are Type 2.

**280g**  1939      **'BENTALLS'**
• Green body, Yellow upper side panels,
White roof, 'Bentalls Kingston on Thames'
and 'Phone Kin: 1001' in Yellow.
Two examples known............. **£10,000-12,500**

**280h**  1939      **'MAISON de BONNETERIE'**
• Dark Red, 'Maison de Bonneterie,
Leverancier'............................ **£10,000-12,500**

**280i**  1939      **'LIVERPOOL ECHO'**
• Type 2, no details available.... **£10,000-12,500**

**280j**  1939      **'FENWICK'**
• Apple Green body, White roof,
'Newcastle on Tyne'.
Two examples known............. **£10,000-12,500**

**280k**  1939      **'H. G. LOOSE'**
• Dark Green body, 'H. G. LOOSE' on
Cream panel, 'Looe' and 'Phone 123'.
One example known ............. **£10,000-12,500**

**280L**  1939      **'DE BIJENKORF'**
• 'Amsterdam DenHaag Rotterdam'
............................ **£10,000-12,500**

**280m**  1939      **'LAND'S FOR BAGS'**
• Green, 'Land's for Bags' in Gold.
One example known (in very
poor condition).......................................NGPP

Type 1

Type 2

Type 3

---

### 28 / 280 Series Delivery Van Identification

**Type 1:**  **(1933-35)**, two-piece lead body with *'HORNBY SERIES'* (early issues) or *'DINKY TOYS'* cast-in under
cab roof, tinplate radiator, no headlamps, thinly-painted coloured solid wheel/tyre castings (some
bright plated), 84 mm. (Coloured wheels tend to attract a premium to the price of the model.)

**Type 2:**  **(1935-39)**, one-piece diecast body, cast-in shield-shaped radiator, rear wheel spats, cast smooth wheel hubs
with  rubber tyres (usually white), 81 mm. All carried advertising.

**Type 3:**  **(1939-41)**, one-piece diecast body with rear wheel spats, cast smooth wheel hubs (various colours) with
black tyres, open rear windows, 83 mm. All carried advertising.

**Type 3:**  **(1947-54)**, one-piece diecast body with rear wheel spats, cast ridged wheel hubs (usually black) with
black tyres, filled-in rear windows, cast boss under roof , 83 mm. No advertising.

## 30 Series

**30e Breakdown Car** (Crane Lorry)
1935-40
- Red, Yellow, Green, Brown or Grey body, Black wings, Black or Blue smooth hubs, open rear window ...... **£100-120**
- Blue body, Dark Blue wings, Blue hubs, open rear window ......... **£100-120**
1946-46
- Red or Grey body, Black wings, open rear window, ridged hubs ............ **£60-70**
1947-48
- Red, Grey or Green body and wings, no rear window, ridged hubs ............... **£40-50**

**30j Austin Wagon** (renumbered in 1954 to 412)
1950-54
- Blue body with hook, Mid-Blue hubs.................................. **£100-120**
- Light, Medium or Dark Maroon body, Maroon or Red hubs.............. **£100-150**
- Brown body, Tan hubs ..................... **£400-500**
- Dark Blue body, Mid-Blue hubs...........NGPP
- Red body, Red hubs ............................NGPP

**30m Rear Tipping Wagon**
1950-54 (renumbered in 1954 to 414)
- Maroon cab, Pale Green tipper and hubs, 'Dodge' on baseplate ............. **£500-750**
- Orange cab, Pale Green tipper and hubs, 'Dodge' on baseplate ............. **£500-750**
- Blue or Dark Blue cab, Grey rear ....... **£60-70**

**30n Farm Produce Wagon** (1950-54)
See 'Farm and Garden Models'.

**30p Petrol Tanker**
- 1950-51 'PETROL', Red or Green, cast in aluminium ......... **£80-90**
- 1951-52 'PETROL', Red or Green, cast in mazak ............... **£80-90**
- 1952-54 (renumbered in 1954 to 440) 'MOBILGAS', Red body, Blue lettering on White background .... **£80-90**

**30pa Petrol Tanker** (renumbered in 1954 to 441)
- 1952-54 'CASTROL', Green body and hubs, some aluminium, most mazak.... **£80-90**
**30pb Petrol Tanker** (renumbered in 1954 to 442)
- 1952-54 'ESSO', Red body and hubs, 'MOTOR OIL - ESSO - PETROL'..... **£80-90**

**30r Fordson Thames Flat Truck**
1951-54 (renumbered in 1954 to 422)
- Red or Green body with hook.............. **£60-70**
- Brown body, Brown hubs .................... **£60-70**
- Brown body, Maroon hubs.....................NGPP

**30s Austin Covered Wagon**
1950-54 (renumbered in 1954 to 413)
- Maroon body, Cream cover, Cream hubs, sold unboxed........................... **£100-150**
- Dark Blue body, Light Blue cover, Light Blue hubs, sold unboxed ....... **£300-400**
- Mid-Blue body, Light Blue cover, Light Blue hubs, sold unboxed ....... **£100-150**

**30v Electric Dairy Van 'EXPRESS DAIRY'**
1949-54 (renumbered in 1954 to 490)
- Cream body, Red chassis, hubs and logo ................................ **£75-90**
- Grey body, Blue chassis, hubs and logo .................................. **£90-120**

**30v Electric Dairy Van 'N.C.B.'**
1949-54 (renumbered in 1954 to 491)
- Cream body, Red chassis, hubs and logo ................................ **£75-90**
- Grey body, Blue chassis, hubs and logo .................................. **£75-90**

**30w Hindle-Smart Helecs**
1952-54 (renumbered in 1954 to 421)
- Maroon body, Maroon or Red hubs, 'British Railways', hook, trailer uncouples .................................. **£60-70**

## 31 Series

**31 Holland Coachcraft Van**
1935-35
- Red, Green, Blue or Orange, 'Holland Coachcraft Registered Design', lead body ................... **£2,000-3,000**
1935-35
- Mid-Green body, Gold stripe, Silver advert., Chrome hubs ...... **£2,000-3,000**
- Cream body, Red coachline ....... **£2,000-3,000**
1935-36
- Red, Blue or Orange, 'Holland Coachcraft Registered Design', diecast body............. **£2,000-3,000**
NB A Red variant from 1935/6 was sold by Christie's in 2001 for £2,350.
- Light and Dark Blue with Silver coachlines, Silver grille and Yellow headlights. ......................... NGPP
**31a Trojan 15 cwt Van 'ESSO'**
1951-54 (renumbered in 1954 to 450)
- Red body, Maroon or Red hubs ......... **£80-100**
**31b Trojan 15 cwt Van 'DUNLOP'**
1952-54 (renumbered in 1954 to 451)
- Red body, Maroon or Red hubs, 'The Worlds Master Tyre'................. **£80-100**
**31c Trojan 15 cwt Van 'CHIVERS'**
1953-54 (renumbered in 1954 to 452)
- Green body and hubs, 'CHIVERS JELLIES' and design...... **£80-100**
**31d Trojan 15 cwt Van 'OXO'**
1953-54 (renumbered in 1954 to 453)
- Mid-Blue or Violet-Blue body, Mid-Blue hubs, 'BEEFY OXO'....... **£300-400**

## 33 Series

**33a Mechanical Horse**
1935-36
NB 1st type have long slot and chrome hubs.
- Red, Green, Blue or Yellow body, 2.5 mm. trailer step ....................... **£150-175**
1936-40
- Same but 9.5 mm. trailer step ......... **£125-150**
1946-?
- As previous model but also in Brown, Grey or Khaki .................... **£125-150**

**33b Flat Truck Trailer**
1935-40
- Red, Green, Blue or Yellow body, no sides ............................................. **£45-55**
**33c Open Truck Trailer**
1935-40
- Red, Green, Blue or Yellow body with sides .......................................... **£45-55**
**33d Box Van Trailer**
1935-40
- Green tinplate body on cast chassis, no advertising .................... **£100-125**
- 'HORNBY TRAINS', Dark Blue body, 'Hornby Trains British and Guaranteed' in Gold ....................................... **£300-400**
- 'HORNBY TRAINS', Green body, 'Hornby Trains British and Guaranteed' in Gold **£300-400**
- 'MECCANO', Green body, 'Meccano Engineering For Boys' in Red and Black.............................. **£300-400**
NB Models 33a and 33d combined and given Ref No 33r - see below.

**33e Dust Wagon Trailer**
1935-40
- Blue, Yellow Grey or Green 33c (Open Trailer) Blue, Yellow, Grey or Green tinplate top.............................. **£70-90**
1946-47
- Grey body with Blue or Yellow tinplate top.............................. **£70-90**
- Red body with Blue or Yellow tinplate top.............................. **£70-90**

**33f Petrol Tank Trailer**
1935-40
- Green (33b) chassis/Red tank, or Red chassis/Green tank, no logo ..... **£70-90**
- 'ESSO' Green chassis/Red tank with 'ESSO' in Gold ......................... **£80-120**
- 'CASTROL' Red chassis/Green tank, 'Wakefield Castrol' .................. **£80-120**

**33r Railway Mechanical Horse and Trailer Van**
1935-40 33a Mechanical Horse and 33d Box Van Trailer in railway liveries. These were also available separately as 33ra and 33rd (see below).
- 'L.N.E.R.' Blue and Black, 'L.N.E.R. Express Parcels Traffic'... **£250-350**
- 'L.M.S.' Maroon and Black, 'L.M.S. Express Parcels Traffic'...... **£250-350**
- 'G.W.R.' Brown and Cream, 'G.W.R. Express Cartage Services' . **£250-350**
- 'S.R.' Green (Cream cab roof) and Black, 'Southern Railway'........ **£500-750**

**33ra Mechanical Horse**
1935-40
'L.N.E.R.' Blue and Black, 'L.N.E.R. 901'................................ **£250-350**
- 'L.M.S.' Maroon and Black, 'L.M.S. 2246'.............................. **£250-350**
- 'G.W.R.' Brown and Cream, 'G.W.R. 2742'........................... **£250-350**
- 'S.R.' Green (Cream roof) and Black, '3016 M' ............................... **£250-350**

**33rd Railway Trailer**
1935-40
- 'L.N.E.R.' Blue and Black, 'L.N.E.R. Express Parcels Traffic'... **£250-350**
- 'L.M.S.' Maroon and Black, 'L.M.S. Express Parcels Traffic'.... **£250-350**
- 'G.W.R.' Brown and Cream, 'G.W.R. Express Cartage Services' . **£250-350**
- 'S.R.' Green and Black, 'Southern Railway'.......................... **£350-500**

**33w Mechanical Horse and Open Wagon**
1947-54 (renumbered in 1954 to 415)
- Cab colours: Grey, Fawn, Dark or Mid-Green, Olive, Red, Brown, Blue or Yellow. Trailer colours: Grey, Fawn, Maroon, Brown, Dark or Mid-Green, Olive or Cream ... **£75-95**

## 34 Series

**34a 'ROYAL AIR MAIL SERVICE'**
1935-40
- Blue car, Silver lettering, Gold crest ........................................ **£400-500**

**34b 'ROYAL MAIL' Van**
1938-47
- Red body, open rear windows, Black bonnet/wings/roof/hubs ......... **£150-175**
1948-51
- Red body, Black bonnet/wings/roof, Black or Red hubs, filled rear windows ......................... **£100-125**
1952-52

- Red body/roof/hubs, Black bonnet/front
  wings, filled-in rear windows .......... **£125-150**

**34c Loudspeaker Van** (280 casting)
1948-54 (renumbered in 1954 to 492)
- Fawn, Grey, Green, Brown or
  Blue body  Black loudspeakers............ **£70-80**
- Brown, Blue or Green body,
  Silver loudspeakers .............................. **£70-80**

**60y Thompson Aircraft Tender**
1938-40
- Red with 'Shell Aviation Services' in Gold;
  Black or White solid rubber wheels. **£300-400**

**151b 6-wheel Covered Wagon**
1937-40 (renumbered in 1940 to 25s)
- Gloss Green body, tinplate canopy,
  seat holes, spare wheel..................... **£125-150**
  1947-54 (export only from 1950)
       (renumbered in 1954 to 620)
- Matt-Green or Greenish-Brown body .. **£60-70**

**251 Aveling Barford Road Roller**
1954-63 (renumbered from 25p in 1954)
- Mid or Dark Green body, Red rollers .. **£45-55**
- Lime Green body, Red rollers............. **£70-90**
- Apple Green body, Red rollers ........... **£70-90**

**252 Bedford Refuse Wagon**
1954-60 (renumbered from 25v in 1954)
- Tan body, Green tinplate shutters,
  Red hubs, window glazing in some . **£100-125**
  1960-63
- Lime Green body, Black tinplate
  shutters, Cream hubs, window
  glazing in some ............................... **£125-150**
  1963-63
- Orange cab, Light Grey back, Green
  tinplate shutters and diecast hubs,
  window glazing, Black grille .......... **£300-350**
  1964-64
- Orange cab, Light Grey back and
  diecast hubs, Green plastic shutters,
  window glazing ................................ **£250-350**
  1964-65
- Bright Orange cab, Light Grey back,
  Green plastic shutters, Red plastic
  hubs, window glazing ..................... **£250-350**
- As previous but matt-Black base ..... **£250-350**

**260 'ROYAL MAIL' Van** (Morris 'J')
1955-61
- Red body, Black roof,
  Gold 'E II R' crest............................ **£125-150**
**260 VW 'DEUTSCHE BUNDESPOST'**
1971-72
- Yellow body (129 casting, 100mm),
  made for German Market................. **£100-150**

**261 Telephone Service Van** (Morris 'Z')
1955-61

- Olive-Green/Black, 'POST OFFICE
  TELEPHONES', ladder ................... **£100-125**

**273 Mini Minor Van 'R.A.C.'**
1965-70
- Blue body, White roof, Black base,
  Red interior, 'ROAD SERVICE'
  on sides ........................................ **£175-200**
- Same model but with Blue interior.. **£175-200**
- With Red interior, Silver baseplate
  and redesigned rear doors ............. **£150-175**
**NB** Factory errors have resulted in
  some rear door logos reading
  'ROAD ROAD' instead of
  'ROAD SERVICE' as normal...............NGPP

**274 Mini Minor Van 'A.A.'**
1964-73
- Yellow body, White roof,
  'PATROL SERVICE', original
  'entwined' logo................................ **£125-150**
- Same, but Yellow roof, Blue int....... **£125-150**
- Yellow body, White roof, Red interior,
  'AA SERVICE', modern 'simple'
  logo, Silver or Black base ................ **£90-120**
- Same model but with Blue interior.... **£90-120**
- With Yellow roof and Blue interior ... **£90-120**
**Note**: 'AA' logo designs:
  a) Embossed paint 'AA',
  b) Waterslide transfer in square recess
  c) Waterslide transfer on raised panel
  Rear door casting variations:
  a) Rear door hinge pins extend directly
     into chassis holes
  b) Rear door hinge pins located into slots.
  Central base colour variations:
  a) Red,   b) Blue,   c) White

**274 Mini Minor Van
'JOSEPH MASON PAINTS'**
1969-70
- Promotional in special Red box with
  advert card. 650 issued. Maroon
  body, Red seats and rear van
  body base, roof sign, 'PAINTS'
  labels, spun hubs ........................... **£800-1,000**

**275 Brinks Armoured Car**
1964-66
- Grey/Blue, 'Brinks Security Since 1859',
  2 figures, 2 crates, plastic hubs........ **£300-400**
  1966-70
- Same as previous model but no driver
  or crates, US packaging ................... **£150-200**
- Grey body White roof, Blue base,
  metal hubs, assembled in USA ..............NGPP
- Mexican issue:
  Blue body with Grey doors and
  Red/White/Blue crests,
  plastic hubs................................... **£750-1,000**

**279 Aveling Barford Diesel Roller**
1965-71
- Orange body, Grey engine covers,
  Blue or Green rollers, Blue driver ....... **£75-95**
  1971-80
- Yellow cab, Black roof, Silver rollers.. **£35-45**
- Yellow cab, Black roof, Black rollers.. **£35-45**
- Yellow cab, Blue roof, Yellow square
  engine covers, Silver rollers................ **£35-45**
- Yellow cab, Black roof, Yellow
  square engine covers, Silver rollers ..... **£35-45**
- Yellow cab, Grey Roof, Yellow
  square engine covers, Silver rollers ..... **£35-45**

**280 Series Delivery Vans**
See '28 Series Delivery Vans' listing.
**280 Mobile 'MIDLAND BANK'**
1966-68
- White/Silver, Blue stripe, Gold
  crest, opening doors, figure.............. **£120-140**

**343 Farm Produce Wagon**
See 'Farm and Garden Models'.

**380 Skip Truck**
- 1977-79 Yellow and Orange body ...... **£10-20**
**381 Farm Wagon**
- 1977-80 Yellow and Brown body ....... **£10-20**
**382 Dumper Truck**
- 1978-80 Red body/Grey back,
  Red body/Black back or Yellow
  body/Grey back ................................... **£10-20**
**383 'N.C.L.' Truck**
- 1978-80 Yellow,
  'NATIONAL CARRIERS Ltd' ........... **£10-20**
**384 Fire Rescue Wagon**
- 1977-79 Red body, White fire escape. **£10-20**
**385 'ROYAL MAIL' Truck**
- 1977-79 Red body............................. **£10-20**
**386 'AVIS' Truck**
- 1979 Red body. Catalogued
  but not issued ..........................................NPP
**387 'PICKFORDS' Truck**
- 1979 Red / Blue. Catalogued
  but not issued ..........................................NPP
**? 'HARRODS' Truck**
- 1979 Khaki body................................NGPP
**? 'POST OFFICE TELEPHONES'**
  1979 Khaki body................................NGPP
**? 'A.A.' Truck**
- 1979 Yellow body ..............................NGPP
**? 'AMERICAN FIRE BRIGADE'**
- 1979 No details ..................................NGPP
**NB** See also 687 Convoy Army Truck
  in the Military Vehicles section.

**390 Customised Transit Van**
- 1978 Type 3 Metallic Blue body with
  'VAMPIRE' and 'flame' design............NGPP

Dinky Toys 903 Foden Flat Truck with Tailboard.  PHOTO: VECTIS AUCTIONS LTD.

**400 B.E.V. Truck**
1954-60   (renumbered in 1954 from 14a)
- Dark Blue or Mid-Blue or Grey with
  Blue, Grey or Red hubs, 1 PP ............. **£30-35**

**401 Coventry Climax Fork Lift**
1954-64   (renumbered in 1954 from 14c)
- Orange body, Green forks, Tan driver . **£30-35**
- Red body, Green forks ..................... **£300-400**

**402 Bedford 'COCA-COLA' Truck**
1966-69
- Red cab and back, White roof,
  Blue interior, six trays of crates,
  Red plastic hubs ............................... **£130-160**

**404 Climax Fork Lift**
1967-72
- Red/Yellow with 'CG4' rear logo ....... **£25-35**
- Red/Yellow front with all Red rear,
  plus stick-on 'CG4' label .................... **£20-25**
  1978
- Yellow body with 'Climax' on fork
  guide and 'TC4' on engine cover ....... **£20-25**

**406 Commer Articulated Truck**
1963-66   (424 without accessories, Supertoy)
- Yellow/Grey, Blue plastic hubs ......... **£110-140**

**407 Ford Transit Vans**
See 'Commercial Vehicles Identification'
pages for an explanation of casting
Types 1, 2 and 3.
- 1966-69 **'KENWOOD'**
  Blue/White, promotional. Type 1 ..... **£100-125**
- 1970-71 **'TELEFUSION'**
  White body, 'Colour TV, Telefusion'.
  Intended promotional not issued .............. NPP
  1970-75 **'HERTZ TRUCK RENTALS'**
  Promotionals. Type 1.
- Yellow body, Red interior,
  Blue baseplate .................................... **£80-100**
- Yellow body, Grey interior,
  Black baseplate .................................. **£80-100**
- 1970-73 **'AVIS TRUCK RENTALS'**
  Red body. Kit only but not issued ............. NPP
- **'PELTZ BADKEREI'** (promotional)
  Blue lower, Yellow upper .................... **£50-60**

**408 Big Bedford Lorry**
1956-63   (renumbered from 522 / 922)
- Maroon cab, Light Tan back,
  Fawn or Cream hubs,
  (with window glazing from 1961) ... **£125-150**
- Dark Blue cab, Yellow back,
  Yellow or Cream hubs..................... **£175-225**
- Pink cab, Cream back,
  Cream hubs ............................... **£1,500-2,000**

**409 Bedford Articulated Lorry**
1956-63   (renumbered from 521 / 921)
All have Black knobbly tyres.
- Deep Yellow cab and back, Black
  wings, Red hubs, Yellow box ..... **£175-225**
- As previous model but with window
  glazing. Lighter Yellow box ............. **£150-200**

**410 Bedford End Tipper Truck**
1954-61 (renumbered in 1954 from 25m)
- Red cab, chassis and diecast hubs,
  Cream back ...................................... **£175-200**
- Yellow cab, chassis and diecast hubs,
  Mid-Blue back, window glazing ...... **£150-175**
  1962-63
- Red cab, chassis and plastic hubs,
  Cream back, window glazing .......... **£175-200**
- Yellow cab, chassis and plastic hubs,
  Dark or Mid-Blue back, glazing ...... **£300-350**

**410 Bedford CF Vans**
- 1972-72 **'SIMPSONS'**
  Canadian promotional.
  Red/Black, 'Simpsons' and logos ...... **£75-100**
- 1974 **'DANISH POST'**
  Danish promotional.
  Yellow body, 'Danish Post' emblem .. **£75-100**

- 1974-75 **'JOHN MENZIES'**
  Promotional, Dark Blue body,
  'John Menzies' logo ......................... **£100-125**
- 1974-74 **'BELACO'**
  Promotional, Brown/Black,
  'Brake and Clutch Parts' ................... **£75-100**
- 1975-76 **'M.J. HIRE'** promotional.
  White body, 'M.J. Hire Service' .......... **£25-30**
- 1975-77 **'MODELLERS WORLD'**
  White body, 'Modellers World'.
  This is a Code 2 model ..................... **£25-30**
- 1975-75 **'MARLEY TILES'**
  Red body with 'Marley Building' logo **£25-30**
- 1979 **'COLLECTORS GAZETTE'**
  White body.  A Code 2 model ............ **£25-30**
- 1972-74 **'ROYAL MAIL'**
  Red body with 'ROYAL MAIL' and
  'E II R' crest ..................................... **£15-20**
- 1974-80 **'ROYAL MAIL'**
  As previous model but with raised
  rectangle on roof ............................ **£15-20**
NB   Many Code-2 issues exist (produced
  by John Gay) and include the following
  liveries: 'MOBIL', 'BN',
  'HERTZ TRUCK RENTAL',
  'JIMMY CARTER', 'MATRA',
  'ELF', 'SILVER JUBILEE 1952-1977',
  'KLG', 'PORTAKABIN', 'WIMPEY'.

**411 Bedford Truck**
1954-59   (renumbered in 1954 from 25w)
- Mid-Green cab, chassis,
  back and hubs................................. **£100-125**
  1959-60
- Mid-Green cab and body, Pale Green
  hubs, gloss base, block-tread tyres... **£100-125**

**412 Austin Wagon**
1954-60 (renumbered in 1954 from 30j)
- Powder Blue body, Lemon or
  Dark Blue hubs ............................... **£350-450**
- Maroon body, Red hubs ................. **£120-140**
- Dark Blue body, Mid-Blue hubs ...... **£140-160**
- Lemon Yellow body,
  Mid-Green hubs .......................... **£750-1,000**
- Lemon Yellow body, Blue hubs .... **£750-1,000**

**412 Bedford CF Van 'AA'**
1974-80
- Yellow or Lemon-Yellow body, headboard,
  'AA SERVICE', plastic hubs .............. **£15-20**

**413 Austin Covered Wagon**
1954-60 (renumbered in 1954 from 30s)
- Maroon body,
  Cream tinplate tilt / hubs.............. **£100-150**
- Maroon body and hubs,
  Tan tinplate tilt ............................. **£100-150**
- Dark Blue body, Mid-Blue tinplate
  tilt, Light Blue hubs ....................... **£150-200**
- Mid-Blue body, Mid-Blue tinplate
  tilt, Light Blue hubs ....................... **£150-200**
- Red body, Light Grey tinplate tilt,
  Cream or Grey hubs ....................... **£300-400**
- Red body, Beige tinplate
  tilt, Red hubs ................................. **£300-400**
- Light or Mid-Blue body, Cream
  tinplate tilt, Cream hubs. Plain box . **£400-500**
- Red body, Grey or Beige tinplate
  tilt, Grey hubs................................. **£400-500**
- Maroon body, Beige tilt, Red hubs .. **£300-400**
- Olive-drab body,
  (Royal Army Volunteer Reserve)..........NGPP

**414 Dodge Rear Tipping Wagon**
1954-64 (renumbered in 1954 from 30m)
- Red cab and hubs, Green back......... **£160-190**
- Orange cab and hubs, Green back ... **£160-190**
- Orange cab,
  Mid-Green back and hubs............... **£160-190**
- Greyish-Blue cab, Grey back,
  Mid-Blue hubs ................................ **£160-190**

- Mid-Blue cab and hubs, Grey back . **£160-190**
- Mid-Blue cab, Cream hubs, Grey back.
  In late issue lighter Yellow box....... **£160-190**
- Violet-Blue cab, Grey back / hubs ... **£250-300**
- Royal Blue cab, Grey back / hubs ... **£250-300**
NB  Early issues with or
  without bonnet louvres.

**415 Mechanical Horse and Wagon**  (33a + 33c)
1954-59   (renumbered in 1954 from 33w)
- Blue horse, Cream trailer ................ **£125-175**
- Red horse, Brown trailer .................. **£125-175**

Ford Transit Vans.
See 'Commercial Vehicles Identification'
pages for an explanation of
casting Types 1, 2 and 3.

**416 Ford Transit Van, 'FORD'** promotional.
1975-78
- Orange-Yellow body, cast hubs,
  '1,000,000 TRANSITS', Type 2...........NGPP

**416 Ford Transit 'MOTORWAY SERVICES'**
- 1975-78
  Yellow body, special lights, Type 2,
  with two warning boards and cones..... **£45-55**

**417 Ford Transit 'MOTORWAY'**
- 1978-79  As model 416 but Type 3...... **£30-40**

**417 Leyland Comet Lorry with Stake Body**
1956-58   (renumbered in 1956 from 931)
(Stake body secured by a rivet. Yellow box).
- Violet Blue cab and chassis, Dark Yellow
  back, Mid-Blue hubs, Yellow box .. **£185-225**
- Dark Blue cab and chassis,
  Brown back, Red hubs .................... **£300-350**
  1958-59
- Yellow cab and chassis, Pale Green
  back, Mid-Green hubs, Grey tyres... **£350-400**

**418 Leyland Comet with Hinged Tailboard**
1956-59   (renumbered in 1956 from 932).
Back of model secured by a rivet. Yellow box.
- Dark Green cab and chassis, Orange
  back, Red hubs ............................... **£175-225**
- Dark Blue cab and chassis, Mid-Blue
  back, Blue, Cream or Red hubs ....... **£175-225**

**419 Leyland Comet Cement Lorry**
1956-59   (renumbered in 1954 from 933)
- Yellow body and hubs, 1 packing piece.
  'Portland Blue-Circle Cement'......... **£145-175**

**420 Forward Control Lorry**
1954-61   (renumbered in 1954 from 25r)
- Cream body, Mid-Blue hubs............ **£100-125**
- Red body, Cream hubs .................... **£100-125**
- Red body, Mid-Green hubs ............. **£160-190**
- Mid-Green body, Cream hubs.......... **£190-230**
- Mid-Green body, Red hubs ............. **£140-170**
- Blue body, Cream hubs ................... **£140-170**

**421 Hindle Smart Helecs 'British Railways'**
1955-59   (renumbered in 1955 from 30w)
- Maroon body, Red hubs, hook ........... **£90-110**

**422 Fordson Thames Flat Truck**
1954-60   (renumbered in 1954 from 30r)
- Red body and hubs.......................... **£125-150**
- Bright Green body and hubs ............ **£125-150**
- Dark Green body, Mid-Green hubs.
  In dual-numbered box .................... **£125-150**

**424 Commer Convertible Articulated Vehicle**
1963-66
- Primrose-Yellow cab, Silver-Grey
  back, Blue plastic tilt, Blue plastic
  hubs, plus detachable White
  plastic 'stake' body.......................... **£200-300**
  424 lift-up lid box types:
  1 - Lemon, Green and Orange,
  2 - Grey, Red and Yellow.

**425  Bedford TK Coal Wagon 'HALL & Co.'**
1964-69
- Red body, interior and plastic hubs,
clear windows, 6 bags, scales .......... **£160-190**
- Red body and plastic hubs, Blue windows
and interior, 6 bags, scales ............... **£175-225**

**428  Large Trailer** (all with hook)
1956-66  (renumbered in 1956 from 951)
- Grey body, Red hubs, Grey tyres ....... **£75-100**
- Grey body, Mid-Blue hubs,
Grey tyres.......................................... **£75-100**
- Grey body, Light Green hubs,
Grey tyres ......................................... **£75-100**
- Grey body, grooved Yellow hubs, Black
tyres, late issue lighter Yellow box .. **£100-150**
- Grey body, grooved Red hubs, Black
tyres, late issue lighter Yellow box .... **£75-100**
- Yellow body, Red hubs, Black tyres,
late issue lighter Yellow box ............. **£75-100**
1967-71
- Grey body, Red plastic hubs,
Black tyres...................................... **£100-150**
- Red body, Silver 'button' hubs,
Black tyres...................................... **£100-150**

**429  Trailer**
1954-64  (renumbered in 1954 from 25g)
- Dark Green body, Light Green hubs,
wire drawbar, Black treaded tyres, hook,
axle pivot is part of main casting....... **£80-100**
- As previous model, but with Red body,
Black or Red hubs.............................. **£80-100**

**430  Commer Breakdown Truck**
1954-64  (renumbered in 1954 from 25x)
- 'DINKY SERVICE' logo, operable crane,
late issues have window glazing.
- Tan cab, Mid-Green back with Black
logo, Red hubs. Yellow or
Blue/White striped box .................... **£125-150**
- Cream cab, Mid-Blue back with
Black logo, Red hubs. Yellow box... **£450-550**
- Dark Stone cab, Blue back with
Black logo, Red hubs. Yellow box... **£450-550**
- Red cab, Light Grey back with Blue
logo, Mid-Blue or Red metal hubs.
Yellow box ...................................... **£450-550**
- Red cab (glazed), Light Grey back, Blue
logo, Blue plastic hubs. Yellow box **£450-550**
- Red cab (glazed), Light Grey back
with Blue logo, Red plastic hubs.
Yellow box ...................................... **£500-750**

**430  Johnson 2 ton Dumper**
1977-80
- Orange/Red or Orange/Yellow body,
Blue and Red driver,
Black or Orange engine ...................... **£20-25**

**431  Guy 4 ton Lorry** (2nd type)
1956-58  (renumbered in 1956 from 911)
- Red cab/chassis, Fawn back,
Red hubs, unpainted hook............... **£200-250**
- Violet Blue cab/chassis,
Mid-Blue back, Mid-Blue hubs ....... **£200-250**
- Mid-Blue cab, chassis and back,
Supertoys hubs. Later yellow/blue
card box with lift-off lid............. **£1,000-1,400**

**431  Guy Warrior 4 ton Lorry**
1958-60
- Light Tan cab (no window glazing),
Dark Green back, Mid-Green hubs.. **£300-400**
- Light Tan cab (with window glazing),
Dark Green back, Mid-Green hubs.. **£300-400**
1960-64
- Red cab (with window glazing), Red
chassis and hubs, Dark Green back . **£300-400**

**432  Guy Flat Truck** (2nd type)
1956-57  (renumbered in 1956 from 912)

- Mid-Blue cab/chassis/hook,
Red flatbed, Mid-Blue hubs............. **£200-250**
- Red cab/chassis/hook,
Mid-Blue flatbed and hubs .............. **£375-425**
- Dark Blue cab, Mid-Blue hubs,
Red flatbed, in a lift-off lid box with
'H. Hudson Dobson' label......... **£1,750-2,000**

**432  Guy Warrior Flat Truck**
1958-60
- Green cab (no window glazing),
Red flatbed, Red hubs..................... **£200-300**
1960-64
- Green cab (with window glazing),
Red flatbed, Red hubs..................... **£200-300**

**432  Foden Tipping Lorry**
1976-79  (Same casting as 668).
- White cab, Red chassis, Yellow back .. **£35-45**

**433  Guy Flat Truck with Tailboard**  (2nd type)
1956-57  (renumbered in 1956 from 913)
- Dark Green cab/chassis/hook,
Mid-Green flatbed and hubs ............ **£200-250**
- Violet Blue cab/chassis/hook,
Orange flatbed, Mid-Blue hubs,
one packing piece in box ................. **£200-250**

**433  Guy Warrior Flat Truck with Tailboard**
1958  Listed in catalogue but not issued . NPP

**434  Bedford TK Crash Truck**
1964-66  'TOP RANK Motorway Services'
- White body with Green flash,
Dark Green hubs, Red interior......... **£140-160**
1966-70  'AUTO SERVICES'
- Red or Metallic Red cab, Pale Grey
back, Red metal or plastic hubs ......... **£90-120**
**NB**  Add 15% to price if in detailed
picture box or with Green hubs.

**435  Bedford TK Tipper**
1964-66
- Grey cab, Blue roof, Orange back ..... **£90-120**
1966-68
- Yellow cab with Yellow or Black roof,
Silver back, Yellow sides, Red hubs **£175-225**
1968-71
- White cab / roof, Silver back,
Blue sides, Blue hubs...................... **£175-220**
- Blue cab, Orange and Grey back ..... **£150-175**
- Red cab / sides, Black roof,
Silver back...................................... **£150-175**

**436  'ATLAS COPCO' Lorry**
1963-69
- Yellow, Pale Grey interior,
matt baseplate..................................... **£50-60**
- Yellow, Dark Blue interior,
gloss baseplate..................................... **£50-60**
- Yellow body, Black roof,
Red interior, Silver/Yellow back,
Blue plastic hubs ................................ **£80-100**

**437  Muir Hill 2WL Loader**
1962-70
- Red body with hook, no grille detail. .. **£20-25**
- Yellow body with Red or Silver hubs.. **£20-25**
1970-78
- Yellow with Red arms with hook,
with or without grille detail ................ **£20-25**
- Orange body, Orange or Black arms.... **£30-40**

**438  Ford D800 Tipper Truck**
(with opening doors)
1970-77
- Metallic Red cab, Yellow tipper,
Yellow or Silver hubs........................... **£55-65**
- Metallic Red cab, Metallic Blue tipper,
Yellow plastic hubs, White interior.. **£100-125**
- Orange cab, Orange or Yellow
tipper, Silver hubs............................. **£125-150**
- Bright Red cab, Orange tipper,
Silver hubs.......................................... **£50-60**

- Bright Red cab and tipper, Silver hubs **£50-60**
- Promotional: White cab, Blue back,
Silver chassis, with cardboard load
'POLCARB'. In plain White box
with folded leaflet ........................... **£200-250**

**439  Ford D800 Snow Plough**
1970-76
- Dark Metallic Blue cab, Orange
tipper, Yellow plough, White hubs... **£100-120**
1976-78
- Dark Metallic Blue cab, Pale Blue
tipper, Yellow plough, Silver hubs... **£125-145**
- Light Metallic Blue cab, Orange tipper,
Dark Yellow plough, Silver hubs......... **£50-70**
- Light Metallic Blue cab,
Pale Blue tipper, Red plough .......... **£100-125**
- Medium Blue cab, Yellow plough,
Powder Blue tipper, Silver hubs ......... **£50-70**
- Medium Blue cab, Yellow plough,
Powder Blue tipper, Lemon hubs......... **£50-60**
- Orange cab and tipper,
Dark Yellow plough, Silver hubs ......... **£50-60**
- Orange cab, Dark Yellow tipper and
plough, Silver hubs .............................. **£50-60**
- All-Orange body, cast Silver hubs ....... **£50-60**

**440  Ford D800 Tipper Truck**
(non-opening doors)
1977-78
- Orange cab, Yellow tipper,
Silver or Black chassis........................ **£35-40**
- Orange cab, Orange tipper ................. **£35-40**
- Orange cab, Light Blue tipper............. **£35-40**
- Red cab, Red Tipper, Silver hubs ........ **£35-40**
- Red cab, Orange Tipper, Silver hubs ... **£35-40**
- Red cab, Light Blue Tipper,
Silver hubs.......................................... **£35-40**
- Red cab, Black roof,
Red tipper and hubs ............................ **£35-40**

**440  Petrol Tanker 'MOBILGAS'**
1954-58  (renumbered in 1954 from 30p)
- Red body and hubs, 'MOBILGAS' in
White letters with Blue borders ....... **£135-150**
1958-61
- Red body and hubs, 'MOBILGAS' in
Blue letters on White background ... **£135-150**

**441  Petrol Tanker 'CASTROL'**
1954-60  (renumbered in 1954 from 30pa)
- Mid-Green body and hubs .............. **£135-150**

**442  Petrol Tanker 'ESSO'**
1954-60  (renumbered in 1954 from 30pb)
- Red body and hubs, Dark Blue decal:
'ESSO MOTOR OIL - PETROL' .... **£135-150**
- As previous model but with
Pale Blue outline decal ................... **£125-150**

**443  Petrol Tanker 'NATIONAL'**
1957-58
- Yellow body and hubs, 'NATIONAL
BENZOLE MIXTURE'................... **£200-250**

**448  Chevrolet El Camino Pick-Up with Trailers**
1963-68
- Turquoise and Ivory with Yellow interior,
Red 'ACME HIRE', spun hubs,
open trailer, Red box trailer ............ **£275-325**

**449  Chevrolet El Camino Pick-up**
1961-69  (All have spun hubs)
- Off-White lower body, Turquoise
upper body and roof, Red interior.... **£100-125**
- Off-White lower body, Turquoise upper
body and roof, Yellow interior......... **£175-225**
- Off-White lower body, Turquoise upper
body and roof, Turquoise interior .... **£175-225**
**NB**  Various shades of Turquoise are
known to exist.
South African issues (all with Red interior):
- All-Turquoise body ................... **£1,000-1,200**

- Cream top, Caramel lower ......... **£1,000-1,200**
- Turquoise top, Cream lower....... **£1,000-1,200**
- All-Cream body...................... **£1,000-1,200**

**449  Johnston Road Sweeper**
1977-79   Later version of model 451 but
with cast-in (non-opening) cab doors.
- Yellow or Lime-Green body ............... **£30-35**
- All Yellow promotional with
'JOHNSTON' stickers, normal box ..... **£40-50**
- All Yellow promotional with
'JOHNSTON' stickers, special box ..... **£70-80**
- Orange or Metallic Red cab,
Metallic Green rear ............................ **£40-50**

**450  Trojan Van 'ESSO'**
1954-57   (renumbered in 1954 from 31a)
- Red body, White stripe,
Red or Maroon hubs, 'Esso' logo .... **£150-175**
- Maroon hub version issued in
U.S.A. trade packs ................................. NGPP

**450  Bedford TK Van 'CASTROL'**
1965-70
- Metallic Green body, 'CASTROL' in
thick lettering, gloss chassis, Red
interior and plastic hubs,
'The Masterpiece In Oils' ............... **£135-155**
- Same, but 'CASTROL' in thin
lettering, and with matt chassis........ **£135-155**

**451  Trojan Van 'DUNLOP'**
1954-57   (renumbered in 1954 from 31b)
- Red body and hubs,
'Dunlop The Worlds Master Tyre' ... **£160-200**

**451  Johnston Road Sweeper**
1971-77
- Orange cab (opening doors),
White interior, Metallic Green tank ..... **£40-50**
- Yellow cab and tank, White interior **£125-150**
- Light Metallic Blue cab, White
interior, Metallic Green tank............**£110-130**
- Metallic Green cab, White interior,
Orange tank .......................................... **£40-50**

**452  Trojan Van 'CHIVERS'**
1954-57   (renumbered in 1954 from 31c)
- Dark Green body, Mid-Green hubs,
'CHIVERS JELLIES' logo .............. **£250-300**

**453  Trojan Van 'OXO'** (not boxed)
1954-54   (renumbered in 1954 from 31c)
- Mid-Blue or Violet-Blue body, Mid-
lue hubs, White 'BEEFY OXO'....... **£300-400**

**454  Trojan Van 'CYDRAX'**
1957-59
- Light Green body and hubs,
'DRINK CYDRAX' logo................. **£160-190**

**455  Trojan Van 'BROOKE BOND TEA'**
1957-60
- Dark Red or Cherry-Red body,
Red hubs ........................................ **£160-190**
- Promotional issue: As previous issue with
white label on roof. The red logo states:
'Since 1924 more than 5,700 Trojan 'Little
Red Vans' supplied. Replaced on a long life
basis'. A similar label is attached to
its (normal) box ................................ **£400-600**

**465  Morris 10 cwt Van 'CAPSTAN'**
1959-59
- Light Blue and Dark Blue body, Mid-
Blue hubs, 'Have A CAPSTAN' ..... **£160-190**

**470  Austin A40 Van 'SHELL-BP'**
- Red and Green body with 'SHELL'
and 'BP' decals................................ **£120-140**

**470  Austin A40 Van 'OMNISPORT'**
1954  Factory drawing exists
but not issued ......................................... NPP

**471  Austin A40 Van 'NESTLES'**
1955-60
- Dark Red body, Yellow hubs ........... **£120-140**
- Dark Red body, Beige hubs ............. **£120-140**

**472  Austin A40 Van 'RALEIGH'**
1956-60
- Dark Green body, Yellow hubs ........ **£120-140**

**480  Bedford CA Van 'KODAK'**
1954-56
- Yellow body, 'Kodak CAMERAS
& FILMS' in Red and Black........... **£120-140**

**481  Bedford CA Van 'OVALTINE'**
1955-60
- Blue body with 'Ovaltine' and
'Ovaltine Biscuits' logo on Cream
panel and sides ................................ **£120-140**

**482  Bedford Van 'DINKY TOYS'**
1956-60
- Orange-Yellow lower body,
Lemon upper body and hubs,
'Dinky Toys' in Red ........................ **£160-180**
- Deep Yellow lower body,
Pale Yellow upper body and hubs.... **£160-180**

**490  Electric Dairy Van 'EXPRESS DAIRY'**
1954-60   (renumbered in 1965 from 30v)
- Cream body, Red chassis,
hubs and logo .................................. **£135-150**
- Light Grey body,
Blue chassis/hubs/logo .................... **£135-150**

**491  Electric Dairy Van 'N.C.B.'**
1954-60   (renumbered in 1954 from 30v)
- Cream body with Red chassis,
hubs and logo, export model........... **£135-150**
- Grey body, Blue chassis,
hubs and logo, export model........... **£135-150**
- Trade Pack of Six ............. **£1,200-1,400**
**491  Electric Dairy Van 'JOB'S DAIRY'**
- 1960  Cream/Red. 1,176 Code-2 models
made for promotional purposes ....... **£200-250**
- Trade pack of six models ........**£800-900**

**492  Loudspeaker Van** (280 casting, Type 3)
1954-57   (renumbered in 1954 from 34c)
- Violet-Blue, Fawn or Green body,
Silver, Mid-Blue or Black hubs,
Silver or Black loudspeakers .......... **£125-150**
- Violet-Blue body ............................ **£175-200**

**492  Election Mini-Van** 'Vote for Somebody'
1964-64
- White body, Red interior, Orange
loudspeakers, figure, microphone and
cable. Yellow 'see-through' box........ **£160-190**

**501  Foden Diesel 8-Wheel Wagon**
1947-48
**1st type cab** with flash, spare wheel,
hook on some, no tank slits in chassis,
no chain-post bosses, Black
'herringbone' tyres, Supertoy.
- Pale Grey cab, Red flash
and hubs, Black chassis, no hook .... **£650-750**
- Dark Blue cab, Mid-Blue back
and hubs, Silver flash,
Black chassis, no hook..................... **£400-500**
- Chocolate Brown cab and back,
Silver flash, Brown hubs,
Black chassis, no hook..................... **£400-500**
- (US only issue)
Red cab and back, Silver flash, Red
hubs, Black chassis, no hook ..... **£2,000-3,000**

- Dark Grey cab and back, Red flash,
chassis and hubs, small unpainted
hook on some ................................. **£400-600**
1948-52
- Hook and tank-slits in chassis
(introduced in 1948), Black 'radial
tread' tyres. Violet-Blue cab/chassis,
Mid-Blue flash, back and hubs,
small unpainted hook ............... **£1,000-1,250**
- Red cab/chassis/hubs, Silver flash,
Fawn back, unpainted hook,
slits on some................................. **£300-400**
1952-54   (renumbered in 1954 to 901)
**2nd cab**, no flash, large painted hook,
Supertoy hubs.
- Violet-Blue cab/chassis, Mid-Blue
back and hubs, Grey tyres............... **£500-700**
- Red cab/chassis, Fawn back,
Red hubs, Grey tyres....................... **£250-350**

**502  Foden Flat Truck**
1947-48
**1st type cab** with flash, spare wheel,
hook on some, no tank slits in chassis,
no chain-post bosses, Black 'herringbone'
tyres, Supertoy.
- Dark Green cab and back, Silver flash,
Black chassis, Dark Green hubs,
no hook  ....................................... **£500-750**
- Mid-Blue cab and back, Dark Blue
flash/chassis/hubs, no hook........ **£1,500-1,750**
1948-52
Hook and tank-slits in chassis introduced
in 1948, Black 'radial' tyres.
- Dark Blue cab/wings/chassis,
Red flash and back, Mid-Blue hubs,
slits on some, small hook ........... **£1,000-1,250**
- Burnt Orange cab/chassis,
Mid-Green flash and back, Green hubs,
slits on some. Dark Blue box
showing 2nd cab model .................. **£500-600**
1952-52
**2nd cab**, no flash, large painted hook,
Supertoy hubs.
- Dark Blue cab/chassis, Red back,
Mid-Blue hubs,
chain-post bosses...................... **£1,000-1,500**
1952-54   (renumbered 902)
- Dull Orange cab/chassis, Mid-Green
back and hubs, chain-post bosses .... **£300-400**
- Red cab/chassis,
Green back and hubs....................... **£300-400**
- Yellow cab/chassis,
Green back/hubs........................... **£900-1,100**

**503  Foden Flat Truck with Tailboard**
1947-48
**1st type cab** with flash, spare wheel,
hook on some, no tank slits in chassis,
no chain-post bosses,
Black 'herringbone' tyres, Supertoy.
- Red cab and flatbed,
Black flash and chassis,
Red hubs, no hook ..................... **£1,200-1,500**
- Pale Grey cab and flatbed,
Dark Blue flash and chassis,
Blue hubs, no hook ................... **£1,000-1,250**
- Mid-Grey cab and flatbed, Mid-
Blue flash, chassis and hubs ... **£1,000-1,250**
1948-52
Hook and tank-slits in chassis
introduced in 1948, Black 'radial' tyres.
- Dark Green cab/chassis,
Mid-Green flash/flatbed/hubs,
small hook .................................. **£1,000-1,500**
- Deep Blue cab/chassis,
Dull Orange flatbed,
Light Blue hubs, hook, slits ...... **£1,000-1,500**
- Violet-Blue cab/chassis,
Orange back and flash,
Mid-Blue hubs, hook, slits......... **£1,000-1,500**
1952-52
**2nd cab**, no flash, large painted hook,
Supertoy hubs.

- Dark Green cab/chassis,
Light Green flatbed and hubs,
Grey tyres, bosses ..................... **£1,500-2,000**
- Dark Green cab/chassis, Orange flatbed,
Mid-Green hubs. 1st type picture
box (blue, lift-off lid) ................ **£1,500-2,000**
1952-56   (renumbered 903)
- Violet-Blue cab/chassis,
Orange flatbed, Mid-Blue hubs,
chain-post bosses............................ **£500-700**
1952-53
- Burnt Orange cab/chassis,
Yellow flatbed and hubs,
Grey tyres, bosses ..................... **£3,000-4,000**
1953-54   (renumbered 903)
- Violet-Blue cab/chassis,
Yellow flatbed, Mid-Blue hubs,
chain-post bosses............................ **£500-700**

**504    Foden 14 ton Tanker**
1948-52
**1st type cab** with flash, spare wheel,
tinplate tank, small hook, no advertising,
Black 'fine radial tread' tyres, Supertoy.
- Dark Blue cab/chassis, Silver flash,
Light Blue tank and hubs ................ **£300-400**
- Violet Blue cab/chassis,
Mid-Blue flash, tank and hubs......... **£300-400**
1948-52
- Red cab/chassis, Silver flash,
Fawn tank, Red hubs........................ **£450-550**
1952-57
**2nd cab**, no flash, large painted hook, Supertoy.
1952-52
- Violet-Blue cab/chassis, Mid-Blue
tank and hubs, Grey tyres.
In 2nd type picture box ............. **£1,500-2,000**
1952-53
- Red cab/chassis, Fawn tank,
Red hubs, Grey tyres........................ **£450-550**

**504    Foden 14 ton Tanker 'MOBILGAS'**
1953-54   (renumbered in 1954 to 941)
- Red cab/chassis/tank/filler caps/hubs,
Grey tyres. With Red 'Pegasus' logo
at cab end of tank facing the cab ..... **£400-500**
- Same, but with Red 'Pegasus'
logo at rear of tank facing
away from cab........................... **£1,500-2,000**

**505    Foden Flat Truck with Chains**
1952-52
**1st type cab** with flash, spare wheel,
large hook, slits in chassis, 'dimpled' post
bosses, Black 'fine radial tread' tyres,
Supertoy. Blue covered box
showing 1st type cab.
- Dark Green cab/chassis/flatbed,
Mid-Green flash and hubs ......... **£3,500-4,500**
- Maroon cab/chassis, Silver flash,
Maroon flatbed and hubs ......... **£7,500-10,000**
1952-54
**2nd cab**, no flash, large painted hook,
Supertoys hubs. Early Blue box with
Orange/White label.
- Dark Green cab/chassis/flatbed,
Mid-Green hubs,
'dimpled' chain-post bosses............. **£300-400**
- Maroon cab/chassis/flatbed/hubs,
'dimpled' chain-post bosses............. **£500-600**
1954-56   (renumbered in 1954 to 905)
- Green cab/chassis/body,
Mid-Green hubs, 'rounded' bosses,
Blue/White box ............................... **£250-350**
- Maroon cab/chassis/body/hubs,
'rounded' bosses, Blue/White box ... **£250-350**

**511    Guy 4 ton Lorry**
1947-48
**1st type cab** casting, Supertoy, spare wheel,
small unpainted hook.
- Green cab, back and hubs,
Black chassis and wings ................. **£350-450**

- Brown cab, back and hubs,
Black chassis and wings ................. **£350-450**
- Fawn cab and back, Red chassis,
wings and hubs............................... **£350-450**
- Maroon cab and back,
Black chassis and wings ................. **£350-450**
- Grey cab, back and hubs,
Red chassis and wings .................... **£350-450**
1948-52
**1st type cab** casting, Supertoy,
large painted or unpainted hook.
- Red cab/chassis/wings/ 'ridged' hubs,
Fawn back ....................................... **£300-350**
- Violet-Blue cab/chassis/wings,
Mid-Blue back and 'ridged' hubs .... **£300-350**
1952-54   (renumbered in 1954 to 911)
- Red cab/chassis/wings/'grooved'
hubs, Fawn back.............................. **£300-350**
- Violet-Blue cab/chassis/wings,
Mid-Blue back and 'grooved' hubs . **£300-350**
1954    **2nd type cab** casting.
- Violet-Blue cab and chassis,
Mid-Blue back and hubs ................. **£300-350**

**512    Guy Flat Truck**
1947-48  **1st type cab** casting, Supertoy,
spare wheel, small unpainted hook.
- Maroon cab, flatbed and hubs,
Black chassis and wings ................. **£400-600**
- Dark Brown cab, Mid-Green flatbed
and hubs, Black chassis and wings .. **£400-600**
- Yellow cab and flatbed, Black
chassis and wings, Red hubs........... **£600-800**
- Khaki cab and flatbed, Black
chassis and wings, Green hubs ........ **£400-600**
- Grey cab and flatbed, Red chassis
and wings, Red hubs ....................... **£400-600**
- Grey cab and flatbed, Black
chassis, Black hubs......................... **£400-600**
- Red cab and flatbed, Black
chassis, Black hubs ........................ **£400-600**
1948-48
- Brown cab/chassis/wings, Green
flatbed, Mid-Green 'ridged' hubs .... **£400-600**
1948-54   (renumbered in 1954 to 912)
**1st type cab** casting, Supertoy,
small or large unpainted hook.
- Dark Blue cab/chassis/wings, Red
flatbed, Mid-Blue 'ridged' hubs....... **£300-350**
1949-54
- Orange cab/chassis/wings, Green
flatbed, Green 'ridged' hubs ........... **£300-400**
1952-54
- Dark Blue cab/chassis/wings, Red
flatbed, Mid-Blue 'grooved' hubs.... **£300-350**
1954  **2nd type cab** casting.
- Red cab and chassis,
Mid-Blue back and hubs ................. **£300-350**
- Mid-Blue cab / chassis / hubs,
Red back ........................................ **£300-350**

**513    Guy Flat Truck with Tailboard**
1947-48
**1st type cab** casting, Supertoy,
spare wheel, small unpainted hook.
- Green cab and flatbed,
Black chassis, wings and hubs........ **£200-250**
- Dark Yellow cab and flatbed,
Black chassis, wings and hubs........ **£300-400**
- Dark Yellow cab and flatbed,
Dark Blue chassis, wings and hubs.. **£300-400**
- Grey cab and flatbed,
Black chassis, wings and hubs........ **£300-400**
- Grey cab and flatbed,
Dark Blue chassis, wings and hubs.. **£500-750**
1948-52
**1st type cab**, 'ridged' hubs, Supertoy,
small or large unpainted hook.
- Dark Green cab/chassis/wings, Mid-
Green back and hubs, small hook .... **£200-250**

- Violet-Blue cab/chassis/wings,
Orange back, Mid-Blue hubs,
large hook...................................... **£200-250**
1952-54   (renumbered in 1954 to 913)
**1st type cab**, Supertoy, 'grooved' hubs,
large unpainted hook.
- Dark Green cab/chassis/wings,
Mid-Green body and hubs .............. **£250-350**
- Deep Blue cab/chassis/wings,
Orange body, Mid-Blue hubs .......... **£200-250**
- Yellow cab/chassis/wings,
Green hubs ..................................... **£750-950**
1954
- **2nd type cab**.Violet-Blue cab and chassis,
Orange back, Mid-Blue hubs........... **£200-250**

**514    Guy Vans**

**514**    1950-52
**Guy Van 'SLUMBERLAND'**
- Red **1st type cab**/chassis/body/'ridged'
hubs. 'Slumberland Spring Interior
Mattresses', spare wheel, Supertoy.. **£300-400**
**514**    1952-52
- **Guy Van 'LYONS'**
Dark Blue **1st type cab**/body, Mid-Blue
'ridged' hubs, 'Lyons Swiss Rolls',
spare wheel, Supertoy .................... **£700-900**
- Same model but rear axle in
cast mounts.................................... **£700-900**
**514**    1952-52
- **Guy Van 'WEETABIX'**
Yellow **1st type cab**/body, Yellow 'ridged'
hubs, 'More Than a Breakfast Food',
spare wheel, Supertoy ............... **£2,000-3,000**
1952-54
- As previous model but with
Yellow 'grooved' hubs .............. **£2,000-3,000**
**514**    1953-54
- **Guy Van 'SPRATTS'**
(renumbered 917 in 1954)
Red/Cream **1st type cab**/body,
Red 'grooved' hubs, 'Bonio Ovals &
Dog Cakes', spare wheel, Supertoy . **£300-400**

**521    Bedford Articulated Lorry**
1948-48
- Red body, Black wings, Black or
Red hubs, '20' transfer, 'Supertoys'
on base, Brown box ........................ **£250-350**
1949-50
- Yellow body, Black wings, Black hubs,
'20' transfer, 'Supertoys' on base.
Brown box with Red/White label .... **£250-350**
1950-54   (renumbered in 1954 to 921)
- Yellow or Yellowish-Orange body,
Black wings, Red hubs, '20' transfer,
'Supertoys' or 'Dinky Toys' on base.
Blue box, Orange or White label ..... **£150-200**

**522    Big Bedford Lorry**
(renumbered in 1954 to 922)
1952-54
- Maroon cab, Fawn truck body,
Fawn hubs, Supertoy....................... **£130-160**
Dark Blue cab, Yellow truck body,
Yellow hubs, Supertoy .................... **£175-200**

**531    Leyland Comet Lorry with Stake Body**
1949-54   (renumbered in 1954 to 931)
- Red cab and chassis, Yellow back
and hubs, Blue box.......................... **£350-400**
- Dark Blue cab and chassis, Brown
back, Red or Blue hubs, Blue box ... **£350-400**
- Violet-Blue cab and chassis, Red hubs,
Orange-Yellow back, Blue box........ **£150-200**
- Yellow cab and chassis, Pale Green
back, Mid-Green hubs, Grey tyres... **£300-400**

**NB** Odd colours: Be wary of colour combinations not listed. The screw fitting makes it easy to interchange the chassis and body components.

**532 Leyland Comet Lorry with Hinged Tailboard**
1952-54 (renumbered in 1954 to 932)
- Dark Green cab and chassis, Orange back, Cream hubs, Blue box ............ **£200-250**
- Dark Green cab and chassis, Orange back, Green hubs, Blue box ............ **£150-175**
- Mid-Green cab and chassis, Cherry-Red back, Cream hubs, Blue box ............ **£200-250**
- Dark Blue cab and chassis, Mid-Blue back, Cream hubs, Blue box ............ **£350-400**
- Dark Blue cab and chassis, Mid-Blue back, Red hubs, Blue/White box ..... **£150-175**

**NB** Odd colours: Be wary of colour combinations not listed. The screw fitting makes it easy to interchange the chassis and body components.

**533 Leyland Comet Cement Wagon**
1953-54 (renumbered in 1954 to 933)
- Yellow body and hubs, 'PORTLAND BLUE-CIRCLE CEMENT', Supertoy ........................................ **£175-200**

**551 Trailer** (renumbered in 1954 to 951)
1948-54
- Grey body, Black hubs, hook, Supertoy ........................................ **£30-40**
- Yellow body, Black hubs, hook, Supertoy ........................................ **£90-110**
- Green body, Black hubs, hook, Supertoy ........................................ **£90-110**

1969-73
- Gift Set issue: Red body, Grey front chassis, protruding chromed hubs. Only in Set 399 ........................................ GSP

**561 Blaw Knox Bulldozer**
1949-54 (renumbered in 1954 to 961)
- Red body, Green or Black rubber tracks, driver, lifting blade, Supertoy. Blue box with Orange/White label, or 'natural' card box with Red/White label, 1 packing piece ................................ **£125-150**

**561 Citroën Delivery Van**
1962-64
- Light Blue body, Red/Yellow 'CIBIE' logo, sliding door. French issue ........... **£60-70**

**562 Muir Hill Dump Truck**
1948-54 (renumbered in 1954 to 962)
- Yellow, metal wheels/tyres, hook ........ **£15-20**

**563 Blaw Knox Heavy Tractor**
1948-54 (renumbered in 1954 to 963)
- Red, Orange or Blue 561 without the dozer blade. Buff cardboard box has Red/White label, 1 packing piece ........ **£70-90**
- Dark Blue body, Mid-Blue rollers, Green rubber tracks, Beige driver. Buff box with Red/White picture label .... **£200-250**

**564 Elevator Loader**
1952-54. Renumbered 964 – see that entry for details.

**571 Coles Mobile Crane**
1949-54 (renumbered in 1954 to 971)
- Yellow and Black, operable crane, 1 driver, Supertoy, 3 packing pieces + instructions ............ **£30-40**

**579 Simca Glazier's Lorry**
1961-63
- Yellow and Green body, mirror/glass load, 'MIROITIER'. French-made model for issue in the UK ................... **£90-110**

**581 Horsebox 'BRITISH RAILWAYS'**
1953-54 (renumbered in 1954 to 981)
- Maroon body (aluminium), 2 PP ....... **£80-100**

**581 Horsebox 'EXPRESS HORSE VAN'**
1953-54 (renumbered in 1954 to 980)
- US issue: Maroon, 'Hire Service'. Blue box has Orange/White labels with picture of US model, 2 PP ....... **£500-700**

**581 Berliet Flat Truck**
1962-64
- Red and Grey body, 6 wheels plus a spare, hook. French issue ................. **£70-80**

**NB** The French issues listed above have been included because they were sold in the U.K.

**582 Pullmore Car Transporter**
1953-54 (renumbered in 1954 to 982)
Bedford cab/chassis, aluminium trailer with 'DINKY TOYS DELIVERY SERVICE' logo on sides. Same logo on rear ramp plus '20' sign. No window glazing, 'DINKY TOYS' on baseplate, Black grille/bumper, Silver trim.

1953-53
- Light Blue cab, trailer and hubs, Fawn decks, six lower deck retaining rivets. Model only issued for a very short period ............................. **£400-600**

1953-54
- As previous model but decks may be Fawn or Grey. Four lower deck retaining rivets ....... **£110-140**

1954-54
- Dark Blue cab, trailer and hubs, Fawn decks, four lower deck retaining rivets. Model supplied in 582/982 all Dark Blue box with White end label ........ **£500-750**
- In 582/982 Blue/White striped box.. **£200-300**

**591 A.E.C. Tanker 'SHELL CHEMICALS LIMITED'**
1952-54 (renumbered in 1954 to 991)
- Red/Yellow, Supertoy...................... **£140-175**

**620 6-wheel Covered Wagon**
1950-54 (renumbered in 1950 from 151b)
- Matt-Green or Greenish-Brown body, 'Export only' (to USA) ...................... **£60-70**

**752 Goods Yard Crane**
1953-54 (renumbered in 1954 to 973)
- Yellow operable crane on mid- or Dark Blue base (steps in some). Dark Blue box ... **£50-75**

**893 Unic Pipe Line Transporter**
1962-64
- Beige articulated body, spare wheel, 6 pipes. Made in France for issue in the UK.... **£90-110**

**894 Unic Boilot Car Transporter**
1962-64
- Grey body, 'Dinky Toys Service Livraison'. Made in France for issue in the UK. **£100-120**

**901 Foden 8-wheel Diesel Wagon**
1954-57 (renumbered in 1954 from 501)
**2nd type cab**, Supertoy with spare wheel and large hook.
- Red cab/chassis/hubs, Fawn truck body ............................. **£300-350**
- Red cab/chassis/hubs, Grey truck body ............................. **£300-350**
- Violet-Blue cab and chassis, Mid-Blue truck body and hubs ........ **£700-850**
- Dark Green cab and chassis, Light Green truck body and hubs. 'LF' sticker on Blue/White striped box lid, '1956' stamped inside bottom of box.... **£5,000-7,500**

**902 Foden Flat Truck**
1954-56 (renumbered in 1954 from 502)
**2nd type cab**, Supertoy with spare wheel and large hook.
- Yellow cab and chassis, Mid-Green flatbed body, Green hubs ........... **£1,250-1,500**

1954-57
- Burnt-Orange cab and chassis, Mid-Green flatbed body and hubs ... **£300-400**

1957-59
- Dark Red cab and chassis, Green flatbed, Green hubs (**NB** Red similar to colour of 919 Guy 'GOLDEN SHRED' van)........... **£1,000-1,500**
- Cherry-Red cab, wings and chassis, Green flatbed body and hubs ........... **£500-600**
- Orange cab and chassis, Fawn flatbed body, Mid-Green hubs...................... **£300-400**

**903 Foden Flat Truck with Tailboard**
1954-55 (renumbered in 1954 from 503)
**2nd type cab**, Supertoy with spare wheel and large hook.
- Violet-Blue cab and chassis, Yellow flatbed, Mid-Blue hubs........ **£350-450**
- Orange cab, chassis and flatbed, Green hubs with Grey tyres ....... **£1,250-1,500**
- Yellow cab, chassis and flatbed, Mid-Green hubs. In box with correct colour spot...................... **£2,000-2,500**

1954-57
- Violet-Blue cab and chassis, Orange flatbed, Mid-Blue hubs ....... **£300-350**

1957-60
- Mid-Blue cab and chassis, Fawn flatbed, Mid-Blue hubs, rivetted spare wheel ...................... **£800-1,000**

**905 Foden Flat Truck with Chains**
1954-64 (renumbered in 1954 from 505)
**2nd type cab**, Supertoy with spare wheel and large hook.

1954-57
- Maroon cab, chassis, flatbed and hubs, 'rounded' chain-post bosses ... **£300-350**

1954-58
- Dark Green cab/chassis/flatbed, Mid-Green hubs, 'rounded' chain-post bosses ............ **£300-350**

1956-57
- Maroon cab/chassis/flatbed, Red hubs, 'rounded' chain-post bosses ... **£350-450**

1957-64
- Red cab and chassis, Grey flatbed, Red metal hubs, 'rounded' bosses.... **£300-350**

19??-64
- Red cab and chassis, Grey flatbed, Red plastic hubs .............................. **£400-500**

**NB** A version of 905 with Light Blue cab/chassis and hubs, and Grey flatbed sold for **$3,700** on eBay in 2004.

**908 Mighty Antar and Transformer**
1962-66
- Yellow tractor unit, Light Grey trailer, Red ramp and hubs, transformer, 3 packing pieces .............................. **£500-600**

**911 Guy 4 ton Lorry**
1954-56 (was 511, renumbered in 1956 to 431)
**2nd type cab** casting, Supertoy, 'grooved' hubs, large hook.
- Red cab/chassis/hubs, Fawn back .... **£250-350**
- Violet-Blue cab and chassis, Mid-Blue back and hubs ................. **£200-250**
- Mid-Blue cab/chassis/back and hubs. (Factory trial model)......... **£1,250-1,500**

**912 Guy Flat Truck**
1954-56 (was 512, renumbered in 1956 to 432)
**2nd type cab** casting, Supertoy, 'grooved' hubs, large hook.
- Orange cab and chassis, Green flatbed body and hubs .......... **£400-500**

- Mid-Blue cab and chassis,
  Red flatbed body, Mid-Blue hubs .... **£400-500**
- Dark Green cab and chassis,
  Light Green flatbed body and hubs . **£400-500**

**913  Guy Flat Truck with Tailboard**
1954-56  (was 513, renumbered in 1956 to 433)
**2nd type cab** casting, Supertoy,
'grooved' hubs, large hook.
- (1954 only) Yellow cab and
  chassis, Green body, Green hubs ..... **£750-950**
  1954-56
- Dark Green cab and chassis,
  Mid-Green flatbed body and hubs. .. **£250-300**
- Violet-Blue cab and chassis, Orange
  flatbed body, Light Blue hubs.
  Usually in Blue/White striped box
  with picture of Green lorry ............. **£200-250**
- Deep Blue/Orange model in box
  with correct colours.......................... **£750-950**

**914  A.E.C. Articulated Lorry**
1965-70
- Red cab ('CIA 7392' on doors),
  White interior, Light Grey trailer,
  Red plastic hubs, Green
  tilt 'BRITISH ROAD SERVICES' .. **£140-160**
- With chromed domed hubs,
  pictorial box .................................... **£200-250**

**915  A.E.C. with Flat Trailer**
1973-74
- Orange cab, White trailer,
  'Truck Hire Co Liverpool' .................. **£55-65**
- Orange cab, White trailer,
  'Thames Board Paper Mills',
  bubble-packed. Truck carries load
  of four Brown card tubes with
  'UNILINER' logos in Black ...... **£2,000-2,500**
- Bright Metallic Blue cab,
  White interior, Orange chassis,
  Yellow trailer............................... **£140-160**

**917  Guy Van 'SPRATTS'**
1954-56  (renumbered in 1954 from 514)
- Red **2nd type cab**, chassis and Supertoy
  hubs, Cream/Red van body with
  'Bonio Ovals & Dog Cakes' ............ **£400-500**

**917  Mercedes Truck and Trailer**
1968-74
- Blue cab/chassis (White roof),
  Yellow trailers, White tilts,
  pictorial stand and tray......................**£85-115**
- Blue cab/chassis (White roof),
  Yellow trailers, Yellow tilts,
  pictorial stand and tray......................**£85-115**
- Dark Blue cab/chassis,
  Yellow trailers, Dark Blue tilts,
  pictorial stand and tray................... **£300-350**
- 'MUNSTERLAND' promotional.
  Dark Green cab and trailers, White tilts,
  Green logo, pictorial stand and tray. **£350-450**
- 'HENRY JOHNSON' promotional.
  Dark Green body, White tilts,
  plain White box ............................... **£350-450**

**918  Guy Van 'EVER READY'**
1955-58
- Blue **1st type cab** with small square
  sides to front number plate.............. **£400-500**
- Blue **2nd type cab**/body, Red
  'grooved' hubs, 'Ever Ready Batteries
  For Life', spare wheel, Supertoy ...... **£300-400**

**919  Guy Van 'GOLDEN SHRED'**
1957-58
- All Red **2nd type cab** and body,
  Yellow Supertoy hubs,
  'Robertsons Golden Shred'
  and 'golly' design, spare wheel........ **£700-900**

**920  Guy Warrior Van 'HEINZ'**
1960-61
- Red cab and chassis, window glazing,
  Yellow van body and Supertoy hubs,
  spare wheel, 'HEINZ 57 VARIETIES'
  and 'Tomato Ketchup' bottle design.
**NB** The correct box for this model has
  Blue/White stripes but no model
  illustrations (see Box Type 1D (v) on
  'Commercial Vehicles
  Box Types' page)...................... **£2,500-3,500**

**921  Bedford Articulated Vehicle**
1954-56  (was 521, renumbered in 1956 to 409)
- Yellowish-Orange body, Black wings,
  Red hubs, Supertoy ........................ **£120-140**

**922  Big Bedford Lorry**
1954-56  (was 522, renumbered in 1956 to 408)
- Maroon cab, Fawn back,
  Fawn hubs, Supertoy.....................**£110-130**
- Dark Blue cab,
  Yellow back and hubs ..................... **£200-250**

**923  Big Bedford Van 'HEINZ'**
1955-58
- Red cab and chassis, Yellow back
  and hubs, 'HEINZ 57 VARIETIES'
  plus '**Baked Beans can**' picture.
  Supertoy in Blue/White striped box
  with correct model picture .............. **£350-450**
  1958-59
- As previous model but with
  '**Tomato Ketchup bottle**' advertising.
  Supertoy in Blue/White striped box
  with correct model picture ........ **£2,500-3,500**

**924  Aveling Barford 'CENTAUR'**
1972-76
- Red/Yellow body, tipping dump truck . **£30-40**

**925  Leyland Dump Truck**
1965-69
- 8-wheeled Supertoy with 'SAND
  BALLAST GRAVEL' on tailgate.
  White (tilting) cab and chassis, Blue
  cab roof, Orange diecast
  tipper, Mid-Blue plastic hubs.......... **£175-200**
- As previous model but with tinplate
  tipper in Orange, Pale Grey or Red . **£175-200**

**930  Bedford Pallet-Jekta Van**
1960-64
- Orange and Yellow body, 'Dinky Toys'
  and 'Meccano', 3 pallets,
  1 packing piece, Supertoy ............... **£350-450**

**931  Leyland Comet Lorry with Stake Body**
1954-56  (was 531, renumbered in 1956 to 417)
- Violet-Blue cab and chassis, Orange-
  Yellow back, Red hubs, Supertoy .... **£175-225**

**932  Leyland Comet with Hinged Tailboard**
1954-56  (was 532, renumbered in 1956 to 418)
- Dark Green cab and chassis,
  Orange back, Mid-Green hubs......... **£130-160**
- Dark Green cab and chassis,
  Red back, Cream hubs .................... **£130-160**
- Dark Blue cab and chassis,
  Mid-Blue back and hubs ................. **£130-160**
- Dark Blue cab, chassis and
  truck body, Red hubs....................... **£130-160**
- Dark Blue cab and chassis, Light
  (Powder) Blue back, Cream hubs .... **£250-350**
- Red cab and chassis,
  Mid-Blue back and hubs ................. **£500-750**
**NB** Odd colours: Be wary of colour
  combinations not listed. The screw fitting
  makes it easy to interchange the chassis
  and body components.

**933  Leyland Comet Cement Wagon**
1954-56  (was 533, renumbered in 1956 to 419)
- Yellow body and hubs, 'Portland
  Blue-Circle Cement', Supertoy........**£110-130**

**934  Leyland Octopus Wagon**
1956-58
- Yellow cab and chassis, Green truck
  body secured to chassis by a screw,
  Green band around cab (but without
  Yellow band above radiator), Red
  diecast Supertoy hubs, 1 PP............. **£150-175**
  1958-59
- As previous model but with Green
  diecast hubs. Body held by rivet...... **£150-175**
  1958-63
- As previous model but with Yellow
  band immediately above radiator, Red
  diecast hubs, body held by rivet ...... **£250-300**
  1963-64
- Dark Blue cab/chassis, Pale Yellow
  cab band and rivetted back, Red
  diecast hubs. In picture box ....... **£2,500-3,500**
- Dark Blue cab/chassis, Pale Yellow
  cab band and rivetted back, Grey
  plastic hubs. In picture box........ **£2,500-3,500**
  1964-64
- Dark Blue cab/chassis, Pale Yellow
  cab band and rivetted back, Red
  plastic hubs. In picture box........ **£2,500-3,500**

**935  Leyland Octopus Flat Truck with Chains**
1964-66
  6 chain-posts, 8 wheels, flatbed held
  by rivet, Supertoy, 1 packing piece,
  picture box.
- Mid-Green cab/chassis,
  Pale Grey cab band and flatbed,
  Red plastic hubs ......................... **£1,500-1,750**
- Mid-Green cab/chassis,
  Pale Grey cab band and flatbed,
  Grey plastic hubs........................ **£1,500-1,750**
- Blue cab/chassis, Yellow cab flash,
  Pale Grey flatbed and hubs ........ **£4,000-5,000**

**936  Leyland 8-wheel Chassis**
1964-69
- Red/Silver, 'Another Leyland on Test',
  three '5-ton' weights ...................... **£120-140**

**940  Mercedes-Benz LP.1920 Truck**
1977-80
- White cab, Pale Grey cover,
  Red chassis, hubs and interior............. **£35-45**
- Same, but Black interior, White hubs .. **£40-50**
- 'HALB UND HALB' Promotional
  with 'MAMPE' & 'BOSCH' on
  Blue cab, Elephant design................ **£300-400**
- 'FISON'S' Promotional. White body,
  Red interior, chassis and hubs, Grey
  plastic cover, 'FISON'S THE GARDEN
  PEOPLE' labels, 2 peat samples....... **£300-400**
- 'HENRY JOHNSON' Promotional.
  Green body, White cover ................. **£400-500**

**941  Foden 14 ton Tanker 'MOBILGAS'**
1956-56  (renumbered in 1956 from 504)
- 2nd type cab. Red body and hubs,
  Black filler caps, Black tyres,
  Supertoy ...................................... **£450-550**

**942  Foden 14 ton Tanker 'REGENT'**
1955-57
- 2nd type cab. Dark Blue cab/chassis,
  Red/White/Blue tank, Black tyres,
  Supertoy ...................................... **£400-500**

**943  Leyland Octopus Tanker 'ESSO'**
1958-64
- Dark Red body and diecast hubs, Red
  tinplate tank with waterslide transfers,
  'ESSO PETROLEUM', spare wheel,
  hook, Supertoy, 1 packing piece ...... **£300-400**

- As before but Red plastic hubs ........ **£300-400**
- With Red plastic hubs,
  logos on self-adhesive labels .......... **£350-450**
**944 Leyland Octopus Tanker 'SHELL-BP'**
1963-70
- White/Yellow cab and body,
  Grey chassis and plastic hubs .......... **£225-275**
- White/Yellow cab and body,
  Grey chassis, Black plastic hubs...... **£300-400**
- White/Yellow cab and body,
  Grey chassis, Red plastic hubs........ **£300-400**
- White/Yellow cab and body, White
  chassis, Grey or Black plastic hubs . **£225-275**
- <u>Export issue</u>: Yellow cab, White
  chassis, White plastic tank, Red plastic
  hubs. 'See-through' export box..............NGPP
**NB** Each issue has 'SHELL' and 'BP' sticky
  labels on the front half of the plastic tank.

**944 Leyland Octopus Tanker
'CORN PRODUCTS'**
1963-64
Only 500 of these promotionals issued.
- White body and plastic tank,
  'Sweeteners For Industry' in White on
  Black labels. In 944 'ESSO' box with
  'CORN PRODUCTS' sticker,
  wrapped in Green/Grey
  striped gift paper ..................... **£7,500-10,000**

**945 A.E.C. Fuel Tanker 'ESSO'**
1966-75
- White cab/chassis, White tank, 'ESSO
  PETROLUEUM', 'Tiger in Your Tank'
  logo on rear, 1 packing piece ..............**£90-110**
1975-77
- As previous model but without logo at
  rear, card boxed or bubble-packed....... **£75-95**
- Metallic Blue cab, White tank,
  Black filler caps ............................... **£100-125**

**945 A.E.C. Tanker 'LUCAS OIL'**
1977-77 <u>Promotional</u>.
- Green cab and tank, White design
  on labels, bubble-packed................. **£100-125**

**948 Tractor-Trailer 'McLEAN'**
1961-67
- (i): Red cab, Light Grey trailer, Red
  plastic hubs, Supertoy, 2 PP............. **£200-250**
- (ii): As previous model but with
  Black plastic hubs ........................... **£200-250**
19?? **'ROADWAY DOVER'**
- (iii): As model (i) but with extra graphics
  on the front of the trailer and on the rear of
  the cab: 'Roadway Dover Del Express Inc.'.
  Black plastic hubs ........................... **£300-500**
1964 ? **'BROWN SHOE Co.'**
- (iv): As 'McLean' model but with
  'Brown Shoe Co.' adhesive labels.
  US Promotional (75 only made)............NGPP
**NB** The trailer moulding is light-sensitive
  and varies in shade from Pale Grey to
  Light Grey with a Greenish tinge, through
  to very Pale Brown. The 'McLean'
  logo can be Red or Light Orange.

**950 Foden S20 Tanker 'BURMAH'**
1978-79
- Red cab, Red/White trailer, Black or
  Grey hatches, Red or Cream hubs ....... **£50-75**

**950 Foden Tanker 'SHELL'**
1978-78
- Red cab, Red/White trailer,
  Cream hubs ........................................ **£75-100**

**951 Trailer**
1954-56 (was 551, renumbered in 1956 to 428)
- Grey body with hook, Red hubs .......... **£30-40**
- Dark Grey body, hook, Lemon hubs.... **£50-75**
**958 Guy Warrior Snow Plough**
1961-66
- Yellow/Black body and plough blade,
  spare wheel, 1 PP, Supertoy............ **£145-165**
- Yellow/Black body, Silver blade...... **£200-250**
- Silver blade version in box with
  picture showing Silver blade........... **£250-300**

**959 Foden Dump Truck & Bulldozer**
1961-68
- Red or Deep Red body,
  Silver chassis and blade,
  Red hubs (plastic front; metal rear) . **£350-500**
- Same, but with Pale Yellow plastic
  front hubs, Yellow metal rear hubs .. **£150-175**
- All-Red body version ...................... **£150-175**

**960 Albion Lorry Concrete Mixer**
1960-68
- Orange body, Blue rotating drum with
  two Yellow triangles, Black plastic
  hubs, Grey tyres. Supertoy.............. **£125-150**
- Orange body, Grey drum, Black
  plastic hubs, Grey tyres. Supertoy ... **£150-200**

**961 Blaw-Knox Bulldozer**
1954-62 (renumbered in 1954 from 561)
- Red or Yellow body, rubber tracks,
  Tan driver, Supertoy............................ **£45-55**
1962-64
- Blue body, rubber tracks, Tan driver.... **£45-55**
1963-64
- Red or Yellow body, rubber tracks,
  Blue driver............................................ **£45-55**
1964-64
- Orange plastic body with Silver engine
  detail, Black diecast lifting gear,
  Green plastic blade and exhaust pipe,
  Blue driver, Light Green or
  Olive-Green roller wheels................ **£400-600**

**962 Muir Hill Dumper**
1954-66 (renumbered in 1954 from 562)
- Yellow body, hook, Supertoy, 1 PP...... **£15-20**

**963 Blaw Knox Heavy Tractor**
1954-58 (renumbered in 1954 from 563)
- Red or Orange body, Green or Black
  tracks. Blue/White striped box, 1 PP ... **£50-60**
1958-59
- Yellow body, Green or Black tracks.
  Blue/White striped box, 1 PP.............. **£60-75**

**963 Road Grader**
1973-75
- Yellow/Red articulated body,
  Silver blade, Red lower arm ............. **£20-30**
- White or Yellow lower arm................. **£30-40**

**964 Elevator Loader**
1954-68 (renumbered in 1954 from 564)
- Yellow with Mid-Blue or Dark Blue
  chutes, Blue or Yellow hubs, 1 PP....... **£45-55**
  <u>Boxes</u>: Early Blue boxes were replaced
  by Blue/White boxes, then by Yellow
  'Supertoys' boxes.
- <u>Late issue</u>:
  Mid-Blue with Yellow chutes, as
  shown on late picture box design..... **£100-150**

**965 'EUCLID' Dump Truck**
1955-61
- Pale Yellow body ('EUCLID' cast under
  cab), Yellow hubs, no windows,
  'STONE - ORE - EARTH',
  operable tipper, 1 packing piece ...... **£150-175**
**NB** 1955-56 Grey backed logo;
      1959-61 Red backed logo.
1961-69

- Same model but with glazing.......... **£150-175**
- Pale Yellow body, Red or
  Dark Green hubs, window glazing.
  In detailed picture box ................... **£200-250**
**965 'TEREX' Rear Dump Truck**
1969-70
- Yellow body and hubs, 'TEREX' in red
  on doors, 'EUCLID' cast under cab.
  In 'EUCLID' picture box, one PP... **£300-350**
- Same model but 'TEREX' cast
  under cab. 'TEREX' picture box ..... **£200-250**

**966 Marrel Multi-Bucket Unit**
1960-64
- Pale Yellow body, Grey skip and tyres,
  Black hubs, Supertoy, one PP .......... **£140-160**

**967 BBC TV Control Room**
1959-64
- Dark Green, 'BBC Television Service',
  Supertoy, drawing on box lid, 1 PP . **£125-150**

**967 Muir-Hill Loader/Trencher**
1973-78
- Yellow/Red body, with driver ............. **£25-35**
- Orange/Black body, with driver.......... **£25-35**

**968 BBC TV Roving-Eye Vehicle**
1959-64
- Dark Green body, BBC crest, camera,
  Supertoy, drawing on box lid, 1 PP . **£125-150**

**969 BBC TV Extending Mast**
1959-64
- Dark Green body, BBC crest,
  dish aerial, mast, Supertoy, drawing
  on box lid, 2 packing pieces ........... **£125-150**

**970 Jones Fleetmaster Crane**
1967-71
- (Bedford TK) Red cab, White roof,
  Red interior, Red plastic hubs,
  White jib, two packing pieces........... **£80-100**
1971-77
- Metallic Red cab, White interior and
  jib, chrome domed hubs, two PP ....... **£80-100**
1971-77
- Pale Yellow cab, White interior and
  jib, chrome domed hubs, two PP ....... **£80-100**

**971 Coles Mobile Crane**
1954-62 (renumbered in 1954 from 571)
- Yellow and Black, operable crane,
  one driver, Supertoy ........................... **£30-40**

**972 Coles 20 ton Lorry-Mounted Crane**
1955-62
- Yellow/Orange (no 'Long Vehicle' signs),
  two drivers, Supertoy, one PP ............. **£40-50**
1962-69
- Yellow/Orange (with 'Long Vehicle'
  signs), two drivers, Supertoy .............. **£40-50**
1967-69
- Yellow/Black, Blue metal driver in lorry
  cab only, Yellow plastic hubs, Black tyres,
  Black/White diagonal stripes around jib,
  Yellow 'COLES CRANE' at rear ... **£100-150**
- Variation with Black hubs.
  (In end-flap box) ............................. **£100-150**
- Regular issue model in <u>promotional</u>
  'Coles Crane' box given away at the 16th
  Commercial Motor Show. Box has three
  labels on lid for '16th International
  Commercial Motor Transport Exhibition',
  'Commercial Motor Show at Earls Court
  London September 26 - October 4' and
  'See our Exhibit, Stand No. 137
  Avenue U 1st Floor',
  blue striped box................................ **£400-500**

**973 Goods Yard Crane**
1954-59  (renumbered in 1954 from 752)
- Yellow operable crane on Blue base.
Blue/White striped box, one PP .......... **£30-40**

**973 Eaton 'YALE' Tractor Shovel**
1971-75
- Red/Yellow body with Yellow or
Silver bucket exterior, cast hubs .......... **£20-30**
- Yellow/Red body, Silver wheels,
no engine covers, cast hubs ................ **£25-35**
- All Yellow body, Blue wheels,
engine covers, cast hubs ...................... **£25-35**
- Factory special:
Window in cab roof, yellow plastic
hubs, 'Trojan 6000' tampo prints,
'Eaton' underneath. This unique model
was presented to the man
who designed the actual vehicle. .......... NGPP

**974 A.E.C. Hoynor Car Transporter**
1968-75
- Bright Metallic Blue cab, White interior,
Pale Orange/Dark Orange back,
Grey plastic hubs, three PP ................ **£90-110**
- Dark Metallic Blue cab,
Pale Orange/Dark Orange back,
Grey plastic hubs, three PP ................ **£90-110**
- Dark Metallic Blue cab,
Yellow and Bright Orange back,
chrome domed hubs, three PP ............ **£90-110**

**975 'RUSTON-BUCYRUS' Excavator**
1963-67
- Pale Yellow plastic body, Red jib and
bucket, Black rubber tracks,
with instructions .............................. **£300-350**

**976 'MICHIGAN' Tractor Dozer**
1968-76
- Yellow/Red body, driver, engine covers,
Red hubs, one packing piece .............. **£30-35**
- Promotional: All Yellow with Blue hubs.
(100 / 200 made for Michigan Co.) . **£100-150**

**977 Servicing Platform Vehicle**
1960-64
- Red and Cream body, operable platform,
spare wheel, two packing pieces ...... **£140-160**
**NB** Version seen using 667 Missile
Servicing Platform Vehicle chassis in the
Red/Cream 977 livery ............................ NGPP

**977 Shovel Dozer**
1973-78
- Yellow/Red/Silver, Black or Silver
plastic tracks, bubble-packed.. .............. **£20-25**

**978 Bedford TK Refuse Wagon**
1964-72
Diecast cab, plastic tipping body,
two plastic dustbins.
- Green cab, Grey body, Red hubs,
White (later Grey) plastic roof rack ..... **£50-60**
1973-74

- Dark Metallic Green cab, Grey body,
Red plastic hubs, White (later Grey)
plastic roof rack .................................... **£70-85**
1975-77
- Lime-Green cab, White interior,
Black or Brown chassis, plastic or
cast roof rack ........................................ **£70-85**
1978-80
- Yellow cab, Brown chassis, cast rack .. **£35-45**
**NB** Over its 16-year production run, 978
came in five different types of packaging:
lidded box, pictorial and non-pictorial
end-flap boxes, bubble-pack, and
window box.

**979 Racehorse Transport**
1961-64
- Grey lower body and roof, Lemon-Yellow
upper body sides, two horses, 'Newmarket
Racehorse Transport Service Ltd',
Supertoy, two packing pieces .......... **£350-450**

**980 Horsebox (US issue)**
1954-60  (renumbered in 1954 from 581)
- Maroon body (cast in aluminium),
'Hire Service', 'Express Horse Van',
'Express'. In Blue/White striped box
with picture of model and 'Hudson
Dobson' mark, two packing pieces .. **£500-600**

**980 Coles Hydra Truck 150T**
1972-79
- Lemon-Yellow body, triple extension
crane, handle at side and rear.............. **£30-40**
- Yellow or Orange body, two side
handles, no rear handle ........................ **£50-60**
- 'SPARROWS CRANE HIRE'
Promotional model, Red body ......... **£200-300**

**981 Horsebox**
1954-60  (renumbered in 1954 from 581)
- Maroon body (cast in aluminium),
'British Railways', two PP .............. **£100-125**

**982 Pullmore Car Transporter**
1955-63  (renumbered in 1955 from 582)
Bedford 'O' series cab and chassis plus
aluminium trailer beneath
'*DINKY TOYS DELIVERY SERVICE*' on
sides. Same logo on rear ramp but
without '20' sign. Black grille/bumper,
Silver trim, one packing piece.
1955-61
- Blue cab and back, Mid-Blue hubs,
Fawn decks...................................... **£400-500**
- Dark Blue cab, Mid-Blue hubs,
Light Blue back and decks, no window
glazing. Blue/White striped box has
picture of 994 Loading Ramp
introduced in 1955 .......................... **£125-150**
1961-63
- Same, but with cab window glazing **£140-170**

**983 Car Carrier and Trailer**
(Supertoys 984 and 985)
1958-63
- Red/Grey, 'Dinky Auto Service',
five packing pieces........................... **£225-275**

**984 Car Carrier**
1958-63
- Red/Grey body, Grey hubs, 'Dinky
Auto Service', two PP, Supertoy...... **£250-350**

**984 Atlas Digger**
1974-79
- Red/Yellow body, Yellow arm/cylinders,
Silver or Yellow bucket...................... **£30-40**
- Red/Yellow body, Black plastic arm,
Black or Yellow cylinders,
Silver bucket ...................................... **£30-40**

**985 Trailer for Car Carrier**
1958-63
- Red/Grey body, 'Dinky Auto Service',
two packing pieces, Supertoy ............. **£50-60**

**986 Mighty Antar with Propeller**
1959-61
- Red cab (window glazing on some),
Grey low-loader, Bronze propeller,
three packing pieces......................... **£300-350**

**987 'ABC TV' Control Room**
1962-69
- Blue/Grey/Red, 'ABC TELEVISION',
camera/operator/cable ..................... **£175-225**

**988 TV Transmitter Van 'ABC-TV'**
1962-69
- Blue/Grey body, Red stripe,
revolving aerial dish, Supertoy ........ **£175-225**

**989 Car Transporter**
**'AUTO TRANSPORTERS'**
1963-65
- Lemon Yellow cab, Pale Grey back,
Metallic Light Blue ramps, Red plastic
hubs, Supertoy boxed in all-card
picture box or export-only Gold
'see through' window box,
two packing pieces .................... **£2,500-3,000**

**990 Pullmore Car transporter with Four Cars**
See Gift Sets section.

**991 Large Trailer**
1954-70   Renumbered in 1954 from 551 –
see that entry for details.

**991 A.E.C. Tanker**
1954-55  (renumbered in 1954 from 591)
- Red/Yellow, Supertoy,
'SHELL CHEMICALS LIMITED' . **£130-160**
1955-58
- Red/Yellow, Supertoy,
'SHELL CHEMICALS'.................. **£120-140**

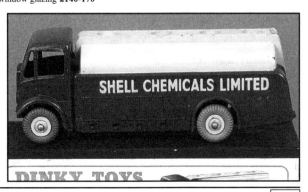

---

**Ford Transit casting types:**

**Type 1**: (1966-74), has sliding driver's door, opening hinged side door, and twin rear doors.
**Type 2**: (1974-78), non-sliding driver's door, one side-hinged door, one top-hinged rear door.
**Type 3**: (1978-80), as Type 2 but with a slightly longer bonnet (18 mm.)

---

**24a  Ambulance**
1934-38
Types 1 or 2 criss-cross chassis,
types 1, 2 or 3 grille, plated chrome
or Black hubs, open windows.
- Cream body, Red chassis ................. **£250-350**
- Cream body, Grey chassis................. **£250-350**
- Grey body, Dark Grey chassis ......... **£200-250**
- Grey body, Maroon chassis.............. **£200-250**
1938-40
Type 2 criss-cross chassis, open
windows, type 3 grille. See 30f.
- Cream body, Red chassis ................. **£200-250**
- Cream body, Grey chassis................. **£200-250**
- Grey body, Dark Grey chassis ......... **£250-300**
- Grey body, Maroon chassis.............. **£250-300**
- Black body, Black chassis
(thought to be for export only) ........ **£500-750**

**25h  Streamlined Fire Engine**
(renumbered in 1954 to 250)
1936-37
- Red body, no tinplate baseplate,
tinplate ladder and bell, White tyres. **£175-225**
1937-40
- Red body, tinplate baseplate, ladder
and bell, Black or White tyres ......... **£125-150**
1948-54
- Red body and ladder, tinplate
baseplate, brass bell, Black tyres ........ **£80-100**

**25k  Streamline Fire Engine**
1937-39
- Red body, tinplate base, 6 firemen,
ladder, bell, White tyres ................... **£400-500**

**30f  Ambulance**
1935-38
- Grey body, Red wings/criss-cross chassis,
plain radiator, open windows............ **£150-200**
1938-40
- Grey body, Black moulded chassis,
radiator badge, open windows .............**£90-110**
1938-40
- South-African issue:
Grey body, Red cross,
'Bentley type' radiator ..................... **£750-950**
1946-47
- Grey body, Black moulded
chassis, open windows........................ **£80-100**
1947-48
- Cream body, Black moulded chassis,
filled-in or open windows.................. **£80-100**

**30h  Daimler Ambulance**
1950-54   (renumbered in 1954 to 253)
- Cream body, Red crosses and
wheels, no window glazing.................. **£80-90**
**30hm  Daimler Military Ambulance**
1950-54   (renumbered in 1954 to 624)
- Military-Green body, Red crosses on
White backgrounds, (US issue) ........ **£200-300**

**123-P  Austin Princess 'POLICE' Car**
1977
- White body, Black roof and interior,
plastic wheels .................................... **£300-350**
**NB**   This model was not officially
released. A prototype (?) was sold by
Vectis Auctions for £360.
**195  Fire-Chief's Range Rover**
1971-78
- Red or Metallic Red, 'Fire Service',
Speedwheels, bubble-packed ............... **£35-40**

**243  Volvo 'POLICE' Car**
(Some made in Italy by Polistil under license)
1979-81
- White body, plastic chassis .................. **£35-40**
**244  Plymouth Fury Police Car**
1977-81
- Black/White, 'POLICE', warning
lights, plastic chassis and wheels.......... **£25-30**

**250  Streamline Fire Engine**
1954-62   (renumbered in 1954 from 25h)
- Red body and hubs, Silver tinplate
ladder, bell and trim ........................ **£100-120**
- Red body, hubs and tinplate ladder..... **£80-100**

**250  Police Mini Cooper 'S'**
1967-71
- White body, Austin Cooper 'S' boot
lid transfer, roof sign and aerial,
'POLICE' on doors ............................ **£55-65**
1971-73
- As previous model but cast boot
detail, no aerial.................................. **£45-55**
1973-75
- Same model but with Speedwheels ..... **£35-45**
**NB**   Boot casting variations:
(1) 'Morris Mini-Minor' cast-in,
(2) 'Austin Mini-Cooper S' cast-in.

**251  U.S.A. 'POLICE' Car**   (Pontiac Parisienne)
1971-72
- White body, Black textured roof,
Off-White interior, twin aerials,
siren, rooflight...................................... **£60-75**

**252  R.C.M.P. Police Car**   (Pontiac Parisienne)
1969-74
- Dark Blue body, White door panels and
interior, driver, twin aerials, Red light.. **£60-75**

**253  Daimler Ambulance**
1954-58   (renumbered in 1954 from 30h)
- Cream body, Red crosses and cast
hubs, no window glazing ..................... **£75-85**
1958-60
- White body, Red crosses and cast
hubs, no window glazing ................. **£100-125**
1960-62
- White body, Red crosses and cast
hubs, with window glazing................. **£80-100**
1962-64
- White body, Red plastic hubs,
with window glazing...........................**£90-110**

**254  'POLICE' Range Rover**
1971-81
- White body, Orange side stripes,
twin aerials on some, Speedwheels ...... **£30-35**

**255  Mersey Tunnel Police Van**  (Land Rover)
1955-61
- Gloss or Matt Red body, smooth or
treaded Black tyres, hook, 'POLICE'
and 'MERSEY TUNNEL'................ **£125-150**
**255  Ford Zodiac 'POLICE' Car**
1967-71
- White body, driver, 'POLICE' on
doors and roof sign, aerial ................... **£55-65**
- As previous model but with paper
labels on door and blue base................ **£45-55**
**255  Police Mini Clubman**
1977-79
- Blue/White body, 'POLICE', opening
doors and bonnet, plastic wheels ......... **£30-35**

**256  Humber Hawk 'POLICE' Car**
1960-64
- Black body, Cream interior, White
'POLICE' sign on roof,
'PC 49' licence plates,
driver and observer, spun hubs .......... **£80-100**

**257  Canadian 'FIRE CHIEF' Car**
(Nash Rambler)
1960-69
- Flashing light, suspension,
window glazing.................................... **£55-65**

**258  U.S.A. 'POLICE' CAR**  (De Soto Fireflite)
1960-61   (192 casting)
- Black body, White front doors,
'POLICE' on doors, roof and
bonnet, Red roof-light...................... **£100-125**
- Same, but with Red interior............. **£100-125**
**258  U.S.A. 'POLICE' CAR**  (Dodge Royal)
1961-62   (191 casting)
- Black body, White front doors,
'POLICE' on doors, roof and
bonnet, Red roof-light...................... **£100-125**
**258  U.S.A. 'POLICE' CAR**  (Ford Fairlane)
1962-66   (149 casting)
- Black body, White front doors,
'POLICE' on doors, roof and bonnet,
Red light, open window...................... **£80-90**
- Same but Dark Blue/White,
with closed windows............................ **£80-90**
**258  U.S.A. 'POLICE' CAR**  (Cadillac 62)
1966-68   (147 casting)
- Black/White, suspension/steering ..... **£100-125**

**259  Fire Engine**  (Bedford Miles)
1961-69
- Red body and hubs, 'FIRE BRIGADE'
and crest, Red tinplate ladder and
bell, Yellow box ............................... **£125-150**
- Same model but with 'AIRPORT
FIRE TENDER' (from 276) ............. **£125-150**
- Red body, spun aluminium hubs....... **£125-150**
**261  Ford Taunus 'POLIZEI'**
1967-77   (German issue)
- White and Green body, box has card
packing ring and label:
'Special contract run for
Meccano Agent in W. Germany'....... **£200-300**

**263  Superior Criterion Ambulance**
1962-68
Bright or Dull White body, Red side stripes,
cab siren and roof beacon. 'AMBULANCE'
in Red/White on rear windows, cast hubs.
Two attendants + patient on stretcher.
Versions:
- Bright White body, Turquoise int. ...... **£80-100**
- Dull (dirty) White body, Red interior ... **£70-80**
- Same but with Yellow interior............. **£60-70**
- Same but with Pale Turquoise interior . **£50-60**
- Same but with White interior............... **£70-80**

**263  E.R.F. Fire Tender 'Airport Rescue'**
1978-81
- Yellow body, flashing light.................. **£40-50**

**264  R.C.M.P. Ford Fairlane**
1962-65
- Dark Blue body, White doors,
aerial, red beacon, two Mounties...... **£100-125**
**264  R.C.M.P. Cadillac**
1965-68
- Dark Blue body, White doors,
aerial, red beacon, two Mounties.........**£90-110**

**264 Rover 3500 Police Car**
1978-80
• White body, Yellow stripe with 'POLICE'
and crest (some made in Hong Kong).. **£20-30**

**266 E.R.F. Fire Tender**
1976-79
• Red body, 'Fire Service',
White wheeled escape ladder............... **£50-60**
1979-80
• Same but with Metallic Red body ....... **£50-60**
1976-79
• Danish issue: Red body, 'FALCK' ....... **£70-85**

**267 Superior Cadillac Ambulance**
1967-71
• Cream and Red, 'AMBULANCE' on
roof, flashing light, stretcher, patient.... **£50-65**

**267 Paramedic Truck**
1978-79
• Red, Yellow cylinders, two figures,
lapel badge, (TV Series 'Emergency') . **£20-30**

**268 Range Rover 'AMBULANCE'**
1973-77
• White body, stretcher, bubble-packed... **£20-30**

**269 Jaguar Motorway 'POLICE' Car**
1962-66
• White body, Red interior, two figures,
spun hubs,
Grey plastic aerial, Blue roof-light... **£120-140**
• Same but with White interior............. **£80-120**
• Same but with Cream interior............ **£80-120**
• Matt White body, Light Grey int. ..... **£125-150**

**269 Ford Transit 'POLICE' Van**
1978-79
• White/Red/Blue, with figures, lights,
signs and cones. Type 3 casting............ **£35-45**

**270 Ford 'POLICE' Panda Car**
1969-72
• Turquoise body, White doors,
Blue/White roof sign, cast hubs........... **£45-55**
1972-77
• Same model but with Speedwheels ...... **£40-50**

**271 Ford Transit 'FIRE'**
1975-76
• Red body, with hose/axe/bells/plastic
ladder, bubble-packed, Type 2 ............. **£55-65**
• Danish issue:
Same model but with 'FALCK' logo.... **£65-75**

**272 'POLICE' Accident Unit**
1975-78
• White body, with radar gun, beacon,
aerial, cones and signs, Type 2 casting. **£35-45**

**274 Ford Transit Ambulance**
1978-79
• White, 'AMBULANCE', Red crosses,
beacon, Type 3 casting......................... **£35-45**

**276 Airport Fire Tender**
1962-69
• Red body, 'AIRPORT FIRE CONTROL',
bell, packing ring in box .................... **£75-100**
• Same but in yellow/red Export box .. **£200-250**
• Same model but 'FIRE BRIGADE'
logo (from 259), no crest ................... **£75-100**

**276 Ford Transit Ambulance**
1976-78
• White body, 'AMBULANCE',
Type 2 casting, packing ring in box...... **£30-40**

**277 Superior Criterion Ambulance**
1962-68
• Metallic Blue, White roof and tyres,
flashing light, box has lift-off lid and
one packing piece.................................. **£75-85**
• As previous model but in Gold
'see-through' box ................................. **£80-90**

**277 'POLICE' Land Rover**
1977-80
• Black body, White tilt, Blue beacon ..... **£20-30**

**278 Vauxhall Victor 'AMBULANCE'**
1964-69
White body, Red Cross on doors, Blue roof
beacon, driver, opening tailgate, Red/White
stretcher with patient. Versions:
• With Pale Brown interior..................... **£70-85**
• With Blue interior ................................ **£70-85**
• With Sea Green interior ........................ **£60-75**
**NB** Baseplates: Examples of 278 will be
found with either 'VAUXHALL VICTOR'
or just 'VICTOR' imprinted on their
baseplates.

**282 Land Rover Fire Appliance**
1973-79
• Red, 'Fire Service', metal ladder,
bubble-packed ..................................... **£30-40**
1974-78
• Danish issue:
Same model but with 'FALCK' logo.... **£35-45**

**285 Merryweather Marquis**
1969-79
• Metallic Dark Red body, escape ladder,
working pump, 'FIRE SERVICE' ........ **£55-65**
• With non-Metallic Red body ............... **£55-65**
• Danish issue: Same model but Red or
Metallic Dark Red body, 'FALCK' ...... **£85-95**

**286 Ford Transit 'FIRE'**
1968-74
• Red, 'Fire Service', hose,
Type 1 casting, bubble-packed ............. **£75-90**
• Same but with Metallic Red body ...... **£75-90**
• Danish issue: Same model but with
'FALCK ZONEN' logo........................... **£85-95**

**287 Police Accident Unit**
1967-71
• White body, Orange panels,
roof rack and sign, radar gun,
aerial, Type 1 casting ...................... **£100-125**
1971-74
• White body, Red panels, Type 1 casting,
roof rack and sign, radar gun, traffic
cones, two 'POLICE' warning boards .. **£65-75**

**288 Superior Cadillac**
1971-79
• White body with Red lower panels,
'AMBULANCE', stretcher and
patient, no flashing light ...................... **£40-45**
• Danish issue: Black body/White roof,
Blue interior and roof bar, 'FALCK'
on roof bar and tailgate.................... **£100-125**

**442 Land Rover Breakdown Crane**
1973-79
• White and Red body, 'Motorway
Rescue', operable winch ...................... **£25-30**

1975-78
• White body, Red bonnet and door panels,
Blue interior, 2 Orange rooflights,
Black jib, 'FALCK'.............................. **£40-50**
• All Red body, Blue interior, Light Blue
header board, Black jib, Speedwheels,
'FALCK' .............................................. **£50-60**
• All Red body, Black interior, deeper
Blue header board, Black jib,
Speedwheels, 'FALCK' ........................ **£50-60**

**555 Fire Engine** (Commer)
1952-54 (renumbered in 1954 to 955)
• Red body with Silver trim and ladder,
no windows ......................................... **£75-85**

**624 Daimler Military Ambulance**
1954-? (renumbered in 1954 from 30hm)
• Military-Green body, Red crosses on
White backgrounds, (US issue) ........ **£200-300**

**954 Fire Station**
1961-64
• Red, Yellow and 'brick' plastic,
base 252 mm. x 203 mm.................. **£200-250**

**955 Fire Engine** (Commer)
1954-64 (renumbered in 1954 from 555)
• Red body and diecast Supertoy hubs,
no window glazing.............................**£90-110**
1964-70
• Red body, Red diecast or plastic hubs,
window glazing, Black or Grey tyres,
housed in Yellow box with drawing
or scene, card packing....................... **£150-175**

**956 Turntable Fire Escape Lorry** (Bedford cab)
1958-60
• Red body and diecast hubs,
no window glazing, Silver deck and ladder... **£80-100**
1960-70
• Red body, diecast then plastic hubs,
window glazing, instructions,
'Tested' label, card packing ............... **£80-100**
**NB** A version of 956 has been discovered
(in Norway) that has 3 ladders instead of 2.

**956 Turntable Fire Escape Lorry** (Berliet cab)
1970-74
• Metallic Red body and hubs, windows,
'ECHELLE INCENDIE',
Black platform ................................. **£150-200**
• Same but with Silver platform.......... **£175-225**
1974-?
• Danish issue: Metallic Red body
and hubs, windows, 'FALCK' .......... **£175-225**

**2253 Ford Capri Police Car**
1974-76
• White/Orange, 'POLICE', Blue light,
suspension. (1:25 scale) ..................... **£80-100**

# Dinky Toys Farm and Garden models

| Model and details | MPR |
|---|---|

**22e** **Farm Tractor**
1933-40
- 'Modelled Miniature' with
'HORNBY SERIES' cast-in, no hook,
Yellow/Dark Blue (lead) body,
Red or Yellow (lead) wheels ........... **£300-400**

**22e** 'DINKY TOYS' cast-in, with hook,
Red or Yellow wheels are lead, diecast
or both, body colours:
- Green/Yellow.................................... **£300-400**
- Yellow/Blue/Red .............................. **£300-400**
- Red/Blue........................................... **£300-400**
- Red/Red............................................ **£300-400**
- Cream/Blue ...................................... **£300-400**
- Cream/Red........................................ **£300-400**
- Blue/Cream/Red ............................... **£300-400**

**27a** 'MASSEY-HARRIS' Tractor
1948-54  (renumbered in 1954 to 300)
- Red body, Yellow cast wheels,
driver, hook ........................................ **£80-100**

**27ak** **Tractor and Hay Rake**
1952-54  (renumbered in 1954 to 310)
- 27a Tractor and 27k Hay Rake ....... **£150-200**

**27b** **Halesowen Harvest Trailer**
1949-54  (renumbered in 1954 to 320)
- Brown body, Red racks,
Yellow metal wheels ............................ **£25-35**

**27c** **M.H. Manure Spreader**
1949-54  (renumbered in 1954 to 321)
- Red body with drawbar, hook,
working shredders ............................... **£30-35**

**27d** **Land Rover**
1950-54  (renumbered in 1954 to 340)
- Orange body, Dark Blue interior,
Tan driver, Red hubs ........................... **£85-95**
- Orange body, Dark Green interior,
Tan driver, Red hubs ........................... **£75-85**
- Mid-Green body, Light Brown
interior, Tan driver, Green hubs .......... **£75-85**
- Promotional: Very Dark Green body.
(Ministry of Food promotional). **£1,000-1,500**
1952-53
- Gift Set model: Dark Brown body,
Beige driver. Only issued in
Commercial Vehicles Gift Set No.2.
If sold individually (unboxed) ...... **£800-1,100**

**27f** **Estate Car**
1950-54  (renumbered in 1954 to 344)
- Pale Brown body with Dark Brown panels,
rear axle pillars, Fawn hubs, small
lettering on matt or gloss baseplate ..... **£60-80**
- Grey body with Red side panels ..... **£100-125**

**27g** **Moto-Cart**
1949-54  (renumbered in 1954 to 342)
- Brown and Green body, driver,
three metal wheels/tyres...................... **£40-50**

**27h** **Disc Harrow**
1951-54  (renumbered in 1954 to 322)
- Red/Yellow body, Silver disc blades,
tinplate hook...................................... **£20-25**

**27j** **Triple Gang Mower**
1952-54  (renumbered in 1954 to 323)
- Red frame, Yellow tines,
Green wheels, cast-in hook ................. **£20-25**

**27k** **Hay Rake**
1953-54  (renumbered in 1954 to 324)
- Red frame, Yellow wheels, wire tines,
operating lever.................................... **£20-25**

| Model and details | MPR |
|---|---|

**27m** **Land Rover Trailer**
1952-54  (renumbered in 1954 to 341)
- Green body and hubs ......................... **£25-35**
- Blue body and hubs............................ **£25-35**
- Red body and hubs............................. **£25-35**
- Orange body,
Red, Cream or Beige hubs .................. **£25-35**
- Militarised version:
see 'Military Vehicles' section.

**27n** 'FIELD MARSHALL' Tractor
1953-54  (renumbered in 1954 to 301)
- Burnt Orange body and exhaust, Silver
metal wheels, Tan driver, hook ....... **£100-130**
- As previous model but with
Green metal wheels ......................... **£150-200**

**30n** **Farm Produce Wagon**
1950-54  (renumbered in 1954 to 343)
Model has stake sides to rear body;
Black cast base and hook;
hubs same colour as rear body.
- Yellow cab with Green back ................ **£60-70**
- Green cab with Yellow back ................ **£60-70**
- Red cab with Blue back ...................... **£60-70**

**105a** **Garden Roller**
1948-54  (renumbered in 1954 to 381)
- Green handle and Red roller sides ....... **£15-25**

**105b** **Wheelbarrow**
1948-54  (renumbered in 1954 to 382)
- Brown or Tan and Red body,
single metal wheel............................... **£15-25**

**105c** **4 wheeled Hand Truck**
1948-54  (renumbered in 1954 to 383)
- Green/Yellow or Blue/Yellow ............. **£10-15**

**105e** **Grass Cutter**
1948-54  (renumbered in 1954 to 384)
- Yellow handle, Green metal wheels,
Red blades .......................................... **£25-30**
- Yellow handle, unpainted metal
wheels, Green blades .......................... **£50-75**

**107a** **Sack Truck**
1948-54  (renumbered in 1954 to 385)
- Blue or Pale Green body,
two Black metal wheels ....................... **£10-15**

**192** **Range Rover**
1970-74
- Bronze body, various interior colours,
cast detailed or Speedwheels .............. **£25-35**
1973-79
- Black or Yellow body, Speedwheels.... **£25-35**

**300** 'MASSEY-HARRIS' Tractor
1954-62  (renumbered in 1954 from 27a)
- Red body, cast wheels (Yellow centre,
unpainted 'tyres'), Tan cast driver ... **£145-175**
1962-64
- Red body, Yellow hubs (cast rear,
plastic front, rubber tyres),
Blue plastic driver, no decals .......... **£300-400**
1964-66
- Cherry Red body, Yellow/Black plastic
hubs, Yellow exhaust, Blue plastic
driver, Yellow/White box ................ **£225-275**

**300** 'MASSEY-FERGUSON' Tractor
1966-71
- As earlier 'Massey-Harris' model,
but renamed 'MASSEY-FERGUSON',
Yellow plastic hubs and exhaust,
Silver steering wheel........................ **£300-400**

**301** 'FIELD MARSHALL' Tractor
1954-61  (renumbered in 1954 from 27n)
- Orange body, cast wheels (Green or
Silver centres, unpainted 'tyres'),
Tan driver, hook ............................. **£150-200**

| Model and details | MPR |
|---|---|

- Same, but with Yellow or
unpainted wheel centres.................. **£150-180**
1962-66
- Orange body, Green hubs (plastic front,
cast rear, rubber tyres), Blue driver . **£300-400**
Same, but with Green plastic hubs
(front and rear) ............................... **£300-400**
1964-66 Orange body, Green
plastic hubs, Blue plastic driver....... **£200-250**

**305** 'DAVID BROWN' 990 Tractor
1964-67
- Yellow cab and hubs, Red cowl, Black
engine, stickers: 'David Brown 990'.
Detailed picture box ........................ **£150-200**
1967-73
- White cab/hubs/cowl,
Brown engine, stickers:
'David Brown Selectamatic 990'..... **£100-130**
- Promotional issue: In Red box with
'IT WAS MADE BY MECCANO
DINKY TOYS' logo. Brown engine,
Black engine stickers: 'David Brown
990 Selectamatic Tractor',
Red exhaust ................................... **£150-200**
1974-75
- White cab and cowl, Red hubs and engine,
stickers: 'Case David Brown 995'.
Bubble-packed................................ **£130-160**

**308** 'LEYLAND' 384 Tractor
1971-72
- Metallic Red body, Cream hubs,
no driver, plastic dome box............. **£125-150**
1973-74
- Metallic Red body, White hubs,
with driver, Yellow/Red box ........... **£125-150**
1975-77
- Dark Blue body, White exhaust
and hubs, Blue plastic driver,
Yellow/Red box.............................. **£125-150**
1978
- Orange body, White exhaust and
hubs, Blue plastic driver,
Red/Blue 'hanging' box .................. **£125-150**
1978-79
- Metallic Red body, White exhaust
and hubs, Blue plastic driver,
Red/Blue 'hanging' box .................. **£100-150**
- Factory error: Blue body and plastic
driver, Red hubs, White exhaust
stack. Bubble-packed ..................... **£200-250**

**310** **Tractor and Hay Rake**
1954-60  (renumbered in 1954 from 27ak)
- 300 Tractor and 324 Hay Rake in
Blue/White box ............................. **£200-250**
- Same, but late issue in Yellow box
with single packing piece................. **£200-250**

**319** **Weeks Tipping Trailer**
1961-71
- Red/Yellow body, cast or Brown plastic
wheels, plain or planked trailer bed.
One packing piece............................. **£25-30**

**320** **Halesowen Harvest Trailer**
1954-60  (renumbered in 1954 from 27b)
- Red/Brown body, Red or Brown racks,
drawbar, hook, cast or plastic wheels .. **£25-35**
- Same, but Red body, Yellow racks ...... **£25-35**

**321** **M.H. Manure Spreader**
1954-62  (renumbered in 1954 from 27c)
- Red body, Yellow cast wheels,
'MASSEY-HARRIS'........................... **£25-35**
1962-73
- Red body, Red or Yellow plastic
hubs, no logo ..................................... **£25-35**

144

**322   Disc Harrow**
1954-67   (renumbered in 1954 from 27h)
• Red/Yellow body, Silver disc blades,
tinplate hook..................................**£25-35**
1967-73
• White/Red, Silver blades, no hook ......**£25-35**
• All White version ................................**£40-50**

**323   Triple Gang Mower**
1954-63   (renumbered in 1954 from 27j)
• Red frame, Yellow tines,
Green wheels, cast-in hook .................**£35-45**

**324   Hayrake**
1954-64   (renumbered in 1954 from 27k)
• Red frame, Yellow wheels,
Black or Silver lever ...........................**£25-35**

**325   'DAVID BROWN' Tractor and
Disc Harrow**
1967-73
• 305 and 322 in White and Red.
Box has inner packing piece ...........**£175-225**
• 305 and 322 in Yellow and Red.
Box has inner packing piece ...........**£175-225**

**340   Land Rover**
1954-66   (renumbered in 1954 from 27d)
• Green body, Pale Brown interior and
cast driver, Green cast hubs ..............**£80-100**
1966-69
• Orange body, Dark Green interior,
Red or Green cast hubs, Tan driver .**£150-175**
• With Red plastic hubs,
Blue cast or plastic driver ................**£110-130**
1969-71
• Red body, Yellow interior,
Red plastic hubs, Blue plastic driver,
Light Yellow box ..............................**£125-150**
• Red body, Yellow interior,
Yellow plastic hubs, Blue plastic
driver, Light Yellow box .................**£125-150**
1971
• Red body, Yellow interior, Green
plastic hubs, Blue plastic driver,
Light Yellow box ..............................**£125-150**

**341   Land Rover Trailer**
1954-66   (renumbered in 1954 from 27m)
• Orange, Green or Red, drawbar and
hook, cast or plastic hubs....................**£25-30**
• Militarised version:
see 'Military Vehicles' section.

**342   Moto-Cart**
1954-61   (renumbered in 1954 from 27g)
• Light Green with Tan back and
driver, Red hubs .................................**£65-75**
• Dark Green with Tan back and
driver, Red hubs .................................**£65-75**

**343   Farm Produce Wagon**
1954-64   (renumbered in 1954 from 30n)
• Mid-Green cab and chassis,
Yellow back and hubs ......................**£130-160**
• Yellow cab, Green back and hubs....**£130-160**
• Dark Red cab,
Mid-Blue back and hubs .................**£160-190**
• Cherry Red cab,
Mid-Blue back / hubs......................**£160-190**
• Late issues with plastic hubs and
in the late lighter Yellow box ..........**£160-190**

**344   Estate Car**
1954-61   (renumbered in 1954 from 27f)
• Fawn with Brown or Red panels,
Cream or Beige diecast hubs,
treaded tyres, large print on base .....**£130-160**
• Fawn with Brown panels,
spun hubs.........................................**£130-160**

**344   Land Rover Pick-Up**
1970-72
• Metallic Blue body, White back,
bubble-packed ....................................**£20-30**
1973-78
• Metallic Red body, White back,
bubble-packed ....................................**£20-30**

**381   Garden Roller**
1954-58   (renumbered in 1954 from 105a)
• Green and Red....................................**£15-25**

**381   Convoy Farm Truck**
1977-80
• Yellow cab, Brown plastic high-sided
truck body .........................................**£15-20**

**382   Wheelbarrow**
1954-58   (renumbered in 1954 from 105b)
• Brown and Red body, metal wheel ......**£15-25**

**383   4 wheeled Hand Truck**
1954-58   (renumbered in 1954 from 105c)
• Green or Blue body............................**£10-15**

**384   Grass Cutter**
1954-58   (renumbered in 1954 from 105e)
• Yellow handle, Green metal wheels,
Red blades..........................................**£25-30**
• Yellow handle, unpainted
metal wheels, Green blades .................**£50-75**

**385   Sack Truck**
1954-58   (renumbered in 1954 from 107a)
• Blue with two small metal wheels.......**£10-15**

**386   Lawn Mower**
1954-58   (renumbered in 1954 from 751)
• Green/Red, separate grassbox,
'Dinky Toys' cast-in...........................**£80-90**

**399   Tractor and Trailer**
1969-75
• 300 combined with 428....................**£200-250**

**428   Large Trailer**
1955-71
See 'Commercial Vehicles' section
for variations.

**561   Blaw Knox Bulldozer**
1949-54   (renumbered in 1954 to 961)
• Red body, Green or Black rubber tracks,
driver, lifting blade, Supertoy.  Blue box
with Orange/White label, or 'natural'
card box with Red/White label,
one packing piece................................**£40-50**

**563   Blaw Knox Heavy Tractor**
1948-54   (renumbered in 1954 to 963)
• Red, Orange or Blue 561 without the dozer
blade.  Brown cardboard box has
Red/White label, one packing piece ....**£60-70**
• Dark Blue body, Mid-Blue rollers,
Green  rubber tracks, driver.  Brown
box, Black/White picture label ........**£175-200**

**564   Elevator Loader**
1952-54   (renumbered in 1954 to 964)
• See 964 (below) for details.

**751   Lawn Mower**
1949-54   (renumbered in 1954 to 386)
• Green/Red, 'Dinky Supertoys' cast-in .**£80-90**

**961   Blaw-Knox Bulldozer**
1954-62   (renumbered in 1954 from 561)
• Red or Yellow body, rubber tracks,
Tan driver, Supertoy............................**£40-50**
1962-64
• Blue body, rubber tracks, Tan driver....**£40-50**
1963-64
• Red or Yellow body, rubber tracks,
Blue driver..........................................**£40-50**
1964-64
• Orange plastic body, Silver engine
detail, Black diecast lifting gear,
Green plastic blade and exhaust,
Blue driver, Light Green or
Olive-Green roller wheels.................**£200-250**

**963   Blaw Knox Heavy Tractor**
1954-58   (renumbered in 1954 from 563)
• Red or Orange body, Green or Black
tracks. Blue/White striped box,
one packing piece................................**£60-70**
1958-59
• Yellow body, Green or Black tracks.
Blue/White striped box, one PP.......**£100-125**

**964   Elevator Loader**
1954-68   (renumbered in 1954 from 564)
• Yellow with Mid-Blue or
Dark Blue chutes, Blue or Yellow
hubs, one packing piece ......................**£45-55**
Boxes:  Early Blue boxes were replaced
by Blue/White boxes, then by Yellow
'Supertoys' boxes.
• Late issue:  Mid-Blue with Yellow
chutes, as shown on late picture
box design ......................................**£100-150**

Dinky Toys Massey-Harris Tractor with Hay-Rake and a Field Marshall Tractor
PHOTO: VECTIS AUCTIONS LTD.

| Model and details | MPR | Model and details | MPR | Model and details | MPR |
|---|---|---|---|---|---|

**041    Police Motor Cyclist**
1952-54
• Post-war reissue for US market of 37a.NGPP

**042    Civilian Motor Cyclist**
1952-54
• Post-war reissue for US market of 37b.NGPP

**043    Police Motorcycle Patrol**
1952-54
• Post-war reissue for US market of 42b.NGPP

**044    'R.A.C.' Motorcycle Patrol**
1952-54
• Post-war reissue for US market of 43b.NGPP

**045    'A.A.' Motorcycle Patrol**
1952-54
• Post-war reissue for US market of 44b.NGPP

**14z    'Triporteur'**
1938-40
• Three-wheel delivery van with Green,
Red, Grey, Blue or Yellow body,
Black hubs, White tyres, rider is always
a different colour from van.
French model, imported into
England in very small numbers....... **£200-300**

**37a    Civilian Motor Cyclist**
(renumbered in 1954 to 041)
1937-40
• Black motor cycle, Silver engine/exhaust
detail; Blue, Maroon, Green or Black
rider, SWRW or thick SBRW............. **£40-50**

1946-49
• Black motor cycle without Silver detail,
Green or Grey rider, thin SBRW........ **£40-50**
1950-54
• As previous version, but export only .. **£40-50**

**37b    Police Motor Cyclist**
(renumbered in 1954 to 042)
1937-40
• Black motor cycle with Silver
engine/exhaust detail, Dark Blue
rider, SWRW or thick SBRW............. **£75-85**
1946-49
• Black motor cycle without Silver
engine/exhaust detail,
Dark Blue rider, thick SBRW............. **£40-50**
1950-54
• As previous model, but export only.... **£40-50**

**37c    Royal Signals Dispatch Rider**
1937-41
• Green body, Khaki rider,
White or Black rubber wheels.
Sold unboxed.................................. **£150-175**
• Boxed version:
It is believed that only 1,000 were
sold boxed. Blue box/lid with
insert, 'A2237'....................................NGPP

**42b    Police Motorcycle Patrol**
(renumbered in 1955 to 043)
1935-40
• Black motor cycle, Silver engine
and exhaust detail, Dark Green and
Black sidecar, Dark Blue figures,
SWRW or thick SBRW ...................... **£75-95**
1946-49
• As previous model but without Silver
detailing and with thin SBRW ............ **£45-55**
1950-55
• Blue/Green, Blue figures, little
detailing, SBRW, export only.............. **£40-50**

**43b    'R.A.C.' Motorcycle Patrol**
1935-40
• Blue/Black motor cycle/sidecar,
Silver engine/exhaust detail,
Blue/Black rider with
Red sash, SWRW or thick SBRW....... **£75-95**
1946-49
• As previous model but no Silver
detailing, thin SBRW.
**NB** - two shades of Blue used post-war .. **£45-55**

**44b    'A.A.' Motorcycle Patrol**
1935-40
• Black/Yellow, Brown rider, more
detailing, 5mm 'AA' badge,
solid white rubber wheels ............... **£100-125**
1946-50
• Black/Yellow, Tan rider, little detailing,
7mm 'AA' badge, SBRW .................... **£50-60**
**NB**   This version remained in the catalogue,
was renumbered in 1954 to 270 but was
not re-introduced until 1959 - see 270 below.
1950-55
• As previous model but export only
(renumbered in 1955 to 045)............... **£50-60**

**270    'A.A.' Motorcycle Patrol**
1959-62   (renumbered in 1954 from 44b)
• Black/Yellow, Tan rider,
'AA' sign, SGPW ............................... **£40-50**
• Black/Yellow, Tan rider, 'AA' sign,
solid knobbly Black plastic wheels. **£100-150**

**271    'T.S.' Motorcycle Patrol**
1959-62
• Yellow motorcycle combination,
Belgian equivalent of the A.A......... **£150-200**

**272    'A.N.W.B.' Motorcycle Patrol**
1959-62
• Yellow motorcycle combination,
Dutch equivalent of the A.A........... **£250-300**

**SWRW =** solid White rubber wheels,
**SBRW =** solid Black rubber wheels
(both are of a larger diameter
than those used on the small cars).
**SGPW =** solid Grey plastic wheels.

# Dinky Toys Military Vehicles

See also Action Kits, Aircraft, Ships, Gift Sets and Factory Samples sections.

**Colour finish of Dinky Toys Military models.**
Military colours tend to be described by collectors, dealers and observers variously as 'Olive Drab' or 'Military Green' or 'Khaki' or 'Matt Green'. This is a less than satisfactory method of describing the colour finish of these models, especially when there are also shades of colour and depth of gloss (or lack of it).
We are of the opinion that they fundamentally relate to the same finish anyway, so for the sake of simplicity, this listing contains colour information ONLY where it is clearly specific (sand, camouflage or German grey, for example). Assume that all the

models in this listing are finished in one form or another of this 'Military Green' unless specifically stated otherwise. For all other descriptions of single colour finishes, the following **general** comments may be noted:

**Pre-war issues** have variations in shade, depth and degrees of gloss or matt surface. Some have a distinct brownish bias. None of these variations affect the price.

**1950's Military Vehicles** finish is generally regarded as Khaki. Mike and Sue Richardson prefer

to regard pre-war military finish as Matt Green and post-war as Olive Drab.

**US issues** are generally considered to be Olive Drab (a term that seems to have originated in a 1950's US Army recruitment poster referring to uniforms).

**Late Lines Bros issues** are in various green shades, often quite light green.

**French issues** are said to be more Olive Drab than British Khaki but all generally appear consistent in their groups.

---

| Model and details | MPR |
|---|---|

**1 Military Vehicles (1) Set**
1954-55  See 'Gift Sets' section.

**22f Army Tank**
1933-34
- 'Modelled Miniature' with 'HORNBY SERIES' cast-in. Green lead body, Orange revolving turret, Red, White or Green rubber tracks . **£250-350**
1934-39
- Green/Orange lead body, 'DINKY TOYS' cast-in, Red or Green tracks....................... **£250-300**
- Khaki lead body, 'DINKY TOYS' cast-in, Red or Green tracks........... **£250-300**
- Grey lead body, 'DINKY TOYS' cast-in, Red or Green tracks.......... **£250-300**

**22s Searchlight Lorry**
1939-41
- Green body, (22c casting, open cab rear window), smooth hubs. Not boxed . **£100-150**
- Same, but in yellow lidded box marked 'A2309'.....................................NGPP

**25b Army Covered Wagon**
1948-50
- Military-Green body and hubs. South-African issue ..................... **£750-1,000**

**25wm Bedford Military Truck**
1952-54  (renumbered in 1954 to 640)
- With tow hook. USA export only.... **£200-250**

**27m Land Rover Trailer**
1952-54  (renumbered in 1954 to 341)
- Made to accompany 669, unpainted hook and drawbar clip.... **£300-400**

**28 Army Delivery Van**
1948-56
- South-African issue: Type 3 with Military-Green body and hubs ..... **£750-1,000**

**30hm Daimler Military Ambulance**
1952-54  (renumbered in 1954 to 624)
- Red crosses on White backgrounds. (US export issue)............................ **£200-250**

**30sm Austin Covered Wagon**
1952-54  (renumbered in 1954 to 625)
- Made for export to USA only ........ **£100-125**

**37c Royal Signals Dispatch Rider**
1937-41
- Green body, Khaki rider, White or Black rubber wheels. Sold unboxed................................. **£150-175**
- Boxed version: It is believed that only 1,000 were sold boxed. Blue box/lid with insert, 'A2237'......................NGPP

---

| Model and details | MPR |
|---|---|

**139am US Army Staff Car**
1952-54  (renumbered in 1954 to 170m)
- Ford Fordor with White stars on roof and doors ................................. **£175-250**
- Canadian issue: As previous model but without stars.....NGPP

**150 Royal Tank Corps Set**
1937-41  See Gift Sets section.
1952-55  See Gift Sets section.

**150a Royal Tank Corps Officer**
1937-41
- Khaki uniform, Black beret, binoculars in hand .............................. **£25-30**
1952-54
- Khaki figure. In box of 12 ............. **£100-120**
1954  (renumbered to 600)

**150b Royal Tank Corps Private**
1938-41
- Black overalls, seated......................... **£25-30**
1952-54
- Khaki, seated. In box of 12 ............. **£100-120**
1954  (renumbered to 604)

**150c Royal Tank Corps Private**  (standing)
1937-41
- Diecast figure in Black overalls.......... **£25-30**
1953-54
- Mid-Brown overalls, Black base..... **£100-150**

**150d Royal Tank Corps Driver**  (sitting)
1937-41
- Die-cast figure in Black overalls......... **£25-30**

**150e Royal Tank Corps NCO**  (walking)
1937-41
- Die-cast figure in Black uniform ........ **£10-15**

**151 Medium Tank Set**
1937-41  See Gift Sets section.

**151a Medium Tank**
1937-41
- White markings, bright chain tracks, aerial, round jockey wheels locating tracks ... **£75-90**
- Version with 'flatted' jockey wheels.. **£75-90**
- Version with 'spray hole' cast in ........ **£75-90**
- With Black rubber wheels instead of tracks......................................NGPP
1947-49
- USA export version, no markings, bright tracks.................................... **£150-200**
- USA export version, no markings, black tracks.................................... **£150-200**

**151b 6-wheel Covered Wagon**
1937-41
- Lead body, tinplate canopy, seat holes but no figures.................. **£150-200**

---

| Model and details | MPR |
|---|---|

1937-41
- Diecast body, tinplate canopy, seat holes but no figures.................. **£150-200**
1946
- With smooth hubs and early tyres... **£150-200**
1947-54
- With ridged hubs, no seat holes ...... **£150-200**
1954-55
- USA export model with fixed driver, no other seat holes. (Renumbered to 620)...................... **£200-250**

**151c Cooker Trailer**
1937-48
- Wire stand, hole in seat but no figure . **£50-70**
NB Two styles of baseplate lettering are known for 151c.

**151d Water Tank Trailer**
1937-48
- Gloss Green, sold unboxed ................. **£50-70**

**152 Light Tank Set**
1937-41  See Gift Sets section.

**152a Light Tank**
1937-41
- White markings, chain tracks, aerial. **£75-100**
- Black rubber wheels instead of tracks............................... **£100-125**
1947-50
- No markings, chain tracks, aerial.... **£125-150**
1954-55
- US export model, no markings, bright or black tracks, (renumbered to 650) .. **£150-200**
- Mid (Chocolate) Brown variation ... **£150-200**

**152b Reconnaissance Car**
1937-41
- Six wheels (smooth hubs). Earliest versions had additional front axle support from baseplate ........... **£100-150**
- Later pre-war versions with normal base ............................ **£100-150**
1946
- With smooth hubs, early tyres......... **£100-150**
1947-49
- With ridged hubs ............................ **£100-150**
1953-54
- USA export model (renumbered to 671)...................... **£125-175**

**152c Austin Seven**
1937-41
- Wire windscreen frame, hole in seat, no baseplate ................ **£100-150**
1940-41
- Same, but cast in lead, hole in seat, no baseplate ................ **£100-150**

**153a  Jeep**
1946-47
- US White star on flat bonnet and left rear side, smooth hubs, solid steering wheel, no round hole in base .......... **£100-125**
1947
- With open spoked steering wheel ....... **£60-75**
- Brown body, open steering wheel ... **£100-125**
1948-52
- With raised 'domed' bonnet, round hole in base .............................. **£60-75**
1952-54
- US export model, some have rounded axle ends, (renumbered to 672) ....... **£100-125**

**160  Royal Artillery Personnel Set**
1939-41   See Gift Sets section.

**160a  Royal Artillery NCO**
1939-41
- Khaki uniform; part of 160 Set .......... **£20-30**

**160b  Royal Artillery Gunner**
1939-54
- Khaki, seated, hands on knees; part of 160 Set .................................... **£20-30**
1952-55
- US export issue: Same, but in green box of 12, (renumbered to 608) ...... **£150-200**

**160c  Royal Artillery Gunlayer**
1939-41
- Khaki, seated, hands held out; part of 160 Set ............................. **£20-30**
1952-55
- US export issue: Same, but in green box of 12 .......... **£150-200**

**160d  Royal Artillery Gunner**
1939-41
- Khaki uniform, standing; part of 160 Set ....... **£20-30**
1952-55
- US export issue: Same, but in green box of 12 .......... **£150-200**

**161  Mobile Anti-Aircraft Set**
1939-41   See Gift Sets section.

**161a  Searchlight on Lorry**
1939-41
- 151b casting plus diecast or lead searchlight ................................ **£200-250**

**161b  Anti-Aircraft Gun on Trailer**
1939-41
- Gloss Green, gun elevates, holes for figures, cast drawbar and hook ....... **£200-250**
1946-50
- Matt Green or Dark Brown .............. **£80-100**
1950-54
- US export issue (renumbered to 690) ....................... **£125-175**

**162  18-pounder Field Gun Set**
1939-54   See Gift Sets section.

**162a  Light Dragon Tractor**
1939-41
- Gloss Green, holes in seats, chain tracks .................................... **£100-125**
- Black rubber wheels instead of tracks ............................ **£250-350**
1946-55
- Matt Green, holes in some, chain tracks .................................... **£100-150**

**162b  Ammunition Trailer**
1939-41
- Gloss Green body, baseplate, drawbar and hook ............................... **£20-25**
1946-55
- Matt Green body, Black baseplate ...... **£20-25**

1948-55
- US export issue: Matt Green body, Black baseplate ...... **£20-25**

**162c  18 pounder Gun**
1939-41
- Gloss Green, drawbar cast-in, tinplate shield .................................. **£20-25**
1946-55
- Matt Green body and shield .............. **£20-25**

**170m  Ford US Army Staff Car**
1954-54   (renumbered in 1954 from 139am)
- Ford Fordor Sedan in Matt Olive, US export issue (renumbered to 675) ......................... **£200-250**

**281  Military Hovercraft 'ARMY'**
1973-76
- Olive-Drab body, Gunner, aerial ........ **£25-35**

**341  Land Rover Trailer**
1960   (renumbered in 1954 from 27m)
- Olive-Drab body, drawbar, hook ..... **£300-400**

**600  Royal Tank Corps Officer**
1952-55
- US only re-issue (renumbered from 150) ......................... **£8-12**

**601  Austin Paramoke**
1966-76
- Khaki, Grey top, spun hubs, parachute, in flap-end box, instructions ............... **£50-60**
1976-78
- Dark Grey, Grey top, Speedwheels, parachute, in bubble-pack with card base, instructions ........................ **£40-50**

**602  Armoured Command Car**
1976-77   See 'Novelty', section.

**603  Army Private (seated)**
1957-68
- Diecast, Khaki, Black beret, seated, box of 12 ................................ **£40-50**
1968-71
- Plastic, Khaki, Black beret, seated, box of 12 ................................ **£40-50**

**603a  Army Personnel Set**
1957-68
- 6 diecast figures (Khaki, Black berets, seated) ............. **£20-30**
1968-71
- Same 6 figures, but in plastic ............. **£20-30**

**604  Royal Tank Corps Private**
1954-60   (renumbered in 1954 from 150b)
- Diecast, Khaki uniform, seated, export only (to USA), box of 12 ........ **£50-70**

**604  Army Personnel**
1960-72
- Six driver figures (Khaki uniforms) .... **£20-30**

**604  Land Rover Bomb Disposal**
1976-77
- Olive-Drab/Orange, 'Explosive Disposal', Speedwheels, robot de-fuser kit on sprue. In 'hanging' box ...................... **£55-65**

**608  Royal Artillery Gunner**
1954-55
- Khaki uniform, seated, hands on knees. US export issue (renumbered from 160b) ..................... **£10-15**

**609  105 mm. Howitzer and Crew**
1974-77
- Olive-Drab body, three soldiers, Green metal wheels or Grey plastic wheels, bubble-packed ........................ **£30-40**

**612  Commando Jeep**
1973-80
- Driver (green helmet), solid axles, plastic gearstick, two guns, jerricans, aerial. In 'hanging' box ...................... **£25-35**
- Driver (brown helmet), split axles, metal gearstick. In bubble-pack with card base .................................... **£25-35**

**615  US Jeep and 105 mm. Howitzer**
1968-77
- Based on 612, US Army markings, driver (brown helmet), display box with pull-out tray ............. **£80-90**

**616  AEC with Chieftain Tank**
1968-77
- AEC articulated Transporter 'ARMY' with 683 Tank. Instructions printed on pictorial box ................................. **£90-110**

**617  VW KDF and 50 mm. Gun**
1967-77
- Grey body, German markings, Green metal or Grey plastic wheels, long display box or bubble-pack ........ **£75-85**

**618  AEC with Helicopter**
1976-80
- AEC articulated Transporter 'RESCUE', 724 Helicopter + net. Flap-end box ... **£90-110**

**619  Bren Gun Carrier and Anti-Tank Gun**
1976-77
- Khaki, plastic tracks, 2 figures, gun, 2 sprues each with 6 shells, White '57' on red shield. Bubble-pack .................. **£35-40**
NB  Two variations of markings exist: (i) '2035703 4', (ii) 'T2272616'  plus star.

**620  6-wheel Covered Wagon**
1954-55 (renumbered in 1954 from 151b)
- US export model, blued axles ......... **£200-250**

**620  Berliet Missile Launcher**
1971-73
- UK issue of French 816. 'NORD R20' missile. Yellow flap-end box .......... **£120-150**

**621  3 ton Army Wagon**  (Bedford 'RL')
1954-60
- Tin tilt, no windows, driver in some. In yellow flap-end box ....................... **£60-70**
1960-63
- Same but with window glazing .......... **£60-70**

**622  10 ton Army Truck**
1954-64
- (Foden) driver, tin tilt, Supertoys box . **£70-80**
1954-64
- Same, but in Dinky Toys striped box .. **£70-80**
- Late issue: In yellow lidded picture box .......... **£200-300**
NB  Two types of casting have been observed:
1 - Smooth cab roof, less cab/chassis strengthening.
2 - Ridge across cab roof, thicker strengthening.

**622  Bren Gun Carrier**
1975-78
- White star, driver, passenger, plastic tracks. Bubble-pack also has decal sheet ....... **£25-35**

**623  Army Covered Wagon**  (Bedford 'QL')
1954-63
- Driver in some, no window glazing, flap-end box ........................................ **£35-45**

**624  Daimler Military Ambulance**
1954-?   (renumbered in 1954 from 30hm)
- Red crosses, White backgrounds, US export issue ............................... **£400-500**

**625    Austin Covered Wagon**
1952-54    (renumbered in 1954 from 30sm)
- US export issue .............................. **£400-500**

**625    Six-pounder Gun**
1975-77
- Anti-tank gun, 2 plastic sprues each
  with 6 shells, bubble-pack with
  flat card base ........................................ **£15-20**

**626    Military Ambulance**  (Fordson)
1956-61
- Red crosses cast-in, no windows, deep
  yellow non-picture end-flap box ......... **£60-75**
1961-62
- Same, but with window glazing,
  pictorial end-flap box ....................... **£80-100**
1962-62
- In non-pictorial end-flap export
  box with red side ............................ **£100-125**

**630    Ferret Armoured Car**
1973-78
- Plastic wheels, spare wheel................. **£15-20**

**640    Bedford Military Truck**
1954-?    (renumbered in 1954 from 25wm)
- US export issue .............................. **£250-350**

**641    Army 1 ton Cargo Truck**
1954-61
- Tin tilt, driver in some, no windows,
  flap-end box.......................................... **£35-40**
1961-62
- Same, but with window glazing.......... **£40-50**

**642    R.A.F. Pressure Refueller**
1957-62
- RAF Blue, 'French' roundel, with or
  without driver, blue/white
  striped Supertoys box...................... **£100-130**
1957-62
- Same, but in Dinky Toys box...........**£110-140**

**643    Army Water Tanker**
1958-61
- No window glazing, driver in some,
  yellow box ............................................ **£30-35**
1961-64
- With window glazing,
  yellow box with red side .................... **£30-35**

**650    Light Tank**
1954-55    (renumbered in 1954 from 152a)
- US issue. Black base, no markings . **£100-125**

**651    Centurion Tank**
1954-70
- Matt or Gloss Olive-Drab body,
  metal rollers, rubber tracks, Supertoys
  Blue/White box, packing piece ........... **£80-90**
- US export issue:
  In U.S. Gold 'see through' box ....... **£150-175**
- US export issue:
  In Yellow/Blue Dinky Toys lidded box
  with packing piece and
  'H.Hudson Dobson' sticker ............. **£150-175**
- In Blue/White Dinky Toys lidded
  box with packing piece .................... **£90-120**
- Late issue:
  Plastic rollers, screws (not rivets), in
  Yellow/Blue lidded box or Yellow
  end-flap picture box, one PP .......... **£130-160**

**654    155 mm. Mobile Gun**
1973-79
- Operable gun, 4 plastic shells,
  bubble-packed ..................................... **£15-20**

**656    88 mm. Gun**
1975-79
- German Grey, 6 plastic shells.
  Bubble-packed..................................... **£15-20**

**660    Tank Transporter**
(Thornycroft Mighty Antar)
- 1956 (May only, 1st issue)
  'Dinky Toys' cast under the trailer,
  Yellow lid 'DINKY TOYS' box...... **£120-150**
- 1956 (June to November, 2nd issue)
  'Dinky Supertoys' casting under
  the trailer, Yellow lidded
  'DINKY TOYS' box ........................ **£90-100**
- 1956 (November) - 1957 (September)
  2nd issue in blue/white striped box,
  'DINKY SUPERTOYS' in
  block lettering................................. **£90-100**
- 1957 (October) - 1961 (November)
  2nd issue in a blue/white striped box,
  'DINKY SUPERTOYS' in
  italic printing ................................. **£90-100**
- 1961 (November) - 1963 (December)
  3rd issue with windows, blue/white striped
  box, 'DINKY SUPERTOYS' in
  italic printing ................................. **£120-140**
- 1964 (January - July)
  4th issue, with windows, detachable
  trailer, blue/white striped box,
  'DINKY SUPERTOYS'
  in italic printing .............................. **£140-160**

**660a   Anti-Aircraft Gun with Crew**
1978-80
- With three soldiers. Bubble-packed .... **£15-20**

**661    Recovery Tractor**
1957-65
- Six wheels, driver, operable crane,
  with windows from 1960, Blue/White
  Supertoys box, one packing piece..... **£80-100**
- With plastic wheels,
  in Yellow 'picture' box ................... **£150-200**

**662    88 mm. Gun with Crew**
1975-77
- German Grey (656 without wheels),
  3 crew, bubble-packed........................ **£15-20**

**665    Honest John Missile Launcher**
1964-75
- Green platform, White missile.
  Yellow Dinky Toys end-flap box .... **£120-140**
- Black platform, White missile.
  Yellow Dinky Toys end-flap box .... **£140-160**
- Green platform, Grey missile.
  Yellow scenic Supertoys lidded box . **£90-120**
- Green platform, White missile.
  Bubble-packed..................................... **£70-90**

**666    Missile Erector Vehicle and
         Corporal Missile Launcher**
1959-64
- Metal erector gears, White missile with
  Black fins, Blue/White Supertoys
  box with one packing piece............. **£200-250**
- Black plastic erector gears,
  all-White missile, Blue/White Supertoys
  box with one packing piece............. **£175-200**

**667    Missile Servicing Platform**
1960-64
- With windows, Blue/White
  Supertoys box, one packing piece... **£175-200**

**667    Armoured Patrol Car**
1976-78
- 680 body with 676 turret,
  in 'hanging' box ................................. **£15-20**

**668    Foden Army Truck**
1976-79
- With windows, plastic tilt and
  wheels, in 'hanging' box .................... **£25-35**

**669    U.S.A. Army Jeep**
1955-57
- White star,
  (US issue in 'plain' box) ................. **£200-300**

**670    Armoured Car**
1954-64
- Olive-Drab body, diecast hubs,
  yellow flap-end box............................ **£20-25**
1964-70
- Olive-Drab body, plastic hubs,
  yellow flap-end box............................ **£20-25**
- Late issue in red-sided yellow
  flap-end box........................................ **£25-35**

**671    Reconnaissance Car**
1954-55    (renumbered in 1954 from 152b)
- (Matt) Green body, for export only .... **£75-95**

**672    US Army Jeep**
1954-55    (renumbered in 1954 from 153a)
- US export issue.
  Some have rounded axle-ends............. **£75-95**

**673    Scout Car**  (Daimler)
1953-61
- Driver fixed in position,
  passenger seat hole in some ............... **£20-30**

**674    Austin Champ**
1954-66
- Cast driver fixed in position, cast steering
  wheel and risged hubs, seat holes for
  personnel, deep yellow end-flap box .. **£75-85**
- No driver, plastic steering wheel,
  cast hubs, yellow end-flap box........... **£75-85**
1966-71
- Plastic driver, plastic steering wheel,
  plastic hubs, yellow end-flap box ....... **£65-75**

**674    'U.N.' Austin Champ**
1958-70
- White body, no holes for personnel,
  yellow end-flap box.
  Made for export only...................... **£300-400**

**675    Ford US Army Staff Car**
1954-59    (renumbered in 1954 from 170m)
- Matt Olive body with cross-hatching
  cast inside roof, sheer-cut star transfers
  on doors, White circled star on roof.
  US issue in 'plain' printed box........ **£250-300**

**676    Armoured Personnel Carrier**
1955-62
- 6 wheels, revolving turret,
  yellow end-flap box............................ **£25-30**
- Late issue in red-sided yellow
  end-flap box........................................ **£30-35**

**676a   Daimler Armoured Car**
1973-76
- Speedwheels, (new version of 670) .... **£15-20**
1973-74
- French made version: With camouflage
  net, ('Made in England' on base)..........NGPP

**677    Armoured Command Vehicle**
1957-62
- 6 wheels, yellow end-flap box ............ **£60-70**

**680    Ferret Armoured Car**
1972-78
- Sand or Khaki, Speedwheels,
  bubble-pack ........................................ **£10-15**

**681    DUKW Amphibious Vehicle**
1972-78
- RAF Blue or Army-Green body,
  Speedwheels, bubble-packed ............. **£10-15**

**682    Stalwart Load Carrier**
1972-78
- 6 Speedwheels, bubble-packed ........... **£10-15**

**683    Chieftain Tank**
1972-80
- Black plastic tracks, fires shells.
  End-flap 'window' box with
  polystyrene inner or bubble-packed.... **£25-35**

## Dinky Toys Military models continued

**686  25-pounder Field Gun**
1957-71
- Cast drawbar, cast hubs (1957-68),
plastic hubs (1968-71)......................... **£10-15**

**687  25-pounder Trailer**
1957-67
- Cast hubs, plastic from 1968.
Not individually boxed........................ **£10-15**

**687  Convoy Army Truck**
1978-79
- Khaki tilt 'ARMY'. In 'hanging' box . **£10-15**

**688  Field Artillery Tractor**
1957-61
- Driver in some, no windows,
cast hubs, end-flap box....................... **£30-40**
1961-70
- Driver in some, windows,
(plastic hubs from 1968) ..................... **£30-40**

**689  Medium Artillery Tractor**
1957-65
- Driver in some, holes, 6 wheels,
tin tilt, in Blue/White Supertoys box
with lift-off lid.................................... **£80-100**
- In Yellow picture box,
plastic driver, windows ................... **£150-200**

**690  Anti-Aircraft Gun on Trailer**
1954-55  (renumbered in 1954 from 161b)
- Matt Green, made for export only .... **£80-100**

**690  Scorpion Tank**
1974-80
- Brown or Green camouflage net.
Decal sheet, spare shells. End-flap
'hanging' box or bubble-packed.......... **£15-20**

**691  Striker Anti-Tank**
1974-80
- Plastic tracks, 6 spare missiles.
Bubble-packed...................................... **£15-20**

**692  5.5 Medium Gun**
1955-62
- Twin cast drawbar, elevating barrel.
In yellow end-flap box or later
red-sided yellow end-flap box............. **£15-20**

**692  Leopard Tank**
1974-80
- Grey with German markings, plastic
tracks, 6 shells on sprue, decal sheet,
bubble-pack ........................................ **£40-50**

**693  7.2 inch Howitzer Gun**
1958-67
- Cast drawbar, yellow end-flap box,
packing piece...................................... **£30-40**

**694  Hanomag Tank Destroyer**
1975-80
- Grey, German markings,
plastic tracks/wheels, bubble-packed .. **£40-50**

**696  Leopard Anti-Aircraft Tank**
1975-80
- Grey-Green, German markings,
plastic tracks, 2 plastic sprues each
with 6 shells, bubble-packed.............. **£40-50**

**697  25 pounder Field Gun Set**
1957-71   See Gift Sets section.

**698  Tank Transporter Set**
1957-64   See Gift Sets section.

**699  Military Vehicles (1) Set**
1955-58   See Gift Sets section.

**699  Leopard Recovery Tank**
1975-77
- Grey-Green, German markings,
dozer blade/jib, aerial, tow-rope,
bubble-packed ..................................... **£40-50**

**815  Panhard Armoured Tank**
1962-64
- Olive Drab body, French flag,
French issue....................................... **£75-100**

**816  Berliet Missile Launcher**
1969-71
- Olive Drab, French issue................ **£150-200**

**817  AMX 13-ton Tank**
1962-64
- Olive Drab body, French flag,
French issue....................................... **£75-100**

**822  Half-Track M3**
1962-64
- Olive Drab body, rubber tracks,
French issue....................................... **£75-100**

**884  Brockway Bridge Truck**
1962-64
- Olive Drab, 10 wheels, bridge parts,
inflatables. French issue ................. **£200-250**

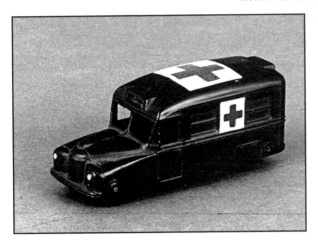

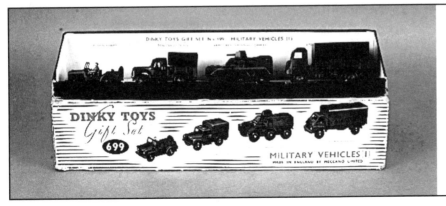

624 US issue Daimler
Military Ambulance

153a Army Jeep

699 Military Vehicles
Set (1)

PHOTO: VECTIS AUCTIONS LTD.

150

| Model and details | MPR |
| --- | --- |

| Model and details | MPR |
| --- | --- |

| Model and details | MPR |
| --- | --- |

**60a  Imperial Airways Liner**
(Armstrong-Whitworth Atalanta)
1934-36
- Cast body, tinplate wings,
  4 x 2-blade propellers.
  Various colours, in three different patterns:
  1: 'Sunray' main colour with contrasting
     radial stripes on wings: Silver/Blue,
     Gold/Blue, Yellow/Blue, Blue/Yellow,
     Red/Cream, Cream/Red, Cream/Green,
     White/Blue, White/Blue/Green.
  2: 'Two-tone' main colour with
     contrasting tail and wingtips:
     Gold/Blue, Yellow/Blue,
     Cream/Green, Gold/Blue, Yellow/Blue,
     Cream/Green, Cream/Red.
  3: 'Striped' main colour with contrasting
     chordwise stripes and tail:
     Cream/Green, White/Blue.
  Other variations on these themes
  may exist, all without registration
  marks. Each ..................................... **£500-600**
  1936-39
- Blue, Pale Blue, Cream, Gold, Red,
  Silver or White; all with
  Black 'G-ABTI' marking ............... **£500-600**
  1939-41
- Gold, Green or Silver, 'G-ABTI',
  'Imperial Airways Liner' under
  wing, (reissued as 66a) .................... **£500-600**

**60b  De Havilland 'Leopard Moth'**
1934-36
- Cast fuselage, tinplate wings, single
  2-blade propeller. Green with Yellow
  tail and wingtips or Dark Blue/Orange,
  Silver/Green, Blue/Yellow, Blue/Red,
  Gold/Red, no markings,
  open windows................................. **£500-600**
  1936-39
- All-over Light Green, Dark Green,
  Gold, Silver, Beige, Blue, Pale Blue
  or Red, 'G-ACPT', open windows . **£300-500**
  1939-39
- As previous model, but with
  'DH Leopard Moth' under wing.
  Green, Gold or Silver, 'G-ACPT' ... **£200-300**
  1939-41
- As previous model, but blank side
  windows. Green, Gold or Silver,
  'G-ACPT', (reissued as 66b) .......... **£200-300**

**60c  Percival 'Gull' Monoplane**
1934-36
- Cast fuselage, tinplate wings, large
  2-blade propeller. Reissued as 60k.
  Blue with Red tail and wingtips,
  Red/Blue, Buff/White, Buff/Blue,
  Buff/Red, Gold/Green, Red/White,
  Silver/Green, White/Green,
  White/Blue, open windows,
  no registration markings................ **£100-150**
  1936-39
- White, Red, Yellow, Light Blue, Blue,
  Silver, Buff, 'G-ADZO' in Black,
  open windows,
  (Silver version renumbered to 60k) **£100-150**
  1939-39
- As 1936-39 version above, but with
  underwing stamped 'PERCIVAL GULL'.
  White, Red, Yellow, Blue,
  'G-ADZO' in Black......................... **£200-300**
  1939-41
- Same but blank or open side windows,
  'Percival Gull' under wing,
  (reissued as 66c)............................ **£200-300**

**60c  'Lewis's' 'Amy Mollinson'**
1936-36
- Souvenir Issue. Mid-Blue with Silver wings
  and a Blue 'G-ADZO' marking. Sold at
  Lewis's of Liverpool department store in
  special 'LEWIS' yellow box.
  (Renumbered 60k when sold in
  normal yellow box) ........................ **£400-500**

**60d  Low Wing Monoplane** (Vickers Jockey)
1934-36
- Cast body, tinplate wings, 2-blade
  propeller. Red with Cream tail and
  wingtips, Orange/Cream, Blue/Yellow,
  Silver/Red or Gold/Blue,
  no markings, no pilot ..................... **£100-150**
  1936-41
- Red, Orange, Blue, Gold, Silver, Black
  or Yellow, 'G-AVYP', pilot's head
  cast-in, (reissued as 66d)............... **£100-150**
- Red with cream tail and wingtips,
  no pilot, with 'G-AVPY' marking.........NGPP
- As previous but with pilot....................NGPP

**60e  General 'Monospar'**
1934-36
- Two-piece diecasting, 2 x 2-blade
  propellers. Pale Blue with White tail
  and wingtips, Cream/Red, Red/Cream,
  Salmon/Blue or Silver/Blue,
  Gold/Red, no markings .................. **£100-150**
  1936-41
- Silver, Lilac or Gold, 'G-ABVP' in
  Black, (reissued as 66e) ................. **£100-150**
- Same but with 'General Monospar',
  Cream, Gold, Lilac, Silver or Blue . **£100-150**

**60f  Cierva 'Autogiro'**
1934-36
- Gold body with Blue rotors and
  trim, no pilot................................. **£200-300**
  1936-41
- Gold body with Blue trim,
  unpainted rotors, pilot cast-in,
  (reissued as 66f) ............................ **£150-200**
  1936-41
- Red body with Cream trim, Cream
  or Silver rotors, pilot cast-in .......... **£150-200**

**60g  De Havilland 'Comet'**
1935-36
- Cast fuselage and wings, enclosed
  wheels, 2 x 2-blade propellers.
  Silver, Red or Gold with Black
  registration 'G-ACSR' (no
  underwing description).................. **£100-125**
  1936-41
- Silver, Red or Gold with Black
  registration 'G-ACSR',
  ('DH COMET' underwing)............. **£100-125**

**60g  Light Racer** (DH 'Comet')
1945-49
- Yellow, Red or Silver, 'G-RACE',
  'Light Racer' under wing,
  2 x 3-blade propellers...................... **£175-225**

**60h  'Singapore' Flying Boat**
1936-36
- Cast fuselage (126 mm.), tinplate
  wings, 4 x 2-blade propellers (early
  hulls lead). Fully-moulded bow,
  no roller, Silver with stencilled
  RAF roundels ................................ **£350-450**
  1936-37
- As previous model but with Red
  or Green plastic roller .................... **£350-450**
  1937-39

- As previous model (with Red or
  Green plastic roller) and with
  'Gliding Game' hole........................ **£350-450**
  1939-40
- With Red or Green plastic roller,
  'Gliding Game' hole and waterslide
  transfer RAF roundels .................... **£350-450**
  1940-40
- Hollowed bow, wooden roller, no
  'Gliding Game' hole, painted or
  transfer roundels............................ **£350-450**
  1940-41
- As previous model, but in Pale
  Grey with transfer roundels............. **£350-450**
  1941 ?
- Same but with name under wing..... **£350-450**

**60k  Percival 'Gull'** (Amy Mollison)
1936-41
- Blue/Silver version of 60c,
  'G-ADZO' in Blue, special box ...... **£300-400**

**60k  Percival 'Gull'** (H. L. Brook)
1936-41
- Blue/Silver version of 60c,
  'G-ADZO' in Black, special box .... **£300-400**

**60k  Light Tourer** (Percival 'Gull')
1945-48
- Red, Silver or Dark or Light Green,
  'Light Tourer' or 'Percival Tourer'
  under wing, no markings,
  small or large 2-blade propeller,
  (renumbered from 60c) ................. **£150-200**

**60m  Four Engined Flying Boat**
1936-41
- Red, Pale Blue, Light Blue, Mid Blue,
  Dark Blue, Light Green, Mid-Green,
  Dark Green, Gold, Cream or Silver.
  'Civilian' version of 60h with
  'G-EUTC', 'G-EUTG', 'G-EVCU',
  'G-EXCF', 'G-EXGF', 'G-EXFE',
  'G-EYCE' or 'G-EYTV' ................ **£175-225**
  **NB**  With or without bow hollow,
        wood or plastic roller or gliding hole.

**60n  Fairey 'Battle' Bomber**
1937-40
- Silver or Grey, RAF roundels,
  1 x 3-blade propeller, undercarriage . **£90-120**
  1938-41
- Silver or Grey, RAF roundels,
  1 x 3-blade propeller, without
  undercarriage, (reissued as 60s) ...... **£120-150**
  **NB**  Early issues did not have name
        of plane cast in.

**60p  Gloster 'Gladiator'**
1936-39
- Silver, stencilled roundels,
  Red 1 x 2-blade propeller,
  no name under wing....................... **£100-140**
  1939-41
- Silver or Grey, transfer roundels,
  'Gloster Gladiator' under wing ....... **£100-140**

**60r  Empire Flying Boat**
1937-40
- Silver, 4 x 3-blade propellers, Red plastic
  roller, hole, own box. Liveries:
- 'CALEDONIA' ('G-ADHM')......... **£250-350**
- 'CALPURNIA' ('G-AETW').......... **£250-350**
- 'CALYPSO' ('G-AEUA') ............. **£250-350**
- 'CAMBRIA' ('G-ADUV') ............ **£250-350**
- 'CAMILLA' ('G-AEUB') ............. **£250-350**
- 'CANOPUS' ('G-ADHL')............. **£250-350**
- 'CAPELLA' ('G-ADUY') ............. **£250-350**
- 'CENTURION' ('G-ADVE')......... **£250-350**
- 'CERES' ('G-AETX')................... **£250-350**

- 'CHALLENGER' ('G-ADVD')...... **£250-350**
- 'CHEVIOT' ('G-AEUG') .............. **£250-350**
- 'CLIO' ('G-AETY') ....................... **£250-350**
- 'CORDELIA' ('G-AEUD')............ **£250-350**
- 'CORINNA' ('G-AEUC') ............. **£250-350**
- 'CORSAIR' ('G-ADVB') .............. **£250-350**
  1940-49 (reissued as 60x)
  As previous models but plastic, wood or
  brass roller, no hole.
- 'CALEDONIA', ('G-ADHM')........ **£200-250**
- 'CAMBRIA', ('G-ADUV')............ **£200-250**

NB Camouflage issues: Early issues have
Red/White/Blue roundels with a Yellow
outer ring. The later (rarer) issues have a
darker camouflage with just Blue/Red
roundels.

**60s    Medium Bomber**
1938-40
- Camouflaged 60n with undercarriage,
  single roundel has Yellow ring,
  (reissue of 60n)................................ **£100-150**

**60s    Fairy 'Battle' Bomber**
1940-41
- Camouflaged body, two Blue/Red
  roundels, no undercarriage,
  1 x 3-blade propeller ...................... **£150-200**

NB Early issues did not have the name
of the plane cast in.

**60t    Douglas DC3 Air Liner**
1938-41
- Silver, 'PH-ALI' 2 x 3-blade propellers,
  'Gliding Game' hole, tail wheel on
  some, own box ................................ **£200-300**

**60v    Armstrong Whitworth Bomber**
1937-41
- Silver body, 'Gliding Game' hole in some,
  RAF roundels, 2 x 3-blade propellers,
  (reissued as 62t)................................ **£200-300**

**60w    Flying Boat 'Clipper III'** (Sikorsky S32)
1938-40
- Silver body, 'USA NC16736',
  4 x 3-blade propellers,
  plastic roller, 'gliding' hole ............. **£150-200**
- US issue: Silver body,
  'NC 16736' markings, 'gliding' hole,
  Red plastic roller, leaflet ................. **£250-350**

**60w    Flying Boat**
1945-48
- Silver, Blue or Green, no markings,
  4 x 3-blade propellers, brass roller.. **£150-200**

**60x    Atlantic Flying Boat**
1937-41 (reissue of 60r)
- Blue/Cream, 4 x 3-blade propellers,
  'DAUNTLESS' ('G-AZBP'),
  name under wing............................. **£500-750**
- Green/Cream,
  'WHIRLWIND' ('G-AZBT') ......... **£500-750**
- Black/White,
  'DREADNOUGHT' ('G-AZBV') .. **£500-750**
- Orange/Cream,
  'SWIFTSURE' ('G-AZBU')......... **£500-750**
- Blue/Cream,
  'ENTERPRISE' ('G-AZBR').......... **£500-750**
- Black/Cream,
  'ENDEAVOUR' ('G-AZBQ')........ **£500-750**
- Red/Cream,
  'VALORIUS' ('G-AZBS') ............. **£500-750**

**62a    Vickers-Supermarine 'Spitfire'**
1939-41
- Silver body (short nose), RAF
  roundels, 1 x 3-blade propeller ....... **£100-130**
  1940-41 'Meccano Spitfire Fund'
- Model 62a in special souvenir box
  (at 2/6 each). Brass ring through fin
  allows use as badge or pendant.
  Proceeds went to Spitfire Fund.

Blue, Green, Grey, Magenta, Red,
Yellow, or Camouflage.................... **£500-750**
- Chromium plated version
  (originally 10s.6d.) .................... **£1,000-1,200**

**62a    'Spitfire'**
1945-49
- Silver, (long nose, bubble cockpit),
  RAF roundels, 1 x 3-blade propeller .. **£35-45**

**62b    Bristol 'Blenheim' Bomber**
1939-41
- Silver body, RAF roundels, Red
  2 x 3-blade propellers,
  name under wing............................. **£100-150**

**62b    Medium Bomber**
1945-49
- Silver body, RAF roundels, 2 x 3-blade
  Red propellers, name under wing ....... **£60-80**

**62d    Bristol 'Blenheim' Bomber**
1940-41
- 62b in Camouflage/Black/White,
  RAF roundels,
  2 x 3-blade propellers..................... **£100-150**

**62e    Vickers-Supermarine 'Spitfire'**
1940-41
- 62a in Camouflage/Black/White, RAF
  roundels, 1 x 3-blade propeller ....... **£100-150**

**62f    D.H. Flamingo Airliner**
1939 ?
Not issued (some unofficial
non-Meccano 'Flamingos' in
white-metal may be found) .................... NPP

**62g    Boeing 'Flying Fortress'**
1939-41
- Silver, 4 x 3-blade propellers,
  'Gliding Game' hole, name under
  wing, 'U.S.A.A.C.'/stars, own box . **£200-250**
- Pale Grey version,
  no 'Gliding Game' hole.........................NGPP

**62g    Long Range Bomber**
1945-48
- Silver body, Red 4 x 3-blade propellers,
  no 'Gliding Game' hole, not boxed. **£125-150**

**62h    Hawker Hurricane Fighter**
1938-41
- Camouflaged body, RAF roundels,
  1 x 2-blade propeller,
  undercarriage on some ................... **£100-130**

**62k    The King's Aeroplane**
1938-41
- Airspeed 'Envoy', Silver/Red/Blue,
  'G-AEXX', 2 x 2-blade propellers,
  own box ......................................... **£300-400**

**62m    Airspeed 'Envoy' Monoplane**
1938-41
- Red ('G-ABDA' or 'G-ACVJ')....... **£300-400**
- Yellow ('G-ACMJ', 'G-ACMT' or
  'G-ACVJ')...................................... **£300-400**
- Silver ('G-ACVI' or 'G-ADCB').... **£300-400**
- Blue ('G-ADAZ' or 'G-ADCA')..... **£300-400**
- Pale Green ('GADCA')................. **£300-400**
- Pale Green ('G-AENA') ................ **£300-400**
- Mid-Green ('G-AENA') ................ **£300-400**
- Gold ('G-AMTC')......................... **£300-400**

**62m    Light Transport Plane**
1945-48
- Red, Yellow, Silver or Blue,
  'G-ATMH', 2 x 2-blade propellers,
  name under wing............................. **£100-125**

**62n    Junkers 'Ju90' Air Liner**
1938-41
- Silver, 4 x 3-blade propellers, own box.
- 'D-AALU'..................................... **£200-300**
- 'D-ADLH'..................................... **£250-350**
- 'D-AIVI'....................................... **£250-350**

- 'D-AURE' ..................................... **£250-350**

**62p    'Ensign' Air Liner**
1938-41
Silver, Red 4 x 3-blade propellers,
gliding hole in some, own box. Liveries:
- 'ECHO' ('G-ADTB')..................... **£250-350**
- 'ELSINORE' ('G-ADST') ............. **£250-350**
- 'ELYSIAN' ('G-ADSZ')................ **£250-350**
- 'ENSIGN' ('G-ADSR')................. **£250-350**
- 'ETTRICK' ('G-ADSX') .............. **£250-350**
- 'EXPLORER' ('G-ADSV')........... **£250-350**

**62p    Armstrong Whitworth Air Liner**
1945-49
As previous casting but no 'Gliding Game'
hole, name under wing, no box,
Silver, Blue or Green, with Silver or
Grey/Green trim.
- 'ECHO' ('G-ADTB') ..................... **£300-400**
- 'EXPLORER' ('G-ADSV') ........... **£300-400**

**62r    D.H. 'Albatross' Mail Liner**
1939-41
- Silver, 'G-AEVV', 4 x 3-blade Red
  propellers, 'Gliding Game' hole,
  name under wing, own box ............. **£300-400**

**62r    Four Engined Liner**
1945-49
- Grey, Light Blue (Red trim) or
  Silver (Red trim), no markings,
  no hole, not boxed........................... **£100-130**
- Grey, Fawn, Light Blue or Silver,
  'G-ATPV',
  4 x 3-blade Red propellers ............. **£100-130**

**62s    Hawker 'Hurricane' Fighter**
1939-41
- Silver body, RAF roundels,
  with or without undercarriage,
  single propeller with 2 or 3 blades.... **£90-120**
  1945-49
- Silver body, RAF roundels, no
  undercarriage, 1 x 3-blade propeller ... **£60-70**

**62t    Armstrong Whitley Bomber**
1939-41 (reissue of 60v)
- Light Green/Brown camouflage,
  Yellow ring roundels,
  2 x 3-blade propellers, box.............. **£200-300**
- Dark camouflage, Yellow roundels . **£200-300**
- Dark camouflage,
  Red / Blue roundels......................... **£200-300**

**62w    'Frobisher' Class Air Liner**
1939-41 (renumbered 68b)
Silver (casting as 62r),
4 x 3-blade propellers, 'Gliding Game'
hole, own box, 3 liveries:
- 'FALCON' ('G-AFDJ')................... **£250-350**
- 'FORTUNA' ('G-AFDK')............. **£250-350**
- 'FROBISHER' ('G-AFDI')............ **£250-350**

**62x    British 40 Seat Airliner**
1939-41 (renumbered 68a)
'G-AZCA', not boxed, with or without
'Gliding Game' hole. Colours:
- Grey/Green, Red/Maroon,
  Two-tone Green, Two-tone Blue,
  Blue/Silver, Yellow/Maroon........... **£200-250**

**62y    Giant High Speed Monoplane**
1939-40
- 'D-AZBK', 'Gliding Game' hole,
  not boxed. Colours:
  Blue/Brown, Blue/Silver, Blue/Cream,
  Olive/Green, Yellow/Maroon,
  Red/Maroon, Two-tone Blue or
  Two-tone Green............................... **£500-750**
  1945-49
- 'G-ATBK', no hole or box. Colours:
  Light/Dark Green, Grey/Green
  or Silver......................................... **£100-125**

**63  Mayo Composite Aircraft**
1939-41
- Models 63a (fitted with special tinplate clip) and 63b together in special box (see below) .................. **£700-800**

**63a  Flying Boat 'MAIA'**
1939-41
- Silver, 'G-ADHK', 'Mayo Composite' under wing, own box ........................ **£100-150**

**63b  Seaplane 'MERCURY'**
1939-41
- Silver, 'G-ADHJ', 'Mercury Seaplane' under wing, 'Gliding Game' hole in some ............................................... **£75-100**

**63b  Seaplane**
1945-49
- Silver, 'G-AVKW', 'Seaplane' under wing, no 'Gliding Game' hole........... **£90-120**
1952-57
- Reissue of 63b Seaplane, same as previous model, (renumbered 700) ... **£90-120**

**66a  Heavy Bomber**
1940-41  (reissue of 60a)
- Camouflaged, RAF roundels, 4 x 2-blade propellers, no name under wing ....................... **£250-300**

**66b  Dive Bomber Fighter**
1940-41  (reissue of 60b)
- Camouflaged, RAF roundels, 1 x 2-blade propeller ....................... **£150-200**

**66c  Two Seater Fighter**
1940-41  (reissue of 60c)
- Camouflaged, RAF roundels, 1 x 2-blade propeller ....................... **£150-200**

**66d  Torpedo Dive Bomber**
1940-41  (reissue of 60d)
- Camouflaged, RAF roundels, 1 x 2-blade propeller ....................... **£150-200**

**66e  Medium Bomber**
1940-41  (reissue of 60e)
- Camouflaged, RAF roundels, 2 x 2-blade propellers, 'General Monospar' under .............. **£150-200**

**66f  Army Co-operation Autogiro**
1940-41  (reissue of 60f)
- Silver body and blades, Red/White/Blue roundels ............... **£150-200**

**67a  Junkers Ju89 Heavy Bomber**
1940-41
- Matt-Black with Light Blue underside, Red propellers, Silver cockpit area, Luftwaffe insignia, with or without 'Gliding Game' hole.................... **£750-1,000**

**68a  'Ensign' Air Liner**
1940-41
- Camouflaged, RAF roundels, no 'Gliding Game' hole, 4 x 3-blade propellers..................... **£300-400**

**68b  'Frobisher' Class Air Liner**
1940-41  (renumbered from 62w)
- Light or Dark Camouflage, RAF roundels, 4 x 3-blade propellers, 'Gliding Game' hole in some .......... **£150-200**

**70a  Avro 'York' Airliner**
1946-49  (renumbered 704)
- Silver body, 'G-AGJC', Red 4 x 3-blade propellers. Early version has Silver propeller pins, tinplate base and blue wash cockpit .................... **£125-150**

**70b  Tempest II Fighter**
1946-49  (renumbered 730)
- Silver with blued canopy, Yellow band on fuselage roundels, pointed spinner ................................... **£35-45**

**70c  Viking Air Liner**
1947-49  (reissued as 705)
- Silver or Grey body, 'G-AGOL', Red 2 x 4-blade propellers, large pointed spinners.......................... **£55-65**

**70d  Twin-Engined Fighter**
1946-49  (reissued as 731)
- Silver body with blued canopy .......... **£35-45**
- Variation:  As previous model but 'N' in 'MECCANO' is reversed ................ **£35-45**

**70e  Gloster 'Meteor'**
1946-49  (renumbered 732)
- Silver body with blued canopy, Black engine intakes, large roundels... **£35-45**

**70f  Lockheed 'Shooting Star'**
1947-49  (renumbered 733)
- Silver body with blued canopy, Black air intakes, USAF star on port wing ... **£35-45**

**700  Seaplane**
1954-57  (renumbered from 63b)
- Silver body, 'G-AVKW' marking...... **£75-100**
- Silver body, 'G-AVKW', no 'Gliding Game' hole, 'Seaplane' under wing .. **£75-100**

**700  Spitfire Mark II ('Jubilee')**
1979
- Plated model on plinth, 1 x 3-blade propeller, 'Diamond Jubilee of the RAF', Blue card display box .......... **£150-175**

**701  Short 'Shetland' Flying Boat**
1947-49
- Silver, 'G-AGVD', 4 x 4-blade Black propellers, first Supertoys aircraft, own box .......................................... **£500-600**

**702  DH 'Comet' Jet Airliner 'BOAC'**
1954-55  (renumbered in 1954 to 999)
- White/Blue body, Silver wings and tail, 'G-ALYV', Gold wheels. Blue/white box ...............................**£110-130**

**704  Avro 'York' Airliner**
1954-59  (renumbered in 1954 from 70a)
- Silver, 'G-AGJC', 4 x 3-blade Red propellers, ('704' beneath wing) ..... **£125-150**

**705  'Viking' Air Liner**
1952-62  (renumbered 70c)
- Silver body with 'G-AGOL' marking, flat head spinners............................... **£60-75**
- Silver or Grey body, 'G-AGOL', 2 x 4-blade Red propellers ................. **£60-75**

**706  Vickers 'Viscount' Airliner**
1956-57
- Silver/Blue/White, 'AIR FRANCE', 'F-BGNL', 4 x 4-blade Red propellers ............. **£100-125**

**708  Vickers 'Viscount' Airliner**
1957-65
- Silver/White or Metallic Grey/White, 'B.E.A.', 'G-AOJA'........................ **£100-125**

**710  Beechcraft S35 'Bonanza'**
1965-76
- Red/White, Bronze/Yellow, or Red/Blue/White body, 1 x 2-blade propeller ........................... **£40-50**
- German promotional:  Green/White, 'GLUCK MIT WICKULER' on towing pennant and box ................. **£400-500**

**712  US Army T.42A**
1972-77
- Military Green (715), Beechcraft plus wing-tip tanks, 2 x 2-blade propellers **£60-75**

**715  Bristol 173 Helicopter**
1956-62
- Turquoise body with Red stripe and Red rotors, 'G-AUXR' ....................... **£65-75**

**715  Beechcraft C55 'Baron'**
1968-76
- White/Yellow or Red/Yellow body, Yellow 2 x 2-blade propellers ............. **£40-50**

**716  Westland Sikorsky 'S-51'**
1957-62
- Red and Cream helicopter body, 2 x 3-blade rotors ................................ **£40-50**

**717  Boeing '737'**
- White/Blue body, 'LUFTHANSA', White or Blue engine pods.................. **£65-75**

**718  Hawker 'Hurricane' Mk.IIc**
1972-75
- Camouflaged body, RAF roundels, Black 1 x 3-blade propeller, guns ....... **£75-95**

**719  Spitfire Mk.II**
1969-77  (renumbered 741)
- Camouflaged, RAF roundels, Black 3-blade propeller is battery-operated................................**£90-110**
- Early issues in 'Battle of Britain' pictorial card box.............................. **£75-95**

**721  Junkers Ju87b Stuka**
1969-80
- Camouflage/Yellow, German markings, 1 x 3-blade propeller, cap-firing bomb ............................. **£150-175**
- Early issues in 'Battle of Britain' pictorial card box.............................**£90-110**

**722  Hawker 'Harrier'**
1970-80
- Metallic Blue/Olive camouflage, RAF markings, pilot, aerial.............. **£80-100**

**723  Hawker Siddeley HS 125**
1970-73
- Yellow/White/Blue or Metallic Blue/White, drop-down door/steps ..... **£35-45**
1973-73
- 'Hawker Executive Jet'. Yellow/White/Blue. In bubble-pack with English and French text. Possibly a promotional sample ....... **£400-600**

**724  'Sea King' Helicopter**
1971-79
- Metallic Blue/White, 5-blade rotors, with 'Apollo' space capsule ............... **£50-60**
- Early issues in card picture box with pictorial inner stand.................... **£40-50**

**725  Royal Navy 'Phantom II'**
1972-77
- Dark Blue body, Black nose, roundels, decals in bubble-pack .......... **£80-90**

**726  Messerschmitt Bf-109E**
1972-74
- Desert camouflage, single 3-blade propeller, decals in bubble-pack...... **£200-250**
1974-76
- Grey/Green camouflage, Yellow wing-tips/nose, decals in bubble-pack...................... **£200-250**

**727  U.S.A.F. Phantom F4 Mark II**
1976-77
- Brown/Olive camouflage, 2 missiles, 2 figures, no transfers, US market .. **£500-750**

# Dinky Toys Aircraft continued

**728    R.A.F. 'Dominie'**
1972-75
- Metallic Blue and camouflage, roundels, retractable wheels, bubble-pack ......... **£40-50**

**729    Multi-Role Combat Aircraft**
1974-76
- Grey/Camouflage, swing-wings, decals in bubble-pack ......................... **£40-50**

**730    Tempest II Fighter**
1952-55    (renumbered from 70b)
- Same as 70b but without blued canopy and with flat spinner ............... **£40-50**

**730    US Navy 'Phantom II'**
1972-76
- Grey/Red, 'NAVY', 'USS Saratoga', fires missiles, retractable wheels......... **£80-90**

**731    Twin-Engined Fighter**
1952-55    (reissue of 70d)
- Silver body, no blued canopy.............. **£25-35**

**731    S.E.P.E.C.A.T. 'Jaguar'**
1973-76
- Metallic Blue and camouflage body, Orange pilot, opening cockpit............ **£40-50**

**732    Gloster 'Meteor'**
1952-62    (reissue of 70e)
- Silver body without blued canopy, small roundels ..................................... **£25-35**
- Shiny Silver body with large roundels..NGPP

**732    Bell 'POLICE' Helicopter**
1974-80
- Orange/Blue/White or Red body, sign boards and cones ........................ **£35-45**

**732    'M.A.S.H.' Helicopter**
1979
- Green body with 'M.A.S.H.' stickers....NGPP

**733    Lockheed 'Shooting Star'**
1952-62    (reissue of 70f)
- Silver body with blued canopy ........... **£25-35**
- Variant with the word 'in' of 'Made in England by Meccano Ltd' missing........NGPP

**733    German 'Phantom II'**
1973-76
- Grey/Green camouflage body, 'Bundesluftwaffe', two white missiles, instructions and transfers, (German/Austrian market) .............. **£500-600**
1976-77
**US F-4K 'Phantom II'**
- Brown camouflage, retractable wheels, fires missiles, (US market only).......... **£80-90**

**734    Supermarine 'Swift'**
1955-62
- Grey/Green camouflaged body, RAF markings ................................... **£30-40**

**734    P47 'Thunderbolt'**
1975-78
- Metallic Silver/Black, Red 4-blade propeller, retractable wheels, 'U.S.A.A.F.'...... **£125-175**

**735    Gloster 'Javelin'**
1956-66
- Camouflaged 'delta-wing' body, RAF markings, smooth (later treaded) wheels ............. **£40-60**

**736    Hawker 'Hunter'**
1955-63
- Camouflaged body, RAF markings..... **£30-40**

**736    Bundesmarine 'Sea King'**
1973-78
- Grey/Orange helicopter, German markings, decals in bubble-pack......... **£45-55**

**737    P.1B 'Lightning' Fighter**
1959-68
- Silver, with metal wheels ................... **£60-80**
- Met. Grey, Black plastic wheels...... **£100-125**

**738    DH 110 'Sea Vixen' Fighter**
1960-65
- Grey/White body, Black nose, RAF roundels, 'ROYAL NAVY'......... **£60-80**

**739    A6M5 'Zero Sen'**
1975-78
- Metallic Blue/Black, Japanese markings, decals in bubble-pack......... **£60-80**
- Same, but in Metallic Green/Black. **£125-175**

**741    Spitfire Mk.II**
1978-80
- Camouflaged body, (non-motorised version of 719)........ **£80-100**

**749    RAF Avro 'Vulcan' Bomber**
1955-56    (renumbered 992)
- Silver body (aluminium). Only 500 models were made (for Canadian market). 992 is the catalogue (and box) number, '749' is cast into the model. Two castings exist; one has pointed wingtips, the other is more rounded ......... **£1,500-2,000**

**997    Caravelle SE 210 Airliner**
1962-65
- Silver/White/Blue, 'AIR FRANCE', 'F-BGNY', metal or plastic wheels, Yellow lidded picture box with card support .................................... **£100-150**

**998    Bristol 'Britannia'**
1959-64
- Silver with 'CANADIAN PACIFIC' livery in Blue/White, 'CF-CZA' in Blue on wing, striped picture box with card support............................ **£250-275**
1964-65
- As previous model but with Silver-Grey wings. Yellow lidded picture box, card support .................................... **£200-250**

**999    DH 'Comet' Jet Airliner**
1955-65    (reissue of 702)
- White body, Blue fin, Silver wings, 'G-ALYV', 'No. 999' cast in underwing.
- Early issues came in Blue/White striped box with an oval '999' sticker over the '702' print. Later boxes were Yellow/Red with printed '999'........ **£100-125**
- As above, but with 'G-ALYX'........ **£100-125**
- As previous but Silver-Grey wings. **£100-125**

**BOX TYPES:**
Many 1970-79 issues were 'vacuform' packed and these include model nos: 710,712, 715, 717, 718, 721 to 734 inclusive, plus 736 and 739.

---

**Recommended reading:**

**'Dinky Toys Aeroplanes - A Collectors Guide and Checklist'**. Contact D.C. Barratt, 230 Earlham Road, Norwich, Norfolk, NR2 3RH. (Tel: 01603-453650).

---

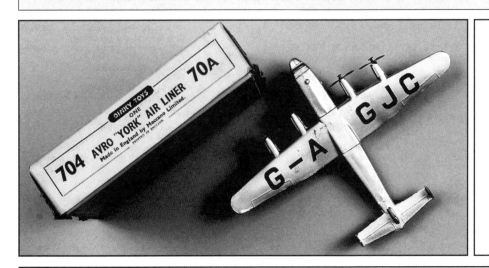

Dinky Toys
70a / 704
Avro 'York'
Air Liner
with
a dual-numbered
trade box

PHOTO: VECTIS AUCTIONS LTD.

# Dinky Toys Public Transport Vehicles

**16 Silver Jubilee Set**
1936-37
- Locomotive and two interlocking coaches, 'LNER' and '2590' cast-in, open windows, smooth hubs with White tyres, special box. Silver loco and coaches, Grey, Mid-Blue, Dark Blue, Red or Orange trim....... **£200-250**
- Silver loco and coaches, Dark Blue trim.............................. **£200-250**
- Cream loco and coaches with Red trim............................. **£250-275**
- Blue loco and coaches, Dark Blue trim.............................. **£250-275**
- Green loco / coaches, Dark Green trim ............................ **£250-275**

**16 Streamlined Train Set**
1937-40
- As previous models but changed name and box .................................. **£200-250**
1946-52
- Blue/Black loco, 'LNER', Brown/Grey coaches, filled windows, Black tyres. Individually boxed in buff box with divisions, yellow label lid end ........ **£125-150**
1952-54
- As previous model but with 'BR' crest on tender ....................... **£100-125**
1954  Model renumbered to 798

**16z Articulated Train**
1935-40
- Two-tone Blue, or Gold/Red, or Cream with Red, Blue or Orange. French issue sold in UK .................. **£200-250**

**17 Passenger Train Set**
1935-40
- Black/Maroon loco 17a, Maroon tender 17b, Maroon/Cream coaches 20a/20b ..... **£200-300**
- Black/Green loco 17a, Green tender 17b, 2 Green/Cream coaches 20a/20b ..... **£200-300**
- Lead and mazak set in 2nd type box with correct colour spot .......... **£400-500**

**17a Locomotive**
1934-40
- Black/Maroon or Black/Green, diecast cab/boiler, lead chassis........ **£100-125**

**17b Tender**
1934-40
- Maroon or Green diecast body............ **£40-50**

**18 Tank Goods Train Set**
1935-40
- Green/Black loco (21a), and 3 Green/Black open wagons (21b).. **£200-300**

**19 Mixed Goods Train**
1935-40
- Maroon/Black loco (21a), Green/Red open wagon (21b), Red/Blue 'SHELL' tanker wagon (21d), Yellow/Red/Green lumber wagon (21e)...... **£400-500**
- Set 19 in 3rd type pictorial landscape box .............................. **£800-1,000**

**20 Tank Passenger Set**
1935-40
- Green/Black loco (21a), 2 Brown/Green coaches (20a), Guard's van (20b)............................ **£300-400**

**20a Coach**
1935-40
- Brown/Cream or Green/White roof, diecast body, lead chassis.................... **£60-75**

**20b Guard's Van**
1935-40
- Brown/Cream or Green/White roof, diecast body, lead chassis.................... **£60-75**

**21 Hornby Train Set**
1932-33
- Blue/Red loco (21a), Green open wagon (21b), Green/Blue crane wagon (21c), Red/Blue 'SHELL' tank wagon (21d), Yellow/Red/Green lumber wagon (21e), 'HORNBY SERIES' cast into lead body. Red card box.......................... **£500-600**

**21 Modelled Miniatures Train Set**
- 1934-35  Contents as previous set, in Red card box ............................. **£400-500**

**21a Tank Locomotive**
1932-34
- Red/Blue 0-6-0 tank loco, 'HORNBY SERIES' cast into lead body ............. **£75-100**
1934-41
- Maroon/Black or Green/Black, 'DINKY TOYS' cast into lead body . **£75-100**

**21b Open Wagon**
1932-34
- Green/Red, Green/Blue, Green/Black, Maroon/Black, 'HORNBY SERIES' cast into lead body............................. **£50-70**
1934-41
- Green/Red, Green/Blue, Green/Black, Maroon/Black, 'DINKY TOYS' cast into lead body ... **£50-70**

**21c Crane Wagon**
1932-34
- Green body, Blue chassis, 'HORNBY SERIES' cast-in, lead....... **£50-70**

**21d Tanker Wagon**
1932-34
- Red tank, Blue or Black chassis, 'HORNBY SERIES' cast-in, lead....... **£50-70**
1934-41
- Red tank, Blue or Black chassis, 'DINKY TOYS' cast-in, lead.............. **£50-70**

**21e Lumber Wagon**
1932-34
- Brown/Blue, Yellow/Red or Yellow/Black, 'HORNBY SERIES' in lead .............. **£50-70**
1934-41
- Brown/Blue, Yellow/Red or Yellow/Black, 'DINKY TOYS', lead ......................... **£50-70**

**26 G.W.R. Rail Car**
1934-40
- Early issues are lead, later issues mazak, plastic rollers. Cream roof, Brown, Green, Yellow or Red body............. **£125-150**
- Green body with Red roof.............. **£125-150**

**26z Diesel Road Car**
1937-40
- Cream roof, Red, Green, Orange, Yellow or Blue body. (French)........ **£100-125**

**27 Tram Car**
1934-38
- Plastic or metal wheels, Red 'OVALTINE' or 'LIPTONS TEA' or no logo. Red, Orange, Green, Yellow or Light or Dark Blue body, Cream upper windows and roof...... **£200-250**
- Light Blue or Dark Blue body, Cream lower/upper windows and roof ....... **£200-250**

**29 Motor Bus**
1934-38  (renumbered to 29a)
- Plastic or metal wheels, no logo, or Silver or Red 'MARMITE'. Blue, Green, Maroon, Yellow or Red body, Cream or Silver roof...... **£200-250**

**29b Streamlined Bus**
1936-46
- Green, Orange or Red coach body, all with Cream wheel covers, Black or White tyres, smooth hubs . **£100-125**
- Two-tone Blue, Yellow/Orange, Red/Maroon, Two-tone Green, or Turquoise/Red, smooth Black hubs, open rear window ................. **£100-125**
1946-47
- Cream and Dark Blue, smooth hubs, open windows ......................... **£100-125**
1947-50
- Grass Green/Light Green, Light Green/Dark Green, Grey/Blue, Grey/Red or Two-tone Blue body, Black tyres on ridged hubs, filled-in rear window ............ **£100-125**

**29c Double Decker Bus**
The different casting types are shown in the attached diagrams.
1938-40
**'DUNLOP TYRES'**
1st Type AEC/STL, cutaway wings, stairs cast-in, smooth hubs, White tyres, crimped axle ends. Advertisement in Black on Yellow rectangle.
- Regular issues:
Cream upper deck and roof with Red, Light Blue, Maroon, Green or Orange lower deck .......... **£300-400**
1938
- Early Grey roof issues:
As previous but with Grey roof ...... **£300-400**
Cream upper body, Grey roof, Mid-Green lower body, Black smooth hubs ......................... **£600-800**
- Late issue:  Dark Blue lower deck, Cream upper deck and roof............ **£300-400**
1938-40
- Without advertisements:
As above but no advertisements ..... **£200-300**
NB  Baseplates:
1st issue 'Made in England', 29 x 2 mm.
2nd issue 'Made in England', 28 x 1.5 mm.
1946
Without advertisements:
1st type AEC/STL grille, cutaway wings, no staircase, six vertical inside body ribs, smooth Black hubs. Colours:
- Green lower deck with Cream or Grey upper-deck, Green hubs ......... **£150-200**
- Red lower deck with Cream or Grey upper deck, Red hubs............. **£150-200**
1947-48
Without advertisements:
- As previous model but with post-war Black ridged hubs............. **£100-125**
- As previous model but with Two-tone Green body..................... **£160-190**
1948-49
Without advertisements:
- 3rd type, Leyland or AEC grille, straight-across wings, Black ridged hubs. Early issues had 6 vertical inside body ribs, later issues had 5 (3 on n/s, 2 on o/s). Red or Green lower deck, Cream upper deck .......................... **£100-125**
1949-53
Without advertisements:
- 2nd type, AEC/Regent grille, straight-across wings, lengthwise chassis strengthener with hole in chassis centre, or (1952) eight vertical inside body ribs, ridged hubs, plus (in 1953) '29c' cast in chassis.

155

Red or Green lower deck,
Cream or White upper deck,
hubs match the lower deck colour .. **£100-125**

**29c 'DUNLOP'** (renumbered to 290)
1954-54
• 3rd type Leyland Titan grille and
straight-across wings, early issues have
recessed stop lights, late issues (1959)
protrude. Logo: 'DUNLOP -The World's
Master Tyre' in Black and Red.
Sloping and upright designs exist.
Red or Green lower deck,
Cream upper deck,
hubs match lower deck colour ....... **£200-250**

**29dz Autobus**
1939-40
• Green or White body, metal wheels,
(French issue sold in UK) ................... **£80-90**

**29e Single Deck Bus**
1948-52
• Mid-Blue body, Dark Blue flashes,
Black hubs ......................................... **£80-90**
• Mid-Blue body /
Dark Blue flashes .............................**£90-110**
• Cream body and hubs, Red flashes ..... **£60-80**
• Cream body, Blue flashes,
Blue or Black hubs ............................. **£60-80**
• Light Green body, Dark Green
flashes, Black hubs.............................. **£80-90**
• Light Green body and hubs,
Dark Green flashes........................... **£140-160**

**29f Observation Coach**
1950-54 (renumbered in 1954 to 280)
• Grey body and hubs, Red flashes........ **£70-80**
• Grey body, Red flashes, Red hubs ...... **£70-80**
• Cream body, Red flashes, Red hubs.... **£80-90**
• Cream body and hubs, Red flashes..... **£80-90**
• Cream body, Red flashes,
Maroon hubs...................................... **£80-90**

**29g Luxury Coach**
1951-54 (renumbered in 1954 to 281)
• Maroon body, Cream flashes / hubs.... **£70-80**
• Orange body, Cream flashes / hubs... **£80-100**
• Fawn body with Orange flashes,
Cream or Green hubs ....................... **£80-100**
• Fawn body, Cream flashes / hubs .. **£100-130**
• Blue body, Cream flashes,
Yellow hubs.................................... **£130-160**
• Cream body, Blue flashes and hubs .. **£80-100**
• Cream body, Red flashes and hubs . **£100-130**
• Cream body, Orange flashes,
Green hubs...................................... **£100-130**
**NB** Market Price Ranges for models
29f, g and h are based on their being
unboxed, as compared to prices for the
boxed renumbered issues 280, 281 and 282.

**29h Duple Roadmaster Coach**
1952-54 (renumbered in 1954 to 282)
• Dark Blue body, Light Blue hubs,
Silver coachlines ............................. **£80-100**
• Red body and hubs, Silver coachlines**£80-100**
• Green lower body,
Cream upper body and hubs .......... **£150-200**
**NB** Early issue had a flat roof underside.
Later issues have a rib front to back.

**36g Taxi with Driver**
'TAXI' cast into Black roof,
driver cast into chassis.
1936-46
• Grey, Dark Blue, Green, Maroon or
Red body, Black roof,
open rear window........................... **£200-250**
• Yellow or Violet body, Black roof,
open rear window........................... **£500-750**
1947-50
• Dark Blue, Green, Light Green, Red,
Maroon or Brown body, Black roof on
all, filled rear windows (a few open
rear window versions exist) ............. **£80-100**

**40h Austin** (FX3) **Taxi**
1952-54
Diecast chassis with cast-in driver
and model number. Not boxed.
• All-Yellow body and hubs,
Black chassis, interior and driver.... **£100-125**
• All-Yellow body and hubs,
Brown chassis, interior and driver .. **£150-250**
• Dark Blue body, Light Blue hubs,
Black chassis, interior and driver.... **£250-350**
• Mid-Blue body and hubs,
Black chassis, interior and driver.... **£400-600**
1954 - 40h was renumbered to 254
**067 Austin Taxi** (FX3)
1959-64 See ref. 067 in the
'Dublo Dinky' section.

**115 United Biscuits Taxi**
1979-79
• Yellow/Blue/Black, casting as 120,
promotional model ............................ **£45-55**

## 29c Double Decker Bus identification

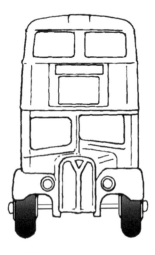

**1st Type 1938-47**
AEC/STL grille, large 'V'
shape. Cutaway wings,
smooth hubs.
No model number on base.

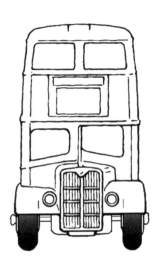

**2nd Type 1949-53 and 1957-59**
AEC/Regent grille, small 'V'
shape. Straight across wings,
ridged hubs. '29c' cast into
base of some issues.

**3rd Type 1948-49 and 1954-63**
Leyland grille, undivided shape.
Straight across wings,
ridged hubs.
'29c', '290' or '291' on base.

**120 Happy Cab**
1979-80
- White/Yellow/Blue, solid wheels, 'flower-power' stickers ...................... **£45-55**

**241 'SILVER JUBILEE TAXI'**
1977-77
- Silver body and hubs, Union Jack on bootlid, 284 casting ....................... **£30-35**

**254 Austin (FX3) Taxi**
1956-59 (renumbered from 40h)
- Dark Blue body, Light Blue hubs ... **£500-750**
- Black body, spun hubs, Grey chassis ('254'), interior and driver...................................... **£140-170**
  *Two-tone issue*:
- Yellow upper body and hubs, Dark Green lower body, Black chassis ('254'), interior and driver .. **£140-170**

**265 Plymouth U.S.A. Taxi**
1960-64
- Yellow/Red body, Blue interior, windows, '25c First 1/5 Mile, 5c Additional', roof sign, white treaded tyres, spun hubs ................. **£150-175**

**266 Plymouth Canadian Taxi**
1960-66
- Yellow/Red body with 'Taxi' and '450 Metro Cab' ............................. **£100-125**

**268 Renault Dauphine Mini Cab**
1962-67
- Red body with 'Meccano', 'Kenwood', and 'Britax Safety Belts' adverts .... **£130-150**

**278 Plymouth Yellow Cab**
1978-80
- Yellow body, 'Yellow Cab Co', plastic chassis and wheels.................. **£20-30**

**280 Observation Coach**
1954-60 (renumbered in 1954 from 29f)
- Grey body, Red flashes and hubs.... **£125-150**
- Cream body and hubs, Red flashes. **£125-150**
- Cream body, Red flashes, Red or Maroon hubs....................... **£130-160**

**281 Luxury Coach**
1954-59 (renumbered in 1954 from 29g)
- Cream body, Blue flashes / hubs..... **£125-150**
- Cream body, Red flashes and hubs . **£175-225**
- Cream body, Orange flashes, Green hubs.................................... **£200-250**
- Cream body/hubs, Orange flashes .. **£125-150**
- Maroon body, Cream flashes and hubs........................................... **£90-120**
- Mid-Blue body, Cream flashes, Yellow hubs................................ **£200-250**
- Fawn body, Orange flashes, Green hubs.................................... **£125-150**
- Fawn body, Cream flashes / hubs ... **£125-150**
NB Prices shown assume that models are in boxes with correct colour spot.

**282 Duple Roadmaster Coach**
1954-60 (renumbered in 1954 from 29h)
- Dark Blue body, Light Blue hubs, Silver coachlines ...............................**£90-110**
- Red body / hubs, Silver coachlines....**£90-110**
- Light Blue body and hubs, Silver coachlines ...............................**£90-110**
- Yellow body, Red or Silver coachlines, Red hubs....................... **£125-150**
US issues:
- Dark Green lower body, Cream upper, Pale Green hubs.................. **£300-350**
- Same model but with Red hubs ...... **£300-350**

**282 Austin 1800 Taxi**
1967-69
- Blue/White body, Red/White 'TAXI' labels on doors and roof..................... **£65-75**

**283 B.O.A.C. Coach**
1956-63
- Dark Blue/White, '*British Overseas Airways Corporation*', White tyres after 1960.................... **£125-150**

**283 Single Deck Bus**
1971-77
- Metallic Red body, Blue interior, 'RED ARROW'. Card box with instructions and packing..................... **£40-50**
- Same, but in bubble pack with unused decal sheet........................ **£35-45**
- Metallic Red body, Yellow interior. Bubble pack...................................... **£45-55**
NB Also available in kit form with 'GREEN LINE' decals. See 1023 in the Dinky Action Kits section.

**284 London Taxi (FX4)**
1972-79
- Black (or very Dark Blue) body, detailed boot on some, Speedwheels, driver, 'TAXI'.............. **£30-40**

**289 Routemaster Bus**
'London Transport', Route '221', 'KINGS CROSS', driver/conductor, cast hubs, spun hubs or Speedwheels.
1964-65
- 'TERN SHIRTS', Red body, 'FOR 8am CRISPNESS' transfers .... **£80-100**
1966-69
- 'SSSCHWEPPES' Red body, Blue-Green logo on White transfers . **£80-100**
1969-80
- 'ESSO' Red body, 'ESSO SAFETY-GRIP TYRES' White label **£60-75**
- Same but with transfers................... **£100-150**
- Deep Purple body, 'London Transport' and 'ESSO SAFETY-GRIP TYRES' logos, Blue driver and clippie ......... **£300-400**
1968-68
- 'LONDON STORES' Promotional, Red body, Black/Gold logo, 'Festival of London Stores'........... **£100-150**
1970
- 'INGERSOLL RAND' Promotional, Red body ................. **£100-125**
1974-74
- 'MECCANO' Gold body, 'MECCANO - DINKY TOYS'. (Very few issued - to Press only).........NGPP
1977-79
- 'MADAME TUSSAUDS' Red body, driver/conductor, White lower deck seating, Blue on White advert., cast wheels........................... **£80-100**
- Red body, driver/conductor, Dark Blue lower deck seating, White on Blue advert., plastic wheels ................. **£80-100**
- Red body, with figures, packed in 'SCHWEPPES' picture box ............ **£100-120**
1977-77
- 'WOOLWORTHS' Silver body, (Silver Jubilee limited issue), figures in some ................................... **£25-30**
1977-77
- 'EVER READY' Silver body, (New Zealand Silver Jubilee issue), no figures.............................................NGPP
1979
- 'THOLLEMBEEK & FILS' Gold body, Pale Blue upper interior, Darker Blue lower interior, 'Thollembeek 1929-79', Belgian promotional........................... **£80-90**

- 'FORDATH' Promotional. Red body, Light Blue upper deck seating, Deep Blue lower deck seating. In plain White box with 'WITH THE COMPLIMENTS OF FORDATH LTD' labels to box ends ..................................... **£175-225**
1979
- 'GREENLINE JUBILEE' Promotional. All-Green body, 'GREENLINE GOLDEN JUBILEE'.. **£70-80**
- 'VISIT BLACKPOOL ZOO' Promotional. Cream body, plastic wheels, 'BLACKPOOL TRANSPORT'..........**£90-110**
19??
- 'NEW ZEALAND CLUB' Red body, Blue/White interior, 'CAR CLUB'S 10th ANNIVERSARY' .......**£90-110**

**290 Double Decker Bus** (renumbered from 29c)
Type 2 (AEC grille), 'DUNLOP - The World's Master Tyre' advert. may be upright or sloping, '290' cast on base, diecast hubs match lower deck.
1954-59
- 'DUNLOP' Green lower deck, Cream upper deck, Light Green hubs .................. **£120-140**
- Red lower deck/hubs, Cream upper deck ......................... **£120-140**
1959-61
- 'DUNLOP' Type 3 (Leyland grille), diecast hubs match lower deck colour, roof route box added, Mid Green or Dark Green lower deck, Cream upper deck.... **£100-125**
- Red lower deck, Cream upper......... **£100-125**
1961-63
- Same colours with sloping lettering but with spun hubs........... **£150-200**
1963
- Same body colours but Green or Red plastic hubs ......................... **£175-200**
1963
- 'EXIDE BATTERIES' Red or Green lower deck, Cream upper deck with '290' cast into base.....NGPP

**291 London Bus**
Type 3 (Leyland grille) with route '73' on destination board.
1961-62
- 'EXIDE BATTERIES' Red body with Red diecast hubs, logo in Black and Yellow............... **£125-150**
- Factory error: As previous model, but with 'CORPORATION TRANSPORT' transfers on sides, crimped axles ..........NGPP
- Promotional: Red body and ridged hubs, White treaded tyres, no route number, Exide dealer promotional leaflet...........NGPP
1962-63
- Same body colours as previous model but with spun aluminium hubs. Plain Yellow box ............................. **£150-175**
1963
- Same body colours as previous but with Red plastic hubs. Box has alternating Red and Yellow panels................... **£175-225**

**291 - 293 Atlantean City Bus**
A Leyland double-decker bus available in several versions:
**291** 1974-77
'KENNINGS'
- Orange body, Blue interior and rear engine cover, Speedwheels.................. **£30-40**
- Same but with White engine cover ..... **£30-40**
- With White engine cover and interior. **£30-40**
- As earlier model but with 'Yellow Pages' stickers .......................NGPP

- White body and lower deck interior,
  Light or Pale Blue upper deck
  interior. Bubble pack ........................... **£40-50**
  1977
  **'LONDON & MANCHESTER**
  **ASSURANCE'**
- White model on plinth. 'Your Best Man
  For Life'. (500 issued to agents) ..... **£400-500**
**292**   1962-65
- **'RIBBLE'** Red and White body,
  'REGENT' advert. on some .............. **£80-100**
- Red and Cream, 'CORPORATION
  TRANSPORT' fleetname .................. **£80-100**
- Same but no fleetname or logo ......... **£80-100**
**292**   1977
- **'LONDON COUNTRY'** Green body,
  shown in 1977 catalogue, but not issued.
**293**   1963-65
- **'BP'** Green/Cream body, Yellow logo and
  smooth roof, 'BP IS THE KEY' ...... **£80-100**
- Same model but with ribbed roof ... **£100-120**

**293**   **Swiss Postal Bus 'PTT'**
   1973-78
- Yellow body with Cream roof, clear
  or tinted windows, (296 casting).............. **£25-35**

**295**   **Atlas Kenebrake Bus**
   1963-69
- Light Blue/Grey body, windows ......... **£50-70**
- All Blue body, Red interior............. **£125-150**
- Blue body, Lemon interior .............. **£150-175**

**295**   **Atlantean Bus**
   1973-74
- **'YELLOW PAGES'** Yellow body,
  'Let Your Fingers Do The Walking',
  Blue or off-White interior,
  Speedwheels ........................................ **£40-50**

   1974-76
- Same, but deeper shade of Yellow ...... **£40-50**
- Same model but finished in Silver,
  no front or rear destination blinds.........NGPP
**296**   **Duple Viceroy 37 Coach**
   1972-75
- Metallic Blue body, clear or tinted
  windows, bubble-packed.................... **£25-35**
- Yellow and Cream body 'P.T.T.',
  bubble-packed, (see also 293)............. **£30-40**

**297**   **Silver Jubilee Bus**
   1977-77
- Leyland Atlantean (291) Silver/Black
  body, 'National'................................. **£30-35**
- 'WOOLWORTHS' Silver Jubilee
  Bus, promotional ............................... **£30-35**

**784**   **Dinky Goods Train Set**
   1972-74
- Blue loco 'GER', one Red Truck,
  one Yellow Truck ............................... **£30-40**

**798**   **Express Passenger Train Set**
   1954-59  (renumbered in 1954 from 16)
- Green/Black loco, BR crest,
  Cream/Maroon coaches (Grey roofs),
  Black hubs/tyres ............................. **£125-150**
- Green/Black loco, BR crest,
  Cream/Maroon coaches/roofs/hubs,
  Black tyres...................................... **£125-150**
- Same but Red hubs, White tyres ..... **£125-150**

**949**   **Wayne 'SCHOOL BUS'**
   1961-66
- Deep Yellow body, Red lines/rear
  bumper, windows, Red plastic hubs.
  Supertoy......................................... **£160-190**
- Same but Black lines/rear bumper .. **£200-300**

**952**   **Vega Major Luxury Coach**
   1964-71
- Pale Grey body, Cream interior,
  Maroon side flash, cast hubs,
  flashing indicators ............................ **£80-100**
- Off-White body, Deep Blue interior,
  Maroon flash, flashing indicators...... **£80-100**
- Late issues:
  Red interior, clear indicators ............... **£70-90**

**953**   **Continental Touring Coach**
   1963-65
- Pale Blue body, White roof, '*Dinky
  Continental Tours*', Supertoy .......... **£300-350**

**954**   **Vega Major Luxury Coach**
   1972-77
- White body, Mid-Blue interior, Maroon
  flash, Lemon-Yellow base, cast hubs .. **£70-90**
- White body, Yellow interior,
  Black base, cast hubs ........................**£90-110**
- White body, Red interior,
  Black base, later cast hubs ................**£90-110**

**961**   **Vega Major Coach 'PTT'**
   1973-77
- Yellow body, Cream roof, Blue interior,
  'P.T.T.' and emblem, Swiss model
  (in normal box)................................ **£100-125**
- Swiss Postal Bus variant:
  Swiss box (Red/White/Yellow,
  'Autocar Postal', 'Postauto', etc),
  plus label: 'Special contract run 1973
  Swiss Post Office Bus', also:
  'Specially boxed for Swiss Meccano
  Agent for sale under their name'.... **£250-300**

Dinky Toys 29c Double Deck Bus Trade Box with two examples of 2nd type radiator grille and four of the 3rd type.   PHOTO: VECTIS AUCTIONS LTD.

# 'Dublo Dinky' models

'Dublo Dinky' models were made in a scale of 1:76.
All their wheels are plastic: smooth wheels are fairly soft and treaded wheels are harder.
The late issues with black treaded ('knobbly') wheels are rarer and may attract a premium. These versions should all be housed in the later issue lighter yellow boxes.

| Model and details | MPR |
|---|---|
| **061 Ford Prefect** | |
| 1958-59 | |
| • Fawn or Grey body, Silver trim, Grey smooth wheels | **£50-60** |
| • With Grey treaded wheels | **£65-75** |
| **062 Singer Roadster** | |
| 1958-60 | |
| • Orange body, Red interior, Grey smooth or knobbly wheels | **£65-75** |
| • Fawn body, Red interior, Grey smooth or knobbly wheels | **£65-75** |
| • Yellow body, Grey knobbly wheels | **£75-85** |
| **063 Commer Van** | |
| 1958-60 | |
| • Blue body, Silver trim, Grey smooth or knobbly wheels | **£100-125** |
| **064 Austin Lorry** | |
| 1957-62 | |
| • Green body, Black or Grey smooth or knobbly wheels | **£60-70** |
| **065 Morris Pick-up** | |
| 1957-60 | |
| • Red body, Silver trim, Grey smooth or knobbly wheels | **£60-80** |
| **066 Bedford Flat Truck** | |
| 1959-66 | |
| • Grey body, Silver trim, hook on some, Grey smooth or knobbly wheels | **£50-60** |

| Model and details | MPR |
|---|---|
| **067 Austin 'TAXI' (FX3)** | |
| 1959-64 | |
| • Blue lower body, Cream upper body, Black or Grey knobbly wheels | **£70-80** |
| **068 'ROYAL MAIL' Morris Van** | |
| 1959-64 | |
| • Red body, 'E II R' crest, Grey knobbly wheels | **£120-150** |
| • Red body, 'E II R' crest, Black knobbly wheels | **£100-120** |
| **069 Massey Harris Tractor** | |
| 1959-64 | |
| • Blue body, Silver trim, Grey knobbly wheels, hole for driver | **£90-110** |
| • With Grey knobbly wheels on front and very Light Tan rear wheels | **£100-120** |
| **070 A.E.C. Mercury Tanker 'SHELL-BP'** | |
| 1959-64 | |
| • Green cab (glazing in some), Red tank, Black or Grey knobbly wheels | **£100-125** |
| **071 VW Delivery Van 'HORNBY DUBLO'** | |
| 1960-64 | |
| • Yellow body with Red logo, Black or Grey knobbly wheels | **£70-90** |
| **072 Bedford Articulated Truck** | |
| 1959-64 | |
| • Yellow cab, Red semi-trailer, Black or Grey smooth or knobbly wheels | **£70-90** |

| Model and details | MPR |
|---|---|
| **073 Land Rover/Trailer/Horse** | |
| 1960-64 | |
| Green car (Grey or Black knobbly wheels), Tan or White horse. Trailers: | |
| • with Bright Green trailer (Green ramp, smooth Grey wheels) | **£120-135** |
| • with Green trailer (Brown ramp, knobbly Grey wheels) | **£120-135** |
| • with Bright Green trailer (Black ramp, knobbly Black wheels) | **£120-135** |
| • with Orange trailer (Grey plastic wheels and ramp) | **£120-135** |
| • with Orange trailer (knobbly Black plastic wheels and ramp) | **£150-175** |
| **076 Lansing Bagnall Tractor & Trailer** | |
| 1960-64 | |
| • Maroon tractor/trailer, Blue driver/seat, Black smooth or knobbly wheels | **£70-90** |
| **078 Lansing Bagnall Trailer** | |
| 1960-64 | |
| • Maroon body, Black smooth or knobbly wheels, hook, wire drawbar | **£40-50** |
| **- Shop Display Stand** | |
| c1959 | |
| • Pale Yellow with Red logo and wording: 'NEW SERIES / DUBLO DINKY', etc. 28 x 19cm overall | **£300-400** |

# Dinky Toys Ships, Boats and Hovercraft

| Model and details | MPR |
|---|---|

**50a  Battle Cruiser 'HMS Hood'**
1934-39
- Battleship Grey, 146 mm,
  'HMS Hood' cast underneath ............. £30-35
  1939-41
- Without name cast underneath ........... £30-35

**50b  Battleship 'Nelson' Class, 'HMS Nelson'**
1934-39
- Battleship Grey, 117 mm,
  'HMS Nelson' cast underneath .......... £30-35
  1939-41
- Without name cast underneath ........... £30-35

**50b  Battleship 'Nelson' Class, 'HMS Rodney'**
1934-39
- Battleship Grey, 117 mm,
  'HMS Rodney' cast underneath ......... £30-35
  1939-41
- Without name cast underneath ........... £30-35

**50c  Cruiser 'HMS Effingham'**
1934-39
- Battleship Grey, 100 mm
  'HMS Effingham' cast underneath..... £30-35
  1939-41
- Without name cast underneath ........... £30-35

**50d  Cruiser 'HMS York'**
1934-39
- Battleship Grey, 98 mm
  'HMS York' cast underneath .............. £30-35
  1939-41
- Without name cast underneath ........... £30-35

**50e  Cruiser 'HMS Delhi'**
1934-39
- Battleship Grey, 81 mm
  'HMS Delhi' cast underneath ............. £30-35
  1939-41
- Without name cast underneath ........... £30-35

**50f  Destroyer 'Broke' Class**
1934-41
- Battleship Grey,
  no wording underneath, 57 mm ......... £15-20

**50g  Submarine 'K' Class**
1935-41
- Battleship Grey, wire mast,
  no wording underneath, 57 mm ......... £15-20

**50h  Destroyer 'Amazon' Class**
1935-41
- Battleship Grey,
  no wording underneath, 52 mm ......... £15-20

**50k  Submarine 'X' Class**
1935-41
- Battleship Grey, wire mast,
  no wording underneath, 61 mm ......... £15-20

| Model and details | MPR |
|---|---|

**51b  Norddeutscher-Lloyd 'Europa'**
1934-40
- Black hull, White superstructure,
  Brown funnels, name under, 165 mm . £35-45

**51c  Italia Line 'Rex'**
1934-40
- Black hull, White decks, name under,
  Red/White/Green funnels, 152 mm .... £35-45

**51d  CPR 'Empress of Britain'**
1934-40
- Canadian Pacific Railway colours –
  White hull, Cream funnels, 130 mm... £30-35

**51e  P & O 'Strathaird'**
1935-40
- White hull, Cream funnels,
  name underneath, 114 mm ................. £30-35

**51f  Furness-Withy Line 'Queen of Bermuda'**
1934-40
- Grey and White hull,
  Red/Black funnels, 99 mm................. £30-35

**51g  Cunard 'White-Star' Liner 'Britannic'**
1934-40
- Black/White/Brown hull,
  Black/Tan funnels, 121 mm ............... £30-35

**52  Cunard White-Star Liner 'No. 534'**
1934-35
- Black/White/Red, '534' cast under,
  boxed, no rollers, 175 mm ................. £70-80
- Same model but '534 Queen Mary'
  cast underneath .................................. £70-80

**52  1935-35** (renumbered in 1935 to 52b)
- As previous model with 'Queen Mary'
  cast underneath, but without '534'...... £70-80

**52a  Cunard White-Star Liner 'Queen Mary'**
1935-41
- Black/White/Red, boxed,
  with plastic rollers, 175 mm................ £70-80
  1946-49
- Same but with brass rollers ................ £70-80

**52b  Cunard 'Queen Mary'**
1935-36  (renumbered in 1935 from 52)
- Black/White/Red, boxed,
  without rollers .................................... £70-80

**52c  'La Normandie'**
1935-40
- Black/White, Red/Black funnels, boxed,
  made in France, pictorial insert.......... £70-80

**52c  Cunard 'Queen Elizabeth'**
1939  Announced in 1939 catalogue
but not produced.......................................NPP

| Model and details | MPR |
|---|---|

**52m  Cunard 'Queen Mary'**
1936-40
- Renumbered from 52b,
  without rollers, supplied unboxed....... £40-50

**53az  Battleship 'Dunkerque'**
1938-39
- Battleship Grey, with or without
  plastic rollers, boxed French issue ...... £40-60

**281  Military Hovercraft**
1973-76
See 'Military Vehicles' section.

**290  SRN-6 Hovercraft**
1970-76
- Red body, Blue or Black skirt............. £20-25
- Same but Metallic Red body.............. £20-25

**671  Mk.1 Corvette**
1976-78
- White/Grey/Brown/Black plastic
  body, fires missiles .............................. £20-25

**672  OSA-2 Missile Boat**
1976-77
- Grey/Whit/Black, fires missiles .......... £20-25

**673  Submarine Chaser**
1977-78
- Grey/White/Black,
  fires depth charges.............................. £20-25

**674  Coastguard Missile Launch**
1977-78
- White/Blue/Red/Yellow,
  'Coastguard', fires missiles................. £20-25

**675  Motor Patrol Boat**
1973-77
- Grey hull with Cream/Black/Red........ £20-25

**678  Air-Sea Rescue Launch**
1974-77
- Grey/Black/Yellow, Orange dinghy,
  pilot/launch......................................... £20-25

**796  Healey Sports Boat on Trailer**
1960-62  All have an Orange cast trailer.
- Mid-Green body, Cream hull ............. £50-75
- Dark Green body, Deep Cream hull.... £50-75
- Red body, Deep Cream hull ............ £150-175
- Yellow body, Cream hull................ £150-175

**797  Healey Sports Boat**
1966
- Sold without trailer from trade box of 6.
  See entry above (796) ..........................NGPP

MECCANO DINKY TOYS NO. 52 CUNARD~WHITE STAR LINER "No 534" Manufactured in England by MECCANO LIMITED, LIVERPOOL.

Dinky Toys
No. 52

Cunard
White Star
Liner 'No.534'
'Queen Mary'.

PHOTO: JOHN KING

# Dinky Toys Novelty, Space, Film and TV-related models

| Model and details | MPR |
|---|---|
| **Model and details** | **MPR** |

**100  Lady Penelope's 'FAB 1'**
1967-75   (TV series 'Thunderbirds')
Non-fluorescent Pink body, clear or tinted sliding roof (Pink stripes on early issues), rockets/harpoons, 'Lady Penelope' and 'Parker' figures.
* With ridged cast wheels. Card picture box with pictorial inner stand ........ **£300-350**
* With ridged cast wheels. Supplied in a bubble pack .............. **£200-250**
* With Fluorescent Pink body ........... **£500-700**
NB   Rare White version reported (but not seen) sold at auction. Details welcomed, please.

**101  Thunderbirds II and IV**
1967-73
* Gloss Dark Green (including loading door), Red thrusters, Yellow legs. Separate plastic Yellow/Red Thunderbird IV model inside. Card box, pictorial inner stand ........ **£700-900**
* Turquoise Green body, Black door, Red thrusters, Yellow legs. Bubble-packed ................................. **£200-300**

**102  Joe's Car**
1969-75   (TV series 'Joe 90')
Metallic Green, White driver, Red engine thruster, battery powered.
* Card picture box with pictorial inner stand ........................ **£250-300**
* Same model, but in bubble-pack ..... **£150-200**
NB   Blue, Silver, Grey version reported (but not seen) sold at auction. Details welcomed, please.

**103  Spectrum Patrol Car**
1968-75   (TV series 'Captain Scarlet')
Shaped hubs, 'screaming motor'.
* Red body with Yellow base, Yellow or Cream plastic interior. Card picture box with pictorial inner stand ......... **£175-200**
* Metallic Red body, White base, Blue tinted windows, Yellow or Cream interior ........................... **£250-300**
* Metallic Gold body, Blue tinted windows, Yellow or Cream interior **£175-200**
* Pre-production prototype: Yellow (resin) body, Lemon interior, aerial, cast wheels........................... **£400-500**
NB   Metallic Blue and Silver versions reported (but not seen) sold at auction. Details welcomed, please.

**104  Spectrum Pursuit Vehicle**
1968-75
* Metallic Blue, Black base, Black or White front bumper, 'SPV'. Card box has inner pictorial stand .. **£240-280**
* Metallic Blue body, Black base, White front bumper. Bubble-pack .. **£175-200**
* Blue body, Light Green base, White front bumper. Bubble-packed....**£110-140**
* Blue body and base, White front bumper. Bubble-packed................. **£100-125**

**105  Maximum Security Vehicle**
1968-75   (TV series 'Captain Scarlet')
* White body, Red base and side stripes, Red or Blue interior, 'RADIOACTIVE' crate ................. **£200-250**
* Late issue without Red stripes ........ **£200-250**
NB   All issues should include a complete and unused decal sheet.
NB   Grey version reported (but not seen) sold at auction. Details welcomed, please.

**106  'The Prisoner' Mini-Moke**
1967-70
White body, Red/White canopy, 'bicycle' decal on bonnet, card box.
* With Black windscreen frame ......... **£250-300**
* With Silver windscreen frame and Brown side panels ......................... **£200-250**

**106  Thunderbirds II and IV**
* Metallic Blue body, Black metal base, Yellow legs. Vacuum-packed . **£150-200**
* Metallic Blue body, White plastic base, Yellow legs............................ **£150-200**
1977-79
* Metallic Blue body, Black plastic base, Red legs................................. **£150-175**
NB   Bubble-packed issues have card bases with Dark Blue sides and (usually) a Light Blue top. Rarer issues have a Yellow top.

**107  'Stripey the Magic Mini'**
1967-68
* White/Red/Yellow/Blue stripes, with Candy, Andy and the Bearandas. Card picture box, pictorial inner stand .... **£350-450**

**108  Sam's Car**
1969-71   (TV series 'Joe 90')
Card box with tray, pictorial backing, 'WIN' badge, instructions.
* Chrome body, Lemon interior ......... **£100-130**
* Gold body, Lemon interior.............. **£120-140**
1971-75
* Pale (Powder) Blue body, Lemon interior, Red engine cover ........... **£140-160**
* Metallic Red body, Red or Silver trim, Lemon interior....................... **£140-160**
* Wine Red body, Lemon interior...... **£150-175**

**109  Gabriel's Model 'T' Ford**
1969-71   (TV series 'The Secret Service')
* Yellow/Black. Card picture box with pictorial inner stand............................ **£75-85**

**111  Cinderella's Coach**
1976-78   (from 'The Slipper & The Rose')
* Pink/Gold, plastic figures and horses.. **£20-25**

**112  Purdey's TR7**
1978-80   (TV series 'The New Avengers')
* Yellow body, Black 'P' logo, Speedwheels ................................... **£55-65**
* As previous model but with Yellow 'P' in Black logo on bonnet ............ **£100-125**
* As previous model but with Silver 'P' logo on bonnet ................... **£35-45**

**113  'The New Avengers'**
**John Steed's Jaguar XJ 5.3 Coupé**
* Metallic Dark Blue, Black interior and base, plastic 'Steed' figure + another. Pictorial window box, inner card tray. Approx. 36 issued unofficially .. **£4,000-5,000**
**?    John Steed's Ford Granada**
* Approximately 6 pre-production samples issued unofficially. No details at present .............................NGPP

**115  United Biscuits Taxi**
1979-79   (promotional)
* Yellow/Blue/Black, casting as 120...... **£50-60**

**120  Happy Cab**
1979-80
* White/Yellow/Blue, solid wheels, 'flower-power' stickers ...................... **£50-60**

**281  'PATHE NEWS' Camera Car**  (Fiat 2300)
1968-70
* Black body, Red interior, cast wheels, cameraman with Brown trousers, camera and stand ............................ **£150-175**
* As previous model but cameraman has Dark Grey trousers.................... **£175-225**

**350  Tiny's Mini Moke**
1970-71   (from 'The Enchanted House')
* Red body, White/Yellow striped top........................................ **£150-175**

**351  U.F.O. Interceptor**
1971-79
(from Gerry Anderson's TV series 'U.F.O')
Light Metallic Green body, 'S.H.A.D.O.' labels. Initially packed in card box with pictorial inner mount (prices 20% higher), later bubble-packed.
* with Black missile holder, White/Black missile, clear canopy, Red legs/skids. ............................... **£175-200**
* with Black missile holder, White/Black missile, Blue canopy, Red legs/skids................................. **£175-200**
* with Red missile holder, Yellow/Black missile, clear canopy, Orange legs/skids. Bubble packed only ....... **£175-200**
* with Red missile holder, Yellow/Black missile, Blue canopy, Orange legs/skids. Bubble packed only ....... **£175-200**

**352  Ed Straker's Car**
1971-75   (TV series 'U.F.O.')
* Gold plated body, Blue interior, keyless motor................................ **£100-120**
* Yellow body, Pale Grey interior, Black engine covers ....................... **£150-175**
* Red body, Silver trim ......................... **£70-80**

**353  'SHADO 2 Mobile'**
1971-79   (TV series 'U.F.O.')
* Green body, Red interior, Brown rollers, Silver tracks, Light Green base. All card box .................................... **£120-140**
* Green body, Black roof, Off-White interior, Dark Green rollers, Black tracks. Bubble-packed.......... **£250-300**
* Green body, Yellow interior, Light Green rollers and base, Silver tracks.................................. **£120-140**
* Metallic Blue body, Off-White interior, Light Green or Black base, Green or Black rollers, tracks and roof. Window box, internal card base...... **£250-300**

**354  Pink Panther**
1972-77
* Pink car and Panther, flywheel drive, card endflap box ................................. **£35-45**
1977-79
* Similar to previous model but without flywheel, bubble-packed .................... **£35-45**
NB   A single experimental Green diecast version exists (Christie's sale 4/95).

**355  Lunar Roving Vehicle**
1972-75
* Metallic Blue, White astronauts, front/rear steering .............................. **£35-45**

**357  Klingon Battle Cruiser**
1977-80   (from TV series 'Star Trek')
* Metallic Blue body, fires 'photon torpedoes'................... **£45-55**

161

**358   'USS Enterprise' ('NCC 1701')**
1976-80
• White body, shuttlecraft,
Yellow or White 'photon torpedoes' ... **£70-90**

**359   Eagle Transporter**
1975-79   (from TV series 'Space 1999')
• White/Green body, Red rear and
side thrusters, clear windows ......... **£100-125**
• White/Green body, Chrome rear
thrusters, Yellow side thrusters,
Orange windows.............................. **£100-125**
• White/Green body, Chrome rear
thrusters, Yellow side thrusters,
Red windows.................................. **£100-125**
• White/Green body, Red rear
thrusters, side thrusters
and windows.................................. **£100-125**
NB   All issues should include a complete
and unused decal sheet.

**360   Eagle Freighter**
1975-79   (from TV series 'Space 1999')
• White/Red, including rear and side
thrusters, 'RADIOACTIVE' drums **£100-125**
• White/blue, Red rear and
side thrusters.................................. **£100-125**
NB   All issues should include a complete
and unused decal sheet.

**361   Zygon War Chariot**
1978-80
• Mid-Green body, two Red spacemen
and rocket motor .............................. **£35-45**

**361   Galactic War Chariot**
1978-80
• Metallic Green body, two White/Yellow
spacemen, Silver rocket motor............ **£35-45**
NB   Light Yellow-Green version
reported (but not seen) sold at auction.
Details welcomed, please.

**361   Missile-firing War Chariot**
1978-80
• Metallic Blue body, two Red
spacemen/rocket motor, blister card.... **£35-45**

**362   Trident Star Fighter**
1978-79
• Black/Orange, fires rockets,
drop-down stairway............................ **£35-45**
• Metallic Gold.
500 only issued to guests at a special
Meccano Dinner in 1979................. **£100-150**

**363   Cosmic Interceptor**
1979-79
• Metallic Silver/Blue, 2 pilots, Marks
& Spencer model ('St.Michael' box) .. **£45-55**

**363   Zygon Patroller**
1979-80
• Metallic Silver/Blue, 2 pilots, ('368' in
some catalogues, '363' on box).......... **£35-45**
• Yellow/Red/Blue version in
'U.S.S. Enterprise' box.........................NGPP

**364   NASA Space Shuttle**
1979
• White booster and shuttle, decals,
instructions, plastic Orange satellite.
Pictorial window box ..................... **£100-150**

**366   Space Shuttle**
1979
• unboxed version of 364 without booster,
with plastic or cardboard load............. **£35-45**

**367   Space Battle Cruiser**
1979-80
• White/Red body, pilot,
plastic weapons .................................. **£35-45**

**368   Cosmic Cruiser**
1979-79
• Blue body, Marks & Spencer model
(in 'St.Michael' box) ........................... **£35-45**

**368   Zygon Marauder**
1979-80
• Red/White, 4 spacemen, ('363' in
some catalogues, '368' on box)........... **£30-35**

**371   Pocket-size 'USS Enterprise'**
1980   (renumbered in 1980 to 801)
• Small version of 358, bubble-packed,
released after factory closure ............. **£45-55**

**372   Pocket-size Klingon Cruiser**
1980   (renumbered in 1980 to 802)
• Small version of 357, bubble-packed,
released after factory closure ............. **£45-55**

**477   Parsley's Car**
1970-72
(TV series 'The Adventures of Parsley')
• Green/Black/Yellow, head swivels. Card
picture box, pictorial inner stand .... **£100-120**

**485   Santa Special Model 'T' Ford**
1964-67
• Red/White body, Santa Claus,
Christmas tree/toys/decals.............. **£100-120**

**486   'Dinky Beats' Morris Oxford**
1965-69
• Pink/Green, 'Da gear',
3 beat-group figures ....................... **£100-150**

**602   Armoured Command Car**
1976-77   (TV series 'The Investigator')
• Green or later Blue-Green body, White
star, driver, scanner, fires sparks ........ **£35-45**

**802   Pocket-size Klingon Cruiser**
1980   (renumbered in 1980 from 372)
• Small version of 357, bubble-packed,
released after factory closure ............. **£45-55**

**803   Pocket-size 'USS Enterprise'**
1980   (renumbered in 1980 from 371)
• Small version of 358, bubble-packed,
released after factory closure ............. **£45-55**

# Dinky Toys 'Action Kits'

These Action Kits were issued in the 1970s. Screws were usually included to attach their bases (which have no model numbers).
Paint supplied with the kit is not always the same colour or shade as on the relative model when supplied built and finished.

| Model and details | MPR |
|---|---|
| **1001 Rolls-Royce Phantom V** | |
| 1971-77  Casting as 152 | |
| • Various colours (usually Blue) | £30-35 |
| **1002 Volvo 1800s Coupé** | |
| 1971-75  Casting as 116 | |
| • Yellow paint | £30-35 |
| **1003 Volkswagen 1300** | |
| 1971-75  Casting as 129 | |
| • Red and White paint supplied | £30-35 |
| **1004 Ford Escort Police Car** | |
| 1971-77  Casting as 270 | |
| • Blue and White paint, 'POLICE' transfers | £30-35 |
| **1006 Ford Escort Mexico** | |
| 1973-77  Casting as 168 | |
| • Red paint and 'MEXICO' transfers | £45-55 |
| **1007 Jensen FF** | |
| 1971-75  Casting as 188 | |
| • Various paint colours (usually Blue) | £30-35 |
| **1008 Mercedes-Benz 600** | |
| 1973-77  Casting as 128 | |
| • Red, Yellow or Green paint supplied | £30-35 |
| **1009 Lotus F1 Racing Car** | |
| 1971-75  Casting as 225 | |
| • Green paint and 'gold leaf' transfers | £30-35 |
| **1012 Ferrari 312-B2** | |
| 1973-75  Casting as 226 | |
| • With Red paint + 'SHELL' transfers | £50-60 |
| **1013 Matra Sports M530** | |
| Catalogued but not issued | NPP |
| **1014 Beach Buggy** | |
| 1975-77 Casting as 227 | |
| • Blue paint included | £20-30 |
| **1017 Routemaster Bus** | |
| 1971-77  Casting as 289 | |
| • Red paint and 'ESSO Safety-Grip Tyres' transfers | £30-40 |
| **1018 Leyland Atlantean Bus** | |
| 1974-77  Casting as 295 | |
| • Various (mostly White) paint, usually 'NATIONAL' transfers | £40-50 |

| Model and details | MPR |
|---|---|
| **? Leyland Atlantean Bus 'YELLOW PAGES'** | |
| • Three variations of transfers exist: | |
| 1) Mid-Blue interior, reversed front 'Yellow Pages' | £40-50 |
| 2) White interior, reversed front 'Yellow Pages' sign | £40-50 |
| 3) White interior, correct reading front 'Yellow Pages' | £40-50 |
| **1023 A.E.C. Single Decker Bus** | |
| 1972-77  Casting as 283 | |
| • Green paint and 'GREEN LINE' transfers included | £30-35 |
| **1025 Ford Transit Van** | |
| 1971-75  Casting as 407 | |
| • Red paint and 'Avis Truck Rental' transfers included | £30-35 |
| **1027 Lunar Roving Vehicle** | |
| 1972-75  Casting as model 355 | |
| • Blue/White paint supplied | £30-35 |
| **1029 Ford D800 Tipper Truck** | |
| 1971-77  Casting as 438 | |
| • Green or Yellow paint supplied | £30-35 |
| **1030 Land Rover Breakdown Truck** | |
| 1974-77  Casting as 442 | |
| • Red or White paint in kit | £30-35 |
| **1032 Army Land Rover** | |
| 1975-77  Casting as 344 | |
| • Military-Green paint and various 'ARMY' transfers in kit | £30-35 |
| **1033 U.S.A. Army Jeep** | |
| 1971-77  Casting as 615 | |
| • Military-Green paint and transfers supplied in kit | £30-35 |
| **1034 Mobile Gun** | |
| 1975-77  Casting as 654 | |
| • Military-Green paint included | £30-35 |
| **1035 Striker Anti-Tank Vehicle** | |
| 1975-77  Casting as 691 | |
| • Military-Green paint and transfer supplied | £30-35 |

| Model and details | MPR |
|---|---|
| **1036 Leopard Tank** | |
| 1975-77  Casting as 692 | |
| • Military-Green paint and transfers supplied | £30-35 |
| **1037 Chieftain Tank** | |
| 1974-77  Casting as 683 | |
| • Military-Green paint and transfers | £30-35 |
| **1038 Scorpion Tank** | |
| 1975-77  Casting as 690 | |
| • Military-Green paint and transfers | £35-45 |
| **1039 Leopard Recovery Tank** | |
| Catalogued but not issued | NPP |
| **1040 Sea King Helicopter** | |
| 1971-77  Casting as 724 | |
| • White with Blue or Orange paint plus 'USAF' transfers | £30-35 |
| **1041 Hawker Hurricane Mk.IIc** | |
| 1973-76  Casting as 718 | |
| • Camouflage paints and RAF roundels in kit | £50-75 |
| **1042 Spitfire Mk.II** | |
| 1971-77  Casting as 719 | |
| • Camouflage paints and RAF roundels in kit | £50-75 |
| **1043 S.E.P.E.C.A.T. Plane** | |
| 1974-76  Casting as 731 | |
| • Blue and Green paints, transfers | £40-60 |
| **1044 Messerschmitt BF-109e** | |
| 1972-75  Casting as 726 | |
| • Brown paint, Luftwaffe transfers | £80-100 |
| **1045 Multi-Role Combat Aircraft** | |
| 1975-76  Casting as 729 | |
| • Camouflage paints, transfers | £40-60 |
| **1050 Motor Patrol Boat** | |
| 1975-77  Casting as 675 | |
| • Black/Blue/White paints and stickers | £20-30 |

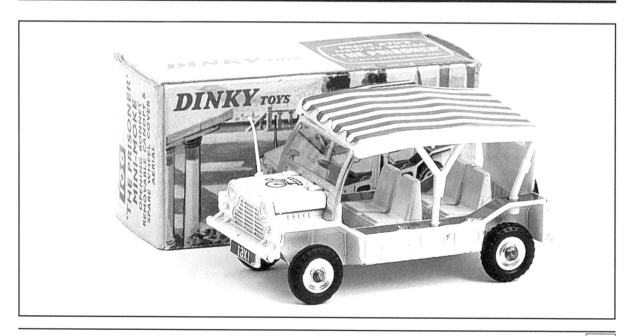

# Dinky Toys Gift Sets

## BOX TYPES

**Sets 001-006**:
Housed in Green card boxes with plain Yellow inserts.

**Sets 1, 2, 3, 4, 5, 6**:
Oblong boxes with Yellow insert card and train picture on lid.
c 1932 Purple marbled 'Modelled Miniatures' box.
c 1936 Blue patterned 'MECCANO DINKY TOYS' box, pictorial insert card.
c 1939 Green box with plain insert, 'DINKY TOYS' label.
1952-56 Green box with Yellow insert, stripe lid label.

**Train sets 17, 18, 19 and 20 box sequence**:
'Modelled Miniatures' :
'Meccano Dinky Toys' :
'Dinky Toys'.

**Sets 24, 25 and 30 series**:
c 1934 Purple marbled 'Modelled Miniatures' box.
c 1935 Purple marbled 'MECCANO DINKY TOYS' box with Yellow/Red label picturing eight assorted cars and lorries. Purple insert with Gold script on two central lines 'MECCANO DINKY TOYS No '24', '25' or '30'.
**NB** The 24 Series and 30 series sets also contained a purple packing card stating: 'PLEASE REMOVE THIS PACKING CARD TO DISPLAY CONTENTS'.
c 1936 Blue patterned box lid with Yellow/Red label picturing eight assorted cars and lorries. Purple insert with no Gold Script on 25 series (no details available on 24 and 30 series).

**Sets 12, 42, 43, 44 and 49** (Pre-war issue):
Blue landscape boxes with inner Blue/Green pictorial inserts.

**Sets 151, 152, 156, 161, 162**:
Grey/Blue or Blue (152) display boxes with inner pictorial scenic backdrop and packing boards.

**Pre-war USA Sets**:
may display 'FAO Schwarz' labels on base of box and 'Meccano Co. of America Inc.' on box lid (e.g., 62h Hurricane Set).

**Early Post-war USA Special Sets**:
Sets for the US market were distributed by H. Hudson Dobson of New York. They are housed in flat boxes with a mottled greenish-blue lid. The picture label on the lid depicts a boy's face plus line drawings of various models. The lid often still retains a red 'H. Hudson Dobson' label. The Set number and type are shown on the main label, e.g. 'No. 6 Commercial Vehicles'. Sets 1, 2, 3 and 6 are listed – the Editor would welcome any new information on the contents of these, and of Sets 4 and 5.

---

Market prices shown here are for guidance only.
They refer ONLY to mint models in pristine boxes (where appropriate) that are complete with **all** of their original contents.

---

| Set and details | MPR |
|---|---|

Pre-war sets without 'fatigue' and with pristine boxes attract a premium, as do early Accessory Sets in 'Modelled Miniatures' boxes.

**001 Station Staff ('0' gauge)** (35mm)
1954-56 (renumbered in 1954 from 1)
- 1b Guard (flag in right hand),
1c Ticket Collector (right arm extended),
1d Driver, 1e Porter (with oblong bags),
1f Porter (standing) .......................... **£90-120**

**002 Farmyard Animals (6)**
1954-56 (renumbered in 1954 from 2)
- 2 x 2a horses, 2 x 2b cows, 1 x 2c pig,
1 x 2d sheep, simplified painting .... **£300-400**

**003 Passengers ('0' gauge)** (35mm)
1954-56 (renumbered in 1954 from 3)
- 3a Woman (with child on left),
3b Businessman (Brown suit and case),
3c Male hiker (no stick),
3d Female hiker (Blue shirt),
3e Newsboy (Grey tray),
3f Woman (Light Red coat,
round case) ........................ **£90-120**

**004 Engineering Staff ('0' gauge)** (35mm)
1954-56 (renumbered in 1954 from 4)
- 2 x 4b Fitter (all-Blue and all-Brown),
4c Storekeeper (all-Brown), 4d Greaser,
4e Engine-Room attendant .............. **£80-100**

**005 Train and Hotel Staff ('0' gauge)** (35mm)
1954-56 (renumbered in 1954 from 5)
- 5a Conductor, 2 x 5b waiters,
2 x 5c Porter (both Brown or Blue) .. **£90-120**

**006 Shepherd Set**
1954-56 (renumbered in 1954 from 6)
- 6a Shepherd (Green hat),
6b sheepdog (all-Black),
4 x 2b sheep.................................... **£250-350**

**007 Petrol Pump Attendants** (35 mm. tall)
1960-67
- 1 male (White overalls),
1 female (White coat), plastic ............ **£30-40**

**008 Fire Station Personnel** (35 mm. tall)
1961-67
- Set of 6 plastic fire-fighters in
Blue uniforms plus hose...................... **£30-40**

| Set and details | MPR |
|---|---|

**009 Service Station Personnel** (35 mm. tall)
1962-66
- Set of 8 plastic figures in various
colours and stances............................. **£30-40**

**010 Road Maintenance Personnel** (35 mm. tall)
1962-66
- Set of 6 plastic workmen using pick,
barrow, shovels, drill etc, plus hut,
brazier, barrier, and 4 lamps................ **£60-70**

**050 Railway Staff ('00' gauge)**
1961-68
- 12 Blue plastic figures in a clear plastic
box. Early issues contained a
Policeman, later ones a Shunter.......... **£40-50**

**051 Station Staff ('00' gauge)**
1954-59 (renumbered in 1954 from 1001)
- 6 plastic figures in a green card box
(re-issue of pre-war
Hornby-Dublo Set D1)....................... **£35-45**

**052 Railway Passengers ('00')**
1961-69
- 11 plastic figures plus a seat,
in a clear plastic box ........................... **£35-45**

**053 Passengers ('00' gauge)**
1954-59 (renumbered in 1954 from 1003)
- 6 coloured plastic figures (re-issue of
pre-war Hornby-Dublo Set D2) .......... **£35-45**

**054 Railway Station Personnel** ('OO' gauge)
1962-70
- 4 plastic figures plus 8 pieces of
furniture in a clear plastic box ........... **£35-45**

**1 Station Staff (6) (large)** (40mm)
1931-39
- 'HORNBY SERIES' (early issues),
'DINKY TOYS' (later)
1a Station Master,
1b Guard (flag in left hand),
1c Ticket Collector (with open arms),
1d Driver, 1e Porter (round/oblong
bags), 1f Porter (walking) .............. **£150-200**

**1 Station Staff (6) (small)** (35mm)
1939-41
- As previous set but smaller figures . **£100-125**

| Set and details | MPR |
|---|---|

**1 Station Staff (6)** (35mm)
1939-41
- 1a and 1d as above,
1b Guard (flag in right hand),
1c Ticket Collector (right arm extended),
1e Porter (oblong bags),
1f Porter (standing) ........................ **£150-200**

**1 Station Staff (5)** (35mm)
1946-54 (renumbered in 1954 to 001)
- 1b Guard (flag in right hand),
1c Ticket Collector (right arm extended),
1d Driver, 1e Porter (with oblong bags),
1f Porter (standing) .......................... **£90-120**

**1 Military Vehicles (1) Set**
1954-55 (renumbered in 1954 to 699)
- 621 3-ton Wagon, 641 1-ton Truck,
674 Austin Champ, 676 Armoured Car.
Blue/White box with Blue cut-out base
plus packing piece on top................ **£400-600**

**No.1 Railway Accessories Set**
1934-39
- 'Miniature Luggage and Truck'.
A Porter's truck and 4 pieces of
luggage (tinplate and cast),
items not available separately ......... **£100-125**

**No.1 Commercial Vehicles Set**
1946-48
- 29c Bus, 25b Wagon, 25d Tanker,
25e Tipper and 25f Market Gardeners
Lorry. In mottled Green, Blue and
Fawn box with inner Green card
cut-out base. Box lid has Light
Green and Blue silhouette label **£2,500-3,500**

**No.1 Farm Gear Gift Set**
1952-54 (reissued in 1964 as 398)
- 27a Massey-Harris Tractor,
27b Harvest Trailer,
27c Manure Spreader, 27h Disc Harrow,
27k Hay Rake. In Blue/White box
with inner cut-out base plus
packing piece on top ................ **£2,500-3,500**

**2 Farmyard Animals**
1934-35
- 2 x 2a horses, 2 x 2b cows,
1 x 2c pig, 1 x 2d sheep,
in 'Modelled Miniatures' box....... **£750-1,000**

1935-40
- Same set but in 'Dinky Toys' box... **£600-800**
1946-54  (renumbered in 1954 to 002)
- Same set but less detailed painting . **£200-300**
**NB** Boxes with a 'H. Hudson Dobson' (of New York) label may sell at a premium of 30% to 35% more.

**No.2   Railway Accessories Set**
1934-?
- 'Milk Cans and Truck'. A 4-wheel barrow and 6 milk churns, not available separately .........................NGPP

**No.2   Private Automobiles Set**
1946-48
- 39a Packard, 39b Oldsmobile, 39c Lincoln, 39d Buick, 39e Chrysler. Inner Green card base in Green, Blue and Orange mottled box, Green and Blue silhouette lid label (export only issue).................... **£2,500-3,500**

**No.2   Commercials Vehicles Set**
1952-53
- 25m Bedford End Tipper, 27d Land Rover (Dark Brown), 30n Farm Produce Wagon, 30p 'Mobilgas' Tanker, 30s Austin Covered Wagon. In Blue/White box with inner cut-out base plus packing piece on top . **£2,500-3,500**

**3   Railway Passengers (large)** (40mm)
1932-39
- 'HORNBY SERIES' (early issues), 'DINKY TOYS' (later).
3a Woman (with child on right), 3b Businessman (left hand on chest), 3c Male hiker (with stick), 3d Female hiker (White shirt), 3e Newsboy (running), 3f Woman (Red jacket, oblong case) ............... **£225-275**

**3   Railway Passengers (small)** (35mm)
1932-39
- As previous set but smaller figures. Oblong Green box, scenic background ......................... **£150-175**

**3   Railway Passengers**
1939-41
- 3a Woman (with child on left), 3b Businessman (case in left hand), 3c Male hiker (no stick), 3d Female hiker (White shirt), 3e Newsboy (standing), 3f Woman (Red coat, round case)... **£125-175**

**3   Railway Passengers**
1946-54  (renumbered in 1954 to 003)
- 3a Woman (with child on left), 3b Businessman (Brown suit and case), 3c Male hiker (no stick), 3d Female hiker (with Blue shirt), 3e Newsboy (Grey tray), 3f Woman (Light Red coat, round case)............. **£90-120**

**No.3   Railway Accessories Set**
1934-?
- 'Platform Machines Etc'. A posting box, ticket machine, label machine and two benches, not available separately ..........NGPP

**No.3   Private Automobiles Set**
1947-52
- (i) 30d Vauxhall, 36a Armstrong, 36b Bentley, 38a Frazer-Nash, 39b Oldsmobile. (Export only issue). Green, Blue and Orange mottled box with inner Green card cut-out base, Green and Blue silhouette lid label .................... **£2,000-2,500**

**No.3   Private Automobiles Set**
1947-52
- (ii) 30d Vauxhall, 36b Bentley, 36d Rover, 38a Fraser Nash, 38c Lagonda. (Export only issue). Green, Blue and Orange mottled box with inner Green card cut-out base, Green and Blue silhouette lid label .................... **£2,500-3,000**

**No.3   Passenger Cars Set**
1952-54
- 27f Estate Car, 30h Daimler Ambulance, 40e Standard Vanguard, 40g Morris Oxford, 40h Austin Taxi, 140b Rover 75. Blue/White box with cut-out tray plus packing piece on top ............................. **£3,000-4,000**

**4   Engineering Staff (6) (large)** (40mm)
1932-41
- 'HORNBY SERIES' (early issues), 'DINKY TOYS' (later)
4a Electrician, 2 x 4b Fitter (Blue/White and Brown/White), 4c Storekeeper (Brown/Black), 4d Greaser, 4e Engine-Room attendant .............. **£150-200**

**4   Engineering Staff (6) (small)**
1932-41
- As previous set but smaller figures. **£150-175**

**4   Engineering Staff (5)**
1946-54  (renumbered in 1954 to 004)
- 2 x 4b Fitter (all-Blue and all-Brown), 4c Storekeeper (all-Brown), 4d Greaser, 4e Engine-Room attendant.............. **£125-175**

**No.4   Railway Accessories Set**
1934-?
- A combination of No.1 ('Miniature Luggage & Truck'), No.2 ('Milk Cans & Truck'), and No.3 ('Platform Machines Etc.'). Individual items not available separately ...............................NGPP

**No.4   Racing Cars Set**
1953-54  (renumbered in 1954 to 249)
- 23f Alfa-Romeo, 23g Cooper-Bristol, 23h Ferrari, 23j HWM and 23n Maserati. Blue/White striped box with one packing piece........................... **£2,000-2,500**

**No.4   Commercial Vehicles Set**
1948-48
- Contains 25d, 25f, 25w, 29c and 30e. Brown/Green box with silhouette lid label. (US export)................ **£2,500-3,000**

**5   Train and Hotel Staff (large)** (40mm)
1932-39
- 'HORNBY SERIES' (early issues), 'DINKY TOYS' (later)
5a Conductor, 2 x 5b waiters, 2 x 5c Porter (1 Red, 1 Green)........ **£300-350**
**NB** Also sold in USA – boxes often display 'H. Hudson Dobson' label.

**5   Train and Hotel Staff (small)**
1932-39
- As previous set but smaller figures. **£150-175**

**5   Train and Hotel Staff**
1939-41
- 5a Conductor, 2 x 5b waiters, 2 x 5c Porter (both Brown or Blue) **£125-175**

**5   Train and Hotel Staff**
1946-54  (renumbered in 1954 to 005)
- 5a Conductor, 2 x 5b Waiter, 2 x 5c Porter (Brown or Blue), less detail ... **£90-120**

**5   Military Vehicles Set**
c1950
- 153a (672) US Army Jeep, 161b (690) Mobile AA Gun, 151a Medium Tank, 151b (620) Transport Wagon, 152b (671) Reconnaissance Car. Green box, inner Green card base and card cut-out packing piece. Blue, Light Green and Red mottled lid has Purple and Yellow label. **£2,500-3,000**

**6   Shepherd Set**
1934-36
- 6a Shepherd (Dark Brown smock, hat and leggings, Black boots, lamb under arm), 6b Collie dog (Black/White), 4 x 2b sheep (Beige, 'Hornby Series' cast-in), set presented in 'Modelled Miniatures' box............. **£500-750**

**6   Shepherd Set**
1936-40
- As previous set but in 'Dinky Toys' box............................. **£250-350**

**6   Shepherd Set**
1946-54  (renumbered in 1954 to 006)
- 6a Shepherd (all Brown below neck, Green hat), 6b Collie dog (all Black), 4 x 2b sheep (without 'Hornby Series')............................. **£150-200**

**No.6   Commercial Vehicles Set**
1946-48
- 29c Bus, 29b Streamline Bus, 25h Fire Engine, 30e Breakdown Car, 30f Ambulance. (US export issue). Mottled Purple-Blue box with inner Purple cut-out card base, Yellow and Maroon silhouette lid label. **£2,500-3,000**

**12   Postal Set**
1937-41
- 12a GPO Pillar Box, 12b Air Mail Pillar Box, 12c Telephone Call Box, 12d Telegraph Messenger, 12e Postman, 34b Royal Mail Van. Blue box with Yellow insert............ **£600-800**

**13   'HALL'S DISTEMPER'**
1931-40
- Advertisement board, White overalled figures (one with Green brush, the other with Blue brush). 'Hornby Series'. Box ('A898')................................... **£300-400**

**15   Railway Signals Set**
1937-41
- 1 x 15a 'Home' (single-arm signal), 1 x 15a 'Distant' (single-arm signal), 2 x 15b 'Home/Distant' (double-arm signals), 1 x 15c 'Home' (double-arm signal), 1 x 15c 'Distant' (double-arm signal). Yellow box with Purple insert, 'DINKY TOYS' on lid ................... **£150-175**

**16   Silver Jubilee Train Set**
1936-37
- Locomotive and two interlocking coaches, 'LNER' and '2590' cast-in, open windows, smooth hubs with White tyres, special box, 300 mm.
1: Silver loco / coaches, Grey, Mid-Blue, Dark Blue, Red or Orange trim....... **£250-350**
2: Silver loco and coaches with Dark Blue trim................ **£250-350**
3: Cream loco and coaches, Red trim. **£250-350**
4: Blue loco/coaches, Dark Blue trim. **£250-350**
5: Green loco and coaches with Dark Green trim ............................ **£250-350**

**16    Streamlined Train Set**
1937-40
• As previous models but with a
  change of name and box ................ **£250-350**
1946-52
• Blue/Black loco, 'LNER',
  Brown/Grey coaches,
  solid windows, Black tyres ............ **£150-175**
1952-54  (renumbered in 1954 to 798)
• As previous model but with 'BR' crest
  on tender. Long portrait 'ladder'
  box with train picture ..................... **£125-145**

**17    Passenger Train Set**
1934-40
• Black/Maroon loco 17a, Maroon
  tender 17b, Maroon/Cream coaches
  20a/20b. Long portrait 'ladder'
  box with train picture ..................... **£300-400**
• Black/Green loco 17a, Green tender
  17b, two Green/Cream coaches 20a/20b.
  Long portrait 'ladder' box with
  train picture ..................................... **£300-400**
• Lead and Mazak set in 2nd type
  box with correct colour spot .......... **£400-500**

**18    Tank Goods Train Set**
1934-40
• Green/Black loco (21a), 3 Green/Black
  open wagons (21b). Long portrait
  'ladder' box with train picture......... **£300-400**

**19    Mixed Goods Train**
1935-40
• Maroon/Black loco (21a),
  Green/Red open wagon (21b),
  Red/Blue 'SHELL' tanker wagon (21d),
  Yellow/Red/Green lumber wagon (21e).
  Long portrait 'ladder' box with
  train picture ..................................... **£400-500**
• Rare box version: Set in 3rd type
  pictorial landscape box................. **£800-1,000**

**20    Tank Passenger Set**
1934-40
• Green/Black loco (21a),
  2 Brown/Green coaches (20a),
  Guard's van (20b)........................... **£300-400**

**21    Hornby Train Set**
1932-33
• Blue/Red loco (21a),
  Green open wagon (21b),
  Green/Blue crane wagon (21c),
  Red/Blue 'SHELL' tank wagon (21d),
  Blue/Red/Black lumber wagon (21e).
  In plain Red 'Hornby Series' box ... **£500-750**

**21    Modelled Miniatures Train Set**
1934-35
• As previous set, but in 'Modelled
  Miniatures' Red card box............... **£500-750**

**22    Motor Vehicles Set**
1933-35
• 22a and 22b Cars, 22c Motor Truck,
  22d Delivery Van, 22e Tractor,
  22f Tank, with 'Hornby Series' or
  'Dinky Toys' cast-in.
  'Modelled Miniatures' box, Purple
  lid, full-size full-colour label
  with pictures of models ......... **£7,500-10,000**

**23    Racing Cars Set**
1936-40
• 23c Mercedes-Benz,
  23d Auto-Union,
  23e 'Speed of the Wind'.
  Blue box ('A2144')........................ **£500-750**

**24    Motor Cars Set**
1934-40
• 1st issue: 24a Ambulance, 24b Limousine,
  24c Town Sedan, 24d Vogue Saloon,
  24e Super Streamlined Saloon,
  24f Sportsman's Coupé,
  24g Sports Tourer (2 seater),
  24h Sports Tourer (4 seater).
  Purple and Gold marbled box, lid has
  colour top label and Yellow/Red
  end label with code 'DT24'..... **£7,500-10,000**
• Later issue: Blue marbled box
  lid (with colour label),
  Purple inner ('A2205').............. **£6,000-8,000**

**25    Commercial Motor Vehicles**
1934-37
• 25a Wagon, 25b Covered Wagon,
  25c Flat Truck, 25d Tank Wagon,
  25e Tipper, 25f Market Gardener's
  Lorry. Mauve 'grained' box lid
  (colour label) ('A1052')............ **£5,000-7,000**
• Revised set:
  Contains 25b, d, e, f, g and h .... **£4,000-5,000**

**27ak  'MASSEY-HARRIS' Tractor and Hayrake**
1952-54  (renumbered in 1954 to 310)
• 27a Tractor and 27k Hayrake .......... **£150-200**

**28/1  Delivery Vans Set in Trade Box**
1934-40
• (1st type castings)
  28a Hornby Trains,
  28b Pickfords,
  28c Manchester Guardian,
  28d Oxo,
  28e Ensign Lukos,
  28f Palethorpes Sausages
  Box numbered 'A1008'......... **£17,500-20,000**
• Revised set:
  28a Hornby Trains,
  28b Pickfords,
  28c Manchester Guardian,
  28e Firestone,
  28f Palethorpes,
  28n Atco Mowers ................. **£17,500-20,000**

**28/2  Delivery Vans Set in Trade Box**
1934-40
• (1st type castings)
  28g Kodak,
  28h Sharps Toffees,
  28k Marsh & Baxter,
  28L Crawfords Biscuits,
  28m Wakefield's Castrol,
  28n Meccano.
  Box numbered 'A1008'......... **£17,500-20,000**
• Revised set:
  28d Oxo,
  28g Kodak,
  28h Dunlop Tyres,
  28k Marsh's,
  28m Wakefield's Castrol,
  28p Crawfords Biscuits......... **£17,500-20,000**

**28/3  Delivery Vans Set in Trade Box**
1936-40
• (2nd type castings)
  28r Swan Pens,
  28s Frys Chocolate,
  28t Ovaltine,
  28w Osram Lamps,
  28x Hovis,
  28y Exide Batteries ................. **£3,000-4,000**

**30    Motor Vehicles**
1935-37
• 30a Chrysler Airflow,
  30b Rolls-Royce,
  30c Daimler,
  30d Vauxhall,
  30e Breakdown Car,
  30f Ambulance ......................... **£5,000-6,000**
1937-41
• As previous set but 30g Caravan
  replaces 30f Ambulance ........... **£4,500-5,000**

**33/1  Mechanical Horse and
        Five Assorted Trailers**
1935-37
• 33a Mechanical Horse,
  33b Flat Truck,
  33c Open Wagon,
  33d Box Van,
  33e Dust Wagon,
  33f Petrol Tank 'WAKEFIELD CASTROL'
  or 'ESSO' logo.
  Blue or Green 'grained' box
  lid, large colour label................ **£1,500-2,000**

**33/2  Mechanical Horse and
        Four Assorted Trailers**
1935-37
• 33a Mechanical Horse, 33b Flat Truck,
  33c Open Wagon and 33e Dust Wagon.
  In Green display box (code 'A2036')
  with Yellow inner tray.............. **£1,250-1,500**

**35    Small Cars Set**
1935-41
• 35a Saloon Car, 35b Racer and
  35c MG Sports Car. In display type
  box ('A2222') with tuck-in flap
  and scenic backdrop .................... **£800-1,100**

**36    Motor Cars with Drivers,
        Passengers and Footmen**
1936-41
• 36a Armstrong-Siddeley with figures,
  36b Bentley with figures,
  36c Humber with figures,
  36d Rover with figures,
  36e British Salmson 2-seater with figures,
  36f British Salmson 4-seater, with figures.
  Set housed in Blue landscape box with
  Yellow tray with Purple inner and Brown
  board top packing piece. Box code
  'A2205', dated '6-38'............. **£7,500-10,000**

**37a   Motor Cycles Set**
1937-41
• Six of 37a civilian Motor Cyclists in
  various colours, hand-painted detail,
  solid White rubber wheels.
  Blue box with Green and White
  pictorial inner ............................... **£400-600**

**37    Motor Cycles Set**
1938-40
• 37a (civilian), 37b (Police),
  37c (Signals Despatch)................... **£400-600**

**39    USA Saloon Cars Set**
1939-41
• 39a Packard, 39b Oldsmobile,
  39c Lincoln, 39d Buick,
  39e Chrysler, 39f Studebaker.
  Mauve box with full colour
  label on lid................................ **£2,500-3,500**

**42    Police Set**
1935-40
• 42a Police Box, 42b Motor Cycle Patrol,
  42c Point-Duty Policeman (White coat),
  42d Point-Duty Policeman (Blue uniform),
  Blue box with pictorial
  inner ('A2114')............................. **£400-600**

**43** **'R.A.C.' Set**
1935-41
- 43a RAC Box, 43b RAC Motor Cycle Patrol,
43c RAC Guide directing traffic,
43d RAC Guide saluting. Blue box,
pictorial inner part, ('A2064')......... **£500-600**

**44** **'A.A.' Set**
1935-41
- 44a AA Box, 44b AA Motor Cycle Patrol,
44c AA Guide directing traffic,
44d AA Guide saluting. Blue box,
pictorial inner part, ('A2065')......... **£500-600**

**46** **Pavement Set**
1937-41
- Dark Grey 'stone' effect (cardboard)
pavement pieces in a box ............... **£100-150**

**47** **Road Signs Set**
1935-41
- 12 road signs, 47e to 47t, (White under
base, triangles usually filled-in).
Yellow box and inner,
box code 'A2073'........................... **£200-250**
1948-54 (renumbered in 1954 to 770)
- US issue: 12 road signs, 47e to 47t,
(Black under base, open triangles). Plain
card box with Yellow label on end
of lift up lid, or in slide-tray box..... **£100-125**
- US issue: White under bases, filled-in
triangles, in a plain box marked 'Made in
England'. Made for sale by H. Hudson
Dobson, 200 5th Avenue, New York.....NGPP

**49** **Petrol Pumps Set**
1935-41
- 'Pratts': 49a, 49b, 49c, 49d, 49e.
White rubber hoses, Blue box ......... **£250-300**
1946-50 (renumbered in 1950 to 780)
- Plain: 49a, 49b, 49c, 49d, 49e.
Yellow plastic hoses, Yellow box... **£100-125**
- 'Pratts': 49, 49b, 49c, 49d, 49e.
White rubber hoses, Yellow box ..... **£150-200**
- Plain: 49, 49b, 49c, 49d, 49e.
White plastic hoses, Yellow box ..... **£100-140**

**50** **Ships of the British Navy**
1934-42
- 50a 'Hood', 50b 'Nelson', 50b 'Rodney',
50c 'Effingham', 50d 'York',
50e 'Delhi', 3 x 50f 'Broke',
50g 'X'-class Submarine,
3 x 50h 'Amazon',
50k 'K'-class Submarine. Blue box
with Green/Blue label on lid .......... **£250-300**

**51** **Great Liners Set**
1934-40
- 51b 'Europa', 51c 'Rex',
51d 'Empress of Britain',
51e 'Strathaird', 51f 'Queen of Bermuda',
51g 'Britannic'............................... **£250-300**

**60** **Aeroplanes Set**
1934-35
- (1st issue)
60a Imperial Airways,
60b Leopard Moth,
60c Percival Gull,
60d Low-Wing Monoplane,
60e General Monospar,
60f Autogiro, no registration letters.
Dark Blue box with Green, Blue
and White 'Atalanta' airliner on
lid label, Yellow/Green side
label dated '5-34'....................... **£2,000-2,500**

**60** **British Aeroplanes Set**
1936-41
- (2nd issue)
60a Imperial Airways, 60b Leopard Moth,
60c Percival Gull,
60d Low-Wing Monoplane,
60e General Monospar, 60f Autogiro.
All the planes in this set (except
60f) have 'GA-' markings ......... **£1,500-2,000**
Box Type i) Blue box with multicoloured
label plus '150 varieties' slogan.
Box Types ii) and iii) Same as previous
but with '200' or '300 varieties'
slogans (code 'A1040').

**60p** **Gloster Gladiator Set**
1938-41
- 6 Silver planes with RAF roundels . **£400-600**

**60s** **'Medium Bomber' Set**
1938-41
- Two renumbered 62n Fairey 'Battle'
Bombers with camouflage finish.
In Stone-colour box ........................ **£250-350**

**60z** **'Avions' Set**
1937-41
- French Aeroplanes Set with
60az 'Arc-en-Ciel', Potez 58,
Hanriot 180t, 61az DeWetoine 500,
Breguet Corsair, 60f Cierva
Autogiro. Blue box...................... **£900-1,200**

**61** **R.A.F. Aeroplanes Set**
1937-41
- 60h 'Singapore' Flying Boat,
2 x 60n Fairey 'Battle' Bombers,
2 x 60p Gloster 'Gladiator' Biplanes.
Contained in Blue box with full
colour label on lid ...................... **£900-1,200**

**61z** **'Avions' Set**
1937-40
- French Aeroplanes Set with DeWoitine
D338, Potez 56, Potez 58,
61az DeWetoine 500d, Farman F360,
60f Cierva Autogiro. Blue box..... **£900-1,200**

**62d** **Bristol Blenheim Bomber Set**
1939
- Six planes, camouflaged, mounted on
card base with 'BRISTOL BLENHEIM
BOMBER MARK IV -
DINKY TOYS 62d'. Green box ..... **£400-600**

**62h** **Hawker Hurricane Set**
1939
- Six planes, camouflaged tops, Black
undersides, mounted on card base with
'DINKY TOYS No.62h HAWKER
HURRICANE SINGLE SEATER
FIGHTER'. Green box, date '7-39' . **£500-750**
- US issue: with
'Meccano Co. of America Inc.' label
on box lid and 'FAO Schwarz'
on box base.................................. **£500-750**

**62s** **Hurricane Fighters Set**
1939-41
- Six Fighters, Silver fuselages, RAF
roundels, undercarriages, Blue box. **£300-400**

**64** **Aeroplanes Set**
1939-41
- 60g Light Racer,
62h 'Hurricane' (Camouflaged),
62k 'Kings Aeroplane',
62m Light Transport,
62s 'Hurricane' (Silver),
63b Seaplane 'Mercury'.
**NB** (In 1940 either 62a 'Spitfire' or
62s were substituted for
62h and 62s) .............................. **£1,000-1,250**

**64z** **'Avions' Set**
193?-4?
- French Aeroplanes Set with
61az Dewoitine 'F-ADBF',
64a Amiot 370,
64b Bloch 220 'F-AOHJ',
64c Potez 63,
64d Potez 662 'F-ARAY'.
Blue box, Yellow inner............. **£2,000-2,500**

**65** **Aeroplanes Set**
1939-41
- 60r Flying Boat, 60t 'DC3',
60v 'Whitely' Bomber, 60w 'Clipper III',
62n Junkers, 62p 'Ensign', 62r 'Albatross',
62w 'Frobisher'. Blue box,
illustrated leaflet enclosed......... **£1,750-2,000**

**66** **Camouflaged Aeroplanes Set**
1940-41
- 66a Heavy Bomber,
66b Dive Bomber Fighter,
66c Fighter, 66d Torpedo,
66e Medium Bomber,
66f Army Autogiro (Silver).
Yellow-Brown box ................... **£2,000-3,000**

**68** **Camouflaged Aeroplanes Set**
1940-41
- 2 x 60s 'Battle' Bombers,
2 x 62d 'Blenheim',
3 x 62h 'Hurricane' (Camouflage),
3 x 62s 'Hurricane' (Silver), 62t 'Whitley',
68a 'Ensign', 68b 'Frobisher'.
Blue or Yellow box, light or dark
camouflage. Models have two roundels:
Red inside Blue on the wings, and
White/Blue/Red on
the fuselage sides....................... **£2,500-3,500**
1940-41
- US issue: Camouflaged versions of:
60s, 62d, 62e, 62h, 62t, 68a and 68b.
Box picture shows civilian aircraft.
Red label states 'Sold by Meccano
Company of America Inc.,
200 5th Avenue, New York' ...... **£2,500-3,500**

**101** **Dining-Room Furniture**
1936-40
- 101a Table, 101b Sideboard,
2 x 101c Carver Chair,
4 x 101d Chair.............................. **£400-500**

**102** **Bedroom Furniture**
1936-40
- 102a Bed, 102b Wardrobe, 102c
Dressing Table, 102d Dressing Chest,
102e Dressing Table Stool, 102f Chair.
Brown or Pink. Green box ............. **£400-500**

**103** **Kitchen Furniture**
1936-40
- 103a Refrigerator, 103b Kitchen
Cabinet, 103c Electric Cooker,
103d Table, 103e Chair. Light
Blue/White or Light Green/Cream.. **£400-500**

**104** **Bathroom Furniture**
1936-40
- 104a Bath, 104b Bath Mat,
104c Pedestal Basin, 104d Stool,
104e Linen Basket, 104f Toilet.
Brown or Pink. Green box ............. **£400-500**

**118** **Towaway Glider Set**
1965-69
- 135 Triumph 2000 (White/Blue),
Cream/Red trailer, Yellow glider..... **£150-200**

**121** **Goodwood Racing Set**
1963-66
- 112 Austin-Healey Sprite, 113 MGB,
120 Jaguar, 182 Porsche,
9 Service Station (009) plastic figures plus
seated and standing drivers. In Buff/Red
display box with stepped insert. **£1,250-1,500**

**122  Touring Gift Set**
1963-65
- 188 Caravan, 193 Station Wagon,
195 Jaguar, 270 'AA' Patrol, 295 Atlas
Kenebrake, 796 Healey Sports Boat
on Trailer. In Buff/Red display
box with stepped insert ............ **£1,500-2,000**

**123  Mayfair Gift Set**
1963-65
- 142 Jaguar, 150 Rolls-Royce,
186 Mercedes-Benz, 194 Bentley,
198 Rolls-Royce, 199 Austin Mini
Countryman, plastic figures (3 male,
1 female). Buff/Red display
box with stepped insert ............ **£2,000-2,500**

**124  Holidays Gift Set**
1964-66
- 952 Vega Luxury Coach,
137 Plymouth, 142 Jaguar, 796 Healey
Sports Boat. In Buff/Red display
box with stepped insert ............ **£1,500-2,000**

**125  Fun Ahoy! Set**
1964-66
- 130 Ford Corsair with driver,
796 Healey Sports Boat with pilot.
Window box ................................... **£350-450**

**126  Motor Show Set**
1967-68
- 127 Rolls-Royce (Gold, Chrome hubs),
133 Cortina (Lemon, spun hubs),
151 Vauxhall Victor (Metallic Red,
Cream interior, Chrome hubs,
171 Austin 1800 (Metallic Blue,
Red interior, Chrome hubs).
In Buff/Red display box with
stepped insert............................. **£1,750-2,500**
1968-69
- As above, but 133 Ford Cortina
is finished in Lemon Yellow ..... **£1,250-1,750**

**149  Sports Cars Set** ('Competition' finish)
1958-61
- 107 Sunbeam Alpine,
108 MG Midget,
109 Austin-Healey,
110 Aston-Martin,
111 Triumph TR2,
Blue/White striped box ............. **£2,500-3,000**

**150  Royal Tank Corps Personnel**
1937-41
- 150a Officer, 2 x 150b Private,
2 x 150c Private, 150e N.C.O. Attached by
cord to Yellow card in Yellow box or
Grey/Blue box with Yellow inner,
code 'A2187'................................. **£200-300**
1946-50
- US export only Set:  Post-war issue of
pre-war figures in original Green box
with 'H. Hudson Dobson' label....... **£200-300**
1952-55
- Reissue, US only:  Contains 1 x 150a,
2 x 150b, 2 x 150c, 1 x 150e.
Green box with one packing piece.. **£200-300**

**151  Medium Tank Set**
1937-41
- 151a Tank, 151b 6-wheel Wagon,
151c Cooker Trailer, 151d Water Tank
Trailer, 150d Royal Tank Corps Driver.
Drop-front Blue box with pictorial inner,
one packing piece with cut-outs...... **£300-400**

**152  Light Tank Set**
1937-41
- 152a Tank, 152b Reconnaissance Car,
152c Austin 7 Car with 150d Royal Tank
Corps Driver. Drop-front Blue box with

pictorial inner, one packing piece
with cut-outs.................................. **£300-400**

**156  Mechanised Army Set**
1939-41
- 151a Tank, 151b 6-wheel Wagon,
151c Cooker Trailer, 151d Water Tank
Trailer, 152a Tank, 152b Reconnaissance
Car, 152c Austin 7 Car with 150d Royal
Tank Corps Driver, 161a Lorry with
Searchlight, 161b AA Gun on Trailer,
162a Light Dragon Tractor, 162b
Ammunition Trailer, and 162c 18-lb
Gun. Drop-front Grey-Blue box
(codes: '11-39', 'A2308') with
contents shown on lid,
four packing pieces. ................. **£4,000-5,000**

**160  Royal Artillery Personnel**
1939-41   (reissued in 1954 to 606)
- 160a N.C.O., 2 x 160b Gunner,
160c Gunlayer, 2 x 160d Gunner (standing).
Grey-Blue box (code: A2308) dated 11-39,
Yellow box (code: A2303) dated 12-39.
Production of this set continued post-war
but only for export to USA ............. **£200-300**
1952-55
- Reissue, US only:
1 x 160a, 3 x 160b, 2 x 160d, 1 x 150e.
Green box with inner card stand ..... **£200-300**

**161  Mobile Anti-Aircraft Unit**
1939-41
- 161a Lorry with Searchlight and
161b A.A. Gun on Trailer. Blue or
Green box ('A2257' on some),
1 packing piece with cut-outs ......... **£500-750**

**162  18-pounder Field Gun Unit**
1939-54
- 162a Light Dragon Tractor,
162b Trailer, 162c Gun. Blue box,
1 packing piece with cut-outs ......... **£150-200**

**201  Racing Cars Set**
1965-68
- 240 Cooper, 241 Lotus,
242 Ferrari, 243 B.R.M. ............... **£800-1,000**

**237  Dinky Way Set**
1978-79
- 178 Mini Clubman, 211 Triumph TR7,
382 Convoy Truck, 412 Bedford 'AA' Van.
**NB**  Export only version of Set 240. ..... **£80-100**

**240  Dinky Way Set**
1978-80
- 211 Triumph TR7, 255 Police Mini,
382 Dump Truck, 412 Bedford, decal
sheet, 20ft 'roadway', 20 road signs ... **£60-80**

**245  Superfast Gift Set**
1969-73
- 131 Jaguar 'E'-type, 153 Aston-Martin,
188 Jensen FF................................. **£125-150**

**246  International Gift Set**
1969-73
- 187 De Tomaso Mangusta, 215 Ford GT,
216 Ferrari Dino............................. **£125-150**

**249  World Famous Racing Cars**
1962-63
- 230 Talbot-Lago, 231 Maserati,
232 Alfa-Romeo, 233 Cooper-Bristol,
234 Ferrari, 239 Vanwall. Bubble-
packed onto large display card.. **£4,000-5,000**

**249  Racing Cars Set**
1955-58   (renumbered in 1954 from 4)
- Cars: 231, 232, 233, 234, 235 ... **£1,000-1,250**

**294  Police Vehicles Gift Set**
1973-77   (Replaces Set 297)
- 250 Mini-Cooper, 254 Range-Rover,
287 Accident Unit .......................... **£200-250**

**297  Police Vehicles Gift Set**
1963-73   (Replaced by Set 294)
- 250 Mini-Cooper, 255 Ford Zodiac,
287 Accident Unit .......................... **£200-250**

**298  Emergency Services Set**
1963-66
- 258 Ford Fairlane, 263 Ambulance,
276 Fire Tender, 277 Ambulance,
Ambulance-man, Ambulance-woman
and Policeman ................................ **£500-750**

**299  Post Office Services**
1957-59
- 260 'Royal Mail' Morris Van,
261 'GPO Telephones' Van,
750 Call Box, 011 Messenger,
012 Postman (but no Pillar Box!).
Blue and White striped box............ **£400-500**

**299  Motorway Services Set**
1963-66
- 434 Bedford Crash Truck, 269 Motorway
Police Car, 257 Fire Chief's Car,
276 Airport Fire Tender, 263 (later 277)
Criterion Ambulance ................ **£1,500-1,800**

**299  'Crash Squad' Action Set**
1978-79
- 244 Plymouth Police Car and
732 Bell Helicopter ........................... **£45-55**

**300  London Scene Set**
1973-77
- 289 Routemaster Bus 'ESSO' and
284 London Taxi ................................. **£80-95**

**302  Emergency Squad Gift Pack**
1979-?
- Paramedic Truck, Fire Chief Car,
figures of Gage and DeSoto. Not issued..NPP

**303  Commando Squad Gift Set**
1978-80
- 687 Convoy Army Truck, 667
Armoured Car, 732 Helicopter.......... **£75-100**

**304  Fire Rescue Gift Set**
1978-79
- 195 Fire Chief Range Rover, 282 Land
Rover, 384 Convoy Fire Truck........... **£70-90**

**306  'Space' Gift Pack**
1979-?
- 358 'USS Enterprise', 357 Klingon
Battle Cruiser, and Galactic
War Chariot. Not issued ...........................NPP

**307  'New Avengers' Gift Pack**
1979-?
- Purdey's TR7, John Steed's Special
Leyland Jaguar, plus a 'fly-off'
assailant! Not issued................................NPP

**309  Star Trek Gift Set**
1978-80
- 357 Klingon Battle Cruiser and
358 'USS Enterprise'....................... **£125-150**

**310  Tractor and Hayrake**
1954-60
- 1st issue:  Red 300 Tractor and 310
Hayrake. Blue/White striped box.... **£250-350**
- 2nd issue:  Cherry Red 300 Tractor
with Yellow hubs. Late issue Yellow
box with lift-off lid......................... **£300-400**

**325** **'DAVID BROWN' Gift Set**
19??-??
- White 305 Tractor,
  Red 322 Harrow .............................. **£150-200**
- Yellow 305 Tractor,
  Red 322 Harrow .............................. **£175-225**

**398** **Farm Equipment Gift Set**
1964-65   (reissue of Set No.1)
- 300 Massey-Harris Tractor,
  320 Harvest Trailer, 321 Manure Spreader,
  322 Disc Harrow, 324 Hay Rake.
  Grey box with hinged lid ......... **£1,250-1,750**

**399** **Farm Tractor and Trailer**
1969-73
- 300 Massey-Harris Tractor and
  428 Large Trailer (Red/Silver).
  Yellow window box........................ **£225-275**

**399** **'Convoy' Gift Set**
1977-79
- 380 Skip Truck, 381 Farm Truck,
  382 Dumper Truck. 'Window' box ..... **£35-45**

**606** **Royal Artillery Personnel**
1954-55
- 1 x 160a, 2 x 160b, 1 x 160c,
  2 x 160d. Export only (to USA)...... **£150-200**

**607** **25-pounder Field Gun Set**
1957-71
- Tractor, Gun, Ammunition Trailer .. **£125-150**

**616** **AEC Transporter and Tank**
1976-78
- Militarised version of 974 with
  683 Chieftain Tank + camouflage net. **£65-80**

**618** **Transporter and Helicopter**
1976-79
- Militarised versions of 974 and
  724 with camouflage netting.............. **£70-80**

**619** **Bren-Gun Carrier Set**
1976-78
- 622 Bren-Gun Carrier and
  625 6-pounder Anti-Tank Gun ........... **£35-45**

**677** **Task Force Set**
1972-75
- 680 Ferret Armoured Car, 681 D.U.K.W.,
  682 Stalwart Load Carrier.................. **£35-45**

**695** **Howitzer and Tractor**
1962-66
- 689 Medium Artillery Tractor and
  693 7.2in. Howitzer........................ **£350-450**

**697** **Field Gun Set**
1957-71
- 688 Field Artillery Tractor, 687 Trailer,
  686 25-pounder Field Gun,
  cast ridged or plastic hubs................ **£80-100**

**698** **Tank Transporter Set**
1957-65
- 660 Mighty Antar Tank Transporter
  and 651 Centurion Tank.
  One packing piece in box................ **£200-250**

**699** **Military Vehicles (1) Set**
1955-58   (renumbered in 1954 from No.1)
- 621 3-ton Wagon, 641 1-ton Truck,
  674 Austin Champ, 676 Armoured Car.
  Blue/White Striped box with inner
  lining and stand .............................. **£350-450**

**754** **Pavement Set**
1958-62
- Twenty various Grey cardboard
  pieces representing paving .................. **£30-40**

**766** **British Road Signs**
1959-64
- Country Set 'A'. Six signs of the times,
  mostly 55 mm high. Yellow box ....... **£80-100**

**767** **British Road Signs**
1959-64
- Country Set 'B'. Six signs of the times,
  mostly 55 mm high. Yellow box ....... **£80-100**

**768** **British Road Signs**
1959-64
- Town Set 'A'. Six signs of the times,
  mostly 55 mm high. Yellow box ....... **£80-100**

**769** **British Road Signs**
1959-64
- Town Set 'B'. Six signs of the times,
  mostly 55 mm high. Yellow box ....... **£80-100**

**770** **Road Signs Set**
1950-54   (renumbered in 1954 from 47)
- 12 road signs, 47e to 47t, (Black under
  base, open triangles) US export ...... **£125-175**

**771** **International Road Signs**
1953-65
- Set of 12 road signs with Silver posts
  and bases. Yellow box with leaflet.. **£100-125**

**772** **British Road Signs**
1959-63
- (Sets 766, 767, 768 and 769). 24
  road signs in a Red/Yellow box ...... **£150-200**

**780** **Petrol Pumps Set**
1950-54   (renumbered in 1950 from 49)
- 49a, 49b, 49c, 49d, 49e (plain).
  Yellow plastic hoses, export only.......**£90-110**
- Version issued in picture box .......... **£100-150**

**784** **Dinky Goods Train Set**
1972-74
- Blue loco 'GER', one Red Truck,
  one Yellow Truck ................................ **£40-60**

**798** **Express Passenger Train Set**
1954-59   (renumbered in 1954 from 16)
- Green/Black loco, 'BR' crest, Cream
  coaches (Grey roofs), Black tyres... **£100-125**
- Green/Black loco, 'BR' crest, Cream
  coaches/roofs/hubs, Black tyres ...... **£100-125**
- Green/Black loco, 'BR',
  Cream coaches/roofs, Red hubs,
  White tyres ..................................... **£100-125**

**851** **Sets of vehicle 'Loads'**
1961-
- 2 each of 846 Oil Drums, 847 Barrels,
  849 Packing Cases and 850 Crates ..... **£30-40**

**900** **'Site Building' Gift Set**
1964-70
- 437 Muir-Hill Loader, 960 Albion
  Mixer, 961 Blaw-Knox Bulldozer,
  962 Muir-Hill Dumper,
  965 Euclid Rear Dump Truck.
  Grey/Red/Yellow box.................. **£900-1,200**

**950** **Car Transporter Set**
1969-70
- 974 AEC Car Transporter, 136 Vauxhall
  Viva, 138 Hillman Imp, 162 Triumph
  1300, 168 Ford Escort, 342 Austin
  Mini-Moke. Not issued ...........................NPP

**957** **Fire Services Gift Set**
1959-65
- 257 Fire Chief's Car, 955 Fire
  Engine, 956 Turntable Fire Escape . **£350-400**

**990** **Car Transporter Set**
1956-58
- Contains 982 Pullmore Car Transporter,
  one packing piece, and these cars:
  154 Hillman Minx (Light Green/Cream),
  156 Rover 75 (Cream/Blue),
  161 Austin Somerset (Red/Yellow),
  162 Zephyr (Green/White)........ **£2,000-2,500**

**1001** **Station Staff ('00' gauge)**
1952-54   (renumbered in 1954 to 051)
- Six Blue figures, Green card box........ **£45-55**

**1003** **Passengers ('00' gauge)**
1952-54   (renumbered in 1954 to 053)
- Six coloured figures, Green card box . **£45-55**

**49N2269** **'Road Racers' Set**
1965
- 113 MGB, 114 Triumph Spitfire,
  120 Jaguar E-type, 237 Mercedes-Benz,
  238 Jaguar D-type, 242 Ferrari Racing
  Car, 243 BRM Racing Car. Special set
  for US mail-order company
  Sears-Roebuck.......................................NGPP

Dinky Toys
No. 4
Engineering Staff.
PHOTO:
VECTIS AUCTIONS LTD.

See also: Public Transport Models, Ships, Motor Cycles and Gift Sets sections.
Approximate size of figures: large 40mm (scale 1:42); small 35mm (scale 1:48).
Pre-war box title sequence: 'Modelled Miniatures'; 'Meccano Dinky Toys'; 'Dinky Toys'.

| Model and details | MPR |
|---|---|
| 1 1939-41 **Station Staff** (large) see Gift Sets. | |
| 1 1939-41 **Station Staff** (small) see Gift Sets. | |
| 1a 1932-41 **Station Master** (large) | |
| • Dark Blue uniform with Gold or Silver buttons on long coat | **£30-35** |
| 1a 1932-41 **Station Master** (small) | |
| • As previous model but smaller | **£20-25** |
| 1b 1932-39 **Guard** (large) | |
| • Dark Blue coat (Gold or Silver buttons), blowing whistle, flag in left hand | **£30-35** |
| 1b 1932-39 **Guard** (small) | |
| • As previous version but smaller | **£20-25** |
| 1b 1939-41 **Guard** (large) | |
| • Dark Blue coat (Gold or Silver buttons), blowing whistle, flag in right hand | **£30-35** |
| 1b 1939-41 **Guard** (small) | |
| • As previous version but smaller | **£20-25** |
| 1c 1932-41 **Ticket Collector** (large) | |
| • Dark Blue uniform (Gold or Silver buttons), slightly open arms | **£30-35** |
| 1c 1932-41 **Ticket Collector** (large) | |
| • As before but only right arm extended | **£30-35** |
| 1c 1932-41 **Ticket Collector** (small) | |
| • As previous version but smaller | **£20-25** |
| 1d 1932-39 **Driver** (large) | |
| • Mid-Blue uniform (Gold or Silver buttons), holding oil-can | **£30-35** |
| 1d 1939-41 **Driver** (small) | |
| • As previous version but smaller | **£20-25** |
| 1e 1932-39 **Porter with Bags** (large) | |
| • Dark Blue uniform, oblong case in right hand, round hat-box in left | **£30-35** |
| 1e 1939-41 **Porter with Bags** (small) | |
| • Dark Blue, small oblong case in each hand | **£20-25** |
| 1f 1932-39 **Porter** (large) | |
| • Dark Blue, walking, no luggage | **£30-35** |
| 1f 1939-41 **Porter** (small) | |
| • Dark Blue, standing, no luggage | **£20-25** |
| 2a 1932-41 **Horses** | |
| • One Light Brown or Dark Brown horse, one White horse | **£20-30** |
| 2b 1932-41 **Cow** | |
| • 3 versions were available; Light Brown, Dark Brown, or Black and White | **£20-25** |
| 2c • 1932-41 **Pig**. A Pink porker | **£15-20** |
| 2d 1932-41 **Sheep** | |
| • White sheep, Black detailing | **£15-20** |
| 3a 1932-39 **Woman and Child** (large) | |
| • Woman in Green coat, child (in Red) is on woman's right | **£30-35** |
| 3a 1939-41 **Woman and Child** (small), | |
| • Woman in Green suit with Grey scarf and Red hat, child on woman's left | **£20-25** |
| 3b 1932-39 **Business Man** (large) | |
| • Dark Blue suit/hat, walking stick in right hand, left hand holds lapels | **£30-35** |
| 3b 1939-41 **Business Man** (small) | |
| • Grey suit, left hand holds attaché case | **£20-25** |
| 3c 1932-39 **Male Hiker** (large) | |
| • Brown clothing, Grey, Brown or Khaki rucksack, walking stick in right hand | **£30-35** |
| 3c 1939-41 **Male Hiker** (small) | |
| • Brown clothing, Khaki rucksack, no walking stick | **£20-25** |
| 3d 1932-39 **Female Hiker** (large) | |
| • Blue skirt, White blouse, walking stick in right hand | **£30-35** |
| 3d 1939-41 **Female Hiker** (small) | |
| • All Blue clothing, or Dark Blue skirt, White blouse | **£20-25** |
| 3e 1932-39 **Newsboy** (large) | |
| • Brown or Blue clothing, running, papers in right hand and under left arm | **£30-35** |

| Model and details | MPR |
|---|---|
| 3e 1939-41 **Newsboy** (small) | |
| • Dark Blue clothing, standing, papers in Cream tray | **£20-25** |
| 3f 1932-39 **Woman** | |
| • Red jacket, White skirt, coat over left arm, oblong case in right hand | **£25-30** |
| 3f 1939-41 **Woman** | |
| • Dark Red coat, Black collar, round case in right hand | **£25-30** |
| 4 1932-39 **Engineering Staff** | |
| See Gift Sets section. | |
| 4a 1932-39 **Electrician** (large) | |
| • Blue overalls, White sleeves, carrying equipment | **£30-35** |
| 4a 1939-41 **Electrician** (small) | |
| • Blue overalls, White sleeves, carrying equipment | **£20-25** |
| 4b 1932-39 **Fitter** (large) | |
| • All-Blue overalls, or Brown overalls with White sleeves, carrying equipment | **£30-35** |
| 4b 1939-41 **Fitter** (small) | |
| • As previous model but smaller | **£20-25** |
| 4c 1932-39 **Storekeeper** (large) | |
| • Brown coat, Black trousers, holding forms in right hand, casting as 1a | **£30-35** |
| 4c 1939-41 **Storekeeper** (small) | |
| • Brown coat, Black trousers, holding forms in right hand, casting as 1a | **£20-25** |
| 4d 1932-39 **Greaser** (large) | |
| • Brown overalls, holding oil-can in right hand, casting based on 1d | **£30-35** |
| 4d 1939-41 **Greaser** (small) | |
| • Brown overalls, holding oil-can in right hand, casting based on 1d | **£20-25** |
| 4e 1932-39 **Engine-Room Attendant** (large) | |
| • Blue overalls, White sleeves on some | **£30-35** |
| 4e 1939-41 **Engine-Room Attendant** (small) | |
| • Blue overalls, White sleeves on some | **£20-25** |
| 5 1932-39 **Train and Hotel Staff**. | |
| See the Gift Sets section. | |
| 5a 1932-39 **Pullman Car Conductor** (large) | |
| • White jacket, Blue trousers, slightly open arms, casting as 1c | **£30-35** |
| 5a 1939-41 **Pullman Car Conductor** (small), | |
| • White jacket, Blue trousers, slightly open arms, casting as 1c | **£20-25** |
| 5b 1932-39 **Pullman Car Waiter** (large) | |
| • White jacket, Blue trousers, two slightly different poses were available | **£30-35** |
| 5b 1939-41 **Pullman Car Waiter** (small) | |
| • White jacket, Blue trousers, two slightly different poses were available | **£20-25** |
| 5c 1932-39 **Hotel Porter** (large) | |
| • Red jacket/Brown trousers, or Green jacket/Blue trousers, casting as 1e | **£30-35** |
| 5c 1939-41 **Hotel Porter** (small) | |
| • Red jacket/Brown trousers, or Green jacket/Blue trousers, casting as 1e | **£20-25** |
| 6 1933-40 **Shepherd Set** | |
| See the Gift Sets section. | |
| 6a 1932-41 **Shepherd** | |
| • Brown with Dark Brown hat | **£50-75** |
| 6b 1932-41 **Sheep-dog** | |
| • Black and White sheep-dog | **£20-30** |
| 12 1937-41 **Postal Set** See Gift Sets section. | |
| 12a 1935-40 **GPO Pillar Box 'GR'** | |
| • Red, with or without Red/Yellow 'Post Office' sign on top, White panel. | **£25-30** |
| 12b 1935-40 **Air Mail Pillar Box** | |
| • Blue body, 'Air Mail', White panel, casting as 12a | **£35-40** |
| 12c 1936-40 **Telephone Box** | |
| • Cream with Silver windows | **£20-30** |

| Model and details | MPR |
|---|---|
| 12d 1938-40 **Telegraph Messenger** | |
| • Dark Blue body, picked out detail in darker Blue, Brown pouch, 35 mm | **£20-25** |
| 12e 1938-40 **Postman** | |
| • Dark Blue body, darker Blue detail, Brown post bag and badge, 35 mm | **£20-25** |
| 13 1931-40 **'HALLS DISTEMPER'**. | |
| • Cream card with Red lettering, 2 painter figures (lead, usually White/Red/Grey), Silver/Green buckets/brushes. 'Hornby Series'. Boxed ('A898') | **£300-400** |
| 15 • 1937-41 **Railway Signals Set**. | |
| See the Gift Sets section. | |
| 15a 1937-41 **Single Arm Signal** | |
| • One Red 'Home' signal, or Yellow 'Distant' signal | **£30-40** |
| 15b 1937-41 **Double Arm Signal** | |
| • One Red 'Home' signal and one Yellow 'Distant' signal on single pole | **£40-50** |
| 15c 1937-41 **Junction Signal** | |
| • Two Red 'Home' signals, OR two Yellow 'Distant' signals on a single pole | **£65-75** |
| 30g 1936-39 **Caravan Trailer** | |
| • 2 wheels, drawbar, body length 81 mm., open roof windows, Blue/Cream, Red/Cream, Green/Cream, Orange/Cream, TT-Green | **£90-120** |
| • Chocolate and Beige, Blue hubs | **£150-175** |
| 1939-40 | |
| • Same, but filled-in roof windows | **£80-110** |
| 42 1935-41 **Police Set**. See the Gift Sets section. | |
| 42a 1936-40 **Police Box** | |
| • Dark Blue box, 'POLICE' in Silver | **£25-35** |
| 42c 1936-40 **Point Duty Policeman**, (42 mm) | |
| • Lead. White coat, Black helmet | **£25-35** |
| 42d 1936-40 **Point Duty Policeman**, (40mm) | |
| • Dark Blue, White gauntlets, lead | **£25-35** |
| 43 1935-41 **'RAC' Set** See the Gift Sets section. | |
| 43a 1935-40 **'RAC' Box** | |
| • Blue and White (tinplate) call-box with 'RAC' emblem | **£90-110** |
| 43c 1935-40 **'RAC' Guide**. (37mm) | |
| • Blue uniform, Red sash, directing traffic, (cast in lead) | **£25-35** |
| 43d 1935-40 **'RAC' Guide** (saluting) (36mm) | |
| • Blue uniform, Red sash, cast in lead | **£25-35** |
| 44 1935-41 **'AA' Set** See the Gift Sets section. | |
| 44a 1935-40 **'AA' Box** | |
| • Black/Yellow tinplate box with 'AA' badge and 3 signs | **£90-110** |
| 44c 1935-40 **'AA' Guide** (37mm) | |
| • Tan uniform, Blue sash, directing traffic, cast in lead | **£20-25** |
| 44d 1935-40 **'AA' Guide** (saluting) (36mm) | |
| • Tan uniform, Blue sash, cast in lead | **£20-25** |
| 45 1935-40 **Garage** | |
| • Cream/Orange (tinplate), Green opening doors, boxed, 127 x 90 mm | **£500-600** |
| 46 1937-40 **Pavement Set** | |
| • Dark Grey 'stone' effect (cardboard) pavement pieces in a box | **£45-55** |
| 47 1935-41 **Road Signs Set** See Gift Sets. | |
| 47a 1935-41 **4-face Traffic Lights** | |
| • Black on White post, Yellow beacon, White base, 62 mm high | **£15-20** |
| 47b 1935-41 **3-face Traffic Lights**. | |
| • Black on White post, Yellow beacon, White base, 62 mm high | **£15-20** |
| 47c 1935-41 **2-face Traffic Lights** | |
| • Back-to-back lights, Black on White post, Yellow beacon, White base | **£15-20** |
| 1935-41 | |
| • Lights at 90 degrees, Black on White post, Yellow beacon, White base | **£15-20** |

**47d** 1935-41 **Belisha Beacon**
- Black on White post, Orange globe, White base, 51 mm high ..................... **£15-20**

**47e** 1935-41 **'30 MPH' Limit Sign**
- Black on White post, Red top, 52 mm. **£15-20**

**47f** 1935-41 **De-restriction Sign**
- Black on White post, diagonal Black bar on White circle, 52 mm high ........ **£15-20**

**47g** 1935-41 **'School' Sign**
- Black on White post, Red top, Black 'beacon' design, 51 mm high .... **£15-20**

**47h** 1935-41 **'Steep Hill' Sign**
- Black on White post, Red top, Black 'incline' design, 51 mm high ..... **£15-20**

**47k** 1935-41 **'S-Bend' Sign**
- Black on White post, Red top, Black 'S-Bend' design, 51 mm high.... **£15-20**

**47m** 1935-41 **'Left-Hand Bend' Sign**
- Black on White post, Red top, Black 'curve' design, 51 mm high....... **£15-20**

**47n** 1935-41 **'Right-Hand Bend' Sign**
- Black on White post, Red top, Black 'curve' design, 51 mm high....... **£15-20**

**47p** 1935-41 **'T-Junction' Sign**
- Black on White post, Red top, Black 'T' design, 51 mm high ............. **£15-20**

**47q** 1935-41 **'No Entry' Sign**
- Black on White post, Red 'bar' design, 48 mm high.............................. **£15-20**

**47r** 1935-41 **'Major Road Ahead' Sign**
- Black on White post, Red top, Black lettering, 54 mm high ............... **£15-20**

**47s** 1935-41 **'Crossing No Gates' Sign**
- Black on White post, Red top, Black 'loco' design, 51 mm high......... **£15-20**

**47t** 1935-41 **'Roundabout' Sign**
- Black on White post, Red top, Black 'arrows' design, 51 mm high..... **£15-20**
  NB Pre-war issues have filled in triangles.

**48** 1935-41 **Filling and Service Station.** Tinplate construction with 'FILLING AND SERVICE STATION' logo. Orange box.
- Green roof and base ......................... **£500-600**
- Turquoise roof and base................... **£500-600**
- Yellow roof, Green base................... **£500-600**

**49** 1935-41 **Petrol Pumps Set**. See Gift Sets.

**49a** 1935-40 **Bowser Petrol Pump**
- Green pump, White rubber hose, 46 mm tall ..................................... **£35-45**

**49b** 1935-40 **Wayne Petrol Pump**
- Turquoise pump, White rubber hose, 39 mm tall ..................................... **£35-45**

**49c** 1935-40 **Theo Petrol Pump**
- Blue, White rubber hose, 58 mm ........ **£35-45**

**49d** 1935-40 **'SHELL' Petrol Pump**
- Red, White rubber hose, 53 mm .......... **£35-45**

**49e** 1935-40 **'Pratts' Oil Bin**
- Yellow bin body and opening tinplate lid, 'Pratts Motor Oil', 32 mm............. **£40-50**
- Post-war, 49e was only available in Set 49 (without 'Pratts' logo)....................GSP

**101** 1935-40 **Dining Room Set** See Gift Sets.

**101a** 1935-40 **Dining Table**
- 'Wood' effect dining table, 64 mm ...... **£30-35**

**101b** 1935-40 **Sideboard**
- 'Wood' effect sideboard with opening doors, tinplate back, 63 mm................. **£30-35**

**101c** 1935-40 **Carver Chair**
- 'Wood' effect chair with armrests, 33 mm high ......................................... **£15-20**

**101d** 1935-40 **Dining Chair**
- 'Wood' effect chair without armrests, raised 'leather' cushion......... **£10-15**

**102** 1935-40 **Bedroom Set** See Gift Sets section.

**102a** 1935-40 **Bed**
- Brown or Pink double bed .................. **£30-35**

**102b** 1935-40 **Wardrobe**
- Brown or Pink wardrobe with opening door, tinplate back, 63 mm .... **£30-35**

**102c** 1935-40 **Dressing Table**
- Brown or Pink, opening drawers, tinplate mirror, 51 mm ........................ **£30-35**

**102d** 1935-40 **Dressing Chest**
- Brown or Pink, opening drawer, tinplate back, 40 mm high.................... **£30-35**

**102e** 1935-40 **Dressing Table Stool**
- Brown or Pink stool, 13 mm high........ **£15-20**

**102f** 1935-40 **Chair**
- Brown or Pink .................................... **£10-15**

**103** 1935-40 **Kitchen Set** See Gift Sets section.

**103a** 1935-40 **Refrigerator**
- Light Blue/White or Light Green/Cream, door, tinplate back and food tray ......... **£35-45**

**103b** 1935-40 **Kitchen Cabinet**
- Light Blue/White or Light Green/Cream, opening doors/drawer, tin back ............ **£35-45**

**103c** 1935-40 **Electric Cooker**
- Light Blue/White or Light Green/Cream, opening door, tinplate back .................. **£35-45**

**103d** 1935-40 **Kitchen Table**
- Light Blue/White or Light Green/Cream, 34 mm high................... **£30-35**

**103e** 1935-40 **Kitchen Chair**
- Light Blue/White or Light Green/Cream, casting as 102f .............. **£10-15**

**104** 1935-40 **Bathroom Set** See Gift Sets.

**104a** 1935-40 **Bath**
- Pink/White or Light Green/White, Gold taps, 69 mm ................................ **£35-45**

**104b** 1935-40 **Bath Mat**
- Mottled Green rubber, 50 x 37 mm ..... **£10-15**

**104c** 1935-40 **Pedestal Hand Basin**
- Pink/White or Light Green/White, Gold taps, tinplate mirror, 63 mm....... **£30-35**

**104d** 1935-40 **Bathroom Stool**
- Pink/White or Light Green/White, 15 mm high ........................................ **£15-20**

**104e** 1935-40 **Linen Basket**
- Pink/White or Light Green/White, hinged lid, 22 mm high ....................... **£15-20**

**104f** 1935-40 **Toilet**
- Pink/White or Light Green/White, hinged lid, 34 mm high ....................... **£35-45**

**---** 1935-40 **'Dolly Varden' Dolls House**
- Not given a reference number, made of 'leather board' (heavy reinforced cardboard), and supplied packed flat. Cream/Brown upper storey, Red brick ground floor, Red roof, 476 x 260 mm base, 476 mm high .. **£500-750**
  NB It is not really possible to give individual prices for single 'Dolly Varden' items as they are very rarely available in collectable condition. Boxed sets sell for £200-300, for example. See also the Gift Sets section.

See also: Public Transport Models, Ships, Motor Cycles and Gift Sets sections.

| Model and details | MPR |
|---|---|
| **001** 1954-56 **Station Staff ('0' gauge)** (renumbered in 1954 from 1) | |
| • 1b Guard (flag in right hand), 1c Ticket Collector (right arm extended), 1d Driver, 1e Porter (with oblong bags), 1f Porter (standing) | **£90-120** |
| **001** 1979-80 **'Space War Station'** | |
| • Dinky Builda card ('54001') | **£15-20** |
| **002** 1954-56 **Farmyard Animals (6)** (renumbered in 1954 from 2) | |
| • 2 x 2a horses, 2 x 2b cows, 1 x 2c pig, 1 x 2d sheep, simplified painting | **£200-300** |
| **002** 1979-80 **'Blazing Inferno'** | |
| • Dinky Builda card ('54002') | **£15-20** |
| **003** 1954-56 **Passengers ('0' gauge)** (renumbered in 1954 from 3) | |
| • 3a Woman (with child on left), 3b Businessman (Brown suit and case), 3c Male hiker (no stick), 3d Female hiker (Blue blouse), 3e Newsboy (Grey tray), 3f Woman (Light Red coat, round case) | **£90-120** |
| **004** 1954-56 **Engineering Staff ('0' gauge)** (renumbered in 1954 from 4) | |
| • 2 x 4b Fitter (all-Blue and all-Brown), 4c Storekeeper (all-Brown), 4d Greaser, 4e Engine-Room Attendant | **£90-120** |
| **005** 1954-56 **Train and Hotel Staff ('0' gauge)** (renumbered in 1954 from 5) | |
| • 5a Conductor, 2 x 5b waiters, 2 x 5c Porter (Brown or Blue) | **£90-120** |
| **006** 1954-56 **Shepherd Set** (renumbered in 1954 from 6) | |
| • 6a Shepherd (Green hat), 6b sheepdog (all-Black), 4 x 2b sheep | **£250-350** |
| **007** 1960-67 **Petrol Pump Attendants** | |
| • 1 male (White overalls), 1 female (White coat), plastic | **£15-20** |
| **008** 1961-67 **Fire Station Personnel** | |
| • Set of 6 plastic fire-fighters in Blue uniforms plus hose, supplied in a bag. (Also present in GS 298) | **£65-75** |
| **009** 1962-66 **Service Station Personnel** | |
| • Set of 8 plastic figures in various colours and stances. Supplied in a bag or a Yellow box | **£65-75** |
| **010** 1962-66 **Road Maintenance Personnel** | |
| • Set of 6 workmen (35 mm tall) using pick, barrow, shovels, drill etc, plus hut, brazier, barrier, and 4 lamps. Plastic. Supplied in a bag or a Yellow box | **£65-75** |
| **011** 1954-56 **Telegraph Messenger** (renumbered in 1954 from 12d) | |
| • Mid-Blue uniform, detailing in darker Blue, Brown pouch, 35 mm | **£10-15** |
| **012** 1954-56 **Postman** (renumbered in 1954 from 12e) | |
| • Mid-Blue body, darker Blue detail, Brown post bag and badge, 35 mm | **£15-20** |
| **013** 1954-56 **Cook's Man** (Agent for the Thomas Cook travel company). (renumbered in 1954 from 13a) | |
| • Dark Blue coat, 40 mm tall | **£20-30** |

| Model and details | MPR |
|---|---|
| **050** 1961-68 **Railway Staff ('00' gauge)** | |
| • 12 Blue plastic figures in a clear plastic box. Early issues contained a Policeman, later ones a Shunter | **£40-50** |
| **051** 1954-59 **Station Staff ('00' gauge)** (renumbered in 1954 from 1001) | |
| • 6 plastic figures in a clear plastic box | **£35-45** |
| **052** 1961-69 **Railway Passengers ('00' gauge)** | |
| • 11 plastic figures plus a seat, in a clear plastic box | **£35-45** |
| **053** 1954-59 **Passengers ('00' gauge)** (renumbered in 1954 from 1003) | |
| • 6 Blue plastic figures | **£35-45** |
| US issue: 6 metal figures in 'Dark Red' box marked 'Made in England, For sale in the United States by H.Hudson Dobson, P.O. Box 254 - 26th Street and Jefferson Avenue, Kenilworth, New Jersey'. | **NGPP** |
| **054** 1962-70 **Railway Station Personnel** | |
| • 4 plastic figures plus 8 pieces of furniture in a clear plastic box, ('OO' gauge) | **£35-45** |
| **1** 1946-54 **Station Staff** See Gift Sets section. | |
| **1a** 1946-54 **Station Master** | |
| • Dark Blue uniform (cap, long coat), (in Set 001 till 1956) | **£20-25** |
| **1b** 1946-54 **Guard** | |
| • Dark Blue uniform, blowing whistle, flag in right hand (see Set 001) | **£15-20** |
| **1c** 1946-54 **Ticket Collector** | |
| • Blue uniform, only right arm is extended (in Set 001 till 1956) | **£15-20** |
| **1e** 1946-54 **Porter with Bags** | |
| • Blue uniform, oblong case in each hand. (In Set 001 till 1956) | **£15-20** |
| **1f** 1946-54 **Porter** | |
| • Dark Blue uniform, standing, no luggage (in Set 001 till 1956) | **£15-20** |
| **2** 1946-54 **Farmyard Animals** See Gift Sets. | |
| **2a** 1946-54 **Horses** | |
| • 3 versions: Dark Brown horse (Black tail / mane), Light Brown horse (Light Brown tail / mane), White horse (2 in Set 002 till 1956) | **£20-25** |
| **2b** 1946-54 **Cows** | |
| • Light Brown, Dark Brown, or Black/White (2 in Set 002 till 1956) | **£20-25** |
| **2c** 1946-54 **Pig** | |
| • Cream body (in Set 002 till 1956) | **£15-20** |
| **2d** 1946-54 **Sheep** | |
| • White body with Black hand-painted detail (in Set 002 till 1956) | **£15-20** |
| **3** 1946-54 **Passengers** See Gift Sets section. | |
| **3a** 1946-54 **Woman and Child** | |
| • Woman in Green suit and hat (Brown scarf), child on left (see Set 003) | **£20-25** |
| **3b** 1946-54 **Business Man** | |
| • Brown suit, left hand holds attaché case (in Set 003 till 1956) | **£20-25** |
| **3c** 1946-54 **Male Hiker** | |
| • Brown clothing, Brown or Khaki rucksack, no stick (in Set 003 till 1956) | **£20-25** |
| **3d** 1946-54 **Female Hiker** | |
| • Blue or Dark Blue skirt and shirt, stick in right hand (see Set 003) | **£20-25** |
| **3e** 1946-54 **Newsboy** | |
| • Dark Blue clothing, standing, papers in Grey tray (in Set 003 till 1956) | **£20-25** |
| **3f** 1946-54 **Woman** | |
| • Light Red coat, round case in right hand (see Set 003) | **£20-25** |
| **4** 1946-54 **Engineering Staff** See Gift Sets. | |

| Model and details | MPR |
|---|---|
| **4a** 1946-54 **Electrician** | |
| • Blue overalls, White sleeves, carrying equipment (in Set 004 till 1956) | **£15-20** |
| **4b** 1946-56 **Fitters** | |
| • 2 versions; one in Blue, the other Brown, carrying equipment (Set 004) | **£15-20** |
| **4c** 1946-56 **Storekeeper** | |
| • Brown coat, Black trousers, holding forms in right hand | **£15-20** |
| **4d** 1946-56 **Greaser** | |
| • Brown overalls, oil-can in right hand | **£15-20** |
| **4e** 1946-56 **Engine-Room Attendant** | |
| • Blue overalls, Blue sleeves | **£10-15** |
| **5** 1946-54 **Train and Hotel Staff** (Gift Sets). | |
| **5a** 1946-56 **Pullman Car Conductor** | |
| • White jacket, Blue trousers, slightly open arms, casting as 1c | **£20-25** |
| **5b** 1946-56 **Pullman Car Waiter** | |
| • White jacket, Blue trousers, two slightly different poses are known | **£20-25** |
| **5c** 1946-56 **Hotel Porter** | |
| • Red jacket/Brown trousers, or Green jacket/Blue trousers, casting as 1e | **£20-25** |
| **6** 1946-54 **Shepherd Set** See Gift Sets section | |
| **6a** 1946-56 **Shepherd** | |
| • Brown with Green hat | **£40-50** |
| **6b** 1946-56 **Sheep-dog** | |
| • All-Black sheep-dog | **£20-30** |
| **12c** 1946-54 **Telephone Box** (renumbered in 1954 to 750) | |
| • Red call-box with Black window frames, 58 mm high | **£20-30** |
| **12d** 1946-54 **Telegraph Messenger** (renumbered in 1954 to 011) | |
| • Dark Blue body, picked out detail in darker Blue, Brown pouch, 35 mm tall | **£15-20** |
| **12e** 1946-54 **Postman** (renumbered in 1954 to 012) | |
| • Mid-Blue body, darker Blue detail, Brown post bag/badge, 35mm tall | **£15-20** |
| **13a** 1952-54 **Cook's Man** (Agent for Thomas Cook travel company) (renumbered in 1954 to 013) | |
| • Blue coat, 40 mm tall | **£20-30** |
| **30g** 1948-50 **Caravan** | |
| • Orange/Cream, 'Caravan Club', steel drawbar | **£45-55** |
| **42a** 1954-60 **Police Hut** (renumbered in 1954 to 751) | |
| • Dark Blue hut, 'POLICE', 66 mm | **£20-30** |
| **47** 1946-50 **Road Signs Set** See Gift Sets. | |
| **49** 1946-50 **Petrol Pumps Set** See Gift Sets. | |
| **49a** 1946-53 **Bowser Petrol Pump** | |
| • Green, White rubber hose, 46 mm | **£35-45** |
| **49b** 1946-53 **Wayne Petrol Pump** | |
| • Pale Blue,Yellow plastic hose, 39mm | **£25-35** |
| **49c** 1946-53 **Theo Petrol Pump** | |
| • Brown, Yellow plastic hose, 58 mm | **£25-35** |
| **49d** 1946-53 **'SHELL' Petrol Pump** | |
| • Red, Yellow plastic hose, 53 mm | **£25-35** |
| **49e** 194?-? **Oil Bin** | |
| • As pre-war 'Pratt's' Oil Bin but only available post-war in Set 49 and without 'Pratts' logo | **£25-35** |
| **117** 1963-69 **Four Berth Caravan** | |
| • Blue/Cream, clear roof, Fawn plastic interior and door | **£35-45** |
| • Primrose Yellow/Cream, Red plastic interior, Yellow plastic door | **£35-45** |
| • Primrose Yellow/Cream, Red plastic interior, Grey plastic door | **£35-45** |
| **188** 1961-63 **Four Berth Caravan** | |
| • Green/Cream or Blue/Cream, windows, detailed interior | **£35-45** |
| • 1963-63 As previous model but larger windows, (model replaced by 117) | **£35-45** |

**190** 1956-62 **Streamline Caravan**
- Mid-Blue lower body, Deep Cream upper body, Cream hubs, drawbar, metal jockey wheel .............................. **£35-45**
- Yellow lower body, Cream upper body, Cream hubs, metal jockey wheel ......... **£35-45**
- 1962-64 As previous models but with knobbly Grey or Black plastic jockey wheel. Two packing rings also in box . **£35-45**

**386** 1954-?? **Lawn Mower**
(renumered in 1954 from 751)
- Green and Red, 140mm. ...................... **£50-75**

**502** 1961-63 **Garage**
- Blue/Grey plastic garage, opening door, 272 mm. (French issue) .............. **£70-80**

**750** 1954-62 **Telephone Box**
(renumbered in 1954 from 12c)
- Red call-box with Red window frames, 58 mm high ........................... **£25-35**

**751** 1949-54 **Lawn Mower**
(renumbered in 1954 to 386)
- Green and Red, 140mm. ...................... **£50-75**

**751** 1954-60 **Police Box**
(renumbered in 1954 from 42a)
- Dark Blue hut, 'POLICE', 66 mm....... **£25-35**

**752** 1953-54 **Goods Yard Crane**
(renumbered in 1954 to 973)
- Yellow with Blue or Dark Blue, mazak or cast-iron base......................... **£40-50**

**753** 1962-67 **Police Crossing**
- Black/White box on traffic island with policeman directing traffic......... **£80-100**

**754** 1958-62 **Pavement Set**
- 20 Grey cardboard paving slabs, box .. **£50-60**

**755** 1960-64 **Lamp Standard (Single)**
- Grey/Fawn/Orange, plastic single-arm lamp on metal base ............................ **£20-30**

**757** 1960-?? **Chocks**
- Pack of 10 for 974 Car Transporter ..... **£15-20**

**756** 1960-64 **Lamp Standard (Double)**
- Grey/Fawn/Orange, plastic double-arm lamp on metal base ............................ **£30-40**

**760** 1954-60 **Pillar Box**
- Red/Black pillar box, 'E II R' cast-in .. **£25-35**

**763** 1959-64 **Posters for Hoarding**
- Six different coloured poster advertisements (on paper) ................... **£25-35**

**764** 1959-64 **Posters for Hoarding**
- Six different coloured poster advertisements (on paper) ................... **£25-35**

**765** 1959-64 **Road Hoardings (6 Posters)**
- Green plastic hoarding, 'David Allen and Sons Ltd' ................ **£50-60**

**766-772** **Road Sign Sets** See Gift Sets section.

**773** 1958-63 **4 face Traffic Lights**
- Black/White, Black base, similar to 47a but without beacon, 62 mm.......... **£15-20**

**777** 1958-63 **Belisha Beacon**
- Black/White post on Black base, Orange globe, casting as 47d, 51 mm.. **£10-15**

**778** 1962-66 **Road Repair Boards**
- Green and Red plastic warning signs, 6 different ................... **£30-40**

**780** 1950-54 **Petrol Pumps Set** See Gift Sets.

**781** 1955-62 **'ESSO' Petrol Station**
- 'ESSO' sign, no kiosk, 2 pumps ('ESSO' and 'ESSO EXTRA')......... **£100-150**

**782** 1960-70 **'SHELL' Petrol Station**
- 'SHELL' sign, Green/Cream kiosk, 4 Red/Yellow 'SHELL' pumps ....... **£100-150**

**783** 1960-70 **'BP' Petrol Station**
- 'BP' sign, Green/Cream kiosk, 4 Green/White 'BP' pumps............. **£100-150**

**785** 1960-64 **'SERVICE STATION'**
- Fawn and Red plastic, with 'BP' sign, 335 x 185 mm. (unbuilt kit, boxed). **£200-250**

**786** 1960-66 **Tyre Rack with Tyres**
- Green tyre rack with 21 assorted tyres and 'DUNLOP' on board ................... **£35-45**

**787** 1960-64 **Lighting Kit**
- Bulb and wire kit for model buildings. **£20-25**

**788** 1960-68 **Spare Bucket for 966**
- For Marrel Multi-Bucket Unit ........... **£10-15**

**790** 1960-64 **Granite Chippings**
- Plastic gravel in plastic bag ('50790'). **£15-20**

**791** 1960-64 **Imitation Coal**
- Packed in a plastic bag........................ **£15-20**

**792** 1960-64 **Packing Cases (3)**
- White/Cream plastic packing cases, 'Hornby Dublo', 38 x 28 x 19 mm...... **£15-20**

**793** 1960-64 **Pallets**
- Orange, Black, Pale Green, Yellow, Lemon, Red, Pink or mottled Purple. For 930 Pallet-Jekta and 404 Conveyancer....... **£15-20**

**794** 1954-64 **Loading Ramp**
(renumbered in 1954 from 994)
- Blue loading ramp for use with 582/982 Pullmore Car Transporter ..... **£15-20**

**846** 1961- **Oil Drums**
- Pack of 6 oil drums. French issue........ **£15-20**

**847** 1961- **Barrels**
- Pack of 6 barrels. French issue ............ **£15-20**

**849** 1961- **Packing Cases**
- Pack of 6 packing cases. French issue . **£15-20**

**850** 1961- **Crates of Bottles**
- Pack of 6 crates. French issue .............. **£15-20**

**851** 1961- **Sets of vehicle 'Loads'**
- Two each of 846 Oil Drums, 847 Barrels, 849 Packing Cases and 850 Crates ...... **£50-60**

**954** 1954-64 **Fire Station Kit** (Plastic)
- Red doors, Cream roof, Grey floor, clear roof, 'FIRE STATION'. 'DINKY TOYS' in Red................... **£200-250**

**994** 1954-55 **Loading Ramp**
- Renumbered from 794 to 994 then back to 794 after only a year! ............. **£15-20**

**973** 1954-59 **Goods Yard Crane**
(renumbered in 1954 from 752)
- Yellow with Blue or Dark Blue mazak or cast-iron base, steps in early issues...... **£40-50**

**1001** 1952-54 **Station Staff** See Gift Sets section.
**1003** 1952-54 **Station Staff** See Gift Sets section.

## Spare Tyres, Tank Tracks, Batteries and Bulbs

| No. | Years | Type | Description | Price |
|---|---|---|---|---|
| **020** | 1968-75 | **Spare tyre...** | Black tyre, 16 mm. dia. YB (12) | **£15-20** |
| **021** | 1970-75 | **Spare tyre...** | Black tyre, 20 mm. dia. YB (12) | **£15-20** |
| **022** | 1971-76 | **Spare tyre...** | Black tyre, 16 mm. dia. YB (12) | **£15-20** |
| **023** | 1971-76 | **Spare tyre...** | Black tyre, 16 mm. dia. YB (12) | **£15-20** |
| **024** | 1971-76 | **Spare tyre...** | Black tyre, 23 mm. dia. YB (12) | **£15-20** |
| **025** | 1976 only | **Spare tyre...** | Black tyre, 17 mm. dia. YB (12) | **£15-20** |
| **026** | 1976 only | **Spare tyre...** | Black tyre, 21 mm. dia. YB (12) | **£15-20** |
| **027** | 1976 only | **Spare tyre...** | Black tyre, 27 mm. dia. YB (12) | **£15-20** |
| **028** | | **Spare tyre...** | Not issued | NPP |
| **029** | 1976 only | **Track** | Black Track. Box of 6 | **£15-20** |
| **030** | 1968-76 | **Track** | Black Track. Box of 6 | **£15-20** |
| **031** | 1976-78 | **Track** | Black Track. Box of 6 | **£15-20** |
| **032** | 1973-76 | **Track** | Black Track. Box of 6 | **£15-20** |
| **033** | 1973-76 | **Track** | Black Track. Box of 6 | **£15-20** |
| **034** | 1964-76 | **Battery** | 1.5 volt battery | NGPP |
| **035** | 1970-76 | **Battery** | 1.5 volt battery | NGPP |
| **036** | | **Battery** | 1.5 volt battery for use with 276 Fire Tender and 277 Ambulance | NGPP |
| **037** | | **Lamp** | Red light-bulb for use with 277 | NGPP |
| **038** | | **Lamp** | Blue (or Orange) light-bulb for use with model 276 Airport Fire Tender | NGPP |
| **039** | | **Lamp** | Clear light-bulb for 952 Vega Coach | NGPP |
| **081** | | **Spare tyre...** | White fine tread tyre, 14 mm. dia. | NGPP |
| **082** | | **Spare tyre...** | Black narrow tread tyre, 20 mm. dia. | NGPP |
| **083** (as 099) | | **Spare tyre...** | Grey tyre, 20 mm. in diameter | NGPP |
| **084** | | **Spare tyre...** | Black 'recessed' tyre, 18 mm. dia. | NGPP |
| **085** (as 092) | | **Spare tyre...** | White tyre, 15 mm. in diameter | NGPP |
| **086** | | **Spare tyre...** | Black fine tread tyre, 16 mm. dia. | NGPP |
| **087** (as 60687) | | **Spare tyre...** | Black big 'tractor' tyre, 35 mm. dia. | NGPP |
| **089** (as 60689) | | **Spare tyre...** | Black 'tractor front tyre', 19 mm. dia. | NGPP |
| **090** (as 60790) | | **Spare tyre...** | Black fine tread tyre, 14 mm. dia. | NGPP |
| **090** (as 60791) | | **Spare tyre...** | White fine tread tyre, 14 mm. dia. | NGPP |
| **091** (as 60036) | | **Spare tyre...** | Black block tread tyre, 13 mm. dia. | NGPP |
| **092** (as 14094) | | **Spare tyre...** | Black block tread tyre, 15 mm. dia. | NGPP |
| **092** (as 14095) | | **Spare tyre...** | White block tread tyre, 15 mm. dia. | NGPP |
| **093** (as 13978) | | **Spare tyre...** | Black medium tractor tyre, 27mm dia. | NGPP |
| **094** (as 6676) | | **Spare tyre...** | Black smooth tyre, 18 mm. diameter | NGPP |
| **095** (as 6677) | | **Spare tyre...** | Black block tread tyre, 18 mm. dia. | NGPP |
| **096** (as 7067) | | **Spare tyre...** | Tyre, 15 mm. in diameter | NGPP |
| **097** (as 7383) | | **Spare wheel** | Solid rubber wheel, 12 mm. dia. | NGPP |
| **098** (as 10118) | | **Spare wheel** | Solid rubber wheel, 12 mm. dia. | NGPP |
| **099** (as 10253) | | **Spare tyre...** | Black block tread tyre, 20 mm. dia. | NGPP |
| **099** (as 10253) | | **Spare tyre...** | Grey block tread tyre, 20 mm. dia. | NGPP |
| **6676** (as 094) | | **Spare tyre...** | Black smooth tyre, 18 mm. diameter | NGPP |
| **6677** (as 095) | | **Spare tyre...** | Black block tread tyre, 18 mm. dia. | NGPP |
| **7067** (as 095) | | **Spare tyre...** | Tyre, 15 mm. in diameter | NGPP |
| **7383** (as 097) | | **Spare wheel** | Solid rubber wheel, 12 mm. dia. | NGPP |
| **10118** (as 098) | | **Spare wheel** | Solid rubber wheel, 12 mm. dia. | NGPP |
| **10253** (as 099) | | **Spare tyre...** | Black block tread tyre, 20 mm. dia. | NGPP |
| **13978** (as 093) | | **Spare tyre...** | Black medium tractor tyre, 27mm dia. | NGPP |
| **14094** (as 092) | | **Spare tyre...** | Black block tread tyre, 15 mm. dia. | NGPP |
| **14095** (as 092) | | **Spare tyre...** | White block tread tyre, 15 mm. dia. | NGPP |
| **60036** (as 091) | | **Spare tyre...** | Black block tread tyre, 13 mm. dia. | NGPP |
| **606087** (as 087) | | **Spare tyre...** | Black big 'tractor' tyre, 35 mm. dia. | NGPP |
| **606089** (as 089) | | **Spare tyre...** | Black 'tractor front tyre', 19 mm. dia. | NGPP |
| **607090** (as 090) | | **Spare tyre...** | Black fine tread tyre, 14 mm. dia. | NGPP |
| **607091** (as 090) | | **Spare tyre...** | White fine tread tyre, 14 mm. dia. | NGPP |

# Dinky Toys Catalogues (UK issues)

> **PRICES:** *Please note that paper ephemera must be in clean, undamaged condition to achieve the prices shown.*
> *French Dinky Toys Catalogues are listed at the end of the French Meccano Dinky Toys section.*

## Pre-war Catalogues, leaflets and listings

Hornby 'Modelled Miniatures' were introduced in 1931 as model railway accessories. The first catalogue listings appeared in Hornby Train catalogues, Meccano catalogues and in the 'Meccano Magazine'.

| Year of intro, publication details | MPR |
|---|---|
| 1932-33   no ref.  **Hornby 'Book of Trains'** First 'Modelled Miniatures' listed as 'Railway Accessories' | **£50-60** |
| 1932 no ref.  **Meccano trade catalogue** First 'Modelled Miniatures' listed as 'Railway Accessories' | **£50-60** |
| 1933 no ref.  **'Meccano Magazine'** 42 Hornby 'Modelled Miniatures' listed in the December issue | **£20-25** |
| 1933-34   no ref.  **Hornby 'Book of Trains'** Accessories are depicted in full colour | **£50-60** |
| 1934 no ref.  **Meccano trade catalogue** 'Modelled Miniatures' briefly renamed 'Meccano Miniatures' | **£70-90** |
| 1934 no ref.  **'Meccano Magazine'** February issue contained the last published 'Modelled Miniatures' listing | **£30-40** |
| 1934 no ref.  **'Meccano Magazine'** April issue contained the first 'Meccano Dinky Toys' listing | **£30-40** |
| 1934 no ref.  **'Meccano Magazine'** The May, June, July, August, September and November issues each reflected the increasing number of varieties of 'Dinky Toys' | **£15-20** |
| 1934 no ref.  **'Meccano Magazine'** '150 varieties of Dinky Toys' on double pages in October and December issues | **£15-20** |
| 1934-35   no ref.  **Hornby 'Book of Trains'** Catalogue shows 150 'Dinky Toys' in full colour on a double page | **£50-75** |
| 1934-35   **13/834/900.  Meccano Catalogue** Boat plane and model plus boy on cover, 3 pages of Dinky Toys | **£40-50** |
| 1934-35   **16/934/100. 'Hornby Trains/Meccano' Catalogue** Blue cover, full colour design of 'The World', lists 150 models of Dinky Toys | **£70-90** |
| 1934-35   **13/834/900.  'Halford's Toys of Interest'** Inc. Dinky, Hornby, Meccano, etc. | **£150-175** |
| 1934-35   no ref.  **Meccano Book** Cover depicts viaduct over river, complete Dinky Toys range is listed | **£70-90** |
| 1935 no ref.  **'Meccano Magazine'** January to November issues have various Dinky Toys listings | **£15-20** |
| 1935 no ref.  **'Meccano Magazine'** December issue shows 200 varieties of Dinky Toys in black and white | **£15-20** |
| 1935-36   **7/835/65.  Hornby 'Book of Trains'** Catalogue features 200 varieties of Dinky Toys in full colour | **£40-50** |
| 1935-36   no ref.  **Hornby/Meccano Catalogue** Same cover as the 1934-35 issue | **£70-90** |
| 1936 no ref.  **'Meccano Magazine'** The February and August issues featured a road layout and a competition; the May issue introduced the 'Queen Mary' model | **£15-20** |

| Year of intro, publication details | MPR |
|---|---|
| 1936-37   no ref.  **Hornby 'Book of Trains'** The catalogue features full colour pictures of the Dinky Toys range | **£50-60** |
| 1937 no ref.  **Hornby/Meccano** Catalogue with 1934-35 'World' cover again. Seven pages of listings | **£50-70** |
| 1937 no ref.  **'Meccano Magazines'** Details given in the monthly listings of the superb new 'Army' range | **£15-20** |
| 1937 **13/637/25.  8-page Leaflet** 8 page fold-out buff leaflet. Front page depicts the 1937 Army models | **£35-45** |
| 1938 **13/638/1150.  Hornby/Meccano** 74 page Catalogue, full Dinky Toys listings. Numerous black and white pictures | **£30-40** |
| 1938 **13/638/1150/UK.  'Wonder Book of Toys'** Two boys with Meccano models plus 11 pages with Dinky Toys | **£30-40** |
| 1938 **8/1238/25.  'DINKY TOYS' Catalogue** (Booklet). Cover shows boy and 6 models inc. 29c Bus, 151a Tank, and 63 Mayo Composite. Brown print on pale-yellow paper | **£100-125** |
| 1938 no ref.  **'Meccano Magazine'** Details of the full range (with pictures) are published each month | **£25-35** |
| 1939 **1/439/10.  'DINKY TOYS' leaflet** 'New Products' leaflet detailing items such as the Presentation Aeroplane Sets Nos 64 and 65. Black printing on pinkish paper | **£40-50** |
| 1939 no ref.  **'MECCANO' booklets** complete Dinky Toys listings, various | **£40-50** |
| 1939 **13/639/1.  Hornby/Meccano Catalogue** 74 pages, full Dinky Toys listings and black and white pictures | **£100-125** |
| 1939 **13/639/11500 UK.  'A Wonder Book of Toys'** Green and Yellow cover depicts two boys with their Meccano models. The booklet includes 13 pages of Dinky Toys information | **£100-125** |
| 1939 **2/739/10 (1P).  'DINKY TOYS' Catalogue** Famous Red/Yellow cover picture of schoolboy with outstretched arm and 17 models. Contains 14 black and white pages | **£150-175** |
| 1939 Same catalogue, but a version with only 10 black and white pages | **£140-160** |
| 1939?   no ref.  **'Toys Of Quality'** Maroon Express train features on cover plus 'The Hornby Railway Co' logo. 13 pages of Dinky Toys listings included | **£40-50** |
| 1939 no ref.  **Trade catalogue** Cover depicts boy with Dinky Toys and Hornby pictures with 'MECCANO TOYS OF QUALITY' logo | **£40-50** |
| 1939 **2/939/20.  'Halford's Toys of Interest'** Inc. all Dinky, Hornby, Meccano, etc. | **£150-200** |

| Year of intro, publication details | MPR |
|---|---|
| 1939 **2/1139/20(3P) UK 'DINKY TOYS' Catalogue** Superb Red and Yellow cover picture of schoolboy with outstretched arm and 17 models. Contains 10 black/white pages of listings and pictures | **£150-200** |
| 1939 no ref.  **'Meccano Magazine'** Each month had Dinky Toys listings | **£15-20** |
| 1940 **1/440/100.  'Meccano Products'** 4 page leaflet, buff paper, brown printing | **£20-30** |
| 1940 **16/1040/100.  'Meccano Products'** Four page leaflet, off-white paper, green printing (no pictures) | **£20-30** |
| 1940 **16/1040/200.  'DINKY TOYS' leaflet** Listing of models with pictures | **£20-30** |
| 1940 no ref.  **'Meccano Magazine'** Wartime Dinky aircraft and the Meccano 'Spitfire Fund' are featured | **£20-30** |
| 1941 **16/541/25 UK.  'DINKY TOYS' leaflet** Wartime camouflaged aircraft featured | **£20-30** |
| 1941 **16/641/20 UK.  'DINKY TOYS' leaflet** Similar to previous leaflet, military models listed | **£20-30** |
| 1941 **16/1141/20 UK.  'DINKY TOYS' leaflet** Listing of models and retail prices | **£20-30** |
| **Full Dinky Toys listings** also appeared in the toy catalogues of major retailers such as Gamages and Bentalls. These are now difficult to find. Each: | **£30-40** |

## Post-War Catalogues, leaflets and listings
## Early Post-War period, 1945 – 1954

There were at least two editions per annum so the following listings are not complete. The 'leaflet' approach reflects the shortage of paper in early post-war years.

| Year of intro, publication details | MPR |
|---|---|
| 1945 **16/1145/75 UK. Meccano leaflet** Leaflet lists the models to be reintroduced after the War and features pictures of 23e, 29c, 39a, 62s, 62p. Sepia print on cream paper | **£15-25** |
| 1946 **16/546/30 UK. Meccano leaflet** Sepia printed listing on cream paper featuring pictures of models 70a, 38c, 29c, 23e | **£15-25** |
| 1946 **16/1146/65 UK. Meccano leaflet** Blue/Black print on cream paper, featuring models 70a, 38c, 70b, 38e | **£15-25** |
| 1947 **16/347/50 UK. Meccano leaflet** Brown print on light cream paper. Models depicted are 70a, 70b, 70c, 70e, 38c, 38e, 38f, and 153a Jeep | **£15-25** |
| 1948 **16/448/30. Meccano General Products** Booklet with green printing on light cream paper | **£15-25** |
| 1948 **16/948/200.** As previous issue but mauve print on light cream paper | **£15-25** |
| 1948 **16/1248/5. 'Dinky Toys Tyre Sizes'** Simple Leaflet giving information on Dinky Toys spare tyres | **£15-25** |
| 1949 **16/449/100. Meccano General Products** Booklet with brown printing on light cream paper | **£15-25** |
| 1949 **13/1049/150. Meccano General Products** 8 pages, cover has boys looking at globe circled by Hornby Trains, Meccano items and Dinky Toys | **£15-25** |

| Year of intro, publication details | MPR |
|---|---|
| 1949 no ref. **Independent shop listings** Full Dinky Toys listings and pictures featured in catalogues published by the larger toy shops such as Bentalls, Gamages, etc | **£15-25** |
| 1950 **16/250/100. Meccano Leaflet** A leaflet of two pages, printed in purple with drawings of 22 models | **£15-25** |
| 1950 **16/450/150. Meccano General Products** booklet with pale Blue/Black printing on light cream paper | **£15-25** |
| 1950 **16/550/75. Meccano Leaflet** A leaflet folded into three 'pages', with listings all Meccano items including Dinky Builder | **£15-25** |
| 1950 **13/1050/80 UK. Dinky Toys Leaflet** 12pp catalogue, printed on cream paper with sepia pictures, 5"x3" approx | **£25-35** |
| 1950 no ref. **Independent shop listings** Full Dinky Toys listings and pictures featured in catalogues of the larger toy shops such as Gamages, Bentalls, etc | **£15-25** |
| 1951 **16/251/33. Meccano General Products** Booklet with brown printing on light cream paper | **£10-15** |
| 1951 no ref. **Independent shop listings** Full Dinky Toys listings and pictures featured in catalogues of the larger toy shops such as Bentalls, Gamages, etc | **£15-20** |

| Year of intro, publication details | MPR |
|---|---|
| 1952 **16/352/120.** Price List A single sheet printed both sides in dark blue, listing 66 models with 23 model drawings | **£10-15** |
| 1952 **13/952/250.** Price List Beige leaflet with pictures and prices | **£10-15** |
| 1953 **13/953/678. Meccano Catalogue** Includes Dinky Toys, Meccano and Hornby Dublo. '1st October 1953' | **£15-20** |
| 1953 **16/453/500. 4-page Leaflet** Buff leaflet; front page shows date '15th April 1953' and boy shouting 'DINKY TOYS' | **£15-25** |
| 1953 **16/753/75 (2P). 4-page Leaflet** Dark brown print, good illustrations | **£15-20** |
| 1953 **16/853/25. Price List** Beige leaflet with pictures and prices | **£15-20** |
| 1953 **16/953/200. Price List** no details at present | **£10-15** |
| 1954 **16/454/50 (7P). 4-page Leaflet** Dark brown print, good illustrations | **£10-15** |
| 1954 **16/854/25. Price List** Beige leaflet with pictures and prices | **£10-15** |
| 1955 **16/255/100 (1P). 4-page Leaflet** Dinky Toys and Dinky Supertoys listed; sepia printing | **£10-15** |

## UK Catalogue editions, 1952 – 1965

The series included fourteen editions although not all issues were given an edition number. More than one catalogue was issued in some years. It was common for catalogues to be overprinted with the name and address of the toy retailer. Original retail prices can be found under each model reference, or on a stapled-in price list in the centre of the catalogue (except for 1956 and 1957 which have separate loose-leaf price lists). In addition to issuing Dinky Toys catalogues, Meccano Ltd continued to issue 'Meccano Toys Of Quality' leaflets which provided a full listing of Dinky Toys with their retail prices plus details of their 'Hornby', 'Hornby-Dublo' and 'Meccano' products. As many as five printings per annum were produced using green, pink, blue or buff paper. When in perfect condition these leaflets sell for **£5-8** each.

1952 **16/152/50. (February) 16 pages** Cover features unknown 'C6321' ... **£55-65**

1952 **16/452/50. (April) 16 pages** As previous issue ... **£55-65**

1952 **15/852/165. (September) 16 pages** Cover shows hands holding 27f Estate Car, 'Dinky Toys' logo ... **£55-65**

1953 ref. ? **24 page catalogue** Cover shows boy wearing green sweater, 'Dinky Toys' and 'Price 3d' ... **£55-65**

1953 **7/953/150. 24 page catalogue** As next item: 7/953/360.

1953 **7/953/360. (1st October) 24 pages** (1) Cover features 555 Fire Engine, 522 Big Bedford Lorry and 25x Breakdown Lorry, price '2d' ... **£55-65**

1953 **13/953/678. (1st October)** (2) Cover shows 'Meccano Magic Carpet', two boys + globe with flag ... **£55-65**

1954 **7/754/600. (1st September) 24 pages** Cover features 157 Jaguar, 480 'Kodak' Van, 641 Army Truck, 'Dinky Toys' logo, price '2d' ... **£40-50**

1955 **7/755/515. 24 page catalogue** 'Dinky Toys','Supertoys', 481 'Ovaltine' Van on cover, ('2d') ... **£40-50**

1956 **7/456/800. (June) 32 pages** Cover has 942 'REGENT' Tanker, 255 Mersey Tunnel 'Police' Land Rover, 157 Jaguar XK120, 'Dinky Toys' and 'Dinky Supertoys', '2d' ... **£40-50**

1956 **7/1056/125 (2P). (October) 32 pages** Same as previous issue, 2nd printing .. **£30-40**

1957 **7/657/820. (August) 28 pages** Cover shows 290 'DUNLOP' Double Decker Bus etc, 'Dinky Toys' and 'Dinky Supertoys', price '2d UK' ... **£40-50**

1958 **7/458/856. 28 pages** Houses of Parliament shown on front cover with 'Dinky Toys' and 'Dinky Supertoys', price '2d UK' ... **£40-50**

1959 **7/559/900. 28 page catalogue** Red Jaguar XK120 Coupe (157) on front cover with 'Dinky Toys' and 'UK Seventh Edition', price '3d' ... **£40-50**

1960 **7/3/800. 32 page catalogue** Motorway bridge on cover, 'Dinky Toys' and 'UK Eighth Edition' ... **£40-50**

1961 **7/561/700. 32 page catalogue** Black/yellow cover with 6 models, 'Dinky Toys', 'UK 9th Edition' ... **£40-50**

1962 **7/562/600. 32 page catalogue** Cover features 120 Jaguar 'E' type, 'Dinky Toys', price '2d' ... **£40-50**

1963 **7/263/400** No details available for this reference number ... **£25-35**

1963 **13/163/200. 32 page catalogue** Motor Show stands featured on cover, '11th Edition', 'UK', '2d' ... **£25-35**

1963 **13/763/400. 32 page catalogue** 11th Edition, 2nd impression ... **£25-35**

1964 **7/164/450. 8 page catalogue** 'Widest Range & Best Value In The World' and 'Dinky Toys' logos Price '3d' ... **£25-35**

1964 **7/764/450 (2nd.Ptg.). 8 page catalogue** (2nd printing). As 7/164/450 except that page 8 shows Bedford TK instead of accessories ... **£25-35**

1965 **7/265/200. 16 page catalogue** Rolls-Royce (127) on cover with 'Dinky Toys by Meccano' Price '3d' .. **£25-35**

1965 **7/865/135 (2 ptg). 16 page catalogue** (2nd printing). Cover features cars 127, 128, 133, 151 and 178 ... **£25-35**

## UK Catalogue editions, 1966 – 1978

Up to 1972, original retail prices were on a refence listing stapled-in to the centre of the catalogue or bound-in at the back. However, no retail prices are shown on the lists for 1972 to 1978. For 1978, this list is found on the last three pages of the catalogue.

| Year of intro, publication details | MPR |
| --- | --- |
| 1966 **72561/2. 106 page catalogue** 1st Edition', '6d', 'Always Something New From Dinky' on the cover. Bound-in (pink) price list | **£25-30** |
| 1966 **72561/2. (2nd edition, after 21st July)** Same cover as 1st, 104 pages plus bound-in (buff) price list | **£20-25** |
| 1967 **72571. 104 page catalogue** 'No.3', '6d' 12 models on cover, same logo as 72561/2. Bound-in (pale-green) price list | **£20-25** |
| 1967 As previous entry, but '2nd Printing' on the first page of the price list | **£20-25** |
| 1968 **72580. 104 page catalogue** 'No.4', '6d', Spectrum Pursuit Vehicle (104) on cover. Logo as 72561/2. Buff price list | **£20-25** |
| 1969 **72585. (May) 24 pages** 'No.5', '3d'. 102 'Joe's Car', and same logo as 72561/2. '1st Printing 1st May 1969' | **£15-20** |

| Year of intro, publication details | MPR |
| --- | --- |
| 1969 **(Sept) 24 pages** 2nd run of 72585 | **£15-20** |
| 1970 **165000. (May) 24 page catalogue** 'No.6', '3d', many models on cover. Same logo as 72561/2 | **£15-20** |
| 1971 no ref. **(Feb) 24 page catalogue** '2nd Printing, 1st February 1971'. This is a '2nd printing' of 165000 | **£15-20** |
| 1971 **100103. 24 page catalogue** 'No.7', '2p', '1971 Meccano Tri-ang Ltd' on rear cover. Same logo as on 72561/2. (Note the change to Decimal Currency in 1971) | **£10-15** |
| 1972 **100107. (June) 28 page catalogue** 'No.8', '2p', 683 Chieftain Tank. '1st Printing, June 1972' | **£10-15** |
| 1972 **100107.** 2nd printing of 100107 | **£15-20** |
| 1972 **100108. 28 page catalogue** 'No.8', 725 Phantom, 784 Goods Train, etc. on cover, but no date or price. No price list | **£10-15** |

| Year of intro, publication details | MPR |
| --- | --- |
| 1973 **100109. 40 page catalogue** 'No.9', '3p', '1st Printing'. Shows 924 'Centaur', 'Dinky Toys' | **£10-15** |
| 1973 **100109. (October) 40 page catalogue** 2nd printing of 100109 | **£15-20** |
| 1974 **100113. (May) 40 page catalogue** 'No.10', '4p', cover shows 731 S.E.P.E.C.A.T. and 'Dinky Toys'. | **£10-15** |
| 1975 **100115 UK. (June) 48 page catalogue** 'No.11', '5p', 'Dinky Toys' and 675 Motor Patrol Boat on cover | **£10-15** |
| 1976 **100118 UK. 48 page catalogue** 'No.12', '5p', 'Dinky Toys' and 358 'USS Enterprise' on cover | **£10-15** |
| 1977 **100122 (UK). 44 page catalogue** 'No.13' and '5p'. Cover features 357 Klingon Battle Cruiser | **£5-10** |
| 1978 **100100. 44 page catalogue** 'No.14', '5p', 180 Rover 3500 on front cover. 'Airfix Group' logo on rear | **£5-10** |

## Leaflets and Price Lists, 1954 – 1978

**Further information**. It is known that other leaflets, literature and price lists were published. The Editor would welcome more information to add to these listings.

1954 **16/854/25. Price List** - no details..... **£30-40**
1955 **16/155/100. Leaflet / Price List** No details...................................... **£30-40**
1955 **7/455/250. (May) 8 page leaflet** 251, 641, 170 and 401 on cover, 'Dinky Toys' and 'Dinky Supertoys' .. **£20-30**
1955 **16/655/25. 'Hamley's' Leaflet** No details...................................... **£30-40**
1956 **16/156/225. Leaflet** - no details ........ **£30-40**
1956 **16/556/500. Leaflet / Price List** No details...................................... **£30-40**
1956 **16/656/525. Leaflet / Price List** No details...................................... **£30-40**
1957 no ref. **Booklet** Yellow cover, 'A NEW SERIES' and 'DUBLO DINKY TOYS' in red ......... **£30-40**
1957 **DT/CF/3 16/257/250 (1P) Leaflet and Price List** Yellow fronted leaflet '1st January 1957', pictures of 716, 162, 626, and 250 Fire Engine, 'Dinky Toys' and 'Dinky Supertoys' in Red............. **£30-40**
1957 **DT/CF/4 UK 16/757/250 (2P) Leaflet and Price List** Yellow fronted folding leaflet. 'July 1957'. Pictures of 418 Leyland Comet, 923 'Heinz' Van, 164 Vauxhall plus 190 Caravan. 'Dinky Toys' and 'Dinky Supertoys' in Red.................... **£30-40**

1957 **16/857/500. Leaflet / Price List.** No details...................................... **£30-40**
1957 **DT/CL/20 16/1157/100 UK Two-sided Leaflet** 'Dublo Dinky Toys' in Red on Yellow. Pictures of first 3 issues: 064, 065, 066...................................... **£30-40**
1958 **16/958/100. Leaflet.** Car Carrier and Trailer leaflet............ **£30-40**
1958 **10/758/450. Leaflet / Price List** No details...................................... **£30-40**
1959 **DT/CF/5 16/159/100. Illustrated Price List** Colour cover showing 983 Transporter and cars, etc. ............ **£30-40**
1959 **DT/CF/6 16/759/100 2ndP. Price List with colour pictures** Leaflet cover shows nos. 998, 967, 968 and 986. Dated '1959/UK' on front .................. **£30-40**
1959 **10/1259/50. Price List** - no details.... **£30-40**
1960 **DT/CF/7 16/160/100 (3P). Illustrated Price List** Colour cover with 666 Missile Vehicle and 785 Service Station, etc................ **£30-40**
1960 **DT/CF/8 16/160/100 (4P). Illustrated Price List** Colour cover with 930 Pallet-Jekta plus GS 951 Fire Service, etc............. **£30-40**

1961 **DT/CF/11 8/561/100. Illustrated Price List** (72535/02) Colour cover with 4 cars and 'Purchase Tax Surcharges 26th July 1961'............................................ **£30-40**
1965 **72557/02. Leaflet** Cover with 133, 127, 128, 151 and 171, with price list............................. **£30-40**
1966 **16/766/50M. Leaflet / Price List** No details...................................... **£30-40**
1967 **72579. Trade Fair Leaflet** 'THUNDERBIRDS'.......................... **£30-40**
1967 **72939. Leaflet / Price List** No details...................................... **£30-40**
1968 **72569. Leaflet** Features 103-105 'Captain Scarlet'.... **£30-40**
1971 **100217. Leaflet** Four page 'Action Kits' leaflet........... **£20-30**
1971 **100261. Single sheet** Full-colour flyer featuring 'All Action Fighting Vehicles' ........... **£20-30**
72-75 no ref. **Dinky Driver's Diary** 6 models shown on the cover; descriptions and diagrams of 1970s models inside .......................... **£20-30**
1979 no ref. **Trade Catalogue 1979** 'Fifty New Models', 11½ x 8¼ inches............................... **£20-30**

## Meccano Trade Catalogues listing Dinky Toys

These were issued for many years but little information has been recorded. For example:
Ref. 100126 – **1978 Trade Catalogue** with 'Todays World', 'Todays Meccano' and Todays Dinky Toys' on the cover plus colour design of late 1970s models on Motorway with 'Meccano' buildings in background.
Ref. 100102 – **1979 Trade Catalogue** 'Today's Meccano & Dinky'.

## Meccano Catalogues 1954 - 1958

with colour 'Dinky Toys' and 'Hornby-Dublo' listing. Details known to the compiler relate solely to issues in the mid-1950's period. 'MECCANO TOYS OF QUALITY' logo on each cover.

1954-55 **13/654/995UK. 24 pages, price '2d'** Cover depicts 4 boys on a desert island. Black/white pictures........... **£20-25**
1955-56 **13/655/797UK. 28 pages, price '2d'** Cover shows boys looking in toyshop window, black/white pictures ........ **£20-25**
1956 **13/756/525UK. 32 pages, price '4d'** Cover depicts Dinky Toys, Hornby-Dublo, and a Meccano

helicopter. This is a large catalogue with colour printing....... **£30-35**
1957 **13/757/500UK. 32 pages, price '4d'** Famous cover showing Meccano Tower, Hornby-Dublo train crossing a viaduct and Dinky Toys passing beneath. Large, with colour pictures............ **£50-75**

1958 **13/758/450UK. 20 pages, price '4d'** Cover depicts boy, Hornby-Dublo train, 8 Dinky Toys and a Meccano model. Includes some superb engine pictures............................. **£30-35**

## Meccano Magazines, 1942 - 1952

During the latter part of the war and especially during the early post-war years when Dinky Toys catalogues were not issued, the Meccano Magazine was the main source of new information for collectors. It advised on the reintroduction of models after the war and of the forthcoming new releases. Consequently the Magazines of this period are highly collectable in their own right.

**1942 - September 1943**. No Dinky Toys adverts or listings appeared.
**September 1943 - December 1944**. Back page adverts for Meccano incorporated listing and pictures of De Havilland Flamingo Aircraft and Buick 'Viceroy' Saloon.
**January - November 1945**. Back page adverts said 'Sorry, not available but will be ready after the war'.
**December 1945**. Advert on back page announced 'Ready during December'.
**1946**. Virtually every month a new model was added to the listing printed on the inside front cover. A picture of each model was shown.
**January - September 1947**. New models added regularly each month.
**October 1947**. First advert appears of Dinky Supertoys with pictures of 501 Foden Diesel Wagon, 502 Foden Flat Truck, 503 Foden Flat Truck with Tailboard, 511 Guy 4 ton Lorry, 512 Guy Flat Truck, 513 Guy Flat Truck with Tailboard, and 701 Short 'Shetland' Flying Boat.
**1948**. Single page advert every month, new models continually introduced.
**1949, 1950, 1951**. Double page advert each month listing new models.
**1952**. Double page adverts each month. The December issue shows Gift Sets No.1 Farm Gear and No.2 Commercial Vehicles.
Prices for Meccano Magazines of this period range between **£10-15** each.

## Meccano Magazines 1952 - 1975

With the introduction of yearly Dinky Toys catalogues from 1952 the Meccano Magazine lost its somewhat unique role as a combined magazine/catalogue. However, with the help of 'The Toyman' and his monthly articles plus superb colour advertising of new models, the Magazine continued to provide a valuable service for collectors. Meccano Magazines of this period are in the price range of **£5-10**.

## Dinky Toys Club Licences, Newsletters, etc.

| | | | |
|---|---|---|---|
| no ref. | 19??-?? | **Dinky Toys Club Certificate** ..............(unused) | **£100-125** |
| no ref | 1955-?? | **Dinky Toys Club Enamel Badge** ........................... | **£35-45** |
| no ref | 1955-?? | **Dinky Toys Club 'Welcome' Letter** ....................... | NGPP |

**Dinky Toys Club Newsletters**

| | | | |
|---|---|---|---|
| ? | 195? | **Dinky Toys Club Newsletter No.1**, '3d', 'Greetings from Australia' on cover .......................... | **£60-80** |
| 19/759/35 | 1959? | **Newsletter No.2**, '3d'. Stirling Moss on cover, 150 Rolls-Royce featured in centre-fold................... | **£60-80** |
| ? | 19?? | **Newsletter No.3**, 'M1' on cover.............................. | **£60-80** |

| | | | |
|---|---|---|---|
| DTC/L/1 | 1958-59 | **Collector's Licence**, Brown cover, 16 pages ........ | **£125-150** |
| DTC/L/2 | 1959-60 | **Collector's Licence**, Red cover, 16 pages ............ | **£100-125** |
| DTC/L/3 | 1960-61 | **Collector's Licence**, Green cover, 16 pages ............ | **£60-80** |
| DTC/L/4 | 1961-62 | **Collector's Licence**, Yellow cover, 16 pages............ | **£60-80** |

## Factory drawings

**UNISSUED MODELS**
A number of models were planned but not actually produced by Meccano. This is list of known factory drawings and plans for such models.
**Austin A40 Van** 'OMNISPORT' drawing dated 31-8-57. **Guy Warrior Van** 'GOLDEN SHRED' drawing dated 26-3-57, Job No. 14794. **Leyland Fuel Tanker** drawing dated 30-9-65, Job No. 62520. **Single-Deck Bus** drawing dated 14-5-34, Job No. 6763. **Jowett Javelin Saloon** drawing dated 10-10-47, Job No. 12886. **Renault Fregate** drawing dated 4-7-57, Job No. 20106. **Triumph Dolomite** (intended 38e) drawing dated 1939. **Vampire Jet** drawing dated 27-11-45, Job No. 12157. **Firebrand Aircraft** drawing dated 18-12-45, Job No. 12159.

**PRODUCTION MODELS**
In October 2000, Christie's South Kensington sold part of the Mike and Sue Richardson collection of Meccano General Assembly Drawings for the Dinky Toys range. The following is a small selection of items from that sale. The reference numbers are 'Job Numbers'.

**Drawings – English Saloon Cars**. 13866/7 **Jaguar XK120 and Base**, 20335 **Base XK150**, 20329 **Spring XK150**, 13381/3 **Austin Atlantic Body and Base**,

20121/2 and 20118/9 **Rolls-Royce Silver Wraith** (various parts), 62035/6/7 **Chauffuer and Passengers**, 13360/1/2 **Rover 75**, 14844/5 **Spring and Base for Humber Hawk**, 14982/4 **Singer Gazelle Body and Base**, 14088/9 **Austin A30 Body and Base**, 14721/3 **Sunbeam Rapier Body and Base**, 14721/3 **Sunbeam Rapier Body and Base**, 14745/7 **Hillman Minx Body and Base**, 7889 **Ford Zephyr Body**, 14097/8 **Vauxhall Cresta Body and Base**, 14937/8 **Fiat 600 Body and Base**, 14847/8 **Austin A105 Body and Base**. (*All 1950s*). In all, 33 items sold in one lot for .................................................................. **£750**

**Drawings – Buses**. 10897/8 **Double Deck Omnibus Body and Base** (both with dyeline copies), **Memo** 15954 about 17693 **'Dunlop' Transfers**, 13480/2 **Luxury Coach and Base**, 13750/2 **Duple Roadmaster Coach and Base**, 13424/6 **Observation Coach and Base**. 12 items in one lot sold for......... **£420**

**Drawings – Fodens**. 12163/6 and 12822 **Cab and Chassis, Body and Tanker Body**, 12164/5/9 **Bogie, Clip and Washer for Spare Wheel** + 7 drawings for **Chains, Stanchions, Tank parts**, etc. 13 items sold for............................ **£550**

**Drawings – Leyland Octopus**. 7874 **Cab and Chassis**, 7875 **Front Bogie**, and **Memo** 20649 **Label for 'ESSO'**. 3 items sold as one lot for.............. **£120**

Catalogues were often adapted so that they could be switched for use in most countries in the world irrespective of the language or the currency used.
An example of this is the 1965 catalogue:

| | | |
|---|---|---|
| 1965 | 72257/02UK | **UK catalogue** |

16 pages. Cover depicts 5 cars namely Nos.127, 128, 133 and 171 plus a description of various model features .......................................**£25-35**

**72557 1965** **Overseas edition**
16 pages. The cover is the same but replacing the features listing is a panel with 'Precision Diecast Scale Models' printed in English, German, French, Spanish, Italian and Swedish.

**72559 1965**

The catalogue pages contain only the basic English model name and number - all the English text having been removed. The models are the same as 72257/02 .......................**£25-35**

**Overseas edition**
24 pages. Whilst the cover is the same as 72557, the listings are entirely different for they feature both English and French Dinky Toys, including the French issues sold in the UK .......**£40-50**

**Price lists.** Prior to the overseas editions being despatched, price lists in the correct language and currency would be inserted. The Editor would like to express his thanks to the many collectors around the world who have contributed to this listing. New information would be welcomed.

---

*For French Dinky Toys Catalogues, please see the Catalogues listing at the end of the French Dinky Toys section.*

---

## AFRICA (Distributor unkown)

**KENYA**
1961 Illustrated List ..................................**£60-80**
**RHODESIA**
1953 Illustrated Price List .......................**£60-80**
1954 Illustrated Price List .......................**£60-80**
**SOUTH AFRICA**
1955 Catalogue '7/655/20',
Ovaltine Van + 7 others, 24 pages ......**£50-75**
**TANGANYIKA & UGANDA**
19?? Combined Catalogue........................**£60-80**

## AUSTRALIA

**Agents** (in 1952): E. G. Page & Co. (Sales) Pty., Ltd., Danks Building, 324 Pitt Street, Sydney.

1950 **Meccano General Products Catalogue '13/550/68',** as 1949 UK Catalogue, 'Meccano World-Famous Toys' .........**£70-90**
1952 **Catalogue '5/352/37.5',** Cover has sepia drawings of hands holding 27f, with 139b, 25x and 532......................**£50-75**
1952 **Catalogue '13/852/12',** Cover shows boy with green sweater. An example sold at auction in 1998 for ......................**£250**
1955 **Catalogue '7/655/30',** 282, 591, 290, 961, 430, 251, 962 and 481 on cover.. **£40-60**
1956 **Leaflet '16/456/15',** 8 page folded leaflet with coloured drawings and price list. Cover has 132, 255 and 781................**£25-35**
1957 **Leaflet '16/357/7.5 (1P)',** folded colour leaflet with 716, 162, 826, 955 on the front..................**£25-35**
1957 **Leaflet '16/757/15 (2P)',** folded colour leaflet with 932, 923, 164, 190 and 'Dinky Toys and Dinky Supertoys' on billboard ...........**£25-35**
1957 **Catalogue '7/757/30',** Piccadilly Circus, colour, vertical, no prices, 28 pages.... **£70-90**
1958 **Catalogue '7/658/40',** UK cover........**£30-45**
1959 **Catalogue '7/559/40',** UK cover........**£30-45**
1960 **Catalogue '23/560/40',** UK cover......**£30-45**
1961 **Catalogue '7/61/40',** UK cover..........**£30-45**
1962 **Catalogue '7/662/40',** UK cover..........**£30-45**
1963 **Catalogue '13/163/100',** UK cover......**£25-35**
1964 **Catalogue '7/364/100',** UK cover.......**£25-35**
1969 **Catalogue '72585',** UK cover .............**£25-35**
1971 **Catalogue '100103',** UK cover .........**£20-25**
1978 **Catalogue '100100'** ('No.14'), '20c' on cover, 44 pages. 'Liberty Trading Pty Ltd, Surrey Hills, Marshall St. NSW' on checklist..........**£20-25**

## BELGIUM and LUXEMBOURG

**French printing. Agents:** P FREMINEUR et Fils, Rue des Bogards 1, Bruxelles 1.

1936 Meccano Catalogue '13/736/265' . **£150-200**

---

1954 **Catalogue '16/1053 /10',** Same cover as 1953 UK issue............**£40-50**
1954 **Catalogue '16/1054 /2',** Same cover as 1954 UK issue...........**£40-50**
1956 **Catalogue '16/656/156'** (DT/CL/5). Cover as 1956 UK issue.....................**£40-50**
1958 **Leaflet '16/1258/12.5 Belgium'** ('DT/CL/32' on cover). Printed in England. 168 Singer and 178 Plymouth on cover. Text in French and Flemish **£40-50**
1959 **Catalogue '7/539/-',** Red Jaguar XK140 on cover ...............**£30-40**
1960 **Catalogue** (no ref.). English and French models in one catalogue, 48 pages. Printed and issued only in Belgium and Luxembourg. Cover depicts Land Rover plus two French Dinky cars. 'Frs 3-'.......**£75-100**

## BELGIUM     French printing.

1954 **Illustrated price list '16/1054 /2'** ......**£40-50**
1966 **1st Edition price list '72551',** in French and Flemish, 164 pages ......**£40-50**

## CANADA

**Agents:** Meccano Limited, 675 King Street West, Toronto and 187 - 189 Church Street, Toronto.

1934 **Leaflet '10/34',** Yellow leaflet with 'LOCKE Bros. of MONTREAL' stamp ..................**£125-150**
1937 **Leaflet '13/637/5',** Eight pages.....**£125-150**
1938 **Leaflet '7/38',** Ten page fold-out leaflet with full range ......................................**£125-150**
1940 **Leaflet '13/840/5',** 12 black and white pages, 8.75" x 5.875". Cover shows boy with outstretched arms plus 62h, 151a, 36g, 43a, and 33r. 'The Fascinating Collecting Hobby'........**£125-150**
1941 **Leaflet '6/41',** 12 page fold-out leaflet with full range ......................................**£125-150**
1951 **Catalogue '16/351/25',** 16 pp, boy + 3 models, blue pictures.. **£60-70**
1953 **Catalogue '7/953/50',** 555 Fire Engine, 522 Big Bedford, 25x Breakdown Truck, 28 pages.........**£50-60**
1955 **Illustrated price list: '16/355/90',** Off-White leaflet .................................**£30-35**
1955 **Catalogue '7/655/90',** Illustration of Bedford 'Ovaltine' Van plus seven other models..............**£50-60**
1956 **Catalogue '7/556/90',** Regent Tanker/Tunnel, 1st June 1956 in colour, 32 pages .......**£50-60**
1956 **Illustrated price leaflet '16/656/18c',** (DT/CL/4) in colour, featuring 131 Cadillac and 660 Tank Transporter .....**£20-30**

---

1956 **Illustrated price leaflet '16/756/18',** in colour, featuring 706 Vickers 'Air France' Airliner.......................... **£20-30**
1957 **Catalogue '7/757/90',** Piccadilly Circus, vertical, in colour, with prices, 28 pages ........................**£50-60**
1959 **Catalogue '7/559/90',** Red Jaguar + 6 models on cover, 28 pages ........................................**£50-60**
1960 **Catalogue '7/560/90',** cover as UK issue .............................**£40-50**
1961 **Catalogue '3/41/25 7252 3/42',** Black with 7 models and '9th' on cover, Canada/English, 32 pages........**£40-50**
1963 **Catalogue '13/163/100 7254 2/42',** Motor Show 11th, Canada/English, 32 pages......................................**£40-50**
1963 **Catalogue '13/1063 /50 7254 8/42',** Flyer 8in x 10¼in. 10 models on cover, 'Canada 1963', 8 pages ...........**£30-40**
1964 **Trade Catalogue '7/364/150',** 8 page catalogue plus 4 page trade price list (half catalogue width, in centre) ... **£30-40**
1964 **Catalogue '7/464/150 72550/42',** '12th', 8in x 11in, Canada/English, 8 pp ........................**£20-30**
1964 **Catalogue (no ref.),** Flyer, 5½ x 3½, shows 6 Hong Kong models, 12 pp ....**£10-15**
1965 **Catalogue (no ref.)** 1st Ed. 8½ x 5½in., 5 models on cover, 16 pp .................**£20-25**
1966 **Catalogue '72561',** 1st Edition, 108 pages ........................**£30-40**
1966 **Catalogue '72561',** 2nd Edition, 106 pages.......................**£30-40**
1967 **Catalogue '72571',** 3rd edition, 106 pages......................**£30-40**
1968 **Catalogue '72580',** 4th Edition, 106 pages......................**£30-40**
1969 **Catalogue '72585',** 5th Edition, 24 pages.........................**£20-30**
1970 **Catalogue '165000',** UK cover .........**£15-25**
1971 **Catalogue '100103',** UK cover .........**£15-25**

## CYPRUS

1969 **Catalogue** (no ref.), Same as UK issue..............................**£50-75**

## EGYPT

1952 **Catalogue '5/652/2',** Different p.9 from UK issue with pictures of US 39 Series cars and British cars .. **£100-150**

## EIRE and Channel Islands

**Agents until 1968:**
S.J. Gearey, 1 St Stephens Green, Dublin.
**Agents from 1969:**
Kilroy Bros Ltd, Shanowen Road, Whitehall, Dublin 9.
1953 **Catalogue '7/953/9',** 'Eire' and 'C.I.' on cover....................**£40-50**

---

1955 **Catalogue '7/755/20'.**
'Eire' and 'C.I.' on cover..................... **£40-50**
1959 **Catalogue '7/659/75'**, 'Eire' on cover **£40-50**
1964 **Catalogue '7/364/7'**, 'Eire' on cover . **£30-40**
1969 **Catalogue 'No.5'**, 'Irish' on cover,
(agents: Kilroy Bros Ltd). .................. **£30-40**

# HONG KONG

**Representatives**: W.R.Loxley & Co. Ltd.,
Jardine House, 11th Floor, 20 Pedder Street,
Hong Kong.
1959 **Illustrated price list 'DT/CF/5'**,
same cover as UK issue ...................... **£50-75**

# ITALY

**Agents**: Alfredo Parodi, Piazza 8, Marcellino 6,
Genova.
1957 **Leaflet '16/657/5'**, with 101-105 ...... **£30-35**
1957 **Leaflet '16/3/57/5'**,
showing 677 and 472 'Raleigh' ... **£30-35**
1957 **Leaflet '16/357/5'**,
642 and 455 'Brooke Bond Tea' ......... **£30-35**
1957 **Leaflet '16/857/5'**,
237 Mercedes front,
136, 236, 238 back ............................ **£30-35**
1957 **Leaflet '16/457/5'**, 697 Military Set .. **£30-35**
1957 **Leaflet '16/457/5'**,
661 and 919 'Golden Shred' ............. **£30-35**
1957 **Leaflet** (no ref.), with 163, 236 and
238 on racing circuit .......................... **£30-35**
1957 **Leaflet** (no ref.), with 237, 661,
and 919 'Golden Shred' ...................... **£30-35**
1957 **Illustrated price list '16/357/5'**,
'Italy' printed after the ref. no............. **£30-35**
1957 **Leaflet '12/757/50'** (DT/CL/15) 642
and 455 'Brooke Bond' ...................... **£30-35**
1957 **Catalogue '7/857/50'**,
Same cover as UK issue 7/657/820 ... **£40-50**
1957 **Leaflet 'DT/CL/12'**,
with 677 and 472 on cover................. **£30-35**
1958 **Catalogue '7/758/50'**,
Same cover as UK issue 7/458/856 ... **£40-50**
1964 **Catalogue '7/364/40 7225 0/37'**,
12th, 8in x 11in, includes four pages
of French Dinky, 12 pages in total...... **£30-35**

# MALAYA and SINGAPORE

**Agents**: King & Co, Singapore.
1957 **Catalogue '16/557/25 (1P)'** (DT/CF/3),
8 pages, cover depicts 170, 626, 716, 955,
other pictures within, price list in $ .... **£40-50**
1958 **Catalogue '7/958/10'**, cover as UK,
4 pages with prices in $...................... **£40-50**

# NETHERLANDS / HOLLAND

**Agents**: Hausemann & Hotte NV,
Kromboomsloot 57-61, Amsterdam.
**Pre-War Editions**
1936 **'1/736/5'**
Yellow paper with Black printing ... **£125-150**
1937 **'13/637/75'**
Yellow paper with Black printing ... **£125-150**
1938 **'13/738/22'**
Yellow paper with Black printing ... **£125-150**
**Post-War Editions** - Some black/white,
later coloured as per UK issues.
1954 **Illustrated price list '16/954/108'**,
Printed in French ................................ **£15-20**
1955 **'8/1255/50'** (DT/L/7), no details......... **£40-50**
1956 **'16/256/30n'** (DT/CL/2)', no details.... **£30-40**
1956 **'16/256/30n'** (DT/L/9)', no details ...... **£30-40**
1958 **'16/1158 /20'**, 'Nederland Frs 3-'.
Cover same as 1958 UK issue .......... **£30-35**
1962 **'16/256/30** (72538/29)', no details...... **£20-25**
1967 **Catalogue '72571'**, 3rd Ed., price list
in Dutch florins, 162 pages ................ **£40-50**
1970 **Catalogue** (no ref.), 6th Edition includes
8pp of French Dinky, 32 pp in total.... **£20-30**

# PORTUGAL

1956 **Illustrated Catalogue** (no ref.) .......... **£40-50**
1957 **Illustrated Leaflet, 'DT/CF/4'**,
no details ............................................. **£50-70**
1958 **Illustrated Catalogue '7/858/5'**,
Houses of Parliament on cover .......... **£50-60**
1959 **Illustrated Catalogue** (no ref.) .......... **£40-50**
1961 **Illustrated Catalogue '5/261/25'**,
9th edition............................................ **£40-50**
1963 **Illustrated Catalogue** (no ref.) .......... **£30-40**
1960s **Illustrated Catalogue '7255049'**,
group of 1960s cars on cover ............. **£30-40**
1969 **'No.5' Catalogue '72585'**,
cover features 'Joe 90's Car'............... **£30-40**

# SPAIN

1957 **Illustrated Leaflet 'DT/CL15 SP 16/457/5'**,
Similar to Italian leaflet with
697 on colour front of single sheet,
unpriced list on reverse ...................... **£10-15**

# SWEDEN

**Agents**: Ludvig Wigart & Cos, AB Helsingborg.
1954 **'7/654/14'**, 4 pages, 3 pages colour
pictures plus price list in Kroner
with Swedish text................................ **£40-50**
1957 **Leaflet '16/357/15'**, Leaflet depicts 455
'Brooke Bond' Trojan plus 642 RAF Tanker.
Price list in Kroner; Swedish text ....... **£15-20**
1957 **Catalogue**, 28 pages .......................... **£70-90**
1961 **Catalogue '14/561/60'**,
as 1961 UK issue, text in Swedish...... **£30-40**
1968 **Catalogue '72580'**, 162 pp,
as UK 1968 edition, but in Swedish ... **£20-30**

# SWITZERLAND

**Agents**: Riva & Kunzmann SA Basel 2,
Switzerland. From 1965 address changed to Prattela,
Switzerland.
1956 **Catalogue '7/356/20'**, Ovaltine + 7
others, prices in Swiss francs, 24 pp... **£40-50**
1958 **Catalogue '7/858/80'**, UK cover........ **£40-50**
1962 **Catalogue '72537/25'**, 10th Edition,
48 pages, same as UK issue 72537/02
plus French Dinky Toys ...................... **£40-50**
1963 **Catalogue '13/163/75'**,
11th Edition, 48 pages, as UK issue
13/163/20 plus French Dinky.............. **£40-50**
1965 **Catalogue '72559'**, 24 pp, cover as
UK 72557 + French Dinky Toys........ **£40-50**

# USA

**Agents**: H. Hudson Dobson, PO Box 254, 26th St
and Jefferson Avenue, Kenilworth, NJ.
**In 1952** the address was: PO Box 254, 906
Westfield Avenue, Elizabeth, NJ.
**From 1957** the address changed to 627 Boulevard,
Kenilworth. New York showroom: 200, Fifth Ave.,
PO Box 255. Models sold by this distributor will
often be found with an 'H.Hudson Dobson' label
**From 1963**: Lines Bros Inc, 1107 Broadway, New
York. **From ?**: AVA International, Box 7611,
Waco, Texas 76710.

**War-Time Issue**
1941 **Large leaflet**
(no ref.), no details available................NGPP
**Post-War Editions**
1951 **Catalogue** (no ref.), boy's side face,
5 models, black and white,
green printing, 16 pages..................... **£70-90**
1952 **Catalogue** (no ref.), hands holding 27f
(139b and 25x in picture). Unlike the
UK edition, 39b, 39c and 39e are
shown in two-tone colours ................. **£70-90**
1953 **Catalogue '7/753/150'**, same cover as
1953 UK issue 7/953/360..................... **£50-75**
1954 **Catalogue '7/954/150'**, same cover as
1954 UK issue 7/754/600..................... **£50-75**
1954 **Catalogue '7/753/150'**, 157 Jaguar,
480 Kodak, 641 Army,
separate price list, 28 pages ............. **£50-75**

1955 **Catalogue** (no ref.), 20 models on
cover, 5 French, black and white,
prices in $, 32 pages........................... **£50-75**
1956 **Catalogue** (no ref.), 'Ever-Ready'
plus 11 others, Feb 57, black/white,
prices in $, 32 pages........................... **£50-75**
1957 **Catalogue** (no ref.), Yellow/Red cover
shows model 697 plus Red lined sections
displaying English and French models.
Red panel with US address of H.Hudson
Dobson. 36 black/white pages of
English and French models ................. **£70-90**
1957 **Catalogue** (no ref.),
Yellow, Red lines, black/white,
'9-30-57', prices in $, 36 pp .............. **£50-75**
1958 **Catalogue '7/958/250'**,
Houses of Parliament on cover,
prices in $, 32pp............................... **£50-75**
1959 **Leaflet '7/7/125'**,
Colour, English and French,
prices in $ ......................................... **£20-30**
1959 **USA Catalogue '7/559/250'**, Cover
depicts Red Jaguar XK140 etc. 26 pages
English models, 6 pages French.......... **£50-75**
1959 **Leaflet '7/8/125'**, 3 pp of colour
pictures plus price list. English and
French items on cover,
(195 Jaguar 3.4, 265 Taxi) ................. **£45-55**
1960 **Leaflet** (no ref.),
6 pages introducing 'Mini-Dinky'...... **£40-45**
1960 **Catalogue '7/3/30 NP'**, 32 pages,
motorway bridge on cover ................. **£40-50**
1961 **Leaflet '16/161/100 72529/22'**,4pp.. **£20-30**
1961 **Catalogue '14/561/200'**, Black with
7 models, USA 1961, 48 pp .............. **£50-75**
1962 **Leaflet '9/762/50'**,
'72542/22' and 'D.T./CL 14'.............. **£10-15**
1962 **Catalogue '725377/22'**, 10th Ed.,
48 pp, UK 7253702 + French ........... **£20-30**
1962 **Catalogue '72537/22'**, 120 Jaguar
'E'-type, 10th Ed. '5c', 16 pages of
French Dinky, 48 pages in total ......... **£50-75**
1963 **Catalogue '13/763/60'**, 11th Ed.,
48 pp, UK 13/763/400 plus French
Dinky Toys ...........................................NGPP
1963 **Leaflet '16/163/50 7254 7/22'**,
illustrated flyer price list, b/w ............ **£20-30**
1963 **Catalogue '13/763/10 7254 5/22'**,
Motor Show 11th USA, 16 pages of
French Dinky, 48 pages in total ......... **£25-35**
1965 **Leaflet** (no ref. no.) Lines Bros flyer
8½in x 11in, includes ......................... **£20-30**
1965 **'Lines Bros' leaflet** (no ref. no.), 4 pp,
Yellow/Red cover with 113 MGB....... **£30-35**
1967 **Leaflet '72577/3'**, 10in x 12³/₄ in.
includes 5 Hong Kong Dinky ............. **£15-20**
1971 **Catalogue '100103'**,
7th Edition, same as UK, 24 pages ..... **£10-15**
1972 **Catalogue '100108'**,
8th Edition, same as UK, 28 pages ..... **£10-15**
1973 **Catalogue '100110'**,
9th Edition, same as UK, 40 pages ..... **£10-15**
1973 **Leaflet '100265'**,
4 pages Dinky Action Kits Catalogue . **£10-15**
1974 **Catalogue '100114'**,
10th Edition, same as UK, 48 pages . **£10-15**
1975 **Catalogue '100/117'**, 11th Ed.,
40 pages, same as UK 100115 .......... **£10-15**
1976 **Catalogue '100/120'**, 12th Ed.,
40 pages, same as UK 100118 .......... **£10-15**
1977 **Catalogue '100/135'**, 13th Ed.,
40 pages, same as UK 100122, but
background on cover is Blue not Red. **£10-15**
1978 **Catalogue '100/101'**, 14th Ed.,
64 pages, same as UK 100/100 .......... **£10-15**

# WEST GERMANY

**Agents**: Bienngraeber of Hamburg.
1969 **Catalogue '72585'**, 32 pages, No.5 features
'Joe's Car' on cover, Catalogue in
English, price list in German ............. **£40-50**

Virtually all Dinky Toys models were supplied in their own individual boxes from around 1954. Before then, most small models were supplied to shopkeepers in 'Trade Boxes' containing 3, 4, 6 or 12 identical models separated by strips of card. (Some aircraft and ship models were an exception to this general rule.) A single item would be sold without further packaging except perhaps for a paper bag.

These Trade Boxes have become collectors items in their own right whether full or empty (the latter selling for between £20 and £50 depending on its rarity and that of its original contents. Most of these boxes that come to auction are full and the listing below derives mostly from surveys of such items undertaken for the 8th, 9th and 10th Editions. We are grateful to David Cooke and Tony Murphy for updating and enhancing the listing for this Edition. The boxes listed here are only those observed or

reported. It is known that other trade packaging of this type exists and the Editor would welcome any additional information on the subject.

Expect Trade Boxes containing rare colour variations to attract a corresponding premium. **NB** See also Gift Sets for 62h and 62d pre-war Aeroplane Trade Box items. **NGPP = No guide price at present.**

| Model and box details | MPR |
|---|---|

### Type 1
Pre-Second World War. Card boxes that have a four-digit reference code number preceded by the letter 'A'. Most have a covering of yellow paper. (The few exceptions that have orange-brown, blue or green paper coverings are noted in the list). Wording: 'Dinky Toys Made in England by Meccano Limited'. Printed information consists of model name and number, often with a date and quantity. The date code is usually a month number and year number separated by a full stop thus: '3.40', in this case indicating March 1940.

| | | | | |
|---|---|---|---|---|
| 22e | Tractor | 6 | A966B | £400-500 |
| 22g | Streamline Tourer | 6 | A2018 | £1,500-1,750 |
| 23 | Racing Car | 6 | A1002 | £1,500-2,000 |
| 24g | Sports Tourer | 6 | A1017 | £1,500-2,000 |
| 24h | Sports Tourer | 6 | A1018 | NGPP |
| 25d | Petrol Wagon | 6 | A1022 | NGPP |
| 25e | Tipping Wagon | 6 | A1023 | NGPP |
| 25f | Market Gardener's Lorry | 6 | A1024 | NGPP |
| 26 | Rail Autocar | 6 | A1001 | NGPP |
| 27 | Tram Car | 6 | | £900-1,200 |
| 28/1 | Delivery Vans, 1st Type | 6 | A1008 | £5,000-7,500 |
| 29a | ('Q') Motor Bus | 6 | | £1,000-1,500 |
| 29c | Double-Deck Bus | 6 | A2226 | £1,200-1,600 |
| 30e | Breakdown Car | 6 | A2060 | £150-200 |
| 30g | Caravan | 6 | A2106 | £100-150 |
| 32 | Chrysler Airflow | 6 | A2032 | £2,000-3,000 |
| 33a | Mechanical Horse, orange-brown | 6 | A2037 | NGPP |
| 36f | British Salmson 4-str with Driver | 6 | A2211 | NGPP |
| 37a | Civilian Motor Cyclist | A2229 | 6 | £150-200 |
| 37c | Dispatch Rider | 6 | A2237 | £150-200 |
| 39e | Chrysler Royal | 6 | A2290 | £1,000-1,500 |
| 47d | Beacon | 12 | A2058 | NGPP |
| 50a | HMS 'Hood' | 12 | A1030 | NGPP |
| 50f/50h | Destroyers 'Broke' and 'Amazon' Class | 12 | A1035 | NGPP |
| 50g/50k | Submarines 'K' and 'X' Class | 12 | A1036 | NGPP |
| 62d | Bristol Blenheim Bombers, green | 6 | | £400-600 |
| 62h | Hawker Hurricane Fighters, green | 6 | '7-39' | £400-600 |
| 62m | Airspeed Envoy | 6 | A2234 | NGPP |
| 62s | Hurricane Fighters, blue | 6 | | £300-400 |
| 63b | 'Mercury' | 6 | A2253 | NGPP |
| 151a | Medium Tank | 6 | A2190 | £3,000-4,000 |
| 152c | RTC Austin Seven | 6 | A2196 | £400-500 |
| 160b | R.A. Gunners | 12 | | £200-250 |
| 160g | R.A. Personnel | ? | A2303 | NGPP |

### Type 2
The first of the post-war trade boxes. Brown card box with yellow contents label affixed to one end (occasionally both ends) No box reference code in the main, but exceptions are noted below.

| | | | |
|---|---|---|---|
| 14a | B.E.V. Truck | 6 | £150-200 |
| 23a | Racing Car | 6 | £500-750 |
| 23d | Racing Car | 6 | £175-225 |
| 25b | Covered Wagon | 6 | £500-750 |
| 25d | Petrol Wagon | 6 | £200-300 |
| 25e | Tipping Wagon | 6 | £250-350 |

| Model and box details | MPR |
|---|---|

| | | | | |
|---|---|---|---|---|
| 25f | Market Gardeners Lorry, 6, 'VK29' / 'AS39' | | | £250-350 |
| 25g | Trailer | 6 | | NGPP |
| 25h | Fire Engine | 6 | | £300-400 |
| 25j | Jeep | 6 | 'M26' | £250-350 |
| 25p | Aveling Barford Diesel Roller | 4 | 'M__' | £150-200 |
| 25r | Forward Control Lorry | 6 | 'M23' | £300-350 |
| 25t | Flat Truck/Trailer | 3 | | £300-350 |
| 25v | Bedford Refuse Wagon | 4 | | £200-300 |
| 27a | M-H Tractor | 3 | | £150-200 |
| 29b | Streamlined Bus | 6 | 'M24' | NGPP |
| 29c | Double Deck Bus (packed vertically) | 6 | | £400-500 |
| 29c | Double Deck Bus (laid flat) | 6 | | £200-300 |
| 29e | Single Deck Bus | 6 | | £300-350 |
| 30b | Rolls-Royce | 6 | | £300-400 |
| 30d | Vauxhall | 6 | | £300-400 |
| 30f | Ambulance, 'M28' / 'M35' | 6 | | £300-400 |
| 33w | Mechanical Horse and Open Wagon | 3 | | £200-250 |
| 34b | Royal Mail Van | 6 | | £300-400 |
| 34c | Loudspeaker Van | 6 | 'VK49' | £150-180 |
| 36a | Armstrong-Siddeley Limousine | 6 | | £350-400 |
| 38c | Lagonda Sports | 6 | | £250-300 |
| 39a | Packard Super 8 Touring Sedan | 6 | | £400-500 |
| 39d | Buick Viceroy | 6 | 'M24' | £400-500 |
| 40a | Riley | 6 | 'M__' | £350-450 |
| 40b | Triumph 1800 | 6 | | £350-450 |
| 40e | Standard Vanguard | 6 | | £350-450 |
| 40e | Standard Vanguard | 6 | 'M50' | £350-450 |
| 52a | 'Queen Mary' | 6 | | £90-120 |
| | (some seen with red 'Hudson Dobson' label). | | | |
| 105a | Garden Roller | 6 | | £100-125 |
| 152b | Reconnaissance Car | 6 | | £400-500 |
| 161b | Mobile A-A Gun | 6 | | £300-400 |

### Type 3
Second design of post-war box. All-yellow with direct printing (no label). All are pre-1953/54 renumbering. No box reference code.

| | | | |
|---|---|---|---|
| 23b | Small Closed Racing Car | 6 | £200-300 |
| 23c | Large Open Racing Car | 6 | £200-300 |
| 23e | 'Speed of the Wind' Racing Car | 6 | £200-300 |
| 25h | Fire Engine | 6 | NGPP |
| 25m | Bedford End Tipper | 4 | £400-500 |
| 25t | Flat Truck and Trailer | 3 | £300-325 |
| 25v | Bedford Refuse Wagon | 4 | £350-400 |
| 25w | Bedford Truck | 4 | £400-500 |
| 25y | Universal Jeep | 4 | £150-225 |
| 27a | Massey-Harris Tractor | 3 | £150-200 |
| 27b | Harvest Trailer | 3 | £75-85 |
| 27c | MH Manure Spreader | 3 | £85-100 |
| 27d | Land Rover | 4 | £150-200 |
| 27f | Estate Car | 4 | £200-250 |
| 27g | Motocart | 3 | £100-150 |
| 27h | Disc Harrow | 4 | £60-80 |
| 29f | Observation Coach | 6 | £350-450 |
| 30h | Daimler Ambulance | 4 | £200-300 |
| 30j | Austin Wagon | 6 | £400-500 |

| Model and box details | MPR |
|---|---|

| | | | | |
|---|---|---|---|---|
| 30m | Rear Tipping Wagon | 6 | | £150-200 |
| 30r | Thames Flat Truck | 6 | | £130-160 |
| 30s | Austin Covered Wagon | 6 | | £150-200 |
| 30v | Electric Dairy Van | 6 | | £250-300 |
| 30v | Electric Dairy Van 'NCB' | 6 | | £250-300 |
| 31a | Trojan 'Esso' Van | 6 | | £600-700 |
| 31b | Trojan 'Dunlop' Van | 6 | | £600-700 |
| 35c | MG Sports Car | 6 | | £250-300 |
| 36a | Armstrong-Siddeley | 6 | | £400-500 |
| 37b | Police Motor Cyclist | 6 | | £150-200 |
| 38b | Sunbeam-Talbot | 6 | | £400-500 |
| 38e | Armstrong-Siddeley | 6 | | £450-550 |
| 39e | Chrysler Royal Sedan | 6 | | NGPP |
| 40b | Triumph 1800 Saloon | 6 | | £350-450 |
| 40d | Austin Devon | 6 | | £350-450 |
| 40f | Hillman Minx Saloon | 6 | | £350-450 |
| 40g | Morris Oxford Saloon | 6 | | £350-450 |
| 40j | Austin Somerset | 6 | | £350-450 |
| 42a | Police Box | 6 | | £140-170 |
| 47c | Two-face Traffic Lights | 12 | | £40-70 |
| 70d | Twin Engined Fighter | 6 | | £100-130 |
| 70e | Gloster Meteor | 6 | | £40-60 |
| 70f | Shooting Star | 6 | | £100-150 |
| 105a | Garden Roller | 6 | | £80-90 |
| 105b | Wheelbarrow | 6 | | £80-90 |
| 105c | 4-wheeled Hand Truck | 6 | | £40-60 |
| 105e | Grass Cutter | 6 | | £90-110 |
| 107a | Sack Truck | 6 | | £90-110 |
| 139a | Ford Fordor | 6 | | £250-300 |
| 139b | Hudson Commodore | 6 | | £500-700 |
| 140a | Austin Atlantic | 6 | | £400-500 |
| 152b | Reconnaissance Car | 6 | | £400-500 |
| 161b | Mobile AA Gun | 6 | | £300-400 |
| 603a | Army Personnel (metal). NB early boxes long, later issues are square | 12 | | £80-110 |
| 603a | Army Personnel (plastic) | 12 | | £40-50 |

### Type 4
As Type 3 but with the addition of a five-digit box reference code.

| | | | | |
|---|---|---|---|---|
| 23f | Alfa Romeo Racing Car '50189' | 6 | | £400-500 |
| 23s | Streamlined R. Car, '50012' | 4 | | £300-400 |
| 25h | Fire Engine, '50019' | 6 | | £300-400 |
| 25m | Bedford Truck, '50021' | 4 | | £400-500 |
| 25p | Aveling-Barford Diesel Roller, '50022' | 4 | | £150-200 |
| 25y | Universal Jeep, '50159' | 6 | | £150-225 |
| 27a | M-H Tractor, '50029' | 3 | | £150-200 |
| 27h | Disc Harrow, '50035' | 4 | | £60-80 |
| 27j | Triple-Gang Mower, '50156' | 3 | | £150-200 |
| 27m | Land-Rover Trailer, '50161' | 4 | | £90-110 |
| 29g | Luxury Coach, '50042' | 6 | | £400-500 |
| 29h | Duple Roadmaster Coach, '50163' | 6 | | £300-400 |
| 30h | Daimler Ambulance, '50049' | 4 | | £200-300 |
| 30j | Austin Wagon, '50050' | 6 | | £400-500 |
| 30m | Rear Tipping Wagon, '50052' | 6 | | £200-250 |
| 30p | Mobilgas Tanker, '50051' | 6 | | £500-600 |
| 30pa | Castrol Tanker, '50146' | 6 | | £500-700 |
| 30pb | Esso Tanker, '50147' | 6 | | £500-700 |
| 30w | Electric Artic. Lorry, '50059' | 3 | | £300-400 |
| 31a | Trojan Esso Van, '50149' | 6 | | £500-600 |
| 31c | Trojan Chivers Van, '50151' | 6 | | £600-800 |
| 33w | Mechanical Horse and Open Wagon, '50060' | 3 | | £200-250 |
| 34c | Loudspeaker Van, '50062' | 6 | | £200-250 |
| 35a | Saloon Car ('Slide-tray' type box), '50063' | 6 | | £300-400 |

| | | | |
|---|---|---|---|
| 35b | Racer | | |
| | ('Slide-tray' type box), 'CZ35' .. | 6 | **£280-330** |
| 40f | Hillman Minx | 6 | **£350-450** |
| 40g | Morris Oxford | 6 | **£350-450** |
| 40h | Austin Taxi, '50097' | 6 | **£350-450** |
| 70a | Avro York Air-Liner, '50123' ... | 1 | NGPP |
| 70b | Hawker Tempest, '50124' | 6 | NGPP |
| 70c | Viking Air-Liner, '50125' | 6 | NGPP |
| 70f | Shooting Star Jet, '50128' | 6 | NGPP |
| 105e | Grass Cutter, '50132' | 6 | **£90-110** |
| 139b | Hudson Commodore, '50135'. | 6 | **£500-700** |
| 140a | Austin Atlantic, '50136' | 6 | **£500-700** |
| 140b | Rover 75, '50137' | 6 | **£350-450** |

## Type 5
As Type 3 (all-yellow, direct printed, no reference code), but these display the 'dual numbering' of the models contained. They generally date from around 1954 when Meccano renumbered most of the Dinky Toys. They are listed here in the order of the earlier model numbering system.

| | | | |
|---|---|---|---|
| 12c/750 | Telephone Call Box | 6. | **£150-200** |
| 23a/220 | Racing Car | 6. | **£400-500** |
| 23e/221 | 'Speed of the Wind' | 6. | **£200-250** |
| 23s/222 | Streamlined R. Car | 4. | **£200-300** |
| 25g/429 | Trailer | 6. | **£80-120** |
| 25h/250 | Fire Engine | 6 | NGPP |
| 25m/410 | Bedford End Tipper | 4. | **£400-500** |
| 25r/420 | Forward Control Lorry | 6. | **£200-250** |
| 25w/411 | Bedford Truck | 6. | **£200-250** |
| 25y/405 | Universal Jeep | 4. | **£200-250** |
| 27a/300 | Massey-Harris Tractor | 3. | **£150-200** |
| 27d/340 | Land-Rover | 4. | **£200-250** |
| 27g/342 | Motocart | 3... | **£80-120** |
| 27m/341 | Land-Rover Trailer | 4... | **£80-120** |
| 29g/281 | Luxury Coach | 6. | **£300-350** |
| 30r/422 | Fordson Thames | 6... | **£70-100** |
| 30s/413 | Austin Cov. Wagon | 6. | **£250-300** |
| 30v/490 | 'Express Dairy' Van | 6. | **£250-300** |
| 30v/491 | 'N.C.B.' Dairy Van | 6. | **£120-160** |
| 30w/421 | Electric Artic. Lorry | 3. | **£125-150** |
| 31b/451 | Trojan Van 'Dunlop' | 6. | **£400-500** |
| 31c/452 | Trojan Van 'Chivers' | 6. | **£400-500** |
| 35b/200 | Midget Racer, 'CZ35' | 6. | NGPP |
| 40b/151 | Triumph 1800 Saloon | 6. | **£250-350** |
| 40j/161 | Austin Somerset | 6. | **£350-450** |
| 42a/751 | Police Hut | 6.... | **£50-80** |
| 63b/700 | Seaplane | 6. | **£250-350** |
| 70c/705 | Viking Airliner | 6. | NGPP |
| 70d/731 | Twin Engined Fighter | 6. | NGPP |
| 70e/732 | Meteor Jet Fighter | 6. | NGPP |
| 70f/733 | Shooting Star Jet | 6. | **£80-100** |
| 105a/381 | Garden Roller | 6. | **£80-120** |
| 105b/382 | Wheelbarrow | 6. | **£60-80** |
| 105c/383 | 4-w. Hand Truck | 6... | **£80-120** |

| | | | |
|---|---|---|---|
| 105e/384 | Grass Cutter | 6. | **£120-150** |
| 107a/385 | Sack Truck | 6. | **£50-70** |
| 140a/106 | Austin Atlantic | 6 | NGPP |
| 140b/156 | Rover 75 | 6. | **£200-250** |

## Type 6
Post 1953-54, all-yellow printed box. These contain the newly-introduced (or re-introduced) models having just a single three-digit reference number.

| | | | |
|---|---|---|---|
| 270 | 'AA' Motor Cycle | 6 .. | **£200-300** |
| 272 | 'ANWB' Motor Cycle | 6 .. | **£250-350** |
| 603 | Army Personnel - | | |
| | Private (seated) | 12 | NGPP |
| 673 | Scout Car | 6 ..... | **£65-85** |
| 687 | Field Gun Trailer | 6 ..... | **£65-85** |
| 705 | Viking Airliner | 6 .. | **£200-300** |
| 750 | Telephone Call Box | 6 .. | **£200-300** |
| 751 | Police Hut | 6 .. | **£150-180** |
| 755 | Lamp Standard, single-arm | 6 ..... | **£30-40** |
| 756 | Lamp Standard, double-arm | 6 .. | **£30-40** |
| 760 | Pillar Box | 6 .. | **£150-200** |
| 768 | Racks with Tyres | 6 ..... | **£75-100** |
| 773 | Robot Traffic Signal | 12 | **£150-175** |
| 777 | Belisha Beacon | 12 ..... | **£65-90** |
| 786 | Tyre Rack | 6 .. | **£120-160** |
| 788 | Spare Bucket for 966 | 6 .. | **£175-225** |
| 797 | Healey Sports Boat | 6 .. | **£150-200** |

## Type 7 (Post-war).
Small boxes, covered in green paper; with 'flap' ends.

| | | | |
|---|---|---|---|
| 12d | Telegraph Messenger | | |
| | '50175' on some | 6 .. | **£100-125** |
| 12e | Postman, '50176' on some | 6 .. | **£100-125** |
| 13a | Cook's Man, '50174' on some. | 6 .. | **£100-125** |
| 43b | 'RAC' M/c Patrol | 6 .. | **£300-400** |
| 44b | 'AA' M/c Patrol | 6 .. | **£300-400** |
| 760 | Pillar Box | 2 | NGPP |

## Type 8 (Post-war).
A box specially designed for
3 x 551 Large Trailer.

| | |
|---|---|
| 'Dinky Toys', brown, yellow label... | **£80-120** |
| 'Dinky Toys', blue card, '50551' .... | **£80-120** |
| 'Supertoys', brown, '50551' | **£80-120** |
| 'Supertoys', green, '(M49)' | **£80-120** |
| 'Supertoys', green, '(IH89)' | **£80-120** |
| 'Supertoys', blue card, '50551' | **£80-120** |
| 'Supertoys' yellow card, '(M44)' .... | **£80-120** |

## Type 9
These began appearing from the mid-1950s. They are 'trade packs' rather than trade boxes as they contain quantities of individually

boxed models. Thin grey (or brownish-grey) card construction with flap ends or tuck-in ends; direct printing mostly in black. The printing on outer boxes for Dublo Dinkys 067 and 069 is in red. The major exception here is 078 which has an outer box of similar design to the individual Dublo boxes inside.

| | | | |
|---|---|---|---|
| 067 | Austin Taxi | 6 | NGPP |
| 069 | Massey-Harris Tractor | 6 | **£300-400** |
| 070 | AEC Mercury Tanker | 6 | **£500-600** |
| 076 | Lansing-Bagnall Trailer | 6 | **£300-400** |
| 104 | 'United Biscuits' Taxis | ? | NGPP |
| 106 | 'Prisoner' Mini-Moke | 6 | **£600-800** |
| 112 | Purdey's Triumph TR7 | 6 | **£150-200** |
| 122 | Volvo 265 DL Estate | 6 | **£55-65** |
| 159 | Morris Oxford | 6 | **£350-450** |
| 161 | Austin Somerset | 6 | **£600-800** |
| 188 | Jensen FF | 6 | **£150-200** |
| 188 | 4-berth Caravan | 6 | **£175-200** |
| 193 | Rambler Station Wagon | 6 | **£400-500** |
| 195 | Jaguar 3.4 Saloon | 6 | **£400-500** |
| 292 | Leyland Atlantean Bus | 6 | **£350-450** |
| 429 | Trailer | 6 | **£100-150** |
| 442 | Land-Rovers | 6 | **£100-125** |
| 471 | Austin Van 'NESTLE' | 6 | **£300-400** |
| 491 | Electric Dairy Van 'N.C.B.', | | |
| | | 6, | **£1,000-1,200** |
| 491 | Electric Dairy Van 'JOB'S' | 6 .. | **£600-800** |
| 252/25v | Refuse Wagon | 4 .. | **£350-400** |
| 260 | Royal Mail Van | 6 | NGPP |
| 260 | VW 'Deutsche Bundespost' | 6 .. | **£150-200** |
| 344/27f | Estate Car | 4 .. | **£200-250** |
| 492/34c | Loudspeaker Van | 6 .. | **£200-250** |
| 668 | Foden Army Trucks | 6 .. | **£80-100** |
| 675 | Ford US Army Staff Car | 6 | NGPP |
| 677 | Armoured Command Vehicle | 6 . | **£200-250** |
| 755/6 | Lamp Standards, | | |
| | yellow/red box | 6 .. | **£100-120** |
| 994 | Loading Ramp (for 982) | 3 ..... | **£55-80** |

## Type 10
Later 1970s trade packs without printing. A small yellow label is attached that shows the model number only. 432 and 662 are exceptions, being shrink-wrapped with no label.

| | | | |
|---|---|---|---|
| 305 | David Brown Tractor | 6 | NGPP |
| 308 | Leyland 384 Tractor | 6 | NGPP |
| 432 | Foden Tipping Lorry, | | |
| | factory shrink-wrapped pack | 6 .. | **£80-100** |
| 662 | Foden Army Truck, | | |
| | factory shrink-wrapped pack | 6 .. | **£100-125** |

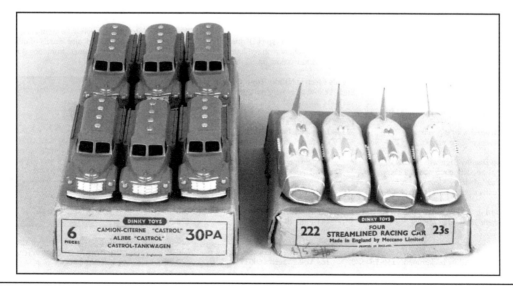

# Dinky Toys Trade Accessories

**'World Famous Racing Cars'**. Retailer's Shop Window / Counter Display Showcard with models 230, 231, 232 and 233 strung into place on the racetrack design. Yellow and Red Showcard.................. **£3,000-4,000**

**Black wooden Trade Display Unit** in plain cardboard box. 'Property of Meccano Ltd Liverpool' in black on gold; 3 shelves in light blue/white/yellow; 4 gold supports with 2 yellow and 2 red supports; 4 red tin flags 'DINKY TOYS'; 3 tin flags 'ASK FOR BOOKLET', 'OVER 200 MODELS', and 'ALWAYS SOMETHING NEW'; plus 2 red and 2 yellow balls............................ **£400-500**

**Glass Display Case.** Oak frame with three glass shelves. Size approx. 32" (80 cm.) wide, 24" (60 cm.) high, 9" (22 cm.) deep. With 'DINKY TOYS' in green lettering on glass front .... **£350-450**

**Large wooden Display Unit** 'DINKY SHOWROOM', 50" x 22" x 38"........ **£1,000-1,200**

**Trade Display Stand** Large yellow folding cardboard stand which non-erected measures approx. 28" (70 cm.) x 14" (35 cm.); three display levels with 'DINKY TOYS' logo in green plus 'MECCANO PRODUCT' in red on top header board. Outer corrugated cardboard packing has green printed instruction leaflet................. **£200-300**

**Trade Display Stand** Small yellow and red folding cardboard stand which non-erected measures approximately 12" (31 cm.) x 7" (15 cm.); with one 'DINKY TOYS' and two 'DINKY SUPERTOYS' logos in red plus yellow 'MASTERPIECES IN MINIATURE' logo on red background. .... **£100-125**

**Display Stand** (circa 1950 - 1960) Large metal stand measures approximately 36" x 21" x 22" (91.5 x 53 x 56 cm.); with nine display shelves covered in black plastic track. Metal advertisement affixed to top states in yellow/red/black 'A MOTOR SHOW FOR GIRLS AND BOYS', 'PRECISION DIE-CAST MODELS BY MECCANO', 'BEST RANGE', and 'BEST VALUE IN THE WORLD'. Lower large transfer also in yellow/red/black repeats the message..................................... **£500-750**

**Window Sign (plastic),** Dark blue top half with white 'MECCANO' logo, bottom half is yellow. Red 'Dinky Toys' logo. Approx. 18"x6"... **£100-125**

**Counter Display (cardboard),** Small display stand for a single model, 'ALWAYS NEW MODELS' logo in white on red background, header states 'DINKY TOYS' in red on yellow. ............ **£100-125**

**Counter Display (cardboard),** retailer's display stand in yellow/blue, 'ALWAYS NEW' logo, 'DINKY TOYS' in red................................... **£50-75**

**Counter Display (cardboard)** 'BATTLE OF BRITAIN' Blue/yellow displaying 719 Spitfire MkII and 721 Junkers JU 87b Stuka. ........ **£150-175**

**Shop Display Carousel** with tripod base supporting four stacks of clear plastic. ...... **£200-300**

**Illuminated Shop Display Sign** with 'DINKY TOYS' in large red wooden letters above a glass panel lettered either 'Made by Meccano Ltd' or 'British and Guaranteed'. ..................... **£500-600**

**Shelf Display Card** in 'landscape' format, featuring the Hesketh 308E 'OLYMPUS' Racing Car .................................................. **£100-150**

**Display Card**, 300 x 250mm, with 'The Wisest Choice Dinky Toys' on yellow background .. **£50-75**

**Freestanding Card**, 'Dinky Toys for Variety and Value', 33 x '17cm .................... **£50-75**

**Illuminated Counter or Window display unit** 13" x 9", perspex front 'DINKY TOYS' + 'NEW MODELS EVERY MONTH' logo. ......... **£100-1500**

**Counter Carousel Unit** with 'Always Something New from Dinky' around its edge. Red/Yellow 'DINKY TOYS BY MECCANO' sign on top, 26" high overall. .................................. **£200-250**

**Metal Counter Display Sign**, triangular in shape with red 'DINKY TOYS' on yellow background, approximately 8" x 1" x 1"....... **£30-40**

**Electric Revolving 'Meccano' Wooden Display Stand**. 'DINKY TOYS - LOOK FOR THE NAME ON THE BASE' logo, (28" square and 10" high) ....................................................................... **£250-350**

**Pre-War 'Meccano Dinky Toys' Advertising Sign.** This double-sided hanging sign shows pictures and details of 22, 24, 25 and 28 series models available in 'Season 1934'. Date code: '16/734/1'. Size: 11in x 9in (28cm x 23cm) ................. **£500-600**

**1938 Cardboard Display Stand** shows boy with green jumper, and 'Dinky Toys 300 Varieties' ............................................ **£150-175**

**1955 Wooden 3-tier Display Stand**. Pale green. 'Dinky Toys' and 'Dinky Supertoys'......... **£300-400**

**c.1959 'Dublo Dinky' Shop Display Stand.** Pale yellow with red logo and wording 'NEW SERIES / DUBLO DINKY', etc. Stand dimensions: 28cm x 19cm overall... **£300-500**

**Dinky Toys Price Tickets.** Aluminium tags to place on toys plus sheet of 200 self-adhesive labels showing model number and price ... **£200-250**

**Wall Chart**. 1963 Dinky Toys and Dinky Supertoys Wall Chart listing all tyre sizes for model vehicles..................................... **£100-125**

**1961 'Mini Dinky'** retailer's counter/window display card, 23 x 16.5cm.......................... **£100-125**

**c1960 Electric 'Dinky Toys' Perspex Hanging Sign.** Yellow sides, red letters, 1,300mm. . **£250-350**

**c1960 'Dinky Toys' Counter-top Stand** for the Italian market. Steel tubular and metal sheet construction approx. 30cm high, triangular back, two shelves, 'Novita', 'Meccano'. Dark cream and white................................. **£90-120**

**1960s Metal and Perspex Display Case,** (33 x 24cm), yellow with red letters with 'Dinky Toys' sign and window for models........... **£200-250**

**c1970s Electric 'Dinky Toys' Perspex Hanging Sign.** Yellow sides with red letters, 1,270mm long ....................................................... **£175-225**

**1960s Window leaflets / posters / stickers**

| | | |
|---|---|---|
| 72569 | Lady Penelope's 'FAB 1' ................... | **£50-60** |
| 72579 | Captain Scarlett and Thunderbirds ..... | **£50-60** |
| ? | 486 'Dinky Beats' Morris Oxford ..... | **£30-40** |
| ? | 107 'Stripey, the Magic Mini' ............ | **£30-40** |
| ? | 101 Thunderbirds ............................... | **£30-40** |
| ? | 153 Aston-Martin DB6 ...................... | **£30-40** |
| ? | 970 Jones Fleetmaster Crane.............. | **£20-30** |
| ? | 281 Pathe News Camera Car.............. | **£30-40** |
| ? | 158 Rolls-Royce Silver Shadow ....... | **£20-30** |
| ? | 131 Ford 40-RV ................................ | **£20-30** |
| ? | 282 Austin 1800................................ | **£20-30** |
| ? | 280 Midland Mobile Bank ................. | **£20-30** |
| ? | 129 Volkswagen Beetle ..................... | **£20-30** |
| ? | 163 Volkswagen 1600TL.................... | **£20-30** |

| | | |
|---|---|---|
| ? | 166 Renault R16................................ | **£20-30** |
| ? | 135 Triumph 2000 and 240 Cooper Racing Car..................... | **£20-30** |
| ? | 141 Vauxhall Victor Estate Car .......... | **£20-30** |

**1970s Shop window self-adhesive posters**

| | | |
|---|---|---|
| 100362 | 1972 Double-sided poster featuring 'All Action Fighting Vehicles' and '10 Great Fighting Vehicles'............. | **£20-30** |
| 100367 | 1973 Double-sided poster featuring 'Highway Action Models'............... | **£20-30** |
| 100482 | 1971 Single-sided poster advertising '451 Road Sweeper'...................... | **£20-30** |
| 100524 | Single-sided poster advertising 'No 410 Bedford Van'...................... | **£20-30** |
| 100537 | Single-sided poster with 'No 654 155mm Mobile Gun' ........ | **£20-30** |
| 100595 | Single-sided poster advertising 'No 694 Hanomag Tank Destroyer' | **£20-30** |
| 100602 | Single-sided poster advertising 'No 293 Swiss PTT Bus' ................ | **£20-30** |
| 100604 | Single-sided poster advertising 'No 656 88mm Gun'..................... | **£20-30** |
| 100734 | Single-sided poster advertising 'No 668 Foden Army Truck'.......... | **£20-30** |
| 100741 | Single-sided poster advertising 'No 432 Foden Tipper Truck'......... | **£20-30** |
| 100742 | Single-sided, advertising 'No 430 Johnson 2-ton Dumper' .... | **£20-30** |
| 100523 | Single-sided, advertising 'No 682 Stalwart Load Carrier'..... | **£20-30** |
| 100531 | Single-sided poster advertising 'No 683 Chieftain Tank' ............... | **£20-30** |
| 100496 | Single-sided poster advertising 'No 725 F-4K Phantom II'............. | **£20-30** |
| ? | Poster advertising '442 Land-Rover Breakdown Crane'....................... | **£20-30** |
| ? | Poster advertising '967 Muir-Hill Loader and Trencher'...................... | **£20-30** |
| ? | Poster advertising '915 AEC with Flat Trailer'........... | **£20-30** |
| ? | Poster advertising 1/25th scale Ford Capri and Police Car................. | **£30-40** |
| ? | Poster adv. 1/25th Saloon Car.......... | **£30-40** |
| ? | Poster advertising 724 Sea King Helicopter................. | **£20-25** |
| ? | Poster advertising 984 Atlas Digger | **£20-25** |
| ? | Poster adv. 977 Shovel Dozer .......... | **£20-25** |
| ? | Poster adv. 963 Road Grader ........... | **£20-25** |
| ? | Poster adv. 726 Messerschmitt........ | **£20-25** |
| ? | Poster adv. 730 US Phantom............ | **£20-25** |
| ? | Poster advertising 731 S.E.P.E.C.A.T. Jaguar and 728 RAF Dominie ....... | **£20-25** |
| ? | Poster adv. 734 P47 Thunderbolt..... | **£20-25** |
| ? | Poster advertising 739 Zero Sen ...... | **£20-25** |

All other late issued leaflets not listed .each: **£20-25**

**Note:** This section is far from complete and the Editor would welcome details of other trade stands, posters, display cards, promotional material and advertising signs.

Retailer's aluminuim price tickets for attachment to Dinky Toys boxes.

Photo: Vectis Auctions Ltd.

# Dinky Toys Numerical Index

# Nicky Toys, 1968 - 1975

In the late 1960s Meccano shipped out to India obsolete model dies and tools. The objective was to overcome exporting difficulties by manufacturing toys in India itself. The Indian manufacturing company was S. Kumar & Co who traded as Atamco Private Ltd. For trade mark reasons the toys were sold as 'Nicky Toys' and the arrangement was that the words 'Meccano' and 'Dinky Toys' would be obliterated from the dies. Similarly an arrangement was agreed in respect of deleting 'Dinky Toys' from the original model boxes.

However, the removal process was not diligently implemented which resulted in Nicky Toys occasionally being sold with 'Dinky Toys' being

displayed both on their baseplates and on their boxes. These models are sought after by collectors and attract a premium at auctions.

After S.Kumar & Co. had made the models from the original dies, they were finished by various firms of outworkers and as a result many different paint, decal and wheel versions exist. The details of the models listed are taken from various recent auction listings so their existence is confirmed.

The figures shown in the 'Market Price Range' column are based on recent auction results and reflect the prices achieved by mint models in good boxes.

**Types of Nicky Toys Boxes**

i) Original yellow box with 'Dinky Toys' on the front and end flaps of the box and with a single model picture on front of box. This is the type of box which should have had all references to 'Dinky Toys' removed or overstamped.
ii) A plain yellow card box with 'Nicky Toys' stamped on the box end flaps and with 'Manufactured by: ATAMCO PRIVATE LTD. CALCUTTA' printed on the box sides.
iii) A yellow box with a full colour picture on the side. 'Nicky Toys' is clearly printed on all sides of the box and on the end flaps.
More information would be welcomed.

| Model and details | MPR |
|---|---|
| **050 Jaguar 'Police' Car** | |
| • Metallic Red body | **£80-100** |
| • Red/White body | **£80-100** |
| **05 VW 'Police' Car** | |
| • Blue, white doors | **£80-100** |
| **051 Mercedes 220E 'Taxi'** | |
| • Black/Yellow, 'Taxi' headboard | **£80-100** |
| • Same but Grey body | **£80-100** |
| • With Orange body | **£80-100** |
| **054 Standard Herald Mk.II** | |
| • Metallic Green body | **£80-100** |
| • Red or Blue body | **£80-100** |
| • Lemon-Yellow body | **£80-100** |
| • White/Red body | **£80-100** |
| • All-White body | **£150-175** |
| **094 Rolls-Royce** | |
| • Gold body | **£80-100** |
| **113 MGB Sports** (with driver) | |
| • Light Blue body | **£100-125** |
| • Navy Blue body | **£100-125** |
| • Metallic Red body | **£100-125** |
| • Light Green body | **£100-125** |
| **115 Plymouth Fury** | |
| • Metallic Green body | **£80-100** |
| • Silver body | **£80-100** |
| • Blue body | **£80-100** |
| **120 Jaguar 'E'-type** | |
| • Metallic Green body | **£100-125** |
| • Red body | **£100-125** |
| • Apple-Green body | **£100-125** |
| • Blue body | **£100-125** |
| • Silver body | **£100-125** |
| • Yellow body | **£100-125** |
| **134 Standard Herald Mk.II** (Triumph Vitesse) | |
| • Red with White stripe | **£80-100** |
| • Turquoise with White body stripe | **£80-100** |
| • Green with Red stripe | **£80-100** |
| • Blue with Red stripe | **£80-100** |

| Model and details | MPR |
|---|---|
| **137 Plymouth Fury Convertible** | |
| • Red, Yellow interior | **£80-100** |
| • Yellow, Black interior | **£80-100** |
| • Apple-Green body | **£80-100** |
| • Metallic Green body | **£80-100** |
| • Red body | **£80-100** |
| • Cream body | **£80-100** |
| **137 Plymouth Fury Sports** | |
| • Silver, Blue interior | **£80-100** |
| • Yellow body | **£80-100** |
| • Blue body | **£80-100** |
| • Apple-Green body | **£80-100** |
| • Red body | **£80-100** |
| • Turquoise body | **£80-100** |
| **142 Jaguar Mk.X** | |
| • Met. Blue, White int. | **£80-100** |
| • Green, White interior | **£80-100** |
| • Metallic Red body | **£80-100** |
| • Metallic Turquoise | **£80-100** |
| • Silver body | **£80-100** |
| • Pale Yellow body | **£80-100** |
| **144 Volkswagen 1500** | |
| • Red body | **£80-100** |
| • White body | **£80-100** |
| • Blue body | **£80-100** |
| • Metallic Green body | **£80-100** |
| • 'Police' version, Blue / White body | **£80-100** |
| **146 Daimler V8 Saloon** (Jaguar 3.4 litre) | |
| • No colour details | NGPP |
| • 'Police' version, Red / White body | **£80-100** |
| **170 Lincoln Continental** | |
| • Blue, White roof | **£100-150** |
| • Silver, White roof | **£100-150** |
| • Pale Yellow body, Black roof | **£100-150** |
| • Cream, Black roof | **£100-150** |
| • Metallic Red body with White roof | **£100-150** |

| Model and details | MPR |
|---|---|
| • Metallic Turquoise, White roof | **£100-150** |
| **186 Mercedes Benz 220SE** | |
| • Metallic Red body, Light Grey interior | **£80-100** |
| • Grey, Light Grey int. | **£80-100** |
| • Metallic Light Green | **£80-100** |
| • Metallic Blue body | **£80-100** |
| • Silver, White int. | **£100-120** |
| **194 Bentley 'S' Coupé** | |
| • Met. Red, White tonneau, Black interior | **£80-100** |
| • Met. Green, Black tonneau, Red or Yellow int. | **£80-100** |
| • Cream with Red int. | **£80-100** |
| • Blue, Red interior | **£80-100** |
| • Silver body | **£80-100** |
| • Gold body | **£80-100** |
| **195 Jaguar 3.4 litre** | |
| • Silver body, Light Grey interior | **£80-100** |
| • Cream, Red interior | **£80-100** |
| • Blue, Red interior | **£80-100** |
| **238 Jaguar 'D'-type** (RN '35' on some) | |
| • Light Blue body, Yellow plastic hubs | **£70-90** |
| • Racing Green body | **£70-90** |
| • Red body | **£70-90** |
| • Silver body | **£70-90** |
| • Metallic Red body | **£70-90** |
| • Metallic Green body | **£70-90** |
| **239 Vanwall Racing Car** (All have a blue plastic driver) | |
| • Dark Metallic Blue | **£70-90** |
| • Red | **£70-90** |
| • Green | **£70-90** |
| • Light Blue body | **£70-90** |
| • Grey body | **£70-90** |
| • Yellow body | **£70-90** |
| **295 Standard '20' Minibus** | |
| • Metallic Red body | **£60-80** |

| Model and details | MPR |
|---|---|
| • Green body | **£60-80** |
| • Silver body | **£60-80** |
| • Pale Blue body | **£60-80** |
| • Red body | **£60-80** |
| • Grey body | **£60-80** |
| • 'Ambulance' version. White, Blue rooflight, red crosses on roof/doors | **£60-80** |
| **405 Universal Jeep** (All have black windscreen frame) | |
| • Gloss Brick Red | **£100-125** |
| • Light Grey | **£100-125** |
| • Blue | **£100-125** |
| • Army versions in Military Green | **£100-125** |
| **626 Military Ambulance** | |
| • Gloss Green body | **£80-100** |
| **660 Mighty Antar Tank Transporter** | |
| • Gloss Green (military) | NGPP |
| • Yellow/Grey (civilian version) | **£300-400** |
| **693 Howitzer 7.2** | |
| • Dark Military Green | NGPP |
| **705 Viscount Airliner 'BEA'** | |
| • Red, White and Blue | NGPP |
| **735 Gloucester Javelin** | |
| • RAF and camouflage liveries | **£90-110** |
| **738 Sea Vixen** | |
| • RAF and camouflage liveries | **£80-100** |
| **949 Wayne School Bus** | |
| • No details available | NGPP |
| **962 Dumper Truck** | |
| • No details available | NGPP |
| **999 Comet Airliner 'BOAC.'** | |
| • 'G-ALYX', boxed | **£140-180** |
| **Nicky Toys Catalogue** Cover depicts Jaguar Mk.10 at Motor Show. Range of models shown in two-tone colour | **£40-60** |

**Nicky Toys 194 Bentley 'S' Coupé.** Note the type iii) box, the simple tinplate baseplate, the plastic wheels and the variable spreading of the spigot heads.

## Bonham's Auctions

Montpelier Galleries, Montpelier Street,
London SW7 1HH
Tel: 0044 (0) 20 7393 3900
E-mail: leigh.gotch@bonhams.com
Website: www.bonhams.com/toys
**Note that** the auction prices shown do not
include premium or tax.
Abbreviations: **M** = Mint, **E** = Excellent,
**G** = Good, **VG** = Very Good,
**F** = Fair, **P** = Poor

### DINKY TOYS CARS
**22a Sports Tourer. 'Hornby Series'**,
Red/Cream, Blue wheels, Good ......................£280
**102 MG Midget Sports.** Orange body
with Red hubs, G in G box ..............................£282
**103 Austin-Healey Sports.** Red,
Grey interior, G-E in G box..............................£235
**157 Jaguar XK120.** Red with Red hubs,
G-E in G-E box................................................£188

### COMMERCIAL VEHICLES
**25d Petrol Tank Wagon.** Type 2,
Blue/Red/Gold, 'Redline-Glico', G.................£376
**25d Petrol Tank Wagon.** Type 4, Orange, G ...£100
**28a Delivery Van.** 1st type,
'Hornby Trains', Blue wheels, Good.............£1,234
**28a Delivery Van.** 1st type, 'Palethorpes',
Fair to Good...................................................£799
**29e Single Deck Buses.** Trade Box of Six:
three Cream, two Green and a Blue,
G - E in G box.................................................£552
**30v Electric Dairy Vans.** Trade Box of Six:
three 'Express Dairy' in Grey, two in Cream and
a 'NCB' in Cream, G-E in G box.....................£306
**455 Trojan Van 'Brooke Bond'.**
Promotional issue with roof label, G in F box ..£548
**501 Foden Wagon.** 1st type,
Grey with Red flash, G-E in F-G box ..............£300
**979 Racehorse Transport 'Newmarket
Transporter'.** G-E in G box ...........................£458
**60h Singapore Flying Boat.**
G-F (some chipping to decals) ........................£150
**Gift Set 398 Farm Equipment.**
As catalogue, E in G box ................................£987

## Christie's

South Kensington, London.
+44 (0)20 7752 3274
**Auction Prices shown include the buyer's
premium. Abbreviations:**
**M** = Mint, **E** = Excellent, **G** = Good,
**VG** = Very Good, **F** = Fair, **P** = Poor

### DINKY TOYS CARS and TRACTORS
**135 Triumph 2000 Promotional.**
Blue-Grey body, Black roof, E in F-G box ......£540
**148 Ford Fairlane** 1965-67.
Metallic Green, White interior.........................£180
**300 Massey Ferguson Tractor.**
Red with Yellow plastic front hubs and
Blue plastic driver..........................................£336

### COMMERCIAL VEHICLES
**31B/451 'DUNLOP' Vans**
Type 3 **Trade box of Six.**
Red body - VG-E in F-G Trade Box ..... **£600**
**448 Chevrolet Pick-up and Trailers.**
As Catalogue. VG-E in VG box ........... **£360**
**701 Short Shetland Flying Boat.**
Good Condition, unboxed.......................£288
**920 Guy Warrior Van.** Tomato Ketchup
advertisements, cab faded + two chips,
VG in G box ........................................£2,040

**930 Bedford Pallet-Jekta Van.**
With 2 pallets/instructions - E in G box ..........£410
**948 Tractor-Trailer 'Mcleans'.**
Late issue - Black Plastic hubs........................£228
**964 Elevator Loader** (late issue).
As per catalogue - G-VG in VG box ...............£288
**979 Racehorse Transporter.**
'Newmarket', 2 horses - VG in VG box ..........£456

### GIFT SETS
**299 Motorways Set.**
Details as per catalogue, F-VG in G box .....
£900
**695 Tractor and 7.2 Howitzer Gift Set,**
inner stay + 2 packing pieces, E in VG box.. £420
**957 Fire Service Gift Set.**
Details as per catalogue - VG in G box **£336**

### FRENCH DINKY TOYS
**21 Mixed Goods Train Set** (pre-war).
G in original G box...............................£720

## Collectoys

Hotel Frank Hornby, Place George Sand,
18000 Bourges, France.
E-Mail: contact@collectoys.fr
Website: www.collectoys.fr

**Model** condition shown in CAPITALS,
i.e., 'A - D' with 'A' being the top grade.
**Box** condition is shown in Lower Case,
i.e. 'a - d' with 'a' being the top grade
('o.' = unboxed)

### ENGLISH DINKY TOYS (PRE-WAR)
**28b 'SECCOTINE' Type 3 Delivery Van**
B.o..................................................................£1,400
**28k 'MARSH'S SAUSAGES' Type 3
Delivery Van.** B.o..........................................£1,400
**28m 'WAKEFIELD'S CASTROL OIL'
Type 3 Delivery Van.** D.o...............................£840
**28t 'OVALTINE' Type 3 Van.** B.o..................£1,260
**28w 'OSRAM LAMPS' Type 3 Delivery Van.**
D.o..................................................................£1,120
**28w 'OSRAM LAMPS' Type Van.** C.o. ........£750
**22c Motor Truck,** 1933-35.
Blue and White body, metal wheels. C.o. .....£1,200
**25b Covered Wagon.** Type 2, Dark Green body,
Cream tilt, Black chassis and hubs, C.o. ..........£455
**25d Tanker 'POOL'** in White. Type 2, 1946,
Grey body, Black chassis, C.o.........................£525
**280a 'VIYELLA Regd.' Type 2 Delivery Van.**
C.o................................................................£1,050
**280b 'HARTLEY'S JAM' Type 2
Delivery Van,** B.o.........................................£2,450
**280 'SHREDDED WHEAT' Type 2
Delivery Van,** C.o..........................................£525
**280e 'YORKSHIRE POST' Type 3
Delivery Van,** C.o........................................£1,960
**280f 'Mackintosh's Toffee' Type 2
Delivery Van,** B.o..........................................£700
**280g 'BENTALLS' Type 2 Delivery Van,**
B.o................................................................£9,800
**280j 'FENWICK' Type 2 Delivery Van,**
D.o................................................................£4,900
**28n 'ATCO MOTORMOWERS'
Type 2 Delivery Van,** B.o..............................£840
**28r 'SWAN PENS' Type 3 Delivery Van,**
E.o..................................................................£525
**28s 'FRY'S COCOA' Type 3 Delivery Van,**
E.o..................................................................£525
**30f Ambulance.** South African,
Military Green, Red Cross, D.o....................£1,350

### ENGLISH DINKY TOYS (POST-WAR)
**30m Dodge Tipper,** 1950-54. Maroon body,
Green tipper and hubs, B.b..............................£700

**252 Refuse Wagon.** Orange/Grey,
Green plastic shutters, A.c..............................£350
**252 Refuse Wagon.** Lime Green,
black shutters, cream hubs, A.c. .....................£525
**412 Austin Wagon.** Lemon Yellow,
green hubs, A.a............................................£1,050
**413 Austin Covered Wagon.** Light Blue body,
Cream back and hubs, A.c..............................£525
**413 Austin Covered Wagon.** Red body,
Grey back and hubs, A.b.................................£525
**413 Austin Covered Wagon.** Maroon body,
Beige back, Red hubs, A.c...............................£350
**419 Leyland Comet 'PORTLAND CEMENT'.**
Yellow body, B.c.............................................£140
**430 Commer Breakdown.** Red cab,
Grey back, Blue hubs, A.b............................£1,050
**432 Guy Flat Truck.** Mid-blue / Red body,
Mid-blue hubs, A.b.........................................£385
**514 Guy Van 'LYONS TEA'.**
Dark Blue body, A.a.....................................£2,300
**514 Guy Van 'WEETABIX'.**
Yellow body, A.a...........................................£3,150
**923 Big Bedford 'HEINZ'
Tomato Ketchup.**
Red/Yellow, A.c...........................................£1,680
**989 Car Transporter
'AUTO TRANSPORTERS'.**
Lemon Yellow body, A.a. ..............................£5,950

### FRENCH DINKY TOYS CARS
**501 Citroen DS19 'POLICE'.**
Blue/Black/White, A.b....................................£190
**506 Aston Martin DB3.** Green, '16', A.a. ........£110
**511 Ferrari.** Red, cross-hatched grille, A.a......£190
**514 Alfa-Romeo Giulia 1600.**
Metallic Grey, A.a..........................................£120
**519 Simca 1000.** South African:
Turquoise, Red interior, A.b.........................£2,000
**520 Fiat 600D.** Cream, A.a. ...........................£100
**24B Peugeot 403 8cv.** Light Grey body, A.b....£105
**521 Peugeot 403 8cv.** Cream body, A.b..........£240
**24CP Citroën DS19.** Ivory/Dark Purple, A.b...£275
**522 Citroën DS19.** Yellow/Grey,
convex hubs, A.a............................................£310
**522 Citroën DS19.** Orange/Cream,
convex hubs, A.b............................................£260
**24D Plymouth Belvedere.**
White body, Blue roof, B.b..............................£380
**24D Plymouth Belvedere.**
Green body, Black roof, A.a............................£105
**24E Renault Dauphine.**
Turquoise, no windows, A,b............................£140
**524 Renault Dauphine.**
Brick Red, windows, A.a.................................£105
**526 Mercedes 190SL.** Silver/Black, A.a. ........£130
**24J Alfa-Romeo Sprint 1900.** Red, A.b............£80
**24K Simca Chambord.** Ivory/Red, A.b. ...........£95
**24K Simca Chambord.**
Light Green/Dark Green body, A.b. ................£330
**24O 1949 Studebaker State Commander.**
Red body, black hubs, B.o...........................£1,150
**106 Opel Kadett.**
Yellow body, Excellent, boxed .....................£1,950
**532 Lincoln Premiere.**
Blue/Silver, concave hubs, B.c........................£300
**536 Peugeot 404 and Trailer.**
Red/Cream, 4 skis on roof, B.a. .....................£310
**545 De Soto Diplomat.** Metallic/Ivory, A.a. ....£210
**546 Opel Rekord Taxi.** Black, A.b..................£450
**550 Chrysler Saratoga.**
Violet/Black flash, B.b....................................£130
**556 Citroën ID 19 Ambulance.**
Grey/Cream, 3rd type, A.a..............................£140
**557 Citroën Ami 6.**
Grey/Blue, white roof, 1st type, A.b. ..............£140
**1401 Alfa-Romeo 1600 Rally.** Red, '8', A.a....£140
**1406 Renault 4L Sinpar 'Michel Tanguy'.**
Khaki Green, A.a............................................£150
**571 Saviem Goelette Horse Box and Sulky.**
Blue/Wood/Pink, A.a.....................................£520
**572 Berliet Quarry Truck.** Red/Yellow, A.b...£300

**577 Berliet Livestock Truck.**
Green/Yellow, A.b....................................................£165
**588 Berliet Beer Lorry.**
Yellow, Red and Brown, A.a. ........................£300
**881 Circus Truck/Trailer 'PINDER',** A.b......£620
**882 Peugeot 404 and Caravan 'PINDER',**
Yellow/Red/White, A.a ...............................£900
**885 Saviem Sinpar Steel Carrier.**
Red/Grey, A.a. ..............................................£260
**898 Berliet Transporter 'ALSTHOM'.**
Orange body, A.c. .........................................£300

**GIFT SETS**
**Passsenger Cars Set,** 1940-48. As per Catalogue,
Very Good model and box ........................£6,080
**Gift Set 64 Aircraft,** 1938-40. As per Catalogue,
some fatigue, Good box............................£1,790
**Gift Set 64 Aircraft.** As per Catalogue,
3 x D., 1 x A., 1xB, 1 x E., Box a. ............£1,520

# Dreweatt-Neate Auctions
Apsley Road Saleroom, St Johns Place,
Apsley Road,
Clifton, Bristol BS8 2ST.

**902 Foden Flat Truck.** 2nd type,
Orange/Green, VGC, boxed ...........................£210
**914 A.E.C. Lorry.** Red/Green,
'British Road Services', E, boxed ...................£110

# Special Auction Services
Kennetholme, Midgeham,
Reading, Berkshire.
Tel: 0118 971 2949   www.invaluable.com

**22e Farm Tractor.**
Yellow/Blue, red wheels G - E ........................£300
**62h Gift Set** with
'Meccano Co.' of America Inc.' & 'FAO
Schwarz' labels. **6 Hawker Hurricanes,**
camouflaged. Damage/some fatigue, box VG..£360
**34b 'Royal Mail' Van.**
Post war, open rear windows, VG-E ..............£170
**100 Lady Penelope's 'FAB1'.**
Sun faded, box G - VG ..................................£150
**101 Thunderbird II and IV.**
Slightly sun faded, box G-VG ........................£210
**102 Joe's Car.**
Vacuform packaging, E overall ......................£150
**103 Spectrum Patrol Car.**
Metallic Red E, box G ...................................£140
**106 The Prisoner Mini-Moke.**
Excellent, box G ............................................£220
**167 AC Aceca.**
Cream/Maroon, spun hubs, VG in VG box......£140
**290 Double-Deck Bus 'DUNLOP'.**
Green/Cream, green hubs, E in G box ............£100
**350 Tiny's Mini-Moke.** Excellent, box VG-E .£170
**958 Guy Warrior Snow Plough.**
VG-E in G box..............................................£119

# Lacy, Scott & Knight
The Auction Centre, 10 Risbygate Street,
Bury St Edmunds, Suffolk, IP33 3AA
E-mail: fineart@lsk.co.uk
Web: www.lsk.co.uk
Abbreviations: **M** = Mint, **NM** = Near Mint,
**E** = Excellent, **VG** = Very Good, **G** = Good,
**B** = Boxed, **BP** = Bubble Pack,
**WB** = Window box, **CD** = Cast detailed,
**CF** = Camouflage.

**ENGLISH DINKY TOYS CARS**
**115 Ford Anglia 105E.**
Turquoise, Red interior, NM in M box............£115

**157 Jaguar XK-120.**
Yellow, Pale Yellow hubs, VG in M box.........£175
**167 A.C. Aceca Coupé**. Matt Cream,
spun hubs, NM, Yellow Mint box .................£370
**180 Packard Clipper.** Orange/Light Grey,
spun hubs, NMB ...........................................£130
**182 Porsche 356A Coupé.**
Cerise, spun hubs, Mint boxed .......................£165
**183 Morris Mini-Minor Automatic.**
Metallic Red body, Matt Black roof, late issue
with 'Austin Cooper S' on boot. M in NM box ..£80
**192 De Soto Fireflite.**
Turquoise/Light Tan, spun hubs, NMB ...........£130

**COMMERCIALS**
**924 Aveling-Barford Diesel Roller.** M boxed .£115
**945 A.E.C. 'Lucas Oil'.** Green/White,
M in VG 'Esso' promotional pack .................£125
**974 A.E.C. Hoynor Transporter.**
Chromed domed hubs, MB.............................£150
**975 Ruston-Bucyrus.** NM in VG box ...........£220

**MISCELLANEOUS  DINKY TOYS**
**22e Farm Tractor.** Green/Yellow,
Red wheels, some fatigue on wheels...............£185
**60h Singapore Flying Boat.** NM in VG box ..£420
**101 Thunderbirds II & IV.**
Metallic Green, Red thrusters, Yellow legs,
M in NM BP ................................................£240
**726 Messerschmitt BF 109.** Grey/Green CF,
unused transfers, M in NM BP .......................£95
**734 P47 Thunderbolt.** Silver/Black,
'USAAF', M in NM bubble pack..................£130

**GIFT SETS**
**19 Mixed Goods Train.**
As per Catalogue, VG in VG box....................£350
**44 'AA' Set.**
As per Catalogue, G - NM in VG box.............£370
**118 Towaway Glider Set.**
As per Catalogue, NM in NM box ..................£165
**151 Medium Tank Unit.**
As per Catalogue, F-G in F-G box ..................£260
**152 Light Tank Set.**
As per Catalogue, F-G in Good box ...............£195
**Gift Set 245 Superfast Set.**
As per Catalogue - 3 models NM in G box......£100
**Gift Set 294 Police Set.**
As per Catalogue, models M in VG-NM box ..£180
**Gift Set 990 Car Transporter.** Only three
F cars plus Transporter in G box + insert......£1,050

**FRENCH DINKY TOYS**
**24A Chrysler 'New Yorker.'**
Red body, Ivory seats, NM in M box ..............£115
**24D Plymouth Belvedere.**
Grey with Red roof, NM in M box .................£120
**24ZT Taxi 'Ariane'.**
Black/Red, M in VG box...............................£130
**550 Chrysler 'Saratoga'.**
Pale Pink/White, NM in VG box ....................£115
**554 Opel 'Rekord'.**
Beige/White, M in NM box............................£110
**561 Camionette Citroën 1200kg 'Cibie'.**
Turquoise body, '25C' on model, M in G box ..£370

# Vectis Auctions Ltd.
Fleck Way, Thornaby,
Stockton -on-Tees TS17 9JZ
Abbreviations:
**M** = Mint, **NM** = Near Mint, **EP** = Excellent
Plus, **E** = Excellent, **GP** = Good Plus,
**G** = Good, **F** = Fair

**ENGLISH DINKY TOYS CARS**
**22g Streamlined Tourer.**
Cream, smooth black hubs, white tyres, F - G ....£60
**24e Streamlined Saloon.** 1st type chassis,
2nd type radiator, 12 bonnet louvres, Red body,
Black chassis, 'Toosietoy' type hubs, GP.........£850

**30a Chrysler Airflow** (post-war issue).
Mid-Green body, black smooth hubs with
thick axles, plated front and rear
bumpers and grille. Excellent Plus ................£300
**30b Rolls-Royce** (pre-war issue). Red body,
Maroon open chassis and wings, Black smooth
hubs, white tyres, thin axles, Excellent ...........£420
**38c Lagonda Sports Coupé.**
Dark Green body, Darker Green seats, EP.......£110
**38d Alvis Sports Tourer.**
Dark Green, Matt Black interior, E unboxed ...£130
**39eu Chrysler Royale.** Two-tone Green,
black ridged wheels, Good ............................£460
**40j Austin Somerset.**
Red including hubs, NM in G box ..................£110
**57/005  Ford Thunderbird.** Blue, Ivory roof,
Red interior cast hubs, NM in EP box............£200
**101 Sunbeam Alpine Tourer.**
Pale Blue body/hubs, Dark blue interior,
EP in GP box................................................£160
**106/140 Austin Atlantic.** Light Blue,
Matt Red interior, Red hubs, Cream steering
wheel, E in G box .........................................£110
**107 Sunbeam Alpine Sports.** Cerise,
Grey interior, Cream hubs, NM in GP box .....£130
**108 MG Midget Sports.** Red, Tan interior,
Red hubs, RN '24', Near Mint Boxed............£180
**109 Austin-Healey 100 Sports.**
Deep Yellow, Mid-Blue interior / hubs,
RN '21', NM in G box .................................£190
**114 Triumph Spitfire.** Met. Gold, Red interior,
no logo on boot, spun hubs, Two-tone Blue
driver, black engine, EP in GP box ................£140
**114 Triumph Spitfire.** Metallic Purple,
Metallic Gold interior, no logo on boot,
spun hubs, Two-tone Blue driver,
silver engine, E in GP-E box .........................£160
**131 Cadillac Eldorado.**
Salmon Pink, Grey interior, E in G box .........£110
**132 Packard Convertible.**
Light Green, Red interior/hubs, NM in E box .£110
**146  Daimler 2.5 V8.** Metallic Pale Green,
Red interior, NM in E box ............................£110
**151 Triumph 1800.** Fawn, Green hubs,
Black base, NM in GP box ...........................£140
**153 Standard Vanguard.**
Cream body and hubs, NM in E box...............£180
**157 Jaguar XK120.** Red, spun hubs,
NM-M in GP box with red spot.....................£400
**161 Austin Somerset.** Black lower/Cream upper
body/hubs, M in E box .................................£280
**162 Ford Zephyr.** Two-tone Blue,
Grey hubs, E in G box ..................................£100
**165 Humber Hawk.** Cream body,
Maroon lower body/roof, NM in E box ...........£100
**165 Humber Hawk.** Green and Black,
chrome spun hubs, M in EP box.....................£130
**167 AC Aceca.** Pale Grey, Red roof and hubs,
EP in EP box ...............................................£110
**170 Ford Fordor Sedan.**
Lowline - Red/Cream, Mint in Good box .......£240
**172 Studebaker Commander.**
Lowline - Cream/Maroon, E in GP box .........£170
**181 VW Beetle.** Pale Blue with
Mid-Blue plastic hubs, EP in G box...............£380
**182 Porsche 356a.**
Pale Blue, Cream hubs, NM in E box ............£110
**187 VW Karmann Ghia.** Dark Green,
Cream roof, spun hubs, M in E box ...............£120
**194 Bentley Coupé.** Light Metallic Bronze,
Matt Black base, Cream interior,
Blue folded hood, spun hubs, E in G box .......£190
**197 Morris Mini Traveller.**
Cream, Pale Lemon interior, G in E box .........£240
**199 Austin 7 Countryman.** Pale Blue,
Red interior, spun hubs, NM in E box.............£90
**199 Austin 7 Countryman.**
Fluorescent Orange, NM boxed .....................£300
**232 Alfa-Romeo Sports Car.** Red body and
hubs, RN '8', M in NM card box ...................£190
**235 HWM Racing Car.** Pale Green/Mid Green
hubs, RN '7', NM in GP card box .................£120

187

**254 Austin Taxi**. Two-tone Green/Yellow
body and hubs, NM in G box ........................£150
**265 Plymouth Plaza US Taxi**.
As per Catalogue, E - EP in Fair box .............£160
**268 Renault Dauphine Minicab**.
Details as per Catalogue, EP in E Box ............£140
**2214 Ford Capri Special** (1/25 scale).
NM in E box .................................................£110

**COMMERCIAL VEHICLES and BUSES**
**274 'Joseph Mason Paints' Austin Mini Van**.
NM model/card, Fair box .............................£620
**410/25M Trade Box for four Bedford Tippers**.
Three Red with Cream back and one with
Yellow cab/Blue back. E in NM yellow box ....£520
**410 Bedford Tipper Truck**. Red cab,
Cream back, windows, matt black baseplate,
red plastic hubs, EP in G late issue
lighter yellow box .......................................£380
**420 Forward Control Lorry**. Mid Green,
Red ridged hubs, Mint in GP card box ...........£160
**420 Forward Control Lorry**.
Red, Green ridged hubs, M in GP card box .....£180
**420 Forward Control Lorry**. Mid Green,
Cream ridged hubs, Mint in G card box ..........£220
**432 Guy Flat Truck**.
Mid-Blue cab/hubs, Red back, NM in E box ...£180
**440 Studebaker Tanker. 'Mobilgas'**
in white letters, EP in EP box .........................£140
**450 Trojan 'Esso' Van**.
Red body, E in G - GP box ............................£120
**451 Trojan Van 'Dunlop'**.
Red body/hubs, Mint in E card box ................£200
**465 Morris 'Capstan' Van**.
Details as per Catalogue, E - EP in E box........£170
**482 Bedford CA Van 'Dinky Toys'**.
E in E box ..................................................£120
**491 Electric Milk Float 'N.C.B.'**.
Cream and Red, E in E plain box ...................£100
**502 Foden Flat Truck (1st)**.
Dark Green body/hubs, E-EP in F-G box.........£280
**504 Foden Tanker, 2nd Type**.
Red cab, Fawn Tank, E in G - GP box ............£260

**505 Foden Flat Truck With Chains, 2nd Type**.
Maroon body and hubs, Mint in G early
blue box with orange and white label with
2nd Type cab picture........................................£540
**505 Foden Flat Truck With Chains, 2nd Type**.
Dark Green cab/chassis and flatbed, Mid-Green
hubs, M in GP-E early blue box, orange/white
label with 2nd type cab picture. ......................£800
**511 Guy Lorry, 1st Type**.
Dark Green/Black - E-EP in GP box................£260
**512 Guy Flat Truck, 1st Type**.
Maroon/Black, E in G-GP 'buff' box ..............£260
**513 Guy Flat with Tailboard, 1st Type**.
Dark Green/Mid-Green, E in GP box..............£190
**514 Guy Van 'Spratts'**.
Details as per Catalogue, E in G blue faded box....£260
**532 Leyland Comet Wagon**. Green,
Orange back, Cream hubs, E in GP box...........£160
**532 Leyland Comet Wagon**. Dark Green cab and
chassis, Mid-blue body, Cream hubs, EP in GP
early blue box with orange and white label .....£360
**533 Leyland Cement Wagon**.
Details as per Catalogue, EP in GP - E box .....£240
**902 Foden Flat Truck, 2nd Type**.
Dark Red cab and chassis, Green back and
Supertoys hubs, M in E-EP box ...................£5,400
**902 Foden Flat Truck, 2nd Type**. Yellow cab
and chassis, Green flatbed, Light Green hubs,
EP-NM in Excellent Blue/White box............£1,400
**903 Foden Tailboard Truck, 2nd Type**.
Violet-Blue, Orange back, G in F-G box .........£150
**903 Foden Tailboard Truck, 2nd Type**.
Mid-Blue cab, chassis and Supertoy hubs,
Fawn (light beige) rear body,
M in E Blue/White striped box ....................£1,400
**905 Foden Chain Lorry, 2nd Type**.
Red/Grey, Red hubs, E in E box ....................£220
**923 Big Bedford Van 'Heinz'**.
Details as per Catalogue, NM in E box............£280
**934 Leyland Octopus Wagon**. Dark Blue cab
and chassis, Lemon Yellow cab band, bumper
and riveted back, Red Supertoy hubs.
NM in EP box ...........................................£2,700

**935 Leyland Octopus Flat Truck**. Green cab
and chassis, Light Grey cab band, bumper and
riveted back, Red plastic hubs and grille.
NM in EP box ...........................................£1,600
**941/504 'Mobilgas' Tanker**.
E in GP dual-numbered box ..........................£460
**944 Leyland Tanker 'Corn Products Ltd'**.
Near Mint in original plain cardboard box. One
of only 550 promotional models issued ........£7,500
**960 Albion Concrete Lorry**. Orange,
Grey barrel, E in G-GP blue/white box ...........£150
**961 Blaw Knox**. Late issue Orange plastic
Bulldozer, NM in NM box ............................£600
**989 Auto Transporters**. With instruction leaflet
and tested tag, Lemon Yellow cab, chassis and
rear ramp, Light Grey back, Metallic Blue ramps,
Red plastic hubs. Near Mint in Good picture
panel Yellow/Red box..................................£2,700

**MILITARY ITEMS and AIRCRAFT**
**22f Army Tank**.
Grey lead body, 'Dinky Toys' cast in, Good ....£280
**Trade Box for four 30h Daimler Ambulance**
Contains only one model. E in GP trade box ...£280
**37c Royal Signals Despatch Rider**.
Details as per Catalogue, GP - E ....................£220
**675 Army Staff Car**.
Military Green. M in E box ............................£280
**62g Long Range Bomber**.
Silver, Excellent, sold unboxed .....................£150
**62p 'Ensign' Class Airliner**. Silver,
'Elsinore', 'G-ADST', Good Plus, unboxed ....£300
**737 Lightning Fighter**.
Metallic Grey, Mint in Excellent box..............£110
**749 Avro Vulcan Bomber**.
Near Mint, unboxed.....................................£850
**998 Bristol Britannia**. As per Catalogue,
EP in GP Blue/White box ..............................£170

**NOVELTY, FILM, and TV-related**
**100 Lady Penelope's 'FAB 1'**.
Pink, NM, with E pictorial stand and box........£380
**100 Lady Penelope's 'FAB 1'**.
Fluorescent Pink, GP-E, stand G, box GP........£480

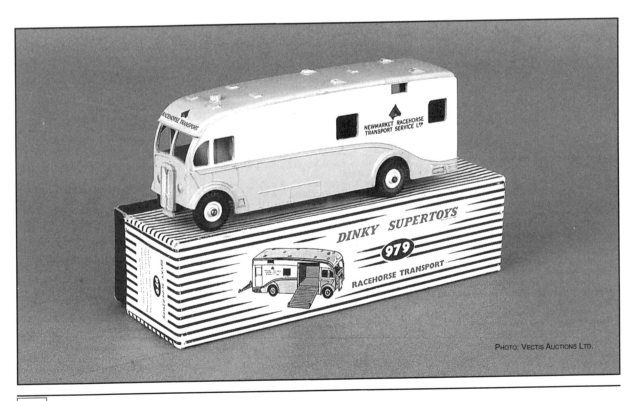

PHOTO: VECTIS AUCTIONS LTD.

**101 Thunderbirds II & IV, 1st issue.**
Gloss Dark Green, Red thrusters,
Yellow legs, Mint, inner pictorial stand,
packing and Box EP ...........................................**£950**
**102 'Joe 90'.** As catalogue,
EP in GP box with pictorial stand ...................**£180**
**103 Spectrum Patrol Car.** Metallic Gold,
Blue windows, G-GP in B box ............................**£140**
**103 Spectrum Patrol Car.** Metallic Red,
Blue tinted windows, cast hubs, White base and
plastic aerial, Mint including inner packing ring,
instructions and outer card picture box ...........**£320**
**104 Spectrum Pursuit Vehicle.** Metallic Blue,
Black base, E with GP stand and box...........**£180**
**106 'The Prisoner' Mini Moke.** White,
brown side steps, chrome hubs, E in G box ....**£190**
**107 'Stripey, The Magic Mini'.**
As Catalogue, EP, NM stand in GP box ..........**£420**
**108 Sam's Car.** Chrome, Lemon interior,
Red engine cover, NM in GP box ......................**£80**
**108 Sam's Car.**
Metallic Red, Yellow interior, EP in E box ......**£120**
**350 Tiny's Mini Moke,**
E in GP box with GP stand...............................**£100**
**353 'UFO' Shado 2 Mobile.** Green,
Yellow interior, silver track, M in G pack........**£140**
**353 'UFO' Shado 2 Mobile.** Metallic Blue,
Pale Green base, Mid-Green plastic rollers,
black rubber tracks, NM, tray E, box GP........**£200**

**FARMING MODELS**
**300 Massey-Harris Tractor.**
Red, tan driver, EP in E lighter yellow box .....**£160**
**300 Massey-Harris Tractor.** Red, blue plastic
driver, M in EP lighter yellow box...................**£160**
**301 Field Marshall Tractor.** Orange, metal
wheels with green centres, E-EP in G -GP ....**£160**
**308 Leyland 384 Tractor.** Blue/white,
blue plastic driver, M in NM pictorial box......**£130**
**325 David Brown Tractor/Harrow Set.**
White, red trim, EP in GP box..........................**£200**
**963 Heavy Tractor.** Pale Yellow,
Green rubber tracks, NM in F-G box .............**£120**

**MISCELLANEOUS ENGLISH DINKY TOYS**
**Dublo Dinky 073 Land Rover and Horsebox.**
Green, Orange, knobbly black plastic wheels,
NM in EP box.....................................................**£160**
**24 Series Cars Gift Set.** Late issue, details as
per Catalogue, models (F) on (G) card in (G)
later issue blue marbled box. With lid label..**£6,750**
**44 AA Patrol Set.** Contents Fair to Excellent
in Good box with Excellent pictorial stand......**£640**
**103 Dolly Varden Kitchen Furniture Set.**
Contents Fair to Excellent. Fair to Good box ...**£520**
**149 Sports Car Set.** Models as in 11th Edition
Catalogue, E - EP, Box G (tape repairs).........**£1,200**
**201 Racing Cars Set.** Models as in 11th Edition,
Good +, inner stand NM, outer box crushed.....**£800**
**299 Post Office Services Set.**
Details as per Catalogue, GP-E in GP box.......**£360**
**990 Transporter Gift Set.**
Models E - EP, inner tray E, outer box G......**£1,200**

**FRENCH DINKY TOYS CARS**
**24K Simca Vedette.**
Two-tone Green, spun hubs, EP in GP box ......**£150**
**24M VW Karmann Ghia.**
Red/Black, EP in GP box....................................**£80**
**24N Citroën Traction-Avant.**
Black, Cream hubs, E unboxed ........................**£110**
**24U Simca Aronde.**
Light Grey body, EP - NM unboxed .................**£70**
**506 Ferrrai 275GTB.**
Red, black interior, GP - E including box .......**£100**
**518A Renault 4 'Autoroutes'.**
Orange, grey interior, EP in EP box ................**£240**
**528 Peugeot 404 Cabriolet.** White,
red interior, concave hubs, NM in GP box.......**£120**
**532 Lincoln Premiere.** Two-tone Green,
chrome hubs, EP in GP - E box ........................**£100**

**535/24T Citroën 2cv.**
Maroon/Grey, NM in G box ..........................**£100**
**552 Chevrolet Corvair.** Red, cream interior,
spun hubs, NM in G box ................................**£150**
**554 Opel Rekord.**
Brown/Cream, M in GP box............................**£80**
**1401 Alfa-Romeo Rally.**
Red, Fawn interior, E in GP box ....................**£100**
**1404 Citroën TV Car**
**'Radio Tele Luxembourg'.** EP in G box ........**£380**
**1421 Opel 1900 GT.**
Blue, Red interior, NM in E box ......................**£70**
**1424 Renault 12 Gordini.**
Blue/White stripes, Mint in Excellent box ......**£130**
**1435 Citroën Presidentialle.** Two-tone Grey,
in blue 'presentation' box, NM in E box.......**£1,000**

**FRENCH DINKY TOYS**
**COMMERCIAL VEHICLES**
**25R Breakdown Truck.** Studebaker,
Red, toolbox outline only, GP unboxed...........**£120**
**32AB Panhard Tractor 'SNCF'.**
Blue, GP - E in F-G Yellow box.......................**£170**
**33C Simca Glazier's Truck.**
Grey/Green, NM in G - GP box ........................**£80**
**34B Berliet Flat Truck.**
Red/Grey, M in GP box ...................................**£100**
**39A Car Transporter.** Silver/Orange,
E (3 tyres perished), in F-G striped box...........**£130**
**541 Mercedes-Benz Autocar Minibus.**
Orange/Cream, NM in G box ...........................**£160**
**560 Citroën Postal Van.**
Yellow, Excellent including box ......................**£150**
**561 Citroën H Van 'Glaces Gervais'.**
White/Blue, E in F picture box.........................**£360**
**561 Citroën Van 'Cibie'.**
Turquoise/Yellow hubs, EP - NM in G box .....**£190**
**570 Peugeot J7 Van 'Allo Fret'.**
NM in GP- E box.............................................**£320**
**577 Beast Carrier.**
Green/Yellow, Excellent in Poor - Fair box ......**£90**
**578 Simca Cargo Tipper.**
Green/Silver, EP in G box ................................**£60**
**580 Berliet Tipper Truck.**
Blue/Black/Orange, EP in G box ....................**£110**
**581 Berliet Flat Lorry.**
Red/Grey, E in GP box ....................................**£60**
**585 GAK Tipper Truck.**
Blue/Orange, EP in G box ...............................**£80**
**587 Citroën Display Van 'Phillips'.**
Yellow, red trim, GP-E unboxed .....................**£300**
**884 Bridge Layer Truck.** Military Green
with bridge sections etc., NM in GP box ........**£320**
**885 Saviem Steel Carrier.**
Red/Grey, GP - E including box.......................**£170**
**888 Berliet Pipe Layer.**
Sand beige, white roof, NM in E box .............**£280**
**60C Super G Constellation 'Air France'.**
As Catalogue, NM in GP box ..........................**£180**
**60D Sikorsky Helicopter 'Sabena'.**
As Catalogue, NM in E card box ....................**£110**
**804 Nord Noratlas.**
As Catalogue, NM in F card box.....................**£140**

## Wallis & Wallis

West Street Auction Galleries, Lewes,
Sussex, BN7 2NJ.
Telephone: 01273 480208,
E-mail: auctions@wallisand wallis.co.uk
Abbreviations: **M** = Mint, **GC** = Good
Condition, **QGC** = Quite Good Condition,
**VGC** = Very Good Condition,
**BMW** = Box has minor wear.

**DINKY TOYS CARS**
**39b Oldsmobile.**
Light Grey, Black hubs, VGC minor chipping...**£70**

**39f Studebaker.**
Light Grey, Black hubs, VGC - Mint .................**£70**
**62p Ensign Airliner.** Silver, 'G-ADSV', 'Explorer',
boxed, VGC (fatigued) ........................................**£100**
**63k The King's Aeroplane.** Silver/Red/Blue
livery, 'G-AEXX' boxed, VGC ........................**£220**
**106 Austin Atlantic.**
Black body, red interior, boxed, VGC ...............**£70**
**151 Triumph 1800.**
Light Blue body and hubs, boxed, VGC-M .......**£70**
**161 Austin Somerset.** Red body and hubs,
boxed, VGC (1 minor chip)................................**£75**
**162 Ford Zephyr.**
Cream/Dark Green, Cream hubs, boxed, VGC ..**£60**
**163 Bristol 450 Sports.** Dark Green,
Mid Green hubs, boxed, vehicle Mint.............**£105**
**167 AC Aceca.** Cream/Dark Brown,
Cream hubs, Mint in creased box ....................**£65**
**182 Porsche 356A.** Cream, spun hubs,
VGC - M in late lighter yellow box ..................**£90**
**252 Refuse Wagon.** Fawn body,
Green shutters, Red hubs, boxed, Mint ..........**£100**
**281 Luxury Coach.** Cream body/hubs,
Orange flashes, M, Box has minor wear .........**£100**
**280 Observation Coach.**
Grey body, Red flashes, Boxed, VGC ...............**£90**
**290 AEC DD Bus.**
Green/Cream, 'Dunlop', Boxed Mint................**£120**
**411 Bedford Truck.**
Mid Green, Boxed, VGC - Mint.......................**£100**
**417 Leyland Comet.** Blue/Yellow, Red hubs,
Box has age wear, model VGC ..........................**£70**
**450 Bedford TK Van.**
'Castrol', box well worn, model VGC .............**£110**
**501 Foden Diesel Wagon.** 1st Type,
Red with Fawn back, boxed, C-GC ..................**£300**
**513 Guy Flat Truck.**
Dark Green/Mid Green, VGC unboxed.............**£110**
**514 Guy Van. 'Lyons Tea',**
VGC minor chipping, boxed ...........................**£680**
**521 Bedford Lorry.** Red with black wings
and hubs, VGC, M in Buff box .......................**£250**
**561 Bulldozer.** Red, dark green tracks,
boxed, Mint with 'Tested' label.......................**£140**
**591 AEC Tanker.**
'Shell Chemicals Ltd', Blue box, GC .................**£75**
**698 Military Gift Set.**
As per Catalogue, boxed in VGC ....................**£180**
**699 Military Gift Set.**
As per Catalogue, some wear damage.............**£230**
**706 Vickers Viscount.** Blue/White 'Air France',
'F-BGNL', VGC, boxed ......................................**£70**
**718 Hurricane Mk.II.**
As per Catalogue, VGC, boxed ........................**£80**
**905 Foden Flat Truck with Chains.** With
original chains, all Maroon, Mint, boxed.........**£320**
**908 Mighty Antar with Transformer.**
As catalogue, GC-VGC, box minor wear........**£440**
**934 Leyland Truck.** 1st issue as per
Catalogue, boxed, minor wear, VGC ...............**£140**
**943 Leyland Tanker 'Esso'.** As Catalogue
with Red plastic hubs, VGC, boxed .................**£240**
**944 Leyland Octopus Tanker 'Shell-BP',**
1st issue as per Catalogue, boxed, VGC ..........**£180**

**FRENCH DINKY TOYS**
**24H Mercedes 109SC.**
Cream/Black, plated hubs, boxed, VGC ............**£95**
**24M VW Karmann Ghia.**
Red/Black, plated hubs, Mint boxed ...............**£110**
**35A Citroën Breakdown.**
'Dinky Service', Red, Black jib, GC unboxed...**£75**
**531 Fiat 1200 Grand Vue.**
Metallic Bronze/Cream, Boxed, VGC................**£85**
**548 Fiat 1800 Familliale.**
Lilac/Black, plated spun wheels, Mint, boxed ...**£95**
**804 Nord 2501 Aircraft.**
Military Metallic Grey, VGC-Mint, boxed.......**£130**
**881 'Pinder' Circus Truck and Trailer.**
As Catalogue listing. Models very good condition
with minor chip, box has some wear................**£400**

# French Meccano Dinky Toys

The history of French Meccano Dinky Toys mirrors that of the Liverpool parent company. The Meccano France subsidiary was set up by Frank Hornby at Rue Ambroise Thomas in Paris in 1912, primarily to import British-made Meccano outfits and components. Having successfully marketed Meccano in France the obvious next step was to manufacture it there and in 1921 a factory was duly established at Rue Rébéval in Paris. This was initially used as offices and warehousing until 1924 when French-made Meccano became available, the Meccano Guild having been created a year before.

Production on French soil proved even more successful and a major new factory was soon required. Building of the famous plant at Bobigny was started in 1929. In 1931, the year in which Frank Hornby became MP for Everton, French Hornby 'Lead Models' nos. 1, 2 and 3 were introduced, followed by 'Miniature Models' nos. 4 and 10 in 1932. 'Modelled Miniatures' made their appearance in England in these years. Early in 1934 'Hornby Modelled Miniatures' were announced in France. Originally intended to extend the growing range of Hornby railway accessories, they were very briefly renamed 'Meccano Miniatures'. Before the year was out they had acquired the name 'Dinky Toys' in both countries. In the same year the Bobigny factory took over all French Meccano production while the Rue Rébéval premises reverted to offices and warehousing.

In 1935, 'Dolly Varden' dolls house furniture was introduced in England and the following year in France. Military vehicles became part of the Dinky range in Britain in 1937 but plans to introduce models of this type in France came to nothing before the War. Some of the English model tanks and guns were sent there between 1938 and 1940 along with some aircraft and ships. A very small part of French production was imported into the Britain in the late 1930s and most of their references were given a 'z' suffix.

During the late pre-war period the names were removed from aircraft dies and the models were given vague generic titles such as 'Long Range Bomber' and 'Medium Bomber'. Some planes like the Gloster Gladiator had no name at all and models of ships were given similar anonymity. It has been said that this was done for the cause of national security – to prevent Nazi intelligence from identifying the actual planes and ships by looking at the toys!

Among resources eagerly seized by the occupying German forces was naturally any factory that could turn instantly to the production of armaments. The French Meccano factory was thus commandeered in 1940 and required to produce various industrial items to satisfy the German war effort and even some toys to be sold under the Märklin name in German-occupied parts of the Continent. Production of conventional Meccano products was of course prohibited. There were very many shortages by the time peace was declared, rubber being a particular problem in France from 1940 since Nazi activities had completely cut off supplies.

When Meccano haltingly returned to production in 1946, Dinky Toys tyres were noticeable by their absence. The metal wheel castings first used in 1940 continued to be fitted right up to the beginning of 1950. Even the 49 series Petrol Pumps had to be sold without hoses for a while! One of the most common vehicles on British and Continental roads during and after the War was the US Army Jeep. Thus in 1946 the 153a Jeep was introduced in England and the 24-M in France.

Any study of the history of Dinky Toys needs documentation from contemporary Meccano sources. Much of the required information is to be found in various catalogues and Meccano Magazines of the period but is not always reliable as an indicator of the date of introduction of models. Advertising did not always coincide with supply of models and distribution was not always even across the country. Most catalogues were generally accurate but occasionally announcements of forthcoming additions to the range could be just wishful thinking or proclamation of intent rather than actual production. Illustrations in early catalogues sometimes present problems with inaccurate line drawings and heavily retouched photographs. French catalogues suffered additional problems in having photos or drawings of English prototypes.

Many French catalogues were printed in England and some were actually English catalogues with a small amount of additional text in French plus a French currency price list. There is a marked similarity between French and English numbering systems and between actual castings, particularly before the War. However, it is important to remember that French castings are different from similar English ones, and come from French dies. All French Dinky Toys carry specific information either cast-in or stamped on a tinplate base as to the country of manufacture or assembly of the item.

In 1951, the Rue Rébéval factory closed and all French production was centralised at Bobigny. The French Meccano Magazine re-appeared in 1953 and 24-U Simca and 25-B Peugeot Van were introduced in their own individual yellow boxes. The first French Dinky Supertoy was issued in 1955.

Promotional opportunities were always being sought by Meccano and the idea of a society for young drivers of toy vehicles was welcomed by Roland Hornby who initiated the French Dinky Toys Club in 1957. 1960 saw the introduction of the French version of 'Dublo' trains ('Hornby ACHO'), production of which continued until 1974. French Hornby 'O' gauge train manufacture came to an end in 1963.

The early 1960s was a time of diversification for Meccano in both England and France with Scalextric and other toys being added to the range of products. In a decade of changing fortunes they continued to design and manufacture an interesting range of Dinky Toys. In 1970 production was moved to a factory at Calais, partly to help relieve the industrial pressure in the Paris area and also to benefit from access to a major port. To cut costs in an increasingly difficult economic climate, manufacture of French Dinky cars was undertaken by Auto-Pilen of Spain in 1975. Other production continued at Calais until 1978 when all remaining French Dinky Toys manufacturing rights were signed over to the Spanish company.

Over the years, French and English Dinkies have had remarkable similarities and some quite paradoxical differences, reflecting the independence of the two companies. 'Speedwheels', for instance, were deemed essential in England to compete with Corgi's WhizzWheels and Lesney Superfast, while in France the need seems not to have been at all apparent. The range of ship models was quite extensive in England but very limited in France. The understandable dominance of French cars in the range resulted in a stream of taxi models in France while motorcycles were completely ignored after the Triporteur was withdrawn. The excellent French idea of a diamond shaped 'viewport' in the famous yellow boxes was restricted to that country and not tried in England. We have no 'Novelty' section in the French Dinky listings since the only Dinkys that would come under that heading would be imported British ones! Indeed, the only film or television-related item to have originated in France is 1406 Michel Tanguy's Renault 4L Sinpar from the French TV series 'Les Chevaliers du Ciel'.

Some interesting models exist as accessories, particularly among the railway items. All the French castings of figures differ from English ones and have distinctly French characteristics, the 'Normandy' farmer and his French countrywoman spouse, the female railway crossing keeper, and the railway cook with his poultry dish are particularly pleasing. Road signs provide another area of interest, some of the later French versions being only available as a free addition with certain models and not sold individually.

# Cars - identification and casting differences

Although French and English reference numbers (particularly pre-war) are strikingly similar, it is very important to treat them as completely different systems in order to avoid confusion. The majority of French castings are different, as are the tyres. Surprisingly, small detail differences occur, as with steering wheels for instance. Post-war French-made open sports cars such as 22-A Maserati and 546 Austin-Healey have cast steering wheels with three spokes while those fitted to English made sports cars have four spokes. Many pre-war French made tyres have 'DUNLOP' moulded into the side-wall; post-war Spanish produced tyres similarly display the name 'PIRELLI'.

The 23b Streamlined Racing Car as made and sold in England from 1935 was based on a French Hotchkiss racing car. Unlike the English version, there were two

French castings with the 23b reference. One is obviously the Hotchkiss (introduced in France in 1940). The other (pre-war) one is said by some to be modelled on a Renault Nervasport or possibly a Delahaye record car.

The 23 Racing Car is generally considered to have been inspired by the MG Magic Midget though it was never actually named as such by Meccano. Many modifications were made to the actual car in the 1930s in attempts to break various endurance and speed records, and both English and French models mirrored these changes during their production. Racing numbers on the French 23 and 23a models were never contained within a circle and were initially stencilled, later mask-sprayed. All the French 23 series castings have either 'Made in France' or 'Fab. en France' cast underneath and also have a number of other differences from the English castings.

The first French Dinky Toys car model to be sold in its own box was the 24-U Simca Aronde in 1953. Many of the French boxes had a 'viewport' or aperture (usually diamond shaped) to allow a glimpse of the model. This enabled dealers and potential buyers to establish the colour of the model without the need to open the box. At the same time it saved the cost of printing a matching colour spot on the outside.

From 1969 a free 595 Traffic Sign was included as an additional attraction with certain models and these are noted in the listings that follow. More than twenty different plastic signs were made (see the 'Accessories' listing for details). They were not sold individually, but selections were available in Gift Sets 592 and 593.

PHOTO: CHRISTIE'S

---

**MARKET PRICE RANGE**
Please note that the prices shown refer to pristine models
and boxes. Items failing to match this standard will sell for less.
Note also that boxes must still contain all their original packing pieces and additional contents where appropriate.

| Model and details | MPR | | Model and details | MPR | | Model and details | MPR |
|---|---|---|---|---|---|---|---|

**22a** **Roadster Sports**
1933-37 (scale 1:53)
Lead two-seater open body, lead wheels.
- Grey body / Blue wings .................. **£500-750**
- Blue body / Yellow wings .............. **£500-750**
- Silver body / Red wings ................. **£500-750**
- Green body / Yellow wings ............ **£500-750**
- Cream body / Red wings ................ **£500-750**
- Yellow body / Black wings ............ **£500-750**

**22-A** **Maserati Sport 2000**
1958-58 (renumbered in 1958 to 505) (1:43)
- Dark red body, Tan seats, plated
convex hubs, white driver. Early
bases are matt; later ones shiny ....... **£300-350**
1958-59
- Dark red body, dark red seats,
plated convex hubs, white driver ...... **£90-110**
- Same, but bright red body and seats .. **£90-110**

**22b** **Sports Coupé**
1934-37 (scale 1:53)
Lead two-seater closed body, lead wheels.
- Cream body with black wings ......... **£500-750**
- Blue body with red wings .............. **£500-750**
- Red body with blue wings .............. **£500-750**
- Green body with yellow wings ...... **£500-750**
- Grey body with green wings .......... **£500-750**
- Buff body, Black wings and hubs ... **£500-750**

**22c** **Sports Roadster**
1934-37
- As 22a, but with white rubber tyres
on smooth silvered lead hubs .......... **£500-750**

**22d** **Sports Coupé**
1934-37
- As 22b, but with white rubber tyres
on smooth silvered lead hubs .......... **£500-750**

**23** **Racing Car**
1933-35 (scale 1:53)
- Lead body with contrasting colour flash
over main colour, smooth lead hubs,
'DUNLOP' tyres coloured to match
body flash. Indication of driver,
4 exhaust stubs, no exhaust pipe.
- Orange (white, blue or green flash) **£150-200**
- Cream (blue, green or red flash) ..... **£150-200**
- Blue (with silver or white flash) ..... **£150-200**
- Yellow (with blue flash) ................. **£150-200**
1934-36
Lead body with contrasting colour flash,
smooth lead hubs, black or white or
coloured tyres matching colour flash.
Helmet detail, 4 exhaust stubs, no pipe.
- Blue (white flash) .......................... **£150-200**
- Green (orange flash) ...................... **£150-200**
- White (blue flash) .......................... **£150-200**
- Silver (blue flash) .......................... **£150-200**
- Silver (red flash) ........................... **£150-200**
- Cream (blue flash) ......................... **£150-200**
- Cream (green flash) ....................... **£150-200**
- Cream (red flash) ........................... **£150-200**

**23a** **Racing Car**
1936-37
Diecast body and smooth hubs; black,
white or coloured 'DUNLOP' tyres that
match colour flash. No driver,
4 exhaust stubs, no exhaust pipe.
- Blue (white flash) .......................... **£200-250**
- Green (orange flash) ...................... **£200-250**
- White (blue flash) .......................... **£200-250**
- Silver (blue flash) .......................... **£200-250**
- Silver (red flash) ........................... **£200-250**
- Cream (blue flash) ......................... **£200-250**
- Cream (green flash) ....................... **£200-250**
- Cream (red flash) ........................... **£200-250**

1937-39
Diecast body and smooth hubs; black,
white or coloured 'DUNLOP' tyres that
match colour flash. Six branch exhaust
pipe, driver helmet detail, 90mm.
Racing numbers '1' or '12'.
- Blue (silver flash) .......................... **£200-250**
- Blue (white flash) .......................... **£200-250**
- Orange (green flash) ...................... **£200-250**
- Orange (blue flash) ........................ **£200-250**
- Yellow (blue flash) ........................ **£200-250**
- Cream (blue flash) ......................... **£200-250**
- Cream (green flash) ....................... **£200-250**
- Cream (red flash) ........................... **£200-250**
1939-40
As previous model but smooth diecast
hubs in assorted colours, black or white
tyres, RNs '1' or '12'.
- Blue (silver flash) .......................... **£200-250**
- Blue (white flash) .......................... **£200-250**
- Orange (green flash) ...................... **£200-250**
- Orange (blue flash) ........................ **£200-250**
- Yellow (blue flash) ........................ **£200-250**
- Cream (blue flash) ......................... **£200-250**
- Cream (green flash) ....................... **£200-250**
- Cream (red flash) ........................... **£200-250**
1940-40
As 1937-39 model but with
unpainted diecast wheels.
- Blue (silver flash) .......................... **£200-250**
- Blue (white flash) .......................... **£200-250**
- Orange (green flash) ...................... **£200-250**
- Orange (blue flash) ........................ **£200-250**
- Yellow (blue flash) ........................ **£200-250**
- Cream (blue flash) ......................... **£200-250**
- Cream (green flash) ....................... **£200-250**
- Cream (red flash) ........................... **£200-250**

**23b** **Streamlined Racing Car**
1935-37 (scale 1:53)
Diecast body, plated smooth hubs,
'DUNLOP' tyres in the colour of the
body flash.
- Blue (red flash, '1') ....................... **£200-250**
- Yellow (red flash, '2') .................... **£200-250**
- Orange (blue flash, '3') .................. **£200-250**
- Cream (blue flash '4') .................... **£200-250**
- White (green flash '5') ................... **£200-250**
- Red (green flash, '6') ..................... **£200-250**
1937-40
Diecast body, plated or black smooth
hubs, white 'DUNLOP' tyres.
- Blue (red flash, '1') ....................... **£200-250**
- Blue (white flash, '11' or '12') ....... **£200-250**
- Red (green flash, '6') ..................... **£200-250**
- Red (silver flash, '2') .................... **£200-250**
- Yellow (red flash, '2') .................... **£200-250**
- Cream (blue flash, '4') ................... **£200-250**
- White (green flash, '5') .................. **£200-250**
- Green (white flash, '7' or '8') ........ **£200-250**
- Green (silver flash, '7' or '8') ........ **£200-250**
- Orange (green flash, '9' or '10') ..... **£200-250**
- Orange (blue flash, '3') .................. **£200-250**
1940-40
As previous model but with cast
metal wheels (black or unpainted) .. **£200-250**
**NB** Many of the pre-war 23b models listed
left the factory without having the racing
numbers applied. The rarity levels for these
is much the same as the numbered ones,
consequently prices are similar.
1949-49
- Re-issue of 1940 model with cast
metal wheels (black or unpainted) .. **£130-180**
1949-49
As 1939 issue but cream painted
smooth hubs, black tyres.
- Red body, silver flash, racing numbers
'1' to '6' on cream background ........ **£110-140**

1952-52
- Brief re-issue of previous model ...... **£110-140**

**23b** **Hotchkiss Racing Car**
1940-40
- Red (silver flash, RNs '1' to '6'),
unpainted mazak wheels, 1:53. ....... **£200-250**
1948-49
- As previous model but with
painted mazak wheels ..................... **£200-250**
1950-51
- Same, but cream painted convex
hubs, black tyres ............................ **£100-150**

**23c** **Mercedes-Benz W154**
1949-49 (scale 1:43)
- Silver, (RNs '1' to '6'), driver,
painted or unpainted metal wheels
(2 sizes known) ............................... **£90-120**
1949-51
- As previous model but black or red
painted convex hubs, black tyres .... **£350-450**

**23d** **Auto-Union Record Car**
1950-? (scale 1:43)
- Light green body, filler cap on some,
RNs '1' to '6', red convex hubs,
black tyres ...................................... **£90-120**
- Same model but with bright green
convex hubs, black tyres, '2' ..... **£3,000-4,000**
**NB** Unlike the UK version, the
rear axle ends are not visible.

**23-H** **Talbot-Lago GP Car**
1953-54 (scale 1:43)
- Blue, (RN's '1' to '6' in white paint),
driver cast in, blue convex hubs,
ribbed tyres ..................................... **£100-125**
1954-55
- Same but numbers '1' to '6' on
yellow transfers .............................. **£100-125**
1955-59 (renumbered in 1959 to 510)
- Blue, (RNs '1' to '6' and '22' to
'27' on yellow transfers),
plated convex hubs .......................... **£100-125**

**23-J** **Ferrari GP Car**
1956-56 (scale 1:43)
- Red, (RN's '1' to '6'), smooth grille,
driver, plated convex hubs .............. **£120-150**
1957-59 (renumbered in 1959 to 511)
- Dark red body (RNs '1' to '6' and
'33' to '38', squared grille,
plated convex hubs .......................... **£150-200**

**24-A** **Chrysler New Yorker**
1956-57 (scale 1:48)
'CHRYSLER NEW YORKER' on base
and on box. All have plated convex hubs.
- Lemon yellow body, green seats ..... **£125-150**
- Red body, ivory seats ..................... **£120-140**
1957-60 (renumbered in 1960 as 520)
'CHRYSLER NEW YORKER 1955'
on base and on box. All have plated
convex hubs.
- Lemon Yellow body, green seats ..... **£300-400**
- Mustard Yellow body, green seats ... **£300-400**
- Red (or orange-red), ivory seats ...... **£300-400**
- Light met. Blue body, ivory seats .... **£300-400**
- Light met. Blue, pale grey seats ..... **£300-400**

**24b** **Limousine**
1934-35 (scale 1:53)
4 doors cast-in, horizontal bonnet
louvres (aligned), large headlights,
no sidelights, black or white
'DUNLOP' tyres on smooth hubs.
- Yellow body (with black wings) ..... **£300-400**
- Yellow body (with red wings) ........ **£300-400**

- Green body (with blue wings)......... **£300-400**
1936-39
4 doors cast-in, horizontal bonnet louvres (stepped), medium or small headlights, sidelights on wings, black or white 'DUNLOP' tyres on smooth hubs.
- Green body (with red wings)........... **£300-400**
- Grey body (with blue wings).......... **£300-400**
1940-48
As previous model but unpainted mazak wheels.
- Grey body (red wings)................... **£300-400**
- Yellow body (red wings) ................ **£300-400**
- Red body (black wings).................. **£300-400**
- Blue body (black wings) ................ **£300-400**
- Green body (black wings) .............. **£300-400**

### 24-B  Peugeot 403 8cv
1956-58  (scale 1:43)
No window glazing, base without towing notch, plated convex hubs, smooth white tyres.
- Blue body........................... **£80-100**
- Black body........................... **£80-100**
1958-59 (renumbered in 1959 to 521)
Base has towing notch, plated convex hubs, smooth white tyres.
- Blue body........................... **£100-120**
- Light grey body .............................. **£100-120**
- Pale Yellow body ........................... **£150-200**

### 24-C  Citroën DS19
1956-58  (scale 1:43)
No window glazing, plated convex hubs, smooth white tyres.
- Green body with white roof ............**£110-130**
- Green body with pale grey roof .......**£110-130**
- Ivory body, very dark purple roof ....**£110-130**

### 24-CP Citroën DS19
1958-59  (renumbered in 1959 to 522)
As 24-C but with window glazing. In 24-C box with '24CP' sticker, later in own box.
- Green body (with white grey roof) . **£200-250**
- Green body (with pale grey roof).... **£200-250**
- Ivory body (very dark purple roof) . **£200-250**
- Dark orange body (cream roof)....... **£200-250**
- Brown body (cream roof)............... **£200-250**
- Yellow body, grey roof.................. **£300-350**

### 24d  Vogue Saloon
1934-35  (scale 1:53)
Spare wheel in wing, large headlights, no sidelights, smooth mazak hubs, black or white 'DUNLOP' tyres.
- Blue body (with black wings) ........ **£300-400**
- Green body (with red wings).......... **£300-400**
1936-37
Spare wheel in wing, medium headlights, sidelights on wings, smooth mazak hubs, black or white 'DUNLOP' tyres.
- Red body (black wings)................... **£300-400**
- Blue body (yellow wings) ............... **£300-400**
- Blue body (black wings) ................ **£300-400**
- Green body (yellow wings) ............ **£300-400**
1938-39
No spare wheel, small headlights, sidelights on wings, smooth mazak hubs, black or white 'DUNLOP' tyres.
- Grey body (with black wings)........ **£300-400**
- Green body (with maroon wings) ... **£300-400**
1940-48
No spare wheel, medium or small headlights, sidelights on wings, painted mazak wheels.
- Yellow body (red wings) ................ **£300-400**
- Grey body (red wings)................... **£300-400**
- Red body (black wings).................. **£300-400**
- Blue body (black wings) ............... **£300-400**

### 24-D  Plymouth Belvedere
1957-59 (renumbered in 1959 to 523) (1:48)
Plated convex hubs.
Model picture on some boxes.
- Green body, black roof and side flash.................... **£100-120**
- Tan body, brown roof / side flash.....**£110-135**
- Grey body, Red roof and side flash... **£80-100**
- White body, blue roof / side flash ... **£275-325**
- White body, blue roof / side flash ... **£350-400**
- Pink body, Pale Maroon roof and side flash.................... **£375-450**

### 24e  Aerodynamic Saloon Car
1934-35  (scale 1:53)
Large headlights, no sidelights, smooth hubs, black or white 'DUNLOP' tyres.
- Green body, blue wings .................. **£200-250**
- Green body, red wings.................... **£200-250**
1936-39
Medium or small headlamps, sidelights in wings, smooth mazak hubs, black or white 'DUNLOP' tyres.
- Blue body (with black wings) ........ **£200-250**
- Red body (with black wings) .......... **£200-250**
- Red body (with yellow wings) ........ **£200-250**
1940-48
Medium or small headlamps, sidelights in wings, cast metal wheels.
- Blue body (black wings) ................ **£200-250**
- Green body (black wings) .............. **£200-250**
- Red body (black wings) ................. **£200-250**
- Yellow body (red wings) ................ **£200-250**

### 24-E  Renault Dauphine
1957-59 (renumbered in 1959 to 524) (1:43)
No window glazing, plated convex hubs, smooth black tyres.
- Olive-green body ............................ **£150-200**
- Brick-red body................................ **£150-200**
- Raspberry-red body ........................ **£120-150**
- Bright Blue body ............................ **£400-500**
- Turqoise body ................................ **£150-200**

### 24f  Sportsman's Coupé
1934-35  (scale 1:53)
Two-door body with spare wheel in wing, large headlights, no sidelights, smooth mazak hubs, black or white 'DUNLOP' tyres.
- Green body (with yellow wings).... **£300-400**
- Blue body (with black wings) ........ **£300-400**
1936-37
Two-door body with spare wheel in wing, medium headlights, sidelights on wings, smooth mazak hubs, black or white 'DUNLOP' tyres.
- Blue body (black wings) ................ **£300-400**
- Blue body (yellow wings) .............. **£300-400**
- Green body (yellow wings) ............ **£300-400**
- Red body (black wings)................... **£300-400**
1938-39
Two-door body, no spare wheel, small headlights, sidelights on wings, smooth hubs, black or white 'DUNLOP' tyres.
- Red body (black wings)................... **£300-400**
- Yellow body (black wings)............. **£300-400**
- Yellow body (red wings) ................ **£300-400**
- Blue body (maroon wings) ............. **£300-400**
- Cream body (blue wings) ............... **£300-400**
1940-40
Two-door body, no spare wheel, medium or small headlights, sidelights on wings, painted mazak wheels.
- Red body (black wings)................... **£300-400**
- Blue (black wings).......................... **£300-400**
- Green (black wings) ....................... **£300-400**
- Yellow body (red wings) ................ **£300-400**
1947-48
Re-issue of 1940 versions (with cast metal wheels):
- Red body, black wings ................... **£300-400**
- Blue body, black wings .................. **£300-400**

- Green black wings ............................ **£300-400**
- Yellow body, black wings................ **£300-400**

### 24-F  Peugeot 403-U Familiale
1958-59 (renumbered in 1959 to 525) (1:43)
- Sky Blue body, no windows, plated convex hubs .......................... **£100-120**
1958
- Dark red body (no windows). Only a few made as gifts for 1958 visitors to Meccano factory ....... **£2,000-3,000**

### 24g  4-seat Sports Car
1934-35  (scale 1:53)
Spare wheel, open windscreen, large headlights, no sidelights, black or white 'DUNLOP' tyres.
- Blue body (with black wings) ......... **£300-400**
- Green body (with red wings).......... **£300-400**
1936-37
Spare wheel, solid windscreen, medium headlights, sidelights in wings, black or white 'DUNLOP' tyres.
- Yellow body (with red wings) ........ **£300-400**
- Grey body (with blue wings) .......... **£300-400**
1938-39
Spare cast-in, solid windscreen, small headlights, sidelights in wings, black or white 'DUNLOP' tyres.
- Green body, red wings ..................... **£300-400**
- Cream body, red wings ................... **£300-400**
1940-40
Spare wheel cast-in, solid windscreen, medium or small headlights, sidelights in wings, unpainted mazak wheels.
- Grey body (red wings).................... **£200-300**
- Yellow body (red wings) ................ **£200-300**
- Red body (black wings).................. **£200-300**
1947-48
Re-issue of 1940 versions (unpainted mazak wheels).
- Grey body (red wings).................... **£200-300**
- Yellow body (red wings) ................ **£200-300**
- Red body (black wings).................. **£200-300**

### 24h  2-seat Sports Car
1934-35  (scale 1:53)
Spare wheel, open windscreen, large headlights, no sidelights, black or white 'DUNLOP' tyres.
- Green body (blue wings) ................ **£300-400**
- Black body, (blue wings)................ **£300-400**
- Black body, (red wings) ................. **£300-400**
- Red body (black wings).................. **£300-400**
1936-37
Spare wheel, solid windscreen, medium headlights, sidelights in wings, black or white 'DUNLOP' tyres.
- Yellow body (black wings)............. **£300-400**
- Blue or green body (red wings)....... **£300-400**
1938-39
Spare cast-in, solid windscreen, small headlights, sidelights in wings, black or white 'DUNLOP' tyres.
- Green body (red wings).................. **£300-400**
- Red or body (black wings) ............. **£300-400**
- Yellow body (black wings)............. **£300-400**
1940-40
Spare cast-in, solid windscreen, medium or small headlights, sidelights in wings, unpainted mazak wheels.
- Cream body (red wings).................. **£200-300**
- Yellow body (red wings) ................ **£200-300**
- Green body (black wings) .............. **£200-300**
- Red body (black wings).................. **£200-300**
1947-48
Re-issue of 1940 versions with unpainted mazak wheels.
- Cream body (with red wings).......... **£200-300**
- Yellow body (with red wings) ........ **£200-300**
- Green body (with black wings) ...... **£200-300**
- Red body (with black wings) ......... **£200-300**

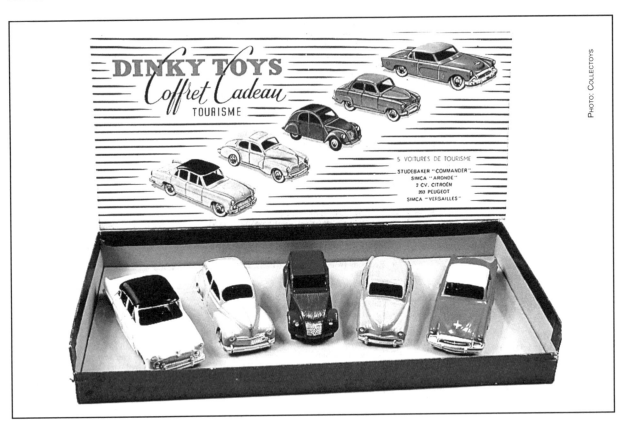

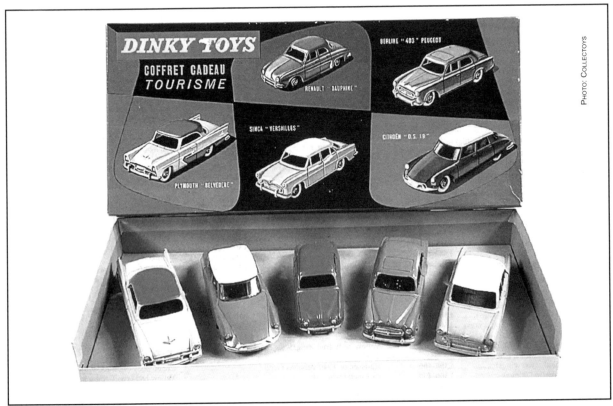

**24-H  Mercedes-Benz 190sl**
1958-59  (<u>renumbered in 1959 to 526</u>) (1:43)
- Cream body (various shades), black
  hard-top. Picture on some boxes ..... **£100-120**
- Silver body, Black roof,
  plated convex hubs .......................... **£140-160**

**24-J  Alfa-Romeo 1900 Sprint**
1959-59  (<u>renumbered in 1959 to 527</u>) (1:43)
- Red body, windows, plated convex
  hubs, smooth black tyres .................. **£80-100**
- Blue body, windows, plated convex
  hubs, smooth black tyres .................. **£80-100**

**24k  Peugeot 402**
1939-40  (scale 1:53)
No baseplate (and no base retainers cast
inside body), black or white 'DUNLOP'
tyres on smooth painted mazak hubs.
- Maroon body ................................. **£300-400**
- Blue body ...................................... **£300-400**
- Light blue body ............................. **£300-400**
- Red body ....................................... **£300-400**
- Yellow body .................................. **£300-400**
1947-48
No baseplate (and no retainers cast
inside), unpainted mazak wheels.
- Maroon body ................................. **£500-750**
- Blue body ...................................... **£500-750**
- Light Blue body ............................. **£500-750**
- Red body ....................................... **£500-750**
- Yellow body .................................. **£500-750**
1948-48
With tinplate base/front bumper (and
with base retainers cast inside body),
unpainted mazak wheels.
- Maroon body ................................. **£500-750**
- Blue body ...................................... **£500-750**
- Light Blue body ............................. **£500-750**
- Red body ....................................... **£500-750**
- Yellow body .................................. **£500-750**

**24-K  Simca Vedette Chambord**
1959-59  (<u>renumbered in 1959 to 528</u>) (1:43)
- Ivory/red body, plated convex hubs **£150-200**
- Light green/dark green body .......... **£130-150**

**24 l  Peugeot 402 Taxi**
1939-40  (all have a tinplate taxi-meter)
- Royal Blue/Yellow, smooth cast
  hubs, no base ................................. **£500-700**
- Maroon/Cream, smooth cast hubs,
  no base .......................................... **£500-700**
1947-48
- Royal Blue/Yellow, metal wheels,
  no base .......................................... **£500-700**
- Maroon/Cream, metal wheels,
  no base .......................................... **£500-700**
1948-48
- Royal Blue/Yellow, metal wheels,
  with base ....................................... **£500-700**
- Maroon/Cream, metal wheels,
  with base ....................................... **£500-700**

**24-L  Vespa 400 2cv**
1959-59  (<u>renumbered in 1959 to 529</u>) (1:43)
- Blue/Grey or Orange/Grey,
  plated convex hubs, '24L' on box ....... **£65-75**

**24m  Military Jeep**
1946-48  (scale 1:43)
- US Military olive-drab body and khaki
  painted mazak wheels (mounted inside-out
  for effect), white star on bonnet, cast star
  at rear, tinplate windscreen frame (bonnet
  castings exist with and without frame
  supports), wire steering wheel......... **£700-900**
NB  24m was the first new French made
Dinky Toys model to appear after the war.
They were supplied to shops in trade boxes
of twelve units. A trailer was designed to

complement the Military Jeep but was
never produced, nor did 24m ever
acquire a towing hook.

**24m  Civilian Jeep**
1948-49
Castings as military version, usually
with unpainted wheels (a few painted).
- Red body.................................... **£400-500**
- Green body ................................ **£400-500**
- Blue body................................... **£400-500**
- Orange body .............................. **£400-500**
- Sand body .................................. **£400-500**
- Yellow body ............................... **£400-500**
- Metallic Grey body....................... **£400-500**
- Metallic Gold body....................... **£400-500**

**24-M  VW Karmann-Ghia**
1959-59  (<u>renumbered in 1959 to 530</u>) (1:43)
- Black/Red, plated convex hubs ........ **£90-120**

**24-N  Citroën 11BL**
1949-58  (scale 1:43)
<u>1st version</u>: Small rear window, small
lettering on base, widely spaced grille
bars, spare wheel cover, tinplate front
bumper, no direction indicators,
smooth roof interior.
<u>2nd version</u>: With 16mm wide rear window,
small lettering on base, boot replaces spare
wheel cover, shallow rear axle supports, with
direction indicators, smooth roof interior.
<u>3rd version</u>: With 17mm wide rear window,
large lettering on base, boot replaces spare
wheel cover, deep rear axle supports, cast
front bumper, with direction indicators,
hatched roof interior.
1949-49
- Navy blue, black mazak wheels ...... **£750-900**
1950-51
As first version but the front wheel arch
casting extends below the baseplate.
- Metallic gold body, black convex
  hubs, black tyres ......................... **£500-700**
- Metallic grey body and red convex
  hubs, black tyres ......................... **£450-650**
- Black body and yellow convex
  hubs, black tyres .......................... **£300-400**
1951-52
As first version but with large rear window.
- Black body, yellow or cream
  hubs, black tyres .......................... **£300-400**
1953-55
Integral front bumper, big or small rear
window, rounded boot, narrow grooves
on grille, small print on base, straight
windscreen base, smooth inside roof.
- Black body, cream convex hubs,
  black tyres.................................... **£130-160**
1955-57
As 1953-55 model but large print and '24N'
on base. Inside of roof is cross-hatched.
- Black body, cream convex hubs ...... **£100-125**
- Light grey, yellow convex hubs ...... **£120-160**
1957-58
As 1953-55 model but large print and '24N'
on base, arched base to windscreen.
- Black body (cream convex hubs).... **£100-125**
- Light Grey body and convex hubs .. **£100-125**
1958-58
As previous but with plated convex
hubs, white tyres.
- Black body.................................. **£100-125**
- Light grey body, grey hubs............. **£120-140**
NB  24-N Citroën models were all
supplied to shops in grey trade boxes
each containing six models.

**24-N  Fiat 1200 Grand Vue**
Announced only in the 1959 Swiss
catalogue but not made as 24-N.
<u>Renumbered and produced as 531</u>.

**24-O  Studebaker State Commander**
1949-49  (scale 1:48)
Casting as the English 39f model but
the black tinplate base is marked
'Fabriqué en France'.
- Cream body,
  painted mazak wheels................... **£800-1,100**
- Red body, painted mazak wheels . **£800-1,100**
- Metallic blue-green body,
  painted mazak wheels................... **£800-1,100**
1950-50
- Cream body, red convex hubs,
  black tyres.................................... **£400-600**
- Metallic blue-green, red convex
  hubs, black tyres .......................... **£400-600**
- Cream or Red body, Black hubs...... **£175-250**
NB  24-O Studebaker was supplied to
shops in trade boxes of six units.

**24-P  Packard Super 8 Limousine**
1949-49  (scale 1:48)
Casting as English 39a but with black
tinplate base marked 'Fabriqué en France'.
Painted convex hubs.
- Blue body................................... **£750-850**
- Turqoise body.............................. **£750-850**
- Metallic Gold body....................... **£750-850**
NB  24-P Packard was supplied to
shops in trade boxes of six units.

**24-Q  Ford Vedette**
1950-51  (scale 1:43)
- Navy blue body and convex
  hubs, small baseprint .................... **£900-1,000**
- Metallic blue body (red hubs) ......... **£200-250**
- Grey body and hubs...................... **£200-250**
- Turquoise body and hubs .............. **£200-250**
- Sand body and hubs...................... **£200-250**
1952-55
- Metallic blue, red convex hubs,
  large base print. ........................... **£150-175**
- Turquoise body and hubs .............. **£150-175**
- Grey body and hubs...................... **£150-175**
- Sand body and hubs...................... **£150-175**
NB  24-Q was supplied to shops in
trade boxes of six units.

**24-R  Peugeot 203**
1951-52  (scale 1:43)
Small rear window, smooth inside roof,
round filler cap on right rear wing.
- Maroon body, cream convex hubs .. **£150-200**
- Metallic Gold body,
  cream convex hubs ....................... **£450-600**
- Metallic Gold body,
  red convex hubs ........................... **£450-600**
- Iridescent Violet body,
  cream convex hubs ....................... **£750-1,000**
- Grey body, grey convex hubs.... **£2,000-3,000**
- Metallic Blue body,
  cream convex hubs ....................... **£150-175**
- Metallic Green body,
  creamy-yellow convex hubs........... **£150-200**
1953-55
Small rear window, cross-hatching
inside roof, no filler cap.
- Grey body, grey convex hubs.......... **£140-160**
- Metallic Blue-Green body,
  cream convex hubs ....................... **£140-160**
- Grey-Blue body,
  cream convex hubs ....................... **£140-160**
1955-56
- Grey or Grey-Blue body, spun hubs,
  white tyres, small rear window,
  no filler cap.................................. **£100-130**
1956-57
- Grey-Blue, spun hubs, white tyres,
  big rear window, square filler cap... **£100-130**
- Pale Grey-Green, spun hubs,
  white tyres, big rear window,
  square filler cap ........................... **£100-130**

1957-59
- Same but with Lime Green body . **£800-1,000**
  1959  (renumbered in 1959 to 533)
  Promotional: Lime Green body,
  'Club Dinky Toys' ........................ **£750-1,250**
  NB  24-R was supplied to shops in
  trade boxes of six units.

**24-S  Simca 8 Sport**
  1952-54  (scale 1:43)
  1st type: thin windscreen frame,
  unpainted convex hubs, white tyres.
- Grey body, red seats, ...................... **£90-120**
- Black body, fawn seats ................... **£300-400**
- Black body, red seats ...................... **£100-130**
  1954-56
- Grey body, red seats, chrome hubs,
  white tyres ...................................... **£80-100**
- Black body, red seats ...................... **£90-120**
  1956-59
  2nd type: thick windscreen frame,
  spun hubs, white tyres.
- Grey body, red seats ...................... **£150-200**
- Black body, red seats ...................... **£200-300**
- Ivory body, red seats ...................... **£100-120**
- Duck-egg Green body, red seats..... **£125-150**
- Duck-egg Blue body, red seats........ **£125-150**
  NB  24-S was supplied to shops in
  trade boxes of six units.
  1959  (renumbered in 1959 to 534)

**24-T  Citroën 2cv** (1951-53 car)
  1952-52  (scale 1:43)
- Mid-Grey or Metallic Grey (grey hood),
  Grey-Gold hubs, one rear lamp,
  rear axle ends not rounded.
  Sold unboxed (supplied to
  shops in trade boxes of six units)...... **£90-120**
  1953-54
- Mid-Grey or Metallic Grey (gloss or matt
  grey hood), grey-gold hubs, one rear lamp,
  rounded rear axle ends. In individual box
  with '24T' and 'MECCANO' in large
  print on ends ......................................... **£80-90**
- Dark Grey body, matt grey hood,
  cream convex hubs ........................... **£80-90**
- Light Grey body, matt grey hood,
  cream convex hubs ........................... **£80-90**
  1955-59
- Light Grey body, gloss or matt grey hood,
  cream hubs, three red rear lamps, rounded
  rear axle ends. In own box with '24T' and
  'MECCANO' in small print on ends... **£75-85**
- Maroon body, matt-grey hood,
  cream convex hubs ........................... **£75-85**
- Grey-Blue body, dark grey-blue hood,
  grey concave or convex hubs .......... **£100-120**
  1959  (renumbered in 1959 to 535)

**24-U  Simca 9 Aronde**
  1953-55  (scale 1:43)
  1st type: 'stepped' grille, painted convex hubs.
- Olive Green body .......................... **£100-150**
- Light Grey-Green body ................... **£90-120**
- Mid Grey or Light Grey body ......... **£150-200**
**24-U  Simca Aronde Elysée**
  1956-57
  2nd type: 'wide' ('shark') grille, spun hubs.
- Light Grey or
  Light Grey-Green body ................... **£150-200**
- Sky Blue body ............................... **£100-150**
  1958-59
- Light Grey-Green body,
  dark green roof .............................. **£100-150**
- Blue or Sky-Blue body, white roof . **£200-250**
  NB  24-U Simca was the first French
  Dinky Toy to be supplied in its own
  individual box (in 1953).
  1959  (renumbered in 1959 to 536)

**24UT  Simca Aronde Elysée Taxi**
  1956-58  (scale 1:43)
- Red/Blue body, meter and roof sign,
  painted convex hubs, second grille ... **£90-120**
  1958-59
- Same but with plated convex hubs.... **£90-120**
  NB  24-UT was supplied to shops in
  trade boxes of six units.
  1959  (renumbered in 1959 to 537)

**24-V  Buick Roadmaster**
  1954-56  (scale 1:48)
  1st type: smooth inside roof,
  unpainted convex hubs, white tyres.
- Blue body, dark blue roof .............. **£160-200**
- Yellow body, green roof ................. **£160-200**
  1956-59
  2nd type: cross-hatched inside roof,
  plated convex hubs, white tyres.
- Blue body, dark blue or cream roof. **£160-200**
- Yellow body, green roof ................. **£160-200**
- Lemon-Yellow body, green roof.. **£750-1,000**
- Salmon-Pink body, black roof........ **£500-700**
- Ivory body, blue roof...................... **£400-600**
- Ivory/Metallic Blue body ............... **£500-600**
- Red/Yellow with blue roof ........ **£1,000-1,250**
  1959  (renumbered in 1959 to 538)

**24-X  Ford Vedette**
  1954-56  (scale 1:43)
  With or without 'Made in France,
  Imprimé en France' on individual boxes.
- Dark Blue body and convex hubs ... **£120-140**
- Pale Grey-Blue body
  and convex hubs ............................. **£100-125**
**24XT  Ford Vedette Taxi**
  1956-59
- Black body, Beige or Cream roof,
  meter, taxi sign, spun hubs ........... **£125-150**
  1959  (renumbered in 1959 to 539)
  NB  24-XT was supplied in trade boxes of
  six units. It was never individually boxed.

**24-Y  Studebaker Commander Coupé**
  1955-57  (scale 1:48)
  1st type: Base has no towing eye,
  plated convex hubs, smooth tyres.
  '24Y' on box but no illustration.
- Red body, dark cream roof .............. **£150-200**
- Light Green body, dark green roof.. **£150-200**
- Ivory body, maroon roof................. **£200-250**
- Orange body, tan roof..................... **£200-250**
  1957-58
  2nd type: Base has a towing eye, plated
  convex hubs, smooth tyres.
  '24Y' and picture of model on box.
- Red body, cream roof ..................... **£100-125**
- Light Green body, dark green roof.. **£100-125**
- Ivory body, dark red roof .............. **£300-350**
  1958-59
  3rd type: Towing eye in base, plated convex
  hubs, smooth tyres. '540-24Y' and picture
  of model on box.
- Red body, cream roof and panels .... **£300-350**
- Ivory body, maroon roof / panels .... **£300-350**
- Pale Grey body,
  maroon roof and wing panels......... **£300-350**
  1959  (renumbered in 1959 to 537)
  NB  The 1959 catalogue shows a two-tone
  blue version of 24-Y/540 but it has not
  been seen. Also, a photo exists showing
  a 24-Y prototype of the 1953-54
  Studebaker, but only the 1955 car
  was actually modelled.

**24-Z  Simca Vedette 'Versailles'**
  1956-58  (scale 1:43)
  1st type: No towing eye, plated convex
  hubs, white tyres, picture on some boxes.
- Yellow body, black roof ................. **£100-120**
- Light Blue body, white roof ........... **£100-120**

**24-Z**  1958-59
  2nd type: Base has towing eye, plated convex
  hubs, white tyres, picture on box.
- Yellow body, black roof ................. **£100-120**
- Light Blue body, white roof ........... **£100-120**
  1959  (renumbered in 1959 to 541)

**24ZT  Simca Ariane Taxi**
  1959-59  (renumbered in 1959 to 542)
- Black body, red roof, plated
  concave hubs. '542-24ZT' on box... **£120-140**

**30a  Chrysler Airflow**
  1935-39  (scale 1:48)
  English castings painted and assembled in
  France. Smooth hubs, black or white
  'DUNLOP' tyres.
- Green body ................................... **£200-250**
- Blue body....................................... **£200-250**
- Red body........................................ **£200-250**

**35a  Simca 5**
  1939-40  (scale 1:50)
  No base, black rubber wheels. Colours:
- Red, Dark Red, Maroon, Light Blue,
  Mid-Blue, Royal Blue, Grey, Grey-Blue,
  Green, Light Green, Brown, Silver,
  Yellow, Gold, Cream ..................... **£250-300**
  1939-40
  Export version of 35-A with white
  rubber wheels. Body colours:
- Red, Dark Red, Maroon, Light Blue,
  Mid-Blue, Royal Blue, Grey, Grey-Blue,
  Green, Light Green, Brown, Silver,
  Yellow, Gold, Cream ..................... **£250-300**
  1940-40
  No base, black painted mazak wheels.
- Red, Dark Red, Maroon, Light Blue,
  Mid-Blue, Royal Blue, Grey, Grey-Blue,
  Green, Light Green, Brown, Silver,
  Yellow, Gold, Cream ..................... **£250-300**
  1948-50  No base, black rubber wheels.
- Red, Dark Red, Maroon, Light Blue,
  Mid-Blue, Royal Blue, Grey, Grey-Blue,
  Green, Light Green, Mid-Brown, Silver,
  Yellow, Gold, Cream ..................... **£100-125**
- Green, Dark Brown ........................ **£150-200**

Numbers 100 to 106 were produced as 'Dinky
Juniors' --a pocket-money budget series. Most
fitted with spun steel hubs or Silver hubs
with 'DUNLOP' tyres. Scale 1:43.
**100  Renault 4L**
  1963-68
- Pale Green body ............................ **£400-500**
**101  Peugeot 404** (553 casting)
  1963-66
- Orange, no frame to rear
  number plate ................................. **£400-500**
  1966-69
- Orange or Red-Orange,
  rear number plate has frame............ **£400-500**
**102  Panhard PL17**
  1963-68
- Grey-Blue body ............................. **£400-500**
- Bright Blue body ........................... **£400-500**
**103  Renault R8**
  1964-68
- Red body........................................ **£400-500**
**103  Renault R8S Gordini**
  1969-69
- Red body, painted headlights ......... **£450-600**
**104  Simca 1000**
  1964-68
- Pale Yellow body........................... **£300-400**
- Lime-Green body............................ **£300-400**
**105  Citroën 2cv**
  1964-68
- Grey body,
  light grey concave hubs.................. **£400-500**
**106  Opel Kadett**
  1965-69
- Yellow body.............................. **£1,600-1,900**

**500   Citroën 2cv**
1967-71
* Beige (dark grey open top),
painted concave hubs.
'Made in France' on aperture box ....... **£80-90**
* Blue-Grey body (dark blue open top) . **£80-90**
* Pale Grey body (mid-grey open top)... **£80-90**
1974-? Spanish issues:
1974-75  Beige (dark grey open top),
painted hubs. 'Made in Spain'
over-stamped on box.......................... **£80-90**
1975-76
* Beige (dark grey open top), painted hubs.
'Made in Spain' and 'Meccano' on
large non-aperture box........................ **£80-90**
1976-78
* Orange body, 'square' headlamps, rivetted
base, plated concave hubs. 'Made in Spain,
imprimée en France, ref 500' on box .. **£70-80**
1978-?
* Orange body, 'square' headlamps,
screwed base, plated concave hubs.
'Made in Spain, imprimeé en Espagne,
ref 011500' on box............................... **£70-80**

**501   Citroën DS19 'POLICE' Car**
1967-70  (scale 1:43)
* Very dark blue/white, roof beacon,
concave hubs ................................... **£200-250**

**503   Porsche Carrera 6**
1967-69  (scale 1:43)
* White/Red, 'Carrera' in black. Box has
'moteur...280km/h' printed outside
of yellow lines ................................ **£100-120**
1969-71
* Same model but box has 'moteur..
..280km/h' within yellow lines ........ **£100-120**

**505   Maserati Sport 2000**  (1:43)
1959-60 (renumbered in 1959 from 22a)
* Dark or Bright Red, shiny baseplate,
convex chromed hubs,
white driver..................................... **£100-125**
1960-61
* Same but concave chromed hubs .... **£125-150**

**506   Aston-Martin DB3S**
1960-61  (scale 1:43)
* Emerald Green, concave hubs, driver,
racing numbers '1' to '17' .............. **£100-130**
**NB** 506 used the English 104 body casting
with 'Made in France' base and a French
three-spoke steering wheel.

**506   Ferrari 275 GTB**
1967-72  (scale 1:43)
Cast base, cast detailed wheels, nylon tyres.
* Red body............................................ **£100-120**
* Yellow body......................................**£110-130**
* Yellow body, 'hybrid' with
Red doors/bonnet/boot.......................**£90-110**

**507   Simca 1500 Estate Car**
1967-71  (scale 1:43)
* White, Metallic Dark Grey or Silver-Grey
body, camping table, concave hubs,
black tyres........................................ **£100-120**

**507-P Simca 1500 'POLICE' Car**
1967-71
* White and Dark Blue body, red interior,
aerial at one side of roof........... **£5,000-6,500**

**508   Daf 33**
1966-71  (scale 1:43)
* Dark Red body, cast base, concave
hubs, black tyres, female driver ........ **£80-100**
* Metallic Bronze, concave chromed
hubs, black tyres .............................**£110-130**
* Beige body, concave chromed
hubs, black tyres .............................**£90-110**

**509   Fiat 850**
1966-68  (scale 1:43)
* Red body, white tilting seats,
concave hubs ...................................... **£70-90**
* Yellow body, red tilt seats,
concave hubs .................................... **£100-125**
* White body, red tilt seats,
concave hubs ...................................... **£80-100**
1968-71  Spanish issues:
* Red, Yellow or White body, 'PIRELLI'
tyres, Barcelona number plate.
'DINKY-POCH' on box. ................. **£400-500**

* Turquoise-Green body, white interior,
'PIRELLI' tyres, Barcelona number
plate. 'DINKY-POCH' on box. ....... **£450-600**

**510   Talbot-Lago GP Car**
1959-59  (renumbered in 1959 from 23-H)
* Blue body, (RN's '1' to '6' and
'22' to '27' on yellow transfers),
driver cast in, plated convex hubs... **£100-150**

**510   Peugeot 204**
1965-68  (scale 1:43)
Two-part rear bumper, rivetted floor,
concave hubs.
* Metallic Dark Red body.
'Par autorisation des automobiles
PEUGEOT' on box.......................... **£100-125**
* Same but Greenish-Beige body....... **£100-125**
1968-68  Spanish issues:
Two-part rear bumper, rivetted floor,
concave hubs, 'PIRELLI' tyres.
* Bright Red body, 'DINKY-POCH'
on box. Assembled in Spain ........... **£500-750**
1968-71
* Same, but White body.
Made for export to Spain................. **£400-450**
1977-78
One-piece rear bumper, screwed floor.
* Beige-Pink body. Made in Spain,
box printed in Spain .......................... **£50-75**
1981
Promotional issue:
Off-White body with 'VGE' in
Blue/White/Red with
Presidential Election decor............. **£400-500**

**511   Ferrari Racing Car**  (1:43)
1959-63  (renumbered in 1959 from 23-J)
* Red body, 'cross-hatched' grille, racing
numbers '1' or '22' to '27', driver, concave
hubs, radial or block tread tyres ...... **£150-200**

**511   Peugeot 204 Cabriolet**
1968-71  (scale 1:43)
Cast base, aluminium concave hubs,
tilting seats.
* Sky-blue  open body, black interior **£140-170**
* Red open body, black interior.......... **£170-200**

PHOTO: COLLECTOYS

**512  Leskokart Midjet Kart**
1962-66  (scale 1:43)
- Blue body, Black plastic wheels. Plastic
  driver (white with yellow jacket) ...... **£80-100**
  Same but with blue jacket ................ **£80-100**
- Same but driver with red jacket ..... **£200-250**

**513  Opel Admiral**
1966-68  (scale 1:43)
- Metallic Blue or Metallic Red,
  detailed hubs, luggage ...................... **£90-120**
1968-69  Spanish issue:
- Same but with 'PIRELLI' tyres.
  'DINKY-POCH' on box ................. **£250-300**

**514  Alfa-Romeo Giulia 1600ti**
1966-71  (scale 1:43)
Plated concave hubs, working
windows, headlights and rear lights.
- Beige or White or Metallic Grey
  body, red interior ............................ **£100-130**
- Pale Green body, red interior ......... **£125-150**
- Spanish export issue:
  Metallic Grey body, 'PIRELLI'
  tyres, Barcelona number plate........ **£200-300**

**515  Ferrari 250GT 2+2**
1963-70  (scale 1:43)
- Red body, white interior,
  concave hubs, black tyres .............. **£100-125**
- Metallic Blue body,
  concave hubs, black tyres.................**£90-110**

**516  Mercedes-Benz 230SL**
1964-65
Removable hard-top, concave hubs,
'MERCEDES 230SL' on base,
French box.
- Metallic Silver/Cream body ........... **£130-160**
- Metallic Red-Orange/Cream body .. **£100-120**
- Metallic Red/Cream body .............. **£120-140**
1965-66
- Same as previous model but with
  'MERCEDES-BENZ 230SL' on
  base. French box.............................. **£100-125**
1966-70
- Metallic Red-Orange/Cream as
  1965-66 version but in British box
  for export to UK and USA ................ **£70-90**

**517  Renault R8**
1962-64  (scale 1:43)
- Blue body, concave hubs ................ **£100-125**
- Primrose-Yellow, concave hubs ...... **£100-125**
1964  (renumbered in 1964 to 1517)
**NB** Model was introduced on the
same day as the actual car.
1968-70  Spanish issues:
- Cream body, concave hubs, 'PIRELLI'
  tyres, silver rear number plate.
  'DINKY-POCH' on box ................. **£400-600**
- Dark Blue body, concave hubs,
  'PIRELLI' tyres, Silver rear number
  plate. 'DINKY-POCH' on box ........ **£400-600**

**517-P  Renault R8 Police Car**
1969
- Dark Blue/White, 'POLICE'.
  Commissioned for use by Police..... **£600-700**

**518  Renault R4L**
1961-64  (scale 1:43)
- Pale Blue or Light Blue body,
  first grille, concave hubs .................... **£50-60**
1964
- Brick-Red or Brown body .................. **£50-60**
- Grey-Green body .............................. **£95-125**
1964  (renumbered in 1964 to 1518)
1964-64
- Red body, 'POMPIERS de PARIS'.
  Commissioned by Fire Service . **£1,200-1,600**
1964-64
- Yellow/blue 'PTT' livery. Commissioned
  for use by Postal Service ................ **£500-600**
1968-70  Spanish issues:
- As standard 1964 French model but
  Violet body, 'PIRELLI' tyres.
  'DINKY-POCH' on box ................. **£400-600**
1975-77
- Dark Blue, second grille,
  concave hubs. 'Made in Spain' and
  pink '4L' on box ................................ **£55-65**
1977-?
- Sky Blue, second grille, concave hubs.
  'Made in Spain' and blue '4L' on box. **£55-65**

**518-A  Renault 4L, 'AUTOROUTES'**
1970-71
- Orange body, first grille, plated concave
  hubs. Box also contains
  595r Traffic Sign 'Road Works' ..... **£200-250**

**519  1961  Facel Vega Facellia**
Announced in the 1961-62 catalogue
but not produced.......................................NPP

**519  Simca 1000**
1962-63
- Red or Light Blue-Grey body,
  cream interior, black base.
  '519' in black oval on box.................. **£70-90**
- Lime-Green body, cream interior .... **£220-260**
- Light Yellow body, cream interior... **£220-260**
- Sky-Blue body, white interior ............ **£80-90**
1962-64
- Light Blue-Grey body, red interior,
  Black base, concave hubs, rubber tyres.
  '519' in black oval on box.................. **£55-65**
1963-64
- Metallic Grey body, black or green
  interior. Existence not confirmed ...........NPP
**NB**  The 1962-64 version of 519 was
renumbered in 1964 as 1519.
Production of 519 continued as follows:
1964-66
- Light Blue-Grey body, white interior.
  Anodised base, concave hubs, nylon
  tyres. '519' in black band on box........ **£70-90**
1966-68  South-African issues:
- Turquoise body, red interior,
  concave hubs. Assembled / painted
  in South Africa.......................... **£1,500-2,000**
- Dark Red body, white interior,
  concave hubs. Assembled / painted
  in South Africa.......................... **£1,500-2,000**
1968-70  Spanish issues:
- Metallic Blue body, Cream interior,
  concave hubs, 'PIRELLI' tyres.
  'DINKY-POCH' on box ................. **£500-700**
- Red body, cream interior,
  concave hubs, 'PIRELLI' tyres.
  'DINKY-POCH' on box .................. **£250-300**

**520  Chrysler New Yorker**  (1:48)
1960-61  (renumbered in 1960 from 24-A)
'CHRYSLER NEW YORKER 1955' on
base and on box. Concave hubs.
- Yellow body, green seats ................. **£200-250**
- Red body, ivory seats ..................... **£100-120**
- Light Met. Blue body, ivory seats ... **£275-350**

PHOTO: COLLECTOYS

**520  Fiat 600D**
1963-64 (scale 1:43)
* White body, red int., concave hubs ..... **£85-95**
1964-64
Red or Cream body, concave hubs.... **£90-100**
1964 (renumbered in 1964 to 1520)
1968 Spanish export issues:
* Pale Yellow, concave hubs, 'PIRELLI'
tyres.'DINKY-POCH'on box ......... **£200-250**
* Light Blue body, concave hubs, 'PIRELLI'
tyres. 'DINKY-POCH' on box ........ **£300-400**
* Off-White body, concave hubs,
'PIRELLI' tyres, Silver number plate.
'DINKY-POCH' on box ................. **£250-300**

**521  Peugeot 403 8cv**
1959-60 (renumbered in 1960 from 24-B)
No windows, base has towing notch,
plated convex hubs, smooth white tyres
* Light Grey body .............................**£90-110**
* Cream body ................................... **£175-225**
1960-62
With windows and towing notch, plated
concave hubs, smooth or treated white tyres.
* Light Grey body. (Light Blue-Grey
picture and Black picture on box)... **£100-125**
* Cream body. (Light Blue-Grey
picture and Black picture on box).. **£150-200**
1962-64
521 became individually unavailable in 1962
but was included in Gift Set 503 up to 1964.

**522  Citroën DS19** (1:43)
1959-60 (renumbered in 1960 from 24-CP)
With windows, convex hubs, smooth
white tyres, '24CP' on box.
* Green/White....................................**£225-275**
* Ivory/very Dark Purple....................**£225-275**
* Yellow/Grey....................................**£225-275**
* Orange/Cream.................................**£225-275**
1960-63
With concave hubs, smooth white tyres.
'522' on box.
* Orange/Cream body.........................**£110-140**
* Yellow/Grey body............................**£100-130**
1963-68
With concave hubs, treaded white tyres.
'522' on box.
* Orange body, Cream roof ................ **£100-130**
* Yellowish-Beige body,
pale grey roof................................. **£150-200**
* Pale Yellow body, grey roof ............ **£100-130**

**523  Simca Driving School Car**
Announced (but not illustrated) in the
1962 price list. Not produced ..................NPP

**523  Plymouth Belvedere** (1:48)
1959-60 (renumbered in 1960 from 24-D)
Convex hubs. Picture on some boxes.
* Green body, black roof and panel ......**£90-110**
* Tan body, metallic brown
roof and panel................................ **£150-200**
* Grey body, orange-red roof / panel ... **£85-100**
* White body, blue roof and panel ..... **£300-350**
1960-61 With concave hubs.
* Tobacco-Brown body,
maroon roof and panel .................. **£200-300**
* White body, blue roof and panel ..... **£375-450**

**523  Simca 1500**
1963-64 (scale 1:43)
* Light-Blue body, concave hubs........... **£60-80**
1964 (renumbered in 1964 as 1523)
* Light Blue body, concave hubs............ **£60-80**
* Metallic Grey body, concave hubs...... **£60-80**
1968-69 Spanish issue:
* Bright Blue body, plated concave hubs,
'PIRELLI' tyres.
'DINKY-POCH' on box ................. **£400-600**

**524  Renault Dauphine**
1959-60 (scale 1:43)
With windows (some without), convex hubs,
smooth black tyres. '524 - 24E' on box.
* Turquoise body ...............................**£120-150**
* Brick-Red body ...............................**£120-150**
* Raspberry-Red body........................**£120-150**
* Ivory-White body ............................**£150-200**
1960-60
As previous models but box has 'DINKY
TOYS' in upright lettering plus '524'.
* Turquoise body ...............................**£150-175**
* Brick-Red body ...............................**£100-120**
* Raspberry-Red body........................**£150-175**
* Ivory-White body ............................**£150-200**
1960-61
* Bright Blue-Green body. Box has 'DINKY
TOYS' in upright lettering plus '524'.
Special limited edition for Paris
Dinky Toys Club............................**£500-750**
1960-61
With windows, concave chromed hubs
with smooth or treaded black tyres.
Box has 'DINKY TOYS' in oblique
lettering plus '524'.
* Turquoise body ...............................**£100-140**
* Brick-Red body ...............................**£100-140**
* Raspberry-Red body........................**£100-140**
1961-64
524 became individually unavailable
in 1961 but remained in Gift Set 503
up till 1964.

**524  Panhard 24CT**
1964-66 (scale 1:43)
* Metallic Grey body, concave
chromed hubs, 'DUNLOP' tyres.
In French box................................... **£80-100**
* Pale Yellow-Green body, concave
chromed hubs, 'DUNLOP' tyres.
In French box.................................... **£70-90**
1966-69
* Metallic Grey body; steel hubs,
in English box (model made for
export to UK and USA)................... **£80-100**

**525  Peugeot 403 Estate Car**
1959-60 (renumbered in 1960 from 24-F)
* Sky Blue, no windows, convex hubs,
rear bumper over-riders .................... **£80-100**
1960-62
* Sky Blue, concave hubs,
no rear bumper over-riders............. **£120-140**
**NB**  Model was originally shown in
catalogues as being available in black.
It was never produced in that colour.

**525  Peugeot 404 Commercial Traveller's Car**
1964-70 (scale 1:43)
With yellow or black rear number
plate, spun hubs, windows.
* Ocean Blue body ............................ **£100-125**
* Cream body .................................... **£100-125**

**525  Peugeot 404 Fire Car**
1964-64
* Red body, 'Pompiers de Paris',
concave chromed hubs,
'DUNLOP' plastic tyres, aerial . **£1,500-2,000**

**526  Mercedes-Benz 190sl** (1:43)
1959-60 (renumbered in 1960 from 24-H)
No windows, convex hubs.
Picture on some boxes.
All 526 models have a black hard-top.
* Cream body (various shades) ........... **£75-100**
* Silver body.....................................**£100-120**
1960-62
With windows, convex hubs.
'526' and picture on box.
* Cream body (various shades) ........... **£75-100**
* Silver body...................................... **£80-100**

**526  Mercedes-Benz 190sl Hard-Top**
1961-63
With windows, concave hubs.
'526' and picture on box.
* Cream body (various shades) ........... **£80-100**
* Silver body......................................**£100-130**

**527  Alfa-Romeo 1900 Sprint** (1:43)
1959-63 (renumbered in 1959 from 24-J)
* Red or Blue body, cream interior,
windows, concave hubs,
smooth (later treaded) black tyres ..... **£80-100**
* Red body with red interior ............. **£150-200**
* Turquoise body ........................ **£4,000-5,000**

**528  Simca Vedette Chambord** (1:43)
1959-60 (renumbered in 1959 from 24-K/2)
* Ivory and Red body, concave hubs........ **£150-200**
* Light and Dark Green, convex hubs........ **£75-90**
1960-61
* Ivory and Red body, concave hubs ..... **£150-200**
* Light and Dark Green, concave hubs ..... **£75-90**

**528  Peugeot 404 Cabriolet**
1966-71 (scale 1:43)
With female driver, steel hubs.
* White open body, red interior.......... **£140-180**
* Metallic Blue body, red interior ..... **£140-180**
* Pale Grey body, red interior ........... **£170-200**
* Light Beige body, red interior ........ **£170-200**

**529  Vespa 400 2cv** (scale 1:43)
1959-60 (renumbered from 24-L)
* Blue/Grey, plated hubs. '24L' on box . **£70-80**
1960-63
* Blue/Grey, convex hubs,'529' on box . **£70-80**
* Orange/Grey, convex hubs,
'529' on box....................................**£300-400**

**530  VW Karmann-Ghia** (1:43)
1959-59 (renumbered in 1959 from 24-M)
* Black/Red ('pointed' bonnet),
convex hubs ..................................... **£80-100**
1960-62
* Black/Red body ('rounded' bonnet),
convex hubs ....................................**£100-120**
1961-62
* Same, but with concave hubs .......... **£150-200**

**530  Citroën DS19**
1964-70
Steel hubs. French '522' box with '530'
labels, later in own '530' box.
1964-64
* Metallic Grey body................... **£1,500-2,000**
1964-66
* Red/Cream body, ivory interior,
silver base ..................................... **£175-225**
* Lime Green/grey body,
pale grey interior, silver base ......... **£175-225**
1966-68
Steel hubs. British box. Model made for
export to UK and USA.
* Red/Cream body,
ivory interior, silver base..................**£90-110**
* Lime Green/Grey body, pale grey
interior, silver base ..........................**£90-110**
1968-70 Spanish issues:
Spun hubs, 'PIRELLI' tyres.
'DINKY-POCH' on box.
* Red/Cream body, ivory interior,
black base ..................................... **£500-600**
* Lime Green/Grey body,
pale grey interior, black base.......... **£500-600**
* Bright Blue body ........................... **£700-900**
* Silver-Grey body ........................... **£700-900**

**530  Citroën DS23**
1976-78 (scale 1:43)
* Metallic Red/Black body,
concave hubs. Made in Spain......... **£120-140**

**NB**  530 Citroën DS23 was shown in the 1974 catalogue but production did not start until Auto-Pilen took over the dies in 1976. The plastic base on this model (and some other Spanish models) was made in different colours and some are held in place by screws rather than rivets.  Consequently, beware the 'rare combination' of base and body colours as they are easily interchanged.

**531   Fiat 1200 Grande Vue**  (1:43)
1959-60  (renumbered in 1960 from 24-N)
With convex hubs, smooth tyres.
- Metallic Bronze/Cream body .............**£90-110**
- Cream/Metallic Blue body ............. **£120-140**

**NB**  531 was shown in the 1959 Swiss catalogue with the reference '24N'.
1960-62
With concave hubs, smooth or treaded tyres.
- Metallic Bronze/Cream body ........... **£90-100**
- Cream/Metallic Blue body ............. **£130-160**

**532   Lincoln Premiere**
1959-60  (scale 1:43)
- Silver body, dark red roof, convex hubs. Box has no view window ................ **£225-275**
- Light Blue body, silver roof ........... **£100-125**
- Metallic Green, dark green roof...... **£100-125**

1960-65
- Bright Blue body, silver roof, concave hubs, white smooth or treaded tyres. View window in box ...................... **£500-650**
- Light Blue body, silver roof ............. **£90-100**
- Metallic Green, dark green roof........ **£90-100**

196?-?
- Export model: Dark Blue body, silver roof. In gold card and cellophane box ..... **£300-400**

**NB**  A dark green wooden prototype of 532 exists.................................NPP

**533   Peugeot 203**
1959-59  (renumbered in 1959 from 24-R)
- Grey-Blue or Pale Grey-Green body, convex hubs, white tyres, big rear window, square filler cap ................ **£90-120**

**533   Mercedes-Benz 300 SE**
1963-70  (scale 1:43)
With plated concave hubs.
- Metallic Blue body .......................... **£150-175**
- Metallic Orange-Red body ............. **£150-175**
- Metallic Red body ........................... **£150-175**

**534   Simca 8 Sport**  (1:43)
1959-59  (renumbered in 1959 from 24-S)
Thick windscreen, convex hubs.
- Grey body, red seats ...................... **£100-125**
- Black body, red seats ..................... **£100-125**
- Pale Greenish-Blue body, red seats. **£100-125**
- Cream body, red seats..................... **£100-125**

**534   BMW 1500**
1963-68  (scale 1:43)
- Red body, steel hubs........................ **£90-100**
- Lime Green, plated concave hubs ... **£100-120**

1968-?  Spanish issue:
- Metallic Blue, plated concave hubs, 'PIRELLI' tyres, 'DINKY-POCH' on box ................ **£500-750**

**535   Citroën 2cv**
1959-60
- Red or Brighter Red body, painted steel hubs, glossy baseplate. Box has '535-24T' printing ............ **£100-120**
- Maroon body, grey top ................... **£100-120**
- Blue body with brighter blue roof.. **£150-175**

1960-63
- Red or Blue body, chromed steel hubs, blued-steel baseplate. Box has '535' printing......................**£90-110**

**536   Simca Aronde Elysée**  (1:43)
1959-59  (renumbered in 1959 from 24-U)
- Light Grey-green/Dark Green, second grille, convex hubs ............. **£100-125**
- Pale Green/Dark Green, second grille, convex hubs ............. **£100-125**
- Blue body, ivory roof ..................... **£100-125**
- Sky blue body, ivory roof.............. **£300-400**

**NB**  Though renumbered from 24-U to 536, no boxes have yet been seen bearing the new number.

**536   Peugeot 404 and Trailer**
1965-70  (scale 1:43)
- Red car, ivory interior, concave hubs, black skis on yellow rack (or yellow skis on black rack), cream plastic single-wheel trailer (no. 812), luggage ................ **£250-300**

**537   Simca Aronde Elysée Taxi**  (1:43)
1959-60  (renumbered in 1960 from 24-UT)
- Red/Blue body, convex plated hubs, second grille......................... **£80-90**

**537   Renault R16**
1965-67  (scale 1:43)
Concave hubs, black treaded rubber tyres, '537' on base. Box has single viewport, R16 leaflet in early issues.
- Sky-Blue body, gloss Black base ........ **£70-90**
- Metallic Grey body, gloss Black base . **£60-80**

1967-70
Concave hubs, 'DUNLOP' nylon tyres, '537' on base. Box has single viewport, R16 leaflet discontinued in 1967.
- Light Blue body, matt black base....... **£50-65**
- Metallic Grey body, matt black base... **£50-65**

1968-69  Spanish issue:
- Bright Blue, '537' on base, concave hubs, 'PIRELLI' tyres, 'DINKY-POCH' box ...................... **£250-350**

1969-70
- Sky-Blue body, matt black base without '537' reference, concave hubs, 'DUNLOP' plastic tyres. Box has single viewport ...................... **£60-75**

1974-78  Spanish issue:
- Metallic Grey body, base without '537', concave hubs, 'DUNLOP' plastic tyres. 'MECCANO' and 'Made in Spain' on box (no viewport) ...................... **£60-75**

**538   Buick Roadmaster**
1959-59  (renumbered in 1959 from 24-V)
All have convex hubs. Scale 1:48.
- Blue/Dark Blue body...................... **£130-170**
- Yellow/Green body.......................... **£100-150**
- Blue/Cream body............................ **£100-150**
- Ivory/Metallic Blue body .............. **£500-600**
- Salmon-Pink/Black body................ **£500-600**

**538   Ford Taunus 12M**
1963-70  (scale 1:43)
- Turquoise body, steel or spun hubs ....**£90-110**
- Brick Red body, steel or spun hubs..... **£80-95**

**538   Renault R16 TX**
1976-78
- Metallic Plum, concave hubs, rear number plate on sticker. Made in Spain .......... **£70-90**

**NB**  538 Renault R16 was shown in the 1974 French catalogue, but production was delayed until 1976.

**539   Ford Vedette Taxi**
1959-59  (renumbered in 1959 from 24-XT)
- Black/Beige (various shades), meter, taxi sign, plated convex hubs, white tyres . **£75-85**

**NB**  539 was never individually boxed (supplied to shops in trade boxes of six).

**539   Citroën ID19 Estate**
1963-66  (scale 1:43)
- Gold/Cream body, red or white seats, black or white steering wheel, steel hubs, black or white tyres ....... **£100-125**
- Green-Gold body, darker cream roof, spun hubs ............................... **£125-150**

**540   Studebaker Commander**
1959-60  (renumbered in 1959 from 24-Y)
With convex hubs, smooth tyres. Tinplate base has towing notch. '540-24Y' and picture of model on box.
- Ivory body, maroon roof and wing panels ...................................... **£120-150**
- Orange body, dark cream roof and panels ...................................... **£140-180**

1960-61
With concave hubs, treaded tyres. Towing notch in base. '540-24Y' and picture on box.
- Ivory body, maroon roof and wing panels ...................................... **£150-200**
- Orange body, dark cream roof and wing panels. Existence not confirmed .....NPP

**540   Opel Kadett**
1963-64
- Red or Pale Green body, steel hubs..... **£85-95**

1964
- Bright Blue body, plated steel hubs **£200-300**

1964  (renumbered in 1964 to 1540)
**NB**  540 Opel was available with either the standard size hubs or smaller hubs. Both types were concave and were steel or spun aluminium with black tyres.

**541   Simca Vedette Versailles**
1959-60  (renumbered in 1959 from 24-Z)
With convex hubs, white tyres, towing notch. Picture on box.
- Yellow/Black body ......................... **£100-125**
- Light Blue/Ivory body .......................**£90-110**

**542   Simca Ariane Taxi**
1959-62  (renumbered in 1959 from 24-ZT)
'Ariane' on base, '542-24ZT' on box, window glazing, scale 1:43.
- Black body, red (later orange-red) roof, meter, taxi sign, convex hubs (concave from 1961) ...................... **£125-150**
- Reversed colours: Red body, black roof ...................... **£300-400**

**542   Opel Rekord**
1964-69
With concave hubs. Scale 1:43.
- Metallic Blue two door body............ **£80-100**
- Metallic Gold-Cream two door body **£80-100**
- Metallic Grey two door body .......... **£80-100**

**543   Renault Floride**
1960-63  (scale 1:43)
Concave hubs, smooth or treaded white tyres.
- Metallic Green body ........................ **£90-120**
- Metallic Green-Gold body................ **£90-120**
- Metallic Bronze body ...................... **£90-120**
- White body ................................. **£750-1,000**

**NB**  A wooden prototype of 543 is known to exist. It was painted pink. ....................NPP

**544   Simca Aronde P60**
1959-60  (scale 1:43)
Convex hubs. Box without (later with) viewport.
- Two-tone Grey body (with silver flash)................................**£90-110**
- Brick Red body (with cream or pinkish-cream roof) ...........................**£90-110**

1960-63
Concave hubs. Box with one viewport.
- Two-tone Grey body...........................**£90-110**

- Brown body (with off-white roof and
  silver flash).................................**£90-110**
- Cream body, red roof,
  smooth white tyres.................... **£4,000-5,000**

**545  De Soto Diplomat**
1960-63  (scale 1:43)
Concave hubs, (usually) treaded white tyres.
- Salmon-Pink/Black body,
  silver flash ..................................... **£100-125**
- Metallic Green body, ivory roof..... **£200-250**

**546  Austin-Healey 100-6**
1960-61  (scale 1:43)
- White body (different shades reported),
  driver, 3-spoke steering wheel,
  concave hubs .................................. **£120-150**

**546  Opel Rekord Taxi**
1964-67  (scale 1:43)
- Black body, aluminium or steel concave
  hubs, white tyres. Box has German text
  as this model was made only for export
  to Germany for this period. The taxi sign
  lettering may be white or yellow..... **£400-500**

**547  Panhard PL17**
1960-64
1st type: Sidelights to front and rear of
centre-hinged doors, black painted
baseplate, steel hubs, rubber tyres.
2nd type: As 1st type but without
rear sidelights.
3rd type: Front-hinged doors, sidelights
under headlamps, black painted baseplate,
steel hubs, rubber tyres.
4th type: As 3rd type but with blued-steel
baseplate, steel or aluminium hubs.
5th type: Aluminium hubs with
plastic 'DUNLOP' tyres.
1960-60
- 1st type, Violet body...................... **£130-160**
- 1st type, Brick Red body................ **£130-160**
1960-61
- 2nd type, Violet body ..................... **£130-160**
- 2nd type, Brick Red or Orange ....... **£130-160**
1962-63
- 3rd type, Violet body ......................... **£70-85**
- 3rd type, Orange body ....................... **£60-80**
1963-64
- 4th type, Violet or Brick-Red body . **£100-120**
1964-70
- 5th type, Blue-Grey body ............... **£120-150**
- 5th type, Blue body ........................ **£300-350**
1964  (renumbered in 1964 to 1547)

**548  Fiat 1800 Familiale Estate Car**
1960-63  (scale 1:43). Concave hubs.
- Lilac body with black roof ............... **£90-120**
- Lavender body, black or blue roof ... **£90-120**
- Yellow body, metallic brown roof... **£100-125**
- Yellow body, black roof ................. **£100-125**
- Two-tone Blue body, black roof...... **£100-125**
1962  South African issues:
- Ivory body (with red interior) ........ **£600-800**
- Lime Green body............................ **£500-600**
- Green-Bronze body ........................ **£500-600**
- Yellow body, metallic maroon roof. **£400-500**

**549  Borgward Isabella TS**
1961-61  (scale 1:43)
Concave hubs, black or white tyres.
- Turquoise body ...............................**£110-140**
- Light Green body.............................**£110-140**
- Metallic Grey body..........................**£110-140**

**550  Chrysler Saratoga**
1961-65
Plated concave hubs,
smooth or treaded white tyres.
- Pale Pink with white flash.............. **£120-140**
- Deep Pink with white flash ............ **£120-140**
- Violet with black flash.................... **£175-200**

**551  Rolls-Royce Silver Wraith**
1959-61  (scale 1:43)
- Light Grey/Dark Grey body,
  concave hubs .................................... **£90-100**

**551  Ford Taunus 17M Police Car**
1965-67  (scale 1:43)
- Dark Green/White, 'POLIZEI',
  concave hubs, German text on box . **£500-700**

**552  Chevrolet Corvair**
1961-64  (scale 1:43)
Concave hubs, indication of filler
cap on some.
- Turquoise body, cream interior..........**£90-110**
- Blue-Grey body, cream interior.........**£90-110**
- Red body, cream interior ................ **£120-140**
1963  South African issues:
(All have off-white interior)
- Silver body.................................... **£700-800**
- Light Grey-Blue body ................... **£700-900**
- Smokey-Green body................. **£1,000-1,500**
1964  (renumbered in 1964 to 1552)

**553  Peugeot 404**
1961-68
1st type: Round 'O' on bonnet,
steel hubs, smooth black or white tyres,
painted baseplate.
2nd type: Squared 'O' on bonnet, steel hubs,
treaded black tyres, painted baseplate.
3rd type: As 2nd type with reinforcement
behind front number plate, revised glazing
moulding common to 536 with opening
roof, blued-steel baseplate. Aluminium hubs
and plastic 'DUNLOP' tyres.
1961-62  1st type,
- Cream body, dark red interior ......... **£100-120**
- Cream body, dark brown interior .... **£125-150**
- Pale blue body, bright red interior... **£100-120**
1962-64  2nd type,
- Cream body,
  dark (later bright) red interior ........ **£100-125**
- Cream body, dark brown interior .....**£110-150**
1963-66  3rd type,
- Pale Blue body, bright red interior .. **£100-120**
1963  South African issues:
- Pale Green body,
  bright red interior...................... **£1,000-1,250**
- Metallic Charcoal Grey body,
  bright red interior...................... **£1,000-1,250**
- Cream body, dark red interior ...... **£800-1,000**
1964  (renumbered in 1964 to 1553)
1968-68  Spanish assembled model:
- 3rd type, but with 'PIRELLI' tyres,
  'DINKY-POCH' on box.
  Bright Blue body, bright red interior,
  Barcelona number plate............... **£900-1,100**

**554  Opel Rekord**
1961-63  (scale 1:43)
Concave hubs, (usually) white tyres.
- Coral-Pink/Ivory body......................**£90-110**
- Dark Yellow/Ivory body.................**£110-130**
- Beige body, cream roof ...................**£115-135**
- Turquoise/Ivory body ..................... **£500-600**
1962  South African issues:
- Pale Blue body, light grey int....... **£800-1,000**
- Bright Blue body, light grey int. .. **£800-1,000**
- Dark Blue body, light grey int...... **£800-1,000**
- Metallic Dark Green body,
  grey interior .............................. **£1,000-1,250**

**555  Ford Thunderbird**
1961-69
1st type: Black painted baseplate,
steel hubs, smooth white tyres.
2nd type: Blued-steel baseplate,
steel hubs, treaded white tyres.
3rd type: Blued-steel baseplate,
aluminium hubs, treaded white tyres.
**NB**  Driver may wear bright or dark suit,
steering wheel may be cream or black.

- White body, red interior ................... **£110-130**
- Red body, sky-blue interior .............**£110-130**
- Dark Brown body, sky-blue int. .....**£110-130**
- Dark Brown body, pale green int. ... **£100-150**
1966-?  South African issues:
- Bright Blue open body, red int. .... **£900-1,200**
- Metallic Blue open body, red int.. **£900-1,200**
- Sand open body, red interior ....... **£900-1,200**
- Red open body, red interior.......... **£900-1,200**

**556  Citroën ID19 Ambulance**
1962-70
1st type: Steel hubs, metal steering wheel,
centred transfer lettering.
2nd type: As 1st type, but with plastic
steering wheel.
3rd type: As 2nd type, but with
aluminium hubs.
4th type: Aluminium hubs, plastic
'DUNLOP' tyres, plastic steering wheel,
transfer lettering aligned to left.
1962-67
- 1st/2nd/3rd types: Grey/cream body.
  In standard box until '64, then in
  'Super detail' box .......................... **£120-140**
1967-70
- 4th type: Grey/cream body.
  In 'Super detail' box ...................... **£100-125**

**557  Citroën Ami 6**
1962-70
1st type: Steel hubs, spare wheel under
bonnet, black painted base.
2nd type: Steel hubs, engine detail under
bonnet, black painted base.
3rd type: As 2nd type, but with
blued-steel baseplate.
4th type: As 3rd type, but with aluminium
hubs and plastic 'DUNLOP' tyres.
1962-62
- 1st type, Pale Green body,
  white or pale grey roof.................... **£120-140**
- Light Blue body,
  with white or pale grey roof............ **£120-140**
- Light Blue body, pale blue roof....... **£120-140**
1963-64
- 2nd type. Pale Green body,
  white or pale grey roof......................**£90-110**
- Light Blue body, pale blue roof.........**£90-110**
- Bright Blue body,
  white or pale grey roof......................**£90-110**
1964  (renumbered in 1964 to 1557)
1964-70
- 3rd/4th types. Pale Green body,
  white or pale grey roof......................**£90-110**
- Light Blue body,
  white or pale grey roof......................**£90-110**

**558  Citroën 2cv Azam**
1962-64
- Yellow body, Brown roof ............... **£100-125**
- Beige body, Brown roof ................. **£150-175**
- Green body, Dark Green roof............ **£75-85**
- Greyish-Green body, Black roof ....... **£75-85**
1964  (renumbered in 1964 to 1558)

**558  Citroën 2cv**
1968-70  Spanish issues:
- Yellow/Maroon body, concave hubs,
  'PIRELLI' tyres,
  'DINKY-POCH' on box ................. **£300-400**
- Green/Dark Green body, concave
  hubs, 'PIRELLI' tyres,
  'DINKY-POCH'on box .................. **£300-400**

**559  Ford Taunus 17M**
1962-64  (scale 1:43)
Steel or aluminium hubs, smooth or
treaded black or white tyres.
- Ivory body ...................................... **£80-100**
- Pale Grey body ............................... **£80-100**
- Metallic Brown body........................ **£80-100**

- Metallic Grey-Brown body .............. **£80-100**
  1964 (renumbered in 1964 to 1559)
  1968-69 Spanish issue: Yellow body,
  concave hubs, 'PIRELLI' tyres,
  'DINKY-POCH' on box ............ **£1,400-1,600**

**1400  Peugeot 404 G7 Taxi**  (536 casting)
  1967-71  (scale 1:43)
- Black body, red top with sunroof, taxi
  sign and aerial, 'Ampere 28.30' and 'G7'
  shield on doors, concave hubs, black
  'DUNLOP' tyres, yellow box.......... **£250-350**

**1401  Alfa-Romeo Guilia 1600Ti**  (514 casting)
  1967-70
- Dark Red 'rally' finish with yellow
  stripe, spotlights, concave hubs.
  Yellow box...................................... **£120-140**

**1402  Ford Galaxie Sedan**
  1968-71  (scale 1:43)
  Detailed wheels. Perspex box.
- Dark Red (cream interior).........**£90-110**
- Metallic Gold body (red interior).......**£90-110**

**1402  Ford Galaxie Police Car**
  1968-68
- Black/white body, 'POLICE'.
  Commissioned for
  use by Police........................... **£2,000-3,000**

**1403  Matra M530**
  1967-71
- White or Orange body, concave hubs,
  two-part roof can be stowed in boot.
  Perspex box ...................................... **£80-100**

**1404  Citroën ID19 Estate Car**
  1968-69
- Grey/red, 'RADIO TELE LUXEMBOURG',
  camera/operator, concave hubs.
  Yellow box............................... **£500-750**
  1969-71
- Grey/red, 'RTL LUXEMBOURG',
  ('RTL' in black), concave hubs.
  Yellow box............................... **£500-750**
  1971-71
- Grey/red, 'RTL LUXEMBOURG'
  ('T' of 'RTL' in black/white check).
  Yellow picture box ................... **£3,500-4,500**
- Same model but with Grey and
  Orange-red body. Yellow box.... **£2,000-2,500**

**1405   Opel Rekord 1900s**
  1968-70  (scale 1:43)
- Metallic Blue body. In perspex box .... **£70-80**

**1405E  Opel Rekord 1900s**
  1970-71  (scale 1:43)
- Metallic Blue. Export model in
  card box ................................... **£150-250**

**1405P  Opel Rekord 1900s**
  1968-68
  Prototypes using the 1405 casting were
  prepared for the 1420 Opel Commodore.
  '1405' on the base.
- Silver body, black 'vinyl' roof,
  Black interior, paper number plate...... **£85-95**
- Red body, black 'vinyl' roof,
  Black interior, paper number plate...... **£85-95**

**1406  Renault 4L Sinpar 'Tanguy'**
  1968-71
- Khaki-green camouflage body, driver
  (Michel Tanguy), passenger, painted
  concave hubs. From TV serial 'Les
  Chevaliers du Ciel'
  ('Knights of the Sky') .................... **£140-170**

**1407  Simca 1100**
  1968-71
- Metallic Grey body, concave hubs. 'Made
  in France' yellow viewport box......... **£80-100**
- Dark Red body. This was the intended
  colour when 1407 was introduced but its
  existence is doubtful................................NPP
  1974-78 Spanish issue:
- Metallic Green body, concave hubs.
  'Made in Spain' overprinted on French
  box (later in Spanish box also printed
  'Made in Spain')................................. **£60-70**

**1408  Honda S800**
  1969-70  (scale 1:43)
- Yellow body, concave hubs.
  Yellow box.................................**£90-110**

**1409  Simca 1800**
- 1970. A prototype for the 1409 Chrysler
  180 but with 'Simca 1800' on the base.
  Just a few were sold - they were finished
  in the same metallic blue-grey paint
  as the production version................. **£200-250**

**1409  Chrysler 180**
  1970-71  (scale 1:43)
- Metallic Blue-Grey body, 'Chrysler' on
  base, 'DUNLOP' tyres. Yellow box .... **£75-90**
  **NB**  595w Traffic Sign 'Danger - Cyclists'
  included with 1409.

**1410  Moskvitch 408**
  1968-71  (scale 1:43)
- Red body, plated concave hubs.
  Yellow box.................................. **£50-60**

**1411  Renault Alpine A310**
  1971-72  (scale 1:43)
- Bright Red body, plastic hubs.
  Yellow box.................................... **£70-90**

**1413  Citroën Dyane**
  1968-70  (scale 1:43)
- Off-White body, luggage, concave hubs.
  Box has 'DYANE CITROËN' in
  white on yellow ................................. **£60-70**
  1969-71
- Same model but box has 'DYANE
  CITROËN' in white on green............. **£60-70**
  1977-78 Spanish issue:
- Off-White body, concave hubs ........... **£50-60**

**1414  Renault R8 Gordini**
  1969-70
- Blue body, White stripes, driver, RN '36',
  jewelled lights, concave hubs.......... **£200-300**

**1414  Renault R8-S**
  1969-70
- Promotional model:
  Yellow or Mustard-Yellow
  body, driver in some ................. **£1,500-2,000**

**1415  Peugeot 504**
  1969-71  (scale 1:43)
- Pale Blue body, concave hubs.
  Clear plastic box.................................**£90-110**
- Dark Blue body .............................. **£500-600**
  1974-76 Spanish issue:
- Pale Yellow body, concave hubs or
  special wheels. Card box .................... **£60-80**

**1416  Renault R6**
  1969-70
- Bright Red body, first grille (round
  headlamps), concave hubs. Side view
  of white model on box......................... **£60-70**
  1970-74
- As previous model but with rear view
  of dark grey model on box .................. **£60-70**
  1974-76 Spanish issue:
- Red or Yellow body, second grille (square
  headlamps), concave hubs.
  Side view of white model on box ..... **£80-100**

**1416  Renault Postal Car**
  1974-75
- Code 2 model based on Spanish-made
  components, commissioned by the Postal
  Service. Yellow, second grille (square
  headlamps), plated concave hubs.
  Side view of white model on box. ...... **£70-90**

**1416P  Renault R6 Fire Car**
  1970-70
- Code 2 model based on Spanish-made
  components, commissioned by the
  Fire Service. Red body and hubs,
  'POMPIERS de PARIS', second grille,
  side view of white model on box. ... **£100-125**

**1417  Matra V12 F1**
  1969-71  (scale 1:43)
- Blue body, driver (J.P.Beltoise), RN '17'
  (transfer, later on label), special wheels.
  Yellow box ...................................... **£60-70**
  **NB**  595c Traffic Sign 'Dangerous Bend To
  Right' included with 1417.

**1419  Ford Thunderbird**
  1969-71  (scale 1:43)
- Battery in base for rear lights, special wheels.
  Perspex box. Metallic green body
  (black 'vinyl' roof on some)................ **£75-85**
  **NB**  Prototype with Metallic Red body and
  black 'vinyl' roof. (Not issued) ................NPP
- Metallic Grey body,
  dark metallic grey roof ................. **£800-1,100**
  **NB**  595g Traffic Sign 'Caution - Animals
  Crossing' included with 1419.

**1420  Opel Commodore GS**
  1970-71  (scale 1:43)
- Red body, Black 'vinyl' roof, special wheels.
  Some boxes have a printed design in
  a panel................................................
  **£90-100**
  **NB**  The Opel Commodore had a 6-cylinder
  engine, but as 1420 was produced using the
  1405 casting, the model retains a 4-cylinder
  engine and the 'Rekord' badges. 595o Traffic
  Sign 'Customs' included with 1420.

**1421  Opel GT 1900**
  1969-71  (scale 1:43)
- Dark Blue body, detailed chromed
  wheels, luggage rack. Yellow box ... **£100-140**
  **NB**  595f Traffic Sign 'Speed Limit'
  included with 1421.

**1422  Ferrari 3L V12 F1**
  1969-71  (scale 1:43)
- Red body, driver (Jacky Ickx),
  RN '26', detailed chromed wheels.....**£90-110**
  **NB**  595e Traffic Sign 'Road Narrows'
  included with 1422.

**1423  Peugeot 504 Convertible**
  1969-71  (scale 1:43)
- Dark Blue, plastic base, plated
  concave hubs. Yellow box ............. **£200-300**
  **NB**  595i Traffic Sign 'Two Way Traffic'
  included with 1423.

**1424  Renault R12**
  1969-70
- Mustard-Yellow body, opening doors,
  red interior, reversed 'V' shape on grille,
  aluminium concave hubs, sidelights.
  Yellow box.......................................... **£70-80**
  **NB**  595h Traffic Sign 'Danger - End of Quay'
  included with French-made 1424.

**1424  Renault R12-TL**
  1977-78
- Spanish issue:
  Yellow body, fixed doors, aluminium
  concave hubs, second (corrected) grille,
  no sidelights. Yellow box ................... **£70-80**

**1424G Renault R12 Gordini Rally Car**
1971-71
- Blue, white stripes, RN '5', silver headlights, fixed doors, aluminium concave hubs, second grille, sidelights. Yellow box ..................... **£125-150**
  1974-78 <u>Spanish issue:</u>
- Blue (slightly darker than 1971 model), white stripes, yellow headlights, fixed doors, aluminium concave hubs, second grille, sidelights. Yellow box ........... **£100-125**

**1425 Matra 630 Le Mans**
1969-71 (scale 1:43)
- French Blue body, driver (Pescarolo), RN '5'. Plastic box .............................. **£60-70**

**1425E Matra 630 Le Mans**
1971-71 (scale 1:43)
- French Blue body, driver (Pescarolo), RN '5'. Yellow card box ................... **£80-100**
**NB** 595k Traffic Sign 'Road Narrows from Left' included with 1425.

**1426 Alfa-Romeo Carabo P33**
1969-71 (scale 1:43)
- Metallic Green/plain Green/Black/Orange, special wheels. Yellow box ................. **£70-80**
- Orange-Yellow/Green/Black/Orange-red, special wheels. Yellow box ............. **£100-125**
**NB** 595m Traffic Sign 'Danger - Loose Chippings' included with 1426.

**1428 Peugeot 304**
1970-74 (scale 1:43)
- White, concave hubs. Yellow box ..... **£80-100**
**NB** 595p Traffic Sign 'Humpback Bridge' included with French made 1428.
  1974-78 <u>Spanish issue:</u>
- Metallic Green, concave hubs. Yellow box............................................ **£70-90**

**1429 Peugeot 404 Police Car**
1970-71 (scale 1:43)
- Blue/White body, 'POLICE', plastic base, concave hubs. Yellow box...... **£250-350**
**NB** 595n Traffic Sign 'Cycling Prohibited' included with 1429.

**1430 Fiat Abarth 2000**
1970-71 (scale 1:43)
- Orange body, special wheels. Plastic box also contains a 595u Traffic Sign 'Dangerous Bends' ............................. **£30-40**

**1431 1970 Porsche 917**
Model planned but not actually issued.....NPP

**1432 Ferrari 312P**
1970-71 (scale 1:43)
- Red body, no driver, RN '60', special wheels. Plastic box also has a 595v Traffic Sign 'All Vehicles Prohibited' .................... **£60-75**

**1432E Ferrari 312P**
1971-?
- Red body, no driver, '60', special wheels. Card box .................... **£60-75**

**1433 Surtees TS5 V8 F1**
1971-74 (scale 1:43)
- Red body, white driver, yellow helmet, RN '5' or '14'. Yellow card box.......... **£40-50**

**1435 Citroën Présidentielle**
1970-71 (scale 1:43)
- Metallic Grey and plain Charcoal Grey body, chauffeur, felt carpet, flag, electric interior light, Speedwheels. Special plastic and rigid card box........................... **£450-600**

**1435E Citroën Présidentielle**
1971
- As 1435 but in blue presentation box (200 made) ..... **£1,500-1,750**

**1450 Simca 1100 'POLICE' Car**
1977-78
- <u>Spanish issue:</u> Blue/white or black/white body, plated concave hubs.................. **£50-60**

**1451 Renault R17-TS**
1978-? (scale 1:43)
- <u>Spanish issue:</u> Orange-Yellow, plated concave hubs .. **£50-60**
**NB** 1451 was announced in the 1976 French catalogue but production only took place in Spain from 1978.

**1452 Peugeot 504**
1977-78 <u>Spanish issues:</u>
- Metallic Copper body, fixed doors, special wheels. 'réf. 1452' on box....... **£50-60**
  1978-78
- Metallic Bronze body, fixed doors, special wheels. Box has: 'réf. 011452' and 'conformité du produit aux normes francaises'.......................................... **£50-60**
**NB** Different registration numbers (on labels) may be found on 1452.

**1453 Renault R6**
1977-78
- <u>Spanish issue:</u> Blue-grey, fixed bonnet, square headlamps, concave hubs ................... **£75-85**
**NB** Although only available in blue-grey, 1453 continued to be shown in yellow in contemporary catalogues.

**1454 Matra Simca Bagheera S**
1978-78 (scale 1:43)
- <u>Spanish issue:</u> Green body, concave hubs.................. **£35-45**

**1455 Citroën CX Pallas**
1978-78  (scale 1:43)
- Spanish issue:
Metallic blue body, concave hubs ....... **£50-60**
NB 1455 was announced (but not
illustrated) in the 1977 catalogue but
was not available before May 1978.

**1517 Renault R8**  (1:43)
1964-65  (renumbered in 1964 from 517)
- Blue, concave hubs. In blister pack... **£80-100**
- Yellow, concave hubs. Blister pack... **£80-100**

**1518 Renault R4L**
1964-65  (renumbered from 518)
First grille. Blister-packed.
- Pale Blue body............................... **£80-100**
- Light Blue body............................... **£80-100**
- Brick-Red body ............................... **£80-100**
- Maroon body ............................... **£80-100**
- Grey-Green body ...................................NGPP

**1519 Simca 1000**
1964-65  (renumbered in 1964 from 519)
- Light Blue-Grey, Red interior,
Black painted base. Blister pack ....... **£80-100**

**1520 Fiat 600 D**
1964-65  (renumbered in 1964 from 520)
- Red body, concave hubs. Bister pack.. **£70-90**
- Pale Yellow, concave hubs.
Bister pack ............................... **£70-90**

**1523 Simca 1500**  (1:43)
1964-65  (renumbered in 1964 from 523)
Blister-packed.
- Mid-Blue body, concave hubs ............. **£70-90**
- Light Blue body, concave hubs .......... **£70-90**
- Metallic Grey body, concave hubs ..... **£70-90**

**1539 VW Scirocco**
1980?  (scale 1:43)
- Spanish issue: Metallic Light Green
body, special wheels ........................... **£60-70**

**1540 Opel Kadett**
1964-65  (renumbered in 1964 from 540)
Blister-packed.
- Red body, concave hubs,
sliding windows................................. **£70-80**
- Pale Green body, concave hubs.......... **£70-80**
- Blue body, concave hubs ................. **£130-170**

**1540 Renault R14**
1980?  (scale 1:43)
- Spanish issue:
Metallic Bright Green body,
special wheels ................................... **£60-70**

**1541 Ford Fiesta**
1981?  (scale 1:43)
- Spanish issue:
Metallic Light Blue body,
special wheels ................................... **£50-60**

**1542 Chrysler 1308 GT**
1980?  (scale 1:43)
- Spanish issue:
Metallic Green, special wheels........... **£35-45**

**1543 Opel Ascona**
1980?  (scale 1:43)
- Spanish issue:
Orange-Yellow, special wheels........... **£60-70**

**1547 Panhard PL17**  (1:43)
1964-66  (renumbered in 1964 from 547)
- Violet body, anodised base, concave hubs,
sidelights under headlights.
In blister pack ................................... **£80-100**

- Brick Red body, anodised base, concave
hubs, sidelights under headlights.
In blister pack ................................... **£80-100**

**1552 Chevrolet Corvair**
1964-66  (renumbered in 1964 from 552)
Raised filler cap on some. Blister pack.
- Turquoise Blue body ........................... **£65-75**
- Orange-Red body............................ **£65-75**

**1553 Peugeot 404**
1964-66  (renumbered in 1964 from 553)
- Ivory body, dark red interior.
Blister pack.....................................**£90-110**

**1557 Citroën Ami 6**
1964-66  (renumbered in 1964 from 557)
- Green/White, no spare wheel.
Blister pack..................................... **£60-70**
- Blue/White, no spare wheel.
Blister pack..................................... **£60-70**

**1558 Citroën 2cv Azam**  (1:43)
1964-66  (renumbered in 1964 from 558)
- Yellow/Maroon body, grey concave
hubs (black tyres). In blister pack ....... **£45-60**
- Light Yellow/Maroon body, grey concave
hubs (black tyres). In blister pack ....... **£60-70**
- Green/Dark Green body, grey concave
hubs (black tyres). In blister pack ....... **£60-70**

**1559 Ford Taunus 17M**  (1:43)
1964-69  (renumbered in 1964 from 559)
(All have concave hubs).
- Metallic Gold body. Blister pack ........ **£70-90**
- Metallic Grey-Gold. Blister pack ........ **£70-90**
- Ivory body. Blister pack ..................... **£70-90**

---

**SOLIDO-COUGAR** Models. Cast by Solido in France, all the models are in
1:43 scale, all have plastic wheels and 'Dinky Toys France' on the plastic
base, and all were supplied in a 'Dinky Toys GB' box. Compare this list with
the 'COUGAR Model Toys' list that follows it.

| | | | |
|---|---|---|---|
| 1401 | 1981 | **Citroën 2cv6** | |
| | | Orange-red body (beige open top) with `ducks' decal ... | **£25-35** |
| | | Green body (grey open top) with `ducks' decal ............. | **£25-35** |
| 1402 | 1981 | **Citroën 2cv6** | |
| | | Orange-red body (beige closed top) with `ducks' decal. | **£25-35** |
| | | Green body (grey closed top) with `ducks' decal .......... | **£25-35** |
| 1402 | 1981 | **Citroën Visa** | |
| | | Metallic jade green (white base, tinted windows), | |
| | | no decals.................... | **£25-35** |
| | | Metallic red, (grey base, clear windows), no decals....... | **£25-35** |
| 1403 | 1981 | **Fiat Ritmo/Strada** | |
| | | Metallic orange body (dark cream base), no decals ...... | **£25-35** |
| | | Metallic blue body (yellow base), no decals ................. | **£25-35** |
| 1404 | 1981 | **BMW 530** | |
| | | Metallic green with `Cougar' decal .............................. | **£25-35** |
| | | Metallic purple with `flames' decal .............................. | **£25-35** |
| 1405 | 1981 | **Alfa-Romeo Alfetta GTV** | |
| | | Red body, `shamrock' decal.................................... | **£25-35** |
| | | Yellow body, `shamrock' decal ................................. | **£25-35** |
| 1406 | 1981 | **Peugeot 504** | |
| | | Metallic yellow with `cougar' decal ............................. | **£25-35** |
| | | Metallic blue with `flames' decal................................. | **£25-35** |
| | 1983 | Black body, `Dinky France' decal, plastic wheels. | |
| | | (Lyons 1983 promotional)........................................ | **£35-45** |

**COUGAR Model Toys**. Many of the 'Airfix Dinky Toys' appeared erratically
in the early 1980s (in France then in the UK) under the name of 'Cougar Model
Toys'. Every one had a plastic base marked 'Dinky Toys made in France' and
the code '1/43 07 80'. They were presented in card backed blister-packs with
'Metal Cougar' and 'Fabriqué par Solido' printing. Numbers printed on card are
100 less than numbers moulded on base.

| | | |
|---|---|---|
| 1301-1401 | **Citroën 2cv6** | |
| | Orange-red body with `ducks' decal, | |
| | Grey base/interior/open top........................................... | **£15-25** |
| | Green body, 'ducks' decal, grey base, orange interior, | |
| | tan open top.................................................................. | **£15-25** |
| 1302-1402 | **Citroën Visa** | |
| | Metallic jade green, no decal, white base, | |
| | dark cream interior........................................................ | **£15-25** |
| | Metallic red, no decal, grey base and interior........ | **£15-25** |
| 1303-1403 | **Fiat Ritmo** | |
| | Metallic orange (dark cream base/interior), no decal ..... | **£15-25** |
| | Metallic blue (yellow base/interior), no decal ............... | **£15-25** |
| 1304-1404 | **BMW 530** | |
| | Metallic green, 'cougar' decal, grey base, | |
| | black/grey interior, green tinted windows ..................... | **£15-25** |
| | Metallic purple, 'flames' decal, grey base, | |
| | black/grey interior, yellow tinted windows ................... | **£15-25** |
| 1305-1405 | **Alfetta GTV** | |
| | Red body, 'shamrock' decal, tan base, | |
| | black/tan interior, yellow tinted windows..................... | **£15-25** |
| | Yellow body, 'shamrock' decal, tan base, | |
| | black/tan interior, blue tinted windows........................ | **£15-25** |
| 1306-1406 | **Peugeot 504 Berline** | |
| | Metallic yellow, 'cougar' decal, brown base and tinted | |
| | windows, black/brown interior ...................................... | **£15-25** |
| | Metallic blue body, 'flames' decal, blue base and | |
| | interior, clear windows................................................. | **£15-25** |

# French Dinky Toys Commercial Vehicles

French Dinky commercial vehicles (in keeping with other ranges) have very similar series numbering to their English counterparts. But, like the cars, the French castings are different in many ways from the Liverpool produced versions and of course are marked 'Made in France' or 'Fab en France'.

An interesting point about the 25 Series is that although there was a range of body styles on offer at any one time, there was only one chassis casting for a particular period. This meant that the chassis dies wore out at a disproportionate rate to the body dies. Chassis castings are found that come from either a crisp new die or from one that is weary from over-use, and the appearance can be so different that some collectors have thought these to be the result

of intentional design changes. The only differences however are the ones noted in this listing.

On the French 25 series the headlights are larger and more pointed than the English equivalent. They were originally silver plated, later silver painted. The size of the headlights was reduced over the years and are best classed as large, medium and small. Modern replacement parts (radiator/grille/bumper) which are intended for the English lorries are not suitable for use on the French 25 Series. Like the cars, the lorries had 'DUNLOP' tyres, first in the colour of the body, later black or white. The problem of shortage of rubber affected the lorry production in 1940 and for four years after the war ended, so that in those periods the lorries had to be produced with all-

metal wheels. Metal failure affects pre-war mazak castings whether they are of French or English origin though the commercial vehicles seem not to be so drastically affected as for instance aircraft or ship models.

The first French Dinky Toys commercial vehicle model to be issued in an individual yellow box was 25-B Peugeot D3a Van in 1953. In England the Supertoys range was introduced in 1947 but it was not till 1955 that a French Supertoys model appeared. The 'Auto-Echelle de Pompiers' (Delahaye Fire Escape) was the first French model to be presented in the famous blue and white striped Supertoys box and was given the number 32-D.

| Model and details | MPR |
|---|---|
| **14 Triporteur** | |
| 1935-39 | |
| Tinplate base, smooth hubs (various colours), black or white 'DUNLOP' tyres, scale 1:40. The driver may be found as a solid casting or hollow-cast. His cap is usually the same colour as his jacket. His trousers and boots were black or very dark brown (hand applied paint that may vary in shade or extent). | |
| • Vehicle colours: Yellow, Red, Light Blue, Navy Blue. Driver's jacket: Blue, Grey or Green | **£750-1,000** |
| NB The 1935 catalogue illustration (a drawing) shows 14 with a front bumper but the existence of this version is very much in doubt. | |
| 1940-49 | |
| Plain cast wheels (black or unpainted), tinplate base, scale 1:40. Vehicle colours: | |
| • Yellow, Red, Light Blue, Navy Blue. Driver's jacket: Blue, Grey or Green | **£500-750** |
| 1950-52 | |
| • Painted ridged hubs with black rubber tyres, no base. Vehicle colours: Yellow, Red, Light Blue, Navy Blue. Driver's jacket: Blue, Grey or Green | **£250-500** |
| **14-C Coventry Climax Fork Lift Truck** | |
| 1950-59 (scale 1:43) | |
| • Orange/green/black, painted ridged hubs, grey tyres, made in England. French box (orange-red outer, yellow inner) | **£40-50** |
| NB 14-C was renumbered in 1959, then assembled in France and issued as 597. | |
| **25a Open Lorry** | |
| 1935-39 (scale 1:65) | |
| Open chassis, grille/headlights casting, front bumper, cast-in tow hook, painted smooth hubs, black or white 'DUNLOP' tyres. | |
| • Green/black | **£250-350** |
| • Blue/black | **£250-350** |
| • Yellow/brown | **£250-350** |
| **25a Open Lorry** | |
| 1940-48 | |
| Same, but with unpainted cast wheels. | |
| • Green/black or Red/black | **£250-350** |
| • Red/grey or Brown/grey | **£250-350** |
| **25-A Ford Livestock Truck** | |
| 1950-52 (scale 1:65) | |
| • Metallic Grey or Metallic Light Blue body, painted ridged hubs | **£150-200** |
| • Silver body, red ridged hubs | **£250-350** |
| • Yellow cab, Red back and ridged hubs | **£3,000-4,000** |

| Model and details | MPR |
|---|---|
| **25b Covered Lorry** | |
| 1935-39 (scale 1:65) | |
| Open chassis, grille/headlights casting, front bumper, cast-in tow hook, smooth hubs, black or white 'DUNLOP' tyres, removable tilt. | |
| • Green/black (green tilt), Blue/black (beige tilt), Red/brown (green tilt), Blue/red (beige tilt) | **£350-450** |
| **25b Covered Lorry** | |
| 1940-48 | |
| Open chassis, grille/headlights casting, front bumper, cast-in hook, unpainted cast (or Cream) wheels, removable tilt. | |
| • Red/black (green tilt), Blue/black (green tilt), Red/black (cream tilt), Red/grey (green tilt) | **£150-200** |
| **25-B Peugeot D3a Van** | |
| 1953-53 (scale 1:50) | |
| • Navy blue body (cross-hatching on inside of roof), no advertising, red ridged hubs | **£600-750** |
| • Grey body (cross-hatching on inside of roof), no advertising, red ridged hubs | **£600-750** |
| 1953-54 | |
| • Yellow and Green body (smooth inside roof), 'LAMPE MAZDA' logo, painted ridged hubs | **£200-300** |
| NB This was the first French Dinky Toys commercial vehicle model to be issued in an individual yellow box. | |
| **25BV Peugeot Post Van** | |
| 1954-59 (renumbered in 1959 as 560) | |
| • Dark Green body (smooth or cross-hatched inside roof), 'POSTES' (thin lettering, tampo). Box print: '25BV, marque déposée' only | **£130-160** |
| • Same model, but with box print: '25BV, marque déposée, Made in France, Imprimé en France' | **£130-160** |
| **25c Flat Truck** | |
| 1935-39 (scale 1:65) | |
| Open chassis, grille/headlights casting, front bumper, cast-in tow hook, smooth hubs, black or white 'DUNLOP' tyres. | |
| • Turquoise/black, Blue/black, Grey/red, Green/black or Red/brown | **£225-275** |
| 1940-48 | |
| Open chassis, grille/headlights casting, front bumper, cast-in tow hook, unpainted mazak wheels. | |
| • Blue/black, Green/black, Cream/red or Grey/red | **£100-125** |

| Model and details | MPR |
|---|---|
| **25-C Citroën H Van** | |
| 1954-57 (scale 1:50) | |
| • Metallic Grey and Gold body (official Citroën colours), painted ridged hubs. Yellow box (grey model shown) | **£100-125** |
| **25CG Citroën H Van** | |
| 1957-59 | |
| • Cream body, 'FROMAGE CH GERVAIS', in 25-C yellow box but with '25CG' sticker | **£160-190** |
| 1959-59 (renumbered in 1959 as 561) | |
| • Turquoise body (various shades), 'CIBIE', ridged or concave hubs, box with '25C' or '25CG' printed | **£300-400** |
| **25d Tanker Lorry** | |
| 1935-35 (scale 1:65) | |
| • Red body (smooth inside tank), no advertising, maroon open chassis (no hook), grille/headlights casting, front bumper, smooth hubs, red 'DUNLOP' tyres. | **£300-400** |
| 1936-37 | |
| • Red body (smooth or ridged inside tank), 'STANDARD ESSOLUBE', black open chassis, smooth hubs, black or white 'DUNLOP' tyres | **£300-400** |
| 1938-39 | |
| • Red body (ridged inside tank), 'ESSOLUBE - ESSO', black or red open chassis, smooth hubs, black or white 'DUNLOP' tyres | **£300-400** |
| **25d Tanker Lorry** | |
| 1940-49 | |
| • Red body (ridged inside tank), 'ESSOLUBE - ESSO', black open chassis, mazak wheels | **£200-300** |
| • Maroon body (ridged inside), 'ESSO' or 'ESSOLUBE', grey or black open chassis, mazak wheels | **£200-300** |
| **25-D Citroën 2cv Van 'BÉBÉ LORRAIN'** | |
| 1959-59 | |
| • Grey body, cream hubs. Only 80 made of this Code-2 promotional (see 562) | **£6,000-8,000** |
| **25e Tipping Lorry** | |
| 1935-39 (scale 1:65) | |
| Tipping rear truck body, open chassis, grille/headlights casting, front bumper, cast-in tow hook, smooth hubs, black or white 'DUNLOP' tyres. | |
| • Blue cab, Yellow body, black or brown chassis | **£240-300** |
| • Green cab, Blue body, black or red chassis | **£240-300** |
| • Green cab, Yellow body, red, black or brown chassis | **£240-300** |

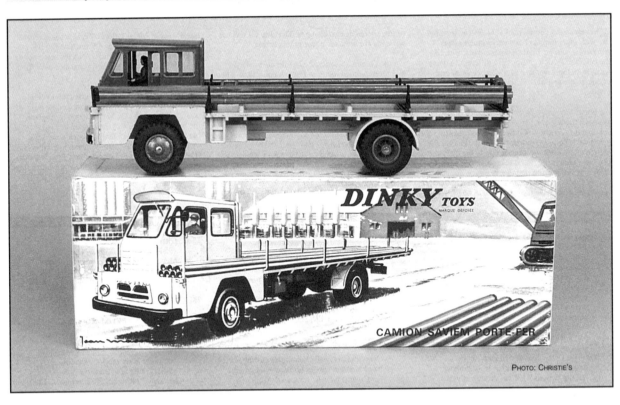

French Dinky Toys 885 Saviem Sinpar Steel Carrier
PHOTOGRAPHS: VECTIS AUCTIONS LTD.

French Dinky Toys 563 Renault Estafette Pick-up and 25C Citroën 1200Kg Van

1940-48
As previous version, but with painted
mazak wheels. Cab/body/chassis colours:
- Blue/yellow/black, Green/yellow/brown,
or Cream/green/red.......................... **£130-180**

### 25f  Market Gardener's Lorry
1935-39   (scale 1:65)
Open chassis, grille/headlights casting,
front bumper, cast-in tow hook, smooth
hubs, black or white 'DUNLOP' tyres.
- Violet body (black chassis)............. **£240-300**
- Cream body (black chassis) ............ **£240-300**
- Green body (red chassis)................ **£240-300**
- Grey body (black chassis).............. **£300-400**
1940-48
As previous version, but with unpainted
mazak wheels. Body/chassis colours:
- Cream/Red, Turquoise/Black,
Yellow/Red, Light Green/Grey ....... **£240-300**

### 25g  Flat Trailer with Headboard
1935-39   (scale 1:65)
- Blue, red or green, 4 mazak hubs,
black or white tyres............................ **£30-40**
1940-48
- Turquoise, red or green, two axles,
unpainted or black mazak wheels. ...... **£30-40**

1949-50
- Red or green, two axles, painted
ridged hubs, black tyres. .................... **£30-40**

### 25-H  Ford Beverage Truck
1949-49   (scale 1:65)
Flat truck with removable tailboard,
cast-in tow hook, spare wheel.
- Blue, Cream, Turquoise, Red, Brown,
Metallic Green, Bright Green body,
painted mazak wheels ..................... **£250-350**
1950-50
- Blue, Cream, Red, Brown, Bright
Green body, with ridged hubs......... **£300-400**
- Metallic green, bright green hubs ... **£300-400**
- Turquoise body, ridged hubs........ **£750-1,000**

### 25-I  Ford Open Wagon
1949-49   (scale 1:65)
- Blue, Red, Green, Dark Grey, Maroon,
or Brown body, cast-in towing hook,
painted mazak wheels ..................... **£150-200**

1950-50
- Beige or Metallic Grey body,
cast-in hook, painted ridged hubs
(colour as body) ............................. **£300-400**
1951-52
- Dark Red or Light Blue body, separate
rivetted hook and spare wheel,
matching ridged hubs..................... **£200-300**
- Cream body, separate rivetted hook
and spare wheel, matching
ridged hubs ............................... **£2,000-2,500**

### 25-J  Ford Covered Wagon
1949-50
(plain) Tinplate tilt (no advertising),
cast-in towing hook, spare wheel,
painted mazak wheels or ridged hubs.
- Metallic Gold (green tilt) ............... **£375-475**
- Red (green or red tilt).................... **£375-475**
- Light Blue (cream tilt) ................... **£375-475**
- Dark Blue (brown tilt).................... **£375-475**
- Brown (brown tilt) ........................ **£375-475**
- Brown (green tilt)........................... **£375-475**
- Cream body, brown tilt .................. **£375-475**

### 25-JB  'SNCF'
1949-50
- Blue (dark blue tilt), 'SNCF' round logo,
cast-in hook, black mazak wheels or
ridged hubs ............................... **£1,000-1,500**
1951-52
- Blue (dark blue tilt), 'SNCF' round logo,
separate hook, black ridged hubs.... **£400-500**

### 25-JJ  'CALBERSON'
1949-52   (scale 1:65)
Wide spacing to letters, plus map of
France, cast-in (later separate) hook.
- Yellow or Yellow Ochre body with black
tilt, painted mazak wheels or Red or
Black ridged hubs............................ **£600-800**

### 25-JV  'GRAND MOULINS DE PARIS'
1953-53
- Grey body, black tilt, separate hook,
painted ridged hubs ........................ **£300-400**

### 25-K  Studebaker Farm Produce Truck
1949-49   (scale 1:55)
Short lateral bonnet mouldings, small
windows, tool-box, painted mazak
wheels (usually black).
- Red/Blue, Blue/Turquoise,
Red/Yellow, Turquoise/Red ............ **£350-450**

- Blue/Greyish-Green ........................ **£350-450**
1950-50
- Red/Blue, Blue/Red, Blue/Turquoise,
Red/Turquoise-Green,
painted ridged hubs ........................ **£200-250**
1951-52
Long curved bonnet mouldings, large
windows, outline of tool-box only,
painted ridged hubs.
- Red/Yellow, Blue/Red,
Blue/Maroon ................................. **£150-200**
- Red cab, Blue back ........................ **£400-500**

### 25-L  Studebaker Covered Truck
1949-50
Short lateral bonnet mouldings, small
windows, tinplate tilt, tool-box,
painted mazak wheels or ridged hubs.
- Red body, yellow tilt ................... **£750-1,000**
- Blue body, yellow or brown tilt ... **£750-1,000**
- Turquoise body, cream or yellow
tilt, red or cream hubs .................. **£750-1,000**
1951-52
Long curved bonnet mouldings,
large windows, tool-box outline only,
painted ridged hubs
- Blue (brown tilt, blue hubs) ........... **£300-400**
- Red (yellow tilt, red hubs) ............. **£300-400**

### 25-M  Studebaker Tipping Truck
1949-50   (scale 1:55)
Short bonnet mouldings, small windows,
tool-box, painted mazak wheels or
ridged hubs.
- Dark Green/Metallic Grey ............. **£100-130**
- Dark Green/Plain Grey................... **£100-130**
1951-52
Long bonnet curved bonnet mouldings,
large windows, tool-box outline only,
painted ridged hubs.
- Dark Green/Metallic Grey ................ **£70-85**
- Dark Green/Plain Grey...................... **£70-85**
- Khaki/silver (cream hubs).............. **£700-900**

### 25-M  Ford Tipping Truck
1950-55   (scale 1:65)
- Green cab, Metallic or Plain Grey
tipper, black or green ridged hubs. ..... **£65-75**

PHOTO: COLLECTOYS

**25-O  Studebaker Milk Truck**
1949-50  (scale 1:55)
- Blue/Eggshell Cream or Blue/White,
'NESTLÉ' (transfer), short bonnet
mouldings, small windows, tool-box,
painted wheels or ridged hubs,
ten milk churns. Red box with
yellow interior ................................ **£400-600**
1951-54
- Blue/White, 'NESTLÉ' advertising on
some, long curved bonnet mouldings,
large windows, tool-box outline only,
painted ridged hubs, ten churns.
Red box with yellow inner ............. **£350-450**

**25-O  Ford Milk Truck**
1950-50
- Blue/White body, 'NESTLÉ' (transfer,
thick lettering). Long red box with
yellow inner, card spacer ............... **£400-500**
1954-55
- Blue/white body, 'NESTLÉ' (tampo,
plain or open (later) lettering).
Shorter (correct length) box ........... **£450-550**

**25-P  Studebaker Pick-Up**
1949-49  (scale 1:55)
- Mustard-Yellow and Dark Red body, painted
mazak wheels, short bonnet mouldings,
small windows, tool-box ................. **£500-600**
1950-55
- Yellow/Red, ridged hubs, short or long
bonnet mouldings, small or large
windows, box outline only. ............. **£100-150**

**25-Q  Studebaker Covered Pick-Up**
1949-49  (scale 1:55)
- Green cab and tilt, Red body, short bonnet
mouldings, small windows, tool-box,
painted wheels ................................ **£500-750**
- Dark Grey-Green cab and tilt, Yellow
ochre body, painted wheels ............. **£500-750**
1950-52
- Green/Yellow, Green hubs, short or long
bonnet mouldings, small or large
windows, box outline only ............. **£500-700**

**25-R  Studebaker Breakdown Truck**
1949-50
- Red body, 'DINKY SERVICE' on some,
short bonnet mouldings, small windows,
tool-box, painted mazak wheels or
ridged hubs ................................... **£400-500**
1951-54
- Red body, 'DINKY SERVICE', long curved
bonnet mouldings, large windows, tool-box
outline only, painted ridged hubs .... **£150-200**

**25-R  Ford Breakdown Truck**
1954-54  (scale 1:65)
- Red body, 'DINKY SERVICE',
red ridged hubs, black tyres. .......... **£300-400**
1954-55
- Red body, no logo, plated ridged
hubs, white tyres. ................................NGPP

**25-S  Single-axle Trailer**
1949-49  (scale 1:55)
- Red body, concave rear lamps,
painted wheels .................................... **£30-35**
1950-50
- Red (Cream hubs), Yellow (Red hubs),
Green (Yellow hubs). Concave or
raised rear lamps ............................... **£30-35**

**25-T  Single-axle Covered Trailer**
1949-49
As 25-S but with tinplate tilt, concave
rear lamps, painted mazak wheels.
- Red body (green tilt), or
Yellow body (brown tilt) ................... **£30-35**

1950-55
- Red (green tilt, green ridged hubs),
Yellow (brown tilt, yellow ridged hubs).
Concave or raised rear lamps ............. **£30-35**

**25-U  Ford Tanker**
1950-50  (scale 1:65)
- Red body, 'ESSO', painted ridged
hubs, hook and spare wheel support,
pierced base ................................... **£400-500**
1951-51
- As previous model but without the
support for hook/spare wheel ......... **£120-140**
1952-53
- As 1951 version but with smaller
transfers and non-pierced base ........ **£100-125**

**25-V  Ford Refuse Tipper**
1950-51  (scale 1:65)
- Dark Green body, Dark or Mid-Green
ridged hubs, smooth tailgate
interior surface ................................ **£80-100**
1952-55
- Dark Green body, dark-green ridged
hubs, cross-braced tailgate
interior surface ................................ **£70-90**

**27AC  Massey-Harris Tractor
and Manure Spreader**
1950-50  (scale 1:43)
- Red tractor and implement made in
England, painted wheels,
French display box (Red) ............... **£400-600**

**30e  Breakdown Lorry**
1936-39  (scale 1:65)
Fitted with the (lead) crane from 21d
Railway Crane Truck. , smooth hubs,
'DUNLOP' tyres.
- Yellow body, green crane, brown or
black chassis ................................... **£300-350**
- Red body, green crane, red or Black
chassis; or Blue body, green crane,
black chassis ................................... **£300-350**
1938-39
- Green body, green crane, brown
chassis; or Red body, red crane,
black chassis ................................... **£300-350**
1940-40
- With mazak wheels. Blue body
with blue crane, or Yellow body,
black chassis ................................ **£900-1,200**

**PANHARD ARTICULATED LORRIES:**
**32-A**  (plain)  (scale 1:60)
1952-52
- Blue body, plain or silver grille,
painted ridged hubs. Sold unboxed. **£200-250**
**32-AB**                            **'SNCF'**
1952-52
- Blue body, 'SNCF' (locomotive in round
logo), painted ridged hubs.
Sold unboxed (3 to a trade box) ...... **£400-500**
1954-59  (renumbered in 1959 as 575)
- Blue body, 'SNCF' (pale green French
map logo), painted ridged hubs.
Sold unboxed (three to a trade box)
or later in own yellow box
(add £30 to price) ........................... **£150-200**
**32-AJ  'KODAK'**
1952-53
- Yellow body (smooth inside cab roof),
'KODAK', painted ridged hubs,
Sold unboxed (supplied to shops in
trade boxes of three) ....................... **£400-500**
1955-57
- Yellow body (cross-hatching in cab roof),
'KODAK', painted ridged hubs. Sold
unboxed (supplied to shops in
trade boxes of three) ....................... **£450-550**
- US issue:
Yellow body, (different letter shape
from the French issue) ................ **£800-1,100**

**32C  Panhard Titan-Coder Tanker, 'ESSO'**
1954-55
- Red body, 'ESSO' (large transfers), painted
ridged hubs, '32C TRACTEUR
PANHARD' on Yellow box ........... **£160-200**
1956-59  (renumbered in 1959 as 576)
- Red body, 'ESSO' (medium transfers), '32C
TRACTEUR PANHARD' in 5 languages
on Yellow box ............................... **£130-160**

**33A  Simca Cargo Van**
1955-56  (scale 1:55)
Indented (early) or raised (later) cab
step-plate, no hook mounting,
spare wheel held by screw.
- Olive-Green/Yellow (green/yellow
picture on yellow box), painted
ridged hubs .................................... **£140-200**
- Olive-Green/Orange (green/orange
picture on yellow box), painted
ridged hubs .................................... **£140-200**
**33AN  Simca Cargo Van, 'BAILLY'**
1956-59  (renumbered in 1959 as 577)
Indented or raised cab step-plate, with hook
and mounting, spare wheel held by screw.
- Yellow/White body, 'BAILLY
DEMENAGEMENTS' logo, painted
ridged hubs, yellow box ................. **£200-250**

**33-B  Simca Cargo Tipper Truck**
1955-59  (renumbered in 1959 as 578)
Indented (later raised) cab step-plate, no
hook mounting, smooth or grooved tipper
surface, indented (later raised) tailgate
central reinforcement, painted ridged hubs.
- Dark Green/Grey, Dark Green/Metallic
Grey, Metallic Dark Green/Metallic
Grey. Yellow box ............................ **£90-110**
- Later version of previous models, with
hook and mounting. Yellow box ........ **£90-110**

**33-C  Simca Glazier's Truck**
1955-59  (renumbered in 1959 as 579)
- Grey/Dark Green, indented or raised cab
step-plate, hook mounting on later issues,
grey ridged hubs.  Scale 1:55.
'MIROITIER SAINT-GOBAIN'.
Yellow box has '33C MIROITIER'
in French, later in 5 languages ........ **£120-170**

**34-A  Berliet Quarry Truck**
1955-59  (renumbered in 1959 as 580)
No spare wheel support, ridged and concave
painted hubs, scale 1:55.
- Blue/black, orange tipper. Box first
without then with picture and '34A' .. **£90-110**
1957-59
Promotional: Blue/black, Orange tipper.
In 'BERLIET' yellow box .............. **£500-750**

**34-B  Berliet Container Truck**
1956-57  (renumbered in 1959 as 581)
Spare wheel screwed on, iron container-
lifting eye, ridged and concave painted hubs.
- Red/Black/Light Grey, matt grey container.
No picture on yellow box ............... **£100-120**
1957-59
- As previous model but with cast-in lifting
eye, yellow box has picture and
'34B plateau avec container' .......... **£100-120**
- Promotional: Yellow body,
'BAILLY' on container .................. **£120-140**

**35-A  Citroën U23 Breakdown Truck**
1955-55  (scale 1:50)
- Red body, large tool-box, closed fuel
tank, 'DINKY TOYS' logo.
'35A' on box ..................................**£110-140**
1956-59  (renumbered in 1959 as 582)
- Dark Red body, small tool-box, open fuel
tank, Yellow 'DINKY TOYS' logo.
'35A' on box ..................................**£110-140**

**36-A  Willeme Log Lorry**
1956-59  (renumbered in 1959 as 897)
• Orange cab, Yellow semi-trailer (pierced
beam), wooden logs, black painted base,
painted ridged and concave hubs,
radial tread tyres, scale 1:55.
'36A' on Supertoys box .................. **£100-130**

**36-B  Willeme Tractor & Closed Trailer**
1958-59  (renumbered in 1959 as 896)
• Red tractor, Orange semi-trailer with
removable green plastic tilt, painted ridged
and concave hubs, 4 rollers on trailer
prop. '36B' on Supertoys box ......... **£150-200**

**38-A  Unic Marrel Multi-Skip Truck**
1957-59  (renumbered in 1959 as 895)
• Grey and Golden-Yellow (or Lemon-Yellow)
body (windows in some), fixed skip,
ridged and concave painted hubs, black
radial or block tread tyres.
'38A' on Supertoys box .................. **£130-170**

**39-A  Unic Boilot Car Transporter**
1957-59  (renumbered in 1959 as 894)
• Silver/orange, ridged and concave hubs,
black radial tread tyres, scale 1:55,
'39A' on Supertoys box .................. **£180-200**
• With all-Red trailer, Black hubs...... **£500-750**

**39-B  Unic Sahara Pipe Transporter**
1959-60  (renumbered in 1960 as 893)
• Beige body (various shades), White roof,
'open' trailer, painted ridged and concave
hubs, 6 black tubes, scale 1:55.
'893' on Supertoys box .................. **£120-150**

**50  Salev Mobile Crane**
1957-59  (1:43)  (renumbered in 1959 as 595)
• Grey body, Red crane, Blue driver,
ridged and concave painted hubs  ... **£120-150**

**70  Two-Axle Covered Trailer**
1957-59  (1:60)  (renumbered in 1959 as 810)
• Red or Yellow, green tilt, ridged or
concave hubs. '70' on yellow box ...... **£30-40**

**90-A  Richier Diesel Roller**
1958-59  (renumbered in 1959 as 830)
• Yellow body, blue driver,
red roller wheels, '90A' on
Yellow box. Supertoy ......................... **£90-110**

**560  Muir-Hill Dumper**
1951-?
• Yellow body, metal wheels. Imported
from England; sold in special blue
box, French printing on label ............. **£55-65**

**560  Peugeot D3A Van**
1959-60 (1:50) (renumbered from 25-BV)
• Dark or Light Grey body,
painted ridged hubs ........................ **£550-625**

**560  Peugeot Post Van, 'POSTES'**
1959-60
• Dark Green body, 'POSTES' (thick letters,
transfer). Box print: '25BV, marque
déposée' only .................................... **£150-200**
• Same model, but box print reads:
'25BV, marque déposée, Made in
France, Imprimé en France' ........... **£150-200**
1960-61
• Same model, but 'POSTES' transfer
has oval or more square letter 'O'.
Box reads '25BV/560' .................... **£150-200**
1960-61
• Same model (transfer with oval 'O' of
'POSTES'), concave painted hubs.
'560' on box .................................. **£150-200**

**560  Peugeot D3a Van 'CIBIE'**
1960
• Promotional: Turquoise body,
yellow ridged hubs .................. **£2,500-3,500**

**560-P  Citroën 2cv Van 'PHILIPS'**
1961
• Promotional: Yellow cab, Silver back,
red  logo and design on door .... **£4,000-5,000**

**560  Citroën 2cv Postal Service Van**
1963-70
• Yellow body and concave hubs,
blue 'swallow' logo. Yellow box print reads:
'C'est une fabrication MECCANO', or
(later): 'C'est une fabrication
MECCANO TRI-ANG' .................. **£125-150**

**560-E  Citroën 2cv Azam Van**
1968-70
• Pale Green body, plated concave hubs,
'PIRELLI' tyres, 'DINKY-POCH' on
box. Export to Spain ................. **£1,750-2,250**

**561  Blaw-Knox Bulldozer**
1951-59  (renumbered in 1959 as 885)
• Red/black, with driver. Model made in
England, Blue box made in France. **£100-125**

**561  Citroën H Van**
1959-59 (1:50)  (renumbered from 25-CG)
• Cream body, 'FROMAGE CH GERVAIS',
In own box with
'25CG GERVAIS' print................... **£200-250**
1959-63
• Turquoise body (various shades), 'CIBIE',
painted ridged hubs (concave from 1961).
In 25CG box with '561 CIBIE' sticker
over the number ............................ **£300-400**
1963-66
• White/blue body, 'GLACES GERVAIS',
blue concave hubs. Picture box....... **£400-500**
1964-64
• Code-2 promotional: Blue body,
'BAROCLEM', aluminium concave
hubs. Special picture box .......... **£4,000-6,000**

**561  Renault 4L Van**
1972-72  (scale 1:43)
• Yellow body, 'PTT', first grille, grey
security window, plastic base,
chromed concave hubs ............. **£2,500-3,000**

**562  Muir-Hill Dumper**
1951-?  (scale 1:43)
• Golden Yellow, with driver, model made
in England, Blue box made in France. **£50-60**

**562H  Citroën 2cv Van, 'WEGENWACHT'**
1965-68
• Yellow body, concave hubs, '25D' on
black painted base or anodised base
without '25D'. Model made for export
to Netherlands. Yellow box marked
'WW' from 1968 ............................ **£500-750**

PHOTO: COLLECTOYS.

**563 Renault Estafette Pick-Up**
1960-62  (scale 1:43)
- Orange or Green body, green tilt, painted concave hubs. Yellow box without, later with, illustration .......................... **£60-80**

**564 Renault Mirror Truck**
1963-65  (scale 1:43)
- Red-Orange body, 'SAINT-GOBAIN / MIROITIER', painted concave hubs. Yellow box ............................... **£150-175**
- As previous model but with Brick Red body. Yellow box .......... **£150-175**

**565 Renault Estafette Camper**
1965-71  (scale 1:43)
- Blue body, Ivory plastic roof, chromed concave hubs. Yellow box............... **£200-250**

**566 Citroën H Currus Van 'POLICE'**
1965-70
- Blue/White body, painted concave hubs, working warning lights.......... **£200-300**

**567 Unimog Snow Plough**
1967-70  (scale 1:50)
- Yellow/black body, brown removable top, painted concave hubs. Yellow box.. **£120-140**

**569 Berliet Stradair Side Tipper**
1967-71  (scale 1:43)
- Light Green/Dark Green body, painted hubs, green or black motor. Yellow box, instruction leaflet ........ **£250-400**

**570 PEUGEOT J7 TAXI VANS:**
**570 'ALLO-FRET'**
1967-67  (scale 1:43)
- Blue body, blue or white roof, aluminium concave hubs, aerial. Yellow box.... **£300-400**

**570 'IMPERIAL CHEMICAL INDUSTRIES'**
1968-68
- Blue/White. Code 2 promo ....... **£1,000-1,500**

**570A 'AUTOROUTES'**
1970-71  (scale 1:50)
- Orange body, two workmen plus equipment, On diorama base in yellow box (also containing a 595s Traffic Sign 'Pedestrians Prohibited') ................ **£600-750**

**571 Coles Mobile Crane**
1951-57  (scale 1:50)
- Yellow and Black, painted hubs. Model made in England, Blue box made in France (see 972).............................. **£70-80**

**571 Saviem Goelette Horse Box and Sulky**
1969-71  (scale 1:43)
- Blue/'wood'/White, painted concave hubs, racehorse, Green two-wheel racing cart (sulky) with driver. Yellow picture box ....................... **£900-1,200**

**572 Berliet Quarry Truck**
1970-71  (scale 1:43)
- Red body, Yellow plastic tipper, plastic hubs, 595d Traffic Sign 'No Overtaking For Heavy Vehicles' also in yellow box **£400-650**

**575 Panhard Articulated Lorry, 'SNCF'**
1959-63 (renumbered in 1959 from 32-AB)
- Blue body, 'SNCF' on Pale (later Dark) Green French map logo, painted ridged or concave hubs. Sold unboxed (three to a trade box), later in own Yellow box (add £30 to price) ........................... **£120-150**

**576 Panhard Titan-Coder Tanker, 'ESSO'**
1959-60 (renumbered in 1959 from 32-C)
- Red body, 'ESSO' (medium lettering), painted ridged hubs. '32C TRACTEUR PANHARD' in 5 languages on yellow box............. **£175-200**
1960-61
- Red or Dark Red body, 'ESSO' (smaller lettering), painted ridged hubs (concave from 1961). Yellow box has 'DINKY TOYS' in italics, '576' and description in 5 languages on flap ..................... **£160-200**
1961-61
- Same, but with concave hubs......... **£200-250**

**577 Simca Cargo Van, 'BAILLY'**
1959-61 (renumbered in 1959 from 32AN)
- Yellow/White body, 'BAILLY DEMENAGEMENTS'. Indented or raised cab step-plate, with hook support, spare wheel held by screw (later by rivet), painted ridged hubs (later concave) **£540-200**

**577 Berliet Livestock Truck**
1965-71  (scale 1:43)
- Yellow and Green, two black and white cows, painted concave hubs. Yellow box ....................................... **£150-200**

**578 Simca Cargo Tipper Truck**
1959-70 (renumbered in 1959 from 33-B)
- Dark or Mid-Green/Metallic Grey, indented or raised cab step-plate, with hook mounting, spare wheel held by screw (later by rivet), scale 1:55. Yellow box ...... **£80-100**

**579 Simca Mirror Truck, 'SAINT-GOBAIN'**
1959-61 (renumbered in 1959 from 33C)
- Grey/Dark Green, 'MIROITIER SAINT-GOBAIN'. Indented or raised cab step-plate, with hook mounting, spare wheel screwed on, Grey or Yellow ridged hubs, scale 1:55. Yellow box has '33C MIROITIER' in 5 languages.................................. **£120-160**
1961-67
- Yellow/Dark Green, Yellow ridged hubs, spare wheel rivetted. Yellow box changed to read: '579-33C'........................... **£140-180**
- Yellow/Dark Green or Grey/Dark Green, Grey ridged hubs or Cream concave hubs ....................... **£150-200**
196?-6?
- Export model: Pale Grey/Pale Green, without 'SAINT-GOBAIN', Cream ridged or concave hubs. ..... **£100-150**

**580 Berliet Quarry Truck**
1959-61 (renumbered in 1959 from 34A)
- As 34-A but with spare wheel support, ridged and concave painted hubs, block tread tyres. Blue/Black, Orange tipper. Picture on yellow box .................... **£150-175**
1961-70
- Same model but with cast-in spare wheel location, concave painted hubs and anodised base .................. **£150-175**

**581 Berliet Container Truck**
1959-60 (renumbered in 1959 from 34B)
Spare wheel held by screw, ridged and/or concave painted hubs, round (later square) section tyres.
- Red/Black/Light Grey, Dark Grey container. Picture on yellow box..... **£100-120**
1960-65
- Same, but spare wheel rivetted on. Yellow box has picture and '34B plateau avec container' in 7 languages ........ **£120-140**

**582 Citroën Breakdown Truck, 'DINKY TOYS'**
1959-69 (renumbered in 1959 from 34A)
Painted ridged hubs, smooth black tyres, small tool-box, open fuel tank, 1:50.
- Dark red body, yellow 'DINKY TOYS' logo. '35A' on box.......................... **£100-150**
1969-71
- Red body and concave hubs, yellow logo, plastic hook, smooth or treaded black tyres. '582' on box .......................... **£120-160**

**584 Berliet Covered Lorry**
1961-65  (scale 1:43)
- Red or Yellow body (either with Green tilt), concave hubs. Yellow box (picture on later ones)................ **£100-120**

**585 Berliet Builders Lorry**
1961-64  (scale 1:43)
- Blue/Orange/Grey, wide (later narrow) boards in tipping body, painted concave hubs. Yellow box............... **£100-125**

**586 Citroën 55 Milk Lorry**
1961-65  (scale 1:43)
- White/Blue body, 30 bottle crates, painted concave hubs. Yellow box.. **£500-700**

**587 Citroën H Display Van, 'PHILIPS'**
1964-70  (scale 1:43)
- Yellow/Silver body, red concave hubs, household appliances. Yellow picture box .......................... **£600-800**

**588 Berliet Beer Lorry**
1964-70  (scale 1:43)
- Yellow/Red/Brown, 'BIERES, LIMONADES, EAUX MINÉRALES', painted concave hubs, crates and barrels. Yellow picture box ............. **£250-300**

**588K** 1970-71
- Code 1 Promotional: Red body, 'KRONENBOURG LE GRAND NOM des BIERES d'ALSACE'......... **£3,500-4,500**

**589 Berliet Breakdown Lorry**
1965-69  (scale 1:43)
- Red body, 'DEPANNAGE' in yellow or white, chromed concave hubs..... **£250-300**
1970-71
- Orange body, 'DEPANNAGE AUTOROUTES', chromed concave hubs, aerial. 595t Traffic Sign 'Maximum Height 3.5 metres' included in box . **£250-300**

**595 Salev Mobile Crane**
1959-61
- As reference 50 but crane pillar not held by rivet, painted concave hubs...**£80-110**

**596 LMV Road Sweeper/Washer**
1960-63  (scale 1:43)
- Cream and Green body, rotating and pivoting brush mechanism. Yellow box .......................................**£80-110**

**597 Coventry Climax Fork Lift Truck**
1959-61 (renumbered in 1959 from 14-C)
- Orange/Yellow (or Green)/Black, ridged or concave hubs, 'assemblé en France' on base............. **£60-75**

**803 Unic Articulated Lorry, 'SNCF'**
1967-69  (scale 1:43)
- Dark Blue body, cream trailer roof, 'SNCF' and 'PAM-PAM', plastic hubs. Yellow picture box................ **£250-350**

**805  Unic Multi Skip and Gas Tanker**
1966-71   (scale 1:55)
• Red/Black/White, interchangeable skip
  and 'PROPANE-PRIMAGAZ' gas tank
  (from Hornby ACHO range), painted
  concave hubs. Yellow picture box .. **£300-400**

**810  Two-Axle Covered Trailer**
1959-62   (renumbered in 1959 from 70)
• Red or Yellow, Green tilt, ridged or
  concave hubs, scale 1:60.
  '70' (later '810') on Yellow box ......... **£40-50**
  1962-?
• **Two-Axle Covered Trailer, 'ESSO'**
  Red body and tilt, 'ESSO' transfers,
  painted concave hubs. Yellow box...... **£55-65**

**830  Richier Diesel Roller**
1959-69   (renumbered in 1959 from 90A)
• Yellow body, Blue driver, Red wheels,
  '90A-830' (later '830') on Yellow box,
  scale 1:43. Supertoy .......................... **£90-120**

**881  GMC Circus Truck and Animal Trailer**
1969-70   (scale 1:43)
• Red/Yellow/Black, 'PINDER FAUVES',
  no hole in seat for driver, plastic animals,
  card supports, 'SUPER DINKY MECCANO
  FRANCE' on chassis, painted
  concave hubs. Yellow box......... **£1,000-1,500**
  1970-71
• Same, but with hole in seat for driver, and
  'DINKY-TOYS MECCANO TRI-ANG'
  on chassis ................................. **£1,000-1,500**

**882  Peugeot 404 + Circus Caravan**
1969-70
• Red/Yellow/White Peugeot 404 (536) and
  Caravelair Armagnac 420 Caravan (564),
  **'Le SUPER CIRQUE PINDER'** roof
  hoardings, chromed concave hubs. Yellow
  box also contains : a 595L Traffic Sign
  'Maximum Width 2 metres', 'Martin'
  the circus bear and a leaflet ...... **£1,500-1,800**

**885  Blaw-Knox Bulldozer**
1959-61   (scale 1:43)
• Orange/Grey/Black, driver.
  'Assemblé en France' on base (see 561).
  Blue/White striped picture box ....... **£150-175**

**885  Saviem Sinpar Steel Carrier**
1966-71   (scale 1:43)
• Red cab, grey chassis, driver, plastic
  hubs, steel load held by magnets.
  Yellow picture box (showing
  yellow/grey vehicle)....................... **£300-350**

**886  Richier Road Profiler**
1960-65   (scale 1:43)
• Yellow body, driver, plastic hubs.
  Supertoys box.................................. **£200-250**

**887  Muir-Hill Dumper**
1959-61   (scale 1:43)
• Yellow-Cream body, driver, painted ridged
  hubs. English components,
  'Assemblé en France' on base............. **£40-50**

**887  Unic Articulated Tanker, 'BP'**
1963-71   (scale 1:43)
• White/Green/Lemon Yellow, 'AIR BP',
  plastic hubs, hoses for filling tank,
  electric lights switched by spare wheel.
  Supertoys blue/white box with
  full colour picture on lid ................ **£150-200**

**888  Berliet Sahara Pipe-Layer**
1960-66   (scale 1:50)
• Sand body (various shades), White roof,
  operable crane, most with White or Beige
  plastic hubs (a few cast metal), most
  with tow hook (a few without)........ **£175-225**
  1968
• Promotional:  As previous model but with
  'Société Languedocienne de
  Forages Pétroliers'.................... **£1,000-1,200**

**889  Coles Mobile Crane**
1959-62
• Orange/Yellow, 2 drivers, painted concave
  hubs, 'Assemblé en France' on base.
  Renumbered in 1959 from 972;
  reissued in 1962 as 972 ...................... **£60-80**

**893  Unic Sahara Pipe Transporter**
1960-70   (renumbered in 1960 from 39B)
• Beige body (various shades), White roof,
  window glazing, pierced (later solid) trailer
  painted ridged and concave hubs, 6 tubes,
  scale 1:55. Supertoys box without
  (later with) '893' ............................ **£150-175**
  196?
• Code 2 Promotional:  Beige body, White
  roof, window glazing, 'solid' trailer, painted
  concave hubs. 'DESTINATION: PETROLE
  DU SAHARA' on box...........................NGPP

**894  Unic Boilot Car Transporter**
1959-68   (renumbered in 1959 from 39A)
• Silver/Orange, 'DINKY TOYS SERVICE
  LIVRAISON', painted concave hubs,
  black block tread tyres, scale 1:55.
  '894' on Supertoys box .................. **£150-180**

**895  Unic Marrel Multi-Body Truck**
1959-65   (renumbered in 1959 from 38A)
• Grey and Golden-Yellow body, fixed skip,
  ridged and concave (or all concave) painted
  hubs, black block tread tyres, scale 1:55.
  '895' on Supertoys box .................. **£120-140**

**896  Willeme Tractor and Covered Trailer**
1959-71   (renumbered in 1959 from 36B)
• Red tractor, inclined (later straight) chassis
  members, Orange semi-trailer, Green tilt,
  painted ridged and/or concave hubs,
  4 (later 2) rollers on trailer prop.
  '36B-896' (later just '896') on
  Supertoys box................................. **£140-180**

**897  Willeme Log Lorry**
1959-71   (renumbered in 1959 from 36A)
• Orange tractor (chassis members on spindle),
  Yellow semi-trailer (pierced, later solid),
  black painted base, painted concave hubs,
  radial or block tread tyres, 1:55.
  '897-36A' (later just '897') on
  Supertoys box................................. **£125-165**

**898  Berliet Transformer Carrier,'ALSTHOM'**
1961-65
• Orange body, Grey transformer (loose parts
  within), painted ridged (later concave) hubs.
  Supertoys box................................. **£400-500**

**972  Coles Mobile Crane**
1957-62   (renumbered in 1959 to 889)
• Orange and Yellow, two drivers, painted
  concave hubs, scale 1:50. English parts,
  'Assemblé in France' on base ............. **£60-80**

**1412  Hotchkiss Willys Recovery Jeep**
1968-71   (scale 1:50)
• Red and Yellow body, Orange or
  Black jib with lamp, painted
  concave hubs .................................. **£100-130**

211

# French Dinky Toys Emergency Vehicles

| Model and details | MPR |
|---|---|

**25BR  Peugeot D3a Fire Service Van**
1959
- A prototype exists with a light red body (cross-hatching inside roof), dark red ridged hubs and identical transfers to the 25D Citroën van ...........................NPP

**25D  Citroën 2cv Fire Service Van**
1958-59 (1:43) (renumbered in 1959 to 562)
- Red body and ridged hubs, 'Pompiers Ville de Paris'. Yellow box. ........... **£130-170**
1959-59
Grey body, 'BÉBÉ LORRAIN', cream hubs. Only 80 were made of this Code-2 promotional model ................... **£3,500-5,000**

**32D  Delahaye Fire Escape**
1955-59 (renumbered in 1959 to 899)
- Red body, chromed ladder, painted ridged hubs, smooth White tyres (specially made for this model), scale 1:55. Blue/White striped Supertoys box. (32-D was the first of the French Dinky Supertoys).............................**£150-200**

**32E  Berliet First-Aid Vehicle** (see picture below)
1957-59 (renumbered in 1959 to 583)
- Bright Red (occasionally Brownish-Red) twin-cab body (no markings), detachable hose reel, painted ridged (concave through 1959) hubs, white tyes, scale 1:55, '32E' on Supertoys box..................**£150-200**

**80F  Renault Military Ambulance**
1959-59 (renumbered in 1959 to 820)
- Renault Goelette in Gloss or matt finish, painted ridged hubs, scale 1:55. Yellow box ........................**£60-75**

**501  Citroën DS19 'POLICE' Car**
1967-70
- Very dark blue/white, roof beacon, plated concave hubs, scale 1:43 ......**£160-200**

**507P  Simca 1500 'POLICE' Estate Car**
1967-71
- Dark blue/white body. Commissioned for use by Police.............................**£300-350**

**517P  Renault R8 'POLICE' Car**
1969
- Dark blue/white. Commissioned for use by Police ..................................**£400-450**

**518  Renault 4L**
1964-64
- Red body, 'POMPIERS de PARIS'. Commissioned by Fire Service ....... **£375-425**

**525  Peugeot 404 Fire Car**
1964-64
- Red body, 'Pompiers de Paris', concave chromed hubs. Commissioned for use by Fire Service. ...............................**£400-500**

**551  Ford Taunus 17M Police Car**
1965-67 (scale 1:43)
- Green/white, 'POLIZEI', plated concave hubs, German text on box. Made for export to Germany and Benelux countries........................**£800-1,000**

**556  Citroën ID19 Ambulance**
1964-67
- Same, but 'A' of 'Ambulance' and 'M' of 'Municipale' are not aligned. 'Super detail' box ..............................**£80-100**
1967-70
- Grey/cream body, plated concave hubs, 'DUNLOP' nylon tyres, plastic steering wheel, without '556' on base, 'A' of 'Ambulance' and 'M' of 'Municipale' are not aligned. 'Super detail' box ...**£110-140**

**562  Citroën 2cv Van**
1959-61 (renumbered in 1959 from 25-D)
- Red body and ridged hubs, 'POMPIERS VILLE de PARIS', scale 1:43 .........**£130-170**
1961-63
- Red body and concave hubs, 'POMPIERS VILLE de PARIS', smooth or treaded black tyres .........**£140-180**

**566  Citroën H Currus Van, 'POLICE'**
1965-70
- Blue/white body, painted concave hubs, working warning lights..........**£200-300**

**568  Berliet Gak Fire Escape**
1968-70 (scale 1:43)
- Red twin-cab body, extending chromed ladder, painted concave hubs. Yellow picture box .........................**£250-300**

**570P Peugeot J7 VSAB Fire Van**
1971-72
- 'POMPIERS', Red body, painted hubs, 'MECCANO FRANCE SA' on diecast base. Yellow box ................. **£300-450**
1972-
- Later version, with 'MECCANO TRI-ANG' on plastic base. Yellow box............. **£300-450**

**583  Berliet First-Aid Vehicle**
1959-63 (renumbered in 1959 from 32-E)
- Bright Red twin-cab body (no markings), detachable hose reel, painted concave painted hubs, white tyes, scale 1:55, '32E' (later '583-32E') on Supertoys box................................**£140-180**
1962-63
- Fire Service promotional: Red twin-cab body with 'POMPIERS de PARIS' shield, concave hubs ...................................**£200-250**

**820  Renault Goelette Ambulance**
1959-70 (renumbered in 1959 from 80-F)
- Gloss or matt finish, painted concave hubs, treaded rubber (later nylon) tyres, scale 1:55. Yellow box ........................**£60-75**

**899  Delahaye Fire Escape**
1959-65 (renumbered in 1959 from 32-D)
- Red body, black steering wheel, painted ridged hubs, smooth white tyres, 1:55. '32D' on Supertoys box .........**£200-250**
1965-70
- Red body, white steering wheel, painted concave hubs, treaded white tyres. '899' on Supertoys box ...................**£200-250**

**1402  Ford Galaxie 'POLICE' Car**
1968-68
- Black/white body. Commissioned for use by Police ........................................NGPP

**1416P  Renault R6 Fire Car 'POMPIERS de PARIS'**
1970-70
- Code 2 model based on Spanish-made components, commissioned by the Fire Service. Red body, second grille (square headlamps), red concave hubs. Side view of white model on box.......................**£400-500**

**1429  Peugeot 404 'POLICE' Car**
1970-71 (scale 1:43)
- Blue/White body, plastic base, plated concave hubs. Yellow box ......................................**£200-300**
**NB** 595n Traffic Sign 'Cycling Prohibited' included with 1429.

**1450  Simca 1100 'POLICE' Car**
1977-78
- Blue/white or black/white body, plated concave hubs. Made in Spain ....................................**£25-40**

# French Dinky Toys Military Vehicles

A number of military vehicle models were designed in the late 1930s and the prototypes were shown in the June 1940 French catalogue. They were never put into production because of the Nazi Occupation.

It came as no surprise that, following liberation by the Allies, the first new French Dinky Toy to be introduced was a model of the US Army Jeep so common at the time. The unavailability of rubber meant that all-metal wheels had to be used instead of hubs and tyres. The wheels used on the Jeep were mounted inside-out to give a heavy duty off-road effect. During the 1960s and 1970s a number of military models from the English range were imported into France.

These are listed in the Imports section. 681 DUKW Amphibious Vehicle was not one of those imported as the French factory produced a much more detailed version (number 825). Note that the letters 'DUKW' are not initials nor are they an abbreviation - they are simply part of the General Motors design reference system of the time.

All the models listed are finished in various shades of military green unless otherwise stated. The paint can be found to be either gloss, semi-gloss or matt but this does not affect the price range. Some military items are also noted in the Accessories section.

| Model and details | MPR |
|---|---|

**24M Military Jeep**
1946-48 (scale 1:43)
- US Military olive-drab body and mazak wheels (mounted inside-out for effect), white star on bonnet, tinplate windscreen frame (some bonnet castings have frame supports), wire steering wheel ......... **£400-600**
  NB 24-M was the first French made Dinky Toy to appear after the War. Trade boxes contained twelve units.

**80A Panhard EBR75 FL11**
1957-59 (renumbered in 1959 to 815) (1:55)
- Painted hubs, radial tread tyres, side headlamps or red lights. '80A' on base and box (picture on some boxes) ......... **£50-70**
**80-B Hotchkiss Willys Jeep**
1958-59 (scale 1:50)
- No driver (but hole in some), no hook, convex or ridged painted hubs, smooth black tyres. '80B' printed on deep yellow end-flap box (picture on some) ........... **£50-70**

**80-BP Hotchkiss Willys Jeep**
1959-59 (renumbered in 1959 to 816)
- With driver, no hook, convex or ridged painted hubs, smooth black tyres. There are two end-flap box types:
  1 - '80B' Yellow box (with picture) has '80BP' stickers
  2 - '80BP' printed on Yellow box (with picture) ........................... **£50-70**

**80-C AMX 13 Tank**
1958-59 (renumbered in 1959 to 817) (1:55)
- Gloss or matt finish, no aerial, rubber tracks, rear roller treads indented or raised. '80C' on Yellow end-flap box .............. **£50-70**
**80-D Berliet 6x6 All-Terrain Truck**
1958-59 (scale 1:55)
- Tinplate tilt, black cab floor, painted hubs. '80D' (no picture) on yellow end-flap box ............................ **£50-70**
1959-59 (renumbered in 1959 to 818)
- Tinplate tilt, khaki cab floor, painted hubs. '80D' and picture on yellow end-flap box ............................ **£50-70**

**80-E Obusier ABS 155mm Gun**
1958-59 (renumbered in 1959 to 819) (1:55)
- Gloss or matt finish, painted concave hubs. Yellow end-flap box with or without picture, one packing piece................... **£40-50**
- Same but with painted ridged hubs...... **£50-60**

**80-F Renault Goelette Ambulance**
1959-59 (renumbered in 1959 to 820) (1:55)
- Gloss or matt, no roof vent or red crosses, ridged hubs. Deep yellow end-flap box (model picture faces left) .................... **£60-75**

**676 Daimler Armoured Car**
1972-72 (scale 1:55)
- Painted concave hubs, camouflage net. Model first made in France though 'Made in England' wrongly stated on base. 'MECCANO FRANCE' on yellow box .............................................. **£150-200**

NB 676 was replaced after a short time by the Liverpool-made model with new reference '676L'.

**800 Renault 4x4 Sinpar**
1974-? (revised and renumbered from 815)
- Khaki body, grey-green-khaki top, camouflage net, no gear lever, no aerial support, black or white plastic radio, painted concave hubs, scale 1:43. 'MECCANO' on base and box ('camouflage' effect on yellow end-flap box) .................................... **£90-120**

**801 AMX 13 Tank**
1973-75 (renumbered in 1973 from 817)
- Matt Khaki body, grey nylon tracks, plastic rollers, camouflage net, aerial (a few without), scale 1:55. '801' on yellow, part camouflaged box ............. **£55-75**

**802 Obusier ABS 155mm Gun**
1974-? (renumbered in 1974 from 819)
- Khaki body with camouflage net, 'OBUSIER 155' replaces '80E' on base, painted concave hubs, scale 1:55. 'Camouflage' effect on yellow box...... **£40-50**

**804 Mercedes-Benz Unimog**
1973-?
(revised and renumbered in 1973 from 821)
- Khaki body and camouflage net, 'MERCEDES TOUS TERRAINS, 804' on chassis, grey-blue base without '821', painted concave hubs, ridged tyres. 'MECCANO TRI-ANG' on yellow box with 'camouflage' effect (box also contains unused transfer sheet).........**£110-140**

**806 Berliet Recovery Truck**
1973-?
(revised and renumbered in 1973 from 826)
- Khaki body and base, driver, plastic hook, camouflage net, without 'TOUS TERRAINS BERLIET' on chassis, painted concave hubs. 'Camouflage' effect on yellow box.. **£200-250**

**807 Renault All-Terrain Ambulance**
1973-? (scale 1:55)
- Khaki body with roof vents and red crosses, plastic concave hubs and base. Yellow end-flap box ......................... **£150-175**

**808 Dodge WC56 Command Car**
Announced in the 1971 catalogue but made as reference 810 from 1972.

**808 GMC US Army Recovery Truck**
1972-74 (scale 1:43)
- Sand body (hole for driver), painted concave hubs, black removable top. Yellow box with insert .................... **£200-250**
1974-?
- Olive-drab body (hole for driver in some), painted concave hubs, black top. Yellow box with insert .................... **£200-250**

**809 GMC US Army 6x6 Truck**
1970- (scale 1:43)
- Olive drab/black body (white stars), driver (white or khaki helmet), painted concave hubs. Yellow box has design panel and insert ............. **£125-150**

**809 GMC 6x6 Truck**
197?-?
- Khaki/black (white stars), driver (grey helmet), painted concave hubs. 'MECCANO' on box but no design panel, box has insert ............. **£175-225**
NB 595q Traffic Sign 'Automatic Level Crossing' included with 809, plus additional 'white star' transfer sheet.

**810 Dodge WC56 Command Car**
1972-74 (scale 1:43)
- Removable top, soldier, camouflage net, concave hubs. 'Camouflage' effect yellow box, transfers ....................... **£150-200**

**813 AMX with 155mm ABS Gun**
1969-71 (scale 1:55)
- Gloss or matt finish, nylon tracks. Yellow end-flap box ........................ **£140-190**
1972-?
- Gloss or matt finish, nylon tracks, simplified gun, camouflage net. 'Camouflage' effect on yellow box.. **£140-190**

**814 Panhard Armoured Car**
1963-71 (scale 1:52)
- Khaki finish, painted concave hubs, black (later Grey-Blue) base. 'C'est une fabrication MECCANO' printed on plain side of yellow end-flap box, insert, aerials in packet .. **£40-50**
**815 Panhard EBR75 FL11**
1959-63 (renumbered in 1959 from 80-A)
- Gloss or matt finish, '80A' on base, painted hubs, block tread tyres, 1:55. Picture and '815' on box ...................... **£40-50**

**815 Renault 4 Sinpar Gendarmerie**
1969-74
(revised in 1974 and issued as 800) (1:43)
- Khaki body, green-khaki top, two military policemen, gear lever, aerial, light grey plastic radio, painted concave hubs. 'MECCANO TRI-ANG' on base..... **£140-170**

**816 Hotchkiss Willys Jeep**
1959-61 (renumbered in 1959 from 80-BP)
- Driver, no hook, painted ridged hubs, smooth black tyres, scale 1:50. Picture and '816-80BP' on yellow box ........... **£50-70**
1962-63
- Driver, cast-in hook, concave hubs, smooth or treaded black tyres. Picture and '816' on yellow box ......... **£50-70**

**816 Berliet Rocket Launcher**
1969-71 (scale 1:55)
- Khaki/grey body, white/red rocket ('NORD, R-20'), painted concave hubs. Yellow end-flap box ........................ **£200-250**

**817  AMX 13 Tank**
1959-64 (renumbered in 1959 from 80-C)
- Gloss or matt khaki, no aerial, rubber tracks, rear roller treads raised. 1:55. '80C' on yellow box.............................. **£50-70**
1965-70
- Same but only in gloss khaki and with aerial. With (later without) '80C' on base. '817' on yellow box..................... **£50-70**
1973-75 (renumbered in 1973 to 801)
- Same but matt khaki body, grey nylon tracks on plastic rollers, Yellow box with 'camouflage' effect ...................... **£50-70**

**818  Berliet 6x6  All-Terrain Truck**
1959-65 (renumbered in 1959 from 80-D)
- Tinplate tilt, khaki cab floor, painted concave hubs, scale 1:55. '80D' and picture on yellow box ......... **£50-70**
1965-70
- Same, but 'TOUS TERRAINS BERLIET' on base (a few without), '818' and picture on yellow box .......................... **£50-70**

**819  Obusier ABS 155mm Gun**
1959-65 (renumbered in 1959 from 80-E)
- Khaki body, painted ridged hubs, '80E' on base, scale 1:55. Fully illustrated yellow box ................. **£40-50**
1965-74
- Gloss khaki body, painted concave hubs. Fully illustrated yellow box ................. **£40-50**
1974 (revised in 1974; issued as 802)

**820  Renault Goelette Ambulance**
1959-70 (renumbered in 1959 from 80-F)
- No roof vents, no red crosses, concave hubs, treaded plastic tyres, Yellow box (picture faces left)............. **£60-75**
- Same but with roof vents. Model picture on later boxes faces right........ **£60-75**

**821  Mercedes-Benz Unimog**
1960-63
- 'MERCEDES-UNIMOG' on chassis, '821' on black painted base, painted concave hubs, smooth tyres. No picture on yellow end-flap box ..... **£50-70**
1963-65
- 'MERCEDES-BENZ UNIMOG' on chassis, '821' on black painted base, painted concave hubs, smooth tyres. Picture and 'MECCANO' on yellow end-flap box. **£45-55**
1965-66
- As previous model. but with ridged tyres. Picture and 'MECCANO TRI-ANG' on yellow end-flap box ....................... **£45-55**
1966-70
- Same but with grey-blue base without '821'. Picture and 'MECCANO TRI-ANG' on yellow box ................... **£45-55**
1973 (revised in 1973 and issued as 804)

**822  White M3 Half-Track**
1960-63  (scale 1:50)
- Matt finish, no machine gun, black painted chassis, painted concave hubs (smooth black tyres). Picture of model on yellow end-flap box ............................ **£70-80**
1963-65
- Matt or gloss finish, with machine gun, anodised chassis, painted concave hubs (treaded black tyres). Picture of model plus scene and 'C'est une fabrication MECCANO' on some yellow end-flap boxes ........... **£70-80**
1965-71
- Same, but with picture of model plus scene and 'C'est une fabrication MECCANO TRI-ANG' on box ........... **£70-80**

**823  Marion Mobile Kitchen**
1962-66  (scale 1:50)
- Khaki body, black or khaki base, painted concave hubs. 'Cuisine Roulante' on Yellow box ....... **£50-60**

**823  GMC Military Tanker**
1969-70  (scale 1:43)
- Khaki/Black, plastic tank, removable cab canopy, painted concave hubs. Yellow end-flap box has insert and also contains a 595b Traffic Sign 'Maximum Weight 5.5 tonnes'........ **£200-300**

**824  Berliet Gazelle 6x6 Truck**
1963-64  (scale 1:55)
- Removable cab canopy and tilt, painted concave hubs. 'Cabine vitrée' ('cab window glazing') on illustrated yellow end-flap box ............... **£120-140**
1964-70
- Same model, but 'Cabine vitrée aménagée' ('cab window glazing fitted') on yellow end-flap box ......................... **£120-140**

**825  GMC DUKW Amphibian**
1963-71  (scale 1:55)
- Gloss or matt finish, drums and boxes, painted concave hubs, driver with later issues. Yellow box has (picture on later boxes) ................... **£120-140**

**826  Berliet Recovery Truck**
1963-70  (scale 1:55)
- Plastic driver, metal hook, black base, 'TOUS TERRAINS BERLIET' on chassis, painted concave hubs. Deep yellow end-flap box also contains pink instruction leaflet....... **£140-170**
1973
(revised in 1973 and issued as 806).

**827  Panhard EBR75 FL10**
1964-71  (scale 1:55)
- Khaki body, aerial/aerial point in some, painted concave hubs. Yellow scenic end-flap box with packing piece .......... **£60-70**

**828  Jeep SS10 Missile Launcher**
1964-71  (scale 1:50)
- Driver, missile battery, concave hubs. Yellow scenic end-flap box has instructions printed on side ................. **£55-70**

**829  Jeep 106SR Gun Carrier**
1964-71  (scale 1:50)
- Driver, plastic gun, painted concave hubs. Yellow scenic end-flap box (instructions on side)........................... **£55-70**

**834  Mobile Bridge Pack**
1963-70
- Khaki plastic 6 part bridge plus inflatable boats (as supplied with 884) ....................NPP

**841  Tank Tracks Pack**
1959-71
- Twelve tracks for AMX tanks...................NPP

**843  Military Tyre Pack**
1962-71
- Twelve treaded black tyres (large for 818 and similar) .......................NPP

**852  Tank Tracks Pack**
1962-71
- Ten replacement tracks for 822 White M3 Military Half-Track .........NPP

**856  Machine Gun**
1963-71
- Plastic armament for use on 822 White M3 Half-Track........................NPP

**883  AMX 13 Bridge Layer**
1964-66  (scale 1:55)
- Gloss or matt, '13t AMX' on base. Yellow box reference on black oval, instructions enclosed .............. **£150-200**
1966-71
- Same, but 'Char AMX poseur de pont, réf.883' on base. Yellow box has reference on violet band.................. **£150-200**

**884  Brockway Bridge Layer**
1961-70  (scale 1:55)
- 10 element bridge, 2 inflatable boats. Supertoys box ('884' on some) also contains leaflet/map ........................ **£275-325**

**890  Berliet T6 Tank Transporter**
1959-63  (scale 1:55)
- Gloss or matt finish, painted ridged hubs, Supertoys box has no illustration .................................. **£160-250**
1963-70
- Gloss or matt finish, painted ridged or concave hubs. Illustration on blue/white Supertoys box................. **£130-160**

PHOTO: VECTIS AUCTIONS LTD.

# French Dinky Toys Aircraft

In comparison with the English factory, Meccano France produced only a small range of model aircraft. They are nonetheless rather attractive and much sought after. Pre-war planes are especially difficult to find in good stable condition since the metal deterioration problem equally affected production on both sides of the Channel.

Some interesting models were designed at the end of the 1930s in the French 64 series (listed below). These were announced in the 1939 Meccano Magazine but with the advance of the occupying German forces production did not take place. Around this period a few small (normally silver) planes were given a camouflage finish and advertised as 'Reconnaissance' or 'Spotter' planes

though it is very unlikely that serious production of these was actually undertaken.

Some of the English 60 series were imported into France before the war, and very few post-war (see the Imports section for details). Of the few new French made aircraft models to appear in the late 1950s, the Caravelle is perhaps the most desirable, particularly in the Swiss, Scandinavian or Algerian liveries with their specially printed Supertoys boxes.

As in England the French factory produced a number of boxed sets of model aircraft in the 1930s. They are fully described in the Gift Sets section.

| Model and details | MPR |
|---|---|
| **60a** **DeWoitine D388 Rainbow** ('L'Arc en Ciel') 1935-40 Three engines, each with 2-blade propellers and no tinplate surrounds. | |
| • Silver/Red | £200-300 |
| • Gold /Red | £200-300 |
| • Cream/Red | £200-300 |
| • Cream/Green | £200-300 |
| • Gold/Green | £200-300 |
| • Gold/Blue | £200-300 |
| **60A** **Dassault Mystere IVa Jet** 1957-59 (renumbered in 1959 to 800) | |
| • Metallic Grey, single jet, Blue cockpit. Yellow box | £70-80 |
| **60b** **Potez 58** 1935-40 Tinplate main wings, 2-wheel undercarriage, 2-blade propeller, 2-part windscreen. | |
| • Yellow/Grey | £150-250 |
| • Red/Silver | £200-300 |
| **60B** **Sud Aviation Vautour 'SNCASO'** 1957-59 (renumbered in 1959 to 801) | |
| • Metallic Grey, twin jet, Blue cockpit. Yellow box | £80-100 |
| **60c** **Henriot H180T** 1935-40 Tinplate main wings, 2-wheel undercarriage, 2-blade propeller, 3-part windscreen. | |
| • Green/White, Green/Red | £150-250 |
| • Blue/White, Red/Silver | £150-250 |
| **60C** **Lockheed Super G Constellation** 1956-59 (renumbered in 1959 to 892) | |
| • Silver, 'AIR FRANCE', 'FB-HBX', 4 x 3-blade propellers, scale 1:190. Supertoys box | £150-200 |
| **60d** **Breguet Corsaire** 1935-40 Open two-seater fuselage with tinplate main wings and 2-blade propeller. | |
| • Silver/Red | £200-300 |
| • Red/Green | £200-300 |
| • Red/Yellow | £200-300 |
| **60D** **Sikorsky S58 Helicopter** 1957-59 (renumbered in 1959 to 802) | |
| • White/Grey/Blue, 'SABENA', Black rotors. Yellow box | £100-125 |
| **60e** **DeWoitine 500 Hunter** 1935-40 Open cockpit, tinplate main wings, 2-wheel undercarriage, 2-blade propeller. | |
| • Cream/Red or Light Cream/Green | £200-300 |
| **60E** **Vickers Viscount** 1957-59 (renumbered in 1959 as 803) | |
| • White/Grey/Blue, 'AIR FRANCE', 'FB-GNX', 4 x 4-blade propellers, scale 1:190. Yellow box | £125-175 |
| **60f** **Cierva Autogiro** 1935-40 Cast body, with or without pilot. | |
| • Gold (Red rotors) | £200-300 |
| • Cream (Red or Blue rotors) | £200-300 |
| • Silver (Red or Blue rotors) | £200-300 |
| • Red (Cream rotors) | £200-300 |

| Model and details | MPR |
|---|---|
| **60F** **Caravelle SE210, 'AIR FRANCE'** 1959-59 (renumbered in 1960 to 891) | |
| • Metallic Grey/White/Blue, 'FB-GNY', operable steps, scale 1:190. Supertoys box | £130-180 |
| **61a** **Dewoitine D338** 1938-40 Casting as 60a L'Arc en Ciel but different arrangement of decoration, 3 x 3-blade propellers and tinplate engine surrounds. | |
| • Green/Silver | £150-250 |
| • Red/Gold | £150-250 |
| 1939-40 Different casting from first version of 61a (and also has the reference 64). Three engines, each with 3-blade propellers and tinplate engine surrounds, gliding hole. 'FA-DBF' marking on body. | |
| • Silver body | £150-250 |
| • Light Green body | £150-250 |
| **61b** **Potez 56** 1938-40 Fitted with 2 x 2-blade propellers. | |
| • Blue/Silver | £150-250 |
| • Red/Silver | £150-250 |
| • Yellow/Silver | £150-250 |
| **61c** **Farman F360** 1938-40 Open two-seater, single 2-blade propeller. | |
| • Silver/Blue or Silver/Red | £150-250 |
| • Silver/Yellow or Silver + roundels | £150-250 |
| **61d** **Potez 58 Air Ambulance** 1938-40 | |
| • Silver body with red cross on Silver or White ground | £200-300 |
| **61e** **Henriot H180M** 1938-40 | |
| • Silver wings and fuselage with roundels, 2-blade propeller | £200-300 |
| **61f** **Dewoitine 500 Hunter** 1938-40 | |
| • Silver wings and fuselage with roundels, 2-blade propeller | £200-300 |
| **64** **Dewoitine D338** 1939-40 Different casting from previous version with more prominent tailfin and also having the reference 61a. Three engines, each with 2-blade propellers, gliding hole. 'FA-DBF' marking. | |
| • Silver body | £150-200 |
| • Light Green body | £150-200 |
| **64a** **Amiot 370** 1939-40 Twin engine monoplane, 2 or 3-blade propellers, gliding hole. | |
| • Beige, Pink, Red or Blue; or Pale Green with red circles on wings; or Silver with French roundels | £150-250 |
| 1948-49 | |
| • A small number of pre-war castings were issued in various colours | £150-250 |

| Model and details | MPR |
|---|---|
| **64b** **Bloch 220** 1939-40 Twin engine airliner marked 'FA-OHJ', 2 x 3-blade propellers, gliding hole. | |
| • Silver or Dark Red | £150-250 |
| • Pale Green or Ivory | £150-250 |
| **64c** **Potez 63** 1939-40 Twin engines, twin tailplanes, 3-blade propellers. | |
| • Beige, Red, Blue, Silver, Silver with French roundels | £150-250 |
| 1948-49 | |
| • A small number of pre-war castings were issued in various colours | £150-250 |
| **64d** **Potez 662** 1939-40 Four engines, 'FA-RAY', 3-blade propellers, twin tailplanes, gliding hole. | |
| • Silver, Red, Light Blue, Yellow | £150-200 |
| **800** **Dassault Mystere IVa Jet** 1959-64 (renumbered in 1959 from 60-A) | |
| • Metallic Grey, single jet, Blue cockpit. Yellow box | £70-80 |
| **801** **Sud Aviation Vautour 'SNCASO'** 1959-64 (renumbered in 1959 from 60-B) | |
| • Metallic Grey, twin jet, Blue cockpit. Yellow box | £80-100 |
| **802** **Sikorsky S58 Helicopter** 1959-61 (renumbered from 60-D) | |
| • White/Grey/Blue, 'SABENA', Black rotors. Yellow box | £100-125 |
| **803** **Vickers Viscount, 'AIR FRANCE'** 1959-61 (renumbered in 1959 from 60-E) | |
| • White/Grey/Blue, 'FB-GNX', scale 1:190, 4 x 4-blade propellers. Yellow box | £125-175 |
| **804** **SNCAN Noratlas** (French military) 1959-63 | |
| • Metallic Grey, twin-fuselage, 2 x 4-blade propellers. Yellow box | £150-200 |
| **891** **Caravelle SE210** (renumbered in 1959 from 60-F) All have 'Escalier escamotable' (operable steps) and Supertoys box. Scale 1:190. | |
| • 1959-59 **'AIR FRANCE'** Silver/White/Blue, 'FB-GNY' | £200-250 |
| • 1959-68 **'AIR FRANCE'** Metallic Grey/White/Blue. '60F' under wing of early issues only | £250-350 |
| • 1960-? **'SWISSAIR'** on box, 'HB-ICX', Metallic Grey/White/Red | £900-1,200 |
| • 1960-? **'SAS'** on box, 'SE-DAA', Metallic Grey/White/Blue | £900-1,200 |
| • 1960-? **'AIR ALGERIE'** Metallic Grey/White/Red. 'FO-BNH'. Supertoys 'Air Algerie' on box | £900-1,200 |
| **892** **Lockheed Super G Constellation** | |
| • 1959-62 **'AIR FRANCE'**, (scale 1:190) Silver, 'FB-HBX', 4 x 3-blade propellers. Supertoys box | £200-250 |

# French Dinky Toys Trains

| Model and details | MPR | | Model and details | MPR | | Model and details | MPR |
|---|---|---|---|---|---|---|---|

**16**   **Northern Sector Railcar**
1935-40
'Autorail' with 3 articulated coaches in
mazak, tinplate base, silvered or black lead
hubs, white rubber tyres. Boxed.
- Blue-Grey/Dark Blue ..................... **£100-125**
- Grey/Blue ......................................... **£100-125**
- Grey/Red .......................................... **£100-125**
- Gold/Red ........................................... **£100-125**
- Cream/Red ....................................... **£100-125**
- Cream/Green .................................... **£100-125**

**16a**   1940   **Two-Car Railcar**
A two-part version of 16a. Advertised
in the 1940 catalogue but not issued........NPP

**17**  1935-38  **Electric Goods Train**. See 'Gift Sets'.
**18**  1934-38  **Steam Goods Train** ... See 'Gift Sets'.
**19**  1935-38  **Electric Passenger Train**.. 'Gift Sets'.

**19a**   **Electric Locomotive**
1935-36
- Cast in lead. Various basic colours ..... **£60-80**
1936-40
- Cast in mazak.
Silver/Red; Light Green/Red; Green/Black;
Gold/Blue; Two-tone Blue ................. **£50-70**

**20**  1935-38  **Steam Passenger Train** .... 'Gift Sets'.
**20a**   **Passenger Coach**
1935-40
Cast in lead
- Red/Blue............................................. **£25-35**
- Green/Blue.......................................... **£25-35**

**21**  1934-38  **Steam Mixed Goods Train**
........................See 'Gift Sets' section.

**21a**   **Steam Tank Locomotive**
1934-40
Cast in lead.
- Red/Blue............................................. **£30-45**
- Green/Blue.......................................... **£30-45**
- Green/Black........................................ **£30-45**

**21b**   **Timber Wagon**
1934-40
- Red/Green wagon cast in lead,
Yellow mazak 'log' ......................... **£30-45**

**21c**   **Coal Wagon**
1934-40
Cast in lead.
- Green/Red wagon .............................. **£30-45**
- Green/Black wagon ........................... **£30-45**

**21d**   **Crane Wagon**
1934-38
Cast in lead, crane has 'open' jib.
- Blue and Green.................................. **£25-35**
- Green and Blue .................................. **£25-35**
- Red and Blue ..................................... **£25-35**
- Yellow and Red ................................. **£25-35**
1938-40
Cast in lead, crane has 'solid' jib.
- Blue and Green.................................. **£25-35**
- Green and Blue .................................. **£25-35**
- Red and Blue ..................................... **£25-35**
- Yellow and Red ................................. **£25-35**

**26**   **Bugatti Autorail**
1934-35
Cast in mazak, smooth sides, small windows.
May have silvered metal cast wheels or
bakelite moulded rollers in red, green or blue.
- Cream body with Blue, Yellow,
Green, Red or Orange sides .............. **£90-120**
1934-40
Same, but with ridged sides and
larger windows.
- Yellow body (Red or Green sides).... **£90-120**
- Green (Red sides)............................. **£90-120**

# Caravans and Campers

**564**   1969-71  **Caravelair Armagnac 420**
Blue/white, plated concave hubs, scale 1:43. Yellow box has
595a Traffic Sign 'Danger of Falling Rocks' ............................. **£100-150**
**565**   1965-71  **Renault Estafette Camping Car**
Light blue body, ivory roof, floral curtains, aluminium
concave hubs, scale 1:43. Yellow box ......................................... **£140-180**

**811**   1959-59  **Caravan** ('Henon' style)
Cream/White, smooth roof casting, window glazing in most,
tinplate drawbar, plated ridged hubs, scale 1:43........................... **£80-100**
1960-63 As previous model, but with ribbed body casting........... **£70-90**
**812**   1965-69  **Camping Trailer**
Cream body with luggage, single plated ridged hub and
black tyre, scale 1:43. Sold only in plastic bag .............................. **£40-50**

# Ships

Most of the Dinky Toys model ships sold in France were imported English issues (see the Imports section for details). Those of French design and manufacture are listed below. No boxed sets made entirely in France appear to have been produced, though the Liverpool made castings of the British Naval Warships set were imported into France between 1938 and 1940. They were sold in a French version of the presentation box. The 'Locomotion Moderne' set was intended to contain ship models but was another of those proposals which fell victim to the outbreak of war (see the Gift Sets section for details).

| | | | | |
|---|---|---|---|---|
| **52c** | **Steamship 'Normandie'** | 1937-40 | Black/white/red, no rollers, 175mm. Blue box has coloured picture of the ship at sea on the lid, and a picture of the ship and the port of Manhattan on the inner part................................ | **£175-250** |
| | | 1940-40 | Black/white/red, no rollers, 175mm. Blue box has no inner picture....................................... | **£120-170** |
| **52d** | **Steamship 'Normandie'** | 1937-40 | Black/white/red, with metal rollers, 175mm. Blue box has coloured picture of the ship at sea on the lid, and a picture of the ship and the port of Manhattan on the inner part................. | **£175-250** |
| | | 1940-40 | Black/white/red, with metal rollers, 175mm. Blue box has no inner picture.............................. | **£120-170** |
| | | 1947-48 | Black/white/red, with metal rollers, 175mm. Blue box has no inner picture.............................. | **£120-170** |
| **53a** | **Battleship 'Dunkerque'** | 1937-40 | Battleship grey, with metal rollers, 120mm. Light yellow one-piece illustrated box ................ | **£100-150** |
| **53b** | **Battleship 'Dunkerque'** | 1937-40 | Battleship grey, no rollers, 120mm. Light yellow one-piece illustrated box ............................. | **£100-150** |
| **870** | **Steamship 'France'** | 1962-71 | White/black/red, scale 1:1200, 263mm. ....................................................................... | **£150-200** |

# 'Dolly Varden' Doll's House Furniture

Models of 'Dolly Varden' Dolls House Furniture were available in France and England. They are very similar in range and appearance but are definitely different castings with a different finish. French boxed sets generally appear to have much bigger boxes than the English equivalent. It is thought that the 'Dolly Varden Dolls House' was never advertised in France and is consequently almost impossible to find there.

**101**   1936   **Dining Room Furniture Set** 'Gift Sets'
**101a**  1936-40  **Dining Table**
  Light or Dark mottled brown ..... **£10-15**
**101b**  1936-40  **Sideboard**
  Light or Dark mottled brown ...... **£15-20**
**101c**  1936-40  **Carver**
  Light or Dark mottled brown ..... **£10-15**
**101d**  1936-40  **Chair**
  Light or Dark mottled brown ..... **£10-15**
**102**   1936-40  **Bedroom Furniture Set** ..... 'Gift Sets'.
**102a**  1936-40  **Bed**, Mottled lilac....................... **£10-15**
**102b**  1936-40  **Wardrobe**, Mottled lilac ........... **£15-20**

**102c**  1936-40  **Dressing Table**
  Mottled lilac, with mirror .......... **£15-20**
**102d**  1936-40  **Chest of Drawers**,
  Mottled lilac................................ **£15-20**
**102e**  1936-40  **Stool**, Mottled lilac ................... **£10-15**
**102f**  1936-40  **Chair** (as 101d), Mottled lilac .... **£10-15**
**103**   1936-40  **Kitchen Furniture Set** See 'Gift Sets'.
**103a**  1936-40  **Refrigerator**
  Pale green/cream or Blue/ivory .. **£15-20**
**103b**  1936-40  **Sideboard**
  Pale green/cream or Blue/ivory .. **£15-20**
**103c**  1936-40  **Cooker**
  Pale green/cream or Blue/ivory .. **£15-20**

**103d**  1936-40  **Table**
  Pale green/cream or Blue/ivory ..**£10-15**
**103e**  1936-40  **Chair** (casting as 101d)
  Pale green/cream or Blue/ivory ..**£10-15**
**104**   1937-40  **Bathroom Furniture Set**.... 'Gift Sets'.
**104a**  1937-40  **Bath**, Pink............................... **£10-15**
**104b**  1937-40  **Bath Mat**, Pink rubber
  (prone to deterioration)..............**£10-15**
**104c**  1937-40  **Hand Basin**, Pink, with mirror ..**£15-20**
**104d**  1937-40  **Stool**, Pink .............................**£10-15**
**104e**  1937-40  **Linen Basket**, Pink ..................**£10-15**
**104f**  1937-40  **Toilet**, Pink ............................**£10-15**

# French Dinky Toys Buses

**29d  Renault TN4H Paris Bus**
All have Dark Green cast lower body,
Cream tinplate top, scale 1:80. Variations:
1939-40
- Base on some, cast hubs, black or white
  'DUNLOP' tyres.............................. **£300-400**
1940-40
- No base, painted mazak wheels ...... **£200-250**
1940-49
- Base on some (may be black or silver
  painted), painted mazak wheels ...... **£200-250**
1950-51
- Driver set high; with base (may be
  black or silver painted),
  yellow ridged hubs .......................... **£250-300**

**29D  Somua-Panhard Paris Bus**
1952-54  (scale 1:70)
- Dark Green/Cream, smooth inside roof,
  painted ridged hubs. Not boxed ...... **£150-175**
1954-59  (renumbered in 1959 to 570)
- Dark Green/Cream, cross-hatched inside
  roof, painted ridged hubs.
  Yellow box marked '29D'............... **£150-175**

**29E  Isobloc Autocar**
1950-50
Smooth sides and roof,
painted ridged hubs, scale 1:70.
- Blue/Cream.................................... **£250-350**
- Dark Green/Light Green ................. **£200-250**
- Blue/Silver.................................... **£250-350**

1951-52
All have side detailing in this period.
- Blue/Silver body, smooth roof ........ **£185-225**
1953-55
All have side detailing in this period.
- Red/Silver, smooth roof ..................**£110-130**
- Orange/Silver, smooth roof............ **£125-150**
- Blue/Silver, ridged roof...................... **£75-95**

**29F  Chausson AP521 Autocar**
1956-58  (scale 1:65)
Painted ridged hubs. Box flap reads '29F
AUTOCAR CHAUSSON' in French only.
- Blue/Cream body............................ **£125-150**
- Red/Cream body............................. **£125-150**
1958-59  (renumbered in 1959 to 571)
- As previous models, but concave hubs.
  Box flap reads '29F AUTOCAR
  CHAUSSON' in 4 languages.......... **£125-150**

**541  Mercedes-Benz Autocar**
1963-71  (scale 1:43)
All have 18 seater body, chromed concave
hubs. Yellow box.
- Mid-Red and Cream...........................**£90-110**
- Orange-Red and Cream.....................**£90-110**
- Deep Pink (various shades)
  and Cream ........................................**£90-110**
1966-?  South African issue:
- Blue/Cream body........................ **£800-1,200**
19??  'PTT SUISSE'
- Orange/Silver body .................. **£3,500-4,500**

**570  Somua Paris Bus OP5**
1959-61  (renumbered in 1959 from 29-D)
- Dark Green/Cream, cross-hatched inside
  roof, painted ridged hubs.
  In Yellow box marked '29D'............ **£90-120**

**571  Chausson AP521 Autocar**
1959-60  (renumbered in 1959 from 29-F)
Painted concave hubs, scale 1:65.
Box flap reads '29F AUTOCAR
CHAUSSON' in 4 languages.
- Blue/Cream body............................ **£130-150**
- Red/Cream body............................. **£120-140**

**889  Berliet Paris Autobus**
1965-70  (scale 1:49)
- Green/Greenish-White, 'DUNLOP',
  'PEPSI-COLA', painted concave hubs.
  Supertoys blue/white box,
  colour picture on lid ....................... **£200-250**

**889U  Berliet Urban Bus**
1965-70
'DUNLOP' and 'PEPSI-COLA' adverts.,
painted concave hubs.
Supertoys blue/white box with colour
picture of the Place Bellecour in Lyons.
- Red/Cream...................................... **£225-275**
- Orange/Cream ................................ **£225-275**
**NB** 889 Paris Bus was modelled on a Berliet
vehicle though the 1965-66 catalogue
attributes it to Saviem.

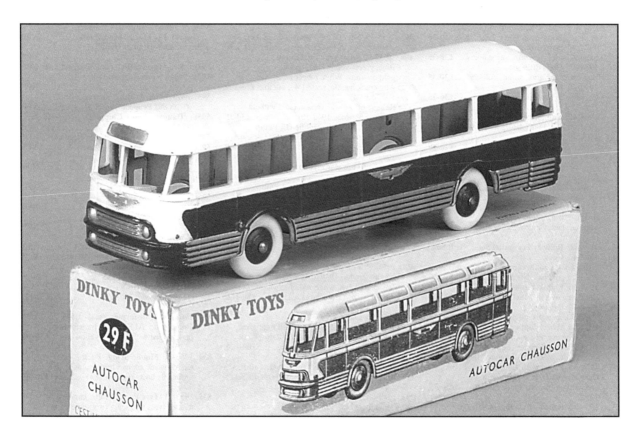

French Dinky Toys 29F Chausson AP521 Autocar

PHOTO: VECTIS AUCTIONS LTD.

# French Dinky Toys Accessories

Pre-war figures 1 to 10 inclusive were hollow cast in lead and individually hand painted. The colours stated are therefore those observed but any other colours and shades are possible especially with painted detail. The bases are usually brown, beige or grey (some blue ones seen) and are usually marked 'MECCANO DINKY TOYS' though some early ones may be found with 'HORNBY' marked under them. Early boxes were blue-grey (often marked 'Série Hornby'), later ones were red (usually printed 'Dinky Toys' and with

various shades and degrees of surface gloss). They vary greatly as far as the printing is concerned. After the War, Meccano-France considered most of the figures to be primarily railway accessories so they reverted to listing them in the 'Hornby Railway Accessories' range. Their boxes generally reflect this thinking after 1948, and between 1950 and 1955 most of models 1 to 10 were issued in plastic as 'Hornby unbreakable figures'.

| Model and details | MPR |
|---|---|

**1** 1934-40 **Station Staff Set** ....... See 'Gift Sets'.
**1a** 1934-40 **Station Master**
• Dark blue coat, grey or
grey-green trousers ............................... **£30-35**
**1b** 1934-40 **Porter**
• Light blue uniform with red belt,
no luggage .................................................. **£30-35**
**1c** 1934-40 **Railway Guard**
• Dark blue coat, grey or
grey-green trousers ................................ **£30-35**
**1d** 1934-40 **Policeman**
• Dark blue uniform ................................ **£30-35**
**1e** 1934-40 **Controller**
• Dark blue coat, grey or
grey-green trousers ................................ **£30-35**

**2** 1934-40 **Railway Passengers Set** ... 'Gift Sets'
**2a** 1934-40 **Normandy Farmer**
• Various rustic colours ............................ **£30-35**
**2b** 1934-40 **Farmer's Wife**
• A 'Peasant type Bécassine' with basket
and umbrella, red or orange dress
(later turquoise) ..................................... **£30-35**
**2c** 1934-40 **Young Woman**
• Bag under right arm, various colours .... **£30-35**
**2d** 1934-40 **Boy Scout**
• Boy in French scout uniform (all khaki
or khaki shorts/green shirt) ..................... **£30-35**
**2e** 1934-40 **Boy (sitting)**
• Satchel under right arm, var. colours..... **£30-35**
**2f** 1934-40 **Girl (sitting)**
• Bag under left arm, various colours ...... **£30-35**
**2g** 1934-40 **Bench Seat**
• Green or brown painted tinplate............ **£30-35**

**3** 1934-40 **Animals Set** ...See 'Gift Sets' section
**3a** 1934-40 **Pig.** Pink (shades may vary) .. **£20-30**
**3b** 1934-40 **Sheep**
• Cream, white or dark brown (shades) .. **£20-30**
**3c** 1934-40 **Horse**
• Grey or reddish-brown 'mottled' finish
(painted using a 'run' technique).
Various shades known .......................... **£20-30**
**3d** 1934-40 **Bull**
• White or reddish-brown 'mottled' finish
(painted using a 'run' technique).
Various shades known .......................... **£20-30**

**4** 1934-40 **Railway Personnel Set** ..... 'Gift Sets'
**4a** 1934-40 **Cook**
• White cook's outfit, carrying a
(usually gold painted) fowl on a dish... **£30-35**
**4b** 1934-40 **Engine Fireman**
• Dark blue overalls, coal shovel ............ **£30-35**
**4c** 1934-40 **Greaser.**
Dark blue overalls, oilcan...................... **£30-35**
**4d** 1934-40 **Wheel Tapper**
• Dark blue overalls, sounding mallet...... **£30-35**
**4e** 1934-40 **Gate Keeper** (Female)
• Green shirt, black skirt, with red flag... **£30-35**
**4f** 1934-40 **Porter with Luggage**
• Dark blue uniform, carrying case
and hat-box (various shades seen)......... **£30-35**

**5** 1934-40 **Railway Passengers Set** .. 'Gift Sets'.
**5a** 1934-40 **Woman and Child**
• Green or brown (various shades).
Single hollow casting............................. **£30-35**
**5b** 1934-40 **Businessman**
• Grey or brown (shades), with briefcase **£30-35**

| Model and details | MPR |
|---|---|

**5c** 1934-40 **Male Tourist**
• Brown (various shades),
with walking stick and camera ............. **£30-35**
**5d** 1934-40 **Clergyman**
• Black garb, brolly (usually red/grey) .... **£30-35**
**5e** 1934-40 **Newsboy**
• Grey or brown (various shades known),
papers under left arm ............................. **£30-35**
**5f** 1934-40 **Woman with Tennis Racket**
• Green, grey or beige (various shades),
tennis racket in right hand ................... **£30-35**
**6** 1934-40 **Shepherd Set** .See 'Gift Sets' section
**6a** 1934-40 **Shepherd**
• Light brown (various shades), with crook
in right hand and lamb under left arm... **£30-35**
**6b** 1934-40 **Sheepdog**
• Black, with or without white detail ....... **£30-35**

**10** 1934-40 **Assorted Figures Set**
• Consists of Sets 1, 2 and 4.
Box has two illustrations ................... **£250-350**
• 1938-40 Same set but box has
no illustration .................................... **£220-270**
**40** 1953-59 **Traffic Signs 'Town' Set** .. 'Gift Sets'
**41** 1953-59 **Traffic Signs 'Route' Set** . 'Gift Sets'
**49** 1935-40 **Set of Fuel Pumps** ..... See 'Gift Sets'
**49** 1949-50 **Set of Fuel Pumps** ..... See 'Gift Sets'
**49a** 1935-40 **Pillar type Fuel Pump**
• Blue, green, yellow, red, cream,
gold or white. White rubber hose,
wire crank handle, scale 1:43, 60mm.. **£75-100**
1948-53
• Reissue of pre-war version (sold without
the hose between 1948-50)................... **£30-35**
**49b** 1935-40 **'SHELL' Mobile Oil Pump**
• Blue, green, yellow, red, cream, gold or
white. White rubber hose, 1:43, 47mm. . **£75-100**
1948-50
• Reissue of pre-war version
(without hose) ...................................... **£30-35**
**49c** 1935-40 **Double Output Fuel Pump**
• Blue, green, yellow, red, cream,
gold or white. Two white rubber hoses,
scale 1:43, 55mm............................... **£75-100**
1948-52
• Reissue of pre-war version
(without hoses 1948-50) ...................... **£30-35**

**49D** 1954-59 **Pump Island, 'ESSO'**
(renumbered in 1959 to 592)
• Two pumps (red/white and blue/white),
'ESSO' sign. Yellow box ................... **£80-100**

**502** 1959-66 **Garage**
• Yellow/grey, sky-blue/grey or all light grey,
plastic, with parking numbers '0' to '9'.
Yellow box...................................... **£100-120**

**590** 1959-68 **Traffic Signs 'Town' Set** . 'Gift Sets'.
**591** 1959-68 **Traffic Signs 'Route' Set** 'Gift Sets'.

**592** 1959-63 **Pump Island, 'ESSO'**
(renumbered in 1959 from 49-D)
• Two pumps (red/white and blue/white),
'ESSO' sign, scale 1:43.
'DINKY TOYS 592-49D' on box ......... **£65-75**

**592** 1969-71 **Traffic Signs 'Town' Set**. 'Gift Sets'.

| Model and details | MPR |
|---|---|

**593** 1969-71 **Traffic Signs 'Route' Set** 'Gift Sets'.
**594** 1969-71 **Traffic Lights (3-colour)**
• Battery operated grey/black plastic
traffic lights, scale 1:43. Yellow box ..... **£65-75**

**TRAFFIC SIGNS.** Since the messages given on road signs are often more graphical than textual, the list that follows contains literal interpretations that reflect the general meaning of the signs rather than attempting accurate translations. **Traffic Signs 595a** to **595w** were not available for purchase; they were included free in the box of the model mentioned. Scale 1:43.
**595a - 595L** were available from 1969-72,
**595m - 595w** were available from 1970-72.

**595a** 'Danger of Falling Rocks',
(with model 564 Caravan) ........................NPP
**595b** 'Maximum Weight 5.5 tonnes',
(823 GMC Tanker) ...................................NPP
**595c** 'Dangerous Bend to Right',
(1417 Matra F1) .......................................NPP
**595d** 'No Overtaking for Heavy Vehicles',
(572 Berliet Truck) ...................................NPP
**595e** 'Road Narrows', (1422 Ferrari F1).........NPP
**595f** 'Speed Limit', (1421 Opel GT)......NPP
**595g** 'Caution - Animals Crossing',
(with 1419 Ford Thunderbird) ..................NPP
**595h** 'Danger - End of Quay',
(1424 Renault R12)...................................NPP
**595i** 'Two-Way Traffic', (1423 Peugeot 504) .NPP
**595k** 'Road Narrows from Left',
(with 1425 Matra)......................................NPP
**595L** 'Maximum Width 2 metres',
(with 882 Peugeot 'Pinder')......................NPP
**595m** 'Danger - Loose Chippings',
(1426 Alfa)................................................NPP
**595n** 'Cycling Prohibited', (1429 Peugeot).....NPP
**595o** 'Customs', (1420 Opel Commodore) ......NPP
**595p** 'Humpback Bridge',
(1428 Peugeot 304)...................................NPP
**595q** 'Automatic Level Crossing',
(809 GMC)................................................NPP
**595r** 'Road Works',
(518 Renault 'Autoroutes') ........................NPP
**595s** 'Pedestrians Prohibited',
(with 570 Peugeot 'Autoroutes') ..............NPP
**595t** 'Max. Height 3.5 metres',
(with 589 Berliet 'Autoroutes') ...............NPP
**595u** 'Dangerous Bends', (1430 Abarth) .........NPP
**595v** 'All Vehicles Prohibited',
(1432 Ferrari) ...........................................NPP
**595w** 'Danger - Cyclists',
(1409 Chrysler 180) .................................NPP

**833** 1962- **Transformer** (scale 1:55)
Grey plastic 'ALSTHOM' transformer
(as supplied with 898). In yellow box... **£30-50**

**834** 1963-70 **Mobile Bridge Pack**
Khaki plastic six part bridge plus
inflatable boats (as with 884) ............. **£20-30**

**835** 1959-71 **Tyre Pack.** Twelve large black
treaded tyres for racing cars and commercial
vehicles (smooth till 1961). Was 6676 .... **£5-10**
**836** 1959-71 **Tyre Pack.** Twelve white treaded
tyres (smooth till 1960). Previously 6677 **£5-10**
**837** 1959-71 **Tyre Pack.** Twelve black smooth
tyres (small). Previously 7067 ................ **£5-10**

**837** 1961-71 **Tyre Pack**. Twelve black treaded tyres (small) ................................. **£5-10**

**837** 1965-71 **Tyre Pack**. 12 black nylon tyres (small). French versions often marked 'DUNLOP', Spanish usually 'PIRELLI'. **£5-10**

**838** 1961-71 **Tyre Pack**. Twelve white treaded tyres (small). Was 7068. 'DUNLOP' or 'PIRELLI' markings not seen.................. **£5-10**

**839** 1959-63 **Tyre Pack**. Twelve tyres, round or square section (treaded version of 11190). Sold in paper (later, plastic) packet ....... **£10-15**

**839** 1971-71 **Rally Pack**. Two sheets of rally transfers, scales 1:32 and 1:24.......... **£15-20**

**840** 1959-70 **Elastic Cord Pack**. Pack of 6 (later 10) elastic cords for 32D and 899 Delahaye Fire Escape. Was 11146.... **£5-10**

**841** 1959-70 **Tank Tracks Pack**. 12, black rubber, for AMX tanks. Was 11924....... **£10-15**

**842** 1959-64 **Tyre Pack**. Twelve tyres for 24-L Vespa. Was 12110 ........................ **£10-15**

**843** 1962-71 **Military Tyre Pack**. Twelve treaded black tyres (large square section for 818 and similar) ....... **£10-15**

**844** 1959-70 **Pipe-Line Pack**. Six black tubes (as with 893 Sahara Pipe Transporter) .. **£15-20**

**845** 1959-70 **Barrier Pack**. Ten grey plastic barriers (Vauban-Samia), scale 1:43 ...... **£15-20**

**846** 1959-70 **Oil Drum Pack**. Ten grey plastic oil drums ..................... **£15-20**

**847** 1959-70 **Barrel Pack**. Ten brown plastic barrels........................ **£15-20**

**848** 1959-70 **Trunk Pack**. Ten brown plastic travelling trunks with hinged lids.......... **£15-20**

**849** 1959-70 **Packing Case Pack**. Ten ivory plastic packing cases with lifting lids, in plastic 'Bobigny' bag......................... **£15-20**

**850** 1959-70 **Bottle Crate Pack**. Ten white or cream plastic crates with transparent or orange bottles.............................. **£20-25**

**851** 1959-70 **Assortment Pack**. Ten items - two each of: 846 (barrels), 847 (barrels), 848 (trunks), 849 (packing cases), 850 (bottle crates) ....... **£20-25**

**852** 1962-71 **Half-Track Tracks Pack**. Ten replacement tracks for 822 White M3 Half-Track, (black rubber) .............. **£10-15**

**853** 1962-64 **Tyre Pack**. Twelve extra large black tyres for use on 803 Unic and 888 Berliet...................................... **£10-15**

**854** 1962-68 **Milk Crates Pack**. Ten grey plastic milk crates with white bottles, as with 586 Citroën P55 Milk Lorry .. **£20-25**

**855** 1962-65 **Tyre Pack**. Twelve small black rubber treaded tyres (Renault R4, etc.). **£10-15**

**855** 1965-70 **Tyre Pack**. As previous, but made of black nylon ............................. **£10-15**

**856** 1963-71 **Machine Gun**. Black plastic (822 White Half-Track) ... **£10-15**

**857** 1970-71 **Racing Tyre Pack**. Two small tyres for use on the front wheels of Formula 1 racing cars... **£10-15**

**858** 1970-71 **Racing Tyre Pack**. Two larger tyres for F1 rear wheels....... **£10-15**

**859** 1970-71 **Tyre Pack**. 4 tyres for 1419 Ford ............................ **£10-15**

**860** 1963-? **1.5 volt Battery** for 276L .......... **£5-10**

**861** 1964-? **Lamp Bulb**. 1.5 volt bulb for 887 BP Tanker ............. **£5-10**

**862** 1965-? **Lamp Bulb**. 1.5 volt bulb for use with 566 Citroën .... **£5-10**

**863** 1964-? **Battery**. Mazda battery for use with 887 then 952L................................... **£5-10**

**864** 1968-? **Lamp Bulb**. Bulb for use with 276L, 160L and 952L............................ **£5-10**

**6676** 1950-59 **Tyre Pack**. Twelve large black smooth or treaded tyres (racing cars, articulated commercials). With letter 'M' on sidewall till 1958. (Renumbered to 835) ........................... **£10-15**

**6677** 1950-59 **Tyre Pack**. Twelve large white treaded tyres (some smooth). 'M' on sidewall till 1958. (Renumbered to 836 in 1959) ............. **£10-15**

**7067** 1950-59 **Tyre Pack**. Twelve smooth black tyres (small) for touring cars 25-BV, 25-CG, 25-D, 29-D and 80-BP. 'M' on sidewall till 1958. (Renumbered to 837 in 1959) ............. **£10-15**

**7068** 1953-59 **Tyre Pack** Twelve smooth white tyres (small). Letter 'M' on sidewall till 1958. (Renumbered in 1959 to 837) ............. **£10-15**

**11146** 1958-59 **Elastic Cord Pack** Six elastic cords for 32-D and 899 Delahaye Fire Escape. (Renumbered in 1959 to 840) ................. **£5-10**

**11190** 1953-59 **Tyre Pack**. Twelve large black ribbed tyres originally for racing cars. Design was changed in 1958 to make them suitable for use with military vehicles. Paper packets marked either 'Racing Tyres' or 'Cross Country Tyres'. (Renumbered in 1959 to 839) ............ **£10-15**

**11924** 1958-59 **Tank Tracks Pack**. Twelve black rubber tracks for AMX Tanks. (Renumbered to 841 in 1959) ............. **£10-15**

**12110** 1959-59 **Tyre Pack** Twelve tyres for 24-L Vespa. (Renumbered to 842 in 1959) ............. **£10-15**

**---** 1935-40 **Milk Churn (large)**. 2 fixing holes in base, scale 1:43 ......... **£30-40**

**---** 1948-50 **Milk Churn**. Smaller churn, scale 1:43, as supplied with 25-O 'NESTLE' Trucks ...................... **£30-40**

**---** 1969-? **Driving Test Circuit**. Printed road layout with town and country elements, 1:43, boxed ............ **£25-40**

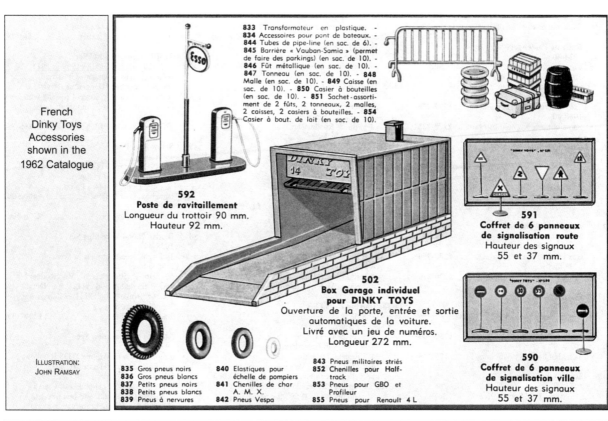

French Dinky Toys Accessories shown in the 1962 Catalogue

**833** Transformateur en plastique. - **834** Accessoires pour pont de bateaux. - **844** Tubes de pipe-line (en sac. de 6). - **845** Barrière « Vauban-Samia » (permet de faire des parkings) (en sac. de 10). - **846** Fût métallique (en sac. de 10). - **847** Tonneau (en sac. de 10). - **848** Malle (en sac. de 10). - **849** Caisse (en sac. de 10). - **850** Casier à bouteilles (en sac. de 10). - **851** Sachet-assortiment de 2 fûts, 2 tonneaux, 2 malles, 2 caisses, 2 casiers à bouteilles. - **854** Casier à bout. de lait (en sac. de 10).

**592**
**Poste de ravitaillement**
Longueur du trottoir 90 mm.
Hauteur 92 mm.

**502**
**Box Garage individuel pour DINKY TOYS**
Ouverture de la porte, entrée et sortie automatiques de la voiture.
Livré avec un jeu de numéros.
Longueur 272 mm.

**591**
**Coffret de 6 panneaux de signalisation route**
Hauteur des signaux 55 et 37 mm.

**590**
**Coffret de 6 panneaux de signalisation ville**
Hauteur des signaux 55 et 37 mm.

ILLUSTRATION: JOHN RAMSAY

**835** Gros pneus noirs
**836** Gros pneus blancs
**837** Petits pneus noirs
**838** Petits pneus blancs
**839** Pneus à nervures

**840** Elastiques pour échelle de pompiers
**841** Chenilles de char A. M. X.
**842** Pneus Vespa

**843** Pneus militaires striés
**852** Chenilles pour Half-track
**853** Pneus pour GBO et Profileur
**855** Pneus pour Renault 4 L

# French Dinky Toys Gift Sets

**1  Station Staff Set**
1934-40
- Six figures: 1 x 1a Station Master,
2 x 1b Porter (no luggage), 1 x 1c Guard,
1 x 1d Policeman, 1 x 1e Inspector.
Two pictures on lid of card box ...... **£250-300**

**1  Station Staff Set**
1938-40
- Same but box has no illustration..... **£225-275**

**2  Railway Passengers Set**
1934-40
- Contains a tinplate bench (2g) and
six figures:
2a Normandy Farmer, 2b Farmer's Wife,
2c Young Girl, 2d Boy Scout (with stick),
2e Boy (sitting), 2f Girl (sitting). Red
box has illustrations, yellow inner .. **£225-275**
1938-40
- Same set but in red box (yellow inner)
with no illustration .......................... **£200-250**

**3  Animals Set**
1934-40
- Contains six animals: 3a Pig,
3b Sheep (dark brown), 3c Horse (grey),
3c Horse (brown), 3d Bull (mottled White),
3d Bull (mottled reddish-brown).
Box has two pictures on lid............ **£300-350**
1938-40
- Same but box has no illustrations ... **£250-300**

**4  Railway Personnel Set**
1934-40
- Six figures: 4a Cook (with fowl),
4b Engine Fireman, 4c Greaser (with oilcan),
4d Wheel Tapper (with mallet),
4e Female Gate-Keeper (with flag),
4f Porter (with luggage).
Box has two illustrations................ **£225-275**
1938-40
- Same but box has no illustration..... **£175-225**

**5  Railway Passengers Set**
1934-40
- Contains six figures: 5a Woman and Child,
5b Businessman, 5c Male Tourist (with
camera), 5d Clergyman, 5e Newsboy,
5f Female Tennis Player.
Two different pictures on box ........ **£225-275**
1938-40
- Same but box has no illustration..... **£175-225**

**6  Shepherd Set**
1934-40
- 6a Shepherd (light brown), 6b Sheepdog
(black), 4 x 3b Sheep (white or cream).
Box has two illustrations................ **£400-500**
1938-40
- Same but box has no illustration..... **£300-400**

**10  Assorted Figures Set**
1934-40
- Consists of Sets 1, 2 and 4.
Box has two illustrations................ **£250-350**
1938-40
- Same but box has no illustration..... **£220-270**

**17  Electric Goods Train**
1935-38
- 19a Electric Locomotive, 21b Timber
Wagon, 21c Coal Wagon, 21d Crane
Wagon. Diorama box....................... **£250-300**
1938-40
- Same but box has no diorama ........ **£175-225**

**18  Steam Goods Train**
1934-38
- 21a Steam Tank Locomotive,
3 x 21c Coal Wagon, diorama box.. **£250-300**

1938-40
- Same but box has no diorama ........ **£175-225**

**19  Electric Passenger Train**
1935-38
- 19a Electric Locomotive, 3 x 20a
Coach, diorama box ....................... **£250-300**

**20  Steam Passenger Train**
1935-38
- 21a Steam Tank Locomotive,
3 x 20a Coach, diorama box ........... **£250-300**
1938-40
- Same but box has no diorama ........ **£175-225**

**21  Steam Mixed Goods Train**
1934-38
- 21a Tank Locomotive, 21b Timber Wagon,
21c Coal Wagon, 21d Crane Wagon,
diorama box.................................... **£350-450**
1938-40
- Same but box has no diorama ........ **£225-275**

**24  Passenger Cars Set**
1935-36
- 6 cars: 24b Limousine, 24d Vogue Saloon,
24e Aerodynamic Saloon,
24f Sportsman's Coupé,
24g 4-seat Sports Car,
24h 2-seat Sports Car.
Yellow box / no illustration......**£8,000-11,000**
**NB** The basic box for this set was
adapted to contain the 25 series
Commercial Vehicles Set.
1936-39
- 6 cars: 24b Limousine, 24d Vogue Saloon,
24e Aerodynamic Saloon,
24f Sportsman's Coupé,
24g 4-seat Sports Car,
24h 2-seat Sports Car.
Purple box with picture (two different
designs exist) ............................ **£7,000-8,000**
1940-48
- The same set, but in Blue box
without illustration ................... **£6,000-7,000**

**24-55  Touring Cars Gift Set**
1955-55
- 24-R Peugeot 203, 24-T Citroën 2cv,
24-U Simca Aronde 9,
24-V Buick Roadmaster,
24-X Ford Vedette .................... **£1,500-2,000**

**24-56  Touring Cars Gift Set**
1956-56
- 24-R Peugeot 203, 24-T Citroën 2cv,
24-U Simca Aronde Elysée,
24-Y Studebaker Commander,
24-Z Simca Vedette Versailles .. **£1,500-2,000**

**24-57  Touring Cars Gift Set**
1957-57
- 24-A Chrysler New Yorker,
24-B Peugeot 403 8cv,
24-E Renault Dauphine,
24-Y Studebaker Commander,
24-Z Simca Vedette Versailles .. **£1,500-2,000**

**24-58  Touring Cars Gift Set**
1958-58
- 24-B Peugeot 403 8cv,
24-C (or 24-CP) Citroën DS19,
24-D Plymouth Belvedere,
24-E Renault Dauphine,
24-Z Simca Vedette Versailles.
Red/yellow/green/black box...... **£1,500-2,000**
**NB** The annual '24 series' of Gift Sets
was renumbered in 1959 ; the next issue
in the series is 500.

**25  Commercial Vehicles Gift Set**
1935-37
- 25a Open Lorry, 25b Covered Lorry,
25c Flat Lorry, 25d Tanker Lorry,
25e Tipping Lorry,
25f Market Gardeners Lorry.
Purple and gold box. ................ **£2,000-2,500**
**NB** The basic box for this set was
adapted from that used for the
24 series Passenger Cars Set.
1938-39
- Same, but in a long Blue box.... **£1,500-2,000**
1940-48
- Same set, but all wheels are solid metal.
Long blue box with printed ends
(yellow base, blue inner). .......... **£1,500-2,000**

**25S  Commercial Vehicles Gift Set**
1948-48
- The same set, all models having solid
metal wheels. Light blue box. .... **£2,500-3,500**

**25N  Commercial Vehicles Gift Set**
1949-49
- 25-H Ford Beverage Truck,
25-I Ford Open Wagon,
25-J Ford Covered Wagon,
25-K Studebaker Market Gardeners Truck,
25-L Studebaker Covered Delivery Truck,
25-M Studebaker Tipping Truck.
Blue or yellow box. .................. **£3,500-5,000**
1950-50
- The same set, but in a Red box. **£3,500-5,000**

**40  Traffic Signs 'Town' Set**
1953-59  (renumbered in 1959 to 590)
- 6 diecast signs: 'No Entry', 'No Waiting',
'30km/hr', 'No Overtaking',
'Maximum Weight 5.5 tonnes',
'Right (or Left) Turn'. Each 55mm. high,
scale 1:43. Yellow box with
'Code de la Route' leaflet.................. **£65-75**

**41  Traffic Signs  'Route' Set**
1953-59  (renumbered in 1959 to 591)
- 6 diecast signs: 'Danger - Crossroads',
'Priority' marker, 'Dangerous Bends',
'Caution - School', 'Level Crossing with
Gates'. Small signs 37mm. high; large
signs 52mm., scale 1:43.
Yellow box with leaflet ...................... **£65-75**

**49  Set of Fuel Pumps** (5)
1935-40
- 2 x 49a Pillar type Fuel Pump,
1 x 49b Mobile Oil Pump,
2 x 49c Double Output Pump.
Blue box, later Yellow.................... **£400-500**
1949-50
- Same set, Yellow box .................... **£300-400**

**50  British Naval Warships Set**
1938-40
- 14 English-made models in French
printed box:
50a 'Hood', 50b 'Nelson', 50b 'Rodney',
50c 'Effingham', 50d 'York', 50e 'Delhi',
3 x 50f 'Broke', 50g 'X' class Submarine,
3 x 50h 'Amazon',
50k 'K' class Sub ........................... **£200-300**

**60  Aircraft Presentation Set**
1935-37
- 6 models: 60a DeWoitine D338 Rainbow,
60b Potez 58, 60c Henriot H180T,
60d Breguet Corsaire,
60e DeWoitine 500 Hunter, 60f Cierva
Autogiro. Purple and gold box (models
are set out in a straight formation along

French Dinky Toys Gift Sets: No.25 Commercial Vehicles Set and No.60z Aeroplanes Set.
PHOTOGRAPHS: COLLECTOYS, BOURGES, FRANCE

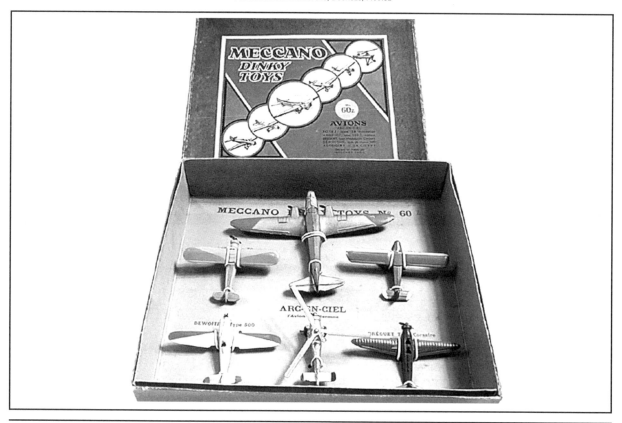

the length of the box).
Picture on lid .............................. £1,500-1,750
1937-39
- The same 6 models but set out in a
  diagonal formation within a bright
  blue box. Picture on box lid ...... £1,500-1,750
  1939-40
- The same 6 models but set out in a
  diagonal formation within a Dark
  Green box. Picture on box lid ... £1,500-1,750
  1957-59   (renumbered in 1959 to 501)
- 4 models: 60-A Dassault Mystere IVa,
  60-B Sud Aviation Vautour,
  60-D Sikorsky S58, 60-E Vickers Viscount.
  Supertoys box, picture on lid ......... £300-400

**61   Aircraft Presentation Set**
1938-39
- 5 models: 61a DeWoitine D338,
  61b Potez 56, 61d Potez 58,
  61e Henriot H180M,
  61f DeWoitine 500 Hunter.
  Blue box .................................... £1,500-2,000
  1939-46
- 6 models: 61a DeWoitine D338,
  61b Potez 56, 61c Farman F360,
  61d Potez 58, 61e Henriot H180M,
  61f DeWoitine 500.
  Green box .................................. £1,250-1,750

**64   Aircraft Presentation Set**
1939-48
- Five models: 61a DeWoitine D338,
  64a Amiot 370, 64b Bloch 220,
  64c Potez 63, 64d Potez 662.
  Green box with illustration ....... £1,250-1,750

**70   Modern Travel Set
('Locomotion Moderne')**
1939?
- Five different forms of travel represented by:
  23b Racing Car, 26 Railcar,
  52c Steamship 'Normandie',
  53a Steamship 'Dunkerque',
  60a DeWoitine Rainbow.
  Advertised in 1939(?)
  catalogue but no production known .........NPP

**101   Dining Room Furniture Set**
1936
- 101a Table, 101b Sideboard, 2 x 101c
  Carver, 4 x 101d Dining Chair.
  Light or dark mottled brown .......... £300-350

**102   Bedroom Furniture Set**
1936-40
- 102a Bed, 102b Wardrobe, 102c Dressing
  Table, 102d Chest of Drawers,
  102e Stool, 102f Chair. Lilac .......... £300-350

**103   Kitchen Furniture Set**
1936-40
- 103a Refrigerator, 103b Sideboard,
  103c Cooker, 103d Table, 103e Chair.
  Pale Green/Cream or Blue/Ivory ...... £300-350

**104   Bathroom Furniture Set**
1937-40
- 104a Bath, 104b Bath Mat, 104c Hand
  Basin, 104d Stool, 104e Linen Basket,
  104f Toilet. Pink veined ................. £300-350

**500   Touring Cars Gift Set**
1959-59
- 521 Peugeot 403 8cv, 522 Citroën DS19,
  523 Plymouth Belvedere,
  524 Renault Dauphine,
  541 Simca Vedette Versailles .... £2,000-3,000

**501   Aircraft Presentation Set**
1959-62   (renumbered in 1959 from 60)
- 800 Dassault Mystere IVa, 801 Sud
  Aviation Vautour, 802 Sikorsky S58,
  803 Vickers Viscount...................... £300-400

**503   Touring Cars Gift Set**
1963-64
- 521 Peugeot 403 8cv, 522 Citroën DS19,
  543 Renault Floride, 544 Simca Aronde,
  545 DeSoto Diplomat.
  Blue/Yellow/Grey box.............. £2,000-3,000

**536   Peugeot 404 and Trailer**
1965
- Red car, Black skis on Yellow rack or
  Yellow skis on Black rack, Cream
  plastic trailer (no. 812), luggage ..... £175-200

**590   Traffic Signs 'Town' Set**
1959-68   (renumbered in 1959 from 40)
- 6 signs 55mm. high: 'No Entry', 'No
  Parking', 'Maximum Weight 5.5 tonnes',
  'Right (or Left) Turn', '30km/hr',
  'No Overtaking'.  Yellow box
  with 'Code de la Route' leaflet .......... £70-80

**591   Traffic Signs 'Route' Set**
1959-68   (renumbered in 1959 from 41)
- 6 metal signs: 'Danger - Crossroads',
  'Priority' marker, 'Dangerous Bends',
  'Caution - School',
  'Level Crossing with Gates'.
  Signs 37mm. and 52mm. high.
  Yellow box, leaflet .............................. £70-80

**592   Traffic Signs 'Town' Set**
1969-71  (scale 1:43)
- Twelve plastic signs on diecast bases:
  'Caution - Gyratory System', 'No Entry',
  'Parking', 'No Parking', 'Caution - School',
  'No U-Turn', '45km/hr', 'No Overtaking',
  'Do Not Use Horn', 'Blue Zone', 'Taxis',
  'No Left Turn'. In 'window' box .... £100-125

**593   Traffic Signs 'Route' Set**
1969-71  (scale 1:43)
- Twelve plastic signs on diecast bases:
  'Autoroute', 'End of Autoroute', 'Autoroute
  Toll Point', 'End of Speed Limit',
  'Crossroads - Give Way', 'Dangerous
  Crossing', 'Stop', 'Priority' marker,
  'Dangerous Bend', 'Caution',
  'Gradient 10%', 'Low Flying Aircraft'.
  In 'window' box .............................. £100-125

**1460   Touring Cars Gift Set**
1969-70
- 6 models: 501 Citroën DS19 'POLICE',
  507 Simca 1500GLS Estate, 508 Daf 33,
  509 Fiat 850, 513 Opel Admiral,
  514 Alfa-Romeo 1600.
  Blue/yellow box ........................ £2,500-3,500

**1462   'Three Days' Gift Set**
1969-69
- 4 models: 507 Simca 1500GLS Estate,
  508 Daf 33, 509 Fiat 850,
  514 Alfa-Romeo 1600. Sold in a special
  'Sac-cadeau'(plastic Gift-Bag)........ £600-800
**NB** 'Galeries Lafayette' is a Paris department
  store with branches in several French towns.
  Annually '3J' sales are held in these shops.
  Selection 1462 was specially made for the
  1969 'Trois Jours' ('Three Days') sale.

# French Dinky Toys Trade Boxes

Meccano distributed Dinky Toys, from factories to shops via warehouses, in the same way in France as in England, through the use of Trade Boxes. Our knowledge of the French versions is not extensive and readers help is required in adding to this short list of known French Trade Boxes and Packs.

| Model ref. and name | Quantity in box | MPR |
|---|---|---|
| 507 Simca 1500 (Estate Cars) | 6 | £400-500 |
| 24UT Taxi (Simca) Aronde | 6 | £700-800 |
| 24R 203 Peugeot | 6 | £600-700 |
| 245 Simca 8 Sport | 6 | £600-700 |
| 24N Citroën Traction Avant 3rd type | 6 | £700-800 |
| 23H Talbot-Lago Racing Cars | 6 | £500-600 |
| 24XT Taxi (Ford) Vedettes | 6 | £500-600 |
| 508S Dafs. Shrink wrapped in acetate. Models M in E boxes | | £400-500 |
| 24V Buick Roadmasters boxes, Outer Pack G-VG | 6 | £700-800 |
| 828 Rocket-Carrier Jeeps. Original boxes and acetate, M in VG boxes | 6 | £300-350 |
| 810 Military Command Car. Original boxes and acetate -boxes | 3 | £600-700 |
| 25P Studebaker Open Lorries | 6 | £1,000-1,200 |
| 32AB Panhard Tractors and 'SNCF' Semi-Trailers | 6 | £400-500 |
| 29D Paris Buses | 6 | £350-400 |
| 25V Ford Dust Carts | 6 | £600-700 |
| 1412 Breakdown Jeeps. Original boxes and acetate | 6 | £600-700 |

# French Dinky Toys Catalogues and Magazines

Note that some post-war catalogues have '57B.16273' or '60B.3844' printed at the bottom of the back cover or in some inconspicuous corner. These are not catalogue reference numbers but a form of 'registered design' for publicity material. As they have no other meaning to collectors they are therefore not shown in the following list. French Dinky Toys are also mentioned in catalogues from other countries, notably Spain and Holland. We are in need of details of Meccano advertising in other countries and would welcome any help our readers could provide.

| Year of intro, publication details | MPR |
|---|---|
| 1949 **Catalogue** (no ref.) Sepia cover, 'Nouveauties Dinky Toys' | **£50-60** |
| 1950 **Catalogue** (no ref., 12 page booklet) Blue on white cover shows 'Dinky Toys Miniatures' issuing from Meccano factory through arched gateway. 'Meccano 78-80 Rue Rébéval Paris (XIX)' on back cover. No price list | **£50-60** |
| 1951 **Catalogue** no ref. Green / sepia, 'Miniatures Dinky Toys'in black | **£60-70** |
| 1952 **Catalogue** '175-5-52' (10 page booklet) Glossy pages fold out to twice the size of the cover. Cream cover with green and red printing. Black and white photographic illustrations, no prices, 'Imp. HENON PARIS' on last page | **£60-70** |
| 1953 **Catalogue** (no ref., 20 page booklet) Pale grey stylized car of the period and trees on cover overprinted with 'Miniatures Dinky Toys' and 'C'est une fabrication Meccano' in red. Black and white inside pictures; no price list | **£40-50** |
| 1954 **Catalogue** (no ref., 20 pages). Blue and white striped cover with Buick Roadmaster, Esso Tanker and Citroën 'H' van. Black and white pictures inside. No prices | **£40-50** |
| 1954 **Leaflet** (no ref.) Various, advertising new issues | **£10-15** |
| 1955 **Catalogue** (no ref., 16 page booklet) No price list. Blue/white stripes on cover, plus Marrel truck and 32-D Delahaye fire appliance | **£40-50** |
| 1956 **Catalogue** (no ref., April, 16 pages) Colour printing inside, no prices. 'Supertoys look' covers with Berliet Container Truck, Autocar Chausson and Citroën car on front with Willème Log Lorry and rear view of 32-D on back cover | **£40-50** |
| 1956 **Catalogue** (no ref., September, 20 pages) Similar to April catalogue but cover has Log Lorry, Citroën car and Dassault plane. No price list | **£40-50** |
| 1957 **Summer Catalogue** (no ref., 16 pages) Driverless vehicles emerging from tunnel on front cover. Printed in France | **£40-50** |
| 1958 **Summer Catalogue** (no ref., 16 pages) Maserati and Mercedes on front cover. Two to five models per page (drawn). Printed in France | **£40-50** |
| 1958 **Meccano Catalogue 'DL 1958/3'** (32 pp). The colourful cover shows a boy's face, an electric train at speed on a blue/gold Meccano track and three Dinky Toys. | |

| Year of intro, publication details | MPR |
|---|---|
| 8 pages of Dinky Toys. September price list enclosed. Printed in France | **£40-50** |
| 1959 **Catalogue** (no ref., 20 pages) Colour booklet like 1958 issue. Cover shows Simca and lorry at an Esso station. No price list | **£40-50** |
| 1960 **Catalogue** (no ref., 24 page booklet) Full colour with Renault Floride and Panhard on the front cover. Printed at Mulhouse in France | **£40-50** |
| 1961 **Catalogue** (no ref., 20 pages) Full colour booklet printed in Belgium. Pictures of real vehicles plus parts of a road map of France with various Dinky Toys on it. No price list | **£30-40** |
| 1962 **Catalogue** (no ref.) Includes mention of Hornby boats and Hornby Acho trains | **£30-40** |
| 1962 **Catalogue** (no ref., 24 pages) Cover shows Renault R4 parked on quayside next to Steamship 'France'. Printed in Belgium | **£30-40** |
| 1963 **Catalogue** (no ref., 32 pages) 'First half' catalogue. Cover shows Dinky Mercedes against photo of the actual car. February price list (on very pale green pages) stapled in. Printed in England | **£30-40** |
| 1963 **Catalogue** (no ref., 32 pages) 'Second half' catalogue (cover as 'first half'). Includes price list dated 'Juillet 1963' in centre | **£30-40** |
| 1964 **Catalogue** (no ref.) Full colour pages with April price list (on orange paper) stapled in. Five new models pictured and described on the cover which also has photo of car showroom interior. Printed in England | **£25-35** |
| 1964 **Catalogue** (no ref., 16 pages) Booklet with October price list | **£25-35** |
| 1965 **Catalogue** (no ref., 20 pages) Full colour 'first half' catalogue. Front cover shows 128L Mercedes and 537 Renault. April price list (1965/1, orange paper) stapled in. Printed in England | **£25-35** |
| 1965 **Catalogue** (no ref., Winter 1965-66) 28 pages; includes October price list 1965/2 on red paper. Cover depicts 889 Autobuses and 510 Peugeot. The only photo within is of an actual AMX Bridge-Layer in action. Printed in England | **£25-35** |
| 1966 **Catalogue** (no ref.) 'First half' | **£25-35** |
| 1966 **'Second half' Catalogue** (no ref., 122 pages). Simca and Opel on the cover. September price list on blue paper. | |

| Year of intro, publication details | MPR |
|---|---|
| Printed in England | **£25-35** |
| 1967 **'First half' Catalogue** (no ref.) | **£25-35** |
| 1967 **Catalogue** (no ref., 128 pages) Porsche Carrera on cover. September price list (on pink paper) fixed in at rear. Lady Penelope's 'FAB 1' shown as newly introduced. Printed in England. '2e édition' printed inside back cover | **£25-35** |
| 1968 **'First half' Catalogue** (no ref., 130 pages). With February price list | **£25-35** |
| 1968 **'Second half' Catalogue** (no ref., 122 pages). Simca and fast-cornering Opel on the cover. Printed in England | **£15-20** |
| 1969 **'First half' Catalogue** (no ref., 24 pages). Front cover shows hard-braking Ford Thunderbird avoiding errant daschund, yellow Opel GT in foreground. Rear cover advertises 'free' Traffic Signs. Printed in England | **£25-35** |
| 1969 **'Second half' Catalogue** (no ref.) | **£20-30** |
| 1970 **Catalogue '91.761'** (24 pages) '1970.1' printed on cover which also shows a Porsche and a Ferrari 312P racing round a banking which has 'La Marque du Connaisseur' on it in yellow. Printed in England | **£20-30** |
| 1970 **Catalogue '91.762'** As previous catalogue but with '1970.2' on front cover. Printed in England | **£20-30** |
| 1971 **Catalogue '91.786'** (24 pages) Cover depicts a Citroën Présidentielle and a Renault R12. Printed in England | **£20-30** |
| 1971 **Meccano Tri-ang leaflet '91.780'** (full colour). Nearly A4 size; one side depicts 1971 Dinky Toys. 'Gyro-Jets' and 'Spirofoil' on reverse | **£6-10** |
| 1976 **Meccano Catalogue** (no ref., 108 pages) Only 10 pages of Dinky Toys (English and French). Brown cover | **£25-35** |

## MAGAZINES

| | MPR |
|---|---|
| 1924-38 **Meccano Magazine** Published monthly from 1924 to 1938, large format | **£5-10** |
| 1953-57 **Meccano Magazine** Published monthly from October 1953 to October 1957, small format | **£5-10** |
| 1957-59 **Meccano Magazine** Published monthly from November 1957 to September 1959, large format | **£5-10** |
| 1959-60 **'Actualités Meccano' Journal** Published between October 1959 to October 1960 (5 issues), each | **£5-10** |

# Promotional Material

| | MPR |
|---|---|
| 1957- **Membership Certificate**. 'Parchment' style 'CLUB DINKY TOYS' certificate | **£45-55** |
| 1960- **Membership Certificate**. As above, but amended | **£45-55** |
| 1960- **Subscription Reminder**. Reminder form. | **£10-20** |
| 1961- **Subscription Reminder**. As above, but updated | **£10-20** |
| 1957- **Membership Document**. Printed details of Club membership | **£10-20** |
| 1954- **Dinky Toys Driver's Licence** | **£35-45** |
| 1957- **Button Insignia**. A round metal badge, 'CLUB DINKY TOYS', screw fitting through button-hole | **£35-45** |
| 1957- **Brooch Insignia**. As above, but with 'safety pin' lapel fitting | **£35-45** |
| 1957- **Key Ring**. Round metal badge within stitched 'leather' surround | **£35-45** |
| 1957- **Key Ring**. Round metal badge encapsulated in clear plastic | **£35-45** |
| **Display Case**. A small display case (no other details) | **£150-250** |
| 1961- **ESGE Display Case**. A larger display case (cream/yellow/red) with 5 shelves, 'DINKY-TOYS MECCANO' on glazing | **£400-500** |
| ? **Illuminated Display Case**. Large display case with 6 shelves and electric lighting | **£450-600** |
| ? **Illuminated Curved Case**. Large curved display case with 6 shelves and electric lighting | **£450-600** |
| ? **Counter Sign**. Diecast triangular block painted red/cream, 'DINKY TOYS'. | **£75-100** |
| 1950s/60s **Shop Display Stand**, freestanding 68 x 16 x 49cm., 'DINKY TOYS' and 'MECCANO' logos, Yellow/Red | **£1,500-2,000** |
| 1950s/60s **Electric Metal Display Stand**, 'DINKY TOYS' and 'MECCANO', illuminated centre piece with 5 shelves | **£1,500-2,000** |

# English Dinky Toys imported into France

The models in the following list were those manufactured in Liverpool and sent to France for sale over different periods of time. In the main they were complete English made models but some were supplied in component form for assembly in the French factory.

It is understood that the boxes were either made in England and printed "Fabriqué en Angleterre" and "Imprimé en Angleterre", or were made in France and printed "Fabriqué en Angleterre" and "Imprimé en France". In some cases the model and the box were sold just as they came from Binns Road with no modification or overprinting of any kind. It is therefore important when seeking variations to make sure whether the model was only imported fully built, imported as plain castings for assembly in France, or both (at different times). They were also on occasions supplied complete except for the baseplate which was fitted in France. The degree of painting often varied, some items being supplied fully finished while others were still "raw" from the dies.

Some models were supplied with English tyres, some without, so that French tyres could be fitted. Body colours were much the same as the UK versions though could be different shades, unique colours or a different range of colours. The 60h Singapore Flying Boat was for instance painted in a camouflage finish

for the French market, and 108L Sam's Car was only available in silver or blue in France. Some renumbering also took place when models previously assembled in France (imported only as components) were later imported ready made. A couple of examples of this practice are 150/551 and 885/961. Virtually every post-war import from England carries the suffix 'L' after its reference number to indicate its Liverpool origin.

Note also that from time to time various factory items were exchanged between Liverpool and Bobigny (this included equipment components and complete or partial dies and tools). This was done either to make up an end of run deficiency, to replace worn or broken dies, to experiment with prototypes or simply to evaluate a new idea. Consequently there may well be oddities still to be found which do not conform to the known output. If you have knowledge of any item or variation not listed, do please communicate it to the Editor so that we may share the information with others in the collecting fraternity. Thank you.

The prices you should expect to see asked for these essentially English productions are likely to be much the same as for the same items sold in British shops or auction houses.

| French ref.no. | Years imported | Model |
|---|---|---|
| 14-C | 50-51 | Coventry Climax Fork Lift Truck |
| 23c | 38-39 | Mercedes Racing Car |
| 23d | 38-39 | Auto-Union Record Car |
| 23e | 38-39 | 'Speed of the Wind' |
| 23m | 38-39 | 'Thunderbolt' |
| 25h | 38-39 | Streamlined Fire Engine |
| 27AC | 50-50 | Tractor and Manure Spreader |
| 29b | 39-39 | Streamlined Bus |
| 30a | 35-39 | Chrysler Airflow |
| 30b | 35-37 | Rolls-Royce |
| 30g | 38-39 | Camping Trailer |
| 50 | 37-38 | Battleship Gift Set |
| 51b | 37-39 | Norddeutscher- Lloyd 'Europa' |
| 51c | 37-39 | Italia Line 'Rex' |
| 51d | 37-39 | 'Empress of Britain' |
| 52a | 36-39 | 'Queen Mary' |
| 60h | 38-38 | Singapore Flying Boat (camouflaged) |
| 60m | 38-39 | Singapore Flying Boat (civilian) |
| 60r | 38-39 | 'Empire' Flying Boat |
| 60w | 38-39 | 'Clipper III' Flying Boat |
| 62k | 38-39 | 'King's Aeroplane' |
| 62n | 39-39 | Junkers 'Ju90' |
| 62p | 39-39 | 'Ensign' Air Liner |
| 63 | 39-39 | Mayo Composite |
| 100L | 68-71 | Lady Penelope's 'FAB 1' |
| 101L | 68-69 | Thunderbirds II / IV |
| 104L | 69-71 | Spectrum Pursuit |
| 106L | 69-70 | 'The Prisoner' Mini-Moke |
| 108L | 70-71 | Sam's Car |
| 110L | 65-68 | Aston-Martin DB5 |
| 114L | 64-66 | Triumph Spitfire |
| 116L | 67-71 | Volvo P1800 |
| 118L | 67-70 | Towaway Glider |
| 127L | 65-68 | R-R Silver Cloud |
| 128L | 65-70 | Mercedes 600 |
| 129L | 68-68 | Volkswagen 1300 |
| 131L | 69-71 | Jaguar 'E'-type |
| 132L | 68-71 | Ford RV40 |
| 142L | 63-67 | Jaguar Mark 10 |
| 150L | 62-64 | R-R Silver Wraith |
| 151a | 38-38 | Medium Tank |
| 152a | 38-38 | Light Tank |
| 152L | 67-70 | R-R Phantom V |
| 153L | 68-70 | Aston-Martin DB6 |
| 155L | 62-65 | Ford Anglia |
| 160L | 68-71 | Mercedes 250 |
| 161 | 39-40 | Mobile A-A Gun |
| 161L | 67-71 | Ford Mustang |
| 162 | 39-40 | Light Dragon Tractor |
| 163L | 67-71 | VW 1600TL |
| 165L | 69-70 | Ford Capri 1600 |
| 172L | 67-71 | Fiat 2300 Estate |
| 173L | 69-71 | Pontiac Parisienne |
| 174L | 69-70 | Ford Mercury Cougar |
| 175L | 69-71 | Cadillac Eldorado |
| 176L | 69-71 | NSU Ro80 |
| 182L | 62-64 | Porsche 356a |
| 186L | 62-63 | Mercedes 220 |
| 187L | 69-71 | De Tomaso Mangusta |
| 188L | 69-71 | Jensen FF 542 |
| 189L/1 | 62-64 | Triumph Herald |
| 189L/2 | 69-71 | Lamborghini Marzal |
| 190L | 71-? | Monteverdi 375L |
| 192L | 71-? | Range Rover |
| 194L | 62-63 | Bentley 'S' |
| 195L | 62-65 | Jaguar 3.4 |
| 198L | 63-66 | R-R Phantom V |
| 199L | 62-67 | Austin 7 Countryman |
| 200L | 71-? | Matra 630 |
| 202L | 71-? | Fiat Abarth 2000 |
| 204L | 71-? | Ferrari 312 P |
| 205L | 69-71 | Lotus Cortina |
| 208L | 71-? | VW Porsche 914 |
| 210L | 71-? | Alfa-Romeo 33 |
| 213L | 70-71 | Ford Capri 1600 |
| 215L | 65-71 | Ford GT Le Mans |
| 216L | 68-71 | Ferrari Dino |
| 217L | 69-71 | Alfa-Romeo Scarabeo |
| 218L | 70-71 | Lotus Europa GT |
| 220L | 70-71 | Ferrari P5 |
| 221L | 70-71 | Chevrolet Corvette |
| 223L | 70-71 | McLaren Can-Am |
| 224L | 71-? | Mercedes C111 |
| 225L | 71-? | Lotus 49B F1 |
| 238L | 71-? | Ferrari 3L F1 (not issued) |
| 240L | 63-70 | Cooper RacingCar |
| 241L | 63-70 | Lotus Racing Car |
| 242L | 63-70 | Ferrari Racing Car |
| 243L | 64-70 | BRM Racing Car |
| 252L | 62-64 | Bedford Refuse Truck |
| 253L | 62-62 | Daimler Ambulance |
| 258L | 62-63 | De Soto USA Police |
| 258L | 63-64 | Dodge USA Police |
| 258L | 65-66 | Cadillac USA Police |
| 258L | 67-68 | Ford Fairlane USA Police Car |
| 263L | 63-68 | Super Criterion Ambulance |
| 270L | 69-71 | Ford Escort Police |
| 276L | 63-69 | Airport Fire |
| 300L | 62-70 | Massey-Harris Tractor |
| 308L | 71-? | Leyland Tractor |
| 320L | 62-70 | Halesowen Trailer |
| 321L | 62-71 | Massey-Harris Manure Spreader |
| 324L | 62-64 | Hay Rake |
| 340L | 62-67 | Land Rover |
| 341L | 62-67 | Land RoverTrailer |
| 344L | 71-? | Land Rover Pick-up |
| 351L | 71-? | 'SHADO' Interceptor |
| 370L | 70-71 | Dragster / Launcher |
| 401L | 62-64 | Coventry Climax Fork Lift Truck |
| 437L | 63-71 | JCB Shovel |
| 439L | 71-? | Ford Snow Plough |
| 449L | 62-63 | El Camino Pick-up |
| 451L | 71-? | Ford D800 Johnston Road Sweeper |
| 475L | 64-68 | Ford Model 'T' 1908 |
| 476L | 65-69 | Morris Oxford 1913 |
| 485L | 64-70 | Ford Model 'T' 'Father Christmas' |
| 601L | 67-70 | Austin Para-Moke |
| 615L | 68-71 | Jeep / Field Gun |
| 617L | 69-71 | VW KDF / Field Gun |
| 620L | 71-? | Berliet Gazelle with Missile |
| 651L | 62-70 | Centurion Tank |
| 661L | 62-63 | Recovery Tractor |
| 665L | 65-71 | Honest John Carrier |
| 666L | 61-65 | Corporal Missile |
| 667L | 62-64 | Servicing Platform |
| 676L | 72-? | Scout Car |
| 697L | 62-70 | Artillery Set |
| 719L | 70-71 | Spitfire |
| 721L | 70-71 | Stuka Ju 87b |
| 722L | 70-71 | Hawker Harrier |
| 724L | 71-? | Sea Rescue Helicopter |
| 796L | 62-68 | Dinghy on Trailer |
| 930L | 61-64 | Bedford 'Pallet-Jekta' |
| 936L | 65-68 | Leyland Test Chassis |
| 952L | 64-70 | Vega Major Coach |
| 958L | 62-65 | Guy Snow Plough |
| 960L | 62-69 | Albion Cement Mixer |
| 961L | 62-63 | Blaw-Knox Bulldozer |
| 962L | 62-64 | Muir-Hill Dumper |
| 964L | 62-63 | Elevator Loader |
| 965L | 61-64 | Euclid Quarry Truck |
| 971L | 62-63 | Coles Mobile Crane |
| 972L | 62-69 | Coles Lorry Crane |
| 973L | 71-? | Yale Diesel Shovel |
| 974L | 69-71 | AEC Hoynor Car Transporter |
| 976L | 69-71 | Michigan Shovel Dozer |

# French Dinky Toys Numerical Index

# Lone Star and DCMT

Robert Newson has provided the following information on Lone Star models.

'Lone Star' was the trade name of Die Casting Machine Tools Ltd (DCMT) who started in 1939 as manufacturers of diecasting machines. They were based at Palmers Green in North London. After the war they started making diecast toys which were distributed by The Crescent Toy Co Ltd. In the Crescent Toys section of this catalogue, the items listed as 'early post-war models' were all made by DCMT with the exception of the Locomotive and the Racing Car. From 1950 DCMT arranged their own distribution direct to wholesalers. Over the next four decades DCMT Lone Star made several ranges of diecast vehicles including 'Slikka Toys' (early 1950s), 'Modern Army Series' (mainly 1960s), 'Roadmaster Majors' (1960s and 1970s), 'Farmer's Boy' (1980s) and the well known 'Lone Star Locos' miniature railway system (later called 'Treble-O-Lectric' or 'Treble-O-Trains'). The four ranges of most interest to collectors are listed here - the original DCMT 'Roadmasters' of 1956, the 1:50 scale 'Roadmasters' (1960s), the 'Impy' and 'Flyers' series made in various forms from 1966 to the mid 1980s, and the miniature 'Tuf-Tots' (1970s). The Editor would welcome any further information on Lone Star products.

| Model and details | MPR |
|---|---|

## DCMT Lone Star Roadmasters

This was a short-lived series introduced in 1956, consisting of three sports cars and four veteran cars, all around 1:35 to 1:40 scale. The models had diecast bodies but all other components were plastic. Plastic drivers and passengers were included with the models.

| | | |
|---|---|---|
| --- | **1904 Darracq 'Genevieve'** Black or Red body, Yellow plastic chassis; Metallic Blue or Silver body, Black plastic chassis | **£250-350** |
| --- | **1904 Daimler 'Windsor' Phaeton** Red body, Yellow plastic chassis | **£70-80** |
| --- | **1912 Ford Model 'T'** Silver body, Black plastic chassis | **£70-80** |
| --- | **1912 Morris Oxford 'Bullnose'** Met. Blue body, Black plastic chassis | **£80-100** |
| --- | **Daimler Conquest Roadster** Red, Metallic Light Blue, Pale Yellow, Pale Green or Pale Blue | **£80-100** |
| --- | **Ford Thunderbird** Red, Metallic Light Blue, Pale Yellow, Pale Green or Pale Blue | **£80-100** |
| --- | **MG Midget TF** Metallic Light Blue or Red | **£80-100** |

## Lone Star Roadmasters

In 1960 Lone Star produced four American cars on behalf of the US firm of Tootsietoy. These were the first four models listed below and they had 'Tootsietoy Classic Series' cast underneath. This arrangement only lasted for a couple of years, as by 1962 there were eight models available, all now marked 'Lone Star Roadmasters'. The models featured plated grilles, bumpers and wheels, and had windows but no interior detail. Around 1964 the plated parts were replaced by less attractive painted or self-coloured plastic, and vacuum-formed interiors were fitted. Later issues have yellow interiors, white wheels, plastic grille and bumpers. Five further numbers were added to the range before they were withdrawn around 1966.

| | | |
|---|---|---|
| 1258 | **Farm King Tractor and Trailer** Red tractor, 'Farm King' paper label, Blue trailer, 'Farm Estates Co.' paper label. (Roadmaster Major) | **£70-80** |
| 1470 | **Chevrolet Corvair** Red or Orange-Red | **£70-80** |
| 1471 | **Rambler Rebel Station Wagon** Sea-Green, Metallic Blue-Green or Green with Cream roof, Metallic Brown with White roof or all Green | **£70-80** |

| | | |
|---|---|---|
| 1472 | **Cadillac 62** Pale Blue, Blue (Cream roof) or all Blue | **£70-80** |
| 1473 | **Ford Sunliner Convertible** White or Light Blue; Red interior | **£70-80** |
| 1474 | **Chevrolet El Camino Pick-Up** Yellow or Orange | **£70-80** |
| 1475 | **Dodge Dart Phoenix** Metallic Dark Blue or Mid Blue | **£70-80** |
| 1476 | **Rolls-Royce Silver Cloud II** Grey with Black upper half or Metallic Blue | **£70-80** |
| 1477 | **Dodge Dart Police Car** Black, 'POLICE PATROL' or 'POLIZEI' | **£70-80** |
| 1478 | **Rambler Ambulance** White, Red Cross transfer on bonnet | **£70-80** |
| 1479 | **Chevrolet Corvair** Red, 'FIRE CHIEF', 'FEUERWEHR' or 'BRANDWEER' | **£70-80** |
| 1480 | **Chevrolet Corvair** Army Staff Car (continued after 1966 as no.1273 in 'Modern Army' series), Olive Green | **£70-80** |
| 1481 | **Rambler Military Ambulance** (continued after 1966 as no.1274 in 'Modern Army' series), Olive Green | **£70-80** |
| 1482 | **Citroën DS19** Turquoise | **£70-80** |
| --- | **Rambler Police Car** White body, 'POLIZEI' on bonnet | **£70-80** |

## Lone Star 'Tuf-Tots'

The first thirteen Tuf-Tots were introduced in 1969, and the next five followed in 1970. The remainder had appeared by 1972. They were available boxed or bubble-packed, and when bubble-packed there was an additional '2' in front of the model number to give a four-digit reference. Later, models were sold in open counter-top trays.

The trucks were based on a common US Ford chassis. Most models exist in numerous colour variations. The series was discontinued after 1980. Market Price Range is £10 to £15.

| | |
|---|---|
| 601 | **Ford Petrol Tanker** 'ESSO' labels Same, but 'ESSO' cast into sides |
| 602 | **Citroën DS Convertible with Driver** |
| 603 | **Chevrolet Corvette Stingray Conv. with Driver** |
| 604 | **Dodge Dart Convertible with Driver** |
| 605 | **Mercedes-Benz 280SL Convertible with Driver** |
| 606 | **Ford 'TT' Tow Truck** |
| 607 | **Ford 'Big L' Dumper Lorry** |
| 608 | **Jeep and Trailer** 'Herts. Farm', scale 85:1 |
| 609 | **Ford 'Autos' Flat Truck** with metal petrol pump island with plastic petrol pump island |

| | |
|---|---|
| 610 | **Ford Tipper Lorry** 'LS Construction Co.' labels with ribs cast onto body instead of labels |
| 611 | **Ford Luton Van** with 'Express Freight' labels with ribs cast onto body instead of labels |
| 612 | **Ford Articulated Low-Loader** 'Apache' |
| 613 | **Chris Craft Capri Speedboat** (plastic) **on Trailer**, scale 86:1 |
| 614 | **Ford Refuse Lorry** with 'City Refuse' labels with 'City Refuse' cast lettering |
| 615 | **Ford Cement Mixer** |
| 616 | **Ford Milk Float** 'Milk, Milk, Milk' cast on each side |
| 617 | **Ford Cattle Transporter** |
| 618 | **Ford Skip Lorry** |
| 619 | **Citroën DS Coupé** |
| 620 | **Chevrolet Corvette Stingray Coupé** |
| 621 | **Dodge Dart Coupé** |
| 622 | **Mercedes-Benz 280SL Coupé**, scale 86:1 |
| 623 | **Routemaster Bus** with 'London Bus' advertisements |
| 624 | **ERF Fire Engine** with ladder, 'Fire Brigade' labels |

| | |
|---|---|
| 625 | **Caravan** |
| 626 | **Ford Circus Cage Lorry** with plastic lion, 'Circus' cast-in |
| 627 | **Tractor Shovel** |

**Gift Sets**

| | |
|---|---|
| 579 | **Commercial Vehicle Set** 6 models |
| 580 | **Car and Trailer Set** 6 models |
| 581 | **12 Vehicle Set** 12 models |
| 582 | **Highway Set** 3 models plus sand hopper, car ramp, street and traffic lights |
| 583 | **Travel Set** 3 models plus girder bridge, windmill and 'Stop' barrier |
| 2570 | **Building Site Playset** 4 models plus sand hopper |
| 2571 | **Garage Playset** 4 models plus car ramp |
| 2572 | **Highway Playset** 4 models plus street and traffic lights |
| 2573 | **Travel Playset** 4 models plus 'Stop' barrier |
| 2574 | **Dutch Farm Playset** 4 models plus windmill |
| 2575 | **Bridge Playset** 4 models plus girder bridge |

# The greatest *IMPY* yet!

**No 24**

# FODEN Tilt-Cab TRUCK

Here's a really great model for you—with *all* the authentic details! $3\frac{3}{4}''$ long, this die-cast metal model has all these features :–

★ Tilting Cab
★ Windows, seats and steering wheel
★ Die-cast chassis
★ Die-cast engine
★ Non-scratch tyres
★ Tipping back with hinged loading flap

**3!**

**LONE ★ STAR**
*Roadmaster* **IMPY**
*Super Cars have everything*

Remember, IMPYs are the die-cast models with ALL the Real-Car features! Additions to the series are coming along all the time!

*Next on the list are:*

★ Ford Taunus
★ Tractor
★ Rolls Royce
       Silver Cloud III
★ Merryweather
       Fire Engine

An advertisement for **Lone Star Impey** models as it appeared in the 'Eagle and Boy's World' comic of 24th June 1967.

In the following listing the year shown is the date of introduction. Most models remained in production until 1976. **IW** = Impy wheels, **FW** = Flyers wheels, **HSW** = Hi-Speed wheels, **BPW** = black plastic wheels.

| | | | |
|---|---|---|---|
| 7 | 71 | **Vauxhall Firenza** IW / FW, RHD and LHD | **£25-30** |
| 8 | - | **Ford Capri**, not issued | NPP |
| 9 | 70 | **Maserati Mistral**, IW or FW | **£20-30** |
| 10 | 66 | **Jaguar Mk.X**, IW or FW | **£20-30** |
| 11 | 66 | **Chevrolet Corvette Stingray GT** IW or FW | **£20-30** |
| 12 | 66 | **Chrysler Imperial**, IW or FW | **£20-30** |
| 13 | - | **Ford Thunderbird**, not issued | NPP |
| 13 | 71 | **Toyota 2000 GT**, Flyers wheels | **£20-30** |
| 14 | 66 | **Ford Zodiac Mk.III Est.**, IW or FW | **£20-30** |
| 15 | 66 | **VW Microbus**, IW or FW | **£20-30** |
| 16 | 66 | **Ford Zodiac Mk.III Est. 'POLICE' Car.** IW or FW | **£20-30** |
| 16 | - | **Chrysler Imperia 'POLICE' Car**, IW or FW | **£20-30** |
| 16m | - | **Mercedes-Benz 220 SE 'POLIZEI' Car.** Impy wheels | **£20-30** |
| 17 | 66 | **Mercedes-Benz 220 SE**, IW or FW | **£20-30** |
| 18 | 66 | **Ford Corsair**, IW or FW | **£20-30** |
| 19 | 67 | **Volvo 1800 S**, IW or FW | **£20-30** |
| 20 | 67 | **VW Ambulance**, IW or FW | **£20-30** |
| 21 | 67 | **Fiat 2300 S Coupé**, IW or FW | **£20-30** |
| 22 | 67 | **Rolls-Royce Silver Cloud III Convertible.** IW or FW | **£20-30** |
| 23 | 67 | **Alfa Romeo Giulia 1600 Spider** IW or FW | **£20-30** |
| 24 | 67 | **Foden Tilt-cab 8w Tipper** black plastic or HSW | **£20-30** |
| 25 | 67 | **International Harvester Tractor Shovel** | **£20-30** |
| 26 | 67 | **Foden Tilt-cab Petrol Tanker** 'MOBIL', BPW or HSW | **£20-30** |
| 27 | 67 | **Ford Taunus 12M**, IW or FW | **£20-30** |
| 28 | 67 | **Peugeot 404 Saloon**, IW or FW | **£20-30** |
| 29 | - | **Cement Mixer Lorry**, not issued | NPP |
| 29 | 71 | **Foden Tilt-cab Box Van**, 'LUCAS', BPW or HSW | **£15-20** |
| 29 | 72 | **Foden Tilt-cab Box Van**, BPW, 'EXPRESS FREIGHT' labels | **£25-35** |
| 30 | 67 | **AEC Merryweather Fire Engine** black plastic or Hi-Speed wheels | **£20-30** |
| 31 | 67 | **Ford Transit Breakdown Lorry** 'ESSO', BPW or HSW | **£20-30** |
| 32 | 68 | **'FIRE CHIEF' Car** Ford Corsair, red, IW or FW | **£20-30** |
| 32 | - | **'FEUERWEHR' Car** Ford Corsair, red, Impy wheels | **£20-30** |
| 33 | 68 | **Austin-Western Mobile Crane** elevating jib | **£20-30** |
| 34 | 68 | **Euclid Crawler Tractor**, rubber tracks | **£20-30** |
| 35 | - | **Articulated Flat Truck**, not issued | NPP |
| 36 | 69 | **Lotus Europa**, Flyers wheels | **£20-35** |
| 37 | - | **Ford GT**, not issued | NPP |
| 38 | 71 | **Chevrolet Corvette Stingray**, Flyers wheels | **£20-35** |
| 39 | 71 | **Ford Mustang**, Flyers wheels | **£20-35** |
| 40 | 73 | **Cadillac Eldorado**, FW | **£20-35** |
| 41 | 72 | **Leyland Builders Supply Lorry** 4 girders, 8 HSW | **£20-35** |
| 41 | 73 | **Leyland Builders Supply Lorry** 4 girders, 6 HSW | **£20-35** |
| 41 | 73 | **Foden Half-cab Builders Supply Lorry** 4 girders,6 HSW | **£20-35** |
| 42 | 72 | **Foden Half-cab Tipper** 'TILCON' labels, 8 HSW | **£20-35** |
| 43 | 73 | **Leyland Flat Lorry with Pipes** 6 HSW | **£20-35** |

| | | | |
|---|---|---|---|
| 43 | 73 | **Foden Half-cab Flat Lorry with Pipes.** 6 HSW | **£20-35** |
| 44 | 72 | **Leyland Marine Transport Lorry** Speedboat, 8 HSW | **£20-35** |
| 44 | 73 | **Leyland Marine Transport Lorry** Speedboat, 6 HSW | **£20-35** |
| 44 | 73 | **Foden Half-cab Marine Transport Lorry** Speedboat, 6 HSW | **£20-35** |
| 46 | 73 | **Leyland Dropside Lorry** 6 Hi-Speed wheels | **£20-35** |
| 47 | 73 | **Leyland High-Side Lorry** 6 Hi-Speed wheels | **£20-35** |
| 47 | 73 | **Foden High-Side Lorry** Half-cab, 6 HSW | **£20-35** |
| 48 | 73 | **Leyland Hopper Lorry**, 6 HSW | **£20-35** |
| 48 | 73 | **Foden Half-cab Hopper Lorry** 6 HSW | **£20-35** |
| 49 | 73 | **Foden Half-cab Tipper**, 6 HSW | **£20-35** |

## IMPY GIFT SETS

| | | | |
|---|---|---|---|
| 301 | 67 | **Six-piece Gift Set** | **£100-150** |
| 302 | 67 | **Six-piece Gift Set** | **£100-150** |
| 303 | 68 | **'MOBIL' Gift Set** | **£100-150** |
| 304 | 68 | **Five-piece Commercial Vehicle Set** | **£100-150** |
| 309 | 68 | **Twelve-piece Gift Set** | **£200-300** |

## IMPY ACCESSORIES

| | | | |
|---|---|---|---|
| 401 | 67 | **Car Lifting Ramp** | **£10-20** |
| 402 | 67 | **Lock-Up Garage** (plastic) | **£10-20** |
| 403 | - | **Service Station** (not issued) | NPP |
| 404 | 68 | **'MOBIL' Petrol Pump Island** Canopy, Forecourt Sign | **£10-20** |
| 406 | - | **Fire House** (not issued) | NPP |

## IMPY TWO-PACKS

| | | |
|---|---|---|
| 422 | **VW Ambulance** (20) and **Mercedes-Benz 'Polizei'** (16M) | **£30-40** |
| 423 | **Fiat 2300S** (21) and **Breakdown Lorry** (31) | **£30-40** |
| 424 | **Foden Tanker** (26) and **Ford Taunus** (27) | **£30-40** |
| 425 | **Ford Zodiac** (14) and **Tractor** (25) | **£30-40** |
| 427 | **Alfa Romeo** (23) and **'MOBIL' Petrol Pumps** (404) | **£30-40** |
| 431 | **Chevrolet Corvette** (11) and **Fiat 2300S** (21) | **£30-40** |
| 432 | **Fire Engine** (30) and **Ford Corsair 'FEUERWEHR'** (32) | **£30-40** |

## IMPY series, post-1976

The Market Price Range is shown as £5 - £10 but as yet there is little collectors' interest in these recent models.

| | | |
|---|---|---|
| 50 | **Six-wheel Tipper** | **£10-20** |
| 51 | **Six-wheel High Side Lorry** | **£10-20** |
| 52 | **Six-wheel Flat Lorry with Crane** | **£10-20** |
| 53 | **Six-wheel Flat Lorry with Speedboat** | **£10-20** |
| 54 | **Six-wheel Cement Mixer** | **£10-20** |
| 55 | **Six-wheel Luton Van** | **£10-20** |
| 56 | **Six-wheel Dropside Lorry** | **£10-20** |
| 57 | **Six-wheel Flat Lorry with Water Tank** | **£10-20** |
| 58 | **Six-wheel Hopper Lorry** | **£10-20** |
| 59 | **Six-wheel Flat Lorry with Pipes** | **£10-20** |
| 60 | **Six-wheel Flat Lorry with Planks** | **£10-20** |
| 61 | **Six-wheel Petrol Tanker** | **£10-20** |
| 71 | **Range Rover** | **£10-20** |
| 72 | **Cadillac Eldorado** | **£10-20** |
| 73 | **Chevrolet Corvette Stingray** | **£10-20** |
| 74 | **Toyota 2000 GT** | **£10-20** |
| 75 | **Range Rover Police Car** | **£10-20** |
| 76 | **Chevrolet Corvette Stingray 'GT Rally'** | **£10-20** |
| 77 | **Jaguar Mk.X** | **£10-20** |

| | | |
|---|---|---|
| 78 | **Maserati Mistral** | **£10-20** |
| 79 | **Ford Mustang** | **£10-20** |
| 80 | **Lotus Europa** | **£10-20** |
| 81 | **Volvo Coupé** | **£10-20** |
| 82 | **Mercedes-Benz** | **£10-20** |
| 181 | **Articulated Flat Lorry with Crane** | **£10-20** |
| 182 | **Articulated Petrol Tanker** | **£10-20** |
| 183 | **Articulated Low Loader with Tuf-Tots car** | **£10-20** |
| 184 | **Articulated Flat Lorry with Pipes and water tank** | **£10-20** |
| 185 | **Cadillac Eldorado with Tuf-Tots Speedboat on trailer** | **£10-20** |
| 185 | **Range Rover with Tuf-Tots Speedboat on trailer** | **£10-20** |
| 185 | **Range Rover 'RNLI' with boat on trailer** | **£10-20** |
| 185 | **Jaguar Mk.X with Cabin Cruiser on trailer** | **£10-20** |
| 186 | **Crane Lorry** (no.52) with Impy car | **£10-20** |
| 187 | **Luton Van** (no.55) with Trailer | **£10-20** |
| 188 | **Articulated Low Loader with Cabin Cruiser** | **£10-20** |
| 189 | **Articulated Flat Lorry with Planks** | **£10-20** |
| 190 | **Petrol Tanker** (no.61) with Trailer | **£10-20** |
| 191 | **High Side Lorry** (no.51) with Trailer. | **£10-20** |
| 192 | **Cement Mixer** (no.54) with Flat Trailer | **£10-20** |
| 1251 | **Articulated Car Transporter** | **£10-20** |
| 1252 | **AEC Merryweather HTTL Fire Engine** (re-packed no.30) | **£10-20** |
| 1256 | **Car Transporter** (no.1251) with four Impy cars | **£65-75** |

## LONE STAR SETS

**'International Peace Force Vehicles' Set** (made 1974) contains: 1271 Small Tank, 1272 Searchlight on Trailer, 1273 Mortar Launcher, 1274 Radar Detector Unit, 1275 Ack-Ack Gun, 1276 Silver Small Canon, 1277 All Blue Military Jeep ..................... **£300-400**

**'GULLIVER COUNTY' Series.**
**Boxed set of three Coaches.**
White card box with scene depicting a coach, fire engine, articulated lorry and two cars.
i) Mid-Green Coach, Grey wheels, 'SCHOOL BUS' logo on sides
ii) Cream Coach, Grey wheels, 'SCHOOL BUS' logo on sides
iii) Mid-Green Coach, Grey wheels, 'GREENLINE' logo on sides .......... **£150-200**

**'War in the Desert' Set**
includes 3 German and 3 US military vehicles ........ **£200-250**

**Miscellaneous items**
**1259 Routemaster Bus**. Made 1972-89, paper adverts 'SEE LONDON BY BUS' and 'BUY LONE STAR'.
Route is '29 VICTORIA', Plastic wheels...... **£15-20**
**RAC Land Rover and Caravan** - no details. NGPP

**'Aircraft of the World' Series**
(boxed, spare transfers, 1:250 scale)
'Scandinavian Airlines' Caravelle .............. **£60-70**
'Pan American' Boeing 707 .................... **£60-70**
'BOAC' De Havilland Comet 4c ................. **£60-70**
'BOAC' Bristol Brittania ...................... **£60-70**
'British and Commonwealth' Bristol Brittania ........................ **£60-70**
'Aer Lingus' Vickers Viscount ................... **£60-70**
**'Modern Army' Series**
'Lorry', 'Bren Gun Carrier' and 'Jeep' ....................... each: **£20-35**
'Small Mobile Fighting Unit' ....................... NGPP
'Farm' Series, 'Jeep' ............................... **£20-30**

## The process of casting

Collectable cast metal models are made mostly of lead or of a zinc alloy. Casting molten metal in a mould is an established engineering process.

Some forms of casting have changed little since early man discovered how to make arrow heads from iron or bronze. The chosen metal is simply heated to the point at which it becomes liquid and is poured into a container and allowed to cool. It then solidifies and makes a near-perfect three-dimensional mirror image of its container. This is called gravity casting since the metal enters all parts of the mould under its own weight. Lead toy soldiers were often made by gravity casting as it was a quick and cheap way of producing toys.

## Developments in casting

Slush casting was a development suitable for larger items in non-ferrous metals. Since the molten metal cools rapidly on entering the mould it can start to solidify before reaching the extremities resulting in incomplete castings. By tilting and turning the mould the metal can be slushed around it to cover all surfaces. The finished item may have a depression at the back and would not be of even thickness. The process is often used for cheap brass door-knockers or crude metal ornaments.

To overcome the 'flat-back' problem, a method of joining two (sometimes more) moulds was devised, using hinges or sliding jigs. This allowed a complete casting to be made with one pouring and released when solid by opening the mould halves. Castings from multi-part moulds can easily be identified by the presence of a join line (along the roof of a model car or the back of a model horse, for instance).

## Hollow casting

Another problem for producers was the sheer amount of metal required to make solid castings. A logical step towards using less metal and improving the product was the development of hollow casting. Several makers used this process here and in America but the masters of this art must be Britains Ltd whose delightful hollow cast figures were available for decades. The technique is developed from slush casting but uses a closed rotating mould. A small amount of molten metal is deposited evenly over just the mould surface, producing a lighter model of fairly uniform thickness. Entry and exit ports are required as the metal must actually flow through the mould.

One result is the rather obvious 'hole in the head' appearance on some figures!

## Centrifugal casting

In centrifugal casting the metal also flows through the mould but produces a solid casting. The mould is in two halves, each half on the surface of a disc. The discs are placed together to close the mould. Molten metal is poured in at the centre and the discs spun till sufficient centrifugal force drags the metal through to exit points at the rim. The process was originally developed by the jewellery trade and was really only suitable for smaller solid items such as cheap base castings for ear-rings and brooches. Suppliers of spare parts for Dinky or Corgi models have successfully developed it in recent times, however, and find it a useful way of making chain posts for Foden lorries or additional parts for Code-3 models.

## Die casting

None of the casting methods described so far could be considered an exact science. Molten metal in adequate amounts was all that was required to obtain a basic casting. But with the desire to make more accurate models on a commercial scale came the need for more detailed moulds and improved control over the flow of metal.

An alloy was also required that had different qualities of flow-rate, and expansion and contraction characteristics. It needed to be stable under pressure and to exit cleanly from the mould. Pressure diecasting was thus developed as a technically precise process, one that was reliable and controllable and could be automated and adapted to the demands of industry. The system has two important differences from previous processes – the volume of metal required is decided before use, and it is forced into the mould (a steel die) under pressure. The alloy best suited to the production of model vehicles would typically consist of 95 percent zinc, 3.5 percent aluminium and 1.5 percent copper. A trace of magnesium is usually added to the mix to improve flow and handling characteristics. Trade names for the alloy are 'Mazak' in the UK and 'Zamak' in America and France.

Other alloys have been used for various reasons: The Dinky Toys 581 Horse Box and 749 Vulcan Bomber are examples of models cast almost entirely in aluminium. Pewter and white metal are zinc alloys with a high tin or lead content, hence their increased softness or weight. Virtually instant solidification takes place in the mould when the Mazak enters.

 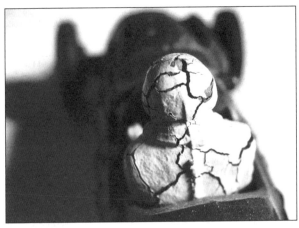

*Self-inflicted wounds. The driver figure is an extension of the baseplate component in the Crescent range of racing cars. In this example of a Connaught model, the base has expanded, cracked and is shedding paint. The driver is racing to an early finish as the deterioration is even more extensive higher up in the casting. Believe it or not, this is actually a mint model that has never been played with!*

## After the casting

When castings are removed from their moulds they must be fettled to remove flash. This is often done by rolling several together in a rotating drum that also contains stones (or ball bearings), water and detergent. Dinky, Corgi and Lesney castings were particularly free of flash as the dies were of such a high standard. Consequently, fettling times for them were usually down to a couple of minutes, but could extend to ten minutes when necessary.

Next, castings are sorted and rejects returned to the foundry for re-melting. Acceptable castings are degreased and primed for automatic spray painting, followed by drying and hardening (at temperatures often above 200°F). Subsequent spraying covers smaller areas (two-tone finishes for instance) while mask spraying applies details like radiators and lights. Models are then tampo printed if required before final assembly, inspection and packing.

## Cracks in the casting

Casting deterioration, so often a problem with pre-war Dinky Toys, is due to the presence of remarkably small amounts of impurities in the alloy. As little as 0.008 percent of lead or 0.006 percent of cadmium can upset the chemical balance sufficiently to give rise to inter-granular or inter-crystalline corrosion.

The impurities attach themselves to grains of the alloy, altering their electro-chemical relationship which becomes increasingly unstable when humidity levels rise. Moisture, always present in the air, acts as an electrolyte - like the acid in a car battery. Minute electrical currents carry chemicals between crystals within the alloy, altering its structure. The corrosion thus formed (along with changes in temperature) keeps pushing the crystals apart, expanding and cracking the casting. Wheels and other simple castings suffer most

because of re-used metal contaminated by lead sweepings. Complex castings demand clean allow that will flow into the areas of finer detail, so are usually less affected. Ships and aircraft models are often a problem as they are simpler and less detailed castings.

Wartime production was the most vulnerable, since shortages of materials meant using whatever materials were to hand, however inferior. For this reason, the Spitfire Fund Badge is notably difficult to find in good condition, while some Dinky aeroplanes are too big for the box that once held them so snugly!

There is, unfortunately, no cure for the problem – usually but incorrectly called metal fatigue – but at least it is possible to arrest the effects of the corrosion. If the model is kept in a dry unchanging environment, preferably at a temperature above 20°C, the condition will remain stable. Models that have deformed cannot be reset or straightened, but broken parts can be glued back in place using a cyano-acrylate adhesive ('SuperGlue').

Reassuringly, models produced since the War seem hardly to suffer at all from this problem, though some from the 1940s and early 1950s have a certain brittleness and will shatter if dropped onto a hard surface. This effect has been observed with early DCMT-produced toys, Major Models, and Crescent's racing car range, for example.

## Caution with your casting

Be warned. . . that nice soft paper you lovingly wrapped your treasured models in may not be acid-free. Even if it is acid-free, it can still attract moisture from the air to rust axles and baseplates with which it has contact. It may be doing more damage than it prevents, especially in a draughty loft. Why not keep your models in a nice display cabinet in the living room – and enjoy your investment!

Photo: John King

*Sailing into stormy waters. The greatest concern for models afflicted with metal deterioration is with pre-war Dinky Toys. Some 28 Series Delivery Vans and the rarer aircraft models are especially vulnerable. Nevertheless, while condition is always of paramount importance, collectors with a realistic approach do still seem to want to acquire the rarest models and will settle for the best condition available. Fortunately, many examples are still to be found in excellent collectable condition, unlike the model of Dinky Toys 52 'Queen Mary' shown above.*

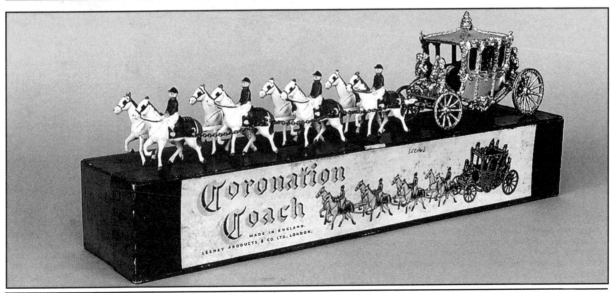

# Matchbox Toys

## Introduction

The company was founded in 1947 by the unrelated Leslie and Rodney Smith who combined their names to form 'Lesney' Products Ltd. They were soon joined by Jack Odell – a recognised die-casting expert.

The most famous of the various early products was the 'Coronation Coach'. During the 1950s the company developed the highly successful Matchbox '1-75' and 'Models of Yesteryear' ranges. Today, certain models in the '1-75' series are highly sought after and fetch very high prices at auction.

Following a difficult trading period Lesney Products Ltd was bought in 1982 by the Universal Toy Co. of Hong Kong. Models issued subsequently fall outside the scope of this publication.

New information in this Edition includes Shop Display Items, Card Layouts and Vinyl Collectors' Cases. Additionally, many new model variations have been listed.

Finally, we have provided a new presentation of details of the various box types used for Regular Wheels and Superfast models.

The Catalogue's listings of the '1-75' variations have been greatly improved by help received from Trevor Bannister and Nigel Cooper. The 'Models of Yesteryear' listings have similarly benefitted from revisions provided by Horace Dunkley.

## 'Moko' Products

**'Moko Products'** was a toy distribution firm founded by Moses Kohnstam who came to Britain from Nuremburg, Germany around 1900.

Moko provided the distribution and storage facilities and, irrespective of the supplier, all toys were marketed as Moko products. The early issues after the Second World War were housed in plain cardboard boxes with 'tuck in' ends. These usually had only single colour printing that did not include a picture of the model. During the early 1950s the packaging became much more attractive with brightly coloured boxes displaying a picture of the model inside. Moko

will best be remembered for their distribution of the early Matchbox '1-75' toys under the name of 'Moko-Lesney'. Moses Kohnstam was succeeded by Richard Kohnstam in 1953.

The following listing of Moko items constitutes all the information available to publish at present. Additional information would be welcomed by the Editor.

| | | |
|---|---|---|
| --- | **Railway Timekeeper's Watch** | |
| | with slide to house matches inside casing ............................**£250-350** | |
| c1948-53 | **Mechanical Tractor** | |
| | Probably early Lesney. Orange body, Green rubber tracks, Black wheels, Green/Black driver, (early issue in plain box)........**£300-400** | |
| 1950-55 | **Mechanical Tractor** | |
| | As previous model but with Orange wheels, (later issue in picture box) ...................................**£300-400** | |
| 1947-50 | **Excavator (with open cab)** | |
| | Orange body and jib, Brown digger and chassis, Green rubber tracks, Orange crank handle. Early card box has 'Moko TOYS OF DISTINCTION' logo......................**£300-400** | |
| 1950-55 | **'RUSTON BUCYRUS' Excavator** | |
| | Yellow over Red body with Black '10 RB' logo. Black or Dark Green chassis, jib, digger, crank wheel and rubber tracks. Later box with full colour picture..........**£200-250** | |
| 1950-55 | **Builder's Crane** | |
| | All Blue crane base and jib with unpainted metal hook. Later card box with full colour picture...................................**£350-450** | |
| 1947-50 | **Crawler Bulldozer** | |
| | Red body and dozer blade (possibly early Lesney). In card box (plain at first, later with colour picture)...........**£250-300** | |
| 1947-50 | **Farm Tractor and Rake** | |
| | Blue / Orange, with two Brown figures...........................**£750-1,000** | |
| 1947-50 | **Farm Tractor and Wagon** | |
| | Blue driver ............................................................**£600-700** | |
| 1950-55 | **'Pop-Pop Series' Motor Scooter** | |
| | Blue, Green or Dark Red scooter, Black seat. Female figure has blonde hair, blue sweater, red or blue trousers. Later box has full colour picture...................**£450-550** | |
| 1950-55 | **Drummer Boy (Mechanical)** | |
| | Red body, Gold trim, Black busby. Cream/Yellow drum, Gold drumsticks ...........................**£1,000-1,250** | |
| 1947-50 | **Hayrake** | |
| | Yellow/Green body or Orange body ...................................**£100-150** | |
| 1947-50 | **Merry-go-Round** | |
| | Blue/Red base and centre column, Maroon/Blue roof, 2 Red and 2 Blue seated figures. Plain card box.................**£400-500** | |
| 1947-50 | **Mechanical Mouse** | |
| | Grey body with Red eyes plus curling tail. Early plain card box.............................................**£175-200** | |
| c1950 | **Peregrine Puppet** ................................................. NGPP | |
| c1950 | **'Jumbo, the Walking Elephant'.** Mechanical / tinplate. | |
| | With diagonal printing ...................................**£1,000-1,250** | |
| | With horizontal printing.................................**£1,000-1,250** | |
| c1950 | **0-4-0 Tank Engine** | |
| | Light Metallic Green, bare metal wheels.............................**£125-150** | |

### Moko 'Farmette' Series

Miniature size models packed in end-flap type boxes with colour picture of the model. The die-cast horses have dark brown bodies and white feet.
**NB** These are delicate models; check for metal deterioration.

| No.1 | 50-53 | **Timber Trailer with two Horses** |
|---|---|---|
| | | Green body, four Red wheels, timber load....................**£150-200** |
| No.2 | 50-53 | **Farm Cart** (4 wheels) **with two Horses** |
| | | Mid or Dark Blue, Red raves, Red 12-spoke wheels.....**£150-200** |
| No.3 | 50-53 | **Bull Wagon with two Horses** (in tandem) |
| | | Green wagon, Brown metal bull, four Red 12-spoke wheels..............................................**£150-200** |

### Moko 'Treasure Chest' Series

Packed in Brown 'chests' with yellow 'strapping'.
**NB** These are delicate models; check for metal deterioration.

| No.10 | 50-53 | **Hay Cart** |
|---|---|---|
| | | Orange body, 2 Green raves, 2 Green wheels, one horse ...**£50-75** |
| No.11 | 50-53 | **Millers Cart** |
| | | Blue body, 2 Red wheels, 3 White sacks, one horse ..........**£50-75** |
| No.12 | 50-53 | **Water Cart** |
| | | Green/Red cart, 2 Red wheels, one horse ...........................**£50-75** |

Moko 'Pop-Pop Series' Motor Scooter
PHOTO: VECTIS AUCTIONS LTD.

# The early 'Lesney' toys

Lesney Products issued their first diecast toys in 1948. Whilst production ceased during the Korean war period (1950-52), the models produced formed the basis from which the 1-75 series was launched in 1953. They were sold in boxes under the name of 'MoKo' who were ultimately to also market all the early 1-75 series models.

**NB Models were sold boxed.**

## Road Roller
All Green (shades) body and flywheel,
unpainted wheels.................................... **£600-800**
As previous but with Red roller wheels
and Yellow flywheel .............................. **£600-800**
With a driver but without a flywheel.... **£250-300**
Without a driver and without flywheel. **£250-300**
Greyish-Brown, driver, Red metal
rollers, no flywheel, rear canopy supports
without cross brace, unboxed .............. **£600-750**

## Cement Mixer
All Green or All-Blue body,
Red wheels............................................ **£250-300**
Pale Green body, Red or
Yellow drum and wheels....................... **£250-300**
Dark Green body, Red or
Yellow drum and wheels....................... **£250-300**
Red body, Green drum and wheels....... **£250-300**
Orange engine cover, Black drum,
Yellow wheels ...................................... **£250-300**
Light Green, Orange barrel and
handle, black wheels ........................... **£800-1,000**

## Caterpillar Tractor
Orange or Yellow body, Red roller wheels,
Black rubber tracks .............................. **£300-400**
Orange body and roller wheels............. **£400-500**

## Caterpillar Bulldozer
Green, Orange or Red body,
Black tracks........................................... **£400-500**
All-Orange body ................................... **£300-400**
Yellow body, Red dozer blade
and wheels............................................ **£200-300**

## Prime Mover 'BRITISH ROAD SERVICES'
Orange tractor (Green engine on some),
Blue trailer, Red/Yellow dozer.......... **£750-1,000**
As previous but with Beige trailer..... **£750-1,000**

## 'MASSEY-HARRIS 745' Tractor
Red body, Cream hubs,
Black rubber tyres................................. **£500-650**
Bright Red variation.............................. **£600-800**

## Horse-drawn Milk Float
Orange body, White driver and six crates,
Black or Brown horse, Black or Grey wheels,
'PASTEURISED MILK' cast-in........... **£500-650**
Same but with Dark Blue body ........ **£900-1,200**

## Soap-Box Racer
Brown box, Grey wheels (16 + 9 spokes),
Brown or Dark Blue boy with
Pink face........................................... **£2,500-3,500**

## Quarry Truck 'LAING'
Yellow body, Black tyres.
Only one known..........................................NGPP

## Covered Wagon with Barrels
Green body, White cover, two Red barrels,
six Mid-Brown horses (with White tails),
with postilion rider and wagon driver .. **£125-175**

## Covered Wagon
Same model but with Chocolate Brown
horses and **no barrels** .......................... **£100-150**

## 'RAG & BONE MERCHANTS' Cart
Yellow body, Red wheels, Black or Tan horse,
Brown driver, with 7 pieces of 'junk':
mangle-wheel, bike frame, bedhead,
bath, bucket, box, cistern. Boxed.... **£1,500-2,000**
Green body, Red wheels..... **£1,500-2,000**

## Coronation Coach (large)
Gold coach with King and Queen, eight
White horses, Gold/Red trappings,
four Red riders. 200 issued.................. **£600-800**
Modified version: Gold, Silver or Gilt coach
with just the Queen inside. Horses and
riders as for previous model ................ **£225-275**

## Coronation Coach (small)
Gold coach, eight White horses,
Red/Gold trappings, four Red riders,
'A MOKO TOY BY LESNEY' cast
into horsebar......................................... **£350-450**
Same but Silver coach ......................... **£120-140**
**NB** 1,000,000 of the small Coach were sold.
The Gold to Silver finish ratio is approx. 50:1.

## 'Muffin The Mule'
White body, Red/Gold harness,
Black trim ............................................ **£300-400**

## Excavator
Digger and chassis are Dark Brown ..... **£250-300**

## Breadbait Press (for anglers)
1st type: Red body, unpainted
'butterfly' press. Boxed........................ **£150-175**
2nd type:
As 1st type but with Green press.......... **£150-175**
3rd type: As 2nd type but with
'MILBRO' cast onto Red body............. **£150-175**

PHOTO: VECTIS AUCTIONS LTD.

# Matchbox '1-75' Series Box Types

## '1 - 75' Series 'Regular Wheels' BOX TYPES and their abbreviations used in these listings.

1. **Moko 'A' type Script box**
   Abbreviation used in listings: **M(A)S box**
   Box Design:
   - A line picture of the model facing left to right in Black/Red.
   - 'A Moko LESNEY 'Product' in Yellow on a Black banner with 'Moko' in Script.
   - 'MATCHBOX SERIES' in Red letters. The box end flaps are blank.
   - 'MADE IN ENGLAND' in Red plus the Model Number in Black.

2. **Moko 'B' type box**
   Abbreviation used in the listings: **M(B) box**
   Box Design:
   - Same as 1. above but 'MOKO' now in CAPITALS.
   - 'MADE IN ENGLAND' not shown on all examples of this type.
   - 'REGD' (Registered) shown in Black on front.
     The box end flaps are blank.

3. **Enlarged Moko 'B' type box**
   Abbreviation used in the listings: **EM(B) box**
   Box Design:
   - Same as 2. above with 'MADE IN ENGLAND' shown on all issues.
   - 'REGD US PAT OFF.' has been added.
     NB The box end flaps display the model number and name in black on a white background.

4. **Lesney 'C' type box**
   Abbreviation used in the listings: **L(C) box**
   Box Design:
   A line picture of the model in Black/Red with 'MATCHBOX SERIES' in Red CAPITALS.
   - 'A LESNEY' is shown in Yellow on a Black banner. On a banner beneath is the word 'PRODUCT'.
   - 'MATCHBOX' SERIES in Red capitals. The model number is shown in Black.
   - 'REGD US PAT OFF' and 'REGD' are shown to the side beneath the banner.
     NB The box end flaps display the model number in Blue on a White circle plus the model name.
     Box variation: A Lesney 'C' type box was issued with 'New Model' displayed in White on the box flaps. The abbreviation of this variation is: **NM L(C) box**.

5. **Lesney 'D' type box**
   Abbreviation used in the listings: **L(D) box**
   Box Design:
   - A colour picture of the model facing left to right
   - 'MATCHBOX Series' in Red across the top
   - 'A LESNEY PRODUCT' and the model number in Black letters.
   - 'MATCHBOX REGD. T.M. G.B. AND ABROAD' in Red
   - 'REGD US PAT OFF' and 'MARCA REGISTRADA' in Red'.
     NB The box end flaps display the model number and name in White on the blue background.
     Box variation: A Lesney type 'D' box was issued with 'NEW MODEL' on the box end flaps.

6. **Lesney 'E' type box**
   Abbreviation used in the listings: **L(E) box**
   Box Design:
   - A colour picture of the model facing right to left
   - 'MATCHBOX' with 'Series' beneath it in Red
   - 'A LESNEY PRODUCT' and the model number in Black
   - 'REGD US PAT. OFF' and 'MATCHBOX REGD' T.M G.M.AND ABROAD.
     NB Box end flaps display a colour model picture plus the model number in Yellow and the model name in White.
     Box variation: A Lesney type 'E' box was issued with 'NEW MODEL' on the end flap; the abbreviation for this variation is: **NM L(E) box**.

7. **Lesney 'F' type box**
   Abbreviation used in the listings: **L(F) box**
   Box Design:
   - A large colour picture of the model facing right to left
   - Red 'MATCHBOX'® with 'Series' below the right side
   - The model number is shown in White on a Blue square background
   - 'A LESNEY PRODUCT' is shown in Black
   - Model features are shown, e.g., 'AUTO-STEER'.
     NB The box end flaps display a colour picture of the model, 'MATCHBOX' is in Red and the model number in Blue. A variation exists with 'NEW' on the end flap.

## Abbreviations used in these Matchbox listings:

| | | | | | |
|---|---|---|---|---|---|
| BPT | Black plastic tyres | KGPW | Knobbly grey plastic wheels | SGPW | Smooth grey plastic wheels |
| BPR | Black plastic rollers | | | | |
| BPW | Black plastic wheels | Met. | Metallic | SGPW | Smooth grey plastic wheels |
| BT | Black tyres | MR | Metal rollers | | |
| CA | Crimped axles | MW | Metal wheels | SPH | Silver plastic hubs |
| GPR | Grey plastic rollers | OPH | Orange plastic hubs | SPW | Silver plastic wheels |
| GPW | Grey plastic wheels | PH | Plastic hubs | ST | Silver trim |
| GRRT | Grey rubber tracks | RA | Rounded axles | SW | Steering wheel |
| GRT | Green rubber tracks | RPH | Red plastic hubs | WB | Window box |
| KBPW | Knobbly black plastic wheels | SBPW | Smooth black plastic wheels | WW | 'Wire' wheels |

**MPR = Market Price Range. This indicates a likely selling price for toys and models that are in the best possible collectable condition, preferably mint in a pristine box that is complete with everything with which it was equipped on leaving the factory (leaflets, spares, accessories, etc.). Items failing to match this criteria will sell for much less.**

## Matchbox Model Identification

**Model Number** is always cast into the base, chassis or body. Obvious exceptions are the early models which were not numbered. 'Lesney' is cast into all issues between 1953 and 1982.

'**Matchbox**' or '**Matchbox Series**' is shown on the base or chassis of all issues after 1965. All issues after 1957 had the model name on the base or chassis. Exceptions include those without a base (e.g., No.24 Excavator).

**Suspension** and **windows**. Car models were fitted with windows after 1961 and suspension after 1965. **Baseplates** are metal castings until the late 1970s when plastic bases introduced. From 1983 they are marked 'Made in Macau'.

**Wheels** were metal castings on early models and were gradually changed to grey, silver or black plastic. **Superfast wheels** introduced in late 1960s and issues from 1968-69 may be found with either type. Novelties such as '**Laser Wheels**' introduced in the late 1980s. '**Rolamatics**' were introduced in the 1970s having working parts that were operated by pushing (see the Superfast section for these).

**Model descriptions**. This Catalogue tries to give original maker's description of model names and colours but early Matchbox listings are known to be inaccurate graphically. Maker's catalogue photographs are often taken of mock-ups months before production starts while model designs become changed before release.

**Dimensions** refer to the greatest overall measurement (usually the length).

**Superfast issues** are listed separately elsewhere in this Matchbox section.

| Model and details | MPR |
|---|---|

### MB 1

1a   53 **Diesel Road Roller** (Aveling Barford)
Red metal roller wheels, Tan driver cast-in, no number, crimped axles, 49mm.
**Type 1**: curved lower canopy ends and thin braces above canopy supports.
**Type 2**: straight ends and thick braces above supports, brace extension.
Dark Green body, Type 1 ......................£150-200
Dark Green body, Type 2 ..........£75-100
Light Green body, Type 2.............£100-150

1b   56 **Diesel Road Roller** (Aveling Barford)
Light Green body, Red metal roller wheels, Lt. or Dk. Tan driver, high peaked canopy, no number, hook, 57 mm ...........................£35-45

1c   58 **Diesel Road Roller** (Aveling Barford)
Light Green body and driver, Red metal roller wheels, number cast-in, high peaked canopy, hook, 62 mm................£100-125
Dark Green body ...............................£40-60

1d   62 **Diesel Road Roller** (Aveling Barford)
Green body and driver, twin-rivet baseplate, Red plastic rollers, 67 mm .................£150-200

1e   67 **Mercedes Truck**
Turquoise body, Orange canopy, BPW .......£8-12

### MB 2

2a   53 **Muir Hill Site Dumper**
Dark Green body, Red dumper, Green painted MW, 42 mm .................£150-200
Same but with unpainted MW.................£40-50

2b   57 **Muir Hill Site Dumper**. Same but:
Tan driver, metal wheels, 46 mm .......£40-50
Same but GPW, crimped axles.................£50-60
Same but GPW, rounded axles.................£50-60

2c   62 **Muir Hill Dumper Truck**
Red body, Green dumper, '*LAING*', Black plastic wheels, 54 mm...................£20-30
Same but '*MUIR HILL*' logo and picture-box (72 only known)....................£60-80

2d   67 **Mercedes Trailer**. Turquoise body, Orange top, BPW ........................................£8-12

### MB 3

3a   53 **Cement Mixer**
Orange MW, Blue main body ..................£30-40
GPW, crimped axles.........................£80-100
GPW, rounded axles ..........................£80-100

3b   61 **Bedford Tipper Truck**
(All have Grey body and chassis)
Maroon back, GPW, 24 treads ............£200-250
Maroon back, GPW, 45 treads .............£200-250
Maroon back, BPW ................................£20-30
Red dump, GPW ................................£90-110
Red dump, BPW.....................................£25-35

3c   67 **Mercedes Ambulance**
Cream or Off-White body ..........................£20-30

### MB 4

4a   54 **Massey Harris Tractor**
(with mudguards over rear wheels), Red body, Gold or Yellow rear hubs, Tan driver........£60-80

4b   57 **Massey Harris Tractor**
(without mudguards over rear wheels), MW, Gold or Yellow rear hubs .............£125-150
Grey plastic wheels ....................................£90-110

4c   60 **Triumph T110 Motor Cycle**
Steel Blue bike/sidecar, Silver spoked wheels, KBPT................£125-150
Same but Copper body (beware fakes) ...........................£2,000-3,000

4d   66 **Dodge Stake Truck**
Yellow cab, Blue stake body, BPW...........£70-80
Yellow cab, Green body, correct box picture.................................£20-25
In L(F) box showing picture of Orange model .......................................£175-200

### MB 5

5a   54 **London Bus** (52 mm)
Red body, 'Buy Matchbox Series' on paper label ........................................£70-100
Green body, MW, gold radiator, white/green 'Buy Matchbox Series' paper labels.
Australian issue in Moko 'B' box ...£5,000-7,500

5b   57 **1957 London Bus** (57 mm)
'Buy Matchbox Series' decal, MW, Moko 'B' box .................................£40-50
'Buy Matchbox Series' decal, GPW .........£60-70
'Players Please' decal, Moko 'B' box ....................................£120-150

5c   60 **Routemaster** (66 mm)
'Players Please' decal, GPW, Lesney 'C' box .....................................£110-130
'Peardrax', GPW or BPW, Lesney 'C' box .................................£700-800
'BP Visco-Static' decal, KBPW, box 'D'.....................................£150-200
'BP Visco-Static' decal, GPW, box 'D'........................................£40-50

5d   65 **Routemaster** (70 mm)
'BP Longlife' decal, box 'D' ....................£20-25
'BP Visco-Static' decal or label, box 'E'...£15-20
'BP Visco-Static' decal, BPW, box 'F'..£100-150
'Baron of Beef' decal, BPW, box 'D'..£400-500
'Pegram Shopfitters' decal, BPW, box 'E'.......................................£600-800

### MB 6

6a   54 **Quarry Truck** 55mm.
Orange body, Grey tipper with six ribs, MW ........................................£40-50
Same, but GPW, domed/crimped axles....................£4,000-5,000

6b   59 '**EUCLID**' **Quarry Truck**
Yellow body, four ribs, six BPW..............£40-50

6c   Knobbly GPW, domed axles ...........£3,000-3,500
63 **Euclid Dump Truck**
Six Black wheels (rear double wheels are one piece) .................................£15-20
Ten Black wheels (rear wheels are normal double wheels) ............................£15-20

6d   68 **Ford Pick Up**
Red body, White canopy, chrome grille...£18-20
Same but White grille...............................£25-35

### MB 7

7a   54 **Horse Drawn Milk Float**
Dark Orange body, White driver, crates and logo, metal wheels...................£70-80
As previous but with GPW .................£110-140
Pale Orange body, metal wheels.............£70-80
Pale Orange body and logo, White hat and crates, GPW .................£110-140
Pale Orange body, Silver driver and crates, GPW (beware fakes) ..........£550-650

7b   61 **Ford Anglia**
Light Blue, Green windows, KGPW, L(F) box ...........................................£90-110
With Silver plastic wheels .......................£45-55
With Black plastic wheels ........................£35-40

7c   67 **Refuse Truck**. Orange-Red body, Grey and Silver dumper .........................£10-15

### MB 8

8a   55 **Caterpillar Tractor** (42 mm)
Yellow body and rollers, Red driver, Green tracks.........................................£350-450
Same but with unpainted rollers...............£50-65
Orange body and driver, Gold or Silver grille, Green tracks............£65-80
Yellow body/driver, Silver or Yellow grille, Green or Grey tracks.....................£40-50

8b   58 **Caterpillar Tractor** (42 mm)
Yellow body and driver, no.'8' cast-in, Green rubber tracks ................................£70-85

8c   61 **Caterpillar Tractor** (48 mm)
Yellow body, metal rollers, Green tracks ..£40-55
If box shows correct model picture.......£125-175
Same but with Silver plastic rollers ......£150-175
Same but with Black plastic rollers...........£30-35

8d   64 **Caterpillar Tractor** (51 mm)
Yellow body, no driver, Green rubber tracks, Black rollers.................................£20-25

8e   66 **Ford Mustang**
White body, BPW with Silver hubcaps.....£25-35
White body, Chrome wheels with BPT.....£20-30
Burnt Orange body, red interior, chrome hubs, BPT, 'F' type box...........£300-350

### MB 9

9a   55 **Dennis Fire Escape** (57mm)
Red body, no front bumper, MW, CA.......£45-55
With small dia. escape ladder wheels ...£125-150

**9b** 58 **Dennis Fire Escape** (58mm).
Red body, with front bumper, MW,
number cast underneath........................**£70-80**
Same but with GPW.........................**£350-450**

**9c** 59 **Merryweather Marquis
Series III Fire Engine**
Red body with Tan ladder,
GPW, crimped axles, 64 mm.............**£60-75**
Same but with rounded axles ............**£40-50**
Same but with Gold ladder................**£40-50**
With Gold ladder and BPW ...............**£30-40**
With Silver ladder, BPW ...................**£80-90**
With Tan ladder, BPW.......................**£65-75**

**9d** 66 **Boat and Trailer** (76mm, 77mm)
Blue/White boat, Blue trailer, BPW....**£15-20**

## MB 10

**10a** 57 **Scammell Mechanical Horse**
Red cab, Gold trim, Grey trailer,
crimped axles, MW, 56mm .................**£85-95**

**10b** 57 **Scammell Mechanical Horse**
Red Cab, Brown trailer,
CA, MW, 75 mm ...............................**£50-60**
Red cab, Gold trim, Light Brown
trailer, Grey plastic wheels.............**£100-150**
Red cab, Silver trim, Light Brown
trailer, Grey plastic wheels.............**£100-150**
If in rare enlarged type 'B'
Moko box .......................................**£150-200**

**10c** 60 **Foden 8-wheel Sugar Container**
Dark Blue body, with crown on rear
decal, Grey wheels ...........................**£90-110**
Without crown, Grey wheels...............**£70-80**
Without crown, Silver wheels .........**£100-130**
Without crown, Black wheels ............**£50-60**

**10d** 66 **Leyland Pipe Truck**
Red body, 6 or 7 Grey pipes,
Silver base and grille .......................**£15-20**
Same but White base and grille..........**£60-75**

## MB 11

**11a** 55 **E.R.F. Road Tanker.** All with metal wheels.
Green body, Gold trim,'B' box..**£1,000-1,500**
Dark Yellow body, Silver trim........**£150-175**
Light Yellow body, Silver trim..........**£85-100**
Red body, Gold trim, small
'ESSO' decal on rear of tank...........**£120-140**
Same but large 'ESSO' decal .............**£75-85**
Same but two small 'ESSO'
decals on tank sides...................**£1,500-1,750**
Same but two large 'ESSO'
decals on tank sides...................**£1,500-1,750**
Rare version: 3 side labels ....... **£750-1,000**

**11b** 58 **'ESSO' Petrol Tanker (E.R.F.).**
All have red body and 'ESSO' decal at rear.
Metal wheels, Gold trim..................**£350-450**
Metal wheels, Silver trim ..................**£75-85**
Grey plastic wheels ...........................**£60-70**
Silver plastic wheels..................**£1,000-1,100**
Black plastic wheels ..........................**£90-100**

**11c** 65 **Jumbo Crane**
Yellow body and weight box.............**£25-30**
Yellow body, Red weight box ............**£15-20**

**11d** 69 **Mercedes Scaffolding Truck**
Silver, Yellow plastic scaffolds, BPW.**£15-18**

## MB 12

**12a** 55 **Land Rover**
Green body, Silver trim on some,
Tan driver, MW, 43 mm .....................**£40-50**

**12b** 59 **Land Rover Series II**
Green body, BPW, crimped axles.......**£75-95**
BPW, rounded axles ..........................**£35-45**
Grey plastic wheels .........................**£400-500**

**12c** 65 **Land Rover Safari**
Green body, Brown luggage, BPW .....**£25-30**
Blue body, Brown luggage, BPW .......**£18-20**
Blue, Red-Brown luggage, BPW ........**£18-20**
Metallic Gold body, BPW,
(beware fakes)..........................**£1,200-1,500**

## MB 13

**13a** 55 (Bedford) **Wreck Truck** (51mm).
Tan body, Red crane/hook, MW, CA ..**£40-55**

**13b** 58 (Ford Thames) **Wreck Truck** (54mm).
Light Brown body, Red crane and
hook, '13' cast-in, MW......................**£40-60**
Same but with KGPW .......................**£100-125**

**13c** 60 **Thames Trader Wreck Truck**
All models with Red body and crane.
Yellow side decals, knobbly Grey MW
(24 treads), Red hook.........................**£70-80**
Grey wheels (45 treads), Grey hook,
closed lattice jib, L(D) box...........**£275-325**
BPW, Silver or Grey hook...............**£100-125**

**13d** 65 **Dodge Wreck Truck**
Green cab, Yellow body,
Grey hook, 'BP' decal ...........**£3,500-4,500**
**NB** Fakes from 1970 have red hooks,
'BP' labels, crimped axles and the thick
crane casting. Only the original Green
cab version (from the Lesney factory)
has a thin crane. But these fakes (only 24
were produced) are now sought after by
some collectors and thus sell for .....**£600-800**
Yellow cab, Green body, Grey hook ...**£20-30**
Same but with Red hook ....................**£20-25**
Same but with Yellow hook ..............**£75-100**

## MB 14

**14a** 55 **Ambulance (Daimler)** (49mm).
Cream body, Silver trim, Red cross on
roof, MW on crimped or-domed/crimped
axles, no number, 'Ambulance' cast
on sides ...........................................**£40-50**

**14b** 58 **Daimler Ambulance** (59 mm).
All have a 'Red Cross' on roof.
Cream body, metal wheels .................**£40-50**
Cream body, KGPW ........................**£80-100**
Off-White body, metal wheels........**£140-160**
Off-White body, GPW......................**£90-110**
Off-White body, SPW ....................**£250-300**

**14c** 62 **Bedford Lomas Ambulance**
All models with 'Red Cross' and
'LCC Ambulance' on sides.
White body, Black plastic wheels ...**£125-150**
White body, KGPW..........................**£90-110**
White body, Silver plastic wheels ...**£275-300**
Off-White body, SPW ....................**£120-150**
Off-White body, locating marks
for Red Cross cast into roof,
Silver grille, SPW ..........................**£100-130**
Off-White body, GPW......................**£100-130**
Off-White body, BPW........................**£30-35**

**14d** 68 **Iso Grifo**
Metallic Blue body, Blue interior........**£25-30**
Dark Metallic Blue, Blue interior........**£20-25**

## MB 15

**15a** 55 **Diamond T Prime Mover**
Yellow body, six MW, hook,
no number, 55 mm...................**£2,000-2,500**
Orange body, six metal wheels...........**£30-35**
Same but with ten GPW .................**£400-500**

**15b** 59 **Rotinoff Super Atlantic Tractor**
Orange body, Black base, hook,
BPW, 67 mm .....................................**£50-60**
Orange body, knobbly GPW ....**£2,500-3,000**
Without tipper body vent hole.........**£100-150**

**15c** 63 **Tippax Refuse Collector.**
All models have Blue body.
Grey container, Black knobbly
24-tread wheels, decal .......................**£60-70**
With fine tread wheels,
'Cleansing Service' decal or label......**£20-25**

**15d** 68 **Volkswagen 1500 Rally Car**
Off-White or Cream,
'137' decals on doors.........................**£35-40**
Same but '137' labels on doors ..........**£25-35**
'Herbie' film promotional:

Off-White, '53' decals, stripes ........**£700-900**

## MB 16

**16a** 55 **Transporter Trailer.** Tan body,
6 MW (CA, or domed _and_ CA)..........**£25-35**

**16b** 60 **Super Atlantic Trailer**
Beige body, Grey plastic wheels .......**£90-100**
Orange body, GPW.....................**£950-1,100**
Bright Orange body, KBPW...........**£150-175**
Orange, BPW,
Black or Orange drawbar ...................**£35-45**

**16c** 63 **Scammell Snow Plough**
Grey body, Orange tipper, Red/White
or Orange/White decal, GPW..........**£110-130**
With Black plastic wheels ..................**£25-30**

**16d** 69 **Case Bulldozer Tractor**
Red/Yellow body, Green rubber
tracks, hook, 64 mm ..........................**£12-15**

## MB 17

**17a** 55 **Bedford Removals Van.** All models with
_'MATCHBOX REMOVALS SERVICE'_
decals and metal wheels.
Light Blue body, Silver trim...........**£200-250**
Maroon body, Silver trim ...............**£250-350**
Maroon body, Gold trim .................**£225-250**
Light or Dark Green body,
Silver trim ....................................**£200-250**

**17b** 58 **Bedford Removals Van**
Green body, MW, decal with or
without Black outline ......................**£75-100**
Green body, GPW, outlined decal ....**£75-100**
Dark Green, GPW, outlined decal...**£175-200**

**17c** 60 **Austin FX3 Taxi**
Maroon body, Mid-Grey interior,
Tan driver, GPW..............................**£45-55**
Same but SPW, Mid-Grey interior ..**£100-120**
With Pale Grey interior and SPW ...**£150-175**

**17d** 64 **Foden Tipper**
Red chassis, Orange tipper,
_'HOVERINGHAM'_, Black base ..........**£30-40**
Same but with Red base ....................**£15-20**

**17e** 69 **Horse Box**
Red cab, dark green box, grey door,
chrome base, 2 white horses on sprue.. NGPP

## MB 18

**18a** 55 **Caterpillar Bulldozer** (46 mm).
Yellow with Red blade, Green tracks..**£40-50**

**18b** 58 **Caterpillar Bulldozer** (50 mm).
Light Yellow body and blade,
Green tracks....................................**£60-70**
Bright Yellow body, Light Yellow
blade, Green tracks, 'C' type box....**£100-150**
Same but with Grey tracks ................**£70-80**

**18c** 61 **Caterpillar Bulldozer** (58 mm).
Light Yellow body and blade,
Green tracks, metal rollers .................**£25-30**
Same but Silver plastic rollers........**£140-160**
Same but Black plastic rollers..........**£25-230**

**18d** 64 **Caterpillar Bulldozer** (62 mm).
Yellow body and blade, no driver,
Green tracks, Silver plastic rollers ..**£140-160**
Green tracks, Black plastic rollers ......**£20-25**

**18e** 69 **Field Car**
Yellow body, Red-Brown roof,
Red hubs...........................................**£10-15**
Same but unpainted base ...................**£10-12**
Same but with Green hubs .............**£500-600**

## MB 19

**19a** 56 **MG Midget TD**
Cream body, Brown driver, Red seats,
MW, no number, 51 mm....................**£80-100**
Off-White body, metal wheels........**£120-140**

**19b** 58 **MG 'MGA' Sports Car**
All models with Off-White body,
Red seats and Tan driver.
Metal wheels, Gold trim................**£300-400**

Metal wheels, Silver trim ...............**£140-160**
Grey plastic wheels, Silver trim ......**£140-160**
Silver plastic wheels.........................**£250-300**

**19c**  62  **Aston Martin DBR5**
All models with Metallic Green body,
'wire' wheels, Grey driver. No. '19',
'New Model', 'C' box.......................**£100-120**
Number '3', '41' or '52'.................**£175-200**
Number '5', 'D' type box...............**£200-250**

**19d**  65  **Lotus Racing Car**
Dark Green body, Yellow wheels,
White driver, RN '3' decal or label.....**£10-15**
Orange body, RN '3' ...........................**£40-50**

## MB 20

**20a**  56  **E.R.F. Stake Truck**
Light Green, Silver trim, MW ...**£2,000-3,000**
Maroon, Gold trim, MW, 'B' box ...**£250-300**
Maroon body, Silver trim, MW..........**£35-45**
Lighter Maroon body, Silver trim,
Grey PW, 'B' box ...........................**£200-300**
Dark Red body, metal wheels............**£45-55**
Dark Red body, GPW ....................**£200-300**

**20b**  59  **E.R.F. 68G Truck**
All have Dark Blue body and 'EVER
READY' decals on sides. Early decals
with Orange outline, later with Red.
Grey plastic wheels, crimped axles.**£125-150**
Grey plastic wheels, rounded axles.**£125-150**
Silver plastic wheels........................**£160-190**
Black plastic wheels...........................**£60-80**

**20c**  65  **Chevrolet Impala Taxi**
Orange-Yellow body, Cream interior,
GPW, Taxi decal ........................**£1,250-1,500**
Orange-Yellow body, Cream interior, BPW,
Silver base, Taxi decal ......................**£30-40**
Same but with unpainted base............**£15-20**
Same but with red interior..................**£20-30**
Yellow, Cream int., Taxi label .......**£120-140**
Same but with Red interior ................**£25-30**

## MB 21

**21a**  56  **Bedford Coach** (57 mm).
Green body and base,
'LONDON-GLASGOW', MW .............**£60-70**

**21b**  58  **Bedford Coach** (68 mm).
All have Black base and
'LONDON TO GLASGOW' decals.
Green body, MW, 'B' type box .......**£100-120**
Light Green, GPW, 'B' type box.......**£90-110**
Dark Green, GPW, 'B' type box .....**£200-250**
Dark Green, SPW .....................**£5,000-6,000**

**21c**  61  **Commer Bottle Float**
All models with Pale Green body and
Black base. On early models the bottles
are Cream, later ones are White.
Bottle on door, SPW, CW...............**£100-130**
Bottle on door, SPW, GW.................**£70-80**
Cow on door, Silver plastic wheels.....**£50-60**
Cow on door, Grey plastic wheels ..**£175-200**
Cow on door, Black plastic wheels ...**£25-30**

**21d**  68  **Foden Concrete Truck**
Yellow body, Red chassis,
Black wheels......................................**£15-20**

## MB 22

**22a**  56  **Vauxhall Cresta**
Body colours and shades from Dark Red
to Maroon, roof White to Cream.........**£35-45**

**22b**  58  **Vauxhall Cresta**
Pale Pink or Cream body,
without windows, metal wheels ......**£600-650**
Same but Grey plastic wheels ........**£120-140**
Same but with windows ................**£175-200**
Pale Pink body, GW, KGPW..........**£100-125**
Pale Pink body, Blue-Green side
panels, Grey plastic wheels .......**£1,000-1,500**

Light Metallic Brown body,
Blue-Green side panels, GPW........**£200-250**
Light Grey body, Lilac side panels,
Grey or Silver plastic wheels ..........**£120-125**
Light Gold body, Grey or SPW.......**£150-170**
Metallic Dark Gold body, SPW......**£150-170**
Metallic Copper body,
Grey, Silver or Black wheels..........**£200-250**

**22c**  65  **Pontiac GP Sports Coupé**
Red body, Pale Grey interior,
BPW, 'E' type box.............................**£25-35**
Same but in 'F' type box ................**£400-500**

## MB 23

**23a**  56  **Berkeley Cavalier Caravan**
Pale Blue, 'On Tow MBS 23',
MW, 65 mm......................................**£40-60**

**23b**  57  **Berkeley Cavalier Caravan**
All have 'ON TOW' rear decal.
Pale Blue, metal wheels .....................**£30-40**
Lime-Green, metal wheels ...............**£110-130**
Lime-Green, Grey plastic wheels........**£60-80**
Metallic Lime-Green, GPW ......**£1,200-1,500**

**23c**  60  **Bluebird Dauphine Caravan**
All models without windows and
with 'ON TOW' rear decal.
Metallic Lime-Green, GPW ......**£1,000-1,200**
Metallic Mauve body,
Maroon base ..................................**£600-800**
Metallic Mauve body / base, GPW .....**£40-50**
Metallic Mauve body / base, SPW .....**£30-40**
Metallic Mauve body / base, BPW .**£300-400**
**NB**  A few issues of 23c are known
with plastic windows ........................ NGPP

**23d**  65  **Trailer Caravan**
Yellow body, knobbly-tread wheels ....**£12-15**
Yellow body, fine-tread wheels ..........**£30-40**
Pink body, knobbly-tread wheels .......**£30-40**
Pink body, smooth BPW ................**£120-150**

## MB 24

**24a**  56  **'Hydraulic' Excavator**
Orange-Yellow body, metal wheels,
'WEATHERILL', 58 mm ....................**£30-40**
Same but Yellow body........................**£50-70**

**24b**  59  **'Hydraulic' Excavator**
Orange-Yellow, GPW, 'C' type box
with 1st type model illustration......**£150-175**
Same but 2nd type
model illustration............................**£150-200**
Orange-Yellow body, GPW,
rounded axles ....................................**£30-40**
Orange-Yellow body, BPW ................**£25-35**

**24c**  67  **Rolls-Royce Silver Shadow**
All models with Metallic Red body
and Black base.
Black wheels with Silver hubcaps.......**£20-25**
Silver wheels with Black tyres ...........**£15-18**

## MB 25

**25a**  56  **Bedford 12 cwt Van**
Dark Blue body, Black base,
'DUNLOP' decals, MW .....................**£40-50**
Grey plastic wheels ...........................**£90-110**
Black plastic wheels .................**£1,200-1,500**

**25b**  60  **Volkswagen 1200**
Metallic Silver-Blue body,
KGPW, clear windows ...................**£120-140**
Same but Green tinted windows .........**£55-65**
Same but with SPW .........................**£100-130**
Metallic Silver-Blue, Green windows,
SBPW, 'D' type box .................**£1,200-1,500**

**25c**  62  **Bedford Petrol Tanker**
Yellow cab, Green chassis,
White tank, 'BP', BPW ......................**£20-25**
Same but smooth GPW ..................**£500-600**
64  German issue: Dark Blue cab and
chassis, White tank, 'ARAL', BPW .**£150-200**

**25d**  68  **Ford Cortina Mk.II**
Metallic Light Brown body, BPW.......**£20-25**
Gift Set issue:
Same but with Yellow roof rack.......**£40-60**
Blue body, Silver base, BPW .......**£800-1,100**

## MB 26

**26a**  56  **E.R.F. Cement Mixer** (45 mm)
Orange body, Gold trim, MW, CA..**£275-300**
Same but with Silver trim ..................**£45-55**
With GPW, Silver trim .......................**£80-90**
With SPW, Silver trim, late box ....**£600-800**

**26b**  61  **Foden Cement Mixer** (66 mm)
Orange body, Dark Grey barrel,
small knobbly GPW ........................**£700-900**
Same but with Light Grey barrel.....**£200-250**
Orange body, Orange barrel,
Grey or Black plastic wheels..............**£20-25**
Orange body, Orange barrel, SPW ..**£800-900**

**26c**  68  **G.M.C. Tipper Truck**
Red cab, Green chassis,
Silver tipper, BPW, 67 mm.................**£10-12**

## MB 27

**27a**  56  **Bedford Low Loader** (78mm)
Pale Blue cab, Dark Blue trailer,
six metal wheels, crimped axles......**£700-900**
Pale Green cab, Tan trailer ..............**£90-110**

**27b**  58  **Bedford Low Loader** (95mm)
Pale Green cab, Tan trailer, MW .........**£80-90**
Same but with GPW ......................**£120-140**
Dark Green cab, Light Brown
trailer, Grey plastic wheels .............**£140-160**

**27c**  60  **Cadillac Sixty Special**
Metallic Pale Green, Cream roof, GG,
Crimson base, SPW, Moko box ......**£350-400**
Silver-Grey body,
Off-White roof, SPW.......................**£110-130**
Metallic Lilac body, Pink roof,
Crimson base, GPW or SPW.........**£125-150**
Same model but with Black base ....**£110-130**
Same but Black base and BPW.......**£110-130**
Same but Blue base .........................**£250-350**
Apple-Green body,
Red interior................................**£2,500-3,500**

**27d**  66  **Mercedes 230 SL**
White body, Red interior ...................**£18-20**

## MB 28

**28a**  56  **Bedford Compressor**
Orange/Yellow body, MW, 47 mm......**£25-35**
Yellow body, MW, domed CA ..........**£90-110**

**28b**  59  **Ford Thames Compressor Truck**
Yellow body, Black wheels, CA...........**£40-50**
Yellow body, KBPW, rounded axles .**£90-110**
Yellow body, Grey wheels...........**£900-1,100**

**28c**  64  **Jaguar Mk.10**
Pale Metallic Brown, Cream seats,
BPW, 74 mm ......................................**£30-40**
With 'Matchbox' lapel badge .............**£50-60**
With Grey plastic wheels and
without 'Matchbox Series' on base .**£800-900**

**28d**  68  **Mack Dump Truck**
Orange body, Red wheels...................**£15-20**
Orange body, Yellow PH,
blister pack......................................**£150-175**

## MB 29

**29a**  56  **Bedford Milk Delivery Van**
Light Brown body, White bottle load,
metal wheels, 57 mm...........................**£35-45**
Same but GPW, White or
Cream bottles....................................**£40-50**

**29b**  61  **Austin A55 Cambridge**
Two-tone Green body,
Green tinted windows, GPW...............**£35-45**
Same but SPW,
clear or tinted windows .....................**£35-45**
Same but with BPW .........................**£20-25**

29c  66  **Fire Pumper Truck**
Red body, with or without
*'Denver'* decal ................................£15-20

## MB 30

30a  56  **Ford Prefect**
Grey-Brown body, Red and
Silver trim, metal wheels, 58 mm .......£30-35
Same but with GPW, rounded axles ..£80-100
Same but Light Blue body, KGPW,
type 'C' Lesney box .......................£350-450

30b  61  **Magirus-Deutz Crane Lorry**
Light Brown body, Red or
Orange crane, GPW..................£5,000-7,500
Silver body, Orange jib and hook,
Grey or Silver wheels .........................£60-70
Silver body, Orange jib, Grey or Silver
hook, Grey or Black plastic wheels ....£30-35

30c  65  **8 Wheel Crane Truck**
Green body, Orange jib ......................£15-20
Turquoise body, Orange jib .............£600-700

## MB 31

31a  57  **Ford Station Wagon**
Yellow body, metal wheels, 66 mm ....£40-45
Yellow body, Grey plastic wheels .......£45-55
Yellow body, Black base, BPW.......£500-600

31b  60  **Ford Fairlane Station Wagon**
Yellow body, Black base, GPW ......£300-350
Yellow body, Black base, SPW .......£250-300
Yellow body, Crimson base,
clear or Green windows, SPW ........£300-400
Metallic Green body, Pink roof,
Crimson base, GPW or SPW...............£40-50
Same but with Black base, SPW ........£60-70
Same but with Black base, GPW ....£100-120
Same but with Black base, BPW....£250-300

31c  64  **Lincoln Continental**

Metallic Dark Blue body, BPW,
'New Model', 'E' type box showing
red model ..........................................£45-55
Metallic Light Blue body, BPW,
'E' type box showing correct
colour model .....................................£45-55
Sea Green body, BPW, 'E' type box
with single-line text to end flaps.........£35-45
Same but two-line text to end flaps.£150-200
Metallic Lime Green, BPW.......£1,000-1,400

## MB 32

32a  57  **Jaguar XK-140**
Off-White body, Black base,
MW, 60 mm .......................................£40-50
Same but with GPW ...........................£50-65
Red body, metal wheels.....................£80-100
Bright Orange-Red, KGPW,
'C' type box ...................................£175-225
Dark Red, Black base, GPW ..........£175-225

32b  62  **Jaguar 'E'-type**
Metallic Red body, Green windows,
Grey tyres, 66 mm ..........................£180-200
Metallic Red, clear windows,
Grey tyres .........................................£45-55
Metallic Red, clear windows,
Black tyres .........................................£40-50

32c  68  **Leyland Tanker**  (All have a White tank).
Green chassis, Silver base and grille,
'BP' decal ..........................................£40-50
Green chassis, Silver base and grille,
'BP' label ...........................................£15-20
Green chassis, White base and grille,
'BP' label ...........................................£80-100
Blue chassis, Silver base and grille,
'ARAL' label ..................................£150-175

## MB 33

33a  57  **Ford Zodiac**
Dark Green body, hook, no windows,

metal wheels, 68 mm..........................£30-40
58  Dark Blue, hook, no windows,
metal wheels ................................£700-800
58  Sea-Green, hook, no windows,
metal wheels ................................£100-120
Same but with GPW ..........................£60-75
59  Metallic Mauve body, Orange
panels, no windows, GPW .............£110-130
60  Same but with Green tinted
windows, GPW or SPW ....................£70-90

33b  63  **Ford Zephyr 6**
Sea-Green body, GPW, 67 mm ..........£40-50
same but with SPW ............................£25-30
same but with BPW............................£20-25

33c  68  **Lamborghini Miura**
(All have White interior).
Yellow body, 71 mm. BPW.................£15-20
Yellow body, Chrome hubs .............£300-400
Metallic Gold body, Chrome hubs ..£300-350

## MB 34

34a  57  **Volkswagen 15cwt Van**
All have Blue body; 'MATCHBOX'
decals.
With metal wheels ..............................£35-45
With Grey plastic wheels .................£75-100
With Silver plastic wheels.........£1,500-2,000

34b  62  **Volkswagen Caravette**
All have Pale Green body;
Green interior. Silver wheels..........£250-300
Knobbly-tread Grey wheels
(24 treads) .........................................£75-100
Fine-tread Grey wheels (45 treads) .....£60-80
SBPW, type 'E' box....................£800-1,100

34c  67  **Volkswagen Camper**
Silver body, with high roof
(7 windows) .......................................£25-30
Same but lower roof (1 window),
box 'F' ..............................................£80-100
Pale Green body, Dark Green base
and interior, SPW ....................£1,500-1,750

239

## MB 35

35a  57  **E.R.F. Marshall Horse Box**
Red cab, Beige back, MW, 52 mm .....**£30-35**
Same but with Grey plastic wheels....**£30-40**
With Silver plastic wheels...............**£175-200**
With Black plastic wheels .............**£110-130**
35b  64  **Snow-Trac**. Red body, Silver base,
White tracks, *'Snow Trac'* cast
on sides ......................................**£25-30**
Same but with *'Snow Trac'* decals
on sides .......................................**£15-20**
Same but without *'Snow Trac'*.......**£15-20**
35c  68  **Merryweather Fire Engine**
Silver body, boxed....................**£4,500-5,500**
**NB** This was one of the extremely rare
Regular Wheels models released during
the transition to Superfast in 1968/69.

## MB 36

36a  57  **Austin A50 Cambridge**
Blue-Green body, Black base, MW.....**£30-35**
Same but with GPW.........................**£30-40**
Pale Blue body, GPW.........................**£50-60**
36b  61  **Lambretta and Sidecar**
Metallic Silver Green, KBPW,
'New Model', 'C' type box with
1st type model picture ...............**£120-140**
Same but 2nd type model on box.......**£50-65**
Same but in 'D' type colour
picture box..........................................**£90-110**
Metallic Dark Green, KBPW,
'D' type colour picture box .............**£150-175**
36c  66  **Opel Diplomat**
Metallic Gold body, chrome engine, BPW,
no tow slot, 'New Model', 'E' type
box showing Dark Green model .....**£200-250**
Same but box shows
Light Green model...............................**£40-50**
With correct colour model on box .....**£20-30**
Met. Gold, Grey engine, tow slot,
'F' type box ..........................................**£40-50**

## MB 37

37a  57  **Karrier Bantam Lorry** (open base)
All models with *'COCA-COLA'* side
and rear decals. Orange-Yellow body,
uneven load, MW .........................**£180-200**
Yellow body, uneven load, MW.....**£180-200**
Orange-Yellow, even load, MW..........**£45-55**
Orange-Yellow, even load, GPW .....**£180-220**
Yellow body, even load, MW ............**£60-80**
Yellow body, even load, GPW .......**£100-150**
37b  60  **Karrier Bantam Lorry** (Black baseplate)
All models with *'COCA-COLA'*
side and rear decals.
Grey plastic wheels, CA.................**£100-120**
Grey plastic wheels, rounded axles.....**£35-45**
Silver plastic wheels..............**£1,500-1,750**
Black plastic wheels ...........................**£70-80**
37c  66  **(Dodge) Cattle Truck**
Yellow body, Grey cattle box,
2 White bulls, Silver plastic base ........**£15-20**
With unpainted metal base .................**£10-15**

## MB 38

38a  57  **Karrier Refuse Collector**
All models with
*'Cleansing Department'* side decals.
Grey-Brown body, MW................**£250-350**
Grey body, metal wheels ....................**£40-50**
Grey body, GPW, crimped axles .........**£75-85**
Grey body, GPW, rounded axles .........**£50-60**
Metallic Silver, with rear ridge
casting, MW, CA ...........................**£400-500**
Silver body, Grey plastic wheels........**£50-60**
Silver body, Silver plastic wheels ...**£600-700**
38b  63  **Vauxhall Victor Estate**

Primrose body, Red interior, GPW..**£200-300**
Same but with Silver wheels ..............**£25-30**
Same but with SBPW.......................**£100-120**
Yellow body, Green interior, GPW .....**£60-70**
Same but with Silver wheels ..............**£30-35**
Same but with Black wheels ..............**£20-25**
38c  **Honda Motorcycle and Trailer**
Metallic Green bike,
Orange trailer without decals ..............**£30-40**
Orange trailer with 'Honda' decals ...**£80-120**
Yellow trailer, 'Honda' decals
or labels ..............................................**£20-25**

## MB 39

39a  57  **Ford Zodiac Convertible**
Pale Peach body, Light Brown
base/interior/driver, MW ................**£500-600**
With Light Green base and
interior, MW ......................................**£70-80**
Same but with Light Green
base, GPW ..........................................**£60-70**
Pale Peach body, SPW....................**£200-250**
Dark Peach body, Blue-Green
base and interior, GPW...................**£150-175**
Dark Peach body, Blue-Green base
and interior, SPW ...........................**£120-150**
Dark Peach body with Sea-Green
base, Grey plastic wheels ...................**£75-85**
39b  62  **Pontiac Bonneville Convertible**
Metallic Purple body, Crimson
base, Red steering wheel, SPW.......**£100-120**
Same but with Grey wheels.............**£450-500**
Lemon body, Crimson base, Red
steering wheel, SPW or GPW .............**£65-75**
Same but Cream steering wheel..........**£25-35**
Lemon body, Black base, SPW .........**£80-90**
Same but with Grey wheels..............**£80-100**
Same but with Black wheels ..............**£30-35**
39c  67  **Ford Tractor**
Blue body, Yellow engine cover,
Black plastic tyres, 55 mm ................**£15-20**
Light Blue body and cover,
Yellow hubs ......................................**£80-90**
All-Orange body, Yellow hubs ...........**£70-80**

## MB 40

40a  57  **Bedford 7 Ton Tipper**, 53 mm
Red body, Brown tipper, MW ............**£35-45**
Same but with GPW, domed CA........**£35-45**
With GPW on rivetted axles................**£30-35**
40b  61  **Leyland Tiger Coach**
Steel Blue body, GPW......................**£90-110**
Silver plastic wheels.........................**£25-35**
Black plastic wheels ..........................**£20-25**
40c  67  **Hay Trailer**. Blue body, Yellow
plastic hay racks and wheels, BPT...**£12-15**
**NB** No. 40c deleted in 1972 but appeared
in Two-Packs between 1976-1981.

## MB 41

41a  57  **Jaguar 'D'-Type** (55 mm)
Green body, MW, No. '41'..................**£70-80**
Green body, MW, No. '52',
'B' type box ....................................**£600-750**
Green body, GPW, No '41' ..............**£90-120**
41b  60  **Jaguar 'D'-Type** (62 mm).
All have Green body and Black base.
Grey plastic wheels, CA, No. '41'......**£70-80**
same but with rounded axles ...............**£60-70**
Wire hubs with Black tyres,
No. '41'............................................**£300-400**
same but with No. '5' or '6' ............**£100-150**
Red hubs, Black tyres, No.'41' .......**£400-500**
41c  65  **Ford GT Racer**
All have the racing number '6'.
White body, Red hubs and
interior, BPT ..................................**£300-400**
White body, Yellow hubs, BPT ..........**£20-25**
Yellow body, Yellow hubs, BPT,

RN '6'. (US set) .............................**£175-200**
White, spoked wheels, BPT ......**£2,000-2,200**

## MB 42

42a  57  **Evening News Van**
Yellow body, *'EVENING NEWS'*
decals, metal wheels, 57 mm............**£35-40**
Grey plastic wheels with 24 treads ....**£35-40**
GPW or BPW with 45 treads .........**£150-175**
BPW with 24 treads........................**£125-150**
42b  65  **Studebaker Lark Wagonaire**
(with hunter and dog figures).
Blue body, sliding rear roof
painted as body ...........................**£100-150**
Same but rear roof is Light Blue.......**£25-30**
42c  69  **Iron Fairy Crane**
Red body, Yellow boom, BPW...........**£15-18**

## MB 43

43a  58  **Hillman Minx**
Apple Green body, Silver/Red trim,
metal wheels, hook .........................**£400-500**
Blue/Grey body, Pale Grey roof,
metal wheels ......................................**£40-45**
Same but with Grey plastic wheels .....**£60-70**
Turquoise body, Cream roof, GPW.....**£50-60**
43b  62  **A.B. Tractor Shovel**
Yellow body, driver and shovel.......**£150-200**
Yellow body / shovel,
Red driver and base .........................**£20-25**
Yellow body, driver and base,
Red shovel .......................................**£40-45**
Yellow body, Red driver,
base / shovel ..................................**£250-300**
43c  68  **Pony Trailer**
Yellow body, Grey ramp,
Light Brown base, BPW....................**£15-20**
Same but with Dark Green base.........**£10-15**

## MB 44

44a  58  **Rolls-Royce Silver Cloud**
Metallic Silver-Blue body, Red trim,
metal wheels, 67 mm.........................**£30-35**
60  Same but with Grey plastic wheels.....**£30-40**
Same but with Silver plastic wheels ...**£60-70**
44b  64  **Rolls-Royce Phantom V**
Metallic Mauve body, BPW...............**£25-30**
Same but with GPW.......................**£200-250**
Same but with SPW.......................**£300-400**
Metallic Silver-Grey, BPW ...........**£150-175**
Same but with SPW.......................**£400-500**
44c  67  **GMC Refrigerator Truck**
Red body, Sea-Green container,
Black wheels, 76 mm ......................**£10-15**

## MB 45

45a  58  **Vauxhall Victor**
Red body, no dashboard casting
bar, MW, 'B' type Moko box ....**£3,000-4,000**
Yellow or Lemon body, MW.............**£35-40**
Yellow body, metal wheels,
no dashboard casting bar ................**£600-700**
Yellow or Lemon body, Grey plastic
wheels, no window glazing ...............**£40-45**
Same but with clear windows ............**£70-80**
Same but with Green windows ...........**£50-60**
Lemon, Green windows, SPW ...........**£80-90**
Yellow body, SPW or BPW...............**£80-90**
45b  65  **Ford Corsair with Boat**
Cream body, Red interior, Black
wheels, Silver painted base .............**£40-45**
Same but with unpainted base............**£25-30**
Same but with Grey wheels..............**£80-100**
Models with White interior are
pre-productions ............................**£600-800**

## MB 46

**46a** 58 **Morris Minor 1000**
Tan body, no windows, MW .....**£2,000-3,000**
Dark Green body, Black base,
metal wheels, domed crimped axles..**£80-100**
Dark Blue/Green body, MW .............**£70-80**
Same but with GPW......................**£100-125**
Blue body, Grey plastic wheels.......**£150-200**

**46b** 60 **'PICKFORDS' Removals Van**
Dark Blue, GPW, three line decal .....**£90-120**
Dark Blue, SPW, three line decal....**£140-160**
Dark Blue, GPW, two line decal......**£150-200**
Dark Blue, SPW, two line decal.....**£250-300**
Green body, GPW, three line decal ..**£80-110**
Green body, SPW, three line decal..**£140-160**
Green, SBPW, three line decal......**£200-250**
**'BEALES BEALESONS' Van**
Light Brown body, *'Beales  Bealesons'*
decal, BPW, without box ................**£600-700**
Same but in special White box with
'sun' and *'It's A Pleasure'* decal ......**£700-800**
**NB** A green version of the 'Beales Bealsons'
van is thought to exist. If you have an
example, please send us details.

**46c** 68 **Mercedes-Benz 300 SE**.Green body ..**£20-25**
69 Metallic Blue body .............................**£15-20**

## MB 47

**47a** 58 **Trojan Van**
Red body, *'BROOKE BOND TEA'*
decals, metal wheels, 58 mm..............**£35-45**
Same but with KGPW, 'B' type box ...**£50-60**
In 'D' type colour picture box............**£700-900**

**47b** 63 **Commer Ice Cream Van** *'LYONS MAID'*,
Metallic Blue body, BPW.................**£120-150**
Same but with Blue body ...................**£30-40**
Blue body, KGPW, 'D' type box.....**£350-450**
Blue body, BPW, White side decals....**£40-50**
Cream body, *'LYONS MAID'* ........**£200-230**
Cream body, White side decals.........**£60-70**
*'LORD NIELSENS ICE CREAM'*,
Cream body, Red/White labels,
Black base, Black plastic wheels .......**£80-90**
Blue body, Black plastic wheels......**£100-130**

**47c** 68 **DAF Container Truck**
Sea Green body, Grey roof,
Yellow container, BPW ......................**£50-60**
Silver body, Grey or Silver roof,
Yellow container, BPW ......................**£12-15**

## MB 48

**48a** 58 **Meteor Sports Boat and Trailer**
Black trailer, Light Brown boat,
Blue hull, metal wheels ......................**£30-40**
With Grey plastic wheels ...................**£50-60**
With SPW, 'B' type Moko box .......**£175-200**

**48b** 61 **Sports Boat and Trailer**
Boat with Cream or White deck and
Red hull or with Red deck and
Cream or White hull.
Dark Blue trailer, BPW......................**£50-60**
Dark Blue trailer, Grey PW.............**£150-175**
Light Blue trailer, BPW......................**£40-50**

**48c** 66 **(Dodge) Dumper Truck**
Red body, Silver trim, wide or narrow
Black plastic wheels, 76 mm..............**£10-15**

## MB 49

**49a** 58 **M3 Personnel Carrier**
Military Green, White bonnet star on
some, metal wheels and rollers ..........**£25-30**
Grey plastic wheels, metal rollers ...**£150-175**
GPW and Grey plastic rollers..........**£350-400**
Grey plastic wheels, Silver rollers .....**£80-100**
BPW and rollers, Grey tracks.............**£30-40**
BPW and rollers, Green tracks...........**£30-40**

**49b** 67 **(Mercedes) Unimog**
Light Brown body,
Sea-Green base, 61 mm......................**£20-25**

---

Light Brown body,
Red base (factory error?)................**£700-800**
Light Blue body, Red base .................**£15-20**

## MB 50

**50a** 58 **Commer Pick-Up**
Pale Brown body, MW, 64 mm..........**£30-40**
Pale or Light Brown body, GPW.....**£35-45**
Light Brown body, SPW..................**£150-180**
Red and White body, SPW ..............**£600-800**
Red / White, KGPW,
'D' type box .............................**£1,500-1,800**
Red and Grey body, SPW...............**£180-200**
Red and Grey, KGPW,
'D' type box ..................................**£180-200**
Red and Grey body, BPW ..............**£180-200**

**50b** 64 **John Deere Lanz Tractor**
Green body, Yellow hubs,
Grey tyres, 50 mm..............................**£20-25**
Same but Black tyres...........................**£10-15**

**50c** 69 **Ford Kennel Truck**
Metallic Green body, White grille,
smooth kennel floor.............................**£20-25**
Same but textured kennel floor
and/or Silver grille...............................**£15-20**

## MB 51

**51a** 58 **Albion Chieftain**
All models with Yellow body,
Tan or Light Beige load.
*'PORTLAND CEMENT'* decals, MW .**£40-55**
With *'BLUE CIRCLE PORTLAND
CEMENT'* decals, MW ......................**£50-60**
Same but with GPW............................**£40-55**
Same but with SPW, 'D' type box ..**£200-230**
Same but with knobbly BPW ..........**£200-230**

**51b** 64 **Tipping Trailer**
Green body, three Yellow barrels,
Yellow hubs, Grey tyres .....................**£10-15**
With Yellow hubs, Black tyres...........**£12-15**

**51c** 69 **AEC Mammoth Major 8 Wheel Tipper**
Orange body, Silver tipper,
*'DOUGLAS'*, White base grille.........**£90-110**
Same but chrome base.........................**£40-50**
Yellow body, Silver tipper,
*'DOUGLAS'* ......................................**£60-80**
Yellow body, Silver tipper,
*'POINTER'* ........................................**£25-35**

## MB 52

**52a** 58 **1948 Maserati 4 CLT**
Red body, Cream driver, no decal,
Black plastic wheels, 61 mm..............**£40-50**
Same with racing number '52'.............**£35-45**
Red body, racing number '52',
wire wheels, BPT .........................**£400-500**
Lemon body, wire wheels, "52".....**£200-240**
Same but number '3', '5' or '30'.....**£120-140**

**52b** 65 **B.R.M. Racing Car**
Blue body, Yellow hubs, BPT, '5' .......**£15-20**
Same but with racing number '3'.......**£60-80**
Dark Blue (Ultramarine) body, RN '5'**£40-50**
Gift Set model: Red body,
Yellow hubs with Black tyres.............**£70-80**
Dark Cherry Red body,
Yellow hubs, racing number '5' ......**£100-120**

## MB 53

**53a** 58 **Aston Martin DB2-4 Mk.I**
Metallic Green body, MW, 65 mm......**£30-40**
Same but with Grey plastic wheels.....**£60-80**
Met. Red, KGPW, 'C' type box ......**£250-300**
Met. Red, KBPW, 'D' type box ......**£200-240**

**53b** 63 **Mercedes-Benz 220SE**
Maroon body, Silver plastic wheels ....**£25-30**
Maroon body, Grey plastic wheels......**£30-40**
Maroon body, Black plastic wheels ....**£60-80**
Dark Red body, GPW ....................**£200-250**
Dark Red body, BPW ..........................**£20-25**

---

Dark Red, SBPW, no rear trim,
'D' type box with Mercedes
promotional card......................**£1,750-2,000**

**53c** 68 **Ford Zodiac Mk.IV**
Light Metallic Blue body, BPW.........**£20-25**
Light Met. Green body, BPW....**£3,000-3,500**

## MB 54

**54a** 58 **Saracen Personnel Carrier**
Olive Green body, six BPW, CA........**£25-35**
Same but with rounded axles .............**£20-25**

**54b** 65 **Cadillac Ambulance**
White, Red cross label or decal and
roof lights, BPW................................**£20-25**

## MB 55

**55a** 58 **DUKW Amphibian**
Olive Green body, metal wheels ........**£20-25**
Same but GPW .................................**£40-50**
Same but KBPW, 'D' type box
with Green model picture
(normally Red picture) ...................**£500-600**

**55b** 63 **Ford Fairlane 'POLICE' Car**
Non-metallic Dark Blue, BPW.....**£280-320**
Metallic Blue, knobbly BPW .........**£400-500**
Metallic Blue, BPW .......................**£70-90**
Metallic Blue, SPW .................**£900-1,200**
Metallic Blue, SPW.......................**£450-500**

**55c** 66 **Ford Galaxie 'POLICE' Car**
White body, *'Police & Shield'*
decal, Blue roof light...................**£300-400**
Same but with Red roof light.............**£18-20**

**55d** 68 **Mercury 'POLICE' Car**
White body, *'Police & Shield'*
labels, Red roof light....................**£350-380**
Same but with Blue roof light............**£25-35**

## MB 56

**56a** 58 **London Trolley Bus 'Drink Peardrax'**
All with Red body and destination decals.
Black poles, MW, (beware fakes) ...**£250-300**
Black poles, GPW, (beware fakes)..**£300-400**
Red poles, metal wheels....................**£45-55**
Red poles, GPW ............................**£300-400**
Red poles, BPW ..............................**£45-55**
Red poles, SPW ..........................**£190-240**
**'BP Visco-Static'**, KBPW,
red poles, 'D' type box ............**£1,000-1,250**

**56b** 65 **Fiat 1500** (all have BPW)
Sea-Green body, Brown luggage........**£15-20**
Same but with Red-Brown luggage ....**£10-15**
Gift Set version:
Red body, Red-Brown luggage ..........**£70-80**

## MB 57

**57a** 58 **Wolseley 1500**
Pale Green body, Grey plastic
wheels, Gold trim, 55 mm..............**£220-250**
Same but with Silver trim ..................**£35-45**

**57b** 61 **Chevrolet Impala**
All versions have Metallic Blue body
and Pale Blue roof.
Clear windows, Black base, SPW ...**£110-130**
CW, Dark Blue base, SPW,
'C' type box ..................................**£140-160**
GW, Dark Blue base, SPW................**£25-30**
GW, Dark Blue base, GPW ................**£50-60**
GW, Pale or Light Blue base,
Silver plastic wheels .....................**£120-140**
Black base, GPW...............................**£75-85**
Black base, SPW................................**£70-80**
Black base, BPW................................**£60-70**

**57c** 66 **Land Rover Fire Truck**
Red body, *'KENT FIRE BRIGADE'*,
Black plastic wheels, 64 mm..............**£25-30**
Same but with GPW ......................**£500-750**

## MB 58

**58a** 58 **AEC Coach 'BEA'**
Dark Blue body, White letters,
Grey wheels, 65 mm...........................**£50-60**
Dark Blue body, Black letters on
White ground, Grey plastic wheels ....**£40-50**
Same but with SPW.......................**£175-200**
Same but with KBPW ...................**£300-350**

**58b** 62 **Drott Excavator**
Red body, Silver base,
Black rollers, Green tracks.................**£20-25**
Same but with Silver rollers...........**£100-120**
Orange body, Silver base,
Black rollers.....................................**£25-30**
Orange body and base, Black rollers ..**£15-20**

**58c** 68 **DAF Girder Truck**
White body, Red base and 12 girders,
6 Black plastic wheels, 75 mm...........**£10-15**

## MB 59

**59a** 58 **Ford Thames Van 'SINGER'**
Pale Green body, Grey plastic wheels.**£75-85**
Same but SPW, rivetted axles .........**£200-250**
Dark Green body, KPW,
rounded axles....................................**£250-300**
Dark Green body, SPW,
rivetted axles....................................**£250-300**

**59b** 63 **Ford Fairlane Fire Chief**
All models with Red body and *FIRE
CHIEF* decals on doors and bonnet,
SBPW..............................................**£150-175**
With Grey plastic wheels ...............**£250-300**
With Silver plastic wheels ..............**£250-300**
With shield decals on doors
(pre-production trial) ......................**£200-250**

**59c** 66 **Ford Galaxie Fire Chief**
Red body, Blue dome light,
*'FIRE CHIEF'*, BPW ..........................**£20-25**
Same but with Red dome light........**£250-350**

## MB 60

**60a** 58 **Morris J2 Pick Up**
All with Light Blue body and
*'BUILDERS SUPPLY COMPANY'* decals.
'Supply Company' in Black,
Grey plastic wheels ..........................**£50-60**
*'SUPPLY COMPANY'* in White,
with rear window, GPW or BPW.......**£30-35**
Same but with SPW...........................**£40-50**
Without rear window, GPW ...........**£180-200**
Without rear window, BPW ..............**£30-40**

**60b** 66 **Site Hut Truck**
Blue body, Yellow and Green plastic
building, Black wheels ......................**£12-18**

## MB 61

**61a** 59 **Ferret Scout Car**
Olive Green body, Tan driver,
BPW, 57mm.......................................**£25-30**

**61b** 66 **Alvis Stalwart 'BP'**
White body, Green wheels with BPT,
smooth carrier bed ............................**£30-40**
Same but with ribbed carrier bed ......**£15-20**
White body, Yellow wheels, BPT.......**£60-80**
Two-Pack version:  Military Olive Green
body, Black wheels............................**£20-30**

## MB 62

**62a** 59 **AEC General Service Lorry**
Olive Green, tow hook, six BPW......**£75-100**
Same but KBPW, rounded axles .....**£140-160**

**62b** 63 **Commer TV  Service Van**
All have Cream body, Red plastic ladder,
aerial and 3 TV's. *'RENTASET'*,
knobbly Grey wheels (24 treads) ....**£300-400**
*'RENTASET'*, SBPW .......................**£140-160**
*'RENTASET'*,
45-tread Grey wheels ...................**£300-350**
*'RADIO RENTALS'*, BPW..................**£50-60**

*'RADIO RENTALS'*,
fine-tread Grey wheels ...................**£450-550**

**62c** 68 **Mercury Cougar**
Cream body, White interior,
Chrome hubs...............................**£4,000-5,000**
Metallic Lime Green, Red interior......**£10-15**

## MB 63

**63a** 59 **Service Ambulance (Ford)**
Olive Green body, Red crosses,
BPW, CA...........................................**£35-40**
Same but with rounded axles .............**£25-30**
Same but in rare type 'D' box with
colour picture.................................**£100-125**

**63b** 63 **Alvis Foamite Crash Tender**
Red body, Silver nozzle,
six BPW, 63 mm..............................**£85-100**
With Gold hose nozzle .......................**£20-30**

**63c** 68 **Dodge Crane Truck**
Yellow body, Red hook, 76 mm..........**£10-15**
Yellow body, Yellow hook..................**£15-18**

## MB 64

**64a** 59 **Scammell Breakdown Truck**
Olive Green body, metal or plastic
hook, Black plastic wheels, 64 mm.....**£35-45**

**64b** 66 **MG 1100**
Green body, White seats, driver,
dog, Black plastic tyres, 67 mm..........**£15-20**

## MB 65

**65a** 59 **Jaguar 3.4 litre**
Blue body, Silver rear no. plate,
GPW ...............................................**£90-120**
Same but with Blue rear no. plate.......**£35-45**
Dark Blue body, KGPW, CA...........**£100-125**
Met. Blue body + no. plate, GPW....**£100-125**
Metallic Blue body, KGPW............**£140-160**

**65b** 62 **Jaguar 3.4 Sedan**
Metallic Red body, Silver base,
Silver plastic wheels, 68 mm .........**£120-140**
Red body, Grey plastic wheels ..........**£50-60**
Red body, Black plastic wheels..........**£30-35**

**65c** 67 **Claas Combine Harvester**
Red body, Yellow blades and front
hubs, no hole in base ......................**£150-250**
Same but with hole in base ................**£10-12**

## MB 66

**66a** 59 **Citroën DS 19**
Yellow body, Silver trim, GPW..........**£50-60**
Same but with SPW.........................**£500-750**

**66b** 62 **Harley-Davidson Motor Cycle**
Metallic Bronze bike and sidecar,
spoked wheels, BPT........................**£100-120**

**66c** 66 **'GREYHOUND' Coach**
Silver-Grey body, CW, BPW.............**£90-110**
Silver-Grey body, AW, BPW .............**£10-15**

## MB 67

**67a** 59 **Saladin Armoured Car**
Olive Green body, six SBPW, CA,
'C' box .............................................**£35-45**
Same but with rounded axles,
'D' type box .....................................**£25-30**
Same but in 'E' type box ................**£100-125**

**67b** 67 **Volkswagen 1600 TL**
Red body, Black wheels,
Silver hubcaps..................................**£25-30**
Red body, Silver wheels with
black tyres........................................**£18-20**
Gift Set version:
Red body, Maroon plastic roof rack....**£80-90**
Met. Purple, Chrome hubs, BPT ....**£300-400**

## MB 68

**68a** 59 **Austin Radio Truck Mk.II**
Olive Green, KBPW, CA,
'B' type box ......................................**£30-35**
Same but with rounded axles .............**£30-35**
Same but in 'E' type box.................**£100-125**

**68b** 65 **Mercedes Coach** (all have BPW)
Turquoise/White body, US issue .....**£140-160**
Orange/White body ...........................**£20-30**

## MB 69

**69a** 59 **Commer Van 'NESTLES'**
Maroon body, driver, Yellow logo,
Grey plastic wheels, 56 mm...............**£45-55**
Red body, GPW with 20 treads..........**£60-70**
Red body, GPW with 36 treads .......**£200-250**

**69b** 65 **Hatra Tractor Shovel**
Orange body, Orange wheels,
Grey tyres, 78 mm ............................**£65-75**
With Red hubs, Grey tyres .................**£30-40**
With Red hubs, Black tyres.................**£25-30**
With Yellow hubs, Black tyres ...........**£20-25**
Yellow body, Yellow hubs..................**£20-25**
Yellow body, Red hubs....................**£100-120**
Orange body, Yellow shovel............**£500-600**

## MB 70

**70a** 59 **Ford Thames Estate Car**
Turquoise and Yellow body,
Grey wheels, no windows ..................**£40-45**
Grey wheels, clear windows...............**£40-50**
Grey wheels, Green windows.............**£25-30**
Silver wheels, clear windows.............**£40-50**
Silver or Black wheels, GW ..............**£35-40**

**70b** 66 **Ford Grit Spreader**
Red body, Primrose Yellow
container, Black slide, BPW...............**£25-30**
Red body, Lemon Yellow
container, Grey slide, BPW .............**£150-175**

## MB 71

**71a** 59 **200 gallon Austin Water Truck**
**(with Badge)**
Olive Green, BPW, with first
*'Matchbox Collectors'* badge ..........**£100-120**
Same, but without badge .................**£50-70**
Same in rare type 'D' box with
colour picture.................................**£300-400**

**71b** 64 **Jeep Gladiator Pick-Up**
Red body, Green int., BPW, 66 mm....**£50-60**
Red body, White interior ...................**£20-25**

**71c** 69 **Ford Heavy Wreck Truck** (all BPW)
Red and White body, Amber
windows, smooth loadbed ...............**£500-700**
Same but with ribbed loadbed........**£400-500**
Same but with Green windows ..........**£20-25**
Military Green body ...........................**£20-25**

## MB 72

**72a** 59 **Fordson Major Tractor**
All models with Blue body, 50 mm.
Grey front wheels,
Orange rear hubs, GPT...................**£140-170**
Black front wheels,
Orange rear hubs, BPT .....................**£35-40**
Orange hubs front / rear, Grey tyres....**£40-45**
Orange hubs front and rear, BPT ........**£30-35**
Yellow hubs front and rear,
GPT or BPT ................................**£1,500-1,750**
Yellow rear hubs, Grey plastic
front wheels, type 'D' box.........**£2,000-2,500**

**72b** 66 **Jeep CJ5**
Orange-Yellow body, Yellow
hubs, White interior .....................**£800-1,000**

Yellow body and hubs, Red interior....**£15-20**

## MB 73

**73a**  59  **Leyland R.A.F. 10 ton Refueller**
Airforce-Blue, roundel, six GPW........**£80-90**
Same but with KBPW ..............**£2,500-3,000**

**73b**  62  **Ferrari F1 Racing Car**
Red body, Grey or White driver,
RN '73', 'spoked' metal hubs, BPT ....**£30-35**
In type 'D' box ................................**£100-125**

**73c**  68  **Mercury Commuter Station Wagon**
Met. Lime Green, Silver hubs, BPT....**£12-15**

## MB 74

**74a**  59  **Mobile 'REFRESHMENTS' Bar**
White body, Pale Blue base,
Blue interior, KGPW ......................**£250-300**
Cream body, Lt. Blue base, GPW ....**£250-300**
Pinkish Cream body, Light Blue
base, Grey plastic wheels ...............**£500-600**
Silver body, Lt. Blue base, GPW ....**£100-125**
Silver body, Turquoise base, SPW ..**£250-300**
Silver body, Mid-Blue base,
KBPW........................................**£800-1,000**
Silver body, Sea Green or
Dark Blue base ............................**£100-120**

**74b**  66  **Daimler Fleetline Bus**
Cream body, 'ESSO' decals ...............**£15-20**
Cream body, 'ESSO' labels ...............**£30-35**

Green body, 'ESSO' labels .................**£15-20**
Red body, 'ESSO' labels .....................**£30-35**

## MB 75

**75a**  60  **Ford Thunderbird**  All  have Cream
body and Peach side panels.
Blue base, SPW, Lesney (C) box ..**£200-250**
Blue-Green base, SPW ...................**£300-400**
Black base, SPW ...............................**£70-80**
Black base, GPW ...........................**£120-150**
Black base, SBPW...........................**£250-350**

**75b**  65  **Ferrari Berlinetta**
Metallic Green body, Silver base,
wire wheels, 'New Model' on
'E' type box ...................................**£300-400**
Same but unpainted base...................**£20-25**
Met.Green body, Silver wheels, BPT ..**£15-20**
Red body, chrome hubs with BPT...**£400-450**
Red body, wire wheels ...................**£600-650**

# Matchbox '1-75' Series early Accessory Packs

**A1**  1957  **Service Ramp**  Gold/Red, pictorial window box..............**£50-60**
**A1a**  1957  **'ESSO' Petrol Pump Set**  Red pumps, White figure ........**£60-70**
**A1b**  1963  **'BP' Petrol Pump Set**  White pumps...................................**£60-70**
**A2**  1957  **Car Transporter**
Box type 1:  Dark Blue/Yellow front and back
'MOKO - LESNEY' line-drawing box.
Box type 2:  Yellow front/back, Blue end tabs,
'LESNEY MATCHBOX SERIES' logo.
1: Pale blue body, Dark Blue logo 'MATCHBOX
CAR TRANSPORTER', metal wheels on tractor and
trailer, 1st box................................................**£60-70**
2: Pale Blue body, Red 'CAR COLLECTION Ltd CAR
TRANSPORTER', KBPW on tractor and trailer,
1st type box ................................................ **£80-100**
3: Pale Blue body, Red 'CAR COLLECTION Ltd CAR
TRANSPORTER', GPW on tractor and trailer,
1st type box ................................................ **£200-240**
4: Red cab and lower deck, Grey upper deck and sides,
BPW, Red logo: 'CAR COLLECTION Ltd' on
Pale Yellow background, 2nd box....................**£300-350**
**A3**  1957  **Garage**  Yellow/Green/Red, opening doors,
all metal with metal connecting clip, Moko box ..............**£30-40**
In late Lesney picture box........................................**£80-90**

**A4**  1960  **Road Signs Set**  Eight Red/White/Black signs,
'Lesney' on base. Moko Lesney box ................................**£70-90**
**A5**  1960  **'HOME STORES' Shop**  Food shop with window
display and opening door, Lesney box..............................**£40-45**
**MG1a**  1959  **Service Station and Showroom**  'MATCHBOX GARAGE',
Yellow base and roof sign, Red building, Moko box .....**£100-125**
Red base and roof sign, Yellow building, Moko box .....**£100-125**
**MG1b**  1961  **'ESSO' Sales and Service Station**  Red base,
Yellow building, White/Red 'MATCHBOX SALES and
SERVICE' plus clock. Lesney box ................................**£100-150**
**MG1b**  1961  **'BP' Sales and Service Station**  White building,
Yellow/Green 'MATCHBOX SALES and SERVICE'.
Lesney picture box with no background scene..............**£100-150**
**MG1b**  1961  **'BP' Sales and Service Station**  As previous item,
but late issue with roof sign labels instead of decals.
Lesney detailed picture box with background scene
(houses, cars, etc.) ....................................................**£150-175**
**MG1c**  1968  **'BP' Service Station**  with forecourt pumps. White
building, 'BP AUTO SHOP', 'BP SELF-SERVICE CAFE',
'MATCHBOX' decal in yellow/red ...................................**£50-75**
**MF1a**  1963  **Fire Station**  White with Green roof,
'MATCHBOX FIRE STATION'................................**£200-250**
White with Red roof, wording on a Red background.....**£160-190**
White with Red roof, wording on Brown background ...**£160-190**

SW = Steering wheel,   PSW = Plastic steering wheel,   PH = plastic hubs,   MW = Metal wheels,
CA = Crimped axles,   RA = Rounded axles,   SRAB = Straight rear axle bar,   RACO = Rear axle has cut-out

**M1  58  Caterpillar Earthmover**
Yellow body, MW, CA or RA .... **£50-60**

**M1  63  'BP' Petrol Tanker**
Green/Yellow/White body,
KBPW, Moko box ................... **£75-100**
Smooth BPW, Lesney box ......... **£50-75**

**M2  58  Bedford Articulated Truck 'WALLS ICE CREAM'**
All have a Light Blue tractor cab, 101mm.
Cream trailer, MW, Moko box ... **£60-70**
59      Cream trailer, GPW, Moko box .. **£60-70**
59-61   White trailer, GPW, Moko box . **£75-85**

**M2  61  Bedford Tractor and York Trailer 'DAVIES TYRES'**
Orange cab, Silver trailer,
clear windows, KBPW .......... **£150-200**
Green tinted windows, KBPW. **£75-100**
Green tinted windows, GPW.. **£125-150**
Black fine tread wheels
(45 treads)................................. **£75-100**
Grey fine tread wheels
(45 treads)............................... **£160-180**
Silver cab, Dark Red trailer,
Black base.............................. **£225-250**

**M2  64  Bedford Tractor and York Trailer 'LEP INTERNATIONAL'**
Silver cab, Maroon trailer,
Dark Red base, SBPW .......... **£200-250**
Silver cab, Dark Red trailer,
Black base.............................. **£60-70**

**M3  59  Mighty Antar Tank Transporter and Centurion Tank**
Both models in Military Green,
Transporter has KBPW,
tank has metal rollers ................ **£70-80**
Transporter has SBPW,
tank has metal rollers ................ **£70-80**
Transporter has SBPW,
tank has GPR......................... **£275-325**
Transporter has SBPW,
tank has BPR......................... **£275-325**

**M4  59  Ruston Bucyrus Excavator**
Maroon cab, Yellow shovel arms,
Black base, Red decals 'Taylor
Woodrow', Green or Grey tracks,
Moko box .................................. **£75-100**
Same but Yellow decals,
'A Lesney Product' box.............. **£40-50**

Same but the 2nd type of the
'Lesney' box shows the model
operating on the slew ............. **£125-150**

**M4  65  'FREUHOF' Hopper Train**
Maroon tractor, two Silver
trailers, Red hubs, BPT ........... **£75-100**
With Red PH and GPT........... **£175-200**

**M5  59  'MASSEY FERGUSON 780' Combine Harvester**
All with Red body, Yellow blades, driver.
Red metal SW, SPW front,
KBPW rear, SRAB, Moko box .. **£70-90**
Same but bare metal SW,
in 'A Lesney Product' box.......... **£70-90**
Same but Yellow plastic hubs,
in detailed colour picture box. **£300-350**
With bare metal SW, Orange PH on
front, SBPW rear, RACO ......... **£75-100**
Same but Yellow plastic SW .... **£75-100**
With Yellow PSW, Orange PH
front/rear, RACO, late issue
detailed box ........................... **£125-150**
With Silver PH and Grey tyres
(front), rear KGPW, Red PSW,
straight rear axle bar........ **£1,500-2,000**

**M6  60  Scammell Transporter 'PICKFORDS'**
Dark Blue tractor and drawbar,
Maroon loadbed, KBPW,
Moko box ............................... **£100-130**
Dark Blue tractor, Red loadbed,
Black drawbar, KBPW, in 'A
Lesney Product' picture box... **£250-300**
Bright Blue tractor, Red loadbed,
Black drawbar, KBPW,
in 'A Lesney Product' box...... **£100-130**
Same but with SBPW, in late
issue detailed 'Lesney' box .... **£150-175**

**M6  66  Racing Car Transporter 'BP'**
Green body, Silver ramp/rear door,
Red hubs with BPT, 'Monza/Le
Mans/Sebring/Nurburgring'
on sides .................................. **£300-350**
With 'Le Mans/Sebring/Silverstone/
Nurburgring' on sides................ **£40-50**

**M7  60  Thames Trader Cattle Truck 'JENNINGS'**, Dark Red cab,
Light Tan box trailer, KGPW ..... **£60-70**

With Dark Tan trailer, Red rear
lamp, knobbly GPW .............. **£100-120**
Same but with knobbly BPW. **£100-120**
Same but Grey
45-tread wheels..................... **£130-150**
Same but Black
45-tread wheels..................... **£140-160**
Light Blue cab, base and rear ramp,
Metallic Copper back,
GPW ............................... **£2,000-3,000**

**M8  61  'MOBILGAS' Petrol Tanker**
Red body, White 'MOBILGAS'
logo, knobbly GPW.................. **£70-85**
With KBPW (24 treads) ......... **£600-750**
With 45-tread BPW, in 'A Lesney
Product' late issue box...... **£1,000-1,250**

**M8  64  Guy Warrior Car Transporter**
Blue-Green cab, Orange trailer, Orange
wheels with Grey tyres, 209 mm.
'FARNBOROUGH-MEASHAM'
in Black, White outline ........... **£75-85**
'FARNBOROUGH-MEASHAM' in
White, Black outline ..................... **£50-60**

**M9  62  Inter-State Double Freighter 'COOPER-JARRETT'.**
Blue cab/central bogey, Grey trailers
and rear doors, Yellow decals,
detailed BPW,
1st type colour picture box..... **£140-170**
Blue cab/central bogey, Silver trailers,
Blue doors, Yellow decals,
2nd type picture box.............. **£140-170**
Blue cab, bare metal central bogey,
Silver trailers and rear doors, SBPW,
detailed colour picture box... **£140-170**
Same but with Orange decals. **£100-150**

**M10  62  Whitlock Dinkum Dumper**
All have Yellow body.
With Bright Red PSW, bare
metal hubs, 'Lesney' box .......... **£50-60**
With small Maroon PSW,
Red PH ...................................... **£50-60**
With large Maroon PSW,
Red PH ...................................... **£50-60**

# Matchbox Presentation and Gift Sets

## Presentation Sets

The first presentation set was sold in the USA in 1957 and consisted of an enlarged normal 'Matchbox' containing eight of the sixty-four models that Lesney manufactured at that time.  The first sets were not sold in the UK until 1959.

| Ref | Year(s) | Set name and details | MPR |
|---|---|---|---|
| PS 1 | 1957 | **Matchbox Presentation Set** Contains models 1 - 8   (only available in USA)..... | **£5,000-6,000** |
| PS 1 | 1959 | **Private Owner Set** 19 MGA, 43 Hillman Minx, 45 Vauxhall Victor, A-3 Garage ...................................... | **£750-1,000** |
| PS 2 | 1957 | **Matchbox Presentation Set** Contains models 9 - 16   (only available in USA).... | **£5,000-6,000** |
| PS 2 | 1959 | **Transporter and 4 Cars Set** Contains 30 Ford, 31 Ford Station Wagon, 33 Ford Zodiac, 36 Austin A50, and an A-2 Transporter ........ | **£750-1,000** |
| PS 3 | 1957 | **Matchbox Presentation Set** Contains models 17 - 24   (only available in USA)... | **£5,000-6,000** |
| PS 3 | 1959 | **Transporter and 6 Cars Set** 22 Vauxhall Cresta, 32 Jaguar XK, 33 Ford Zodiac, 43 Hillman Minx, 44 Rolls-Royce Silver Cloud, 45 Vauxhall Victor and an A-2 Transporter ............ | **£1,000-1,250** |
| PS 4 | 1957 | **Matchbox Presentation Set** Contains models 25 - 32   (only available in USA)... | **£5,000-6,000** |
| PS 4 | 1959 | **Commercial Vehicle Set** Contains No.5 Bus, 11 Petrol Tanker, 21 Long Distance Coach, 25 'Dunlop' Van, 35 Horse Box, 40 Bedford Tipper, 47 'Brooke Bond' Van and 60 Morris Pickup............ | **£750-1,000** |
| PS 4 | 1959 | **Lastwagen und Omnibuse** German version of PS4; same contents as British issue................................... | **£750-1,000** |
| PS 5 | 1957 | **Matchbox Presentation Set** Contains models 33 - 40   (only available in USA)... | **£5,000-6,000** |
| PS 5 | 1959 | **Army Personnel Carrier Set** M3 Personnel Carrier, 54 Saracen, 55 DUKW, 61 Ferret, 62 General Service Lorry, 63 Ambulance, M-3 Tank Transporter.............................................. | **£750-1,000** |
| PS 6 | 1957 | **Matchbox Presentation Set** Contains models 41 - 48   (only available in USA)... | **£5,000-6,000** |
| PS 7 | 1957 | **Matchbox Presentation Set** Contains models 49 - 56   (only available in USA)... | **£5,000-6,000** |
| PS 8 | 1957 | **Matchbox Presentation Set** Contains models 57 - 64   (only available in USA)... | **£5,000-6,000** |

# Gift Sets

The packaging for the first UK issued sets consisted of a frail blue box with a yellow lid panel on which were displayed (in red) the models making  up the set. Sets in similar packaging were issued for the German market. Note however that contents may vary within the same type of box (the G4 Farm set listed below is an example). Please advise us of any other different model combinations you may have.  NB - Sets containg rare variations will sell for higher prices than the MPR shown here. Each set needs to be priced on its contents.

**GS 1** c1960 **Garage Set 'C'**
'MATCHBOX' Sales and Service Station (Red/Yellow), Roadway Layout, Accessories Pack No.1 (Esso petrol pumps), Accessory Pack No.2 (Car Transporter, Blue/Red lettering), Major Pack No.6 ('Pickfords' Transporter), 1-75 series models (5c, 29b, 31b, 42a, 45a, 46b, 57b, 74a). All models are individually boxed and housed in larger display box printed with 'MATCHBOX SERIES' and pictures of the garage and models, etc. ...........................**£2,000-2,500**

**G 1** 60-61 **Commercial Motor Set**
Contains: 5b 'Players Please', 20b, 37a (even load), 47a, 51a, 59a, 60a and 69a. (All models in G 1 had Grey plastic wheels) ...............................**£550-600**

**G 1** 62-63 **Commercial Vehicle Set**
5c 'Visco-Static', 10c, 12b, 13c, 14c, 21c, 46b, 74a.....**£350-450**

**G 1** 1965 **Motorway Set**
6, 10, 13, 33, 34, 38, 48, 55, 71 and R-1 layout............**£600-800**

**G 1** 1967 **Service Station Set**
A1 Service Station and 'BP' Pump Set, 31c or 32c, 13d and 64b in pictorial display case .............**£1,000-1,400**

**G 2** 60-61 **Car Transporter Set**
A-2 Transporter (metal wheels) and cars 22b, 25b, 33b, 39a, 57b and 75a....................................**£500-700**

**G 2** 60-61 2nd issue: A-2 Transporter (with Grey plastic wheels to tractor and Black plastic wheels to trailer), plus cars 7b, 22b, 25c, 27c, 57b and 75a .....................**£500-700**

**G 2** 62-63 **Car Transporter Set**
Models 25b, 30b, 31b, 39b, 48b, 65b plus Accessory Pack No.2............................................**£500-700**

**G 2** 1965 **Car Transporter Set** (Mail Order issue)
Contains 22c, 28c, 36c, 75b and Major Pack 8b........**£300-350**

**G 2** 1967 **Transporter Set**
Contains K8 Transporter, 14d, 24c, 31c and 53c ..........**£250-300**

**G 3** 60-61 **Building Constructors Set**
Contains 2, 6, 15, 16, 18, 24, 28 and M-1.................**£300-350**

**G 3** 62-63 **Constructional Plant Set**
Contains 2, 6, 15, 16, 18, 24, 28 and M-1.....................**£240-280**

**G 3** 1965 **Vacation Set**
Contains 12c, 23d, 27d, 42b, 45b, 56b, 68b, and Sports Boat on Trailer. Artwork on box ................**£250-300**
Same but in plain white box with red lettering............**£150-200**

**G 3** 1965 **Farming Set (King-Size and Major Models)**
1st issue (with rare components):
Detailed picture box with transit card contains:
M5 Combine Harvester (SPH, KBPW on rear axle),
M7 Thames Trader with KBPW, K3 Caterpillar Tractor with bare metal rollers, K11 Tractor and Trailer.
Orange metal hubs to both.....................................**£1,200-1,500**
2nd issue (with common components):
M5 Combine Harvester (Orange PH, SBPW on rear axle),
M7 Thames Trader with SBPW,
K3 Caterpillar Tractor with Red plastic rollers,
K11 Tractor and Trailer. Orange plastic hubs .............**£400-500**

**G 3** 1968 **Farm Set**
Contains 4d, 12c, 37d, 40c, 39c, 43c, 65c and 72b.......**£400-500**

**G 4** 60-61 **Farm Set**
(1st issue) M-7 Cattle Truck (GPW), 12b Land Rover (BPW), 23b Berkeley Caravan (Lime Green, GPW), 31b Ford (Met.Green/Pink/Maroon, SPW), 35a Horse Box (MW), 50a Commer (Lt.Brown, SPW), 72a Fordson (Orange rear hubs, GPW) ..................**£800-1,100**

(2nd issue) M-7 Cattle Truck (GPW), 12b Land Rover (BPW), 23c Bluebird Dauphine Caravan (Metallic Mauve, SPW), 31b Ford (Yellow, Maroon base, clear windows, SPW), 35a Horse Box (SPW), 50a Commer (SPW), 72a Fordson (Orange rear hubs, GPW) .......................**£350-400**

**G 4** 1963 **Grand Prix Set**
Contains 13c, 14c, 19c, 41b, 47b, 52a, 32b, 73b and Major Pack No.1, R-4 Racetrack, instructions.............**£350-450**

**G 4** 1965 **Grand Prix Racetrack Set**
13d, 19d Green, 19d Orange, 41c White, 41c Yellow, 52b Blue, 52b Red, 54b, Major Pack M-6 29c, 'BP Motor Racing' leaflet................................**£600-700**

**G 4** 1968 **Race 'n' Rally Set**
19d Orange, 19d Green, 52b Blue, 52b Red, 29d, 3c, 41c, 67b, 25d, 8e.....................................**£250-300**

**G 5** 60-61 **Military Vehicles**
Contains 54, 62, 63, 64, 67, 68 and M-3 ...........**£250-300**

**G 5** 1963 **Army Gift Set**
Contains 54a, 62a, 63a, 67a, 68a, 64a and Major Pack No.3....................................**£250-300**

**G 5** 1965 **Army Gift Set**
12, 49, 54, 61, 64, 67 and M-3 (picture box)...............**£250-300**

**G 5** 1965 **Fire Station Set**
Contains MG1 Fire Station, 29c, 54b and 59c...........**£900-1,200**

**G 6** 1965 **Commercial Trucks Set**
Usual contents (may vary): 6, 15, 16, 17, 26, 30, 58 and 62 ..............................................**£600-700**

**G 6** 1966 **Truck Set** 16c, 17d, 25c, 26b, 30c, 69b, 70b, 71b ......**£200-250**

**G 9** 1963 **Major Series Set**
Contains Major Packs 1, 2, 4 and 6................**£250-350**

**G9** ? **Commercial Vehicles Gift Set.** M1 - BPW, Silver rear trim, M2 - 'Davies Tyres' - Orange unit/rear doors, SBPW, M4 Excavator - Yellow side decals,  metal rollers, M6 Scammell - Maroon loadbed, colour picture box ...**£500-600**

**G 9** 1965 **Service Station Set**
Contains 13, 33, 71, A-1, MG-1 .................................**£300-350**

**G 10** 1963 **Service Station Set**
Service Station, 13c, 25b, 31b, and Accessory Pack No.1 ..........................................**£300-350**

**G 10** 1965 **Fire Station Set**
Contains MF-1, 14, 59, 2 of No.9 ..................**£300-350**

**FB 5** 1969 **Matchbox Traffic Game**
Contains two cars (No.45 Ford Corsair and No.56 Fiat 1500) plus game board, etc ........................**£175-200**

**?** ? **'GAF' Racing Car Game**
Belgian game set contains four 24d 'TEAM MATCHBOX' racing cars including the rare Metallic Blue and Yellow variants. Set issued by 'GAF', not by Matchbox..........**£300-400**

**TG 7037** **Gift Pack** (US issue)
MG1 'BP' Service Station (1st issue); R1 Layout; 3c Ambulance; 5d Bus ('BP' labels); 9d Cabin Cruiser; 'BP' Wreck Truck; 14d Iso Grifo; 23d Caravan; 29c Fire Pumper; 36c Opel; 'BP' Tanker; 34c VW Camper; 44c GMC Truck; Red and Yellow square 'GIFT PACK' box........**£500-600**

**?** ? **Display Set** (US issue for the Fred Bronner Corporation)
Contents: 26c GMC Tipper Truck; Leyland 'BP' Tanker; 45b Ford Corsair; 46c Mercedes 300SE Coupé; 68b Mercedes Coach. Contained in interlocking 'see-thru' display case, shrink-wrapped 'DISPLAY SET' box .........................**£400-500**

**?** 1969 **Display Set** (US issue)
12c, 24c, 30c, 46c, 47c. In plastic display case............**£300-400**

## 'King-Size' Gift Sets

| | | | |
|---|---|---|---|
| --- | 1963 | **King-Size Set**............K1-1, K2-1, K3-1, K5-1, K6-1 .......**£250-300** | |
| --- | 1965 | **Construction Set**......K16-1, K7-1, K10-1,K13-1,K14-1 ..**£200-300** | |

**G 3** 1965 **Farming Set (King-Size and Major Models)**
1st issue (with rare components): Detailed picture box with transit card contains: M5 Combine Harvester (SPH, KBPW on rear axle),  M7 Thames Trader with KBPW, K3 Caterpillar Tractor with bare metal rollers, K11 Tractor and Trailer. Orange metal hubs to both ............................................**£1,200-1,500**
2nd issue (with common components): M5 Combine Harvester (Orange PH, SBPW on rear axle),  M7 Thames Trader with SBPW, K3 Caterpillar Tractor with Red plastic rollers, K11 Tractor and Trailer. Orange plastic hubs .....................**£400-500**

**G8** 1965 **Commercials Set**
K1 Tipper, K11-1 Tractor, K12-1 BP Truck, K15-1 ..........**£200-250**

**G8** 1965 **Construction Set**
K1 Tipper, K7 Rear Dumper, K10 Shovel, K13 'Readymix', K14....................................**£300-350**

**G8** 19?? **King Size Models**
K-71 Rear Dumper, K-101 Tractor Shovel, K13-1 Concrete Truck, K14-1 Jumbo Crane and K1-2 Tipper Truck 'Hoveringham' .................................**£225-275**

--- 1966 **King-Size Set**............K11-1, K12-1, K15-1, K16-1 ..........**£200-300**

Following successful sales of Major Models, Lesney Products decided to further develop the range by introducing a larger scale toy. The name chosen was 'King-Size'. In 1966 the popular Major Models were discontinued in name but were themselves built into the King-Size range.   (TW = tinted windows)

| Model and details | MPR | Model and details | MPR | Model and details | MPR |
|---|---|---|---|---|---|

**K1-1** 60 **Hydraulic Shovel**
Yellow body, GPW,
'WEATHERILL' ...................... '£40-45

**K1-2** 63 **Foden Tipper Truck**
Red cab and chassis, Orange
tipper, 'HOVERINGHAM',
Green suspension....................... **£50-60**
White suspension .................. **£80-100**
NB 'HOVERINGHAM GRAVELS LTD'
issued models in their own outer
box to their customers ........... **£120-150**

**K1-3** 71 **'O & K' Excavator**
Red body, Silver shovel,
TW, BPT......................... **£40-50**

**K2-1** 60 **Dumper Truck**
Red body, 'MUIR HILL 14B',
Black or Green MW ................. **£40-50**

**K2-2** 64 **Dumper Truck**
Yellow body, 'KW DART' logo,
6 Red wheels, BPT ..................... **£40-50**

**K2-3** 68 **Scammell Wreck Truck**
White body, Red jib and wheels,
Grey hook, 'ESSO'.................... **£70-80**
71 Gold body version .................... **£40-50**

**K3-1** 60 **Caterpillar Bulldozer**
Yellow body, Red engine,
bare metal rollers ............. **£70-80**
Same but Red metal rollers ....... **£70-80**
Same but Yellow metal rollers ... **£70-80**
Same but Red plastic rollers... **£70-100**

**K3-2** 65 **'HATRA' Tractor Shovel**
Orange body, Red wheels.......... **£35-45**

**K3-3** 70 **'MASSEY FERGUSON'
Tractor and Trailer**
Red body, Yellow trim.............. **£60-70**

**K4-1** 60 **'McCORMICK
INTERNATIONAL' Tractor**
Red body, Green wheels ......... **£80-100**
Same but Red plastic hubs ........ **£60-80**
Large hook, Orange PH.......... **£150-175**

**K4-2** 67 **GMC Tractor and Hoppers
'FREUHOF'**
Dark Red cab, 2 Silver hoppers,
BPT, slide-tray box .................... **£40-50**
GPT, window box ................... **£100-120**

**K4-3** 69 **Leyland Tipper 'W. WATES'**
Maroon cab, Silver tipper......... **£70-80**
Same but Yellow/Green....... **£750-1,000**
Red cab, Green tipper .............. **£50-60**
Orange cab, Lime Green tipper.. **£80-90**
Same but Met. Green tipper ..... **£80-90**
Lime Green cab and tipper..... **£250-300**
Blue cab, Silver tipper, 'Miner'.. **£60-70**
With 'LE TRANSPORT' label... **£30-40**

**K5-1** 61 **Foden Dump Truck**
Orange Yellow body and tipper, Red
wheels, 'FODEN' logo.......... **£100-125**
Dark yellow cab,
Light yellow tipper............... **£120-140**

**K5-2** 67 **Racing Car Transporter**
Green body, Silver drop down
rear door, Red wheels................. **£55-65**

**K5-3** 70 **Tractor and Trailer 'MUIR HILL'**
Yellow body, Red chassis........... **£35-40**

**K6-1** 61 **Earth Scraper
'ALLIS CHALMERS'**
Orange body, bare metal hubs.... **£55-65**
Matt Orange, bare metal hubs ... **£55-65**
Bright Orange, bare metal hubs. **£55-65**

**K6-2** 67 **Mercedes Ambulance**
Off-White body, Red badge,
ambulance-man, stretcher.......... **£50-60**

**K7-1** 61 **Rear Dumper 'CURTISS-WRIGHT'**
Yellow body, Red engine............ **£45-50**

**K7-2** 67 **S&D Refuse Truck**
Red, decals, 1st window box..... **£60-70**
Red, labels, 2nd window box.... **£40-45**
72 Blue body version....................... **£60-70**

**K8-1** 62 **Prime Mover and Transporter
with Crawler Tractor 'LAING'**
Orange bodies, thick print 'Laing'
decals, bare metal hubs. With 'Laing'
'Civil Engineering Contractors' on
trailer, square door decals, Tractor
has bare metal rollers ............. **£150-200**
Large lettered 'Laing' decals, bare
metal hubs. With 'Laing', without
'Civil Engineering Contractors' on
trailer, rectangular door decals,
Tractor has bare metal rollers,
colour picture box.................. **£300-350**
With bare metal hubs, thin lettered
'Laing' decals and the Tractor has
red plastic rollers. colour box. **£120-140**
Thin lettered 'Laing' decals, red plastic
hubs and red plastic rollers.... **£240-280**

**K8-2** 67 **Guy Warrior Transporter
'FARNBOROUGH - MEASHAM'**
Turquoise/Orange, Orange PH ... **£40-50**
Yellow, Red PH ........................ **£40-50**
Dark Aqua cab, Yellow trailer. **£600-800**

**K8-3** 70 **'CATERPILLAR TRAXCAVATOR'**
Yellow body, Orange rams ..... **£175-200**
72 Silver body ........................ **£50-60**

**K9-1** **'AVELING BARFORD'
Diesel Road Roller** Green body,
Red wheels and Red driver ....... **£40-50**
Same, but with Grey driver ....... **£80-90**

**K9-2** 67 **'CLAAS' Combine Harvester**
Red body,
Yellow blades and wheels ......... **£60-70**
Green body, Red blades/wheels . **£60-70**

**K10-1** 63 **'AVELING BARFORD'
Tractor Shovel** Blue/Green body,
bare metal hubs, detailed picture
box with Red end flaps............. **£50-60**
Same but Red plastic hubs, late issue
box, picture on the end flaps.. **£150-175**

**K10-2** 66 **Pipe Truck**. Yellow body,
Red wheels, 6 Grey pipes........... **£45-65**
('Super-Kings' issue) Purple
body, Grey or Yellow pipes....... **£25-30**

**K11-1** 63 **'FORDSON SUPER MAJOR'
Tractor and Trailer**
Blue tractor, Grey/Blue trailer,
bare metal steering wheel ......... **£40-50**
With Blue metal steering wheel . **£80-90**

**K11-2** 69 **DAF Car Transporter**
Yellow body, Yellow/Red decks. **£60-70**
Metallic Blue body, Gold decks. **£60-70**

**K12-1** 63 **Foden Breakdown Truck**
Green, Silver grille/headlights,
'Matchbox Service Station' decal,
Red plastic hubs, window box . **£45-55**
Same but Silver grille only,
colour picture box.................... **£80-100**
Silver Grille only, bare metal
hubs, colour picture box............ **£60-70**

**K12-2** 69 **Scammell Crane Truck**
Yellow, 'LAING' on crane,
Red or Black plastic ram .......... **£40-50**
71 Silver body ................................ **£60-70**

**K13-1** 63 **ERF Concrete Truck
'READYMIX'**
Orange body and barrel,
bare metal or Red PH................. **£70-80**
Same but with 'RMC' logo ....... **£70-80**

**K14-1** 64 **Jumbo Crane**
Yellow body and crane,
'TAYLOR JUMBO CRANE',
Red or Yellow ballast box ......... **£40-45**

**K15-1** 64 **Merryweather Fire Engine**
Dark or Bright Red body, Silver ladder,
'KENT FIRE BRIGADE' ......... **£80-90**

**K16-1** 66 **Tractor and Twin Tippers**
Green cab, Yellow tippers,
'DODGE TRUCKS' in Red ....... **£80-90**
Yellow cab, Blue tippers,
same logo (Superfast)................ **£60-65**

**K17-1** 67 **Ford D800 Low Loader / Bulldozer**
Green cab /trailer, 'LAING', clear
plastic suspension, Red/Yellow 'Case'
Bulldozer (red or green plastic rollers),
'New Model' window box.......... **£50-75**

**K17-2** 71 Same but 'TAYLOR WOODROW'
with screwed baseplate, dozer has
Yellow plastic rollers. In tall
window box ................................ **£60-75**
Same but Light Blue plastic
suspension, short window box ... **£30-35**
Same but Yellow suspension,
pictorial window box................. **£65-75**
Same nut White suspension,
pictorial window box............. **£120-140**

**K18-1** 66 **Kew Fargo Articulated Horse Box**
'ASCOT STABLES', all versions
have Red cab, 4 White horses, and
were sold in window boxes.
Cream/Silver Trailer, Yellow / Grey
trailer interior, cab has decals,
labels on trailer,
'New Model' window box.......... **£70-80**
Grey or Red trailer interior....... **£70-80**
Green or Grey-Green interior..... **£45-55**

**K19-1** 67 **Scammell Tipper**
Red body, Yellow tipper,
Clear or Green suspension ........ **£30-40**

**K20-1** 68 **Ford D800 Tractor Transporter**
Red body, Yellow or Red tank, 3 Blue/
Yellow tractors (MB39c),
Clear or Green suspension ......... **£60-70**
Same but Orange tractors...... **£120-150**
71 Blue cab .............................. **£180-200**

**K21-1** 69 **Mercury Cougar**
Gold body, Cream or Red seats.. **£70-90**

**K22-1** 69 **Dodge Charger**
Blue body, Yellow or
Pale Blue seats........................... **£50-60**

**K23-1** 69 **Mercury 'POLICE' Car**
White, 'HIGHWAY PATROL'.... **£35-45**

**K24-1** 69 **Lamborghini Miura**
Red body, Cream seats .............. **£30-35**

# 'Super-Kings' and 'Speed-Kings' 1971 – 1980

After 1970 the 'King Size' range developed into the larger 'Super-Kings' Series. They were fitted with extra wide speed slick tyres.

During the period 1971-79 certain issues were sold as 'SPEED KINGS' and retailed in different coloured packaging. These have been identified in the listings by the abbreviation (**SPK**).

**Market Price Range.** In general 'Super-Kings' are not very collectable and most models may be purchased for **under £15**. However, a little more price information on some of the rarer items has been received since the previous Edition and this is shown where appropriate. We regret we are unable to provide more specific price information on the remainder at this time.
Further information on the rare issues and price levels would be welcomed.

K2 77 ***'24 HOUR'* Recovery** ..... **£25-35**
K3 74 **Mod Tractor / Trailer** .... **£25-35**
K3 74 **Grain Transporter**,
Green cab (German) ........ **£60-70**
74 Red, *'KELLOGGS'* ......... **£20-25**
K4 74 **Big Tipper**, blue/silver .... **£60-70**
K5 72 **Muir Hill Tractor and Trailer**, Yellow ............... **£25-30**
Blue (German) ................ **£60-70**
K6 76 **Cement Mixer**, blue ....... **£20-25**
K6 74 **Motor Cycle Transporter**,
*'HONDA'* ........................ **£30-35**
K7 73 **Transporter**,
*'TEAM MATCHBOX'* ...... **£30-35**
74 With 'Martini' labels ....... **£45-50**
K9 73 **Fire Tender** *'DENVER'* .. **£30-35**
K10 76 **Transporter**,
*'AUTO TRANSPORT'* ...... **£30-35**
K11 76 **Recovery Truck**,
*'SHELL RECOVERY'* ..... **£50-60**
76 Recovery Truck in Red .... **£70-80**
K12 75 **Hercules** *'LAING'* Crane **£50-60**
K13 71 **Building Transporter**,
'DAF' .............................. **£30-35**
K13 76 **Aircraft Transporter** ..... **£60-70**
K14 71 **Scammell Freight** *'LEP'*. **£50-60**
K14 77 **Breakdown Truck**,
*'SHELL'* .......................... **£50-60**
K15 71 **Merryweather Fire Engine**, *KENT'* ............... **£30-40**

K15 73 **Londoner Bus issues**.
*'HARRODS - ENTER A DIFFERENT WORLD'* .... **£40-50**
*'CARNABY STREET'* ...... **£40-50**
*'SILVER JUBILEE'*, ........ **£40-50**
*'HARRODS - MORE THAN MONEY'*. **£40-50**
*'LONDON DUNGEON'* .. **£40-50**
*'HAMLEYS'* .................... **£40-50**
*'ROYAL WEDDING 81'* .. **£40-50**
*'LONDON WIDE TOUR'* **£40-50**
*'TELEGRAPH&ARGUS'* **£40-50**
*'MACLEANS* .................. **£40-50**
*'HERITAGE OF ENGLAND'* ..................... **£40-50**
*'BUTTERKIST'* ............... **£40-50**
*'TOURIST LONDON'* ..... **£40-50**
*'FIRESTONE'* ................. **£40-50**
*'CHESTERFIELD 1984'*. **£40-50**
*'LONDON PLANETARIUM'* ........... **£40-50**
*'PETTICOAT LANE'* ....... **£40-50**
*'NESTLES MILKY BAR'*. **£40-50**

K16 74 **Ford LTS Tanker**,
*'TEXACO', 'CHEMCO', 'LEP', 'ARAL', 'SHELL', 'EXXON', TOTAL', 'QUAKER STATE'*
*'U.S. M/BOX CLUB'* ....... **£20-30**
75 With 'BP' labels ........... **£200-300**
K16 **Dodge Tractor**,
Yellow/Blue tippers ......... **£80-90**

K17 **Container Truck**
*'DBP', 'PENGUIN', '7 UP', 'GENTRANSCO'*. **£30-50**
*'TAYLOR WOODROW'* ... **£60-70**
K18 74 **Tipper Truck**
*'TARMAC', 'US STEEL', 'HOCH & TIEF'* ............ **£30-40**
K19 79 **Security Truck**
*'GROUP 4', 'FORT KNOX'* ................ **£30-40**
K20 73 **Cargo Hauler** ................ **£30-35**
K20 79 **Peterbilt**
*'HEAVY DUTY'* .............. **£30-35**
K21 71 **Cougar Dragster** (SPK). **£20-30**
K21 74 **Tractor Transporter** ...... **£30-40**
K21 79 **Ford Transcontinental**
*'CONTINENTAL', 'DANZAS', 'POLARA', 'SUNKIST'* ... **£30-35**
K22 71 **Dodge Dragster** (SPK) ... **£20-30**
K22 74 **Hovercraft**,
'SEASPEED' .................. **£30-40**
'HOVERLLOYD' ........... **£30-40**
All-white ......................... **£40-50**

K23 71 **Mercury *'POLICE'* Car**,
(SPK) ............................. **£20-30**
K23 74 **Low Loader**,
*'HOCH & TIEF'* ........... **£30-40**
K24 71 **Lamborghini Muira** ....... **£20-30**
K24 77 **Scammel Truck**
*'LONDON TO GENEVA'* **£30-40**
*'MICHELIN'* .................. **£30-40**
*'GENTRANSCO'* ............ **£30-40**
*'BAUKNECT'* .................. **£30-40**
K25 77 **Powerboat and Trailer**
*'SEABURST'* .................. **£30-35**
*'CHRYSLER'* .................. **£30-35**
K25 78 **Digger**, 'MUIR HILL' ..... **£20-30**

K26 71 **Mercedes Ambulance**
(SPK) ............................. **£30-40**
K26 78 **Bedford Cement Truck**
*'McALPINE' 'HOCH & TIEF'* ............ **£30-40**
K27 71 **Camping Cruiser** .......... **£20-30**
K27 78 **Powerboat Transporter**
*'EMBASSY'* .................... **£40-50**
*'MISS SOLO'* .................. **£40-50**
K28 71 **Drag Pack** (SPK) ........... **£25-35**
K28 78 **Bedford Skip Truck**
*'HOCH & TIEF'* ............ **£25-35**
*'HALES'* ......................... **£25-35**
K29 71 **Muira *'SEABURST'* Set**,
(SPK) ............................. **£25-35**
K29 77 **Ford Delivery Van**,
*'U-HAUL', 'AVIS', 'TAA', 'Mr SOFTY', 'BASSETTS'* ..................... **£30-35**
K30 72 **Mercedes C111** ............... **£20-30**
K30 78 **Unimog/Compressor** ...... **£20-30**
K31 72 **Bertone Runabout**
(SPK) ............................. **£20-30**
K31 78 **Peterbilt Refrigeration Truck**
*'CHRISTIAN SALVESON', 'BURGER KING', 'IGLOO', 'GERVAIS GLACE', PEPSI', 'DR KOCH'S TRINK', 'DURA PENTA'* (S. African) ...... **£30-40**
K32 71 **Shovel Nose** .................... **£20-30**
K33 78 **Cargo Hauler** ................ **£20-30**
K34 72 **Thunderclap** (SPK) ........ **£20-30**
K34 79 **Pallet Truck** .................. **£20-30**
K35 72 **Lightning** (SPK) ............ **£20-30**
K35 79 **Massey Ferguson Tractor and Trailer** .................... **£50-75**
K36 72 **Bandolero** (SPK) ........... **£20-30**
K36 78 ***'LAING'* Transporter** .... **£40-50**
K37 73 **Sandcat** (SPK) ............... **£20-30**
K37 79 **Leyland Tipper**
***'LAING'*** ........................ **£30-40**
K38 74 **Gus's Gulpher** (SPK) ..... **£20-30**
K39 73 ***'MILLIGANS MILL'***
(SPK) ............................. **£20-30**
K40 73 **Blaze Trailer**
*'FIRE CHIEF'* (SPK) ..... **£25-35**
K41 73 **Fuzz Buggy**
*'POLICE'* (SPK) ............ **£25-35**
K41 78 **Brabham F1** (SPK) ........ **£20-30**
K42 73 **Nissan 270X** (SPK) ......... **£20-30**
K42 79 **Traxcavator Road Ripper** ............................ **£20-30**
K43 73 ***'CAMBUSTER'*** (SPK) ... **£20-30**
K44 73 ***'BAZOOKA'*** (SPK) ......... **£20-30**
K44 78 **Surtees F1** ...................... **£20-30**
K45 73 **Marauder** (SPK) ............ **£20-30**
K46 74 **Racing Car pack**
with K34 and K35 .......... **£35-45**
K47 73 **Easy Rider Trike** (SPK). **£30-40**
K48 74 **Mercedes 350**, (SPK) ...... **£20-30**
K49 73 **Ambulance** (SPK) ........... **£20-30**
K49 74 ***'MALTESER'* Truck** ...... **£20-30**
K50 74 **Street Rod** (SPK) ........... **£20-30**
K51 73 **Barracuda** (SPK) ........... **£20-30**
K52 73 **Datsun Rally** (SPK) ........ **£20-30**
K53 76 **Hot Fire Engine** (SPK) .. **£20-30**
K54 76 **AMX Javelin** (SPK) ....... **£20-30**

K55 76 **Corvette**
*'CAPER CART'* (SPK) ... **£20-30**
K56 76 **Maserati Bora** (SPK) ..... **£20-30**
K57 76 **Javelin Drag Racing Set**,
K38 & K39 (SPK) .......... **£30-40**
K58 76 **Corvette Power Boat Set**,
K45 etc. (SPK) .............. **£30-40**
K59 76 **Ford Capri II** (SPK) ...... **£30-40**
K60 76 **Ford Mustang** (SPK) ..... **£20-30**
K61 76 **Mercedes *'POLICE'***
(SPK) ............................. **£20-30**
78 **Mercedes *'POLIZEI'***
(SPK) ............................. **£20-30**
K62 77 **Doctors Car** (SPK) ......... **£20-30**
K63 77 **Mercedes 'Binz'**
*'AMBULANCE'* (SPK) ... **£20-30**
K64 78 ***'FIRE CONTROL'***
Range Rover (SPK) ......... **£20-30**
K65 78 **Plymouth Mountain Rescue**
*'EMERGENCY RESUCE'* ........................ **£50-60**
*'BERGRETTUNG WACHT'* ........................ **£50-60**
K66 79 **Jaguar *'POLICE'* Set** .... **£20-30**
K67 78 **Dodge Monaco** (SPK)
i) *'FIRE CHIEF'* ............ **£20-30**
ii) *'HACKENSACK'* ........ **£20-30**
K68 78 **Dodge Monaco and Trailer** (SPK) ................ **£30-40**
K69 78 **Jaguar XJ12 and Caravan** (SPK) ............. **£40-50**
K70 79 **Porsche Turbo** ............... **£20-30**
K71 79 **Porsche *'POLIZEI'* Set** . **£20-30**
K72 79 **Brabham F1**,
Red or Green .................. **£20-30**
K73 79 **Surtees F1**,
White or Tan .................. **£20-30**
K74 79 **Volvo Estate** ................... **£20-30**
K75 79 **Airport *'FIRE'* Rescue**
*'AIRPORT FIRE TENDER'* ...................... **£20-30**
*'FLUGHAFEN-FEURWEHR'* ................. **£20-30**
*'SECURITE AEROPORT'* .................. **£20-30**
K76 79 **Volvo Rally Set** 'CIBIE'. **£20-30**
K77 79 **Rescue Vehicle**
*'STRASSEN SERVICE'* .... **£20-30**
*'SECOURS ROUTIER'* ... **£20-30**
*'HIGHWAY RESCUE'* ..... **£20-30**
K78 79 **US Police Car**, *POLICE', 'POLIZEI'* or *'CITY POLICE'* ............. **£20-30**
K79 79 **US Taxi** ........................... **£20-30**

## 'Battle-Kings', 1974

Models packed in 'window' boxes. Each has a 'military' theme and includes three plastic soldiers. Expect to pay **£20-25** for any of these items.

**K101 Sherman Tank** ..........
**K102 M48 AS Tank** ............
**K103 Chieftain Tank** ..........
**K104 King Tiger Tank** .......
**K105 Hover Raider** ............
**K106 Tank Transporter** ......
**K107 155mm Gun** .............
**K108 Half Track** ................
**K109 Sheridan Tank** ..........
**K110 Recovery Vehicle** ......
**K111 Missile Launcher** ......
**K112 DAF Ambulance** .......
**K113 Crane Truck** ............
**K114 Army Aircraft Transporter** .............
**K115 Petrol Tanker** ...........
**K116 Troop Carrier and Howitzer**
**K117 Rocket Launcher** ......
**K118 Army Helicopter** ......

## 'Sea-Kings', 1976

These models were packed in 'window' boxes. Expect a Market Price of **£12-18** for any of these 'Sea-Kings'.

**K301 Frigate 'F109'** ...........
**K302 Corvette 'C70'** ..........
**K303 Battleship '110'** ........
**K304 Aircraft Carrier with 4 aircraft '36'** ...
**K305 Submarine Chaser**
**K306 Convoy Escort** ..........
**K307 Helicopter Carrier** ...
**K308 Missile Destroyer** .....
**K309 Submarine '117'** .......
**K310 Anti Air Carrier** .......

## 'Big MX', 1972 -74

Special packaging contained models and accessories powered by an 'Activator Gun' which plugged into them and operated the mechanisms.

**MX1 Incinerator Site** + K7 Refuse Truck ..... **£50-70**
**BM2 Mechanised Tractor Plant** Transporter (K20-1 Ford), blue/yellow MB39c Tractors ........... **£70-80**
with Orange MB39c Tractors ........ **£175-225**
**BM3 Mechanised** (K12 Scammell) **Crane Truck** and Building Site .................. **£50-70**
**BM4 Mechanised Coal Delivery Hopper** and (K4 Leyland) Tipper .............. **£50-70**
**BM5 Mechanised Quarry Site** and (K8, silver/red) Traxcavator ...... **£40-50**
**BM6 Fire Rescue Scene** with mechanised (K15 Merryweather) Fire Engine plus 4 figures and scenery ........ **£120-140**

## "MATCHBOX" SERIES KING SIZE K-5 to K-7

K-7 Curtiss-Wright Rear Dumper
*Length 5¼ ins. 145 mm. 74-1. OO Scale*

K-5 Foden Tipper Truck
*Length 4¼ ins. 108 mm. 74-1. OO Scale*

K-6 Allis-Chalmers Earth Scraper
*Length 5¾ ins. 149 mm. 70-1. OO Scale*

## "MATCHBOX" SERIES KING SIZE K-8 to K-11

K-9 Diesel Road Roller
*Length 3¾ ins. 95 mm. 57-1. O Scale*

K-10 Aveling-Barford Tractor Shovel
*Length 4¼ ins. 105 mm. 62-1*

K-11 Fordson Tractor and Farm Trailer
*Length 6¼ ins. 158 mm. 42-1*

K-8 Prime Mover and Transporter
with Caterpillar Tractor
*Length 12½ ins. 318 mm. 70-1. OO Scale*

| Item and details | MPR |
|---|---|

**1956** **Counter Display.** Wood and card, yellow shelves, dark blue/yellow headboard 'MATCHBOX SERIES', '1/8d each' plus red 5a Double-Decker Bus. Will display all 1-75 models ............................. **£700-800**

**1960** **Counter Display.** Card, yellow shelves, dark blue headboard, 'MATCHBOX SERIES' in yellow, '1/9d' plus 85a Jaguar 3.4 in red............................ **£200-250**

**1965** **'King-Size' carded Counter Display.** Showing K16 Dodge Tractor model. Yellow/red/white .......................... **£200-300**

**1965** **Carded Counter Display Stand.** 'MATCHBOX' King-Size. White shelves, dark blue surround 'Die Cast Metal - Authentic Scale Models'. Holds K1 - K18. (US Fred Bronner issue) .............. **£200-300**

**Late 1960s** **'MATCHBOX' Illuminated Display Sign.** Finished in yellow/red/blue (270 x 100 x 120mm) .................. **£400-500**

**1962** **Card Display Stand.** Wood frame. Displays complete Regular Wheels range. Dark blue/yellow headboard with yellow stepped dislay area. 'MATCHBOX SERIES' '1/9'. Features 65b Jaguar 3.8 ...... **£250-350**

**1967** **Card Display Stand.** Displays complete Regular Wheels range. 'MATCHBOX NOS. 1 – 75', flyover design........ **£200-250**

**1967** **Plastic Revolving Display Unit.** Red/Yellow/White. Designed to display all 75 Regular Wheels models ..... **£200-250**

## FRED BRONNER CORP. U.S. ISSUES (1-75)
**1955** **Card Display Stand.** Pale Blue with Black lettering. Features first 12 models plus Miniature Covered Wagon............ **£400-500**

**--** **Display Unit.** 1950/60s, holds 75 models at '55c each' ..... **£800-900**

**1961** **Card Display Stand** for 'MATCHBOX SERIES Major Packs and Accessory Packs' which contains models A1 - A4, and M1 - M8. Dark Blue/Yellow/Red headboard features Major Pack 4 Ruston Bucyrus Excavator ..................................... **£600-800**
Stand without the models ............ **£250-350**

**1963** **Card Display Stand.** 'MILITARY MATCHBOX SERIES'. Green/Orange headboard, beige stepped display area containing actual models M3, 12b, 49a, 54a, 61a, 63a, 64a 67a, 68a ....... **£900-1,100**
Display stand without models......**£250-350**

**1964** **Aluminium Display Stand.** 'MATCHBOX SERIES' in Red. Features 53b Mercedes 220SE Coupé ............................... **£250-350**

| Item and details | MPR |
|---|---|

**1965** **Card Display Stand.** 'AUTHENTIC MATCHIES', '49c EACH'.......... **£200-250**

**1966** **Card Display Stand.** 'AUTHENTIC MATCHIES', '55c EACH'.......... **£200-250**

**1967** **Wood Framed Display Stand** to display complete range. Red 'MATCHBOX SERIES', black/white 'NOS. 1-75'............... **£200-250**

**1968** **Card Display Stand.** Dark blue/red with yellow shelving. Features Red 53b Mercedes 220SE Coupé. 'MATCHLESS 'MATCHBOX SERIES'................ **£350-450**

**1968** **Card Dispenser Stand** for 24 models, Red/Yellow/Blue 'MATCHBOX', 'ONLY 55c EACH'....................... **£200-250**

**1968** **Card Display Stand** containing the complete 1 – 75 range. Red/Yellow/Blue with White shelving, 'MATCHLESS MATCHBOX SERIES'.......... **£1,200-1,400**
Display Stand without models ...... **£300-400**

**1968** **Card Counter Display.** Holds all 1-75 Regular Wheels issues. 'MATCHLESS MATCHBOX SERIES' on dark blue headboard plus red 85a Jaguar 3.4. Yellow shelves with red surround 'Ask For Free Catalogue', '55c' **£700-1,000**

## WEST GERMAN ISSUES
**58-60** **Single Model Counter Display.** (German). Yellow/blue/red card stand 'MATCHBOX AUTOS' with 44a Rolls-Royce. 'Neuigkeiten Dieses Monats'........ **£400-500**

**1960** **Card Counter Display.** 5 tiers, yellow/dark blue 'MATCHBOX SERIES' in yellow, '1 DM' .......... **£300-400**

## ITALIAN ISSUE
**1968** **Vac-form Display Stand.** Yellow/Red/Black withwhite shelving 'BARAVELLI MATCHBOX BARAVELLI' ............................. **£150-200**

## MODELS OF YESTERYEAR U.K. ISSUES
**1965** **Wooden Counter Display.** Red letters with Yellow shelves designed to display Models of Yesteryear 1 – 16, King Size 1 – 15 and Major Pack models 1 - 6. 'MATCHBOX' in Red plus 'NEW RELEASES' ...................... **£400-500**

**56-60** **Card Display Stand.** 'Models of Yesteryear SERIES'. Dark Blue/Red/Yellow headboard, yellow display area designed to display 1st Series models Y1 - Y9 inclusive ............ **£400-600**

| Item and details | MPR |
|---|---|

**56-60** **Card Display Stand.** 'Models of Yesteryear SERIES'. Dark Blue/Red/Yellow headboard, yellow 'stepped' area to display models Y1 - Y15 inclusive. 'A LESNEY PRODUCT' in red letters............. **£500-700**

**c.1960** **Card Display Stand.** Red/Yellow/Blue with four shelves designed to display models Y1 - Y16 inclusive. 'MATCHBOX' in red letters ........ **£250-300**

**c1966** **Card Display Stand.** Big Ben and a Packard Landaulet are featured on headboard. Displays Y1-Y16. 'MATCHBOX'.............................. **£200-250**

**c1968** Gold/White **Plastic Wall Display Unit** in the shape of a radiator grille - shelves contain Y1-Y16 models, 'MATCHBOX' in black letters .... **£275-325**
Display Unit without models ........ **£100-125**

**1970s** 924276 **Plastic Display Case** for Y1-Y16 'MATCHBOX MODELS OF YESTERYEAR' in top panel. Gold/cream vac-formed, clear perpex front ...... **£80-100**

## FRED BRONNER CORP. U.S. ISSUES (MoY)
**c1958** **Card Display Stand.** Containing 1st Series models Y1 - Y15. Dark Blue/Yellow/Red headboard design which features a Y13 Sante Fe Locomotive emerging from a 1st type box ........................... **£800-1,000**
Stand without the models ............ **£300-400**

**c1960** **Card Display Stand** containing 2nd Series models Y1- Y16. Dark Blue surround featuring a Red Y15 Rolls-Royce emerging from a 2nd type box, yellow shelving 'MATCHBOX'............................. **£450-650**
Stand without the models ............ **£200-300**

**c1956-60** **Card Display Stand.** Models of Yesteryear SERIES'. Dark Blue/Red/Yellow headboard, yellow display area designed to display 1st Series models Y1 - Y9 inclusive ............ **£400-600**

**c1967** **Card Display Stand** containing models Y1-16. Yellow/Red/ Blue design which features a White Y4 Opel Coupé. 'MATCHBOX' 'START YOUR COLLECTION NOW'................ **£300-400**
Stand without the models ............ **£150-200**

## KING-SIZE Sales Aids
**King-Size Shop Display.** 1960s showing K16 Dodge Tractor......... **£250-300**
**'Fred Bronner' King-Size.** US freestanding unit, No.s K1 - K18 . **£400-500**

# Miscellaneous Matchbox items

## Folded Card Layouts
contained inside a paper sleeve.

**No.1**   **Roadway Layout** 1st issue. In 'A Lesney Moko' picture paper sleeve........... **£125-150**

**R1**   **Roadway Layout** 2nd issue. In 'A Lesney' paper sleeve, b/w illustration....... **£125-150**

**R1**   **Roadway Layout** 3rd issue with flyover picture in 'A Lesney Product' detailed colour picture paper sleeve........... **£140-160**

**R1**   **Roadway Layout** 4th issue. 'New Foldaway Flyover' in detailed colour picture paper sleeve............. **£75-100**

**R2**   **Roadway Layout** 1st issue. 'London' layout in 'A Lesney' paper sleeve **£125-150**

**R2**   **Building Construction Site** Early 1st type issue in detailed colour picture sleeve....................... **£75-100**

**R2**   **Building Construction Site** Later 2nd type issue in detailed colour picture sleeve with yellow side panel........ **£75-100**

**R3**   **'London Famous Landmarks' Layout** In 'A Lesney' paper sleeve ............... **£50-75**

**R3**   **'Foldaway Farm' Layout** In detailed colour picture sleeve....... **£50-75**

**R4**   **'Racetrack/Speedway' Layout** In 'A Lesney' paper sleeve, b/w picture. **£100-125**

**R5**   **'Grand Prix Race Track' Layout** Late issue detailed colour picture paper sleeve.................................. **£100-125**

## Collector's Carrying Cases
All are made of vinyl. The US issues were produced on license by the Fred Bronner Corporation.

**1965**   Has picture of 41c Ford GT40, holds 48 models ..................... **£15-20**

**1965**   Pictures of 53b Mercedes and 6c Euclid, holds 40 models. US issue . **£80-100**

**1966**   Pictures of 19d Lotus and 32b Jaguar, holds 48 models............. **£60-80**

**1966**   Garage and Service Station Carrying Case with picture showing boy/E-type/garage. US issue............. **£60-80**

**1967**   Has picture of 8e Ford Mustang, holds 18 models. Lesney issue ..........NGPP

**1968**   Has illustration of a green car with red interior, holds 72 models. US issue .. **£60-80**

**1969**   Pictures of 14d Iso Grifo, 51c AEC Tipper and 53c Ford Zodiac. Holds 24 models ...............................NGPP

**1969**   Pictures of 6d Ford Pickup, 14d Iso Grifo and 62c Mercury Cougar. Holds 24 models. US issue ................NGPP

## Matchbox Jig-Saw Puzzles
These jig-saw puzzles each feature a Matchbox model.

| | | |
|---|---|---|
| 29c | Fire Pumper | **£10-15** |
| 31c | Lincoln Continental | **£10-15** |
| 34c | VW Transporter Camper | **£10-15** |
| 35b | Snow-Trac | **£10-15** |
| 39c and 40c | Ford Tractor and Hay Trailer | **£10-15** |
| 62c | Mercury Cougar (dark green) | **£10-15** |
| 62c | Mercury Cougar (light green) | **£10-15** |
| 66b | Greyhound Bus | **£10-15** |
| 72b | Standard Jeep | **£10-15** |

## Matchbox Book
**Collector's Matchbox Book**
'Matchbox 1-75 Regular Wheels'.
Collector's ringbound book by
Michael Stannard ...........................................NGPP

---

## 'Matchbox' Series Painting Books

Four different types of cover and contents numbered 1 to 4.
Mint unused set of books.........................................................................**£2,000-3,000**

---

## Lincoln Industries 'Matchbox Series'

Collectors should be aware that a range of models exists which were made in New Zealand and which at first sight appear to be Matchbox Miniatures. The packaging in particular is strikingly similar to early Lesney Matchbox boxes, even to the extent of having 'MATCHBOX SERIES' printed in a banner as on the Lesney boxes.

It seems that the makers, Lincoln Industries, were so taken with the Lesney idea of 'a model in a matchbox' that they were tempted to capitalise on it by adopting it themselves. 'Lincoln Industries Ltd' and 'Made in New Zealand' are also clearly marked on the boxes so confusion should be avoidable. The

models are a little cruder than genuine Matchbox products and all seem to have metal wheels. They are nevertheless collectable and include: a Utility Truck, Breakdown Truck, Large Parcels Van, Ambulance, and a sports car resembling a Jaguar XK120 (see illustration).

These auction results were achieved by Vectis Auctions Ltd. in July 2000:

| | | | |
|---|---|---|---|
| **4506** | **Coach** | Green body | **£170** |
| **4509** | **Ambulance** | Red cross on roof | **£140** |
| **4510** | **Jaguar XK120** | Cream, with driver | **£560** |

The Editor would welcome more details of these products.

'Matchbox Series' Miniature Metal Vehicles by Lincoln Industries, New Zealand.

# Matchbox Catalogues

1957 **Folded Leaflet**
Yellow cover has Blue edging and depicts
No.1 Diesel Roller. Colour pictures
of nos. 1 - 42 of '1-75'series .......... **£140-180**

1957 **Folded Leaflet**
Blue/Yellow cover featuring MOY No.1
Allchin 7hp Traction Engine
1st series box. Contents list
first nine Yesteryears ..................... **£180-200**

1958 **16-page catalogue**
Cover shows Rolls-Royce (44)
emerging from box. Models 1 - 60 in
colour inside, early 'Major Packs'
and Accessory Packs ..................... **£100-125**

1959 **Leaflet**
'Everyone buys MATCHBOX TOYS by
LESNEY'. Blue with line drawings.
Gives details of Presentation and
Gift Sets ..................................... **£200-300**

1959 **Folded Leaflet**
First 14 Yesteryears in colour ......... **£100-125**

1959 **16-page catalogue**
Same cover as 1958 catalogue with
'1959 Edition'. Lists 1-75's, Major Packs
and accessories. Colour pictures ..... **£85-100**

1959 **24-page catalogue**
'UK' and '2d' on cover with MOY No.9,
1-75 series, No.'43', and Accessory No.'2'.
Colour contents show MB 1 - 72 and
MoY 1 - 14 plus Accessories
and Major Packs. ......................... **£85-100**

1960 **32-page catalogue**
'UK' and '3d' on cover featuring logo
*'ALL THE MATCHBOX POCKET
TOYS BY LESNEY'* plus semi-circle
picture of MoY and 1-75's.
Contents illustrate all ranges ............ **£80-100**

1961 **32-page catalogue**
*'International Pocket Catalogue'* on cover
with picture of 1-75 series No.5 Bus. New
style smaller catalogue listing all issues in
colour plus International price list...... **£70-80**

1962 **20-page catalogue**
'2d', *'International Pocket Catalogue'* and
*'1962 Edition'* on cover. All issues listed,
European price list included.............. **£50-60**

1963 **20-page catalogue**
No.53 Mercedes-Benz printed on cover
with '2d' and *'1963 Edition'*. Good
Gift Set pictures and listings ............. **£40-50**

1964 **32-page catalogue**
'3d' on cover depicting Blue Mk.10 Jaguar
(No.28). *'1964 Matchbox Prices'* on back
cover. Contents include superb Gift
Set pictures and listings..................... **£40-50**

1965 **32-page catalogue**
Cover features Motor Racing Cars. *'1965
Matchbox Prices'* on back cover.
Excellent full colour Gift Set
pictures. (Price 3d) ....................... **£20-25**

1965 **US Trade Catalogue.**
Fred Bronner's..................................... **£45-65**

1966 **40-page catalogue**
London scene and *'Price 3d'* on cover.
Excellent pictures of mid-sixties
Gift Sets plus history of Matchbox .... **£20-25**

1966 **40-page catalogue**
International issue............................... **£45-55**

1966 **Sales Promotion Guide**
Multi Language Colour Guide ....... **£125-150**

1967 **40-page catalogue**
Cover shows flags and 1-75 issues,
*'Price 3d'*. Contents list and
depict Veteran Car Gifts. ................. **£20-25**

1968 **40-page catalogue**
1968 car picture and *'Price 3d'* on
cover. Includes details of
manufacturing processes ................... **£20-25**

1969 **48-page catalogue**
Cover features Motorway scene.
Contents include detailed history of
real cars making up the MoY range ... **£12-15**
2nd edition: The 2nd edition of the 1969
catalogue including first reference to
*'Superfast'* issues.......................... **£12-15**

1969 **'MATCHBOX' Selector Chart.**
Two-sided leaflet with the complete
range of Matchbox products.............. **£40-50**

1970 **64-page catalogue**
Only drawings of models (no photographs)
throughout. Superfast track featured.
'6d', *'MATCHBOX SUPERFAST'*
and a collage of models on cover......... **£8-10**

1971 **64-page catalogue**
'24p' on Blue/Red cover with scorpion
design. 'Speed Kings' listed plus
pictures of first Superfast Gift Sets ..... **£8-10**

1972 **72-page catalogue**
Yellow *'MATCHBOX'* and '3p' on
cover. Contents feature launch of
'Scream'n Demon' bikes and
excellent Gift Set pictures ................... **£8-10**

1973 **80-page catalogue**
'5p' and '1973' on cover of the largest
Matchbox catalogue produced. Contents
include good 'Super Kings' and
Aircraft Kit listing ............................... **£8-10**

1974 **64-page catalogue**
'2p' and '1974' on cover. Includes
first 'SKYBUSTERS' listing.................. **£5-8**

1975 **64-page catalogue**
'2p' and '1975' on cover. Contents feature
'Rolamatics' and 'Battle Kings' ............. **£5-8**

1976 **64-page catalogue**
'1976' on cover. Feature 'Sea Kings' plus
'Baby Dolls' and 'Disco Girl Dolls'....... **£5-8**

1977 **80-page catalogue**
'1977' on cover. Contents list the 'Two
Pack' (TP) range of 1-75's. Good Gift
Set pictures and listings of 1-75's ......... **£5-8**

1978 **64-page catalogue**
'1978' on cover. Good 'SKYBUSTERS'
and 1-75 Gift Set pictures ...................... **£5-8**

79-80 **80-page catalogue**
'5p' and '1979-80' on cover. The contents
feature good pictures of Gift Sets G1 - G8.
'900' TP series introduced...................... **£5-8**

80-81 **80-page catalogue**
'5p' on cover. All ranges listed inc. 'Walt
Disney' and 'Power Track' equipment ... **£4-6**

81-82 **64-page catalogue**
'5p' and '1981-82' on cover. 'Adventure
2000' space models pictured. 'Playtrack',
'Popeye' and 'Streak Sets' listed........... **£4-6**

82-83 **64-page catalogue**
'1982-83' on cover. 'Convoy' series
introduced, good MoY pictures............. **£2-4**

1984 **64-page catalogue**
'1984' on cover. 'MATCHBOX SPECIALS'
introduced, 'Burnin' Key Cars', 'Rough
Riders' and 'Lock Ups' ........................ **£2-4**

1985 **48-page catalogue**
'1985' and 'chequered flag' design on cover.
All ranges + introduction of 'Trickshifters',
'Power Blasters', 'Matchmates'
and 'Carry Cases'. (Printed in Italy) ..... **£2-4**

1986 **48-page catalogue**
'1986' on cover. 'High Riders',
'Twin-Pack', 'Action Packs' listed
inside. 'Motor City' introduced............. **£2-4**

1987 **72-page catalogue**
'1987' on cover. Includes 'Superfast
Lasers', 'Pocket Rockets', 'Speed Riders',
'Streak Racing', 'Hot Rod Racers',
'Turbo 2' and 'Demolition Cars'............ **£2-4**

1988 **88-page catalogue**
'1988' on cover. Includes Miniatures
Gift Sets pictures, 'Lasers', 'Super GT
Sport' and 'Super Miniatures', 'Team
Convoy', 'Road Blasters', 'Motor City'
and 'Action Matchbox'. Also includes
'MICA' and 'Junior Matchbox Club'
membership details................................ **£2-4**

1989 **80-page catalogue**
'1989' on cover. Include 'Miniatures',
'Twin-Pack', 'Motor City' Gift Sets,
'Dinky Collection', 'Conn-Nect-Ables',
'Flashbacks', 'Super ColourChangers'
and 'Skybusters ColourChangers'.......... **£2-4**

---

## Overseas Catalogue Editions

During the 1960s there were normally six editions of each catalogue:
British, International, U.S.A., German, French and French-Canadian. These
were usually of the same format as UK editions but with the appropriate
language and currency. 'INTERNATIONAL CATALOGUE' was shown on
the front cover together with the edition, e.g. 'EDITION FRANCAISE',
'INTERNATIONAL' or 'U.S.A. EDITION'.
The 1960 'International Pocket Catalogue' listed the national prices for every
product in Australia, Austria, Belgium, Spain, Denmark, Eire, France, Germany,
Great Britain, Holland, Hong Kong, Italy, Kenya and East Africa, Singapore
and Malaysia, South Africa, Sweden and Switzerland. From 1972 the country-
specific editions only listed the model range available in that country.

**Market Price Range** Prices are equivalent to those asked for UK editions.

## Other Matchbox literature

**'Mike and The Modelman'** (1st edition 1970), was a childrens' book issued
by Lesney telling the Matchbox story.
A copy in perfect condition should cost between **£50 - £60**.

**Trade Catalogues** have been published for many years and occasionally
become available for sale. Those before 1970 are scarce and no price
information is possible at present. Those from the 1970-80 period tend to be
in the region of £15-20 while post-1980 editions sell for £5-10 depending on
content and condition.

| Model and details | MPR | Model and details | MPR | Model and details | MPR |
|---|---|---|---|---|---|

This listing refers to Superfast models produced between 1969 and 1983. In this period, most models in the range were presented in picture boxes with some variations being sold in Twin Packs and carded 'bubble packs'. The 'cut-off point' for many collectors of these Matchbox Miniatures is 1983 when picture boxes ceased. 'See-through' window boxes sealed at both ends were then introduced.

All the models listed have 'Made in England' bases. Those with Macau', 'China', 'Thailand' or elsewhere are too numerous to mention and are outside the scope of this listing. There are also many wheel variations for the models listed, such as 5-spoke, 4-spoke, 'dot-dash' etc., but again, only specific wheel variations such as hub colour are noted. Due to limitations of space, it has been necessary to introduce the use of the following abbreviations into the listing. These have been mainly restricted to indicate colour of bases and window glazing.

| Windows | Base colour |
|---|---|
| AG = amber glass | BB = black base |
| BG = blue glass | GB = grey base |
| CG = clear glass | PB = purple base |
| GG = green glass | SB = silver base |
| OG = orange glass | UB = unpainted base |
| PG = purple glass | WB = white base |
| | YB = yellow base |

| Wheels | General |
|---|---|
| BW = black wheels | BE = black engine |
| NW = narrow wheels | CE = chrome engine |
| UW = unpainted | LE = limited edition |
| WW = wide wheels | SE = silver engine |
| | TP = Twin Pack |

## MB 1e   MERCEDES TRUCK

| | | |
|---|---|---|
| 70-70 | Metallic gold body, yellow or orange canopy, green glass, narrow wheels | £25-35 |
| 76 | Military olive drab green body, tan canopy, purple glass, WW, '4TS702K', (TP) | £35-40 |
| 76-80 | Same but military olive green | £8-12 |
| 76-80 | Red body, yellow or orange canopy, PG, wide wheels, 'Transcontinental' (TP) | £8-10 |
| 80-82 | Light blue body, light orange canopy, purple glass, WW, 'IMS' (TP) | £12-15 |

## MB 1e   MOD ROD

| | | |
|---|---|---|
| 71 | Yellow body, OG, SE, red wheels, UB or SB, 'spotted cat's head' label | £30-35 |
| 71-75 | Same but with black wheels | £10-12 |
| | Black wheels and silver base | £18-20 |
| 71-75 | Same but with 'Wildcat' label | £10-12 |
| 73 | Same but with 'Flower' label | £20-25 |
| 74 | Same but with 'Scorpion' label | £50-60 |
| 78 | Striped silver body, BW, UB. (U.S.A. 'Roman Numeral' LE) | £25-30 |

## MB 1g   DODGE CHALLENGER

| | | |
|---|---|---|
| 76-79 | Red body, white roof, silver interior | £15-20 |
| 76-79 | Same but with white interior | £15-20 |
| 76-79 | Same but with red interior | £30-35 |
| 80-82 | Blue body, white roof, red interior | £15-20 |
| 82-83 | Orange body, blue roof, black interior, UB or SB, 'Revin Rebel' | £15-20 |
| 82 | Same but with white roof | £20-25 |

## MB 2d   MERCEDES TRAILER

| | | |
|---|---|---|
| 70 | Metallic gold body, yellow or orange canopy, narrow wheels | £25-30 |
| 76 | Military olive drab green body, tan canopy, WW, '4TS702K' (TP)' | £30-35 |
| 76-80 | Same but military olive green | £10-12 |
| 76-80 | Red body, WW, yellow or orange canopy, 'Transcontinental' (TP) | £8-10 |
| 80-82 | Light blue body, light orange canopy, WW 'IMS' (TP) | £10-12 |

## MB 2e   JEEP HOT ROD

| | | |
|---|---|---|
| 71-75 | Pink body, white or cream seats, light or dark green base | £10-15 |
| | Same but white base | £55-65 |
| 75-76 | Red body, white or cream seats, WB | £12-18 |
| | Same but green base | £45-50 |

## MB 2f   RESCUE HOVERCRAFT

| | | |
|---|---|---|
| 76-78 | Light or dark lime green body, fawn or light brown skirt, red or silver air intakes, amber or red windows, 'Rescue' | £6-8 |
| 76-79 | With Metallic light or dark green body | £6-8 |
| | Same but with red windows | £7-10 |
| 78 | Same but with black skirt | £7-10 |
| | Black skirt, red or purple windows | £10-12 |
| 78-80 | Pale green body, black skirt, purple or AG, '2000' or 'Rescue' | £15-20 |

## MB 2g   S-2 JET

| | | |
|---|---|---|
| 81-82 | Black/yellow, yellow or red glass | £6-8 |
| 82-83 | Metallic light blue and white or grey, clear glass, 'Viper' on some | £7-10 |

## MB 3c   MERCEDES 'BINZ' AMBULANCE

| | | |
|---|---|---|
| 70-73 | Cream or off-white body, light blue glass, NW, opening rear door | £40-50 |
| | Same but with dark blue glass | £30-40 |
| 77-80 | Cream body, dark blue glass, red cross on doors, rear door cast shut (TP) | £10-12 |
| 78-80 | Military olive-green body, WW with silver hubs, rear door cast shut (TP) | £15-25 |
| | Same but with black hubs | £12-15 |

## MB 3d   MONTEVERDI HAI

| | | |
|---|---|---|
| 73-78 | Orange body, pale yellow interior, black or UB, '3' on bonnet | £7-10 |
| | Same but with '16' on bonnet | £35-40 |

## MB 3e   PORSCHE TURBO

| | | |
|---|---|---|
| 78-79 | Metallic brown body, cream interior, clear glass, black base | £10-15 |
| 79-80 | Metallic brown body, UB | £14-18 |
| | Silver body, CG, cream or red interior, black or dark grey base | £8-12 |
| | Tan interior, black or dark grey base | £12-15 |
| | Tan interior, brown base | £18-20 |
| | Red interior, brown base | £8-10 |
| 80-82 | Metallic green body, cream interior, clear glass, black or dark grey base | £14-18 |
| | With light or dark yellow interior | £14-18 |
| | Same but with unpainted base | £14-18 |
| | Red interior, dark GB or BB | £14-18 |
| | Red body, tan interior, opaque glass, black base, 'Porsche Turbo 90' | £14-18 |
| 82-83 | Red body, tan or white interior, CG, black or dark grey base, 'Porsche Turbo 90' on some | £14-18 |

## MB 4d   STAKE TRUCK

| | | |
|---|---|---|
| 70-72 | Orange-yellow cab, green stake body, Green tinted glass | £20-25 |
| | Same but bright yellow cab | £80-100 |

## MB 4e   GRUESOME TWOSOME

| | | |
|---|---|---|
| 71-75 | Gold body, SB or UB, cream interior, PG | £14-18 |
| | With white or yellow interior | £12-15 |
| | Gold body, SB, cream interior, AG | £60-70 |
| 75 | Red body, SB or UB, yellow int., PG | £12-15 |
| | Same but with cream interior | £12-15 |
| | Orange-red body, SB or UB, cream interior, purple glass | £35-40 |
| | Graphite Grey body, PW, yellow interior, bare metal base | £225-275 |

## MB 4f   PONTIAC FIREBIRD

| | | |
|---|---|---|
| 75-77 | Metallic light blue body, UB, AG | £15-20 |
| 78-80 | Same but metallic dark blue | £20-25 |

## MB 4g   '57 CHEVY

| | | |
|---|---|---|
| 80-81 | Purple body, silver interior, UB, CG | £10-15 |
| 82-83 | Red, 'Cherry bomb', SB or UB, CG | £10-15 |
| | Same but with black base | £20-25 |

## MB 5e   LOTUS EUROPA

| | | |
|---|---|---|
| 69-70 | Dark metallic blue body, ivory interior, UB, NW | £40-45 |
| | Same, no 'Superfast' cast on base | £200-300 |
| | Dark metallic blue with '20' and stripe labels from G3 racing set | £25-30 |
| 70-75 | Pink body, ivory int., SB, NW or WW | £25-30 |
| | Same but with unpainted base | £10-12 |
| | Same, but with UB, NW, '20', and stripe decals | £25-30 |
| 77-78 | Black body, ivory interior, UB, NW, 'JPS' (Japanese issue) | £20-25 |
| | Same but without 'JPS' (TP) | £12-15 |

## MB 5f   SEAFIRE BOAT

| | | |
|---|---|---|
| 75-79 | White deck, blue hull, orange-yellow, blue or lemon man, black or red exhausts | £6-8 |
| 79-82 | Red deck, white hull, orange-yellow or lemon man, red exhausts, black trailer (TP) | £7-10 |
| 81 | Red deck, blue hull, lemon man, red exhausts, black trailer (TP) | £80-100 |
| 81 | White deck, brown hull, lemon or orange-yellow man, red exhausts | £45-50 |
| 82 | Black deck, yellow hull, red man, red exhausts, black trailer (TP) | £30-35 |
| 83 | Red deck, yellow hull, red man, red exhausts, black trailer (TP) | £35-40 |

## MB 5g   US MAIL TRUCK

| | | |
|---|---|---|
| 78-82 | Dark or light blue body, white roof (small or large windows), WB, BW, black or silver hubs, 'US Mail' on some | £10-12 |
| | Same but with black base | £10-12 |
| 78 | Pale blue body, white roof, 'sleet and snow' base, 'US Mail'. US LE | £10-12 |

## MB 5h   4X4 JEEP OFF-ROAD

| | | |
|---|---|---|
| 82-83 | Metallic light or dark bronze body, black base, 'Golden eagle' | £18-22 |

## MB 6d   FORD PICK-UP

| 70-71 | Red body, white roof, white or chrome grille, NW or WW, black base | £30-35 |
| | Metallic green or UB | £30-35 |
| | Green or Grey base | £18-20 |

## MB 6e   MERCEDES 350SL

| 74-75 | Orange body, black roof, UB, ivory or pale yellow interior, amber or CG | £12-15 |
| 75-79 | Yellow body, black roof, UB, pale yellow interior, amber or CG | £12-15 |
| 77 | Silver body, black roof, UB, pale yellow interior, CG, 'Rennservice' (German issue) | £50-60 |
| | Same but without 'Rennservice' | £40-50 |
| 79 | Metallic bronze body, black roof, UB, pale yellow interior, amber glass | £12-18 |
| 79-81 | Metallic bronze, white roof, AG, UB, pale yellow or cream interior | £7-10 |
| 81-82 | Metallic red body, white roof, UB, pale yellow interior, AG or CG | £30-35 |
| | With Cream interior, AG or CG | £10-15 |

## MB 6f   MERCEDES Convertible

| 82-83 | Metallic blue body, white interior, UB or SB, silver side stripe on some | £8-10 |
| 83-84 | Maroon body, BB, SB or UB | £8-10 |

## MB 7c   FORD REFUSE TRUCK

| 70-72 | Orange or orange-red cab, grey back | £18-20 |

## MB 7d   HAIRY HUSTLER

| 71-74 | Metallic bronze body, AG, '5' on yellow side stripe and bonnet, GB or BB | £15-20 |
| | Same but purple glass | £55-60 |
| | Metallic bronze body, AG, '5' on blue side stripe and bonnet, UB or BB | £15-20 |
| | Same but green base | £20-25 |
| | Same but green base, plain sides | £20-25 |
| | Same but black base, plain sides | £15-20 |
| | Metallic bronze body, AG, '3' on side labels, '5' on bonnet, BB | £25-30 |
| | Met. bronze, AG, '3' or '137' on sides, 'Scorpion' on bonnet, GB or BB | £80-100 |
| 75-77 | White 'Streakers' version, AG, red stripes with black/white check, GB or BB | £10-15 |
| | Same but with black base | £10-15 |
| 78 | White body, AG, grey base | £25-35 |
| 78-79 | Yellow body, AG, 'flames', BB, US 'Roman Numeral' Ltd. Edition | £18-20 |

## MB 7e   VOLKSWAGEN GOLF

| 76-77 | Metallic lime green body, yellow interior, AG, BB, roof-rack, black surfboards | £15-20 |
| 77-81 | Same but metallic light green body | £15-20 |
| 77-81 | Metallic dark green body, yellow or lemon interior, AG, BB or GB | £15-20 |
| | Same but with orange glass | £15-20 |
| | Red interior, grey base | £20-30 |
| 77 | Yellow body and interior, matt black base, 'ADAC', (German issue) | £25-30 |
| 79-80 | Red body, yellow interior, CG or AG, BB, roof rack, surfboards, (TP) | £12-15 |
| | Same but red interior, CG, (TP) | £40-45 |
| 81-82 | Yellow body, red interior, CG, BB or GB, roof rack and black surfboards | £12-16 |
| 82-83 | Silver body, red interior, CG, BB or GB, green stripes and 'Golf' | £10-14 |
| | Same but with tan interior | £15-20 |

## MB 8e   FORD MUSTANG

| 70 | White body, red interior, BB, CG | £275-350 |
| 70-71 | Red body, red interior, BB, CG | £200-250 |
| | Same but with ivory interior | £120-140 |
| | Orange-red body, red interior | £300-400 |
| | Same but with ivory interior | £150-175 |

## MB 8f   WILDCAT DRAGSTER

| 71 | Pink body, yellow interior, black and orange 'Wildcat' labels, BB | £12-15 |
| 71-75 | Same but Orange body, BB | £40-50 |
| | Same but with UB or orange base | £40-50 |
| | With dark or bright yellow base | £40-50 |
| | Same but with grey base | £18-20 |
| | Orange body, yellow interior, yellow/orange 'Wildcat' labels on some, BB | £30-35 |
| | Same but grey base | £15-20 |
| | Same but with UB or green base | £50-60 |
| | Orange body, yellow interior, black base, 'Rat Rod' labels | £30-40 |
| | Same but with 'Sailboat' labels | £50-60 |

## MB 8g   DE TOMASO PANTERA

| 75-81 | White body, red interior, blue base, '8' and 'Pantera' labels on some | £15-20 |
| | Same but orange interior | £10-15 |
| | With unpainted base | £10-15 |
| | White body, orange interior, '9' or yellow 'Sun' in black or green circle bonnet label, blue base | £20-25 |
| 81-82 | Blue body, black interior, '8' and 'Pantera' labels on some, BB, US issue. | £10-15 |
| NB | MB8g can be found with the larger rear wheels swapped with the smaller front. | |

## MB 8h   ROVER 3500

| 81 | Yellow body, red interior, sunroof, black base, (G1 Gift set) | £225-250 |
| | Metallic bronze body, white interior, sunroof, black base | £15-20 |
| | Same but dark or light tan interior | £10-15 |

## MB 8i   ROVER 'POLICE' CAR

| ? | White with blue logo/stripe | £14-18 |

## MB 9d   BOAT AND TRAILER

| 70-72 | White hull, light turquoise deck, dark blue trailer | £30-35 |
| 76-83 | White hull, light blue deck, light blue trailer (TP) | £30-35 |
| 82 | White hull, black deck, light or dark blue trailer (TP) | £40-50 |
| | Same but with black trailer | £20-25 |

## MB 9e   AMX JAVELIN

| 72-78 | Metallic lime green body, opening doors, yellow int., AG, black air intake, UB or SB, 3rd series box | £12-16 |
| | Same but with silver air intake | £20-25 |
| | Metallic lime green body, orange interior, AG, black air intake, UB or SB | £25-30 |
| | Same but with 5-spoke wheels | £50-60 |
| | Same but white interior, UB | £60-70 |
| | Same but with blue interior | £40-50 |
| 76-78 | Metallic light blue body, yellow or orange-yellow interior, AG, UB or SB | £8-11 |
| 78-81 | Metallic dark blue body, cast-in doors, orange-yellow interior, AG, UB or SB, (TP) | £8-11 |
| 80-81 | Blue body, cast-in doors, UB or SB, orange-yellow interior, AG, black air intake, white '1', (US Ltd.Ed.) | £20-25 |
| 81-83 | Metallic dark green body, cast-in doors, orange-yellow interior, AG, UB or SB, black air intake, (TP) | £4-6 |
| 82 | Red body, cast-in doors, UB or SB, orange-yellow interior, AG, (TP) | £20-25 |

## MB 9f   FORD ESCORT RS2000

| 78-82 | White body, tan interior, BB, CG, '9', 'Ford', 'Shell', and 'Dunlop' decals | £10-12 |
| | Same but with grey base | £10-12 |
| | Same but red interior, black base | £90-100 |
| | White body, tan interior, BB, CG, 'Phantom' decals, (TP) | £18-20 |
| 80-82 | Blue body, tan interior, BB or GB, CG, 'Phantom' decals, (TP) | £10-12 |
| | Same but with blue-grey base | £20-25 |
| 82-84 | Green body, tan interior, BB or GB, CG, 'Phantom' decals (TP) | £20-25 |
| | Green body, white interior, BB, CG, 'Phantom' decals, (TP) | £40-50 |
| | Same but with red interior | £90-100 |

## MB 10d   LEYLAND PIPE TRUCK

| 70 | Red body, silver base and grille, 6 grey pipes on sprue | £80-100 |
| 70-73 | Same but orange-red body | £20-25 |
| | Orange body, silver base and grille, 6 grey or yellow pipes on sprue. | £20-30 |
| | Same but grey base and grille | £80-100 |

## MB 10e   PISTON POPPER

| 73-80 | Metallic blue body, yellow interior, AG, 'Superfast' on UB | £80-100 |
| | Same but 'Rola-Matic' on UB | £10-15 |
| | Same but with silver base | £40-45 |
| | With CG, 'Rola-Matic' on UB or SB | £18-20 |
| 80 | White body, yellow interior, AG, 'Rola-Matic' on UB, (German multi-pack issue) | £250-300 |
| 80-81 | Yellow body (red flames) and interior, AG, 'Rola-Matic' on UB. US LE. | £15-20 |

## MB 10f   PLYMOUTH GRAN FURY POLICE CAR

| 79-81 | White body, black panels, blue or pale or dark yellow glass, UB, 'Police' | £14-18 |
| 82-83 | Same but with 'Metro Police Traffic Control', shield and '012', UB or SB | £8-11 |
| | Same but 'Mercury' base from no 55 | £10-15 |

## MB 11d   SCAFFOLDING TRUCK

| 70-72 | Silver body, red base / grille, GG, yellow scaffold, NW, 'Builders Supply Company' | £25-35 |

## MB 11e   FLYING BUG

| 72-77 | Red body, SB or UB, grey glass, yellow exhausts, silver helmet, square cut or heart-shape bonnet decal | £25-30 |
| | Heart-shape decal, UB, blue glass | £70-80 |
| 78 | Orange body, UB, black glass and exhausts, flying beetle bonnet decal, US Ltd. Ed. | £25-30 |
| | With '4' on bonnet, BB | £40-45 |

## MB 11f   CAR TRANSPORTER

| NB | Usually comes with 1 red, 1 blue and 1 yellow car. Other combinations are common (e.g., 1 blue and 2 yellow) but this does not affect the price. | |
| 77-80 | Orange cab, white or beige back, BB or UB, blue, purple or green glass | £8-11 |
| 80-83 | Red (later Dark Orange) cab, beige or grey back, BB, SB or UB, blue or purple glass | £8-11 |

## MB 12c    SAFARI LAND-ROVER

| | |
|---|---|
| 70 | Metallic blue body, white interior,<br>UB, NW, brown luggage..............**£1,500-2,000** |
| 70 | Green body, fine GPW.....................**£150-200** |
| 70-71 | Metallic gold body, white interior,<br>UB, NW, brown luggage......................**£20-25** |

## MB 12d    SETRA COACH

| | |
|---|---|
| 71 | Metallic gold, grey roof, UB, CG..........**£20-25** |
| | Same but with white roof......................**£18-20** |
| 72-73 | Yellow body, white roof, UB, CG.........**£30-40** |
| | Same but with green glass ...............**£150-200** |
| 73-74 | Metallic crimson, UB, CG or GG........**£20-25** |
| 74-75 | Met. purple, UB or PB, CG or GG.......**£12-15** |

## MB 12e    BIG BULL

| | |
|---|---|
| 75-79 | Orange, green shovel, black rollers ......**£30-40** |
| | Same but with yellow rollers................**£15-20** |
| | Same but with orange rollers...............**£10-15** |

## MB 12f    CITROËN CX

| | |
|---|---|
| 79-82 | Light or dark metallic blue body,<br>pale yellow or cream or ivory interior,<br>SB or GB or BB or UB,<br>clear or blue glass ...................**£10-14** |
| | Light metallic blue, tan interior ...........**£12-16** |
| | Dark metallic blue, red interior...........**£80-90** |
| 82-83 | Yellow body, red interior, black base,<br>dark blue glass, (TP)..................**£12-16** |
| | With clear glass, BB, GB or SB, (TP)...**£10-14** |
| | Yellow, red interior, BB, CG, 'Team<br>Matchbox' in black or blue, (TP)........**£15-20** |
| 83 | White body, red interior, BB or UB,<br>blue glass/lights, 'Ambulance', (TP).......**£8-10** |
| | Same but 'Police', 'Marine Division'<br>and '8' prints, blue stripes, (TP) ............**£8-10** |

## MB 13d    DODGE WRECK TRUCK

| | |
|---|---|
| 70-71 | Yellow (or lighter yellow) cab, green<br>back, yellow crane, red hook 'B.P.'.....**£50-75** |

## MB 13e    BAJA BUGGY

| | |
|---|---|
| 71-78 | Metallic light green body, orange interior,<br>UB, black or red exhausts, red or<br>orange bonnet flower label ...................**£12-15** |
| | With red exhausts, no bonnet label.......**£12-15** |
| | With red exhausts, 'Police' bonnet<br>label from 55d...................**£40-45** |
| | Same but with red interior ...................**£40-45** |
| | Metallic light green body, orange<br>interior from 47c, UB, red exhausts,<br>orange bonnet flower label ...............**£150-200** |
| 78 | Metallic dark green body, orange interior,<br>UB, red exhausts, orange flower label...**£10-15** |
| | Same but 'Sun' label from 47c .............**£18-20** |

## MB 13f    SIMON SNORKEL

| | |
|---|---|
| 78-80 | Light red body, SB or UB, blue glass,<br>blue lights, yellow crane and man ...........**£6-8** |
| | Same but amber glass and lights...........**£25-30** |
| 80-82 | Dark red body, SB or UB, blue glass,<br>blue lights, yellow crane and man ............**£6-8** |
| 82 | Same but white crane and man ...............**£8-10** |

## MB 14d    ISO GRIFO

| | |
|---|---|
| 69-71 | Metallic dark blue body, pale or dark<br>blue interior, UB, NW............................**£30-40** |
| | Same but with white interior............**£250-300** |
| 71-75 | Lighter metallic blue body, white<br>interior, UB or SB, NW ....................**£18-20** |
| | Sky blue, white interior, UB, NW .........**£18-20** |
| 77-78 | Lighter powder blue, white interior, |

| | |
|---|---|
| | UB, WW, (Japanese issue).....................**£25-30** |

## MB 14e    MINI HA HA

| | |
|---|---|
| 75-82 | Red body, dark blue glass, UB,<br>'flesh' coloured man, brown helmet,<br>4 circle side labels...................**£20-25** |
| | Same but with purple man ...................**£30-35** |
| | 'Flesh' man, light blue glass.................**£20-25** |
| | Purple man, light blue glass.................**£15-20** |
| | Pink man, light blue glass....................**£15-20** |
| | Red body, light blue glass, 'flesh' or<br>pink man, 2 circle side labels................**£30-35** |

## MB 14f    LEYLAND TANKER

| | |
|---|---|
| 82-83 | Red cab, white tank, 'ELF' with red/blue<br>stripes or orange/turquoise stripes ........**£10-15** |
| 19?? | Yellow cab, White tank, 'SHELL' .........**£20-25** |

## MB 15d    VOLKSWAGEN 1500

| | |
|---|---|
| 69-70 | Off white or cream body, cream<br>interior, '137', 'Monte Carlo' ...............**£35-45** |
| 70-72 | Metallic red body, cream interior,<br>'137', 'Monte Carlo' on some.................**£30-40** |
| 77-78 | Off white body, cream interior, '137',<br>no bumper decal (Japanese issue).........**£30-40** |
| **Promotional issue** linked to Walt Disney<br>film 'Herbie' with correct RN '53'<br>and racing stripes.........................**£600-800** |

## MB 15e    FORKLIFT TRUCK

| | |
|---|---|
| 72-77 | Red body, yellow hoist, grey forks, UB,<br>black steering wheel, 'horse' and<br>'Lansing Bagnall' labels ...........................**£5-7** |
| | Same but with green or black base ..........**£6-8** |
| 77-82 | Red body, unpainted hoist, yellow forks,<br>UB, black steering wheel, 'horse' and<br>'Lansing Bagnall' labels ...........................**£5-7** |
| | Same but with green or black base ..........**£6-8** |
| | Same but no steering wheel ....................**£5-7** |
| | Same but with black or grey forks...........**£5-7** |
| | With red forks, no steering wheel.........**£12-15** |
| 82-83 | Orange body, unpainted hoist, black<br>forks and roof, UB or SB or BB, no<br>steering wheel, 'Hi-Lift' labels ................**£7-9** |
| NB | Models can be found with 'horse' label<br>facing forwards or backwards and<br>before or after 'Lansing Bagnall'. |

## MB 16d    CASE BULLDOZER

| | |
|---|---|
| 69-74 | Red body, yellow cab, shovel, engine<br>and base, green rubber tracks.................**£8-10** |
| | Same but with black tracks ...................**£10-12** |
| 77 | Military olive drab green body, black<br>shovel, BB, black tracks (TP) ...............**£55-60** |
| | Same but olive green body (TP)...........**£20-25** |

## MB 16e    BADGER

| | |
|---|---|
| 74-80 | Metallic bronze body, SB, silver radar,<br>green glass (Rola-Matic)........................**£10-12** |
| | Same but BB or SB, cream radar............**£8-10** |
| | Same but with light or dark grey base......**£8-10** |
| | Dark grey or black base, black radar......**£8-10** |
| | Same but with purple glass ..................**£10-12** |
| | Black base, white radar, green glass .......**£8-10** |
| | Same but with dark grey base................**£8-10** |
| 76 | Military olive drab green body, light grey<br>base, cream radar, green glass(TP) ......**£35-40** |
| 76-78 | Same but olive green body (TP)...........**£18-20** |

## MB 16f    PONTIAC FIREBIRD

| | |
|---|---|
| 80-81 | Metallic light brown body, red interior,<br>UB, 'Eagle' bonnet label on most..........**£14-18** |
| 81-82 | Same but metallic light gold body.......**£14-18** |

| | |
|---|---|
| | Same but metallic dark gold body.........**£14-18** |
| 82-83 | White body, red interior..........................**£23-28** |

## MB 16g    PONTIAC T-ROOF

| | |
|---|---|
| 1982 | Black body, red interior, 'Lesney' base .**£15-20** |

## MB 17e    HORSE BOX

| | |
|---|---|
| 70 | Red cab, dark green box, grey door,<br>chrome base, 2 white horses on sprue ...**£55-60** |
| 70-71 | Same but orange-red cab.......................**£30-35** |
| | Orange-red cab, light grey-white box,<br>brown door....................**£40-45** |
| | Same but orange cab ............................**£30-35** |
| | Mustard-yellow cab, dark green<br>box, grey door.........................**£30-35** |

## MB 17f    DAIMLER<br>'LONDONER' BUSES

The 'Londoner' bus models are loosely based on the Daimler Fleetline design of double-decker buses. Unless otherwise stated all issues have red bodies and white interiors. Most have metal bases in gloss or matt black, grey, brown or unpainted. Before changing to the Titan bus (17g) some were fitted with plastic bases. Factory issued models are listed first, then Lesney issued promotional models.

| | |
|---|---|
| 72-74 | 'Swinging London', 'Carnaby Street'......**£8-10** |
| 73 | Chrome plated Gift Ware version ......**£150-175** |
| 73 | Gold-effect plated Gift Ware version.....**£70-80** |
| 73-80 | 'Berger Paints'. ('Brush' logos may<br>be at front or rear of label).......................**£5-7** |
| 73 | Same but silver body.............................**£70-80** |
| 73 | Same but gold body .........................**£200-300** |
| | Same but orange body...........................**£45-50** |
| 73 | Same but cream body, brown roof........**£60-65** |
| 75 | 'Esso Extra Petrol'................................**£65-70** |
| 77 | 'Silver Jubilee 1952-77'. Silver body<br>with red interior, special issue box ....**£12-15** |
| | Same but red body, white interior..........**£70-80** |
| 78 | 'Matchbox 1953-78'................................**£4-6** |
| | Same but orange body...........................**£65-70** |
| | Same but blue body...............................**£45-50** |
| 72 | 'Preston Guild Merchant'......................**£75-80** |
| 73 | 'Impel 73' Trade Fair ............................**£34-40** |
| | 'London and Kensington Hilton'...........**£75-80** |
| | 'The Baron of Beef'...........................**£100-120** |
| | 'Sellotape Selbstklebebander'.............**£250-300** |
| | 'Sellotape Packaging Systems'...........**£250-300** |
| | 'Sellotape Electrical Tapes'...............**£250-300** |
| | 'Barclays Bank'.....................................**£80-90** |
| | 'Chambourcy Yogurt'............................**£55-65** |
| | 'Interchemicals and Plastics'...........**£200-250** |
| 74 | 'Typhoo puts the 'T' in Britain'............**£80-90** |
| 76 | 'Impel 76' Trade Fair. Cream body<br>with brown roof, white interior..............**£25-30** |
| | 'British Airways Busch Gardens' .........**£60-70** |
| | 'Ilford HP5 Film' ..............................**£150-180** |
| | 'A.I.M. Building Fund 1976'................**£35-40** |
| | 'Selfridges'...........................................**£15-20** |
| | 'Santa Claus, Aviemore Centre'............**£35-40** |
| | 'Amcel takes you places'.......................**£65-75** |
| | 'Eduscho Kaffee'.............................**£140-160** |
| 77 | 'New! The Museum of London'..............**£18-20** |
| | 'Army and Navy' ...................................**£18-20** |
| | 'Jacob's the Biscuit Makers'<br>Red body with white interior.................**£35-40** |
| | Orange body with white interior............**£18-20** |
| 78 | 'Aral-Deutschlands Autopartner'<br>Blue body with white interior................**£45-50** |
| | Same but red body................................**£90-100** |
| 79 | 'Impel 79' Trade Fair ............................**£25-30** |
| 80 | 'You can't kid a Bisto kid'......................**£8-10** |
| | 'Borregaard Paper'.............................**£90-100** |

## MB 17g    LEYLAND TITAN BUS

| | |
|---|---|
| 82 | 'Berger Paints'.......................................**£5-8** |

'Laker Skytrain' .........................................**£5-8**
82  'Chesterfield Transport Centenary'...........**£5-8**
'Matchbox No.1, Montepna'
Pale blue/white (Greek issue) ...............**£18-20**
Same but red body .................................**£20-25**

## MB 18e    FIELD CAR

70-75  Light yellow body, light brown roof,
white interior, SB, NW or WW ...........**£30-40**
Same but WW, UB.................................**£15-18**
Black roof, UB, WW ............................**£30-40**
76  Military olive drab green body, tan roof,
black interior, BB, 'A' square door
labels, black wide wheels (TP) .............**£35-45**
76-80  Same but olive green body (TP)............**£18-20**
Same but 'RA391' bonnet label............**£18-20**
With circled star bonnet label (TP)........**£20-25**
77-78  White body, black roof, black interior,
BB, Black/white checked bonnet
label, black wide wheels (TP)...........**£200-300**
Same but silver wheel hubs (TP)......**£200-300**
Orange body, black roof, black interior,
BB, black/white checked bonnet label,
black wide wheels (TP)..........................**£12-15**
Same but silver wheel hubs (TP)..........**£12-15**
Orange body, black roof, black interior,
SB, black/white checked bonnet label,
black wide wheels (TP)..........................**£30-35**
78-80  Metallic ruby-red body, tan roof, black
interior, SB or BB, '44', 'Champion' and
'Goodyear' bonnet label (TP) .................**£8-10**
80  Dark orange body, black roof, black
interior, BB or SB, 'AC Filters' and '179
Scout Racing' labels, US Ltd. Ed. .........**£30-35**
Same but no labels, US Ltd. Ed............**£30-35**
82-83  Dark yellow body, black or tan roof,
black interior, SB, black/white
checked bonnet label, (TP) ...................**£25-30**
Orange, black roof and interior, BB,
black/white checked bonnet, (TP)........**£18-20**
Orange body, black or tan roof, white
interior, BB, '44', 'Champion' and
'Goodyear' bonnet label, (TP) .............**£30-35**

## MB 18f    HONDARORA

74-75  Red body, chrome forks, SE, black
seat, 'Honda' tank labels, WW .............**£18-20**
75-80  Same but no labels or with BW.............**£15-20**
Red body, black forks, SE, white
seat, 'Honda' tank labels, WW .............**£85-95**
Same but with black seat .......................**£15-20**
76  Orange body, black forks, SE, black seat,
'Honda' labels, (King Size set 6) ...........**£20-25**
76  Military olive drab green, black forks,
BE, black seat, no labels, WW (TP) ......**£25-30**
76-78  Same but military olive green (TP) .......**£15-18**
81-82  Metallic green body, black forks,
BE or SE, black seat, no labels, BW .....**£10-15**
82-83  Yellow body, black forks, SE, black
seat, no tank labels, black wheels .........**£10-15**
Same but with brown or tan rider .........**£10-15**

## MB 19d    LOTUS RACING CAR

70  Metallic purple body, UB, SE, white
driver, round No.'3' side labels..............**£35-40**

## MB 19e    ROAD DRAGSTER

70-75  Light red body, UB or SB, off-white
interior, '8' labels normal or sideways...**£15-20**
Same but with 'Scorpion' labels............**£40-50**
72  Promotional: Fluorescent red body, UB,
off-white interior, 'Wynns' labels ......**£125-150**
Same but smaller 'Wynns' labels.......**£125-150**
75  Metallic purple body, UB, off-white
interior, 'Scorpion' labels......................**£40-50**
Same but with '8' labels or no labels.....**£15-20**
Metallic red body, UB, off-white

interior, '8' labels as normal .............**£200-250**

## MB 19f    CEMENT TRUCK

76-81  Red body, yellow barrel,
red stripes, UB, GG...............................**£6-8**
Same but black stripes or no stripes .........**£6-8**
79  Same but grey barrel with red stripes........**£6-8**
Same but with purple glass ....................**£10-12**
81-82  Red body, lemon barrel,
red stripes, UB, GG...............................**£6-8**
Same but black stripes or no stripes .........**£6-8**
Same but with purple glass .....................**£8-10**

## MB 19g  PETERBILT
##          CEMENT TRUCK

82-83  Metallic green body, orange barrel,
yellow or white 'Big Pete'......................**£9-12**

## MB 20d LAMBORGHINI Marzal

69  Metallic red body, white interior, UB ....**£15-18**
Met. red body, yellow/orange interior ....**£30-35**
70  Same but with 'Avon' and '2' labels
from G3 Racing Specials set..................**£20-25**
71  Bright pink body, white interior, UB ....**£30-40**
Bright pink, silver base ..........................**£30-40**
Same but with 'Avon' and '2' labels
from G3 Racing Specials set..................**£20-25**
71-75  Orange or orange-pink body, white
interior, unpainted base .........................**£10-12**
72  Yellow body, white interior, UB,
('Brroom Stick' blister pack issue)........**£40-50**

## MB 20e    POLICE PATROL

75-80  White, UB, orange or red 'Police' stripe,
orange light and interior (Rola-Matic).....**£7-10**
White body, UB or SB, orange 'Police'
stripe, blue or yellow light and interior .....**£6-8**
Same but with black base ........................**£8-10**
White body, UB, 'Ambulance' and Red
Cross, orange light and interior ............**£15-18**
76-78  White body, UB, orange 'Site Engineer'
stripes, orange light / interior,
(G3 Consruction Set) ............................**£30-35**
Same but with orange body ...................**£25-30**
Orange body and 'Police' stripe, orange
light and interior, UB, (G3 Set) ............**£25-30**
76  Military olive drab green body, UB,
yellow and red 'Police' arrow, orange
light and interior (TP) ...........................**£40-50**
Same but 'Ambulance' labels ................**£40-50**
76-77  Military olive green body, UB, yellow
and red 'Police' arrow, orange light
and interior (TP)....................................**£18-20**
Same but with 'Ambulance' labels ........**£18-20**
80  Blue body, UB, yellow 'Paris-Dakar 81'
stripe, (French issue blister pack)..........**£40-45**
81  White body, UB, blue 'County Sheriff'
labels, blue light and interior ................**£12-15**
Same but '017', 'Sheriff', blue roof........**£15-18**
81-83  White body, UB, yellow 'Police' and
'shield' stripe above chequered stripe.....**£8-10**
Same but with black base ........................**£8-12**
White body, UB, black 'Police' on
sides, yellow light and interior ...............**£12-15**
83  Light brown or beige body, UB, yellow
'Securite-Rallye Paris-Dakar 83'..........**£24-28**

## MB 20f    DESERT DAWG

82  US issue. White body, orange canopy .......**£7-9**

## MB 21d  FODEN
##          CONCRETE TRUCK

70-73  Dark yellow cab, yellow barrel, red
body and shute, green base ...................**£25-30**

Same but bright yellow cab,
green or dark green base ........................**£25-30**

## MB 21e    ROD ROLLER

73-78  Yellow body, black wheels with
metallic red  hubs, GB, 'flame' label.....**£30-35**
Same but with matt red hubs .................**£15-20**
Yellow or darker yellow body, black
wheels, GB or BB, 'flame' or no label ..**£15-20**

## MB 21f    RENAULT 5TL

78-79  Metallic blue, red interior, BB or SB.....**£15-20**
Metallic blue body, tan interior,
black, dark grey or silver base .................**£8-10**
Yellow body, red interior, BB or SB,
'Le Car' and stripe prints ......................**£12-15**
Yellow body, tan interior, BB or SB
or dark grey base, 'Le Car' prints............**£8-10**
79-81  Silver body, red interior, BB or SB,
'A5' and stripe prints ............................**£12-15**
Same but no tampo prints .......................**£8-10**
Silver body, red interior, SB..................**£32-38**
81-82  Silver body, red interior, dark grey or
BB or SB, 'Le Car' and stripe prints .....**£10-12**
82-83  White body, tan interior, BB,
'Renault' and '4' on green prints ............**£8-10**
Same but 'Renault' roof prints.................**£8-10**
White body, white interior, BB,
'Renault' and '4' on green prints .............**£8-10**
White body, tan interior, BB, 'Roloil'
and '21' on yellow prints ........................**£8-10**
Same but with orange base ....................**£20-25**
White body, white interior, BB,
'Roloil' and '21' on yellow prints...........**£8-10**
White, Orange interior, 'Roloil'.........**£50-60**

## MB 22c    PONTIAC GP SPORTS

70  Red body, grey interior, BB.........**£1,250-1,500**
Light purple, grey interior, BB .........**£100-150**
Dark purple, grey interior, BB ..........**£100-150**

## MB 22d    FREEMAN INTERCITY

70-71  Metallic purple body, off-white interior,
UB, yellow arrow labels on some..........**£15-20**
71-72  Metallic gold body, off-white interior,
UB, yellow arrow labels .......................**£30-35**
72-75  Metallic red body, off-white interior,
UB or SB, arrow labels on some ...........**£15-20**

## MB 22e    BLAZE BUSTER

75-80  Red body, silver interior, UB,
yellow ladder, 'Fire' labels.....................**£8-10**
Same but with black ladder....................**£42-48**
Same but with white ladder ...............**£130-150**
Red body, silver or white interior,
black or dark grey base, yellow ladder....**£8-10**
80-82  Dark red body, white interior, grey or
BB, yellow ladder, 'Fire' labels .............**£8-10**
83  Light red body, white interior, BB, dark
yellow ladder, 'Fire' labels.....................**£8-10**
Same but 'No.32' on yellow labels........**£12-15**

## MB 22f    BIG FOOT

19??  Silver body and base,
light or dark blue glass. (US)................**£12-15**

## MB 23e    VW CAMPER

70-72  Blue body, orange interior and hinged
roof, UB, CG, rear sailboat side labels
on some, petrol filler cap, NW.............**£80-100**
Same but no filler cap ............................**£20-25**
72-75  Orange body, orange interior and hinged
roof, UB, CG, sailboat labels, NW ....**£100-120**
Light or dark orange body, white interior,

orange hinged roof, UB, CG, sailboat
labels on some, NW ...............................**£30-40**

77-80   Military olive green, no interior, cast roof,
BB, BG, Red Cross labels, WW (TP)....**£15-18**

80      White body, no interior, cast roof, BB,
GG, 'PizzaVan', WW. US LE...............**£30-35**

## MB 23f    ATLAS TRUCK

75-81   Metallic blue body, orange tipper, yellow/red
arrow labels, chrome interior, AG, UB..**£12-14**
Same but without tipper labels .............**£12-14**
Same but grey interior, CG, UB ...........**£12-14**
Same but grey interior, AG, SB or UB..**£12-14**
With grey interior, CG and SB ..............**£12-14**

81      Metallic blue body, silver tipper, grey
interior, CG, SB ..................................**£12-14**

81-82   Same but red body ..............................**£12-14**
Same but black interior..........................**£12-14**

## MB 24c ROLLS SILVER SHADOW

70-73   Light metallic red body,
cream interior, BB..................................**£18-20**
Same, but Dark metallic red body ........**£30-40**
Same but with pink base ........................**£30-40**
Same but SB or grey base......................**£15-18**
Same but with metallic green base ........**£30-40**

77-78   Light metallic gold body, cream
interior, UB, (Japanese issue) ..............**£30-40**
Same but BB (Japanese issue) ..............**£25-30**

## MB 24d    TEAM MATCHBOX

73      Bright yellow body, white man, '4' (or '8')
and 'Team Matchbox' bonnet label ...**£200-250**
Metallic blue body, white man,
'1' and 'Team Matchbox' label..........**£125-175**
With '5' and 'Team Matchbox'..........**£125-175**

73-75   Metallic green, white man, '5' (or '8'),
'Team Matchbox' label, (G4 set) ...........**£30-50**

73-78   Metallic red body, white man,
'8' and 'Team Matchbox' label..............**£10-15**

78-80   Metallic ruby-red body, white man,
'44', 'Champion', 'Goodyear',
black trailer (TP) ..................................**£10-12**

82-83   Same but orange body, yellow man.......**£60-70**

## MB 24e    DIESEL SHUNTER

78      Metallic dark green body, light brown
control panel, 'Railfreight'......................**£6-8**
Same but with 'D1496-RF' labels ............**£4-6**

78-83   Light or dark yellow body, light brown
control panel (or none), 'D1496-RF'........**£3-5**

## MB 25d    FORD CORTINA GT

70      Metallic light brown body, off white
interior, unpainted base ....................**£130-150**

70-72   Same but metallic light blue body ........**£25-30**
Same but metallic dark blue body ........**£40-45**

## MB 25e    MOD TRACTOR

72-78   Metallic purple body, BB, yellow seat,
headlights cast on rear mudguards........**£40-50**
Without lights on rear mudguards .........**£15-20**
Metallic purple body, BB, red seat ........**£80-90**
Metallic purple, UB, yellow seat ...........**£15-20**

76-79   Red body, BB, yellow seat (TP) ............**£15-20**

## MB 25f    FLAT CAR CONTAINER

78-80   Light beige container red roof, black flat
car, 'United States Lines' labels...............**£8-10**
Same but 'N.Y.K.' labels ..................**£4-5**
Same but with 'Sealand' labels ..............**£5-7**
Dark beige container, red roof, black
flat car, 'N.Y.K.' or 'Sealand' labels .........**£4-5**

Same but with 'OCL' labels...................**£10-12**
Dark brown container, red roof, black
flat car, 'N.Y.K.' labels...........................**£12-15**

## MB 25g    AUDI QUATTRO

82-83   White and black, 'Audi' and '20' ..........**£10-12**

## MB 26c    GMC TIPPER TRUCK

70-72   Red tipping cab, silver tipper, green
chassis, green glass, wide wheels ..........**£15-18**

## MB 26d    BIG BANGER

72-76   Red, UB, 'Big Banger', dk. blue glass ..**£20-25**
Same but with amber glass ...................**£18-22**

78      Dark brown, 'Brown Sugar', WB,
amber, black or blue glass (USA)..........**£25-30**

81-83   White body, BB, 'Cosmic Blues'
clear or blue glass, (US issue) ...............**£15-20**

## MB 26e    SITE DUMPER

76-78   Yellow body, yellow dumper,
black seats, black base ...........................**£5-7**

78-81   Same but with red dumper......................**£4-6**
Same but dark grey base ........................**£8-12**
Same but brown base ...........................**£12-15**

81-82   Orange-red body, silver dumper,
white seats, black base ...........................**£4-6**
Same but wheels have yellow hubs ........**£7-10**
Orange-red body, silver dumper, white
seats, dark grey base ..............................**£4-6**
Same but wheels have yellow hubs ........**£7-10**

## MB 26f    CABLE TRUCK

82-83   Orange-yellow body, red base, blue
glass, two light grey cable drums ..........**£15-18**
Same but dark grey or BB ......................**£7-10**

83      Bright yellow body,
BB, BG, 2 grey drums .........................**£50-60**
Same but dark red body ........................**£12-15**

## MB 27d    MERCEDES 230SL

70-71   White body, red interior, CG, UB, NW .**£40-45**
Same but in 'F2' box...............................**£80-90**

71      Same but yellow body............................**£50-60**

71-73   Yellow body, black interior,
CG, UB, NW or WW...........................**£35-40**

## MB 27e    LAMBORGHINI
##              COUNTACH

73-75   Yellow body, BB, red glass, '3' ...........**£14-18**
Same but amber glass ...................**£10-15**
Same but with purple glass ...................**£30-40**
Yellow body, UB, red glass, '3'............**£10-15**
Same but with purple glass ...................**£14-18**

75      Orange body, UB, red glass, '3' ...........**£30-35**
Same but with amber glass ...................**£30-35**

75-81   **Lamborghini 'Streakers'**. All have
green/black 'Streaker' prints and a
red '8' on the bonnet.
Orange body, chrome interior, BB.........**£20-30**
Same but with amber or green glass......**£20-30**
Orange body, grey interior, BB, GG......**£20-30**
Same but with purple glass ...................**£20-30**
Orange body, grey interior, UB, GG......**£20-30**
Same but with brown base .....................**£20-30**
Orange body, yellow interior, BB or
dark grey base, green glass ...................**£20-30**
Orange, chrome int., UB, GG or AG......**£20-30**
Orange body, grey interior, dark grey
base, green glass ..................................**£20-30**
Same but with purple glass ...................**£20-30**
Orange, chrome int., red windows ....**£45-55**
Orange body, beige interior,
dark grey base,GG ...............................**£20-30**

Same but with purple glass ....................**£20-30**
Orange body, beige interior, BB, GG ....**£20-30**

## MB 27f    SWING WING

81-83   Red/white, red glass ..............................**£10-15**
Red/white, dark yellow-orange glass.....**£10-15**
Red/white, red or black 'Jet Set'............**£10-15**

## MB 28d    MACK DUMP TRUCK

70-73   Metallic lime green body and dumper,
UB, cab steps cast closed.......................**£18-20**
Same but with steps cast open ...............**£18-24**

77-79   Military olive drab green body/dumper,
BB, cab steps cast closed (TP)...............**£40-50**
Military olive green (TP).........................**£20-25**

## MB 28e    STOAT

73-76   Metallic gold body, UB or BB, dark
brown man, (Rola-Matic issue) ...............**£5-10**

77      Military olive drab green body, BB,
dark brown man, (TP).............................**£40-50**

77-79   Military olive green body, BB, dark
brown man, (TP) ...................................**£20-25**

## MB 28f    LINCOLN CONTINENTAL

79      Light red body, white roof,
beige interior, clear glass, UB................**£10-15**

79-81   Dark red body, beige, dark brown
or grey interior, clear glass, UB.............**£15-20**

## MB 28g    FORMULA RACING CAR

81-83   Metallic brown-grey body, BB or UB,
white driver, 'Exxon' and '8' prints.......**£10-12**

## MB 29c    FIRE PUMPER TRUCK

70      Red body, white back and ladders,
UB, blue glass, narrow wheels ..............**£35-40**

81      Same but 'P1' and 'Los Angeles Fire
Dept.', wide wheels ('Code Red') .........**£18-20**

## MB 29d    RACING MINI

70-72   Metallic bronze body, SB or UB,
off-white interior, '29' on yellow
labels (orange edges)............................**£30-35**

72-76   Orange body, SB or UB, cream or
off-white interior, '29' on yellow
labels (orange edges)........................**£125-150**
Same but with green label edges ..........**£12-15**

76-81   Red body, SB or UB, off-white or
cream interior, '29' on yellow
labels (green edges) (TP)......................**£35-40**
Red body, SB, cream interior, '3' on
white circle door labels (TP).................**£35-40**
Same but with no labels.........................**£15-20**

## MB 29e    TRACTOR SHOVEL

76-78   Light yellow body, red shovel, silver
engine and seat, yellow base...................**£8-10**

77      Lime green body, yellow shovel and
base, silver engine and seat,
(German PS1000 set issue)....................**£60-70**

78-81   Yellow body, red shovel, silver or
black engine and seat, yellow base...........**£6-8**
Same but with cream base ......................**£8-10**
Same but with black base ........................**£6-8**
Yellow body, red shovel, black engine
and seat, yellow base, yellow hubs...........**£6-8**
Yellow body, black shovel, black engine
and seat, yellow base ..............................**£6-8**
Same but with cream base ......................**£8-10**
Same but with black base ........................**£6-8**

79      Yellow body, black shovel/engine/seat/stripes,

BB, 'C' prints on some, (G5 Set)...............**£6-8**

81    Orange-red body, red shovel, dark grey
engine and seat, black base...................**£20-25**

82-83   Same but with black shovel .................**£12-15**

## MB 30c   8-WHEEL CRANE

70    Red body, dark orange crane arm
with yellow hook, UB.........................**£240-280**

Same but with gold crane arm ..............**£35-45**

## MB 30d   BEACH BUGGY

70-76   Light metallic purple body, yellow
spots, UB, white interior .......................**£20-25**

Same but with orange interior...............**£10-15**

Same but dark metallic purple body .....**£10-15**

**NB**    The yellow spots on this model can vary
from only a few spots to almost an
entire body covering.

## MB 30e   SWAMP RAT

76-81   Military green deck, light brown hull,
'Swamp Rat' labels on some...................**£9-12**

## MB 30f   ARTICULATED TRUCK

81-83   Metallic steel-blue cab, WB,
red glass, silver trailer.........................**£9-12**

Blue cab, WB or YB, silver trailer .........**£9-12**

83    Blue cab and trailer, 'Pauls' white labels,
pale YB or WB, (Ltd. blister-pack
issue of 900).....................................**£35-45**

Blue cab, WB or YB, yellow
trailer, 'International' labels ....................**£8-10**

Red cab, YB and trailer,
'International' labels ............................**£10-12**

Red cab, YB, silver trailer ...................**£10-12**

## MB 30g   PETERBILT
## QUARRY TRUCK

82    Yellow cab/chassis, grey tipper.............**£12-14**

## MB 31e   LINCOLN CONTINENTAL

70    Sea-green body, white interior,
unpainted base, CG, NW ..............**£750-1,000**

Metallic lime-green body, white
interior, UB, CG, NW ..........................**£25-30**

Same but with wide wheels ..................**£20-25**

## MB 31d   VOLKSDRAGON

71-77   Red body, PG, UB or SB, yellow or
cream interior, 'eyes' label on some .....**£15-20**

Red body, purple glass, UB or SB,
yellow interior, 'flower' label ...............**£20-25**

78    Black body, purple glass, UB, yellow
interior, 'bug'/ 'flames' (US issue) ........**£30-35**

## MB 31e   CARAVAN

77-83   White body, off-white, light yellow or
light brown interior, UB, AG, orange,
light blue or yellow door, orange stripe
(white bird labels on some).....................**£9-12**

Same but light yellow interior ...............**£9-12**

Same but dark blue door, blue stripe .......**£9-12**

## MB 32c   LEYLAND TANKER

70-73   Dark green cab and body, BG, 'B.P.' labels
in centre or front of white tank,
SB, NW ............................................**£18-20**

Dark green cab and body, white tank,
GB, 'B.P.' labels in centre of tank ........**£40-50**

Same but with grey grille....................**£80-100**

Blue cab and body, SB, 'Aral' labels

on white tank, (German,
'Aral Tankwagen' box) ......................**£130-160**

Metallic purple cab and body,
silver tank, SB, no labels .................**£100-125**

Same but with 'N.A.M.C.' labels.......**£250-300**

Red cab and body, white tank,
SB, 'N.A.M.C.' labels ......................**£300-400**

## MB 32d   MASERATI BORA

73-78   Metallic crimson body, lime green base,
yellow interior, stripe and '8' label.........**£8-10**

Same but with dark green or UB ...........**£10-12**

Same but dark green base, '3' label......**£15-20**

Same but with no label ..........................**£6-8**

79    Metallic gold, SB, yellow interior,
no bonnet label, tow hook, (TP) ...........**£60-75**

## MB 32e   FIELD GUN

77-81   Military green body, light or dark brown
base, 2 soldiers and 4 shells on sprue,
black WW..........................................**£11-14**

Same but black wheels, silver hubs ......**£30-40**

78    Military olive green body, no base,
soldiers or shells, black wheels (TP) ........**£3-5**

## MB 32f   EXCAVATOR

81-82   Orange-red body, silver-grey tracks.........**£8-10**

82-83   Yellow body, black tracks and
'CAT' prints........................................**£8-10**

Same but with no 'CAT' print..................**£6-8**

## MB 33c   LAMBORGHINI MIURA

69    Yellow body, red interior, UB, NW ...**£250-300**

70    Light met. bronze body, red int.,
UB, NW ............................................**£30-40**

Dark met. bronze body, red int.,
UB, NW ..........................................**£100-120**

70 -73   Light metallic gold body, off-white
interior, UB, NW ...............................**£35-40**

Same but dark metallic gold body ........**£35-40**

Dark met. gold body, red interior,
UB, NW ............................................**£30-35**

Light met. gold body, off-white interior,
red or pink-red base, NW or WW ........**£30-35**

77-78   Light gold body, off-white interior,
UB or BB, WW (Japanese issue)..........**£30-35**

## MB 33d   DATSUN 126X

73-75   Yellow body, orange base, AG..............**£10-15**

Same but with unpainted base ..............**£30-40**

75-77   Yellow body, orange base, AG,
red/orange or red/black flame prints,
('Streakers' issue)..............................**£15-18**

78    Yellow body, BB, AG, red/black flame
prints, (US Roman Numeral issue)........**£18-20**

Gold plated body, BB, black glass,
green prints, (US Roman Numeral).......**£18-20**

## MB 33e   POLICE MOTORCYCLE

77-79   White frame, chrome or black engine,
white bars, UW, blue man, white or
black seat and panniers, 'Police'.............**£8-11**

79    White frame and bars, chrome engine,
UW, green man, seat and panniers,
'Polizei' (German)...............................**£15-18**

79    Same but cream frame, man has white
helmet and gloves (KS71 German
Polizei Patrol set)..............................**£15-18**

79    All black bike / wheels, dark blue man,
white helmet, seat and panniers.
3 stripes and shield, 'Police',
gold star tank labels (KS 66 set)...........**£20-25**

79    White frame, bars, helmet, gloves, seat,
and 'Police' labels, black engine/wheels,

blue man....................................................**£8-10**

79-81   White frame/bars, BE/wheels, green
man, seat and panniers, 'Polizei' labels
(German) ...........................................**£10-12**

79    Same but white helmet and gloves ........**£12-15**

79-81   Same but white helmet and gloves,
UW, (KS 66 Police Patrol set).............**£20-25**

81    White frame, bars, seat and panniers, green
man, BE/wheels, 'LAPD' labels .........**£20-25**

81    White frame, seat and panniers,
CE, black bars, black wheels,
no man, 'Police' labels...........................**£10-12**

81-82   Black frame, CE, white bars/seat/panniers,
black wheels, blue man,
'LAPD' (Code Red) .............................**£12-15**

## MB 34d   F-1 RACING CAR

71-72   Metallic purple body, UB, CG, yellow
or blue stripe, '16' label, 4 NW .............**£20-25**

71    Same but yellow stripe, 'Wynns'
labels (Promotional issue)....................**£60-70**

72-75   Yellow body, UB, CG, blue bonnet
stripe, '16' label, 4 NW or WW................**£6-8**

Same but front NW, rear WW.................**£8-10**

Yellow body, UB, CG,
'16' label, 4 NW ...................................**£8-10**

Yellow body, UB, AG, blue or yellow
stripe, '16' label, 4 WW ......................**£12-15**

73-75   Metallic blue body, UB, CG, yellow or blue
stripe, '15' label, 4 WW (or front NW,
rear WW) (G4 set)...............................**£70-80**

Orange body, UB, CG, blue or yellow
stripe, '16', 4 WW (or front NW, rear
WW) (G4 set)......................................**£30-35**

Orange-yellow body, UB, CG, blue
stripe, '16' label, 2 NW, 2 WW ............**£15-18**

## MB 34e   VANTASTIC

75-78   Orange, WB, GG, white int.,
stripes labels.....................................**£12-16**

Same but motif instead of stripes ...........**£8-10**

Same but with stripes and UB ..........**£100-150**

78    Orange body, WB, GG, white interior,
'Jaffa Mobile', (Promotional)..........**£200-230**

78    Orange body, WB, GG or CG, white
interior, bonnet 'Sun' label....................**£25-30**

78-81   Orange body, WB, GG, white interior,
'34', rear stripes labels on some ...........**£10-14**

## MB 34f   CHEVY PRO-STOCKER

81-83   White body, UB, blue '34' prints.............**£8-12**

Same but with no tampo prints ...............**£8-12**

White body, red base, blue '34'.............**£12-15**

## MB 35c   MERRYWEATHER
## FIRE ENGINE

69-71   Metallic red body, GB, white ladder,
'London Fire Service', NW ..................**£40-50**

71-75   Red body, GB, white ladder, 'London
Fire Service', NW or WW ...................**£25-30**

Red, GB, 'Flame-Proof Wool' .........**£125-150**

Same but in promotional box.............**£400-500**

Red body, BB, ladder, 'London
Fire Service', wide wheels.....................**£25-30**

Same but with tan base ........................**£25-30**

Red body, GB, different style ladder,
'London Fire Service', WW, (TP) ........**£20-25**

81    Red body, GB, white ladder and man
from 13f, 'Los Angeles City Fire Dept.'
prints, WW, (Code Red)......................**£20-25**

## MB 35d   FANDANGO

75-77   White body, red interior, red base,
red or silver rear disc, arrow and '35'
bonnet label (Rola-Matic)....................**£12-16**

White body, red interior, UB, red rear
disc, arrow and '35' bonnet label...........**£25-30**

# MATCHBOX SUPERSETS!

"MATCHBOX" Supersets contain exciting collections of "MATCHBOX" Models. Whether you like garages, racing cars, trucks or vintage and veteran models, there is a Super Set to suit your taste, plus two great new additions – a super size cross channel ferry set and a drag racing set.

**G2** Transporter Set
Price £1.75

**G4** Truck Set
Price £1.50

**G6** Drag Race Set  Price £1.25

**G1** Service Station Set
Price £1.80

**G3** Superfast Racing Specials
Price £1.15

**G5** "Models of Yesteryear"
Price £1.90

**G7** Ferry Boat
Price £1.20

64

65

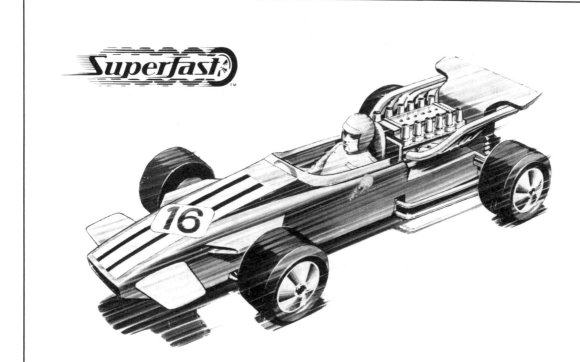

# "MATCHBOX" Nº 34 FORMULA 1. RACING CAR  "MATCHBOX"

LESNEY PRODUCTS & CO. LTD. LEE CONSERVANCY ROAD, LONDON, E.9
01·985 5533

White body, red interior and base, silver rear disc, stripe and '6' bonnet label from 41c ............................**£15-20**

77-82  Red body, red interior, red base, blue arrow and '35' bonnet label, blue or silver rear disc ........................**£85-100**

Red body, purple windows, dark blue spinner, UB ........................**£25-30**

Red body, off-white interior, WB, blue arrow and '35' label, blue, silver or red rear disc ........................**£10-15**

Red body, off-white or white interior, UB, blue rear disc, arrow and '35' ........**£12-16**

Red body, white interior, UB, blue rear disc, 'Sun' bonnet label from 47d .........**£35-40**

## MB 35e   ZOO TRUCK

82  Red body, blue cage, light brown lions, BG, BB .................................**£9-12**

Same but with red base ........................**£25-30**

Same but with grey base ........................**£10-12**

Orange body, blue cage, 5 arch wheels .**£40-45**

83  Red body, silver cage, light or dark brown lions, blue glass, black base .......**£14-18**

## MB 36c   OPEL DIPLOMAT

70  Metallic light or dark gold body, silver grille, white interior, BB .............**£20-25**

Same but without silver grille.................**£18-20**

## MB 36d   HOT ROD DRAGUAR

70-73  Metallic dark red body, off-white or light yellow interior, silver 'Draguar' label....**£15-20**

Same but with orange interior...................**£25-30**

Same but lemon or white interior .........**£15-20**

73-75  Metallic pink body, light yellow interior, silver 'Draguar' label.................**£15-20**

Met. pink body, cream interior, no boot label......................................**£18-22**

Metallic pink body, light or dark yellow interior, no boot label.............**£15-20**

Same but with amber glass ....................**£15-20**

## MB 36e   FORMULA 5000

75-77  Orange body, blue or yellow man, 'Formula 5000' and orange or yellow '3', '5000' on rear spoiler.................................**£6-8**

77  Same but red body, yellow man.................**£6-8**

77-78  Red body, yellow man, 'Texaco 11' on bonnet, no spoiler label or 'Marlboro'.......**£6-8**

78-80  Same but 'Champion' on rear spoiler .....**£8-10**

## MB 36f   REFUSE TRUCK

80-82  Met. red cab/load, yellow container, no labels ..........................................**£8-10**

Same but no 'Collectomatic' on container.............................................**£50-75**

82-83  Blue cab, yellow or orange container, black or red load, 'Metro DPW66' on side labels...........................................**£7-9**

Same but orange container with yellow opening back, red load .................**£8-10**

## MB 37c   CATTLE TRUCK

70-71  Orange-yellow cab and body, grey back and 2 white cattle ..........................**£25-30**

71  Same but orange cab and body .............**£30-40**

Orange cab and body, silver back........**£80-90**

72  Bright-yellow cab/body, grey back ......**£70-80**

## MB 37d   SOOPA COOPA

72-75  Metallic light blue body, yellow interior, AG, unpainted or silver base .................**£10-15**

75-76  Metallic light purple body, yellow

interior, AG, UB, 'flower' label............**£12-15**

Same but with red base ......................**£150-200**

Purple, yellow interior, UB...................**£25-30**

77  Orange body, yellow interior, AG, SB, 'Jaffa Mobile' (Promotional) ......**£100-120**

Orange, yellow interior, UB...................**£80-90**

## MB 37e   SKIP TRUCK

76-81  Red cab, yellow skip, chrome int., AG, BB ...........................**£11-14**

Same but grey interior, clear glass..........**£8-10**

Same but with brown base ......................**£8-10**

Red cab, yellow skip, orange int., CG, BB ..............................**£10-12**

Red cab, blue skip, grey interior, CG, BB.........................**£90-100**

77  Orange cab/body, yellow skip, grey interior, CG, BB (German issue) ......**£90-100**

Red skip (German PS1000 set) ............**£60-70**

81-82  Metallic blue cab, yellow skip, grey interior, CG, gloss or matt BB ...........**£8-10**

Same but with silver base ......................**£10-12**

## MB 37f   MATRA RANCHO

82  Blue body, blue base, black interior ........**£8-10**

83  Yellow body, yellow base, black interior, red side stripe prints ................**£15-20**

## MB 38c   HONDA MOTORCYCLE and TRAILER

70-71  Metallic blue-green bike, yellow trailer, 'Honda' labels.................**£35-40**

71  Same but metallic pink bike .................**£30-35**

72-73  Same but metallic purple bike .............**£30-35**

77  Metallic green bike, orange trailer with 'Honda' labels on some (TP) .......**£35-40**

82  Same but yellow trailer (TP)..................**£15-18**

## MB 38d   STINGEROO

73-76  First issue: Metallic purple body, purple forks, white horse's head ..........**£15-20**

Later issue with pale blue forks............**£50-65**

Same but with chrome forks .............**£600-700**

## MB 38e   JEEP

76-80  Military green body, gun, BB/seats, '21*11' or 'star' label.............................**£8-10**

77  Military olive drab green body, no gun, BB/seats, 'star' label, (TP).......**£55-65**

Same but military olive green body......**£25-30**

Same but with '21*11' label (TP).........**£20-25**

Yellow body, BB/seats, 'Gliding Club', (TP with yellow glider trailer) ..............**£15-20**

Same but with white base, (TP with yellow glider trailer) .............**£35-40**

Red body, BB/seats, 'Gliding Club', (TP with red glider trailer)..................**£450-550**

## MB 38f   FORD CAMPER

80-82  Orange-red body, green glass, cream back with AG, UB with no.'35' ...........**£90-110**

Same but camper back with no glass.......**£7-10**

## MB 38g   FORD MODEL 'A' VAN

The 'collectable cut-off point' for this Catalogue is generally 1983. However, the MB38g casting was used well into the 1990s and proved popular as a promotional item. This section therefore includes issues up to the end of 1989 but excludes items likely to be priced below £5.

84  'TOY FAIR 84' (US), roof label ............**£70-85**

Same but without roof label...................**£40-50**

84  'PEPSI COLA', 'COME ALIVE' ...........**£8-12**

Same but without 'COME ALIVE' .........**£8-12**

'PEPSI COLA', 'Matchmates'.................**£8-12**

84  'BEN FRANKLIN' ..............................**£250-350**

84  'MATCHBOX USA' ...............................**£15-20**

86  'WEET-BIX'/'SANITARIUM'...............**£8-12**

86  'H.H. BRAIN'........................................**£8-12**

87  'W.H.SMITH & SON Ltd', Red............**£8-12**

87  'MICA' 2nd CONVENTION .............**£100-125**

87  'SILVO 1912-1987`................................**£8-12**

87  'This Van Delivers', with phone no.........**£8-12**

without phone no...............................**£250-350**

87  'RICE KRISPIES', Dark Blue, (US).......**£8-12**

88  'MICA 3rd CONVENTION'...................**£8-12**

88  'MICA 1st  N.A. CONVENTION'...........**£8-12**

with black 'island'...............................**£18-22**

88  'W.H. SMITH & SON Ltd', Yellow.......**£8-12**

88  'UNIROYAL' (Canada)............................**£8-12**

89  'MB US COLLECTORS CLUB' ............**£18-22**

89  'JACKY MAEDER' (Swiss)....................**£8-12**

89  'SWARFEGA'.........................................**£8-12**

89  'CAMPERDOWN' (Australia) ...............**£12-15**

## MB 39d   CLIPPER

73-79  Metallic crimson body, yellow interior, AG, UB, chrome or white exhausts, (Rola-Matic).........................................**£20-25**

With green base and amber glass..........**£10-15**

With green base and clear glass............**£12-15**

## MB 39e ROLLS SILVER SHADOW

79-81  Silver body, Red interior, SB or UB ......**£10-12**

81-82  Metallic red body, off-white or yellow interior, silver or unpainted base.............**£8-12**

82-83  Metallic gold-brown body, white interior, silver or unpainted base..............**£8-10**

83  Ruby red body, white interior, matt black or matt silver base ......................**£12-15**

## MB 40c   HAY TRAILER

67-70  Dark blue body, yellow sides, BPT with yellow hubs...........................**£8-10**

79-79  Lt. yellow body, no sides, BPT (TP) .........**£4-6**

Same but with black fixed sides (TP).......**£4-6**

Orange-yellow body, black fixed sides, black wheels (TP)....................................**£8-10**

79  Same but with light blue body, (TP)......**£10-12**

80  Same but with red body, (TP) .............**£10-12**

81  Same but with beige body, (TP) ..........**£50-60**

## MB 40d VAUXHALL GUILDSMAN

71-74  Pink body, GG, cream interior, UB, blue circle flame bonnet label...............**£15-20**

Same but with silver base ......................**£15-20**

With UB, black circle flame label .........**£15-20**

Same but with silver base ......................**£15-20**

75  Pink body, GG, cream interior, UB, blue '40' print (Streakers issue).........**£100-120**

75-76  Red body, AG or GG, cream interior, UB or SB, blue '40' (Streakers).............**£15-20**

76  Red body, GG or AG, cream interior, UB, Blue circle flame bonnet label, (TP)......**£30-40**

Red body, AG, UB, cream interior, no bonnet label, (TP) ............................**£15-20**

## MB 40e   HORSE BOX

77-80  Orange cab, cream horse box, light or dark brown door, BB, SB, GB or UB ........**£10-12**

Same but red horse box.........................NGPP

80-83  Light metallic green cab, cream box, dark brown door, unpainted base ..........**£10-12**

Same but with white door ......................**£10-12**

Dark metallic green cab, cream box, dark brown door, UB, SB or BB ..........**£10-12**

Same but lime green door, SB or BB ....**£12-15**

83  Dark metallic green cab, dark brown

box, white door, unpainted base ............**£12-15**
Yellow cab, dark brown box, lime
green door, black base............................**£20-25**
Same but with white door ....................**£18-20**
Orange cab, dark brown box, lime
green door, BB, SB or UB ....................**£14-18**
Same but with white door ....................**£14-18**

## MB 41c    FORD GT

69-70    White body, light or dark green or BB,
red interior, '6' on bonnet, NW............**£25-30**
71-72    Metallic bronze body, dark green or
BB, red interior, '6', NW or WW ..........**£30-35**
Same but WW, cream base ...................**£30-35**
Same but WW, grey base ....................**£18-20**
WW, light or dark yellow base .............**£30-35**
Blue body, Yellow interior ....................**£40-45**
77    White body, red interior, 'Wildcat'
or '6' label, BB, (Japanese issue)...........**£30-35**
79    Yellow body, red interior, BB, no
bonnet label, MP1 Italian issue....**£2,000-2,500**

## MB 41d    SIVA SPYDER

72-75    Metallic red body, cream interior, black
band, unpainted base, clear glass...........**£10-14**
Same but with chrome band .................**£15-18**
Metallic red body, white interior, black
band, unpainted base, clear glass.............**£8-10**
75-78    Metallic dark blue body, white or cream
interior, black band, UB, CG, stars &
stripes, '8', (Streakers issue).................**£15-20**
77    Light blue body, off-white interior, black
band, UB, black glass or CG, 'Spider'
print, (US Roman Numeral issue) ........**£20-25**

## MB 41e    AMBULANCE

78-81    White body, grey interior, side stripe
with 'Ambulance', red cross labels .......**£10-12**
Same but with yellow interior...............**£12-14**
White body, grey interior, side stripe
with 'Emergency Medical Services'......**£10-12**
Same but with yellow interior...............**£12-14**
White body, grey interior, no stripe -
only 'Ambulance' in grey letters ...........**£12-15**
80    Silver body, grey interior, 'Paris-Dakar
81' (French blistercard issue)................**£35-40**
Same but with white rear doors .............**£35-40**
White body, small 'Ambulance' labels ..**£20-25**
81    Red body, grey interior, 'Notarzt' and
red cross prints, (German issue) ...........**£25-30**
White body, grey interior, side stripe
with 'Ambulance', Blue Cross labels ....**£10-12**
Same but with 'Pacific Ambulance,
Emergency, 101' prints (Code Red)......**£25-30**

## MB 41f    KENWORTH TRUCK

80    Red body, white canopy..........................**£9-12**

## MB 42c    IRON FAIRY CRANE

70    Red body, yellow boom/hook/base....**£150-175**
Light or dark orange-red body, lime
boom, yellow hook, yellow base ..........**£45-55**

## MB 42d    TYRE FRYER

72-77    Metallic light blue body,
yellow interior, UB ............................**£25-35**
Same but with black base .....................**£12-16**
Met. dark blue body,
orange-yellow int., BB.......................**£20-25**
77    Orange body, yellow interior, BB,
'Jaffa Mobile' (Promotional) ............**£100-120**

## MB 42e    MERCEDES TRUCK

77    All-yellow body, BG, BB, 'Deutsche

Bundespost' labels (German issue)........**£20-25**
77-80    Red cab/body, cream container with
red doors and roof, BG, UB,
'Sealand' or 'NYK' labels....................**£11-14**
Same but with black base .....................**£11-14**
Same but with UB, 'OCL' labels ...........**£11-14**
81    Same but with 'Confern Mobeltransport-
betriebe' labels, PG (German issue) ......**£18-20**
Dark blue cab and body, blue container
BG, UB, 'Karstadt'(German issue).......**£20-25**
81-82    Red/white, 'Matchbox', BG or PG ...........**£6-8**
Metallic green/yellow, BG or PG,
'Mayflower' and ship labels ...................**£8-11**
Same but with red glass .........................**£10-14**
Same but red/white body, BG or PG ......**£8-11**

## MB 42    '57 THUNDERBIRD

82-83    Red body, white interior, UB or SB.........**£7-10**

## MB 43c    PONY TRAILER

70-71    Yellow body, grey door, light green
base, 2 white horses, NW......................**£30-35**
Same but with dark green base ..............**£25-30**
76-79    Orange body, brown door, BB or GB,
2 horses, 'horse head' labels (TP).........**£25-30**
79-83    Same but light brown body, BB.............**£15-20**
83    Light brown body, brown door,
BB, 2 horses, 'Silver Shoes' or no
labels (TP) ...........................................**£10-15**

## MB 43d    DRAGON WHEELS

72-77    Dark green, BB, 'Dragon Wheels'.........**£12-18**
Same but with unpainted base ..............**£45-55**
Light green, BB, 'Dragon Wheels'........**£18-20**

## MB 43e    STEAM LOCOMOTIVE

78-82    Red cab/sides, black engine, '4345'..........**£4-5**
Same but with 'NP' labels .......................**£5-7**
81    Green cab/sides, black engine, '4345' .....**£8-10**
81-83    Same but with side 'NP' labels (TP) ........**£7-9**

## MB 44c    REFRIGERATOR TRUCK

70    Red cab and body, green back, grey
rear door, green glass, UB, NW........**£175-225**
70-71    Yellow cab and body, red back, grey
rear door, green glass, UB, WW ...........**£10-15**

## MB 44d    BOSS MUSTANG

72    Yellow body, black bonnet, UB, WW....**£20-25**
Same but with silver base .....................**£20-30**
80    Green, UB, 'Cobra', (US Ltd. Ed.).......**£15-20**
82-83    Dark or light orange body, off-white
interior, UB, 'The Boss' and '5'...........**£15-20**

## MB 44e  PASSENGER COACH / CABOOSE

78-83    Red/black, off-white roof, green glass,
red '431 432' side labels .........................**£6-8**
Same but with clear glass ......................**£8-10**
Same but with no glass ............................**£6-8**
Red/black, off-white roof, no glass,
red '5810 6102' side labels ......................**£6-8**
Same but with cream or tan roof ............**£6-8**
Red/black, off-white roof, no glass,
green '5810 6102' side labels ..................**£6-8**
Red/black, off-white or cream roof,
no glass, green 'GWR' side labels..........**£8-10**
81-83    Green/black, off-white raised roof, no
glass, green '5810 6102' labels (TP) ........**£6-8**
Red/black, off-white raised roof, no
glass, red '431 432' labels (TP) ................**£6-8**
Same but red '5810 6102' labels (TP)......**£6-8**

## MB 45c    FORD GROUP 6

70    Non-metallic green body, white interior
CE, CG, UB, '7' label, NW .............**£300-400**
70-71    Dark metallic green body, CE,
CG, UB or BB, '7' label, NW..............**£30-35**
Same but 'Burmah' labels (G3 set).......**£30-35**
Dark metallic green body, CE,
CG, BB or GB,'45' label, NW.............**£20-25**
Same but with pink base ......................**£35-40**
71-73    Metallic lime green body, CE,
AG, BB, '45' label, WW ......................**£15-20**
Same + 'Burmah' labels, (G3 set) ........**£20-25**
Metallic lime green body,
grey engine, AG, BB, '45', NW ...........**£15-20**
Same but grey or CE, GB, WW............**£15-20**
73-76    Metallic dark or light purple body,
grey or CE, AG, BB, '45', WW ............**£15-20**
Metallic dark purple body, CE, AG,
BB, 'eyes' label from 31d, WW ...........**£30-35**

## MB 45d    BMW 3.0 CSL

76-81    Light or dark orange body, cream
interior, GG, 'BMW' label on some ......**£12-15**
Same but with clear glass .....................**£18-22**
77    White body, cream interior, GG,
'BMW' and 'Manhalter' signature
label, (Austrian 50,000 issue) ..............**£30-35**
White body, GG, 'Polizei 123', blue
or yellow light, (German issue) ............**£50-60**
Same but no light or 'Polizei 123'.........**£50-60**
82    Red body, GG, 'BMW' (G15) .............**£80-100**

## MB 45e    KENWORTH CABOVER

82-83    White body, AG, blue/brown stripes......**£10-12**
With orange/yellow tampos ..................**£40-50**

## MB 46c    MERCEDES 300SE

70    Metallic blue body, white interior, UB,
opening doors and boot, NW ............**£150-200**
70-71    Metallic light or dark gold body,
opening doors and boot, NW ...............**£45-50**
Metallic light gold body, opening boot
but doors cast shut, NW .......................**£30-35**
77    Military olive green body, boot and
doors cast shut, 'Staff' labels (TP) ........**£18-20**
81    Silver body, WW, (Multi Pack).............**£70-80**

## MB 46d    STRETCHA FETCHA

72-77    All-white body, red base, BG,
'Ambulance', large Red Cross labels ........**£6-8**
Same but no 'Amulance', small RC ......**£15-18**
All-white body, UB, BG, 'Ambulance'
and large Red Cross labels....................**£8-10**
All-white body, red base, 'Ambulance',
large Red Cross labels, AG ..................**£15-20**
Same but no 'Amulance', small RC ......**£20-25**
77    All-red body, red base, BG, 'Unfall
Rettung' labels (German issue).............**£40-50**
80    Lime green/white, WB or BB, AG,
'Viper Van' prints (US Ltd. Ed.)............**£20-25**

## MB 46e  FORD TRACTOR and HARROW

78-81    Blue body, yellow interior, UB, black
wheels, yellow plastic harrow.................**£9-12**
Same but black wheels, yellow hubs.......**£9-12**
Blue body, white interior, UB, black
wheels, yellow hubs, yellow harrow........**£9-12**
79    Blue body, yellow interior, UB, black
wheels, no harrow (TP).........................**£9-12**
81    Metallic lime green, yellow interior,
BW, yellow hubs, no harrow (TP)..........**£9-12**
81-83    Metallic green body, yellow interior,
BW, yellow hubs, yellow harrow ...........**£9-12**
83    Blue body, white interior, GB, BW

with gold hubs, no harrow (TP)..............£9-12

## MB 47c    DAF   TRUCK

70-72   Silver cab/body, yellow tipper ..............£20-30

## MB 47d    BEACH HOPPER

73-78   Blue body with paint spots, pink base,
        orange interior, light brown man,
        clear or no windscreen,
        'Sun' label, wide WW (Rola-Matic)......£15-18
        Same but UB, no windscreen..............£15-18
        With light pink base, yellow interior,
        no windscreen, dark brown man...........£30-35

## MB 47e  PANNIER LOCOMOTIVE

79-82   Dark green and black, BB, 'G.W.R.'......£8-10
        Same but with unpainted base ................£8-10
        Same but with brown or grey base ........£15-20

## MB 47f    JAGUAR SS100

82-83   Red body, light brown interior, BB..........£8-10
        Same but with grey base ......................£10-12

## MB 48c DODGE DUMPER TRUCK

69-71   Blue cab and body, yellow tipper,
        chrome base, NW or WW.....................£35-40

## MB 48d    PIE-EYED PIPER

72-77   Metallic blue body, silver engine and
        exhausts, BG, UB, '8' and stars............£15-20
        Same but with amber glass .................£20-25
        Red body, 'Big Banger', CE and
        exhausts, BG, UB.............................£150-200
78      White body, silver/black engine, black
        exhausts, glass and base, orange
        prints, (US Roman Numeral issue)........£20-25
81-83   Red body, SE, black exhausts, AG,
        BB, 'Red Rider' prints (USA) .............£20-25

## MB 48e   SAMBRON JACK LIFT

77-81   Yellow body, BB, red 'Sambron'.......£600-800
        Same but with no tampo prints ................£5-7
        Yellow body, BB, yellow hubs ................£6-8
        Same but with grey or brown base ........£7-10
81-83   Yellow body, black forks, BB or GB........£6-8

## MB 49b    UNIMOG

70      Blue body, red base, GG,
        silver or plain grille..............................£25-30
70-71   Same but metallic steel-blue body..........£20-25
71-72   Same but sky blue body, plain grille ......£18-20
78      Military olive green body, BB, GG,
        tan load, 'A' label in square (TP)...........£35-40
        'Star' circle label,
        tan load on some, (TP).......................£35-40

## MB 49c    CHOP SUEY

73-76   Metallic red-purple frame, chrome
        forks, CE, 'bull's head' .....................£400-500
        Same but with red forks...........................£8-10
        With black or orange forks ..................£35-40

## MB 49d    CRANE TRUCK

76-79   Yellow body and crane arm,
        red hook, BB, GG ...................................£6-8
77      Red body, yellow crane arm, red hook,
        BB, GG (German PS1000 set) ...........£70-80
        Same but GG (German PS1000 set) ......£60-70
80-82   Yellow body, black crane arm, red

hook, black base, purple or red glass.....£15-18
        Same but green glass...........................£15-18
82-83   Same but 'A1 Crane Service' on arm
        + 'Safety First', 'C', 'Cat' on some .......£15-18

## MB 50c    KENNEL TRUCK

70-71   Dark or light metallic green body, BB,
        silver grille, 4 white dogs, NW .............£18-20
        Dark Metallic Green body, Grey base,
        silver grille, 4 white dogs, NW .............£15-18
        Same but with yellow base ...................£25-30
72-73   Lime Green body, BB or GB,
        chrome grille, 4 white dogs, WW ........£70-80
        Same but white grille, BB or GB..........£30-35
        Same but with unpainted base .............£35-40

## MB 50d    PETERBILT  TRUCK

73-79   Yellow cab/body, BB, light blue trailer
        with yellow chevron side labels, yellow
        or orange trailer body, red or PG .........£10-15
        Same but no labels .................................£8-12
        Yellow cab/trailer, 'KODAK' logo .........NGPP
80      Red cab/body, BB, light blue trailer, no
        labels, red trailer body, PG ..................£40-45
        Yellow cab/body/trailer body,
        light blue trailer, no labels, white tow
        hook, purple glass (TP)...........................£8-11
        Red cab/body, silver trailer (red body),
        white hook on some, PG (TP) .............£35-40
80      **Articulated Trailer**
        Light blue trailer (yellow body) (TP) ........£6-8
        Silver trailer, red trailer body (TP) .......£35-40

## MB 50e    HARLEY-DAVIDSON

80-82   Light gold frame, black handlebars .......£13-16
82-83   Dark bronze frame, black bars..............£13-16
        Light bronze frame, with rider ..............£13-16

## MB 51c LEYLAND 8-wheel TIPPER

70-71   Yellow cab and body, silver tipper,
        BG, SB, 'POINTER' labels on some.....£30-35
        Same but with grey base .....................£80-100
        Promotional issue: 'Alcon Laboratories Inc.
        Fort Worth, Texas'. Chrome grille,
        plastic bottle, special box..................£250-350

## MB 51d    CITROËN SM

72-74   Metallic bronze body,
        cream int., UB, NW ...........................£12-15
        Same but with orange interior...........£120-150
        Same but with yellow interior...............£20-25
        With cream interior, silver base ...........£12-15
75      Metallic blue body,
        yellow int., UB, WW ..........................£30-40
        Same but with off-white interior, UB ....£50-65
75-78   Same plus '8', UB (Streakers issue) ......£12-14
        With '8', UB and off-white or orange
        interior (Streakers issue) .....................£15-18
79      Metallic blue body, orange interior, UB,
        roof rack, 'Yamaha Shell STP' (TP)......£15-18

## MB 51e   COMBINE HARVESTER

78-81   Red body, yellow blades/arm, BB,
        black 'regular wheels'............................£8-11
        Same but with black Superfast wheels ....£8-11
        Same but with yellow hubs...................£12-15
        Red body, yellow blades/arm,
        no base, black Superfast wheels .............£8-10
        Same but with yellow hubs...................£12-14
        Yellow body, red blades/arm, no base,
        '2' print, Superfast wheels (Gift Set).......£8-10

## MB 51f   PONTIAC FIREBIRD SE

82-83   Red body, tan interior, silver base............£8-10

Red body, yellow interior......................£14-18

## MB 51i MOTORCYCLE TRAILER

79-82   Metallic blue body, 3 orange-yellow or
        yellow bikes (TP)..................................£7-10
        Same but with 3 red bikes (TP)...........£10-12
82-83   Red body, 3 yellow bikes (TP) .............£12-15

## MB 52c DODGE CHARGER Mk.III

70-71   Metallic light or dark red body,
        black interior ........................................£8-12
        Same but with '5' labels (G3 set) ........£30-35
71      Metallic purple body, black interior......£15-20
71-75   Metallic lime green, black interior..........£8-12
        Same but with '5' labels (G3 set) ........£25-30
        Same but with UB (G3 set)..................£25-30

## MB 52d    POLICE LAUNCH

76-80   White deck, light blue hull,
        lt. or dk. BG, orange stripes, 'Police',
        2 light blue men, 2 horns ....................£10-13
81      Same but with no roof horns.................£8-11
        White deck, red hull, roof and rear, BG,
        'Los Angeles Fire Department',
        2 light blue men (Code Red issue) ......£25-30
        Same but 2 yellow men (Code Red).......£18-20

## MB 52e    BMW M1

81-83   Silver body, red interior, BB, CG, black
        stripes and '52' tampo prints.................£11-14
        Same but blue-grey base .....................£10-12
        With BB, amber glass .........................£25-30
        With BB, CG, no tampo prints .............£10-12
        With BB, green glass .......................£120-140

## MB 53c    FORD ZODIAC Mk.IV

70      Metallic light blue body, NW ...........£450-500
70-71   Metallic light green body, NW .............£50-60
        Metallic dark green body, NW...............£35-40
        Metallic emerald green body .................£30-40
72      Lime green body, wide wheels .............£70-80

## MB 53d    TANZARA

72-74   Orange body, SE,
        silver interior, UB, AG .......................£10-15
        Same but with green glass ...................£10-15
75-76   White body, SE, silver interior, UB,
        AG, blue/orange stripes/stars, '53' .......£12-15
        Same but with no tampo prints .............£18-20
        With blue/red stripes/stars, '53'............£12-15
        Same but with green glass ...................£18-20
        White body, red engine, red interior,
        UB, AG, blue/red stripes/stars, '53'......£80-90

## MB 53e    CJ6 JEEP

77-80   Red body, yellow interior,
        lt. brown roof, UB, WW .........................£8-10
        Same but with black interior...................£8-10
        With yellow interior, silver base ..............£8-10
81-82   Metallic green body, yellow interior,
        light brown roof, UB, WW .....................£8-10
        Same but with black interior...................£8-10
        With yellow interior, silver base ..............£8-10
        Pale yellow body, dark brown roof,
        black interior, BB or GB, 'CJ6' print ....£12-15

## MB 53f    FLARESIDE PICK-UP

82-83   Blue body, '326' and 'Baja Bouncer'......£8-10
        Same but with some or prints or none.....£8-10

## MB 54b CADILLAC AMBULANCE

70    White body, silver grille, red roof lights,
      BB, small Red Cross door labels ...**£75-85**
      Off-white body, plain grille, red roof
      lights, BlB, large Red Cross labels ........**£85-95**

## MB 54c    FORD CAPRI

71    Pink or orange body, black bonnet,
      UB, wide wheels ....................................**£25-30**
72-75  Metallic crimson body UB or SB .........**£20-25**
76    Orange body, UB, (TP) .........................**£35-40**

## MB 54d   PERSONNEL CARRIER

76-79  Military green body, black base, green
      glass, light brown soldiers on some........**£8-10**

## MB 54e    MOBILE HOME

80-82  Cream or white body, brown door,
      side stripes on some, BB.......................**£9-12**
      Same but with grey or brown base .........**£9-12**

## MB 54f    NASA Tracking Vehicle

82-83  White/red/black, BB, 'US Space
      Shuttle Command Centre', 'NASA'.......**£15-18**
      Same but with grey base ......................**£15-18**

## MB 55d  MERCURY POLICE CAR

70    White body, 2 men, blue roof light,
      shields and 'Police' label .....................**£60-70**
      Same but with red roof light .................**£50-60**

## MB 55e MERCURY EST. POLICE

71-74  White body, off-white interior, no men,
      UB, 2 red roof lights, bonnet shield and
      'Police' label and side shield labels .......**£25-30**
      Same but UB or SB, bonnet and side
      'Police' arrow labels ...........................**£15-20**
      Same but UB or SB, bonnet 'Police'
      arrow label, plain sides ........................**£15-20**

## MB 55f    HELLRAISER

75-76  White body, red interior, UB,
      'Stars and Stripes' bonnet label ............**£10-15**
      Yellow body, sun bonnet label...........**£300-350**
      Yellow, Red int., bare metal base......**£90-110**
77-78  Metallic blue body, red interior, SB,
      'Stars and Stripes' bonnet label ............**£12-16**
      Metallic blue body, off-white interior,
      UB or SB, 'Stars and Stripes' ...............**£10-15**
      Metallic blue body, off-white interior,
      SB, bonnet stripe and '3' label..............**£32-38**
      Same but with no label .........................**£10-15**

## MB 55g    FORD CORTINA

79-80  Metallic green body, red interior,
      UB, clear glass, opening doors .............**£15-18**
      Same but with light yellow interior .......**£18-22**
81    Metallic red body, light yellow interior,
      UB, opening doors ...............................**£16-20**
82-83  Metallic light brown body, white interior,
      UB or SB, opening doors, black stripe ..**£19-24**
      Light red body, white interior,
      UB or SB, doors cast shut......................**£8-10**
      Same but with gloss black base ............**£18-20**
      Bright red body, white interior,
      UB or SB, opaque glass,
      doors cast shut (Gift Set issue) .............**£27-32**
83    Light red body, light brown interior,
      UB or SB, doors cast shut,
      black side stripe prints (TP)..................**£20-25**
      Same but white interior (TP) ................**£12-15**

## MB 56c  BMC 1800 PINIFARINA

---

69-70  Metallic gold body, UB, NW .................**£20-25**
      Same with '17', 'Gulf' (G3 set)............**£30-35**
71-73  Peach body, UB, NW.............................**£35-40**
      Orange body, UB, NW or WW..............**£12-15**
      With '17' and 'Gulf' (G3 set) ...............**£20-25**
      Pre-production model. Colour trial,
      Silver body, baseplate without 'Superfast',
      pre-production Superfast wheels
      with silver hubs.............................. **£750-950**

## MB 56d    HI-TAILER

74-78  White body, orange/blue stripes, UB,
      'MB5 Team Matchbox', yellow man.....**£15-18**
      With red labels instead of orange .........**£75-85**
      Same but with silver or red base............**£15-18**
      Same but with blue man .......................**£15-18**
79    Red base, 'Martini 7' (Gift Set) ............**£20-25**

## MB 56e    MERCEDES 450 SEL

79-80  Metallic blue body, red interior ...........**£20-25**
      Same but with light brown interior........**£10-12**
81-83  Light brown body, light or dark brown
      interior, red 'Taxi' sign, UB or SB........**£16-20**

## MB 56f    PETERBILT TANKER

82    US issue: Blue body, white back,
      'Milk's the One'..................................**£12-15**
      Same but white tampo on doors ...........**£13-16**

## MB 57c Land-Rover FIRE TRUCK

70    Red body, 'Kent Fire Brigade' labels ....**£80-90**
      Same but with 'Kent Fire Brigade'
      labels cut around words ......................**£90-110**

## MB 57d    ECCLES CARAVAN

70-71  Cream body, orange roof, green
       interior, maroon side stripe labels.........**£15-20**
      Same but brown side stripe labels .........**£18-22**
      With brown stripe and flower labels......**£15-20**
72    Pale Yellow body, orange roof, green
      interior, brown stripe, flower labels.......**£30-35**
76-78  Yellow body, red-orange roof,
      white interior, black stripe, flowers (TP) ....**£15-20**
      Same but with side red dots label from
       K-27 Camping Cruiser set (TP)...........**£25-30**
79-81  Light brown, red-orange roof, white
      interior, black stripe, flowers (TP) .......**£12-16**
      Same but 'white bird' label (TP) ..........**£20-25**
82    White body, red-orange roof, white
      interior, 'Sunset', palm tree (TP) .........**£18-22**

## MB 57e    WILDLIFE TRUCK

73-80  Yellow body, clear back, red glass,
      'Ranger' (Rola-Matic version)...............**£10-15**
      Same but with amber back....................**£12-16**
81    White body, clear back, red glass, light
      brown lion, black/white camouflage
      prints, (Rola-Matic version)..................**£10-15**
      Same but with amber glass ...................**£12-16**
      Same but with purple glass ..................**£15-20**
      Same but tinted detachable back...........**£15-20**

## MB 57f    CARMICHAEL RESCUE

82    White body, 'Police Rescue'.................**£15-20**
83    Red body, 'Fire'...................................**£15-20**

## MB 58c    DAF GIRDER TRUCK

70    Cream or off-white cab and body,
      red base (with 'Pat App' on some).....**£125-150**
70-71  Metallic lime green cab and body.........**£35-40**

## MB 58d    WOOSH 'N' PUSH

---

72-75  Yellow body, red interior, '2' label ...........**£7-9**
      Same but pale yellow interior...............**£25-30**
      With red interior, 'flower' label ............**£12-15**
76    Metallic red body, pale yellow interior,
      '2' label on roof...................................**£8-10**
      Same but '8' and stars label .................**£12-15**

## MB 58e    FAUN DUMP TRUCK

76-81  Yellow body, yellow tipper .......................**£6-9**
79    Yellow body, red tipper (G5 set)............**£25-30**
82-83  Yellow body, yellow tipper, 'CAT' ........**£10-12**

## MB 59c  FORD GALAXIE FIRE

70    Red body, white interior, 'Fire Chief'
      and side shield labels .............................**£60-75**
      Promotional issue 'Lyons Tea', in
      promotional blister pack with card
      label. Dutch/Belgian market....... **£750-1,000**

## MB 59d  MERCURY FIRE CHIEF

71-74  Red body, '59' or '73', 2 men,
      yellow 'Fire Chief' on bonnet,
      'shield' labels on sides ...........................**£20-25**
      Same but 'helmet & axes' on sides........**£15-20**
      Same but yellow bonnet 'helmet and
       axes' labels, plain sides........................**£12-16**
      Same but yellow 'helmet and axes'
      labels on bonnet and sides ...................**£12-16**
      With nothing or just '59' on base .........**£12-16**
78    Same but with no men (TP)...................**£12-16**
      Red body, CG, 'Fire', shield (TP) .........**£12-16**
      Red body with purple glass (TP)...........**£15-20**
79    White, CG, 'Police', shield (TP) ...........**£20-25**
81    Red body, 'Los Angeles Fire Dept'
      tampo prints (Code Red)........................**£20-25**
      White body, CG or BG, 'Los Angeles
      Police' tampo prints,  (Code Red)..........**£20-25**
82    White body, CG, PG or BG, 'Police'
      and shield, black wing panel prints .......**£20-25**
      White body, CG or BG, 'Metro Police',
      black wing tampo prints as 10f............**£10-15**
      Same but with white wing panels ..........**£12-16**

## MB 59e    PLANET SCOUT

75-77  Metallic green and lime green ...............**£10-15**
78-80  Metallic red and light brown...............**£10-15**
77    Avocado/black, PG or AG (Adventure
      2000 K2005 Command Force set)........**£25-30**
80    Metallic blue/black, PG,
      (Adventure 2000 set)............................**£50-60**

## MB 59f    PORSCHE 928

80-81  Light metallic brown body, brown
      interior, black base, clear glass ...............**£8-10**
      Same but cream or off-white interior......**£10-12**
      With brown interior, amber glass...........**£16-20**
      Dark met. brown, brown interior, BB....**£10-15**
      Same but with amber glass ...................**£16-20**
      Same but with brown glass....................**£10-15**
      With clear glass, brown or grey base .....**£10-15**
      With AG, brown or grey base ...............**£12-15**
81-82  Met. blue body, brown int., CG, BB......**£10-12**
      Same but with grey or silver base..........**£10-15**
82-83  Black body, brown interior, 'Porsche' ...**£12-16**
      Same but with red interior ...................**£10-12**

## MB 60b TRUCK and SITE OFFICE

70    Blue truck, yellow/green office..............**£25-30**
      Dark Blue truck, 2-rivet base................**£40-45**

## MB 60c    LOTUS SUPER 7

71-75  Orange body, black interior and boot,
      bonnet 'flame' label ..............................**£12-15**

Same but with Yellow body ..................£15-20
75-76   Same but blue stripe and check design
+ bonnet '60' prints, (Streakers) ....£15-20

## MB 60d    HOLDEN PICK-UP

77      Metallic ruby red body, yellow interior,
AG, yellow bikes, '500' label .............£12-15
77-80   Bright red body, yellow interior,
AG, yellow bikes, '500' label .............£12-15
Same but with orange glass ................£12-15
Bright red body, red interior, orange or
AG, olive green bikes, '500' label........£12-15
Bright red body, red interior, orange or
AG, olive green bikes, 'Sun' label ......£35-40
Bright red body, yellow interior, AG,
yellow bikes, 'striped' bonnet label ......£15-18
80      Metallic blue body, yellow interior,
OG or AG, yellow bikes,
'Paris-Dakar 81' (French issue) ...........£20-25
81-83   Cream body, red interior, orange or
AG, red bikes, stripes and Superbike! ...£20-25
Same but with yellow bikes ..............£10-14
Cream body, red interior, AG,
red bikes, 'Honda' labels ......................£25-30

## MB 61b    ALVIS STALWART

66-71   White body, yellow detachable top,
clear glass, 'BP Exploration' labels,
regular black wheels, yellow hubs........£35-40
78      Metallic olive green body, fixed top,
GG, black wide wheels (TP)...............£20-25

## MB 61c    BLUE SHARK

71-77   Metallic blue, UB or SB, CG, '86'....£15-20
Same but with '69' label from 69d....£15-20
Metallic blue body, SB, CG or AG,
'Scorpion' label on bonnet ....................£50-60
Metallic blue body, UB or SB, AG,
bonnet arrows and '86' label..............£15-20
Same but with '69' label from 69d .......£15-20

## MB 61d    WRECK TRUCK

78-80   Red body, white arms, red hooks,
BB or GB, AG and 2 roof lights...........£10-12
With red or white arms, black hooks.....£10-12
Red body, red arms, red hooks .............£10-12
Red body, white arms, red hooks,
BB, blue glass and 2 roof lights............£25-30
81      Red body and hooks, off-white arms,
BB, AG, 'Radio Despatches 24 Hour
Towing' (TP) .......................................£15-20
81-82   Light yellow body, red arms, black
hooks, AG, black or grey base..............£10-12
Same but with brown base ....................£10-12
Same but with silver base .....................£10-12
With red arms & hooks, BB or GB ........£10-12
Light yellow body, white arms, red
hooks, BB or GB, AG and lights ...........£20-25
Light yellow body, green arms, red
or black hooks, BB or GB, AG lights....£12-15
Dark yellow body, red arms,
BB/hooks, AG .....................................£10-12
Same but with brown base ......................£8-10
Dark yellow body, red arms, red hooks,
BB or GB, AG and lights .........................£7-9
Dark yellow body, white arms, red
hooks, BB, AG and lights .....................£20-25
Dark yellow body, green arms, red
or black hooks, BB, AG and lights........£12-15
Same but with grey base .......................£15-20

## MB 61e    PETERBILT WRECKER

82-83   Red-orange, white 'Eddies Wrecker'....£8-11
Same but with black tampo prints ........£12-15
Blue body, no tampo print, from
'Highway Express' Gift Set).................£20-25

## MB 62c    MERCURY COUGAR

70      Light metallic gold, red interior............£20-25
Metallic green ......................................£85-95

## MB 62d    MERCURY COUGAR DRAGSTER

70      Light green body, red interior, UB,
'Rat Rod' labels...................................£25-30
70-73   Same but lime green body ....................£15-20
Same but with silver base .....................£25-35
Same but UB, 'Wild Cat' labels............£45-55

## MB 62e    RENAULT 17TL

74-78   Red body, white interior, '9' label .........£10-15
Red-orange body, white interior, '9' ......£10-15
Same but label reversed to read '6' ......£12-16
76      Red body, white interior, 'Fire'
labels, (from G12 Rescue set)..............£25-35

## MB 62f    CHEVROLET CORVETTE

79-81   Metallic ruby red body, grey interior,
UB, CG, white bonnet prints ................£11-14
Same but with black interior.................£11-14
Same but white interior..........................£15-20
Same but with black interior.................£11-14
Same but with grey interior ..................£11-14
81-83   Black body, grey interior, UB, CG,
orange/yellow bonnet stripes ...............£11-14
Same but with silver base ....................£11-14
83      Same but UB, opaque glass, (from
Streak Racing set) ...............................£25-30
White body, black stripes, '09' .............£17-22

## MB 63c    DODGE CRANE TRUCK

70-72   Yellow body, yellow crane, arm
and hook (orange hook on some) ..........£25-30

## MB 63d    FREEWAY GAS TANKER

73      Red/black/white, 'Castrol' labels ...........£60-70
73-77   Red/black/white, 'Burmah' labels .........£10-15
Same but with tow hook hole in rear.....£10-15
76      Military olive drab green and black,
'Canadian' flag labels (TP) ................£300-400
Same but with 'French' flag (TP) .........£70-80
76-77   Military olive green cab black base,
'95 High Octane' (TP) .........................£18-20
77      Light blue/black/white,
'Aral' labels (German) ..........................£30-35
78-79   Red/black/white, 'Chevron' labels,
tow hook hole in rear of tanker...............£6-8
Same but with white tow hook (TP)........£8-10
Red/black/white, 'Burmah' labels,
cream tow hook (TP) ............................£10-12
79-80   White/yellow, 'Shell' labels, PG ...........£10-12
Same but with red glass ......................£12-14
Yellow/black/white, 'Shell', PG ...........£18-22
80-81   White/yellow, 'Exxon' labels ...............£18-22
White/black, 'Exxon' labels..................£18-22
White/yellow, 'Shell',
cream tow hook (TP) ...........................£10-15
Same but 'Exxon' labels (TP)...............£18-22
81-82   White/black/green, 'BP Super' ............£15-20
White/yellow, 'BP Super' (TP).............£25-30

## MB 63dx    FREEWAY GAS TRAILER

78-79   White/red, 'Chevron' labels (TP)..........£10-15
Same but with 'Burmah' labels (TP) .....£10-15
80-81   White/yellow, 'Shell' labels (TP)..........£10-15
White/yellow, 'Exxon' labels (TP) ........£15-18
81-82   White/yellow, 'BP Super' (TP)............£20-25

## MB 63e    4x4 OPEN BACK TRUCK

82-83   Orange (shades),

'24' and 'FWD' or '4x4' ......................£10-15

## MB 63f    SNORKEL FIRE ENGINE

82      Red body, white ladder, UB.................£18-24

## MB 64b    MG 1100

70      Green body, white interior with man and
dog, unpainted base, clear glass........£300-400
70-71   Same but metallic light blue body ........£45-55
Same but metallic dark blue body ........£45-55

## MB 64c    SLINGSHOT DRAGSTER

71-72   Metallic pink body, BB, black exhausts,
bonnet flame and '9' labels...................£15-20
73      Orange body, BB, black exhausts,
bonnet flame and '9' label ................£100-120
Same but red exhausts.......................£150-200
73-75   Metallic blue-green body, UB, red
exhausts, bonnet flame, '9' label .........£18-24
Same but BB, front NW or WW...........£10-15
Same but with '3'..................................£18-20

## MB 64d    FIRE CHIEF CAR

76-79   Red body, 'Fire', some yellow shield
labels have black edging.........................£8-12
Same but with orange body ..................£10-14

## MB 64e    CATERPILLAR D-9

79-81   Yellow body, brown roof, yellow shovel,
black tracks, orange or yellow rollers....£10-15
82      Yellow body, black roof, yellow shovel,
'C' on cab, black tracks, yellow rollers ..£10-15
82-83   Same but black shovel, black or silver
tow hook, 'C' on cab ............................£10-15
Same plus 'CAT' print, (black hook)......£10-15

## MB 65c    CLAAS COMBINE HARVESTER

67-72   Red body, yellow cutters, black base,
black wheels with yellow hubs ...............£8-10

## MB 65d    SAAB SONNET III

73-76   Metallic blue body, yellow interior,
UB, AG, grey rear door...........................£8-10
79      White body, yellow interior, UB,
AG, grey rear door, (Multi Pack).......£200-220

## MB 65e    AIRPORT COACH

**NB All Airport Coach models have white roofs.**
77-81   Metallic blue body, off-white or pale
yellow interior, AG or CG, UB,
'British Airways' .................................£10-15
Same but with labels reversed ..............£10-12
Metallic blue body, off-white interior,
UB, AG, 'American Airlines' labels......£10-15
Same but with clear glass .....................£12-15
Same but pale yellow interior, AG .......£10-15
Same but with clear glass .....................£12-15
Metallic blue, off-white or pale yellow
interior, AG, 'Lufthansa' (German) ......£10-15
Same but with clear glass .....................£12-15
81      Orange body, pale yellow interior, UB,
AG, 'Schulbus' (German issue)............£25-35
81-83   Red body, 'TWA' .....................................£9-12
Red body, 'Qantas'..................................£9-12
82      Red body, 'Fly Braniff'..........................£25-35
White body, 'Stork SB'(Australian) ......£18-20
Metallic Blue,
'Girobank' (Promotional)......................£18-20
83      Metallic Blue, UB or SB, AG,
'British' labels .........................................£9-12
Met. Blue, UB or SB, AG,
'Australian' labels ................................£12-14

White body, UB or SB, 'Alitalia'...........£15-20
White body, UB or SB, 'Lufthansa'......£25-30

## MB 65f    BANDAG BANDIT

82        Black with green/white stripes.................£8-11

## MB 66c    GREYHOUND COACH

70        Silver body, yellow interior, AG, matt
or gloss BB, 'Greyhound', box 'F'........£60-70
Supplied in 'C' type box........£25-30
Same but with yellow or pink base.......£25-35

## MB 66d    MAZDA RX500

71-74    Orange body, SE, white base, PG..............£7-9
Same but with unpainted base..............£15-20
Orange body, SE, white base, AG..........£12-15
75-76    Red body, SE, WB, AG, white/green
'77' and stripes (Streakers version) ..........£7-9
Same but with PG (Streakers)..........£12-14
Same but UB, AG (Streakers)..........£12-14
Red body, light brown engine, WB,
AG, '77' and stripes (Streakers) ..........£12-14
Same but with PG (Streakers)..........£15-18

## MB 66e    FORD TRANSIT

77-80    Orange body, green glass, UB,
brown load, green interior......................£20-25
Same but light brown interior ..............£15-20
Same but light yellow interior ...............£9-12
Orange body, amber glass, UB,
beige load, green interior ......................£25-30
Light brown or light yellow interior ......£15-20
81-82    Yellow-orange body, off-white or green
interior, UB, brown load, green glass ....£10-15
Same but with beige load........................£9-12
Yellow-orange body, green interior, GB,
brown or beige load, green glass ..........£10-15
Same but with black base .....................£15-20

## MB 66f    TYRONE MALONE

82-83    White body, blue/red stripes on some,
'Tyrone Malone' on white aerofoil .........£8-10
With plain white or cream aerofoil ..........£6-8

## MB 67b    VOLKSWAGEN 1600TL

70        Dark or light red body,
white interior, UB, CG, NW .............£120-150
70-71    Metallic purple body (may be dark,
mid or light), white interior,
UB, CG, NW or WW...........................£40-45
71-72    Metallic pink body, white interior,
UB, CG, NW or WW ..........................£40-45
Pre-production model. Colour trial,
Metallic dark blue, no 'Superfast' on
baseplate, pre-production SF wheels
with silver hubs.......................... £750-1,000

## MB 67c    HOT ROCKER

73-74    Metallic green-gold body, white interior,
UB, CG (Rola-Matic version)............£15-20
Same but with silver base .....................£20-30
Same but metallic green body, UB .....£15-20
Same but with silver base .....................£20-30
75-77    Red body, UB, (Rola-Matic version).....£12-16
Same but with silver base .....................£20-30

## MB 67d    DATSUN 260Z 2+2

78-80    Metallic crimson body,
white interior, CG, BB .......................£8-11
Same but with grey base .....................£10-12
79        Metallic blue body, pale yellow
interior, matt black base (TP) ............£15-20

Same but with red interior (TP).............£30-40
Metallic blue body, red int.,
brown base (TP).................................£40-50
80        Metallic red body,
pale yellow interior, BB .........................£15-18
81-83    Silver body, red interior, black base ..... £8-11
Same but grey or blue-grey base ..........£10-12
Same but with brown base ....................£10-12
Silver body, white interior, GB or BB,
red stripes, black 'Datsun 2+2' (TP)......£10-12
Silver body, black interior, BB, blue
stripes, black 'Datsun 2+2' (TP)..........£12-15
83        Black body and interior, BB (TP).........£20-30

## MB 68c    PORSCHE 910

70-74    Metallic red body, pale yellow interior,
UB, AG, '68' label on bonnet, NW .......£15-20
Same + '68' side labels (G3 set).........£25-30
Metallic red body, pale yellow interior,
UB, AG, bonnet '68' label, WW...........£15-20
Same but with '45' label from 45c ........£25-30
Silver body, White interior, UB ........£140-160
72        White body, pale yellow interior, UB,
AG, WW ('Broom Stick' issue) ..........£35-40

## MB 68d    COSMOBILE

75-78    Metallic light blue body, yellow under,
white or silver interior, AG ......................£8-12
77        Avocado body, black under, white
interior, AG, (Adventure 2000 set)........£20-25
Same but with purple glass (set)...........£15-20
Same but with silver interior (set) ........£25-30
78-79    Metallic red body, beige under,
white or silver interior, AG ....................£8-10
80        Metallic dark blue, black under, silver
interior, PG (Adventure 2000 set)..........£50-65

## MB 68e    CHEVY VAN

79-80    Orange body, UB, BG, blue/red or
blue/white stripes ................................£10-15
Same but CG, blue/red stripes ..............£12-16
Same but BG, red/black stripes ............£10-15
Same but with green or red glass..........£10-15
80-81    Orange body, 'Matchbox Collectors
Club' labels, BG (Ltd. Edition)...........£15-18
81-82    White body, 'Adidas' (German)............£25-30
White body, 'USA-1' (US issue) ..........£12-15
Green body, 'Chevy' with brown or
yellow segmented stripes ........................£9-12
82-83    Yellow body, 'Collect Exciting
Matchbox' (Australian issue).................£20-25
Silver body, blue glass, 'Vanpire' ..........£10-15

## MB 69c ROLLS SILVER SHADOW

69-70    Metallic blue body, brown interior,
tan folded top, BB, AG, NW..................£30-40
Same but dark or light yellow base ......£35-40
71-72    Metallic light gold body, brown interior,
tan folded top, BB, AG, WW..................£30-40
Same but dark or light yellow base ......£30-40
Same but with silver base .....................£30-40
With black folded top, BB .....................£40-45
Same but with light yellow base ...........£30-40
Same but with silver or grey base.........£30-40
With off-white interior, black folded
top, black base, AG, WW .....................£40-45
Same but with grey base ......................£25-35
Metallic dark gold body, off-white
interior, black folded top, BB, WW......£30-40
Same but with grey or silver base.........£20-25
Metallic dark gold body, brown interior,
tan folded top, BB, AG, WW..................£30-40
Same but with grey or silver base.........£25-35
72-73    Metallic lime gold body, off-white or
brown interior, BB, AG, WW ..............£40-50
Same but with grey or silver base.........£50-60

## MB 69d    TURBO FURY

73-77    Metallic red body, CG, '69' and
arrows label, (Rola-Matic version)........£10-15
Same but AG (Rola-Matic version)......£12-16
Metallic red body, '86' and arrows
label, (Rola-Matic version) ..................£25-30
Same but 'Scorpion' (Rola-Matic)........£40-45

## MB 69e    SECURITY TRUCK

78-83    Dark red body, cream roof, UB or SB,
BG, '732 2031', 'Wells Fargo' ............£10-12
Light red body, white roof, SB, CG,
'732 2031' and 'Wells Fargo'.................£12-15
Same but BG, UB or SB........................£10-12
Light red body, white roof, SB, BG,
'QZ 2031' and 'Wells Fargo'................£15-20
81        Metallic dark green body, SB, BG,
'Dresdner Bank' (German promo)........£25-30

## MB 69f    WILLYS STREET ROD

82        US issue: White, flame-effect tampo.....£10-14

## MB 70b    GRIT SPREADER TRUCK

70        Red cab and body, dark or pale yellow
grit spreader, UB, GG, NW ..................£15-20
Same but with 5-spoke wheels .............£35-40

## MB 70c    DODGE DRAGSTER

71-75    Dark pink body, BB, 'snake' labels .......£12-16
Supplied in 'J' type box .......................£80-90
With purple, cream, light green, light
yellow, dark yellow or grey base..........£20-25
With brown or unpainted base ..............£35-40
Dark pink body, BB, 'Wild Cat'............£40-50
Dark pink body, 'Rat Rod' labels ......£100-125
Light pink body, BB, 'snake' labels......£15-18
Light pink, BB, blue star labels .........£150-175
Bright pink body, BB, 'snake' labels.....£15-18
78        Yellow body, red glass, GB or BB,
side prints, (US Roman Numeral) ........£18-20

## MB 70d    S.P. GUN

76-80    Military green body, black or brown
tracks, (Rola-Matic version) ...................£8-10

## MB 70e    FERRARI 308 GTB

81-83    Red body and base, black stripe, CG.....£10-14
Red body and base, CG, 'Ferrari'.........£10-14
Same but with AG.................................£12-15
83        Red body, silver base, no 'Ferrari'.......£20-25

## MB 71c FORD HEAVY WRECKER

70-72    Red cab, white body, red crane and
hook, BB, GG, 'Esso' ...........................£55-65
Same but with yellow hook ...................£40-50
79        Military olive green, black hook,
BB, GG, '3LGS64' labels (TP)............£20-25
81        Dark blue, blue crane, black hook,
BB, GG, no labels (Multi Pack) ...........£80-90

## MB 71d    JUMBO JET

73-75    Metallic blue frame, red elephant head,
dark blue handlebars, black wheels ......£10-15
Same but light blue handlebars.............£20-25

## MB 71e    CATTLE TRUCK

76-81    Metallic orange-red cab, dark yellow back,
UB or SB, GG or BG, 2 black cattle ....£10-12
With AG, PG or orange glass, SB ........£10-12

79-83   Dark red cab, off-white back,
SB, BG, 2 black cattle (TP) .................**£10-12**
Same but with red or PG (TP) ..............**£10-12**
Dark red cab, dark or light yellow back,
SB, PG, 2 black cattle (TP)...................**£10-12**

81-83   Metallic light green cab, off-white back,
SB, OG, 2 brown cattle..........................**£8-10**
Metallic light or dark green cab, yellow
back, SB, red or OG, 2 brown cattle ......**£8-10**
Metallic dark green cab, dark brown
back, SB, red or AG, 2 brown cattle.....**£14-18**

83   Yellow cab, brown back, BB, UB or SB,
red or AG, 2 light brown cattle................**£8-10**
Same but with black tow hook (TP)........**£8-10**

## MB 71ex  CATTLE TRUCK TRAILER

79-83   Dark red body, off-white or light or dark
yellow back, SB, 2 black cattle (TP) .........**£5-7**

83   Yellow body, dark yellow back, SB,
2 light brown cattle (TP)...........................**£5-7**

## MB 71f  CORVETTE

82   White, red/yellow tampo.......................**£12-15**

## MB 72b  STANDARD JEEP

70-71   Dull yellow body, red interior, UB .......**£35-40**
Bright yellow body, red interior............**£75-85**

## MB 72c  SRN HOVERCRAFT

72-78   White body, BB, BG, 'R.N.L.I.' ................**£6-8**

## MB 72d  BOMAG ROAD ROLLER

79-82   Yellow/red, black roller, 2 wheels .............**£6-8**
Same but 2 wheels have yellow hubs........**£7-9**

## MB 72e  DODGE DELIVERY

All have red cab, white back,
some have 'gold' hubs.
82-83   'Pepsi'.....................................................**£10-12**
'Kelloggs'..............................................**£10-12**
'Smiths Crisps' (Promotional offer)......**£10-12**

## MB 73c  MERCURY COMMUTER

70-71   Metallic lime green body, UB with '59',
'55' or '73', NW or WW.......................**£35-40**
Metallic lime green, white interior,

---

with filler cap, box type 'F2' .................**£40-50**
Same, but in box type 'G'.....................**£40-50**

71-73   Red body, UB, 'Bull head' label on
bonnet of some, wide wheels.................**£25-30**

## MB 73d  WEASEL

74-76   Metallic green body, metallic green and
green base, (Rola-Matic).......................**£10-12**

76   Military olive drab green body,
metallic green and green base,
(Rola-Matic) (TP) .................................**£35-40**

76-79   Same but with military olive green
body (Rola-Matic) (TP) .........................**£12-15**
Military olive green body, olive green
and green base, (Rola-Matic) (TP) ........**£12-15**
Same but olive green and BB, (TP).......**£12-15**
Met. copper body, Met. green base ...**£60-70**

## MB 73e  FORD MODEL 'A' CAR

79-80   Cream body, dark green wings, GG ......**£10-12**
Same but no spare wheel or glass............**£9-11**

80   White body, dark green wings, GG .......**£10-12**

80-82   Met. green body, dark green wings,
GG or none..................................................**£7-9**

82-83   Lt. brown body, dark brown wings, AG ....**£7-9**
Same but with clear glass .......................**£8-10**

## MB 74b  DAIMLER FLEETLINE

70-72   Red body, white interior, 'Esso'............**£25-30**
Same but fluorescent pink body ...........**£25-30**

72   Red body, 'Inn on the Park' labels.......**£80-100**
Red body, 'The Baron of Beef'............**£80-100**
Red body, 'NAMC', 'The Miniature
Vehicle' labels (Promotional)............**£160-180**
Red body, 'Kensington Hilton'.........**£100-120**
Red body, 'I.C.P. Interchemicals'......**£250-300**
Red body, 'Beefeater' ......................**£200-250**
Light red, 'Fly Cyprus Airways'.......**£150-175**
Light red, 'Big T Scotch Whiskies' .....**£80-100**

## MB 74c  TOW JOE

72-77   Metallic green-gold body, UB, AG and
roof light, green arms, Red hooks..........**£12-16**
Same but with BB or SB......................**£12-16**
With UB and black hooks .....................**£15-20**
Metallic green body, BB, AG and
roof light, green arms, red hooks...........**£10-15**

76-81   Yellow body, BB, SB or UB, AG, red
arms, black hooks (TP) .........................**£10-15**
With matt base, red or black hooks .....**£75-100**
Metallic green body, BB, AG,
red arms, black hooks (TP)....................**£25-30**
Same, BB or SB, white arms (TP).......**£90-100**
Red body, green arms, red hooks,

---

BB, AG, (TP) ....................................**£150-170**
Red body, green arms, black hooks .....**£80-100**
Red body, red arms, black hooks ......**£150-170**

82   Yellow body, UB, AG, red arms, black
hooks, 'Hitch Hiker' labels (TP)........**£100-120**

## MB 74d  COUGAR VILLAGER

78-81   Metallic light or dark green body,
yellow interior, UB, AG........................**£10-12**

81-82   Metallic blue body, yellow or
orange-yellow interior, UB, AG.............**£15-20**

## MB 74e  FIAT ABARTH

82-83   White body, red interior, 'Matchbox' ....**£12-14**
Same but with black interior.............**£140-180**

## MB 75b  FERRARI BERLINETTA

70   Metallic green body, off-white interior,
unpainted base, clear glass.................**£200-250**

70-71   Red body, off-white interior, UB,
CG, silver grille on some.......................**£85-95**

## MB 75c  ALFA CARABO

71-75   Metallic Purple body, YB, NW..............**£10-15**
Same but with unpainted base ...............**£12-16**

75   Metallic light pink body, YB, WW........**£15-20**

75-76   Metallic light pink or red body, WW,
(Streakers) yellow/black/green prints ....**£12-16**

## MB 75d  SEASPRITE  Helicopter

77-81   White body, Red underside, BG or GG,
black rotors, blue 'Rescue' labels ...........**£8-10**
Same but with red glass .........................**£12-15**
Same but with purple glass....................**£15-18**

## MB 75e  HELICOPTER

82-83   White/orange, black interior, black skids,
AG, 'MBTV News' tampo prints ............**£8-11**
White/black, black or grey interior, black
skids, AG or CG, 'Police' and '36'..........**£8-11**
White/black, black or grey interior,
black or grey skids, AG, 'Rescue' ...........**£10-12**

---

## ABBREVIATIONS

| Windows | Wheels | Base colour | General |
|---|---|---|---|
| AG = amber glass | BW = black wheels | BB = black base | BE = black engine |
| BG = blue glass | NW = narrow wheels | GB = grey base | CE = chrome engine |
| CG = clear glass | UW = unpainted | SB = silver base | LE = limited edition |
| GG = green glass | WW = wide wheels | UB = unpainted base | SE = silver engine |
| OG = orange glass | | WB = white base | TP = Twin Pack |
| PG = purple glass | | YB = yellow base | |

# Matchbox Superfast and miscellaneous Sets

| | | | |
|---|---|---|---|
| G 1 | 1968 | **Service Station Set** | |
| | | 13d, 56b, 32c, and 'BP' Service Station | **£250-300** |
| G 1 | 1970 | **Service Station Set** | |
| | | 13d, 15d, 32c, and 'BP' Service Station | **£250-300** |
| | 1970 | **Magnetic Action Farm Centre** US issue | **£150-175** |
| G 1-8 | 1981 | **Transporter Set** | |
| | | Contains Transporter and 5 Superfast Cars | **£150-175** |
| G 1-9 | 1984 | **Transporter Set** Contains K10 plus 4 cars | **£50-60** |
| G 2-7 | 1970 | **Transporter Set** | |
| | | Transporter and 5 Superfast models | **£100-125** |
| G 2-8 | 1973 | **Transporter Set** | |
| | | Transporter and 5 Superfast models | **£100-125** |
| G 2-11 | 1981 | **Railway Set** Contains 43e, 2 x 44e, 25f | **£25-30** |
| G 3-7 | 1970 | **Racing Specials Set** | |
| | | Contains 5e, 20c, 45c, 56c, 52c and 68c | **£150-175** |
| G 3-8 | 1973 | **'WILD ONES' Set.** Contains 5 Superfast Cars | **£80-100** |
| G 3-9 | 1981 | **Racing Car Set** Transporter and 4 Racing Cars | **£50-60** |
| G 4-7 | 1970 | **Truck SuperSet** | |
| | | 47c, 63c, 58c, 49b, 16d, 21d, 11d and 51c | **£100-125** |
| G 4-8 | 1973 | **Team Matchbox Set** | |
| | | Racing Car Transporter + 4 Racing Cars | **£70-80** |
| G 4-9 | 1981 | **Military Assault** Landing Craft + 6 military models | **£60-70** |
| G 5-9 | 1981 | **Construction Set** Contains 5 construction models | **£40-50** |
| G 6-6 | 1970 | **Truck Set** | |
| | | 1e, 10d, 21d, 26c, 30c, 60b, 70b and 49b | **£120-150** |
| G 6-7 | 1973 | **Drag Race Set** Contains 6 Superfast Cars | **£40-60** |
| G 6-8 | 1981 | **Farm Set** Contains 6 farming models | **£50-75** |
| G 7-5 | 1973 | **Ferry Boat** With Plastic Boat and 4 Superfast Cars | **£45-50** |
| G 7-8 | 1978 | **Car Ferry Set 'HERON'** | |
| | | Blue hull, white cabin, red deck, four models | **£50-70** |
| G 7-8 | 1978 | **Car Ferry Set 'OLYMPUS'** | |
| | | Red hull and cabin, yellow deck, four models | **£50-70** |
| G 7-6 | 1981 | **Emergency Set** Contains 5 Rescue models | **£40-50** |
| G 7-7 | 1984 | **Emergency Set** With models 8, 12, 22, 57 and 75 | **£40-50** |
| G 8-5 | 1984 | **Turbo Charged Set** | |
| | | Turbo Charger plus 7, 9, 52, 60 and 68 | **£35-40** |
| G 9 | 19?? | **Commando Task Force Set** | |
| | | with 2, 3, 16, landing craft | **£50-70** |

| | | | |
|---|---|---|---|
| G 10-5 | 1986 | **'PAN-AM' Set** | |
| | | Contains 10, 54, 64, 65 + 'Sky-Buster' Boeing | **£40-45** |
| G 10 | 19?? | **'Thunder Jets' Set** Four SkyBusters | **£25-35** |
| G 11-1 | 1978 | **Strike Force Set** Contains 6 Army Vehicles | **£100-125** |
| G 11-2 | 1986 | **'LUFTHANSA' Set** | |
| | | 30, 54, 59, 65 and 'Sky-Buster' Airbus | **£50-60** |
| G 12 | 1978 | **Rescue Set** Contains 6 Rescue Vehicles | **£40-45** |
| G 13 | 1978 | **Construction Set** Contains 6 Construction Vehicles | **£35-40** |
| G 14 | 1978 | **Grand Prix Set** Transporter and 4 Racing Cars | **£35-40** |
| G 15 | 1978 | **Transporter Set** Transporter and 5 Superfast Cars | **£35-40** |
| G 16 | 19?? | **'Sky Giants' Set** Four SkyBusters airliners | **£25-35** |
| G 40 | 1988 | **40 years Set** | |
| | | ('Made in China' cast under models). | |
| | | Aveling-Barford Road Roller, London Bus, Horse Drawn | |
| | | Milk Float, M-H Tractor, Dennis Fire Engine | **£20-25** |
| C 6 | | **Emergency Gift Set** All Japanese Set | **£25-30** |
| C 11 | | **Airport Gift Set** | |
| | | Japanese Foam Pump, Ikarus Coach + plane | **£30-35** |
| --- | 1971 | **Matchbox Crash Game** | |
| | | With 4 assorted cars, racetrack, dice and instructions | **£60-75** |
| --- | | **Multi-Pack Gift Set** Contains 5 Superfast models | **£20-25** |
| A1 | 70-73 | **Service Ramp** 'CASTROL' | **£30-35** |
| A2 | 1970 | **'Superfast Auto Sales'** | |
| | | Plastic kit includes 'MATCHBOX SALES OFFICE', | |
| | | 'STAR VALUE' stand, 3 'M' flagpoles and | |
| | | 4 lampposts, plus pink card base, signs and | |
| | | advert. stickers. 25 items in total | **£200-300** |
| A2 | 71-73 | **'Matchbox' Sales Park** | |
| | | Pink card sales park + four lampposts | **£35-40** |
| | 1975 | **Auto Sales Pitch** no details | **£75-100** |
| A3 | c1971 | **'Brroooom Stick'** | |
| | | Blister-packed car with steering control. | |
| | | Contains No.20 Lamborghini Marzal in Yellow and | |
| | | No.68 Porsche in White | **£60-70** |
| --- | 1975 | **Military Carry Case Set** with six models | **£100-150** |
| PD1 | 19?? | **Power Driver Set** with No.74 Alfa Carabo | **£40-60** |
| MG3 | 19?? | **'TEXACO' Garage Set** with unused decals | **£75-100** |

# Models of Yesteryear, 1956 - 1983

Many variants of Yesteryears have resulted from long production runs which often required renewal or modification of worn dies. Considerable numbers of model variations have thus been issued over the years, some of them quite minor. The objective of this listing is to identify for the Yesteryear collector all those price-significant variations which really do matter. Collectors requiring details of the all the variations issued should contact:
The Matchbox International Collectors Association (M.I.C.A.)
PO Box 120, Deeside, CH5 3HE, UK.

## Identification

**Common features.** Many models have common identifying features and these are shown below to avoid unnecessary repetition in the Features column.

**Model name and number.** Both 'Models of Yesteryear' and 'Made in England by Lesney' are cast underneath all models issued up to the end of 1982. With the change of ownership this was replaced by 'Matchbox Intl Ltd.' From 1987 'Made in Macau' appears on the base. All models have their 'Y' number shown underneath.

**Wheels.** All the wheels prior to 1970 were of metal construction. From 1972 (approximately), plastic wheels were used on all models. Nevertheless the models issued at this changeover period are to be found with either metal or plastic wheels.

**Scale of models** ranges from 1:34 to 1:130. The scale of each model is usually shown on its box.

**Logos and designs.** The early models had waterslide transfers. Labels have also been used and currently models are tampo printed.

**Catalogue listings.** Do not place too much reliance on the model colours shown in catalogues. Very often the pictures shown are from mock-ups in colours never actually issued. For example, the 1969 catalogue showed a picture of a blue Y-5 Peugeot that was issued in yellow. Similarly the 1973 catalogue showed a silver Hispano Suiza which was then issued in red.

**Bumpers, dashboards, headlights, radiator shells and windscreens.** All assumed to be of metal construction prior to 1974 (approx.), after which plastic was increasingly used.

**Base plate and chassis** are usually of metal construction.

**Tyres** are of treaded black plastic unless otherwise indicated.

**Seats** are all made of plastic unless otherwise indicated.

**Boxes**

| | |
|---|---|
| 1956-57 | All card box with just a plain black number shown on box ends. Line drawing of model on the front of box. |
| 1957-60 | All card box with line drawing of model used for first 15 models issued, blue number shown on white circle on endflap. |
| 1960-61 | As first box but with a red number. All card box with coloured picture of the model (3 varieties of this box exist). All card box with model pictures on the box endflaps. |
| 1968-69 | Pink and yellow box with clear window. |
| 1968-70 | As previous box with hanging display card (developed in the US market and led to blister-pack design). |
| 1969-70 | Mauve and yellow box with window. |
| 1974-78 | 'Woodgrain' window box in various colours |
| 1979-83 | 'Straw' (light cream), window box. |
| 1984-90 | 'Red' (maroon), window box. |

**MPR** = Market Price Range    **GSP** = Gift Set price

| Model and details | MPR |
|---|---|

### Y1-1  Allchin Traction Engine

1956-1965. Scale 1:80.
Early issues have rear wheel treads with a straight-across pattern, second type are diagonal; third type has a smooth tread.

With straight-across treads to rear wheels. **£100-125**
Rear wheel treads in Red (as per spokes)...... **£40-60**
Brass boiler door, Red angled rear treads,
rounded axles ............................................ **£70-80**
Rear wheels with no treads (smooth) ..... **£900-1,100**
Smoke box door in green (as per body) .... **£150-200**
Other versions ................................................ **£25-50**

### Y1-2  1911 Ford Model 'T'

1964-1984. Scale 1:42.
All Y1-2 models have 'brass effect' finish wheels.
Dark Red models with twin brake lever........ **£45-70**
Dark Red or White/Red models with
        Black textured roof) ............................ **£60-75**
Black body, textured roof and seats........... **£120-150**
White/Red body, Bright Red textured roof . **£85-120**
Cream body, Red chassis, Dark Red seats,
        Orange canopy .................................. **£80-100**
Red body and chassis, Black seats,
        Dark Orange canopy ......................... **£80-100**
Other versions ................................................ **£2-10**

### Y1-3  1936 Jaguar SS100

1977-1994. Scale 1:38.
With small sidelights
        (Off-White model only) .................. **£125-150**
Steel-Grey body and chassis..................... **£150-175**
Yellow body, Black seats, large lights.......... **£20-30**

### Y2-1  1911 'B'-type London Bus

1956-1961. Scale 1:100.
The diecast driver may be found in any shade of mid or dark blue, sometimes black.
With 4 over 4 side windows ......................... **£60-70**
With Black wheels ...................................... **£80-100**
Other versions ................................................ **£35-50**

### Y2-2  1911  Renault Two-Seater

1963-1968. Scale 1:40.
Note that the red pigment used in the plastic seats is prone to fading in bright light.
All versions .................................................... **£15-25**

### Y2-3  1914 'Prince Henry' Vauxhall

1970-1979. Scale 1:47.
With Copper petrol tank
        (Red and Silver issue only).............. **£225-275**
Bright Red seats
        (Blue and Silver issue only)............. **£200-300**
Other versions .................................................. **£2-8**

### Y3-1  1907 'E'-class Tramcar

1956-1965. Scale 1:130. All versions have a bright Red body with Yellow 'LONDON TRANSPORT' fleetname and 'NEWS OF THE WORLD' decals.
With thin (Grey) cow-catchers ................. **£100-125**
Grey base (thin or thick cowcatchers)....... **£125-175**
Other versions ................................................ **£30-50**

### Y3-2  1910  Benz Limousine

1965-1984. Scale 1:54.
Cream body / chassis, Light Yellow roof .. **£150-200**
Light Green body / chassis,
        Dark Green roof ............................... **£150-200**
Light Green body and chassis, Light Yellow
        roof, separate rear wing supports..... **£200-275**
Light Green body and chassis, Black roof .... **£60-75**
Dark Metallic Green body and chassis,
        Light Yellow roof............................. **£200-250**
As previous model, but no holes in base... **£300-350**
Other versions ............................................... **£10-15**

### Y3-3  1934  Riley MPH

1974-1979. Scale 1:35.
Dark Purple body and chassis,
        Black seats and grille ..................... **£100-125**
Ruby Red body / chassis,
        Black seats / grille ........................... **£100-125**
Other versions .................................................. **£2-6**

### Y3-4  1912 Ford Model 'T' Tanker

1981-1989. Scale 1:35.
'BP', Green body, Red tank,
        with 'No. Y12' cast on base................ **£40-50**
'BP', other versions ........................................ **£2-4**
'ZEROLENE', with 'No. Y12' cast on base . **£40-50**
'ZEROLENE', other versions .......................... **£2-4**
'EXPRESS DAIRY', all versions...................... **£2-6**

## Y4-1  1928  Sentinel Steam Wagon

1956 only. Scale 1:100.
Blue body, 'SAND & GRAVEL SUPPLIES'.
With Black plastic wheels ........................... **£85-100**
With Grey metal wheels ............................... **£35-55**

## Y4-2 1905 Shand-Mason Fire Engine

1960-1965. Scale 1:63.
Red metal body, two horses,
three plastic firemen.
'KENT' Fire Brigade, Pale Grey Horses .. **£500-600**
'KENT' Fire Brigade, White Horses .......... **£85-125**
'LONDON' Fire Brigade, Bronze horses .. **£300-400**
'LONDON' Fire Brigade,
    White or Black horses....................... **£80-120**
Silver plated, Jack Odell momento..... **£1,000-1,250**

## Y4-3  1909  Opel Coupé

1967-1984. Scale 1:38.
With Tan textured hood + rear window..... **£175-200**
With Maroon grille and seats........................ **£15-25**
Other versions ...................................................... **£2-8**

## Y4-4 1930 Duesenberg 'J' Town Car

1976-1997. Scale 1:43.
White body, Orange-Red or Red chassis,
    Yellow hood and seats............... **£2,000-2,500**
White body, Orange-red or Red chassis,
    Black hood and seats................. **£1,500-2,000**
Dark Red body and chassis,
    Maroon hood and seats .................... **£175-200**
Dark Red body and chassis,
    Dark Green hood and seats .............. **£75-100**
Dark Red body and chassis,
    Dark Green hood, Lt. Brown seats .. **£100-125**
Metallic all-Red body, White hood............. **£80-100**
Light Green body and chassis,
    Lime Green side / rear body panels..... **£45-65**
Dark Green, Blue base................................ **£80-100**
Other versions ...................................................... **£2-5**

## Y5-1  1929  Le Mans Bentley

1958-1961. Scale 1:55.
All are finished in British Racing Green.
With Grey folded hood, Silver radiator ...... **£85-125**
With Grey folded hood, Gold radiator......... **£80-110**
Other versions ................................................... **£35-55**

## Y5-2  1929  4½ litre Bentley

1962-1968. Scale 1:52.
Model has Union Jacks and racing numbers on
its sides, folded windscreen and silver 24-spoke
wheels, (spare on nearside).
Metallic Apple Green body,
    Dark Green or Dark Red seats ........ **£150-200**
Same but with Red seats/tonneau ............. **£100-125**
British Racing Green body, Red RN '6'....... **£60-70**
Other versions ................................................... **£10-15**

## Y5-3  1907  Peugeot

1969-1977. Scale 1:43.
Except where noted, the wheels have 12-spokes.
Yellow body and chassis, Black roof, no rib
    on rear edge of front seat side panels .. **£35-55**
Yellow body/chassis, Black roof,
    clear windows ..................................... **£85-125**
Yellow body and chassis, Gold roof......... **£100-150**

Orange-Gold, or Light-Gold body,
    Black chassis and roof ........................ **£65-85**
Light Gold body and roof,
    Black chassis, Chrome 12 or 24
    spoke wheels, clear windows........... **£100-105**
Other versions ...................................................... **£6-8**

## Y5-4  1927  Talbot Van

1978-1988. Scale 1:47.
'LIPTONS TEA' (1978), all versions ............. **£2-5**
'CHOCOLAT MENIER' (1978-1979),
    all versions ............................................... **£2-5**
'TAYSTEE BREAD' (1980), all versions ...... **£2-5**
'NESTLES' (1981).
    With Matt Black roof ...................... **£100-150**
    With Gloss Black roof ..................... **£100-150**
    All other versions ..................................... **£2-5**
'CHIVERS' (1982), all versions .................... **£2-5**
'WRIGHTS' (1982),
    with Dark Brown roof...................... **£150-180**
    All other versions ..................................... **£2-5**
'EVER READY' (1983), all versions ............. **£2-5**

## Y6-1  1916  AEC 'Y' type Lorry

1957-1961. Scale 1:100.  'OSRAM LAMPS'
Pale Blue or Mid Blue body,
    Grey metal wheels..................... **£1,250-1,750**
Light Grey body, Grey metal wheels........... **£40-60**
Dark Grey body, Grey metal wheels .......... **£60-100**
Dark Grey body, Black plastic wheels **£1,300-1,500**

## Y6-2  1935  Type 35 Bugatti

1961-1965. Scale1:48. Model has a black baseplate
and gold 8-spoke wheels with a spare on the
nearside. Racing number '6' may be upside-down
and appear as '9'.
Blue body, Grey tyres ................................... **£45-65**
Blue body, Blue radiator ............................... **£80-100**
Blue body, White dashboard........................ **£100-125**
Red body, Red radiator ................................. **£80-100**
Red body, Black dashboard ........................ **£100-150**
Red body, Gold radiator............................... **£125-150**
Other versions .............................................. **£15-25**

## Y6-3  1913  Cadillac

1968-1975. Scale 1:48.
Gold body, Dark Red textured roof.............**£80-110**
All other Gold body versions .......................... **£6-12**
Green body, thin spare tyre carrier ............... **£45-65**
Green body with Blue, Pale Green, Metallic Green,
    Beige, Yellow, Pink or Mauve seats .... **£60-80**
All other Green body versions......................... **£2-6**

## Y6-4 1920 Rolls-Royce Fire Engine

1977-1984. Scale 1:48.
Without locating lugs for side label............ **£75-100**
With red front seats, Brown ladders ......... **£250-350**
All other versions................................................ **£2-8**

## Y7-1  1918  Leyland 4-ton Van

1957-1960. 'W. & R. Jacob & Co. Ltd.'
    Scale 1:100.
Dark Brown body ........................................... **£55-75**
Dark Brown body with centre line of
    transfer omitted ............................... **£600-800**
Reddish Brown body ..................................... **£40-60**
Reddish Brown body,
    Black plastic wheels.................. **£1,250-1,500**

## Y7-2 1913 Mercer Raceabout type 35J

1961-1965. Scale 1:46.
Lilac body and chassis................................... **£15-20**
Lilac body and chassis, Grey tyres............... **£60-85**
Yellow body and chassis................................ **£10-15**
Yellow body, chassis and radiator ............... **£15-20**

## Y7-3  1912  Rolls-Royce

1968-1970. Scale 1:48.
Silver body and bonnet, Dark Red chassis
    and smooth or ribbed roof.................... **£5-10**
Silver body/bonnet, Dark Red chassis and
    smooth roof, Yellow seats / grille .... **£550-800**
Silver body and bonnet, Dark Red chassis,
    Grey ribbed roof................................. **£50-75**
Gold body, Silver bonnet, Dark Red
    chassis and ribbed roof ..................... **£75-100**
Gold body and bonnet, Dark Red chassis
    and ribbed roof, thin brass
    12-spoke wheels................................ **£50-75**
Gold body / bonnet, Dark Red chassis
    and ribbed roof, wide chrome
    12 or 24-spoke wheels ......................... **£5-8**
Gold body and bonnet, Dark Red chassis and
    ribbed roof, wide chrome 12-spoke
    wheels, Dark Green seats / grille ..... **£225-275**
Yellow body and bonnet, Red chassis,
    Black ribbed roof ............................. **£200-250**
Yellow body and bonnet,
    Black chassis and ribbed roof................. **£2-5**

## Y8-1  1926  Morris Cowley

1958 only. Scale 1:50.
Tan body, Dark Brown chassis,
    Silver or Light Copper wheels............. **£40-50**

## Y8-2 1914 Sunbeam M/cycle & Sidecar

1962-1967. Scale 1:34
Chrome plated, Black m/cycle seat,
    Dark Green sidecar seat ....................... **£25-45**
Chrome plated, Black m/cycle seat,
    Emerald Green sidecar seat............. **£150-250**
Chrome plated, Black m/cycle seat,
    Black sidecar seat.............................. **£500-600**
Light Gold plated...................................... **£550-750**

## Y8-3  1914  Stutz Roadster

1969-1973. Scale 1:48.
Dark Red body / bonnet, smooth Tan roof...... **£6-10**
Dark Red body / bonnet, brass petrol tank.... **£75-95**
Dark Red body / chassis, textured Tan roof .. **£20-25**
Dark Red body / chassis, textured Tan roof,
    Red grille............................................. **£30-50**
Dark Red body / chassis, textured Tan roof,
    Pinky-Red seats or Maroon seats......... **£50-75**
Metallic Red body, smooth Black roof........ **£80-100**
Metallic Blue body and chassis;
    White, Yellow or Black seats .............. **£80-90**
Blue body and chassis,
    Bright Red seats and grille.................. **£35-45**

## Y8-4  1945  MG 'TC'

1978-1984. Scale 1:35.
Green body and chassis ................................. **£5-10**
Red body and chassis...................................... **£3-5**
Blue body and chassis..................................... **£3-5**

## Y9-1 1924 Fowler Showman's Engine

1958-1965. Scale 1:80.
**'Lesney's Modern Amusements'.**
Dark Maroon body.............................................**£70-80**
Dark Maroon body, Gold cylinder block.....**£85-125**
Light Purple body, Gold or Light Purple
cylinder block.................................**£350-400**
Maroon body.....................................................**£65-75**
Bright Red body................................................**£55-65**
    **NB** Any of the above with a Black
    nameplate in the base usually
    adds a premium of approximately **£10**.

## Y9-2 1912 Simplex

1968-1988. Scale 1:48.
Lime Green or Mid Green body.......................**£8-15**
Dark Gold body, Dark Red chassis.............**£10-15**
Dark Gold body, Bright Red chassis........**£185-235**
Red body, Yellow seats..................................**£70-80**
Red body, Red or Black chassis.....................**£5-10**

## Y10-1 1908 'Grand Prix' Mercedes

1958-1959. Scale 1:54.
Off-White/Pale Cream body,
    Light or Mid Green seats.....................**£20-50**
Pure White body,
    Light or Mid Green seats.................**£100-150**

## Y10-2 1928 Mercedes-Benz 36-220

1963 only. Scale 1:52
White body, Red seats and folded hood,
    single or twin spare wheels.................**£10-20**
White body, Black seats and folded
    hood, twin spare wheels............**£1,500-1,750**

## Y10-3 1906 Rolls-Royce Silver Ghost

1969-1983. Scale 1:51.
Lime Green body, Bronze chassis ..................**£8-12**
White body, Purple or Dark Red chassis...........**£4-7**
White body, Silver chassis, Black seats ....**£275-325**
Silver body, Purple chassis .......................**£275-325**
Silver body and chassis, Dark Red seats ........**£2-4**
Silver body and chassis, Yellow seats .............**£4-6**
Silver body/chassis, White or Ivory seats..**£300-350**

## Y11-1 1920 Aveling & Porter Steam Roller

1958 only. Scale 1:80.
Mid-Green body/boiler/roof;
    Black roof supports ..............................**£30-50**
With Gold maker's plate (front of cylinder
    block), Black supports .....................**£200-250**
With Gold maker's plate (front of cylinder
    block), Green supports ..................**£350-550**

## Y11-2 1912 Packard Landaulet

1964-1984. Scale 1:50.
Dark Red and Orange-Red versions...............**£8-12**
Cream body, only in 1984
    'Connoisseur Collection'.............................GSP

## Y11-3 1938 Lagonda Drophead Coupé

1972-1985. Scale 1:43.
Gold body, Purple chassis,
    Black seats.............................**£1,500-2,000**
Gold body, Dark Red chassis....................**£100-150**
Gold body, Strawberry Red chassis.............**£75-85**

Gold body, Maroon chassis ...........................**£15-20**
Orange body, Gold chassis,
    brass (narrow) 24-spoke wheels ......**£100-125**
Orange or Copper body, Gold chassis,
    Chrome or Red (wide) wheels ..............**£4-15**
Copper body, Gold chassis, Green or Bright
    Red seats, folded hood and grille ....**£200-250**
Copper body, Gold chassis, Black seats ........**£40-50**
Orangey-Blood Red body, Gold chassis.......**£65-85**
Copper body, Black chassis ......................**£175-225**
Dark Cream body, Gold chassis ...............**£175-225**
Dark Cream body, Black chassis ......................**£2-8**
Maroon body version
    (in 1985 'Fathers Day' Set)......................GSP

## Y12-1 1899 Horse-drawn Bus

1959 only. Scale 1:100.
Red body and chassis. All versions ..............**£35-55**

## Y12-2 1909 Thomas Flyabout

1967-1975. Scale 1:48.
Blue body / chassis,
    Yellow seats and grille ..............**£1,000-1,250**
Blue body / chassis,
    Dark Red seats and grille ......................**£5-15**
Purple-Red body / chassis,
    Off-White seats / grille...........................**£4-8**

## Y12-3 1912 Ford Model 'T' Van

1979-1986. Scale 1:35.
**'COCA COLA'** (1979)
With 5 vertical Red printed coach lines .... **£200-300**
With 4 vertical Red printed coach lines ....... **£40-60**
**'COLMANS MUSTARD'** (1979-1981).
    All versions ................................................**£2-4**
**'TAYSTEE'** (1980)
    Yellow body, Black chassis / roof.... **£350-500**
    **NB** There are known to be fakes which
    have the smaller labels as used on the
    Y5-4 Talbot Van. Genuine 'Taystee' labels
    for the Ford Model 'T' Van measure 29mm
    end to end of 'Taystee' oval and 11mm
    top to bottom of the oval.
**'SUZE'** (1980-1981)
    With Gloss Black roof,
    Red double lines on rear doors .........**£85-125**
    All other versions ...................................**£2-4**
**'SMITHS CRISPS'** (1981) All versions..........**£2-4**
**'25 YEARS SILVER JUBILEE'** (1981)
    Silver printed single line
    on rear doors ...................................**£400-475**
    With Yellow 24-spoke wheels..............**£45-65**
    All other versions ...................................**£2-4**
**'BIRDS CUSTARD'** (1982)
    With Metallic Blue body....................**£50-65**
    All other (plain Blue) versions................**£2-4**
**'CEREBOS'** (1982)
    Light Blue body, Black chassis,
    Yellow roof.........................................**£60-75**
    All other versions ...................................**£2-4**
**'ARNOTTS'** (1982)
    Bright Red body, Black chassis,
    Gloss Black roof ............................**£100-135**
    Same but with Matt Black roof...........**£50-75**
**'HARRODS'** (1982). All versions..................**£2-4**
**'SUNLIGHT SEIFE'** (1983)
    Yellow body, Black chassis,
    matt Black roof ..................................**£45-65**
    **NB** Models exist with fake labels. Genuine
    labels have a clothes line post to the right of
    the woman hanging out the washing.
**'ROYAL MAIL'** (1983)
    Bright Red body, Black chassis and
    roof, Yellow printed double lines
    on rear doors ...................................**£175-225**

    All others (cast rear door outline)...........**£2-4**
**'CAPTAIN MORGAN'** (1983-1984)
    Black body, cast hole in
    rear base of body.................................**£45-75**
    All other versions.................................**£2-4**
**'HOOVER'** (1983).
    Blue body, White roof, Black
    chassis, Beige seats .......................**£400-500**
    All other versions.................................**£2-4**
**'MOTOR 100'**, world globe with blue
    land and white oceans ....................**£700-800**

## Y13-1 'Santa Fe' Locomotive (1862)

1959 only. Scale 1:112.
Mid-Green cab and boiler, Dark Red chassis
    and smokebox, Gold chimney
    rim and condenser tops ................**£900-1,200**
Other versions (Dark Green) ........................**£35-55**

## Y13-2 1911 Daimler

1966-1967 + 1984. Scale 1:45.
Yellow body, all versions..................................**£6-8**
Blue body, Powder Blue chassis,
    in 1984 'Connoisseur Collection' ............GSP

## Y13-3 1918 Crossley Lorry

**'RAF' Tender** (1975-1976). Scale 1:47.
RAF Blue cab, body and chassis, Black
    canopy, no strengthening web between
    front mudguards and chassis............**£300-400**
With Dull Dark Red or Green seats.............**£75-100**
With Olive Green canopy and grille...........**£25-35**
With Black canopy and grille ..................**£225-275**
All other versions................................................**£4-6**

## Y13-4 1918 Crossley Lorry

**'EVANS Bros.'** (1979-1982). Scale 1:47.
    Red cab and body, with two cast
    cleats on body sides .........................**£75-125**
    All other versions .................................**£2-4**
**'CARLSBERG'** (1983-1984)
    Cream cab / body,
    'Matchbox Toys Ltd' base.....................**£2-4**
    With 'Lesney Products' cast on base ... **£40-50**
    With Ice Blue canopy and tilt .............**£60-70**

## Y14-1 'Duke of Connaught' Locomotive

1959 only. Scale 1:130.
Dark Green cab and boiler,
    with Gold sand boxes........................**£70-90**
With Silver smoke box door......................**£75-100**
All other versions................................................**£35-50**

## Y14-2 1911 Maxwell Roadster

1965 only (+1984). Scale 1:49.
Turquoise body and chassis,
    Copper petrol tank...........................**£75-100**
Any other versions...........................................**£4-8**
Cream body, Dark Green chassis,
    in 1984 'Connoisseur Collection' ............GSP

## Y14-3 1931 Stutz Bearcat

1974-1995. Scale 1:44. All versions................**£2-8**

## Y15-1 1907 Rolls-Royce Silver Ghost

1960 only. Scale 1:55.
Light Green body and chassis,
    Grey knobbly tyres, Silver rear
    number plate and Red rear light.......... **£20-35**
With Dark Green seats.................................. **£60-80**
Other versions...................................................... **£4-8**

## Y15-2 1930 Packard Victoria

1969-1979 (+1984). Scale 1:46.
Lime Gold body, Dark Brown chassis,
    wide cast rear coach-line...................... **£20-30**
Lime Gold body, Black chassis,
    thin or wide cast rear coach-line...... **£235-285**
Metallic Lime Gold body, Dark Brown
    chassis, Black hood, Brown,
    Red or White seats............................ **£60-70**
Same but with White hood and seats........... **£65-75**
Other versions...................................................... **£2-8**

## Y16-1 1904 Spyker

1961-1968. Scale 1:45.
Pale Cream body / chassis,
    Grey knobbly tyres.......................... **£275-350**
Pale Lemon body / chassis,
    Grey knobbly tyres............................ **£60-80**
With two cast holes in base .......................... **£45-75**
Maroon body and chassis .................. **£1,400-1,900**
Other versions...................................................... **£4-8**

## Y16-2 1928 Mercedes-Benz SS

1972- 1990. Scale 1:45.
Lime Green body, Dark Green chassis,
    Black seats...................................... **£150-200**
Metallic Mid-Green body,
    Lime Green chassis............................ **£50-60**
White body, Black chassis ......................... **£375-500**

Blue body / chassis,
    Duck Egg Blue side panels ................. **£50-60**
Blue body and chassis,
    Milky White side panels ...................... **£75-90**
Metallic Silver, Metallic Red chassis .......... **£55-65**
Other versions...................................................... **£2-8**

## Y17-1  1938  Hispano-Suiza

1975-1995. Scale 1:48.
Silver body (Powder Blue side panels
    on some), Silver or Black chassis,
    Yellow seats.................................... **£135-175**
Red/Black body, Red or Black hood ............. **£70-80**
Other versions...................................................... **£2-6**

## Y18-1  1937  Cord 812

1979-1995. Scale 1:48.  All versions................. **£2-4**

## Y19-1  1936  Auburn Speedster

1979- 1990. Scale 1:42. All versions................. **£2-4**

## Y20-1 1937 Mercedes-Benz 540K

1981-1995. Scale 1:45. All versions................. **£2-6**

## Y21-1  1930  Ford Model 'A' Woody

1981-1985. Scale 1:40. All versions................. **£2-6**

## Y21-2 1930 Ford Model 'A' Woody

1983-1985. Scale 1:40
**'A. & J. BOX'**
With Yellow bonnet, 'Lesney' base ................. **£5-10**
All other versions............................................... **£2-6**

## Y22-1 1930 Ford Model 'A' Van

1982-1991. Scale 1:41.
**'OXO'** (1982)
    Red body, seats / interior,
    'Lesney' base...................................... **£75-125**
    Red body, Gloss Black van roof ......... **£10-15**
All other versions............................................... **£2-4**

## Y23-1 1922 AEC Omnibus

1983-1989. Scale 1:72.
**'SCHWEPPES'** (1983-1984)
    Red body, with Red lettering on
    advertisement labels............................ **£30-45**
    All other versions................................... **£2-4**

## Y24-1  1928  Bugatti T44

1983-1995. Scale 1:72.
Black and Yellow body with Brown,
    Green or White seats........................ **£175-250**
Black and Yellow body with Black seats ..... **£25-45**
Black/Yellow with Grey seats, straw box.. **£100-120**
All other versions.............................................. **£2-4**

## Y25-1 1910 Renault 'AG' Van

1983-1989. Scale 1:38.
**'PERRIER'** (1983)
    Green body, Dark Green chassis,
    roof rack with 3 side struts.............. **£250-300**
    With closed grab handles ................. **£75-125**
    All other versions................................... **£2-4**

# Models of Yesteryear Gift Sets

| | | | | |
|---|---|---|---|---|
| G 6 | 1960 | **Gift Set** ........................................Contains Nos. 1, 2, 5, 10 and 13. Lesney line-drawing box................................................. | £325-375 |
| G 7 | 1960 | **Gift Set** ........................................Contains Nos 3, 8, 9, 12 and 14. Lesney line-drawing box................................................. | £325-375 |
| G 6 | 1962 | **Veteran & Vintage Car Set**.......Contains Nos 5, 6, 7, 15 and 16. Lesney picture box......................................................... | £325-375 |
| G 7 | 1962 | **Gift Set** ........................................Contains Nos 3, 4, 11, 12 and 13. Lesney picture box.................................................... | £325-375 |
| G 7 | 1965 | **Veteran & Vintage Set** .............Contains Y2, Y5, Y10, Y15 and Y16. Picture box............................................................. | £325-375 |
| G 7 | 1966 | **Gift Set** ........................................Y1-2 Model T Ford, Y3-2 Benz, Y11-2 Packard, Y14-2 Maxwell. Picture box ..................... | £250-300 |
| G 7 | 19?? | **Gift Set** ........................................Y3, Y8, Y9, Y12 and Y14 ...................................................................................... | £75-100 |
| G 5 | 1968 | **Gift Set** ........................................Y4-3 Opel, Y6-3 Cadillac, Y9-2 Simplex, Y9-2 Simplex .......................................... | £200-300 |
| G 5 | 1970-72 | **Gift Set**...........................................Contains Y8-3 Stutz Red, Y14 Maxwell, Y16-1 Spyker (Dark Yellow), Y7-3 Rolls-Royce Silver and Red. Picture box................................................................................................................................ | £40-50 |
| Y-50 | 1982 | **Gift Set** ........................................Contains Y3-4 'BP' Tanker, Y5-4 Talbot Van 'Chivers', Y10-3 Rolls Royce, Y12-3 Model 'T' Van, Y13-3 Crossley Coal Lorry.................................................................................................................... | £20-30 |
| | 1984 | **'Connoisseur Collection'** ..........Contains Y1-2 Black 1911 Model 'T' Ford, Y4-3 Red/Beige 1909 Opel, Y3-2 Blue/Black 1910 Benz Limousine, Y11-2 White/Black 1912 Packard Landaulet, Y13-2 Blue 1911 Daimler, Y14-2 Beige/Black 1911 Maxwell. 30,000  certificated and numbered sets issued in beechwood display case ...................................................... | £80-100 |

# Models of Yesteryear plated souvenirs and giftware

Models specially plated to adorn giftware (e.g., cigarette boxes, ashtrays, penstands, boxes and pipestands. Non-plated versions of the models listed will also be found with the two baseplate holes used for fixing the plated models to the various items.
Prices (dependent on type of giftware):
Unboxed, not mounted on original giftware ....**£2-3**
Unboxed, still mounted on giftware ..............**£5-20**
In original box, still on original giftware .....**£30-85**

**SILVER-EFFECT PLATED MODELS**

| | | |
|---|---|---|
| Y1-2 | 1911 | Model 'T' Ford ............................ |
| Y2-2 | 1911 | Renault 2 seater ......................... |
| Y2-3 | 1914 | Prince Henry Vauxhall.................. |
| Y3-3 | 1934 | Riley MPH................................... |
| Y4-3 | 1909 | Opel Coupé................................. |
| Y5-2 | 1929 | 4½ Litre Bentley.......................... |

## Lesney 'Pub Signs'

| | | |
|---|---|---|
| Y6-2 | 1926 | Type 35 Bugatti ........................... |
| Y7-2 | 1913 | Mercer Raceabout........................ |
| Y7-3 | 1912 | Rolls-Royce .................................. |
| Y10-2 | 1928 | Mercedes-Benz 36-220 ............... |
| Y10-3 | 1906 | Rolls-Royce .................................. |
| Y12-2 | 1909 | Thomas Flyabout.......................... |
| Y13-2 | 1911 | Daimler ........................................ |
| Y13-3 | 1918 | Crossley ....................................... |
| Y14-2 | 1911 | Maxwell Roadster......................... |
| Y15-1 | 1907 | Rolls-Royce Silver Ghost............. |
| Y16-1 | 1904 | Spyker ......................................... |

**GOLD-EFFECT PLATED MODELS**

| | | |
|---|---|---|
| Y1-2 | 1911 | Model 'T' Ford ............................ |
| Y2-3 | 1914 | Prince Henry Vauxhall.................. |
| Y3-2 | 1910 | Benz Limousine............................ |
| Y4-3 | 1909 | Opel Coupé.................................. |

| | | |
|---|---|---|
| Y5-2 | 1929 | 4½ Litre Bentley.......................... |
| Y7-2 | 1913 | Mercer Raceabout........................ |
| Y7-3 | 1912 | Rolls-Royce .................................. |
| Y10-2 | 1928 | Mercedes-Benz 36-220 ............... |
| Y10-3 | 1906 | Rolls-Royce .................................. |
| Y12-2 | 1909 | Thomas Flyabout.......................... |
| Y13-2 | 1911 | Daimler ........................................ |
| Y13-3 | 1918 | Crossley ....................................... |
| Y14-2 | 1911 | Maxwell Roadster......................... |
| Y15-1 | 1907 | Rolls-Royce Silver Ghost............. |
| Y16-1 | 1904 | Spyker on tray ...............**£150-175** |

**GOLD PLATED SETS**
**Golden Veteran Set** with 3 models:
Y7-3, Y13-2, Y14-2..................................**£50-65**
**Heritage Gifts**, 2 models: Y7-3, Y10-3 .......**£35-50**

A series of plated figurines made for attachment to giftware. The base of each is marked 'Lesney Co. Ltd. 1975'. They have 'spurs' underneath to aid fixing to such items as ashtrays, etc. The Editor would be pleased to receive more details. NGPP.

| | | | | |
|---|---|---|---|---|
| 'The Cock' ............................ | 'The Unicorn'......................... | 'The Pig & Whistle'............... | 'The Sherlock Holmes'........... | 'The Mermaid' ........................ |
| 'The Lion' ............................. | 'The Bull'.............................. | 'The George & Dragon'.......... | 'The Volunteer' ...................... | 'The Royal Standard'............. |
| 'The Swan'............................ | 'The Rose & Crown'.............. | 'The Dick Turpin' .................. | 'The Britannia'....................... | |

# Models of Yesteryear 'Codes 1 and 2' special issues

A system of categorising models has evolved among collectors to distinguish between authentic manufacturers' output and acceptable but unauthorised alteration of their models for later resale. The explanation which follows refers to a coding system adopted generally (but not officially) throughout the model collecting fraternity in the UK and elsewhere, and may he applied to models produced by any manufacturer.
**CODE 1** Applies to models which have been originated and totally produced by an established manufacturer.
**CODE 2** As CODE 1, but labelled or finished outside the factory WITH the manufacturer's permission.
**CODE 3** Same as CODE 2, but model re-labelled, altered or re-worked WITHOUT authorisation or permission from the manufacturer.

**Y1-2**   76  **1911 Ford Model 'T' Car.** Black body, textured roof, grille and seats, Chrome 12-spoke wheels, brass trim, bare windscreen frame. 900 models made for the USA.........**£325-400**

**Y5-4**   78  **1927 Talbot Van** with 12-spoke wheels and Chrome trim.
'2nd AIM CONVENTION', Dark Green body and wheels, 'Toy Show, Harrisburgh PA May 27/28, 1978' .................**£75-125**
81  'CRAWLEY SWAPMEET 1981', Royal Blue body, Black roof and chassis, 'Follow Us To Crawley'...........**£125-175**
81  'VARIETY CLUB', 'Sunshine Coach Appeal'
1: Yellow body and chassis, Black roof, Red wheels.....**£125-165**
2: As 1 but with Black chassis.....................................**£150-175**
80  'MERITA BREAD', Yellow body, Red wheels .................**£20-40**
80  'LANGENDORF', Yellow body, Red wheels....................**£20-40**
80  'TAYSTEE BREAD', Yellow body, Black roof, Red wheels and Pale Yellow 'Taystee' on Red oval.................**£70-80**
81  'IRONBRIDGE' 1: Yellow body, matt Black roof, Red wheels, 'The World's First Iron Bridge' ................**£125-165**
2: As 1 with gloss Black chassis and mudguards...........**£140-180**

81  'BEES' 1: Yellow body, Black roof, Red wheels, plain or White-wall tyres, 'Bees Art & Model Service'.........**£100-150**
2: As 1 but Black chassis and mudguards ......................**£90-110**
81  'DUTCH MATCHBOX MEET'.
'1st Matchbox meeting in Holland on 4th October 1981'.
1: Blue and Grey body, Black roof and chassis, 'Stoevclaar', with Certificate ........................................**£175-225**
2: Yellow and Red body, Black roof and chassis, 'Stoevclaar', 72 only presented to stallholders .............**£400-500**
81  LAWRENCE FRASER TOYS', Blue body....................**£200-250**

**Y7-3**   82  **1912 Rolls-Royce.** Wedding of Prince Charles and Princess Diana. Bright Yellow and Black, Red wheels, 600 ........**£145-185**

**Y12-3**  81  **Ford Model 'T' Van**
1: 'BANG & OLUFSEN', White/Red, certificate ..........**£275-325**
2: Without certificate ....................................................**£165-185**
81  'RAYLEIGH SWAPMEET', Yellow body, Black roof.....**£75-125**
82  'CADA TOYS Have Moved', Yellow/Black, 600 .........**£180-200**
82  'DEANS of LEEDS', Yellow body, Black roof, Red 'Deans for Toys', telephone no. on some, 800 ......**£125-150**
80  'CAMBERLEY NEWS', Yellow/Black, '75th', 750 .....**£155-185**
83  'HOOVER', Blue body, White roof, Black chassis,
1: With certificate, 500 .................................................**£500-600**
2: Without certificate, 50 ..............................................**£350-400**

**Y13-3**        **1918 Crossley**
79  'UK MATCHBOX CLUB', Red/Yellow, 800....................**£80-90**
81  'ASPECTS and IMAGES', Red/Light Brown ...............**£125-150**
81  'SURREY MODEL FAIR', Red body, 'Tangley Model Workshop' on rear of Grey canopy only, 500 ................**£125-150**

## Collectors notes

## M.I.C.A.
**Matchbox International Collectors Association**
MICA UK, PO Box 120, Deeside, CH53HE.
Tel/Fax:01244 539414. E-mail: kevin@matchboxclub.com
Abbreviations: BPW = Black Plastic Wheels, E = Excellent,
VG = Very Good, GPW = Grey Plastic Wheels, TT = Two-tone,
MW = Metal Wheels, CA = Crimped Axles.

**MATCHBOX '1-75' series Regular Wheels**
**10a Scammell Mechanical Horse**. Red, MW, CA, E in VG box................. **£88**
**11a Petrol Tanker 'ESSO'**. With 2 small side labels, pristine Boxed......... **£705**
**20b E.R.F 'Ever-Ready'**. Dark Blue, GPW, Very Good model and Box.... **£102**
**27c Cadillac Sixty Special**. Metallic Pale Green, 95% Mint Boxed .......... **£278**
**35a E.R.F. Horse Box**. Red/Beige, BPW, Mint Boxed.............................. **£139**
**41b Jaguar 'D' Type**. Green with wire hubs, Mint Boxed ....................... **£218**
**45a Vauxhall Victor**. Red body, (99% Mint), box Fair............................ **£3,211**
**45a Vauxhall Victor**. Yellow body, BPW, Excellent Boxed ...................... **£99**
**53 Aston-Martin DB2-4 Mk.I**. Metallic Red, GPW, 98% mint, good box. **£223**
**55d Mercury Police Car**. With Red dome light, Mint Boxed ................... **£338**
**66c Greyhound Bus**. Silver/Grey, clear windows, Pristine model/box ...... **£101**
**75b Ferrari Berlinetta**. Red, chrome hubs/black tyres, pristine/G box ..... **£501**

**MATCHBOX SUPERFAST**
**14d Iso Griffo**. Metallic Blue, white interior, Pristine model/box ............. **£334**
**17f Londoner Bus. 'Berger Paints'**, a rare gold issue, Mint Boxed.......... **£276**
**22c Pontiac GP Sports Coupé**. Red body, Grey interior,
    99% Mint Boxed................................................................ **£1,295**
**25d Ford Cortina GT**. Metallic Light Brown, Mint in Good box ............... **£128**
**49c Chop Suey**. Metallic Red-Purple, chrome forks, Mint boxed ............. **£402**

**MATCHBOX 'Models of Yesteryear'**
**Y1-2 Model Ford 'T'**. Dark Red, Twin brake lever, Excellent, boxed ........ **£99**
**Y3-3 1934 Riley MPH**. Ruby Red body, BPW, Mint boxed ..................... **£181**
**Y4-2 1905 Shand Mason**. With Grey Horses/Manes, 99% Mint Boxed.... **£658**
**Y4-2 1905 Shand Mason**. With Bronze Horses, Mint Boxed ................... **£410**
**Y5-2 1929 Bentley**. Metallic apple Green, 100% mint Boxed................... **£339**
**Y6-1 1916 AEC 'Y' Lorry**. 'Osram Lamps', pale blue,
    (85% mint) unboxed............................................................ **£718**
**Y7-3 Rolls-Royce**. Silver/Red, Grey ribbed roof, Mint boxed ................... **£81**
**Y8-2 Sunbeam Motorcycle**. Silver, black sidecar seat, E, very clean box. **£423**
**Y10-2 1928 Mercedes-Benz**. White body, Black seats, Mint Boxed........ **£1,636**
**Y11-1 Aveling Steam Roller**. Gold makers plate, green supports, Boxed .. **£604**
**Y-13-1 Santa Fe Locomotive**. Mid Green, Dark Red chassis,
    Excellent boxed............................................................... **£713**
**Y13-3 1918 Crossley Lorry**. 'RAF' Tender, black canopy, M in VG box. **£433**
**Y16-2 Mercedes-Benz**. Blue with Duck Egg Panels, E, Boxed ................. **£69**

**MOKO and LESNEY TOYS**
**Moko Heavy Tractor**. Orange - 98% mint, driver, green tracks, G box ..... **£333**
**Early Lesney Coronation Coach (small)** in the Rare Gold finish.
    NB. The Gold to Silver issues rarity ratio is around 50:1 ................. **£483**
**Early Lesney Bulldozer**. Peppermint Green, Black tracks,
    95% M, unboxed.............................................................. **£233**

## Special Auction Services
Kennetholme, Midgeham,
Reading, Berkshire.
Tel: 0118 971 2949   www.invaluable.com

**MATCHBOX TOYS**
**3b Bedford Tipper**. Red dump with GPW, VG in E box ............................ **£100**
**4b Massey-Harris Tractor**. With Grey Plastic Wheels, E-M in E box....... **£120**
**12b Land-Rover**. Green body, GPW, E-M in E..................................... **£420**
**26a Foden Cement Mixer**. With Dark Grey plastic barrel and small GPW **£880**
**30a Ford Prefect**. Light Blue, GPW, E-M in E box ................................. **£550**
**37a Karrier Bantam 'Coca-Cola' Lorry**. Uneven load, metal wheels,
    E-M in E box................................................................. **£150**
**39b Pontiac Convertible**. Metallic purple, SPW, E-M in E ..................... **£90**
**46b 'Pickfords' Removals Van**. Dark Blue, SPW, 3 lines, E-M in E box .. **£120**
**50a Commer Pick-up**. Red/Light Grey, BPW, E-M in E box ..................... **£200**
**55c Ford Galaxie Police Car**. White with Blue roof light, VG-E in E box **£300**
**59a Ford Thames 'Singer' Van**. Dark Green body, GPW, E-M in G box.. **£200**
**69a Commer 'Nestles' Van**. Red body, GPW, E-M, VG-E box, 36 treads . **£260**
**74a Mobile Canteen**. Silver, pale blue base/interior,GPW, E-M in E ..... **£130**
**74a Mobile Canteen**. Silver, Turquoise base, GPW, E-M in E box ......... **£310**
**75a Ford Thunderbird**. With Blue-green base, SPW, E-M in VG box ..... **£280**
**75a Ford Thunderbird**. With black baseplate, BPW, E in G box.............. **£420**

## Vectis Auctions Ltd.
Fleck Way, Thornaby,
Stockton -on-Tees TS17 9JZ

### Abbreviations used by Vectis Auctions

**Model description:**
**BPW** = Black Plastic Wheels,   **BPT** = Black Plastic Tyres,
**BT** = Black Tyres,   **CA** = Crimped Axles,
**GPW** = Grey Plastic Wheels,   **GRRT** = Grey Rubber Tracks,
**GRT** = Green Rubber Tracks,
**KBPW** = Knobbly Black Plastic Wheels,   **KGPW** = Knobbly Grey
Plastic Wheels,   **Met.** = Metallic,   **MW** = Metal Wheels,
**OPH** = Orange Plastic Hubs,   **PH** = Plastic Hubs,
**RA** = Rounded Axles,   **RPH** = Red Plastic Hubs,
**SBPW** = Smooth Black Plastic Wheels,   **SGPW** = Smooth Grey
Plastic Wheels,   **SPH** = Silver Plastic Hubs,   **SPW** = Silver Plastic
Wheels,   **ST** = Silver Trim,   **SW** = Steering Wheel,
**WB** = Window Box,   **WW** = 'Wire' Wheels.
**Condition:**
**F** = Fair,   **G** = Good,   **GP** = Good Plus,   **E** = Excellent,
**EP** = Excellent Plus,   **NM** = Near Mint,   **M** = Mint.

**EARLY LESNEY TOYS**
**Walking Elephant**. Grey/Red/Yellow/White,
    E in GP 'Moko' picture box with diagonal 'Jumbo' printing .............. **£1,300**
**Road Roller**. Green, Red metal rollers, Yellow flywheel,
    canopy supports without cross brace, Good unboxed......................... **£900**
**Road Roller (large scale)**. Green, unpainted metal rollers,
    no flywheel or driver, G unboxed .......................................... **£320**
**Site Mixer**. Dark Green, Red barrel and handle, Yellow wheels,
    Good unboxed............................................................... **£190**
**Site Mixer**. Dark Green, Red barrel, handle and wheels, GP unboxed....... **£260**
**Site Mixer**. Dark Green body and barrel, red wheels, EP unboxed ......... **£300**
**Site Mixer**. Red body, Green Barrel, handle and wheels, Good unboxed .. **£190**
**Caterpillar Tractor**. Orange including rollers, tan driver,
    Black rubber tracks, E unboxed ........................................... **£600**
**Caterpillar Bulldozer**. All Orange, Black rubber tracks, GP unboxed ..... **£360**
**Caterpillar Bulldozer**. Light Green, Black rubber tracks, Fair unboxed .... **£130**
**Horsedrawn Milk Float**. Dark Blue, 'Pasteurised Milk', White crates
    and driver, Grey wheels, Brown horse, E in all card box ............. **£1,300**
**Horsedrawn Milk Float**. As previous except Orange body,
    G in F picture box......................................................... **£520**
**Rag & Bone Merchants**. Green version as per Catalogue but incomplete,
    F unboxed................................................................. **£380**
**Soap Box Racer**. Metallic Bronze, spoked bare metal wheels,
    Brown/Blue and Pink figure, Excellent unboxed........................... **£2,700**
**Covered Wagon** with Barrels. Green/White, Red barrels,
    Brown horses, E in E box.................................................. **£280**
**Covered Wagon**. Same as previous but no barrels, E in G picture box ..... **£280**
**Bread Bait Press**. Red with Green Press, NM in Mint 'Lesney' box......... **£190**
**Bread Bait Press**. Red, bare metal Press, EP in GP Lesney box ............. **£140**
**Prime Mover / Low-Loader**. Details as per Catalogue,
    G-GP in G 'Lesney' box.................................................... **£500**
**Massey-Harris Tractor**. Red, Beige wheels, missing stack,
    Good in Fair box........................................................... **£220**
**Coronation Coach** (large). Gold with King and Queen, GP in F box......... **£480**
**Coronation Coach** (large). Gold with Queen only, E in G maroon box .... **£300**
**Coronation Coach** (large). Gilt, Queen only, Good in Good box ............. **£200**
**Coronation Coach** (large). Silver plated, Queen only, Good in Good box . **£260**

**MATCHBOX 1-75 Regular Wheels**
**3b Bedford Tipper** with Maroon back. GPW, NM in E, NM L(C) box ..... **£240**
**4c Triumph Motorcycle and Sidecar**.
    Metallic Steel-Blue, BPT, M in NM, L(C) box............................... **£160**
**13d Dodge 'BP' Wreck Truck**. In 'New Model' box, Green cab and jib,
    Yellow base and back, silver grille, grey plastic hook, E in G box ... **£2,800**
**17a Bedford Removals Van**. Maroon, ST, NM in E-EP, M(B) box........... **£480**
**17c Austin Taxi**. Maroon, SPW, Light Grey interior, NM in NM box ....... **£160**
**18e Field Car**. Yellow, Green Plastic hubs, NM in G-GP, L(F) box......... **£560**
**19a MG TD**. Off-White, metal wheels, EP in M, M(B) box ..................... **£170**
**19b MGA**. Off-White, dark red interior, NM in NM box .......................... **£320**
**20a ERF Truck**. Maroon body, Gold trim, MW, EP - NM, M(B) box......... **£320**
**20a ERF Truck**. Light Maroon, ST, GPW, NM in E - EP, M(B) box ......... **£260**

**21b Bedford Coach**. Dark Green, GPW, NM in E, M(B) box .................. £180

**25c Bedford TK 'Aral' Tanker**.
Blue/White, SBPW, E-EP in E, L(E) box ........................ £280

**26a ERF Cement Mixer**. All Orange body, mask sprayed silver grille,
no silver trim to fuel tank, SPW, EP in GP - E, L (C) box ............... £750

**26b Foden Cement Mixer**. Orange, silver grille, dark Grey barrel,
KGPW, E in E, NM L(C) box ........................ £460

**26b Foden Cement Mixer**. Orange, Light Grey Barrel, KGPW,
silver grille, G in GP L(D) box........................ £240

**27c Cadillac Sixty Special**. Metallic Lilac, pale Pink roof, green windows,
black base, SBPW, NM in NM box........................ £140

**28b Compressor Truck**. Yellow, KBPW, RA, EP in EP L (C) box............ £120

**30b Magirus Deutz Crane Truck**. Tan, Red jib, KGPW,
GP in GP, L (C) box........................ £4,200

**33a Ford Zodiac**. Dark Blue, metal wheels, EP in E, M(B) box........... £850

**37a Karrier Bantam 'Coca-Cola'**. Orange, GPW, EP in E, L (C) box .... £170

**39a Ford Zodiac Convertible**. Pale Peach, MW, E in EP, M(B) box ...... £680

**41a Jaguar D-type**, Green, MW, RN '52', NM in GP, M(B) box .......... £600

**41b Jaguar D-type**, tan driver, Green, RN '5', WW, NM-M in EP box .... £300

**41c Ford GT 40**. White, No '6', red plastic hubs, EP-M in M box........... £230

**43a Hillman Minx**. Green, metal wheels, EP in GP, Moko B box ........... £520

**45a Vauxhall Victor**. Primrose Yellow without dashboard casting bar,
E in EP Moko (B) box........................ £750

**45a Vauxhall Victor**. Red body without dashboard casting bar,
E Plus in NM Moko (B) box ........................ £3,800

**46a Morris Minor**. Tan, metal wheels, EP in E Moko B box .......... £1,700

**46a Morris Minor**. Blue, GPW, NM-M in EP Moko box .......... £160

**46b 'Beales Bealesons' Van**. Tan, smooth BPW.
M in EP plain white 'Beales' promotional box........................ £700

**51a Albion Chieftan Cement**. Yellow/lt. Tan, SPW, EP in EP L(D) box ... £240

**51a Albion Chieftan Cement**. Yellow/dk. Tan, KBPW, E in GP L(D) box £180

**53c Ford Zodiac**. Metallic Green, smooth BPW,
NM-M in G-GP type E box (should be F type) ........................ £2,800

**55b Ford Fairlane Police Car**. Met. Blue, GPW. GP in G Lesney D box . £700

**56a London Trolley Bus**. Red body and trolleypoles, SPW,
'Drink Peardrax' logo, NM in G Lesney (C) box ........................ £240

**57c Land Rover Fire Engine**. Red, SGPW - E in GP - E Lesney (E) box. £620

**58a BEA Airport Coach**. Knobbly BPW, E - EP in F Lesney (D) box .... £360

**59b Ford Fairlane Fire Chief**. Red body, ST, GPW, E in GP-E box..... £300

**62b Commer 'Rentaset' Van**. Cream, knobbly GPW, E in G, L(D) box . £240

**65b Jaguar 3.8**. Met. Red, SPW, E in E - EP scarce NM L(C) box .......... £150

**66a Citroën DS 19**. Yellow, SPW, EP in G Lesney (D) box........................ £850

**69a Commer 'Nestles' Van**. Red, knobbly GPW, NM in G, L(D) box .... £120

**72a Fordson Major Tractor**. Yellow PH, NM in NM, L(D) box .......... £1,800

**74a Mobile Refreshments**. White, KGPW, EP in EP Moko (B) box ...... £520

**74a Mobile Refreshments**. Silver, knobbly BPW, EP in NM L(D) box . £1,000

**75b Ferrari Berlinetta**. Red, chrome hubs - EP in NM Lesney (F) box . £520

**5d Routemaster Bus 'The Baron of Beef'**. NM-M in E, L(C) box .......... £800

**5d Routemaster Bus 'Pegram Shopfitters'**. EP in GP, L(E) box .......... £850

**11a ERF Tanker 'Esso'**. Model NM-M in NM Moko box. Red body,
Gold trim, twin large 'Esso' decals on each side of tank,
NM -M in NM box ........................ £1,400

**11a ERF Tanker**. Green body, Gold trim, MW, NM-M in M(B) box ...... £560

**22b Vauxhall Cresta**. Pale Pink, Sea Green lower body, green windows,
KGPW, G - GP in E, M(B) box........................ £580

**55b Ford Fairlane Police Car**. Met. Blue, KBPW, NM, G-GP NM box .. £360

**62c Mercury**. Cream/White, chrome hubs/BT, EP in E, NM L (E) box .£5,000

**G1 Service Station Set**. MG1, A1 - BP Pumps/Sign with plastic parts
sprue,13c - red hook, 31c - Sea Green and 64b, NM - M in F box ... £1,200

**3b Bedford TK Tipper**. Grey cab, maroon back, GPW,
NM in GP –E in C Lesney box ........................ £260

**6b Euclid Quarry Truck**. Yellow dump with brace, knobbly GPW,
E in GP – E type B Moko box........................ £3,600

**8e Ford Mustang**. Burnt orange, chrome wheels, EP in NM type F box. £360

**9b Dennis Fire Escape** with GPW, NM in NM type B box ........................ £440

**10b Scammell Mechanical Horse**. GPW, silver trim,
NM in E type B Moko box........................ £220

**11a ERF Tanker**. Green, gold trim, MW, E in NM type B Moko box..... £1,300

**13c Wreck Truck**. Knobbly grey plastic wheels, EP in NM type C box.... £150

**14b Daimler Ambulance**. Off-white, SPW, EP in E type D box........... £340

**14c Bedford Lomas Ambulance**. Off-white, SPW, EP in EP type C box . £380

**15b Atlantic Tractor**. Orange body, knobbly GPW,
NM – M in GP type B Moko box ........................ £,3400

**15d VW Beetle Rally Car. Promotional issue** linked to Walt Disney
film of 'Herbie'Off-white, numbers'53' and racing stripes,
chrome hubs, black tyres, NM – M in NM type F box ........................ £1,000

**17a Bedford Removals Van**. Maroon, gold trim, MW,
E in NM type B Moko box........................ £150

**17b Bedford Removals Van**. Dk. green, GPW, M in E type B Moko box . £320

**PS3 Car Transporter Set**.
Models as per Catalogue, E - NM in Fair 'Moko' box ...................... £1,000

**PS4 Commercial Vehicles** (German issue).
Models G - EP in Good 'Moko' box........................ £600

**PS5 Army Set**. Models as Catalogue, GP - EP in Good 'Moko' box ....... £1,000

**G1 Commercial Vehicles**. Models as per Catalogue,
E - EP in Good 'Lesney' box........................ £460

**G2 Transporter Set** with K8, 14d, 24c 31c, 53c. NM in NM window box £300

**G3 Building Constructors**. Models as per Catalogue,
G - E in F - G 'Moko' box ........................ £300

**G4 Farm Set** (1st issue). Models as per Catalogue,
NM - M in EP 'Moko' box ........................ £800

**G4 Grand Prix Set**. Models as per Catalogue,
NM - M in NM complete box ........................ £1,300

**G5 Military Vehicles**. Models as Catalogue, E - NM in G 'Lesney' box.... £500

**G5 Fire Station Set**. MG1 - NM, 29c, 54b - decals, (4), 59c Galaxie
- blue roof light, NM - M in GP window box........................ £2,100

**G6 Commercial Vehicles**. 6c - BPW, 15c - BPW, 16c - BPW, 17d,
26b - BPW, 30 - Green, 58b - Black rollers, E-NM in GP box. .......... £750

**2e Jeep Hot Rod**. Pink, White base, NM in M 3rd Series box ...................... £70

**8e Ford Mustang**. White, Red interior, EP in G-GP 1st Series box .......... £160

**8e Ford Mustang**. Orange-Red, Red interior, M in M 2nd Series box ...... £220

**9e AMX Javelin**. Met. Green, White interior, EP in Mint 3rd series........... £80

**13e Baja Buggy**. Metallic Light Green, 'Police' on bonnet, NM in EP box.. £40

**22c Pontiac GP**. Metallic Purple, Grey interior, M in NM box .................. £60

**24d Team Matchbox**. Metallic Blue, racing number '1', EP in GP box ...... £80

**31e Lincoln Continental**. Sea Green, narrow wheels,
EP in E 2nd Series box ........................ £620

**32c Leyland Tanker 'Aral'**. Dark Blue, White tank,
NM in E 2nd series box ........................ £130

**32c Leyland Tanker**. Metallic Purple, Silver tank,
'N.A.M.C.' labels, EP unboxed........................ £70

**37d Soopa Coopa**. Orange, 'Jaffa Mobile', E in NM box ........... £35

**37e Skip Truck**. Red, Blue Skip, black base, NM in E box .................. £80

**42 Iron Fairy Crane**. Red, Yellow jib, EP in E 2nd series box ........... £120

**45d BMW 3.0 CSL**. Red body, yellow interior, green windows,
NM in EP box........................ £80

**46 Mercedes 300SEC**. Metallic Blue, NM in NM 1st Series box .............. £140

**53d Tanzara**. Streaker Version, White, Red interior, NM in M box .......... £50

**64b MG 1100**. Green, NM in M - NM 1st Series box ........................ £170

**70c Dodge Dragster**. Pink, 'Rat Rod' door labels, M in E blister pack ...... £140

**M2 Bedford Articulated**. Orange/Silver, 'Davies Tyres', KGPW,
GP in G box ........................ £150

**M3 Tank Transporter**. Smooth BPW, tank with metal rollers, E in E box .. £90

**M3 Tank Transporter**. SBPW, no silver trim,
tank with black plastic rollers, NM in EP - NM ........................ £340

**M4 Ruston Excavator**. Green tracks, Yellow decals,
NM in GP 'Lesney' box........................ £160

**M4 Hopper Train**. Grey plastic tyres, NM - M in E picture slide-out box. £260

**M4 Hopper Train**. Black plastic tyres, E- EP in G colour picture box......... £60

**M5 Combine Harvester**. Yellow plastic hubs, bare metal steering wheel,
NM in G 'Lesney' box........................ £360

**M6 'Pickfords' Low-Loader**. Dark Blue, Maroon loadbed,
knobbly BPW, E in E 'Moko' box ........................ £130

**M6 'Pickfords' Low-Loader**. Dark Blue, Red loadbed,
knobbly BPW, E - EP in E 'Lesney' box ........................ £300

**M7 TT Cattle Truck**. Red, Dark Tan trailer, GPW, E in GP 'Moko' box. £100

**M8 'Mobilgas' Tanker**. Black plastic wheels, EP in NM 'Lesney' box .. £1,300

**M8 Car Transporter**. Same with White/Black outline decals, GP in E box. £20

**M9 Double Trailers 'Cooper Jarrett Inc'**. Grey trailers and doors,
Yellow/Blue decals, detailed BPW, EP in E - EP 'Moko' box ........... £160

**K1 O&K Excavator**. Red/Grey, Red plastic hubs, 'MH6' on jib,
EP in EP window box ........................ £30

**K2 'Muir Hill' Dumper**. Red, Black metal hubs,
Grey tyres, E in G-GP 'Lesney' box ........................ £60

**K2 'Muir Hill' Dumper**. Green metal hubs, Black tyres,
EP in E colour picture box ........................ £70

**K2 'Esso' Wreck Truck**. White/Green, Amber roof lights, EP in EP WB .... £80

**K2 'Esso' Wreck Truck**. Gold body version, E in E window box.............. £35

**K3 Caterpillar D9 Bulldozer**. Yellow, bare metal rollers,
Green rubber tracks, E in GP 'Lesney' box........................ £80

**K3 Caterpillar D9 Bulldozer**. Yellow, Red plastic rollers,
Green rubber tracks, E in F colour box ........................ £80

**K3 Hatra Tractor Shovel**. Orange, 'Black 'Hatra' decal, GP-E in E WB.... £40

**K3 Massey-Ferguson 165**. Red tractor/trailer, Yellow PH, NM in EP WB .. £70

**K4 McCormick Tractor**. Small hook, Green metal hubs,
NM in E 'Lesney' box ............................................................ **£100**
**K4 McCormick Tractor**. Large hook, Red plastic hubs,
NM in E rare box illustrating model with green hubs. ......... **£100**
**K4 McCormick Tractor**. Large hook, Orange PH, NM in EP box............ **£190**
**K4 Leyland LE Transport**. Maroon, Metallic Silver tipper, E in E WB..... **£30**
**K5 Foden Dump Truck**. Yellow, red plastic hubs, NM in E 'Lesney' box. **£130**
**K5 Racing Car Transporter**. Green/Yellow, correct K5 base, M in WB..... **£70**
**K6 Mercedes Ambulance**. White with decals, EP in EP window box......... **£35**
**K6 Mercedes Ambulance**. White with labels, E in EP box pictorial WB... **£70**
**K6 Earth Scraper 'Allis Chalmers'**. Orange, bare metal hubs,
E-NM in GP-E box .................................................................. **£70**
**K6 Earth Scraper 'Allis Chalmers'**. Matt Orange, bare metal hubs,
E-NM in GP-E box .................................................................. **£70**
**K6 Earth Scraper 'Allis Chalmers'**. Bright Orange, Red plastic hubs,
E-NM in GP-E box .................................................................. **£70**
**K7 'Curtess Wright' Rear Dumper**. Yellow, bare metal hubs,
NM in G 'Lesney' box .............................................................. **£80**
**K8 Guy Warrior Transporter**. Turquoise/Orange, Orange PH, E in E box **£30**
**K8 Guy Warrior Transporter**. Yellow, Red PH, E in F window box ......... **£25**
**K8 Traxcavator**. Lemon Yellow, Orange rams, BRT, EP in EP WB ............ **£50**
**K9 'Claas' Combine**. Green/Red, white driver, E in EP window box ........ **£70**
**K9 'Claas' Combine**. Red/Yellow, light tan driver, NM in E pictorial WB. **£90**
**K11 'DAF' Car Transporter**. Yellow/Orange, Red plastic hubs,
NM in E pictorial window box.................................................. **£70**
**K13 ERF Concrete Mixer**. Orange, 'Readymix', bare metal hubs,
EP in EP picture box ............................................................... **£60**
**K13 ERF Concrete Mixer**. Same but with Red PH, GP in E in GP box ..... **£40**
**K13 ERF Concrete Mixer**. Orange, 'RMC', bare metal hubs,
GP in GP 1st window box ......................................................... **£80**
**K13 ERF Concrete Mixer**. Same but with Red PH, G in E - EP WB ......... **£45**
**K14 Taylor Jumbo Crane**. Yellow ballast box, decals,
front no. plate label, NM in EP box ......................................... **£50**
**K14 Taylor Jumbo Crane**. Red ballast box + decal, NM in NM-M WB.. **£40**
**K15 Turntable Fire Engine 'Merryweather'**.
Dark Red, decals NM in NM box ............................................... **£100**
**K15 Turntable Fire Engine**. Bright Red + labels, NM in NM - M WB..... **£100**
**K16 Dodge Tractor/Trailers**. Green/Yellow, clear plastic suspension,
NM in GP early WB ................................................................ **£100**

**K16 Dodge Tractor/Trailers**. Same but with Green plastic suspension,
E in E window box .................................................................. **£100**
**K21 Mercury Cougar**. Metallic Gold, Red interior, E in NM window box .**£50**
**K22 Dodge Charger**. Metallic Blue, light blue interior, NM-M in EP WB .. **£60**
**K23 Mercury 'POLICE'**. White, 'Highway Patrol', NM in EP WB .......... **£45**
**K24 Lamborghini Miura**. Metallic Red, E in EP- NM pictorial WB ......... **£35**

**MATCHBOX CATALOGUES**
**1958 Catalogue**. No. 44 Rolls-Royce driving out of box ............................ **£140**
**1959 Catalogue**. 24 pages as 11th Ed. Catalogue with dealers stamp, E..... **£130**
**1960 Catalogue**. 32 pages as per 11th Edition Catalogue, Good Plus......... **£110**
**1961 Catalogue**. 32 pages as per 11th Edition Catalogue, Good Plus .......... **£90**
**1963 Catalogue**. 20 pages as per 11th Edition Catalogue, Excellent............ **£30**
**1964 Catalogue**. 32 pages as per 11th Edition Catalogue, Good Plus.......... **£90**

**MATCHBOX 'Models-of-Yesteryear'**
**Y1 Allchin Traction Engine**. Copper boiler door, straight-across rear treads,
maroon wheels, crimped axles, EP in GP box ................................. **£70**
**Y1 Model Ford 'T'**. Black with Black textured roof, NM in E box ............ **£80**
**Y2 London Bus**. 4 over 4 lower deck windows, metal wheels,
Black driver, E in GP box....................................................... **£150**
**Y2 Prince Henry Vauxhall**. Metallic Silver-Blue, Silver bonnet,
EP in EP box........................................................................ **£620**
**Y3 1934 Riley MPH**. Metallic Magenta, Metallic Red chassis, E in G box . **£40**
**Y4 Sentinel Steam**. Dark Blue, knobbly BPW, RA, E in GP 'Lesney' box .. **£50**
**Y4 Fire Engine 'Kent'**. Pale Grey horses, EP in G 'New Model' box ....... **£100**
**Y5 1929 Bentley**. Metallic Green, Dark Red seats, NM in GP box............ **£140**
**Y5 1907 Peugeot**. Metallic Orange/Black, Orange windows, EP in E box ... **£70**
**Y6 Bugatti**. Blue, Red dash, knobly GPW, NM in EP box ......................... **£100**
**Y9 Showman's Engine**. Dark Maroon, Gold cylinder block, EP in G box... **£50**
**Y11 Lagonda Coupé**. Met. Gold/Purple, NM in E purple/yellow WB .... **£1,000**
**Y11 Lagonda Coupé**. Metallic Gold/Strawberry, EP in GP window box..... **£50**
**Y12 Ford Model 'T' Van 'Tastee'**. Yellow body, NM in NM straw box ... **£360**
**Y12 Ford Model 'T' Van 'Coca Cola'**. Cream, 5 lines, EP in EP box....... **£280**
**Y12 Ford Model 'T' Van 'Cerebos'**. Same as previous but with
Red 12-spoke wheels, NM in NM straw box ............................... **£160**
**Y13 Sante Fe Locomotive**. Maroon, Light Green, E in EP 'Lesney' box... **£750**
**Y13 Crossley RAF Tender**. Black canopies, 24-spoke wheels,
NM in E box ......................................................................... **£320**

# MICA – The Matchbox International Collectors Association

MICA was founded in 1985 and provides its Members with a bi-monthly magazine full of useful information about past, present and future issues of Matchbox and the 'Dinky Collection' range of products. Aspects covered include such topics as new releases, variations and past issues and it has a members' advertisement section. Yearly social conventions are held providing talks, exhibitions on Matchbox and special Matchbox-only auctions. A special 'members only' model is issued to commemorate the event.

### HOW TO CONTACT MICA
In the UK:  Kevin McGimpsey, MICA, PO Box 120, Deeside, CH5 3HE, UK
Tel: 01244 539414, Fax: 01244 303335, E-mail: kevin@matchboxclub.com

In the US and CANADA:
Rita Schneider (Membership Secretary), MICA North America,
PO Box 28072, Waterloo, Ontario, Canada, N2L 6JB
Tel: 519 885-0529, Fax: 519 885-1902.
In AUSTRALIA, NEW ZEALAND and SOUTH PACIFIC:

Elaine Winkworth (Membership Secretary), MICA,
PO Box 26, Winston Hills, NSW 2153, Australia.
Telephone: (02) 9686-6685     Fax: (02) 9686-6970

### RECOMMENDED READING
'The Yesteryear Book 1956 - 2000'. Kevin McGimpsey (Editor of the MICA Magazine) and Stewart Orr, assisted by several Club members have produced the ultimate book for MOY collectors. 250 pages packed with details of every variation plus diagrams and superb colour photos. Contact MICA for details.

'Collecting Matchbox Diecast Toys – the First Forty Years'
Published in 1989, it contains chapters on every aspect of Matchbox production since 1947. MICA members provided much of the technical input to this well-illustrated book which is now out of print. (The 'Regular Wheels' section was written by Nigel Cooper; Paul Carr wrote the Superfast section).

A selection of Automobile Association models by Budgie Toys    PHOTO: VECTIS AUCTIONS LTD.

Budgie Toys 'Blue Line Sightseeing' Bus    PHOTO: JOHN RAMSAY

'Tonibell' Ice Crea Van    PHOTO: VECTIS AUCTIONS LTD.

Budgie Toys 'British Railways' Scammell Articulated Delivery Van    PHOTO: VECTIS AUCTIONS LTD.

# Morestone, Modern Products, Budgie Toys and Seerol

The following history and listings have been provided by Robert Newson.

The history of these makes is a fascinating story of inter-linked companies, take-overs and bankruptcies reflecting the ups and downs of the toy trade. In the late 1940s Morris & Stone was a toy wholesaler selling the products of many small toy manufacturers including those from Modern Products who had started as die-casters. Morris and Stone decided to have their own exclusive 'Morestone' branded lines and some were made by Modern Products, who increasingly relied on Morestone for the sole marketing and distribution of their toys. Morestone continued to use several suppliers but in 1954 set up a die-casting company jointly with Rodney Smith (one of the founders of Lesney Products).

From the mid-1950s to 1966 the Morestone and Budgie ranges contained models that came either from the in-house factory or from Modern Products. Morestone's production expanded with new ranges of models, such as the 'Noddy' and 'Big-Ears' vehicles in 1956 and the Esso Petrol Pump Series of miniatures, launched at Christmas of that year. In 1958, the 'Trucks of the World International Series' was introduced, but only ran to three models.

Some of the earlier Morestone and Modern Products models were re-issued as part of the Budgie range which was introduced in 1959. Model numbers were allocated in 1960 and new additions to the range continued every year up to 1966. During 1961, Morris & Stone was taken over by S. Guiterman & Co. Ltd., who changed the name of their new subsidiary to Budgie Models Ltd. Although the range included many interesting and unusual subjects, they failed to compete with Corgi, Dinky and Matchbox, and losses in Budgie Models Ltd. contributed to losses in the Guiterman group. In March 1966 these companies went into voluntary liquidation.

Modern Products was badly hit by this but eventually were able to set up a new company called Budgie Models (Continuation) Ltd and purchase the Budgie trade mark from the receiver. They wanted the Budgie dies as well, but these were destroyed in a fire while negotiations were in progress. The only dies to survive were those in their own factory.

Thus the main range of Budgie commercial vehicles came to an end in 1966. Modern Products continued to produce the Budgie miniatures, mainly for the USA, until 1969 when the stronger competition this time was from Mattel's 'Hot Wheels'. Modern Products direction for the 1970s was to produce models for H. Seener Ltd., distributors of toys and souvenirs to London's tourist shops. The old Budgie Routemaster bus was reintroduced for Seener, followed by a new FX4 Taxi and Rolls-Royce Silver Cloud.

In 1983, following the death of one of the partners in Modern Products, the business was sold to a neighbouring engineering company called Starcourt Ltd (some boxes say Merracroft Ltd - an associated company of Starcourt). The new owners reintroduced several models from the original moulds, starting with the Aveling Barford Road Roller. However, a disagreement developed with Seener who withdrew the dies for the Taxi and Rolls-Royce (which he had paid for), and arranged for these to be made by Corgi together with a completely new Routemaster bus. These 'Seerol' models appeared in 1985 and are still available. Starcourt ceased toy production in 1985.

Some unpainted castings for no.204 Volkswagen Pick-Up and some empty boxes were sold to a Dutch firm and have since appeared in various liveries. These are classed as 'Code 3' models and have not been listed. The die-casting moulds were sold to Autocraft (Dave Gilbert) in 1988, and these include most of the 1950s Modern Products and part of the 1960s Budgie range. Autocraft are now in the process of adapting dies for a range of some 35 various models. Only one model has so far been reintroduced - a run of 1000 of no.258 Daimler Ambulance in kit form.

A complete history of these companies and their products is contained in the book 'Budgie Models' by Robert Newson. This hardback book also has full descriptions of all the models, 58 pages of colour photographs illustrating over 180 models, and reproductions of Budgie leaflets.

# Morestone and Modern Products

| Ref | Year(s) | Model name | Colours, features, details | Market Price Range |
|---|---|---|---|---|
| - | c.1946 | Racing Car | Red, Dark Blue, Dark Green or Light Brown. One piece casting including driver. No identification on model. 135 mm | £50-75 |
| - | 19?? | Monkey Handcarts | Two monkeys on Red handcarts | £200-250 |
| - | 19?? | Teddy Bears on 'Sociable' Cycle | Brown/Yellow and Brown/Green Teddies on a red cycle | £500-600 |
| - | 19?? | Clown on Penny Farthing Cycle | Clown and dog on a bicycle | £400-500 |
| - | 19?? | Tandem Cycling Set | Tandem with sidecar with male and female riders and baby in sidecar | £50-75 |
| - | 19?? | Boy on Tricycle | Various colours | £30-40 |
| - | 19?? | Butcher's Deliveryman on bicycle | (no details) | £40-50 |
| - | c.1947 | Stage Coach with Four Horses | English mail coach with driver and trunk, Yellow body, Red wheels, 173 mm. 'Ye Olde Coach and Four' on box | £100-200 |
| - | c.1948-56 | Fire Escape (large) | Brass bell and wheel hubs. Base consists of sump and prop shaft only. Extending wheeled escape ladder. 108 mm. (excluding ladder) | £250-350 |
| - | c.1950 | Fire Escape (smaller) | Plain flat base, wheeled escape ladder, 66 mm. (excluding ladder) | £150-200 |
| - | c.1948 | Fire Engine | Clockwork motor and bell underneath, 'Morestone Series' cast-in, 135 mm | £250-350 |
| - | c.1948-58 | 0-6-0 Tank Locomotive | Green or Red, 'British Railways' cast in, re-issued as Budgie 224, 119 mm | £35-45 |
| - | 1949-51 | Horse Drawn Snack Bar | 'SAM'S' cast on side below counter, removable roof, separate man, tea urn and two mugs, 117mm. Wide range of colours | £250-350 |
| - | 1949-59 | Horse Drawn Hansom Cab | Black / Yellow, driver, elastic band for reins, 118 mm. (re-issued as Budgie 100) | £70-90 |
| - | 1949-? | Gypsy Caravan | Yellow, Green and Red caravan, step to seat, Grey or Brown horse, Gypsy | £300-400 |
| - | c.1948-61 | Horse Drawn Covered Wagon with Four Horses | Green, Red or Orange, driver, cloth canopy plain or printed with 'Thundering Hooves and Blazing Guns on the Western Trail', or 'Walt Disney's Davy Crockett Frontier Wagon' or 'Last of the Mohicans Chingachgook Hawkeye', later with two barrels, 'Made in England' cast transversely under, 190 mm. (Budgie 404). | £100-200 |
| - | 1949 | 'Wells Fargo' Stage Coach with two 'Galloping' Horses | Brown / Yellow, driver and guard, eccentric wheel for 'galloping' effect, some with 'Copyright F.W. Birch & Co.' cast inside, 164 mm | £100-150 |
| - | c.1950 | 'Wells Fargo' Stage Coach | Various colours, four horses, driver, 172 mm | £100-150 |
| - | 1952-58 | Stage Coach with Two Horses | Red or Orange (no lettering), Black plastic horses, wheels and figures,165 mm | £100-150 |
| - | 1954-59 | Horse Drawn Covered Wagon with Six Horses | Red, Yellow wheels, printed cloth canopy 'The Wild West Land of Buffalo and Covered Wagon', driver, two barrels, 'Made in England' cast transversely underneath, 265mm. | £100-125 |

| | | | | |
|---|---|---|---|---|
| - | 1950-51 | **Mechanical Road Sweeper** | Metallic Green/Black, 'City Cleansing Dept.' cast-in, clockwork motor in some, 91 mm | **£350-450** |
| - | c.1950 | **Compressor** | With man and pneumatic drill. No identification cast on model. 76 mm | **£40-50** |
| - | 1953 | **State Landau with Six Horses** | Coronation souvenir, three figures cast-in. No identification on model. 111 mm | **£40-60** |
| - | 1953 | **Prime Mover with Trailer** | Red prime mover, 'British Road Services', 'NO 311' and 'MAX 20 MPH' cast-in, Black plastic wheels, 83 mm. Orange plastic trailer, 136 mm | **£150-175** |
| - | 1953 | **Sleigh with Father Xmas** | One reindeer. No identification on model. About 140 mm | **£175-225** |
| - | 1953-55 | **RAC Motorcycle and Sidecar** | Cast wheels / tyres and rider, no windscreen, hinged lid on sidecar, 70 mm | **£150-175** |
| - | 1954-55 | **A.A. Motorcycle and Sidecar** | Cast wheels / tyres and rider, windscreen, non-opening sidecar, separate rails | **£75-100** |
| - | 1956-57 | **RAC Motorcycle and Sidecar** | Cast rider, windscreen, separate rails and hinged lid on sidecar, steering front forks, rubber tyres, plain number plates, 82 mm | **£75-100** |
| - | 1956-57 | **A.A. Motorcycle and Sidecar** | Cast rider, windscreen, separate rails and hinged lid on sidecar, steering front forks, rubber tyres, plain number plates, 82 mm | **£75-100** |
| - | 1956-57 | **Solo Motorcycle** | Cast rider, steering front forks, rubber tyres, plain number plates, 82 mm. There are four versions: Police Patrol, Despatch Rider, GPO Messenger and TT Rider. Each | **£75-100** |
| - | ? | **Police Motorcycle and Sidecar** | Black machine, Dark Blue sidecar, Black uniformed figures, cast wheels | **£75-100** |
| - | 1954-55 | **Horse Drawn Gipsy Caravan** | Yellow / Green, tinplate roof and base, separate driver and rear steps, 190 mm | **£400-500** |
| - | 1954-56 | **Bedford Dormobile** | Red or Green body. 90 mm | **£150-200** |
| - | 1955-58 | **Leyland Double Deck Bus** | 'Finest Petrol - ESSO - in the World', Red or Green, route '7', 103 mm | **£150-175** |
| | | | 'ESSO - for Happy Motoring - ESSO', Red body, route '7', 103 mm | **£150-175** |
| | | | 'Motor Oil - ESSO - Petrol', Red body, route '7', 103 mm | **£150-175** |
| - | 1955-56 | **Aveling-Barford Road Roller** | Green, Yellow or Red, with driver, 117 mm. Re-issued as Budgie 701 | **£40-50** |
| - | 1955-59 | **Wolseley 6/80 Police Car** | Black, loudspeaker, aerial, 113 mm. No maker's name. (Budgie 246) | **£150-175** |
| 1 | 1955-57 | **Foden 8-wheel Petrol Tanker** | Red body, 'Motor Oil Esso Petrol' transfers, leaflet, 136 mm | **£200-300** |
| 2 | 1955-56 | **Foden 8-wheel Open Lorry** | Light brown cab and chassis, Red truck body, leaflet, 138 mm | **£200-300** |
| 3 | 1955-56 | **Foden Flat Lorry with Chains** | Green cab and 8-wheel chassis, Beige flatbed, brass chain, leaflet, 138 mm | **£200-300** |
| 4 | 1955-57 | **Foden 8-wheel Flat Lorry** | Yellow or Orange cab and chassis, Grey flatbed, leaflet, 138 mm | **£200-300** |
| - | 1956-57 | **Bedford Car Transporter** | Orange cab, Grey trailer, collapsible top deck, two loading ramps, 243 mm | **£200-300** |
| - | 1956 | **Daimler Ambulance** | White or Cream body (no transfers), Silver base, opening rear doors, no maker's name, 110 mm. Re-issued as Budgie 258 | **£150-200** |
| - | 1955-57 | **A.A. Land Rover** (large) | Yellow / Black, 'AA ROAD SERVICE' cast-in, opening rear doors, driver, passenger, 108 mm | **£500-600** |
| - | 1957-58 | **A.A. Land Rover** (medium) | Yellow / Black, driver, 79 mm. 'AA ROAD SERVICE' transfers, no rear windows | **£150-200** |
| | | | Same but 'AA ROAD SERVICE' cast-in, two rear windows | **£150-200** |
| - | 1958 | **Military Police Land Rover** | Olive Green, driver, 'MP Military Police' and crown cast on sides, 79 mm | **£500-750** |
| - | 1958 | **Breakdown Service Land Rover** | Red body, driver, 'Breakdown Service Unit' cast on sides, 79 mm | **£300-400** |
| - | 1958 | **Foden Dump Truck** | Orange cab and chassis, Grey dumper, 108 mm. Re-issued as Budgie 226 | **£150-200** |

## Morestone 'Trucks of the World International' Series

| | | | | |
|---|---|---|---|---|
| - | 1958 | **Klöckner Side Tipper** | Red cab, Black chassis, Cream tipper, 81 mm. (with 'Driving Licence') | **£40-50** |
| - | 1958 | **Scammell Articulated Tanker** | Orange cab, Cream tank. 'LIQUID IN BULK' cast on sides, 114 mm | **£70-90** |
| - | 1958 | **International Articulated Refrigerator Lorry** | Red / Blue cab, Silver trailer, 'COAST to COAST REFRIGERATION' transfers, 153 mm. Re-issued as Budgie 202 | **£40-50** |

## 'Noddy' items by Morestone and Budgie

| | | | | |
|---|---|---|---|---|
| 301 | 1956-61 | **Noddy and his Car** (large) | Yellow/Red, windscreen, solid rubber wheels, metal or plastic 'Noddy', 98 mm | **£150-200** |
| - | 1957-58 | **Big Ears on Bicycle** (large) | Red bicycle (64 mm.), metal 'Big Ears' with legs that move as the model is pushed along. No maker's name on model | **£150-200** |
| - | c.1959 | **Clown on Bicycle** (large) | Metallic Light Brown bicycle (64 mm. as previous model), metal clown figure with moving legs. No maker's name on model | **£150-200** |
| - | 1958 | **Noddy's Garage Set** | 331 Noddy's Car and 'Esso' series nos. 7, 13, 16 and 20. Box folds into garage | **£150-200** |
| 303 | c.1961 | **Noddy and his Car** (large) with Big Ears | As 301 but with additional metal Big Ears Figure | **£150-200** |
| 305 | 1959-61 | **Noddy's Gift Box** | Contains numbers 331, 333 and plastic Mr. Plod the Policeman | **£600-800** |
| 307 | 1959-61 | **Locomotive and Wagon with Noddy and Big Ears** | Yellow loco with red cab. Red wagon. Plastic figures, 104 mm | **£150-200** |
| 309 | c.1961 | **Noddy and Locomotive** | As no.307 but without wagon, 57 mm | **£100-150** |
| 311 | 1960-61 | **Noddy on Bicycle with Trailer** | Yellow bicycle, red trailer, plastic figure, 81 mm | **£150-200** |
| 331 | 1958-61 | **Noddy and his Car** (small) | Yellow car, red base and wheels, plastic figure, 52 mm | **£150-200** |
| 333 | 1958-61 | **Big Ears on Bicycle** (small) | Red. No maker's name on model, plastic figure, 48 mm | **£150-200** |

# Morestone and Budgie Miniatures

Packed in 'Esso' Petrol Pump boxes from 1956 to around 1959, then in Budgie bubble packs (yellow backing card) till 1964, and from 1965 in bubble packs with 'The Esso Petrol Pump Series' blue backing card. In the early 1960s, conventional boxes marked 'Mobile Vehicle Series' or 'Modern Vehicle Series' were also used.

| | | | | |
|---|---|---|---|---|
| 1 | 1956-58 | **A.A. Motorcycle and Sidecar** | Yellow/Black motorcycle and sidecar, Blue uniformed rider, 46 mm | **£75-100** |
| 2 | 1956-58 | **RAC Motorcycle and Sidecar** | Black motorcycle, Mid-Blue sidecar, Dark Blue uniformed rider, 46 mm | **£75-100** |
| 3 | 1956-58 | **A.A. Land Rover** | 'AA ROAD SERVICE' cast-in, spare wheel (on bonnet) on some, 54 mm | **£75-100** |
| 4 | 1956-58 | **A.A. Bedford Van** | AA badge and 'ROAD SERVICE' cast-in, 57 mm | **£75-100** |
| 5 | 1956-70 | **Wolseley 6/80 Police Car** | Black or green body, 65 mm | **£75-100** |
| 6 | 1956-58 | **Cooper-Bristol Racing Car** | Blue or Dark Blue body, Off-White base and driver, 58 mm | **£75-100** |
| 7 | 1956-65 | **Mercedes-Benz Racing Car** | Silver body, Red base and driver, 60 mm | **£75-100** |
| 8 | 1956-70 | **Volkswagen 1200 Saloon** | Metallic Light Blue body, 58 mm | **£75-100** |
| 9 | 1956-58 | **Maudslay Horse Box** | Red body, 'HORSE BOX SERVICE' cast-in, 57 mm | **£75-100** |
| 10 | 1956-58 | **Karrier GPO Telephones Van** | Dark green body, 57 mm | **£75-100** |
| 11 | 1957-65 | **Morris Commercial Van** | Red body, 'ROYAL MAIL' and 'E-II-R' cast-in, 58 mm | **£75-100** |
| 12 | 1957-70 | **Volkswagen Microbus** | Light Brown, Pale Blue or Metallic Dark Blue, 61 mm | **£75-100** |
| 13 | 1957-64 | **Austin FX3 Taxi** | Black body, Silver base and driver, 58 mm | **£75-100** |
| 14 | 1957-70 | **Packard Convertible** | Beige or Metallic Lt.Blue body, Red base/seats, Lt. Brown or Gold driver | **£75-100** |
| 15 | 1957-70 | **Austin A95 Westminster Countryman** | Blue or Orange, (Silver flash on some); or Metallic Mauve, 66 mm | **£75-100** |
| 16 | 1957-64 | **Austin-Healey 100** | Red body, Off-White base and driver, 57 mm | **£75-100** |
| 17 | 1957-58 | **Ford Thames 5 cwt. Van** | Blue body, 60 mm | **£75-100** |
| 18 | 1957-66 | **Foden Dumper** | Red cab and chassis, Lemon-Yellow or Grey dumper, 60 mm | **£75-100** |
| 19 | 1957-70 | **Rover 105R** | Green or Gold body, 65 mm | **£75-100** |
| 20 | 1957-64 | **Plymouth Belvedere Convertible** | Pale Pink or White body, Red base and driver, 64 mm | **£75-100** |
| 20 | 1968-70 | **Austin A95 Emergency Vehicle** | As 15 but White with Orange beacon, 'EMERGENCY' transfer, Red base | **£75-100** |
| 21 | 1963-66. | **Bedford TK Tipper Lorry** | Dark Green tipper. Yellow, Off-White or Orange cab, 58 mm | **£75-100** |
| 21 | 1968-70 | **Oldsmobile Town Sedan** | Gold body, 66 mm | **£75-100** |
| 22 | 1963-66 | **Bedford TK Crane Lorry** | Dark Green cab, Orange crane, Orange or Dark Green platform, 56 mm | **£75-100** |
| 22 | 1968-70 | **Cattle Transporter** | Adapted from no.58. Light Brown body, Dark Brown rear door, 61 mm | **£75-100** |
| 23 | 1963-66 | **Bedford TK Cement Mixer** | Off-White mixer. Green, Yellow, Red or Orange cab and chassis, 59 mm | **£75-100** |
| 24 | 1963-66 | **Bedford TK Refuse Lorry** | Green, Orange, Red or Yellow cab, Silver back, 59 mm | **£75-100** |
| 25 | 1963-66 | **Bedford TK Cattle Lorry** | Light brown body. Off-White, Orange or Yellow cab, 58 mm | **£75-100** |
| 26 | 1963-66 | **Aveling-Barford Road Roller** | Similar to Lesney Matchbox no.1c. Green body, Red wheels, 55 mm | **£75-100** |
| 27 | 1963-70 | **Wolseley 6/80 Fire Chief Car** | Same as no.5 with altered base lettering. Red body, 65 mm | **£75-100** |

**Models 50 - 55 were designated the 'Road Tanker Series'.**

| | | | | |
|---|---|---|---|---|
| 50 | 1963-66 | **'BP Racing Service' Tanker** | Green with White tank, 61 mm | **£75-100** |
| 51 | 1963-66 | **'Shell' Tanker** | Yellow, 61 mm | **£75-100** |
| 52 | 1963-64 | **'Shell BP' Tanker** | Green or Yellow; White tank, 61 mm | **£75-100** |
| 53 | 1963-66 | **'National' Tanker** | Blue with Yellow tank, 61 mm | **£75-100** |
| 54 | 1963-66 | **'BP' Tanker** | Green with White tank, 61 mm | **£75-100** |
| 55 | 1963-66 | **'Mobil' Tanker** | Red body, 61 mm | **£75-100** |
| 56 | 1966-70 | **GMC Box Van** | 'HERTZ TRUCK RENTAL' transfers and 'TRUCK RENTAL' cast-in. Light Green or Pale Blue body, 61 mm | **£75-100** |
| 57 | 1966-70 | **International Parcels Van** | Green body, sliding door. 'REA EXPRESS' transfers, 67 mm | **£75-100** |
| 58 | 1966-70 | **'Modern Removals' Van** | 'MODERN REMOVALS' transfers. Light Brown or Metallic Green, 61 mm | **£75-100** |
| 59 | 1967-70 | **AEC Merryweather Fire Engine** | Copied from Lesney Matchbox no.9c. Red body, Gold ladder, 65 mm | **£75-100** |
| 60 | 1966-70 | **Rover 105R Squad Car** | As no.19 but with altered base lettering. Black or Red body, 65 mm | **£75-100** |
| 61 | 1966-70 | **Austin A95 'Q Car'** | As no.15 but with altered base lettering. Black or Metallic Dark Blue body | **£75-100** |

**Sets of three vehicles (bubble-packed)**

| | | | | |
|---|---|---|---|---|
| 94 | 1966 | **Interpol Set** | Intended to contain no.5 Police Car, 60 Squad Car, 61 'Q' Car. Not issued | NPP |
| 95 | 1966 | **Road Haulage Set** | Intended to contain 56 Hertz Van, 57 REA Van, 58 Removals Van. Not issued | NPP |
| 96 | 1965-66 | **Road Construction Set** | Contains no.18 Dumper, 23 Cement Mixer, 26 Road Roller | **£125-150** |
| 97 | 1965-66 | **Truck Set** | Contains no.21 Tipper, 22 Crane, 25 Cattle Lorry | **£125-150** |
| 98 | 1965-66 | **Utility Vehicle Set** | Contains no.12 VW Microbus, 24 Refuse Lorry, 55 Mobil Tanker | **£125-150** |
| 99 | 1965-66 | **Traffic Set** | Contains no.8 Volkswagen, 15 Austin, 27 Fire Chief | **£125-150** |
| 95 | 1968-70 | **Town Set** | Contains no.20 Emergency Vehicle, 21 Oldsmobile, 56 Hertz Van | **£125-150** |
| 96 | 1967-70 | **Service Set** | Contains no.5 Police Car, 19 Rover, 59 Fire Engine | **£125-150** |
| 97 | 1967-70 | **Truck Set** | Contains no.12 VW Microbus, 57 REA Van, 58 Removals Van | **£125-150** |
| 98 | 1967-70 | **Utility Vehicle Set** | Contains no.27 Fire Chief, 60 Squad Car, 61 Q Car | **£125-150** |
| 99 | 1967-70 | **Traffic Set** | Contains no.8 Volkswagen, 14 Packard, 15 Austin | **£125-150** |

**Gift Sets**

| | | | | |
|---|---|---|---|---|
| | 1962 | **Gift Set No.8** | Contains numbers 5, 8, 11, 12, 13, 15, 18 and 19 | **£200-300** |
| | 1962 | **Gift Set No.12** | Contains 5, 7, 8, 11, 12, 13, 14, 15, 16, 18, 19 and 20 (Plymouth) | **£200-300** |

| 100 | 1972-84 | **Horse Drawn Hansom Cab**  With driver, elastic band for reins. Re-issue of Morestone/Modern Products model. 'Gold' plated or Metallic Light Brown, 118 mm ............ **£25-30** |

| 101 | 1977-84 | **Austin FX4 Taxi**  Also issued as no.703. Re-issued by Seerol. Black or Maroon. 106 mm .................................. **£25-30** |

| 101 | 1984 | **Austin FX4 Taxi**  Silver body, 'LONDON VINTAGE TAXI ASSOCIATION'. Limited (1,000) commemorative marking 25 years of the FX4. Normal box ...................... **£25-30** |

| 102 | 1981-84 | **Rolls-Royce Silver Cloud**  Re-issued by Seerol. Gold (painted or 'plated'), Black, Silver, Cream, Red, Blue, Metallic Lt.Blue, Metallic Turquoise or Metallic Dark Pink, 107 mm ............................................ **£25-30** |

| 202 | 1959-66 | **International Articulated Refrigerator Lorry**  Re-issued 'Trucks of the World' model. Red / Blue or Red cab (windows later). Silver trailer, 'COAST TO COAST REFRIGERATION', 153 mm...... **£50-75** |

| 204 | 1959-64 | **Volkswagen Pick-Up**  Blue body, Cream base, cloth tilt 'EXPRESS DELIVERY', 92 mm .................... **£50-75** |

| 206 | 1959-64 | **Leyland Hippo Coal Lorry**  Green or Orange cab, Light Brown body, 'COAL AND COKE' cast-in, coal load, 92 mm .......................................................... **£65-85** |

| 208 | 1959-61 | **RAF Personnel Carrier**  RAF blue, roundels, White tilt. 'A MORESTONE PRODUCT', 104 mm .... **£90-120** |

| 210 | 1959-61 | **US Army Personnel Carrier**  As 208 but Army brown body with star, Light Brown tilt, 104 mm.......... **£90-120** |

| 212 | 1959-61 | **British Army Personnel Carrier**  As 208 but Dark Green with Red / White square, Light Brown tilt....... **£90-120** |

| 214 | 1959-64 | **Thornycroft Mobile Crane**  Red cab and chassis, Yellow crane engine, Light Blue crane, 100 mm ............ **£50-60** |

| 216 | 1959-64 | **Renault Truck**  Yellow cab, Red body. Cloth tilt, 'FRESH FRUIT DAILY', 103 mm ........................... **£40-50** |

| 218 | 1959-63 | **Seddon 'Jumbo' Mobile Traffic Control Unit**........................ Yellow cab and trailer with Black flash and catwalk. 'AUTOMOBILE ASSOCIATION' and AA badge transfers, 168 mm .............................................. **£125-150** |

| 220 | 1959-66 | **Leyland Hippo Cattle Transporter**  Orange cab, Light Brown body, Dark Brown base + ramp, 97 mm.... **£35-45** |

| 222 | 1959-65 | **International Tank Transporter with Centurion Tank**  Army brown with star transfers. Cab as no.202. 155 mm. (with ramps up) ...................................... **£175-200** |

| 224 | 1959-66 | **0-6-0 Tank Locomotive**  As Modern Products model. Red, 'BRITISH RAILWAYS' cast-in, 119 mm .......... **£25-35** |

| 224 | 1971-84 | **0-6-0 Tank Locomotive**  Red, Metallic Brown, Black or Dark Green, 'BRITISH RAILWAYS' on transfers or labels .................................................. **£10-15** |

| 226 | 1959-66 | **Foden Dumper**  Re-issue of a Morestone model. Orange cab and chassis, Grey dumper. 'BUD 123' number plate transfers, 108 mm .................. **£30-40** |

| 228 | 1959-64 | **Karrier Bantam Bottle Lorry**  Orange-Yellow, 12 maroon plastic crates. 'DRINK COCA-COLA' transfers, 'COMMER LOW LOADER' cast underneath, 134 mm .................................... **£400-500** |

| 230 | 1959-66 | **Seddon Timber Transporter**  Orange cab (no windows), or Green cab (with windows), Yellow trailer, five 'logs', 178 mm....................... **£250-350** |

| 232 | 1960-66 | **Seddon Cable Drum Transporter**  Red prime mover (windows later), Orange trailer, 3 wooden cable drums 'STANDARD' ................ **£200-300** |

| 234 | 1960-65 | **International Low Loader with Caterpillar Tractor**  Orange cab, Light Brown trailer, Orange tractor, 155 mm. (with ramps up) ................................ **£175-225** |

| 236 | 1960-66 and 1969-84 | **AEC Routemaster Bus**  Also issued as nos.704, 705 and 706. All models have destination transfers for route '9' and 'LONDON TRANSPORT' transfers or labels. They were available with or without windows. 108 mm. Red, 'Esso GOLDEN Esso'..............................**£50-75** Red, 'Esso UNIFLO - the tuned motor oil'......................**£50-75** Red, 'GO ESSO - BUY ESSO - DRIVE ESSO'.............**£50-75** Red, 'UNIFLO sae 10W/50 Motor Oil'........................ Red, Green or Gold, 'Houses of Parliament Tower Bridge' ........................ **£50-75** |

| 236 | 1973 | Promotional issue: Red body (with windows), 'Sheraton-Heathrow Hotel' on sides, 'OPENING 1st FEBRUARY 1973' on roof, Special box................ **£100-150** |

| 238 | 1960-63 | **Scammell Scarab Van**  Crimson / Cream body. 'BRITISH RAILWAYS' and 'CADBURYS', 150mm. |

| | Note: | Chocolate Bar picture may be vertical or horizontal . **£140-170** |

| 238 | 1964-66 | Yellow cab, Black chassis, Yellow trailer. 'Railfreight', 'CADBURYS'.................................. **£140-170** |

| 238 | 1985 | Maroon cab, Maroon / Cream trailer. 'BRITISH RAILWAYS' and 'CADBURYS'.................. **£25-35** Yellow cab and trailer. 'Railfreight' and 'CADBURYS' transfers. Most of these were issued in original 1960s boxes. 150 mm ...................................... **£25-35** |

| 240 | 1960-64 | **Scammell Scarab Wagon**  Red / Cream cab, Yellow chassis, Red trailer, Green cloth tilt, 150 mm..... **£65-85** |

| 242 | 1960-66 | **Euclid Dumper**  Red cab, Orange chassis and dumper. 114 mm .................................................. **£65-85** |

| 244 | 1961-65 | **Morris Breakdown Lorry**  Blue body, Yellow base, tool box and jib. 'BUDGIE SERVICE', 120 mm ........ **£80-100** |

| 246 | 1960-63 | **Wolseley 6/80 Police Car**  Re-issued Modern Products model. Black, loudspeaker, aerial, 'BUDGIE TOYS' cast under, 'POLICE' transfers on grille and boot, 113 mm ............................................ **£50-70** |

| 246 | 1983 | **Wolseley 6/80 Police Car**  Light Blue, 'POLICE' labels, spotlights and roof sign replace the loudspeaker and aerial. Trial run only - did not go into full production .... **£50-70** |

| 248 | 1961 | **Stage Coach with Four Horses**  Listed on this number as 'available later', but issued as no. 434. |

| 250 | ------ | Pack reference only. This number was used for packs of one dozen of the Budgie miniatures. |

| 252 | 1961-63 | **Austin Articulated Lorry with Railway Container**  Crimson / Cream cab, windows, Crimson trailer / container, 'BRITISH RAILWAYS' transfers............... **£125-150** |

| 252 | 1964 | Crimson cab / trailer, windows, Blue container, 'Door to Door' transfers ...................................... **£125-150** |

| 254 | 1961-64 | **AEC Merryweather Fire Escape**  Red, windows, Silver extending turntable ladder. 97 mm. (excl. ladder)................................... **£125-150** |

| 256 | 1961-64 | **Foden Aircraft Refuelling Tanker 'Pluto'**  Red, with windows. 'ESSO AVIATION PRODUCTS' transfers, 149 mm .............................................. **£250-300** |

| 258 | 1961-63 | **Daimler Ambulance**  Re-issued Modern Products model. Cream with Red base ('BUDGIE TOYS' cast-in), 'AMBULANCE' and 'EMERGENCY' transfers, 110 mm. .......................................... **£100-150** |

| 258 | 1991 | **Daimler Ambulance Kit**  Re-issued as a kit of unpainted castings (by Autocraft)........................... **£10-20** |

| 260 | 1962 | **Ruston-Bucyrus Excavator**  Yellow / Red cab, '10-RB', Beige or Olive-Green base and jib, 73 mm . **£400-500** |

| 262 | 1962-64 | **Racing Motorcycle**  No maker's name. Unpainted cycle, tinplate fairing in Metallic Blue, Metallic Lilac, Metallic Brown or Lime Green, Black plastic rider, 104 mm ............ **£75-100** |

| 264 | 1962-64 | **Racing Motorcycle and Sidecar**  Cycle as 262, sidecar and fairing in Metallic Blue, Metallic Pinkish-Red, Metallic Green, Metallic Lilac, Metallic Brown or Lime Green. Black plastic rider / passenger, no maker's name, 104 mm .............................. **£75-100** |

| 266 | 1962-64 | **Motorcycle and Delivery Sidecar**  Blue cycle as 262, Red sidecar, 'EXPRESS DELIVERY' cast-in, no maker's name, Black plastic rider. 108 mm ............... **£100-125** |

| 268 | 1962-64 | **A.A. Land Rover**  Different from Morestone AA Land Rovers. Yellow body, Black roof, windows, opening rear doors, 'AA ROAD SERVICE' transfers, 97 mm ............................................. **£125-150** |

| 270 | 1962-66 | **Leyland Articulated Tanker**  Red, windows, 'ESSO PETROLEUM COMPANY LTD' labels, 132 mm ............................................................. **£100-125** |

| 272 | 1962-64 | **Supercar**  From TV series. Red / Silver body, Red wings (or colours reversed), clear plastic canopy, 'SUPERCAR' transfers, 122 mm .......................... **£500-700** |

| 274 | 1962-66 | **Ford Thames Refuse Lorry**  Blue cab / Silver body, or Yellow cab / Metallic blue body, windows ............. **£45-55** |

| 276 | 1962-66 | **Bedford LWB Tipper**  Red cab with windows, Yellow tipper, 'HAM RIVER GRIT', 128 mm.............. **£40-80** |

| 278 | 1963-64 | **RAC Land Rover**  Casting as 268, Blue, windows, 'RAC RADIO RESCUE' transfers, 97 mm ............... **£150-175** |

| 280 | 1963-64 | **AEC Super Fueller Tanker**  White cab and trailer, windows, Green base / canopy, 'AIR BP', 219 mm ... **£400-500** |

| 282 | 1963-66 | **Euclid Scraper**  Yellow or Lime Green, windscreen, 'EUCLID', Black plastic wheels, 163 mm.................. **£100-140** |

| 284 | 1962 | **Euclid Crawler Tractor**  Not issued................................ **NPP** |

| 286 | 1962 | **Euclid Bulldozer**  Not issued ........................................ **NPP** |

| 288 | 1963-66 | **Leyland Bulk Flour Tanker**  Red cab, windows, Off-White silos, Yellow hopppers, 'BULK FLOUR', 107 mm ..................................................................... **£45-55** |

290 1963-64 **Bedford Ice Cream Van 'TONIBELL'**
Blue body, pink cow's head on roof,
two cows in side transfer ............................................ **£150-200**
Same but with three cows in side transfer .................. **£500-750**

292 1963-66 **Leyland Bulk Milk Tanker** Blue or Red cab,
windows, White tank, 'MILK', 107 mm ......................... **£45-55**

294 1963-66 **Bedford TK Horse Box** Off-White cab, windows,
Brown body, Light Brown doors. two Brown plastic
horses. 'EPSOM STABLE' transfer, 109 mm .............. **£80-100**

296 1963-66 **Motorway Express Coach** Midland Red livery:
Red body, Black roof, 'BIRMINGHAM-LONDON
MOTORWAY EXPRESS' transfers,
windows, 121 mm ...................................................... **£125-150**
USA livery: Light Blue body, Cream roof,
'WASHINGTON D.C.' and 'BLUE LINE
SIGHTSEEING CO.' transfers,
phone number 'LA9-7755' at rear .............................. **£400-500**

298 1963-66 **Alvis Salamander Crash Tender** Red body,
windows, Silver plastic ladder, Yellow engine cover
at rear, Black plastic wheels.
'FIRE SERVICE' transfers, 92 mm. ............................ **£100-125**

300 1963-65 **Lewin Sweepmaster** Blue / Silver, windows,
Black plastic wheels, Black sweeping brush ................ **£75-100**

302 1963-66 **Commer Cabin Service Lift Truck** Blue cab, windows,
Silver body, 'BOAC CABIN SERVICES', 104 mm ... **£100-150**

304 1964-66 **Bedford TK Glass Transporter** Off-white cab and
chassis, windows, Green body. 'TOWER GLASS CO.'
transfers. Four clear plastic 'glass' sheets, 108 mm ........ **£45-55**

306 1964-66 **Fiat Tractor with Shovel**
Orange tractor, Metallic Blue shovel, 108 mm ........... **£100-140**

308 1964-66 **Seddon Pitt Alligator Low Loader** Green cab,
windows, Yellow trailer with Black ramp, 163 mm ........ **£45-55**

310 1964-66 **Leyland Cement Mixer** Orange cab, windows,
Silver mixer, 'INVICTA Construction Co.', 98 mm ....... **£60-80**

312 1964-66 **Bedford Super Tipmaster** Dark Green cab, windows,
Silver tipper. 'SUPER TIP-MASTER', 127mm .............. **£60-80**

314 1965-66 **Fiat Tractor with Dozer Blade** As 306 but enclosed
cab, Orange tractor, Metallic Blue blade, 81 mm ......... **£45-55**

316 1965-66 **Albion Overhead Maintenance Vehicle** Green body,
windows, Silver / Black boom assembly, 107 mm ......... **£40-50**

318 1965-66 **Euclid Mammoth Articulated Dumper**
Modified from no.242. Green cab, Yellow chassis,
Orange tipper, 201 mm ................................................. **£75-95**

322 1965-66 **Scammell Routeman Pneumajector Transporter**
Light Blue cab, Cream or White tank,
'THE ATLAS CARRIER CO.', 111 mm ......................... **£60-80**

324 1965-66 **Douglas Prospector Duomatic Tipper**
Tips in two directions. Blue cab and chassis,
windows, Grey tipper, 112 mm .................................. **£250-300**

326 1965-66 **Scammell Highwayman Gas Transporter**
Two-tone Green cab, clear windows, Dark Green trailer,
Silver plastic hubs, 6 White / Red gas cylinders ......... **£300-400**

328 1966 **Scammell Handyman Artic.** Planned but not issued ....... NPP
330 1966 **Land Rover** Modified 268, planned but not issued ......... NPP
332 1966 **'Kenning' Breakdown Lorry** Planned but not issued..... NPP
334 1966 **Austin Gipsy Fire Tender** Planned but not issued .......... NPP
404 1960-61 **Horse Drawn Covered Wagon** with Four Horses.
For details see Morestone and Modern Products entry.

410 1961 **Stage Coach with Four Horses** Blue or 'Gold' plated
coach, no lettering cast on sides but 'WELLS FARGO
STAGE COACH' and 'A BUDGIE TOY' cast underneath,
plastic horses and driver, bubble-packed, 118 mm...... **£100-150**

430 1960-61 **Wagon Train Set** Contains 3 of no. 432 plus two
more horses with riders, bubble-packed ..................... **£100-130**

432 1960-61 **Horse Drawn Covered Wagon with Two Horses**
Red wagon, ('A BUDGIE TOY' on floor), Grey,
White or Lemon metal canopy, 2 barrels, plastic horses,
driver, passenger, bubble packed, 82 mm ...................... **£35-45**

434 1961 **Stage Coach with Four Horses**
'WELLS FARGO' above windows, 'STAGE LINES' on
doors, luggage cast on roof, Red or Blue,
plastic horses and driver, 189 mm ............................. **£100-150**

452 1958-63 **A.A. Motorcycle and Sidecar** Initially in Morestone
box. Windscreen, plastic rider, integral rails and
hinged lid on sidecar, steerable, rubber tyres,
plain number plates, 82 mm ...................................... **£100-150**

452 1964-66 **A.A. Motorcycle and Sidecar**
New design. Sidecar with transfers and 'BUDGIE'
underneath, plastic rider, windscreen and leg guards,
plain number plates, 84 mm ...................................... **£100-150**

454 1958-63 **RAC Motorcycle and Sidecar**
Initially in Morestone box. Windscreen, plastic rider,
integral rails and hinged lid on sidecar, steerable,
rubber tyres, plain number plates, 82 mm ................. **£100-150**

454 1964-66 **RAC Motorcycle and Sidecar**
New design. Sidecar with transfers and 'BUDGIE'
underneath, plastic rider, windscreen and leg guards,
plain number plates, 84 mm ...................................... **£100-150**

456 1958-66 **Solo Motorcycle** Initially in Morestone boxes.
Two casting versions as 452 and 454 but bikes are
'Silver plated'. Plastic riders:
456 PP Police Patrol (Blue uniform an helmet) ........................... **£70-90**
456 DR Despatch Rider (Light Brown uniform) ........................... **£70-90**
456 GPO GPO Messenger (Light Blue uniform, Red helmet) . **£100-130**
456 TT 'Tourist Trophy' Rider (White racing overalls,
Red helmet) ............................................................. **£100-130**

701 1983 **Aveling-Barford Road Roller** Re-issued Modern
Products model. Dark Green body, Silver / Red wheels,
Dark Blue driver ........................................................... **£10-15**

702 1984-85 **Scammell Scarab Vans** Re-issue of 238.
Very Dark Blue cab and trailer, White 'RN' on doors,
'ROYAL NAVY' on tilt .............................................. **£150-250**
Very Dark Blue cab and trailer,
'HALLS MENTHO-LYPTUS' labels ............................ **£25-35**
Maroon cab and trailer,
'LMS LIVERPOOL ROAD' transfers........................... **£25-35**
Maroon cab and trailer, 'SPRATTS BONIO' transfers ... **£25-35**
Maroon cab and trailer, 'REA EXPRESS' transfers....... **£25-35**

703 1984 **Austin FX4 Taxi** As no.101 but in window box.
Black, Silver, Met.Dk.Pink, Gold, Dark Green,
Grey or White .............................................................. **£25-35**

704 1984 **AEC Routemaster Bus** Yellow / Red body with
windows, 'SHOP LINKER' labels, casting as 236 ......... **£25-35**

705 1984 **AEC Routemaster Bus** Silver body with windows,
'25 FAITHFUL YEARS' labels, casting as 236.............. **£25-35**

706 1984 **AEC Routemaster Bus** Yellow / Red with windows,
'Watford FA Cup Final 84' labels, 236 casting .............. **£25-35**

PHOTO: VECTIS AUCTIONS LTD.

## Budgie Gift Sets

No. 4   1961   **Gift Set No.4** .......................................Contains four models. Price depends on contents which vary .......................**£125-165**
No. 5   1961   **Gift Set No.5** .......................................Contains five models. Price depends on contents which vary.......................**£400-500**

## Seerol Models

-   1985   **Austin FX4 Taxi**...............................Re-issue of Budgie no.101 with amended base lettering and low friction wheels.
                                               .....................................Black body, 106mm. Still available...........................................**£15-25**
-   1985   **Rolls-Royce Silver Cloud** ..................Re-issued Budgie 102, amended lettering, low friction wheels. Black, Silver,
    .............................White, Yellow, Dark Blue, Pink or Maroon, 107 mm. Still available..............**£15-25**
-   1985   **AEC Routemaster Bus** .....................New design, 1:76 scale, 108 mm. Was available from London souvenir outlets till the late 1990s.
-                                .............................Red, Light Green or Dark Green, 'Houses of Parliament Tower Bridge' labels ....**£15-25**
-                                .............................Red, 'The Original London Transport Sightseeing Tour' labels ..............**£15-25**
-                                .............................Red, 'Greetings from London' tampo print.............................**£15-25**
-                                .............................Red, 'Tower of London' tampo print.................................**£15-25**
-                                .............................Red, 'Petticoat Lane' tampo print..................................**£15-25**
-                                .............................Red, 'Buckingham Palace' tampo print...............................**£15-25**

# Budgie Leaflets and Catalogues

A leaflet was included in the box with most Budgie Toys. Dates are not shown on any except the 1963 and 1964 catalogues.

-   1959   **Leaflet**..........................................Printed on one side only. 'Budgie Toys Speak for Themselves' at top.
                      1st version:................................. Includes the Six-horse Covered Wagon...................................**£20-30**
                      2nd version: ............................. Timber Transporter replaces the Covered Wagon............................**£20-30**
-   1960   **Leaflet**..........................................'Budgie Toys Speak for Themselves' on front, 'Budgie Toys for Girls and Boys' on reverse...................**£20-30**
-   1961   **Leaflet**..........................................'Budgie Toys Speak for Themselves' on Black background..................**£20-30**
  1961   **Trade catalogue** ...........................Fold-out leaflet showing Noddy items, Wagon Train and Budgie miniatures as well
                                 as the main Budgie range. Separate price list marked 'Price List 1961' showing
                                 wholesale and retail prices...............................................**£40-50**
-   1962   **Leaflet**..........................................'Die-Cast Models by Budgie They Speak for Themselves' on Black background.
                      1st version: .............................. 268 AA Land Rover on front, 258 Daimler Ambulance on reverse ............**£10-15**
                      2nd version: ............................. 214 Mobile Crane on front, 266 Express Delivery Motorcycle on reverse ........**£10-15**
-   1963   **Leaflet**..........................................'Die-Cast Models by Budgie They Speak for Themselves' on Black background.
                      1st version: .............................. 278 RAC Land Rover on front, 258 Daimler Ambulance on reverse ............**£10-15**
                      2nd version: ............................. 278 RAC Land Rover on front, 266 Express Delivery Motorcycle on reverse ........**£10-15**
-   1963   **Trade Catalogue** (8 pages) ........... Landscape format, includes retail price list...............................**£30-40**
-   1964   **Trade Catalogue** (8 pages) ........... 'Budgie Models' on cover (portrait format). Includes retail price list ..............**£30-40**

## Sales aids

**Shop Display Unit:** Five tiers, yellow / blue / red, with 'BUDGIE DIECAST MODELS' plus perching 'Budgie' logo.........................**£200-250**

**Shop Display Unit:** 'The ESSO Petrol Pump Series': '1/6d each', 'A MORESTONE PRODUCT'. Features twenty models on four shelves...................**£200-300**

## BUDGIE TOYS SELECTED AUCTION RESULTS 2005 — 2007

### Vectis Auctions Ltd.
Fleck Way, Thornaby,
Stockton -on-Tees TS17 9JZ
Abbreviations: M = Mint, NM = Near Mint, EP = Excellent Plus,
E = Excellent, GP = Good Plus, G = Good, F = Fair

**BUDGIE TOYS and MORESTONE**
**218 'AA' Traffic Control Unit**. Yellow/Black, NM in G box ................... **£100**
**238 Scammell Delivery Van 'British Railways'**. Red/Cream, E in G box**£140**
**256 Aircraft Refuelling Tanker 'Esso'**. Red, Blue, White, E in G-GP box**£280**
**262 Racing Motorcyclist**. Unpainted cycle, Metallic Blue fairing,
Black/Silver rider, NM in GP box ........................................ **£130**

**262 'Express Delivery' Motorcycle and Sidecar**. Blue/Silver bike,
Black/White rider, Red sidecar, M in GP box.................................... **£100**
**282 Euclid 21 Yard Scraper**. Yellow, Black plastic wheels, E in GP box. **£140**
**290 Ice Cream Van 'Tonibell'**. Blue, Grey plastic hubs,
EP in G (grubby) box ...................................................... **£320**
**296 Motorway Express Coach 'Birmingham to London'**. EP in G box. **£130**
**306 Tractor with Fork Lift**. Orange, Blue, White, E in G window box.....**£110**
**324 Duomatic Tipper Truck**. Blue, Grey, Yellow decals, GP in GP box .. **£260**
**456/DR Despatch Rider**. Silver bike, Brown rider, M in E box ............... **£100**
**456/GPO GPOTelegraph Boy**. Silver bike, Blue rider, M in NM box......**£110**
**456/PP Police Patrol**. Silver bike, Blue helmeted rider, NM in E box........ **£80**
**456/TT Tourist Trophy Racer**.
Silver bike, White rider with Red helmet, M in GP box...................... **£110**
**No. 5 Gift Set**. Details as Catalogue, E-NM in G picture box ................... **£460**

# The 'River Series'

A trademark owned by M/s Jordan and Lewden of Homerton, London E9. Note that, while 'River Series' models were cast using tools supplied by DCMT, they had no other connection with DCMT. The Jordan and Lewden company started to offer diecast toys to the toy trade from about 1953 and continued to do so for only a few years. Dies were eventually sold to the Habonim firm in Israel and models subsequently appeared in the 'Gamda' series of toys. Some examples are known to have been produced in New Zealand by Lincoln Industries (who were also responsible for some 'lookalike' Matchbox models). Only 'Made in England' and the car name appear on the diecast base of each model.

None of the models acquired window glazing while made as 'River Series' – some did when produced as 'Gamda' toys.

These car models came in various colours and had cast hubs / rubber tyres where friction-motor fitted, otherwise one-piece rubber wheels.

Ford Prefect................................................NGPP
American Buick ..........................................NGPP
Daimler Conquest ......................................NGPP
Austin Somerset.........................................NGPP
Standard Vanguard II Saloon .......................NGPP
Standard Vanguard Estate ...........................NGPP

These larger items were also available in various colours, some have clockwork motor, most have one-piece cast wheels, and some were boxed.

Cattle Truck...............................................NGPP
Car Carrier ................................................NGPP
Excavator Truck .........................................NGPP
Tower Wagon .............................................NGPP
Cattle Truck...............................................NGPP

The Editor would welcome any additional information on the 'River Series'.

'River Series' American Buick

'River Series' Austin Somerset

# Scale Models Ltd. (Scamold)

Manufactured between 1939 and 1950 by Scale Models Ltd from whose title the model name was obtained. The models are extremely accurate 1/35 scale diecast models, with their original measurements being taken from the real racing cars at the famous Brooklands race track. Pre-war boxes state 'MANUFACTURED BY SCALE MODELS LTD, BROOKLANDS TRACK, WEYBRIDGE, ENG.'. This was dropped after the war. The proprietor of Scale Models Ltd was a Mr Tilley who wound up the business in the 1960s.

The model detail and castings are outstanding, with features such as removeable exhausts, spring suspension, steering wheels and dashboards. In addition the back axle could be exchanged for one containing a clockwork motor which was wound up by a long starting handle. The wheel axles were crimped and the hubs were either brass (early) or aluminium (later) with black treaded rubber tyres.

Scamold kits were also available. The kit models had detailed features similar to the production issues including a working differential gear. In addition, it was also possible to fit a flywheel type motor which was activated by turning a 'starting handle'.

This information on Scamold models and kits has been kindly provided by Mr R.N. Eason-Gibson.The Editor would welcome additional information on this small but fascinating range.

**SCAMOLD PRODUCTION MODELS**

| | | | | |
|---|---|---|---|---|
| 101 | 1939-50 | **ERA Racing Car** .................. | Blue (Light or Dark), Green (Light or Dark), Yellow, White or Black body................................ | **£150-200** |
| 103 | 1939-50 | **Maserati Racing Car** ........... | Red, Blue, Green (Mid or Dark), Silver body ............................................................... | **£150-200** |
| 105 | 1939-50 | **Alta Racing Car** .................. | Green (Mid or Dark), Silver, White or Blue............................................................ | **£150-200** |

**SCAMOLD KITS**
Austin 7 Single-seater 750cc, Bugatti Type 35, 'E'-type E.R.A. (prototype only), Brooklands Riley, MG (planned type not known), Bentley LeMans Tourer and Maserati Racing Car.

# Mobil Midget Fun-Ho! Series

Manufactured and distributed by the Underwood Engineering Co. Ltd, Mamaku Street, Inglewood, New Zealand.

**Market Price Range.** Most small cars and trucks etc. **£20-30.** Exceptions: No.7 BOAC Observation Coach **£40-50,** No.9 VW Beetle **£40-50,** No.11 Morris Mini Minor **£80-90,** No.2 Vauxhall Velox **£30-40,** No.? Morris 1100 **£40-50,** No.17 Austin Mini **£80-90,** No.23 Mark 10 Jaguar **£80-90,** No.25 MG Sports **£80-100;** No.43 E Type Jaguar **£80-90.**
Larger Commercials/Emergency vehicles etc.:
Nos.18, 21, 22, 27, 31, 35, 36, 40 **£30-40.**

**Technical Information.** Models from No.10 are 1:80 scale. Early models 1-32 1963-66 were all either chrome or copper plated. Painted finishes were introduced in 1966. Boxed models 1-18 include a folded leaflet in black and white giving details of the first 18 models and all have Black plastic wheels. Similarly the later issues contained leaflets showing the complete 1-46 model range as per the above leaflet.

**'Fun Ho!' Mighty Mover Sets**
**1   Army Construction Battalion Kit Set**: Contains six Military models, Bulldozer, Cement Mixer, Road Roller, Earth Mover, JCB, Land Rover, Brown display box **£50-60**
**2   Civilian Road Construction Set**: Yellow/Silver Bulldozer, Red/Silver Bedford Lorry, Green Aveling Road Roller, Blue Earth Mover, Red/Blue Ford Sand Dumper, Yellow JCB, Red window display box **£50-60**
**3   Fire Service Kit Set**: Contains six Red models, 21 Fire Engine, Jeep, Pick Up, Artic Lorry, Rescue Truck, Fire Van with Blue light, Red window display box **£50-60**

**Later issues (c.1965?) Window Boxes**
48 Ford, Brown/Green, Two-tone Green or Maroon White body **£10-15,**
49 Ford Sand Dumper, Red/Blue body **£10-15,** 50 Ford Dumper **£10-15,**
51 Ford Articulated Truck **£15-20,** 52 Sand Dumper Trailer **£5-10**

# Shackleton Models

The company was formed by Maurice Shackleton and traded as James Shackleton & Sons Ltd. from 1939 to 1952. They had premises in Cheshire and originally produced wooden toys such as lorries and dolls houses. The toy lorries were only made pre-war and had four wheels, a simple wooden chassis and body with a green name badge on the rear of the cab, and were fitted with a highly detailed aluminium radiator grille. Known models are a Chain Lorry, Breakdown Lorry and a Sided Wagon. Their price today is around £100 each.

In 1948 having expanded its staff to nearly 40 people, the company started to produce diecast constructional models based on the Foden FG six-wheel platform lorry. The models consisted of separate parts all of which were, incredibly, made 'in house', including the clockwork motor, its key, and the wheels and tyres. The models were advertised in the 'Meccano Magazine' with the slogan 'You can dismantle it - Just like the real thing', and they were originally priced at £2/19/6.

Eventually the range was extended to include a Dyson Drawbar Trailer and a Foden Tipper. Each model was packed in its own distinctive box which displayed a black and white picture of the model inside.

In 1952, whilst in the midst of producing the David Brown Trackmaster 30 Tractor, a shortage of materials coupled with difficult trading conditions brought about the end of the company. Some remaining models from this period were acquired and distributed by Chad Valley. The unique models produced by the Shackleton company are now highly collectable and difficult to find.

**Note:** It is known that some prototype models of Ploughs and Harrows were made , though it is not known if any were produced for sale.

| | | | | |
|---|---|---|---|---|
| --- | 1948-52 | **Foden FG 6-wheel Platform Lorry** ........ | Yellow, Blue, Grey or Green body with Red wings, Grey chassis and Red or Grey fuel tanks, 12½ inches (305 mm.) long, initially in Blue/Yellow box, later in mottled Green box, (20,000 made) ............................................................. | **£500-650** |
| | | | Same colours as above but with Grey or Black wings and Red chassis ..................... | **£500-600** |
| | | | Same casting but with Red, Orange or Brown cab ................................................... | **£500-600** |
| | | **NB** Box difficult to find: ......................... | Blue box with paper label having picture of chassis. | |
| --- | 1949-52 | **Dyson 8-ton Drawbar Trailer** ................ | Yellow, Blue, Grey or Green body, packed in Red and Yellow box, (15,000) .............................. | **£150-200** |
| --- | 1950-52 | **Foden FG 6-wheel Tipper Lorry** ............ | Yellow, Blue, Grey or Green body with Red wings, Grey chassis and Red or Grey fuel tanks, Silver wheels, (5,000) ................................................................. | **£600-750** |
| | | | As previous models but with Grey wings and Red chassis ..................................... | **£600-750** |
| | | | As previous models but with Blue wings, Grey chassis, Grey wheels .................... | **£600-750** |
| | | | Orange or Red body ............................................................................... | **£600-750** |
| --- | 1952 | **David Brown Trackmaster 30 Tractor** ... | Red body, Black rubber tracks, 10 inches long, boxed. Only 50 models thought to exist ...... | **£1,250-1,500** |
| --- | 1958-60 | **Foden S21 8-wheel Platform Lorry** ....... | Dark Blue, Dark Green or Light Turquoise fibreglass cab with Red metal chassis and wheels, wooden flatbed, length overall 18½ inches (470 mm), plastic injection moulded springs and axle parts, powered by 'Minimax' electric motor. (250 made as a promotional for Foden) ... | **£1,000-1,250** |

The information in this listing has been taken from an original article written by John Ormandy in the 'Modellers World' magazine, Volumes 12 and 13, and is used by kind permission of the Editors, Mike and Sue Richardson. Robert Taylor provided additional information. Gary Irwin contributed information on the DB Trackmaster.

Foden FG 6-wheel Platform Lorry with a Shackleton Dyson 8-ton Drawbar Trailer
(MODELS SOLD BY ROMSEY MODEL AUCTIONS, ROMSEY, HAMPSHIRE; PICTURE USED BY THEIR KIND PERMISSION)

## Taylor and Barrett Lead Vehicles and the Postwar Re-issues
### by Mike Richardson

The firm of Taylor and Barrett dates from the early 1920s when they started producing mainly figures but with a few odd carts. The vehicles themselves were only introduced in about 1935. These were rather crude by comparison with the Dinky Toys of the day as the lead gravity casting process was incapable of working to the fine limits possible with pressure diecasting as used by Meccano Ltd. The majority of the vehicles use a basic chassis incorporating the bonnet and wings. Different bodies are attached to this base unit by tabs and a radiator is plugged into the front. Some versions have the grille cast integrally with the bonnet, and most of these use plain metal wheels instead of having rubber tyres. These vehicles have a tremendous amount of charm as toys while they are only a generic representation of the types of vans and small trucks of the time.

A wide variety of types were made including petrol tankers, a pick-up truck and a couple of mail vans. The breakdown truck is particularly attractive with a working crane on the rear. These toys were made until the production was halted in 1940 when the factory was bombed out of existence. All salvageable tools, moulds and stock was moved to a new location in North Finchley but production stopped very soon after because of the munitions requirements of the war effort. During the war the tools were split between the Taylors and the Barretts for safe keeping but they did not join up again afterwards and two separate companies, F.G.Taylor & Sons and A.Barrett & Sons, started up in 1945. The main part of the range, the small commercial vehicles and the cars, does not seem to have survived the War, only the trolley buses, which became Barretts, and the Leyland coach which appeared in one-piece casting form as a Taylor. It is interesting to note that the trolleybus carries a route board '621 Finchley' which probably means that they went past the factory.

A range of very nice fire engines came along in the late 1930s with a super turntable ladder appliance as the top of the range. These were longer than the main range and had many parts. To mark the advent of the Home Office Fire Precautions scheme (where fire appliances were made available to local areas by central government), Taylor and Barrett painted their range in grey as well as the more traditional red. These grey models are highly sought after now. Personnel were also available to go with these fire engines. A 'Decontamination Squad' being a particular favourite with their gas masks and chemical-proof overalls. There is also a less impressive fire engine in the short chassis range.

The trolley buses came in two sizes. The large one has a separate driver figure (and conductor as well in the T & B version but not the later Barrett), and the body is in two pieces, upper and lower decks. The small one is in one piece and has no driver. Needless to say there is a vast difference in the values of the two sizes.

There are generic cars, roadster, coupé, saloon, on the short base but there is also quite a good model of the 1935 Singer Airstream saloon. This is also the poor man's Chrysler Airflow but never really caught on, the styling made the car look too tall to be appealing. A rather crude one-piece Austin Seven racer was the final car but this was to a larger scale.

Dinky Toys were not the only factory to make a model of the Air Mail Service Car based on the Morris Commercial chassis. T & B also made one and a nice chunky toy it is too. A couple of aeroplanes, a De Havilland Comet and an air liner, completed the range of powered vehicles. A modified version of the Comet seems to have been made by Barrett later but it differs a lot from the T & B, which is a much better model.

Some of the moulds were still around a few years ago and some attempts were made to make models again. These were fairly unsuccessful as casting techniques had changed and the new metals did not have the same flow characteristics as the early lead. Some models are definitely known to have been re-made as they have been seen at a swapmeet some time back, so collectors are advised to be wary.

The following listing is of models issued by Taylor and Barrett between 1920 and 1939 and post war production which was split between F. G. Taylor & Sons and A. Barrett & Sons, each firm inheriting some moulds and continuing to make some but not all of the models until about 1952.

**(FGT)** = produced by F. G. Taylor after 1945, **(AB)** = produced by A. Barrett after 1945, **(-)** = date and company not known for certain.

| | | |
|---|---|---|
| 14 | Trotting Pony Racer with jockey, boxed set of three (FGT) | £200-250 |
| 15 | Turntable Fire Escape and 3 Firemen (AB) | £200-300 |
| 16 | Fire Engine and Escape and 3 Firemen (FGT) | £200-300 |
| 17 | Fire Engine and 3 Firemen (FGT) | £200-300 |
| 20 | Horse Drawn Water Cart (FGT) | £300-400 |
| 21 | Horse Drawn Brewer's Cart (FGT) | £100-200 |
| 22 | Horse Drawn Window Cleaner's Cart (FGT) | £150-200 |
| 23 | Horse Drawn Baker's Cart (FGT) | £100-200 |
| 26 | Roman Chariot (FGT) | £25-35 |
| 27 | Donkey Drawn Coster Cart with Dog and Boy (FGT) | £80-100 |
| 28 | Donkey Drawn Coster Cart, Plants load, Walking Coster (FGT) | £200-250 |
| 28a | Donkey Drawn Coster Cart, Vegetable load, Walking Coster (FGT) | £200-250 |
| 29 | Ice Cream Tricycle, 'ICE BRICKS', 'Stop Me and Buy One' (FGT) | £300-400 |
| 36 | Milk Float and Milkman, 'EXPRESS DAIRY' (AB) | £250-350 |
| 42 | Fire Escape and Team of Firemen (FGT) | £200-300 |
| 43 | Air and Land Postal Service Set (-) | £300-400 |
| 45 | Road and Traffic Set (-) Traffic island with bollards and street lamp, 2 swivelling traffic lights, school and 30mph signs, 2 Belisha beacons, pavement sections (2 straight, 2 corners). 45mm figures of lady and gentleman, 2 children (on base), mounted policeman, traffic policeman. Boxed | £300-350 |
| 49 | Street Cleaner Barrow with two Bins (FGT) | £300-350 |
| 92 | Llama Cart (FGT) | £100-150 |

| | | |
|---|---|---|
| 92a | Donkey Cart (FGT) | £100-150 |
| 109 | Pony Drawn Governor's Cart (AB) | £100-150 |
| 109a | Pony Drawn Cart (AB) | £75-100 |
| 111 | Saloon Car (-) | £80-100 |
| 112 | Transport Lorry (-) | £80-100 |
| 113 | 'ROYAL MAIL' Van (-) | £150-200 |
| 114 | 'AMBULANCE', Grey (Wartime civilian) (-) | £150-200 |
| 114a | 'AMBULANCE', Khaki (Army) (-) | £150-200 |
| 115 | Sports Car (-) | £100-200 |
| 116 | Coupé (-) | £100-200 |
| 117 | 'AMBULANCE', (Street, civilian) (-) | £80-100 |
| 119 | Racer (AB) | £40-60 |
| 120 | Fire Engine (AB) | £60-80 |
| 123 | Atlanta Touring Plane (AB) | £100-125 |
| 124 | 'AIR MAIL' Van (AB) | £100-125 |
| 128 | Petrol Tanker (-) | £100-125 |
| 129 | Breakdown Lorry (-) | £80-100 |
| 137 | DH 'Comet' Aeroplane (AB) | £80-100 |
| 138 | 'AIR MAIL' Streamline Van (-) | £175-225 |
| 139 | Saloon Car (-) | £50-60 |
| 152 | Streamline Motor Coach (-) | £100-150 |
| 163 | Streamline Fire Engine (-) | £100-125 |

| | | |
|---|---|---|
| 177 | **Brewery Dray Wagon & Drayman** 'Ale & Stout', boxed | £200-250 |
| 197 | **Trolley Bus** (small) (AB), boxed | £100-200 |
| 204 | **Trolley Bus** (large) (AB), boxed | £300-400 |
| 302 | **Horse Drawn Covered Wagon** (-) | £75-100 |
| 304 | **Sledge and Dogs** (FGT) | £100-150 |
| 306 | **Aeroplane Set** (Comet, Atlanta and pilots) (FGT) | £120-150 |
| 307 | **Fire Brigade Set** (-) | £300-400 |
| 310 | **Rickshaw pulled by Chinese Coolie** (FGT) | £250-300 |
| | Same, in 'Midwest British Importers' box | £350-500 |
| 311 | **Light Trailer Fire Pump in Action Set** (-) | £150-200 |
| ? | **Space Ship** (-) | NGPP |
| ? | **Coronation Coach** (small) (AB) | £30-50 |
| ? | **State Landau Coach** (-) | £40-60 |
| ? | **Farmer's Gig** (FGT) | £80-100 |
| ? | **Farm Cart with Trotting Horse** (-) | £80-100 |
| ? | **Mobile Animal Trailer and Vet** (-) | £600-800 |
| --- | **Racing Car**, Red body with 'MG Magnette' cast into side, 110 mm. 'FGT & SONS' | £100-125 |
| --- | **Petrol Pumps**, Black/White with rubber hoses (T&B) | £80-100 |
| --- | **'CASTROL' Oil Pump**, Green/Red, sliding cover (AB) | £20-30 |

| | | |
|---|---|---|
| --- | **Village Blacksmith Set**, contains blacksmith, forge with hood, anvil, Shire horse. In 2-part card box | £150-175 |
| --- | **Fire Car**, Red, with 3 figures | £175-200 |
| ? | **Pony-drawn Milk Float**, Yellow with red wheels, brown pony, mikman, milk churn | £250-300 |
| ? | **Zoo Keeper And Animals Set**. In Kay Zoo box | £100-125 |
| ? | **Seal Pond**. With two Seals | £250-300 |
| ? | **'Visitors to the Zoo Tea Party'**, boxed. Waitress, 4 seated persons, table | £1,500-2,000 |
| ? | **'Chimpanzee's Tea Party'**. Three seated Chimps, a table and a Keeper | £275-325 |
| ? | **Elephant Ride Set** with four children. Elephant, howdah etc., Keeper, boxed | £400-450 |
| ? | **Ivy and Brumas Polar Bears**. Two white bears, boxed | £275-325 |
| ? | **Dolls House Pieces** (boxed) - Carpet Sweeper, Vacuum Cleaner, Fireplace, Oil Heater, Electric Fire | £20-25 each |
| ? | **'Decontamination Squad'**. Five Black figures with gas masks£168 | £150-175 |
| ? | **World War Two Firemen**. 3, with gas masks and trailer, | £125-150 |
| ? | **Streamlined Coach**.. white and green, rubber tyres, (illustrated below) | £90-130 |

# Timpo Toys

Robert Newson has provided this history and listing of cast metal Timpo motor vehicles.

The name Timpo comes from 'Toy Importers Ltd'. It was only with the outbreak of war in 1939 that Timpo started to manufacture their own lines, when importing became impossible. A few vehicles were made in 1940-41, but the main Timpo range started in 1946. The models were cheap and sturdy, if somewhat crude, and many have survived. Relatively few suffer from metal deterioration. In 1949 Timpo advertised 'faithful replicas of famous delivery services' and introduced several vans with attractive advertising liveries. An AEC Monarch lorry in the livery of Vaux brewery was introduced around 1950, and this was a far better model than the earlier toys. Sadly it was not the first of a new range - the 1951-2 ban on the use of zinc meant that Timpo discontinued all their diecast vehicles. Some of the dies were subsequently sold to Benbros, including the AEC lorry.

Timpo Toys are very rarely seen in mint condition, and prices are therefore quoted for good original condition. Dates given are the approximate year of

| Intro | Model name | Details | MPR |
|---|---|---|---|
| 1940 | **MG Record Car** | Hollow-cast lead. Red, 'TIMPO TOYS' cast on side, 98 mm | **£50-75** |
| 1940 | **Streamlined Saloon** | Separate body and chassis. 'Timpo' in script underneath. 99 mm | **£30-40** |
| 1940 | **Pick-Up Truck** | Separate body and chassis. 'Timpo' in script underneath. Re-issued post-war with name blanked out. 97 mm | **£30-40** |
| 1940 | **Four-light Saloon** | Possibly re-issue of a Goody Toy | NGPP |
| 1946 | **MG Record Car** | Zinc diecast. 'TIMPO TOYS' cast at rear on offside. 97 mm | **£50-75** |
| 1946 | **'American Star' Racer** | Star transfer on each side, 101 mm | **£40-50** |
| 1946 | **'Timpo Saloon'** | Vaguely like a Morris 8. 93 mm | **£40-50** |
| 1946 | **Austin 16 Saloon** | Black. 'TIMPO TOYS' underneath. 96 mm | **£40-50** |
| | | Re-issued by Betal in four versions: | |
| | | 1. No name on model, brass wheel hubs | **£30-40** |
| | | 2. 'A BETAL PRODUCT' under roof, tin base with friction motor, brass wheel hubs | **£30-40** |
| | | 3. As 2. but with plastic body | **£30-40** |
| | | 4. As 3. but with clockwork motor and solid metal wheels | **£30-40** |

| Intro | Model name | Details | MPR |
|---|---|---|---|
| 1946 | **MG Midget** | Composition wheels. 82 mm | **£30-40** |
| 1946 | **Packard Saloon** | Fitted with aluminium baseplate and friction motor from 1948. 113 mm | **£30-40** |
| 1946 | **'Speed of the Wind' Record Car** | Similar to the Dinky Toy. 99 mm | **£40-50** |
| 1946 | **No.1 'Arctic' Set** | Sledge and dog team, Eskimo with whip, another with rifle, walking stick, 2 penguins, 2 seals, polar bear, snowy hedge and igloo. Boxed | **£400-600** |
| 1947 | **Alvis 14 Saloon** | A big four-light saloon. 106 mm | **£30-40** |
| 1947 | **Utility Van** | With aluminium baseplate and friction motor from 1948. (Early casting 102mm, later 104mm). | |
| | | 1. No transfers, plain colours, without motor | **£10-15** |
| | | 2. Black, 'TYRESOLES SERVICE' transfers, no motor | **£200-300** |
| | | 3. 'HIS MASTER'S VOICE' transfers, pale Yellow, Orange-ellow, pale Blue or Green, motor.in some | **£200-300** |
| 1947 | **Articulated Petrol Tanker** | No transfers. | |
| | | Re-issued by Benbros. 149 mm | **£30-40** |
| | | Red/white body, 'ESSO' logo | **£80-120** |
| 1947 | **Lincoln Convertible** | Vaguely like a 1942 Lincoln. Aluminium baseplate and windscreen. Usually single colours. Late version in cream with blue seats. 115 mm | **£30-40** |

PHOTO: VECTIS AUCTIONS LTD.

1947 **Armstrong-Siddeley Hurricane**  Coupé with top up. 105 mm ...**£30-40**

1947 **Streamlined Fire Engine**  Red, 2 yellow aluminium ladders.
　　　Aluminium baseplate + friction motor from '49. 105 mm ...**£30-40**

1947 **Articulated Box Van**  Re-issued by Benbros. 146 mm. Boxed.
　　　1. Green, Blue or Red trailer with 'TIMPO TOYS' transfers....**£160-190**
　　　2. Black cab and trailer with Grey roof,
　　　　Red wheel hubs, 'PICKFORDS' transfers .......................**£140-170**
　　　3. Orange cab and trailer, Black roof,
　　　　'UNITED DAIRIES' transfers ...................................**£140-170**
　　　4. Light Blue cab, Light Blue and Cream trailer,
　　　　'WALL'S ICE CREAM' transfers..................................**£140-170**
　　　5. Dark Blue cab and trailer with off-White roof,
　　　　'LYONS TEA' transfers...........................................**£140-170**
　　　6. Pale Yellow cab and trailer, transfers with
　　　　'BISHOPS MOVE' logo and 'BISHOP & SONS
　　　　DEPOSITORIES LTD. 10-12 BELGRAVE
　　　　ROAD LONDON, S.W.1'............................................**£140-170**
　　　7. Same, but transfers with 'BISHOPS MOVE' logo and
　　　　'JOHN H. LUNN LTD. 6 HOPE CRESCENT
　　　　EDINBURGH'.......................................................**£140-170**

1947 **London Taxi**  Cast in two parts. 94 mm......................**£20-25**

1947 **Alvis 14 Police Car**  Police sign and loudspeakers at front
　　　of roof, wire aerial behind. Black. 106 mm .........................**£50-75**

1947 **Articulated Low Loader**  Re-issued by Benbros. 168 mm.........**£10-15**

1947 **Buick Saloon**  Crude model, composition wheels. 99 mm.........**£10-15**

1947 **Pick-Up Truck**  With eight cast-in barrels. 104 mm...................**£15-20**

1947 **Forward Control Tipper Lorry**
　　　Cream cab and chassis, Red tipper. 101 mm........................**£15-20**

1947 **Forward Control Luton Van**
　　　Same chassis as the tipper. 97 mm. boxed.
　　　1. No transfers, black lower, light blue upper ...............**£15-20**
　　　2. Dark blue, 'SMITH'S CRISPS' transfers ...................**£120-150**
　　　3. Brown, 'W.D. & H.O. WILLS' transfers ....................**£120-150**

1949 **Forward Control Box Van**
　　　Same chassis as above. Re-issued by Benbros.
　　　Dark blue, 'CHIVERS JELLIES' transfers.....................**£120-150**

1949 **Normal Control Box Van**  Later models with aluminium
　　　baseplate and friction motor. 105 mm. Models were boxed.
　　　1. Dark Blue with White roof, 'EVER READY' transfers,
　　　　motor in some ..................................................**£150-250**
　　　2. Green, 'GOLDEN SHRED', with motor.......................**£150-250**
　　　3. Green, 'MELTONIAN SHOE CREAM' transfers,
　　　　with motor........................................................**£150-250**

1949 **Normal Control Petrol Tanker**  Red,
　　　'MOTOR OIL ESSO PETROL' on paper labels, boxed.
　　　Re-issued by Benbros .............................................**£250-350**

1950 **AEC Monarch Brewery Lorry**  Red. 'VAUX' cast on
　　　headboard behind cab, 'SUNDERLAND' cast on cab sides.
　　　Boxed. Brown hollow-cast barrels with 'VAUX' cast
　　　on ends. Re-issued by Benbros without the
　　　headboard + other changes. 129 mm................................**£150-250**

1940s **Bomber Station Set**  3 x twin-fuselage aircraft, 2 x twin-engined,
　　　single-fuselage aircraft and a single-engined fighter.
　　　Box has a pictorial label on its lift-off lid .........................**£150-200**

249 **Hopalong Cassidy Series Set**
　　　Contains 7 cowboys including Hopalong Cassidy,
　　　Lucky, California, etc., 3(?) horses. Boxed.................**£1,000-1,250**

--- **Wild West Set**, boxed. Covered Wagon with Driver.................**£300-350**

--- **'The Ranch' Set**, boxed. Two cowboys playing guitars and
　　　two playing accordions, cowboy rider, 2 horses, bench ..**£350-400**
--- 　**Individual figures** from this group..............................**£15-20 each**

--- **Petrol Station**  Car plus Pump and Dispenser. Pictorial box.....**£75-100**

--- **Petrol Station No.2 Set**  Saloon Car and Racing Car plus
　　　3 Personnel and 5 Pumps. Pictorial box lid states:
　　　'THE FAMOUS TIMPO CARS'......................................**£150-200**

--- **Petrol Station No.3 Set**  4 Cars, 3 Pumps, 2 Dispensers,
　　　Chauffer, 2 Mechanics. Pictorial box has street scene .....**£150-200**

--- **Car Series No. 1 Set**, boxed. Green open tourer, pump,
　　　oil bin, mechanic...................................................**£150-175**

--- **Racing Set** - 3 Racing Cars + 3 petrol pumps, 4 mechanics.....**£175-200**

--- **Station Figures Set**  Contains Station Master, Porter with trolley,
　　　Porter with luggage, Signalman with flag, Signalman with
　　　whistle, Railwayman with lamps, Mr Brown, boy hiker,
　　　lady with bag, girl in red coat, soldier with kitbag. Box...**£500-750**
--- 　**Individual figures** from this group.............................**£15-20 each**

--- **Railway Porter with Luggage**. Sack barrow,
　　　5 pieces of luggage, boxed .........................................**£175-200**

--- **Tiger Hunt Set**  Elephants, howdahs, mahouts, Maharaja,
　　　hunter, 2 tigers, 4 bears, natives with spears. Boxed .....**£900-1,000**

--- **Farm Series Set**  15 piece dairy / poultry set .........................**£300-350**

--- **Gypsy Organ Grinder with Dancing Bear** ...............................**£50-70**

--- **Clown Circus Band**. Four Clown figures ...............................**£250-300**

--- **Jaunting Cart**, boxed. Brown horse and cart with driver.........**£500-700**

--- **Domestic Sets**. A Kitchen Sets, a Washing Set....................**£40-50 each**

--- **Coronation Coach**. Gilt Coach, 8 grey horses, 4 riders ..........**£200-250**

--- **HM Queen Elizabeth II**. 'Trooping the Colours'
　　　figure on horse, E in G box ........................................**£75-100**

--- **Timpo figures**.
　　　Knights of the Round Table and Ivanhoe figures. Each .............**£75-100**
　　　Knights of the Round Table Set. Nine figures, boxed .............**£500-600**
　　　Policeman, Policewoman, Zoo Keeper, Farm Girls. Each............**£15-20**
　　　Super heroes:
　　　Captain Marvel, Mary Marvel, Marvel Junior. Each ....................**£15-20**

--- **Salesman's 'My Pets' Sample Box** with 18 dogs .............**£1,250-1,750**

Minic ships are accurately detailed waterline models made between 1958 and 1964 to a scale of 1:1,200 (1in to 100ft).
Six sales catalogues were published which nowadays are quite hard to find.
No single catalogue shows the full range.
Minic ships re-introduced in 1976 were fitted with wheels and have 'Hong Kong' on the base.

## Ocean Liners

| Ref | Model name | Colours, features, details | Market Price Range |
|---|---|---|---|
| M701 | RMS 'Caronia' | Green body, one plain Red/Black or detailed funnel, one mast, 178 mm. 'Painted in the correct Cunard green she is a most striking vessel'. | £150-175 |
| M702 | RMS 'Queen Elizabeth' | Black/White, 2 plain Red/Black or detailed funnels, 2 masts, 262 mm. 'The worlds largest ship and the pride of the Cunard fleet'. | £90-110 |
| M703 | RMS 'Queen Mary' | Black/White, plain Red/Black or detailed funnels, 2 masts, 259 mm. 'Her three funnels make her the most easily recognisable'. | £90-110 |
| M704 | SS 'United States' | Black/White body, two Red/White/Blue funnels, 252 mm. 'The present holder of the Blue Riband of the Atlantic'. | £100-125 |
| M705 | RMS 'Aquitania' | Black/White body, four Red/Black funnels, two masts, 231 mm. | £150-200 |
| M706 | SS 'Nieuw Amsterdam' | Grey/White body, two Yellow funnels, two masts, 192 mm. | £120-140 |
| M707 | SS 'France' | Black/White, 2 Red/Black funnels, 5 masts, 262 mm. 'The longest ship in the world – 1035ft, being 4ft longer than Queen Elizabeth'. | £125-150 |
| M708 | RMS 'Saxonia' | Black/White body, one Red/Black or detailed funnel, nine masts, cargo handling gear on stern | £120-140 |
| M708/2 | RMS 'Franconia' | Green body, one Red/Black funnel, nine Green masts, 155 mm, swimming pool on stern.480 made | £500-750 |
| M709 | RMS 'Ivernia' | Black/White or Green body, 155mm, cargo handling gear on stern. | £90-110 |
| M709/2 | RMS 'Carmania' | Green body, one Red/Black funnel, nine Green masts, 155 mm, swimming pool on stern.480 made | £500-750 |
| M710 | RMS 'Sylvania' | Black/White, one Red/Black funnel, nine masts, 155 mm. | £120-140 |
| M711 | RMS 'Carinthie' | Black/White, one Red/Black funnel, nine masts, 155 mm. | £90-110 |
| M712 | NS 'Savannah' | White, no funnels (nuclear powered), four masts, 149 mm. | £125-150 |
| M713 | SS 'Antilles' | Black/White, one Red/Black funnel, ten masts, 152 mm. All White body, one Red/Black funnel, ten masts | £125-150 £150-200 |
| M714 | 'Flandre' | Black/White, one Red/Black funnel, ten masts, 152 mm. All White body, one Red/Black funnel, ten masts | £120-140 £90-110 |
| M715 | RMS 'Canberra' | White body, one Yellow funnel, three masts, 189 mm. | £130-160 |
| M716 | MS 'Port Brisbane' | Grey/White, one Red/Black funnel, eight masts, 140 mm. | £150-200 |
| M717 | SS 'Port Auckland' | Grey/White, one Red/Black funnel, seven masts, 140 mm. | £150-175 |
| M718 | RMS 'Amazon' | White, Yellow funnel, 19 masts, 10 lifeboats, 149 mm. | £200-250 |
| M719 | RMS 'Arlanza' | White, Yellow funnel, 19 masts, 149 mm. | £150-175 |
| M720 | RMS 'Aragon' | White, Yellow funnel, 19 masts, 149 mm. | £150-175 |
| M721 | RMS 'Britannia' | The Royal Yacht. Blue/White body, Yellow/Black funnel, 3 masts, 105 mm. | £75-100 |
| M721/H | RMS 'Britannia' | Hospital Ship. White body, three masts, 105 mm. | £75-100 |

## Smaller craft

### CHANNEL ISLANDS STEAMERS (78mm long)

| | | | |
|---|---|---|---|
| M722 | 'Isle of Jersey' | Black/White, 2 Yellow/Black funnels, 2 masts | £40-50 |
| M723 | 'Isle of Guernsey' | Black/White, 2 Yellow/Black funnels, 2 masts | £40-50 |
| M724 | 'Isle of Sark' | Black/White body, 2 Yellow/Black funnels, 2 masts | £40-50 |
| M726 | 'PILOTS' Boat | Black/White/Yellow, 45 mm | £100-125 |
| M727 | Lifeboat | Blue body | £40-50 |

### PADDLE STEAMERS (all are 78 mm long)

| | | | |
|---|---|---|---|
| M728 | 'Britannia' | Black/white, 2 funnels (black/blue, red/black or yellow/black), 2 masts | £40-50 |
| M729 | 'Bristol Queen' | Black/white, 2 funnels (black/blue, red/black or yellow/black), 2 masts | £40-50 |
| M730 | 'Cardiff Queen' | Black/White, 2 funnels (Black/Blue, Red/Black or Yellow/Black), 2 masts. | £40-50 |

### OIL TANKER

| | | | |
|---|---|---|---|
| M732 | SS 'Varicella' | Black/White body, Black/Yellow funnel ('SHELL' logo), 2 masts, 169 mm. | £90-110 |

### WHALE FACTORY SHIPS

| | | | |
|---|---|---|---|
| M733 | TSS 'Vikingen' | Grey body, six masts, 125 mm. | £100-125 |
| M734 | Whale Chaser | Grey, Yellow/Black funnel, 39 mm. | £40-50 |

### TUGBOATS (all except 'Turmoil' are 38mm long)

| | | | |
|---|---|---|---|
| M731 | Tugboat | Black/Grey/Red, Red/Black funnel | £15-20 |
| M731 | Tugboat | Black/Grey/Red, Yellow/Black funnel | £15-20 |
| M731 | Tugboat | Black/Blue/Red, Yellow/Black funnel. | £15-20 |
| M731 | Tugboat | Black/Grey/Yellow, Yellow/Black funnel | £15-20 |
| M740 | Barge | Intended to match M731, but not issued | NPP |
| M810 | Navy Tug HMS 'Turmoil' | Black/Blue or Grey, Black funnel, 50 mm. | £40-50 |

### LIGHTSHIPS (all are 33mm long)

| | | | |
|---|---|---|---|
| M735 | 'SUNK' | Red body, White logo/name | £40-50 |
| M736 | 'SHAMBLES' | Red body, White logo/name | £40-50 |
| M737 | 'CORK' | Red body, White logo/name | £40-50 |
| M738 | 'VARNE' | Red body, White logo/name | £40-50 |
| M739 | 'St GOWAN' | Red body, White logo/name | £40-50 |

# Tri-ang Minic Warships

**BATTLESHIP**
M741   **HMS 'Vanguard'** ..... Grey or Blue, two masts, 206 mm ............. **£60-80**

**AIRCRAFT CARRIERS**
M751   **HMS 'Bulwark'** ....... Grey or Blue, one mast, 186 mm ........... **£100-125**
M752   **HMS 'Centaur'** ....... Grey or Blue body with one mast .......... **£100-125**
M753   **HMS 'Albion'** .......... Grey or Blue body with one mast .......... **£100-125**

**COMMANDO SHIP**
M754   **HMS 'Albion'** .......... Grey ship with 12 Cream or Brown plastic
       helicopters. 1,000 models issued and given to H.M.S. 'Albion'
       crew members (Capt. Adams in command) ............................. **£500-750**

**CRUISERS**
M761   **HMS 'Swiftsure'** .... Blue or Grey, one crane jib, 145 mm ........ **£35-45**
M762   **HMS 'Superb'** ........ Blue or Grey, one crane jib, 145 mm ........ **£35-45**

**DESTROYERS, FLEET ESCORT, 'DARING' CLASS**
M771   **HMS 'Daring'** ........ Blue or Grey, one mast, 98 mm ............. **£35-45**
M772   **HMS 'Diana'** .......... Blue or Grey, one mast, 98 mm ............. **£35-45**
M773   **HMS 'Dainty'** ........ Blue or Grey, one mast, 98 mm ............. **£35-45**
M774   **HMS 'Decoy'** .......... Blue or Grey, one mast, 98 mm ............. **£35-45**

**DESTROYERS, FLEET, 'BATTLE' CLASS**
M779   **HMS 'Alamein'** ...... Blue or Grey, one mast, 97 mm ............. **£35-45**
M780   **HMS 'Jutland'** ....... Blue or Grey, one mast, 97 mm ............. **£35-45**
M781   **HMS 'Anzac'** .......... Blue or Grey, one mast, 97 mm ............. **£35-45**
M782   **HMS 'Tobruk'** ........ Blue or Grey, one mast, 97 mm ............. **£35-45**

**DESTROYERS, GUIDED MISSILE, 'COUNTY' CLASS**
M783   **HMS 'Hampshire'** ... Grey body with two masts, 136 mm .......... **£55-65**
M784   **HMS 'Kent'** ............ Grey body with two masts, 136 mm ......... **£50-65**

M785   **HMS 'Devonshire'** .. Grey body with two masts, 136 mm .......... **£50-65**
M786   **HMS 'London'** ........ Grey body with two masts, 136 mm .......... **£50-65**

**FRIGATES, FAST ANTI-SUBMARINE, 'V' CLASS**
M787   **HMS 'Vigilant'** ........ Blue or Grey, one mast, 92 mm ................. **£40-50**
M788   **HMS 'Venus'** ......... Blue or Grey, one mast, 92 mm ................. **£40-50**
M789   **HMS 'Virago'** ........ Blue or Grey, one mast, 92 mm ................. **£40-50**
M790   **HMS 'Volage'** ........ Blue or Grey, one mast, 92 mm ................. **£40-50**

**FRIGATES, ANTI-SUBMARINE, 'WHITBY' CLASS**
M791   **HMS 'Whitby'** ........ Blue or Grey body, 94 mm .................... **£40-50**
M792   **HMS 'Torquay'** ....... Blue or Grey body, 94 mm .................... **£40-50**
M793   **HMS 'Blackpool'** .... Blue or Grey body, 94 mm .................... **£40-50**
M794   **HMS 'Tenby'** ......... Blue or Grey body, 94 mm .................... **£40-50**

**MINESWEEPERS, 'TON' CLASS**
M799   **HMS 'Repton'** ........ Blue or Grey body ........................... **£40-50**
M800   **HMS 'Dufton'** ........ Blue or Grey body ........................... **£40-50**
M801   **HMS 'Ashton'** ........ Blue or Grey body ........................... **£40-50**
M802   **HMS 'Calton'** ........ Blue or Grey body ........................... **£40-50**
M803   **HMS 'Picton'** ......... Blue or Grey body ........................... **£40-50**
M804   **HMS 'Sefton'** ........ Blue or Grey body ........................... **£40-50**
M805   **HMS 'Upton'** .......... Blue or Grey body ........................... **£40-50**
M806   **HMS 'Weston'** ........ Blue or Grey body ........................... **£40-50**

**SUBMARINES, 'A' CLASS**
M817   **Sub 'A' Class** .......... Blue or Grey body, 61 mm ................... **£15-25**
M818   **Sub Recon** ............... Blue or Grey body, 61 mm ................... **£15-25**

# Tri-ang Minic Ships Trade Boxes and Sales Aids

**TRADE BOXES**   Note that the MPR refers to full boxes.

M735-M739 **Trade Box for 12 Lightships,** each in cellophane bag..... **£200-250**
M731      **Trade Box for 12 Tug Boats** each in cellophane bag............. **£140-160**
M726      **Trade Box for 12 'PILOTS' Boats,** in cellophane bags ........ **£140-160**
M722 /3/4. **Trade Box for 12 Paddle Steamers** ................................... **£400-450**
M771/2/3/4. **Trade Box for 12 'Daring' Class Destroyers** ................ **£150-200**
M779, 780/1/2. **Trade box for 12 'Battle' Class Destroyers** ............. **£150-200**
M786 **Trade box for 3 HMS 'London'** ..................................... **£150-170**
M787/8/9. M790. **Trade box for 12 Anti Sub 'V' Class Frigates** ...... **£150-200**
M791/2/3/4. 7 **Trade box for 12 Anti-Sub 'Whitby' Class Frigates** ... **£150-200**

M799, M800-6. **Trade box for 8 Minesweepers 'Ton' Class** .............. **£300-350**
M810   **Trade box for 12 HMS 'Turmoil' Tugs** .................................. **£175-200**
M853 **Trade box for 6 Factory Units** ............................................. **£200-250**
M884 **Trade box for 2 'Statute of Liberty'** ................................... **£100-125**

## SHOP DISPLAY and SALES AIDS

**Shop Display Unit.** Over 40 models/accessories displayed,
       48" x 30" ...................................................................... **£1,500-2,000**
**Shop Display Banner.** Paper, 36" long x 8" deep,
       displaying full range ............................................................. **£500-750**

# Accessories, Gift Sets, Hong Kong issues and Catalogues

## DOCKSIDE ACCESSORIES

| | | |
|---|---|---|
| M827 | **Breakwater Straights**, Grey | £5 |
| M828/L | **Breakwater Angle**, Left, Grey | £1 |
| M828/R | **Breakwater Angle**, Right, Grey | £1 |
| M829 | **Breakwater End**, Grey | £1 |
| M836 | **Quay Straights**, Tan | £5 |
| M837 | **Crane Units**, Tan, Brown or Green cargo | £5 |
| M838 | **Storage Tanks**, Grey/Silver and Red | £5 |
| M839 | **Customs Shed**, Green | £5 |
| M840 | **Warehouse**, Brown | £5 |
| M841 | **Ocean Terminal**, White with Black windows | £10 |
| M842 | **Swing Bridge**, Red, no description on base | £8 |
| M843 | **Terminal Extension**, White with Black windows | £10 |
| M844 | **Lock Gates** (pair), Brown | £3 |
| M845 | **Landing Stages**, Cream 'L' shaped, 1in long | £3 |
| M846 | **Lift Bridge**, Silver/Tan | £5 |
| M847 | **Pier centre section**, White | £5 |
| M848 | **Pier entrance section**, White | £5 |
| M849 | **Pier head**, White | £20 |
| M850 | **Pier Shelter**, Green, 35 mm | £10 |
| M851 | **Pier archways** | £5 |
| M852 | **Pier Building**, White/Blue/Green, Silver Cupola, 'RESTAURANT' plus 'DANCING TONIGHT' | £20-25 |
| M853 | **Factory Unit**, Pink and Buff, Black chimneys | £30-40 |
| M854 | **Tanker Wharf Straight**, Cream and Red | £65-75 |
| M855 | **Tanker Wharf Berth**, Red and Green or Cream and Green, Black plastic pipeline | £5 |
| M857 | **26in Sea**, Blue plastic | £25-35 |
| M857 | **52in Sea**, Blue plastic | £40-50 |
| M861 | **Lifeboat set**, Grey, Blue shed, one lifeboat | £60-80 |
| M878 | **Lighthouse**, White | £10 |
| M880 | **Whales**, White or plain Grey | £15-20 |
| M882 | **Beacon**, White/Red or Green | £5 |
| M884 | **Statue of Liberty**, Green/Grey | £30-40 |
| M885 | **Floating Dock**, Grey, 4 Black plastic cranes | £50-60 |
| M - | **Helicopter**, Cream or Brown plastic | £30-35 |

## GIFT SETS and SPECIAL PRESENTATION PACKS

| | | |
|---|---|---|
| M891 | **'Queen Elizabeth'** Gift Set | £250-300 |
| M892 | **'United States'** Gift Set | £250-350 |
| M893 | **'Task Force'** Gift Set | £250-300 |
| M894 | **'Royal Yacht Britannia'** Gift Set containing 'Britannia' plus two Destroyers strung to green backing card | £300-350 |
| M895 | **'Nieuw Amsterdam'** Gift Set | £750-1,000 |
| M702s | **'Queen Elizabeth'** Presentation Set | £200-250 |
| M703s | **'Queen Mary'** Presentation Set | £300-350 |
| M704s | SS **'United States'** Presentation Set | £250-350 |
| M705s | RMS **'Aquitania'** Presentation Set | £200-250 |
| M707s | SS **'France'** Presentation Set | £300-350 |
| M741s | HMS **'Vanguard'** Presentation Set | £180-220 |

## HONG KONG 'BLUE BOX' MODELS (1976-80)

These models are slightly larger than original issues, e.g., Canberra is 207mm.
**'Queen Mary', 'Queen Elizabeth', 'United States', 'Canberra', HMS 'Vanguard', HMS 'Bulwark', 'Missouri', 'Bismark', 'Scharnhorst', 'Yamato'.** Each, boxed £20-30
**RMS 'Canberra'**, boxed £30-40

## HONG KONG SETS of MODELS

| | | |
|---|---|---|
| 1 | **Fleet Anchorage Set**, dockyard entrance scene on lid | £30-40 |
| 2 | **Quay Set** | £30-40 |
| 3a | **Ocean Terminal**, lid shows stern of RMS 'Queen Mary' | £50-65 |
| 3b | **Ocean Terminal**, lid shows bow of RMS 'Queen Mary' | £40-50 |
| 4 | **Naval Task Force**, with HMS 'Bulwark' and 'Vanguard' | £40-50 |
| 5 | **Naval Task Force**, with 'Bismark' and 'Scharnhorst' | £70-90 |

## MINIC CATALOGUES 1958-64

| | | |
|---|---|---|
| 1st Ed. | **Leaflet** ........... with first Minic Ships listed | £100-125 |
| 2nd Ed. | **Booklet** .......... with first Minic Ships listed | £75-80 |
| 3rd Ed. | **Booklet** .......... with Ships and other Tri-ang products | £60-75 |
| 4th Ed. | **Booklet** .......... with Minic Ships only | £25-30 |
| 5th Ed. | **Booklet** .......... with Minic Ships only | £25-30 |
| 6th Ed. | **Booklet** .......... with Tri-ang range | £30-35 |
| M862 | **Leaflet** ........... Minic illustrated leaflet | £10-15 |

## TRI-ANG MINIC SHIPS AUCTION RESULTS 2005 — 2007

### Vectis Auctions Ltd.
Fleck Way, Thornaby,
Stockton -on-Tees TS17 9JZ
Abbreviations: M = Mint, NM = Near Mint, EP = Excellent Plus,
E = Excellent, GP = Good Plus, G = Good, F = Fair

**TRI-ANG MINIC SHIPS**

**M701 RMS 'Caronia'**. Pale Green, M in NM box .......... £170
**M702 RMS 'Queen Elizabeth'**. Complete, NM in E standard box .......... £100
**M703s RMS 'Queen Mary'**. Complete in original cellophane bag, Mint in Good Plus rare presentation box .......... £280
**M704s SS 'United States'**. Missing masts, otherwise Excellent in rare Near Mint presentation box in E. outer card box .......... £190
**M705 RMS 'Aquitania'**. Complete, NM in G box .......... £150
**M706 SS 'Nieuw Amsterdam'**. Complete - M in E standard box .......... £140
**M707s SS 'France'**. Complete in original cellophane bag, Mint in GP rare presentation box .......... £320
**M708 RMS 'Saxonia'**. Complete in original cellophane bag, NM in GP box .......... £140
**M708/2 RMS 'Franconia'**. Pale green, single red/black funnel, complete, EP, unboxed .......... £420
**M709 RMS 'Invernia'**. Complete in original cellophane bag, M, G box .......... £100
**M709/2 RMS 'Carmania'**. Pale green, lacks masts, G - GP, unboxed .......... £190
**M710 RMS 'Sylvania'**. Complete in original cellophane bag, M in E box .......... £140
**M711 RMS 'Carinthia'**. Complete, E in GP box .......... £80
**M712 NS 'Savannah'**. Complete, NM in NM box .......... £150
**M713 SS 'Antilles'**. All White, in original cellophane bag, M in E box .......... £200

**M714 SS 'Flandre'**. Black/White, complete in original bag, M in E box .......... £140
**M7145 RMS 'Canberra'**. In original cellophane bag, M in E box .......... £150
**M716 'Port Brisbane'**. In original cellophane bag, M in GP-E box .......... £200
**M717 'Port Auckland'**. Complete, E in NM box .......... £160
**M718 RMS 'Amazon'**. Complete in original cellophane bag, M in E box .......... £240
**M719 RMS 'Arlanza'**. Complete, E in NM box .......... £180
**M720 RMS 'Aragon'**. Complete in original cellophane bag, M in E box .......... £200
**M732 SS 'Varicella'**. Complete, M in E box (masts in cellophane bag) .......... £110
**M733 TSS 'Vikingen'**. Complete, NM in GP box .......... £110
**M741 HMS 'Vanguard'**. 2 models: Grey and Blue, complete, NM-M in GP standard boxes .......... £140
**M741s HMS 'Vanguard'**. Pale Blue, complete with masts in original cellophane bag, Mint in rare Excellent presentation box .......... £220
**M752 HMS 'Centaur'**. Complete, NM in E box .......... £120
**M753 HMS 'Albion'**. Complete, M in E box .......... £120
**M754 Commando Ship - HMS 'Albion'**. Missing some helicopters, NM .......... £320
**M761 HMS 'Swiftshore'** x 2 and **M762 HMS 'Superb'** x 3. Five Cruisers - All NM - M in GP - E boxes .......... £190
**M885 Floating Dock**. 2 complete examples, Mint in Good boxes .......... £130
**M891 RMS 'Queen Elizabeth' Gift Set**. Mint in Good blue box with Tug Boats, Quay sections and Buildings strung on to 'sea' card .......... £300
**M893 Royal Navy Carrier Task Group Gift Set**. Contains HMS 'Centaur' and 3 Escort vessels attached to original blue base 'sea' card. Mint in Good box .......... £280
**M893 Royal Navy Carrier Task Group Gift Set**. Same as previous but with HMS 'Albion'. Mint in Excellent box .......... £380

Contemporary advertisements for Tri-ang Spot-On models in the 'Eagle' comic (above) and a Gamages catalogue (below)
(ILLUSTRATIONS SUPPLIED BY JOHN RAMSAY)

# Introduction

Spot-On Models were introduced in 1959 by Tri-ang Toys to gain a foothold in the diecast market dominated at the time by Dinky Toys and their recently established rivals Corgi Toys.

Tri-ang realised that they had to offer not only a range of features similar to those of their competitors' products but something more besides. They decided that collectors would appreciate models that were all made to the same precise scale right across the range.

The models would thus look right together and qualify as such rather than toys. Much of the Dinky and Corgi cars range was made to a scale of around 1:45 (with a few exceptions).

Tri-ang advertised the precise nature of their (larger) chosen scale as being 'spot-on' at 1:42 throughout.

A large modern factory was set up in Belfast, Northern Ireland to produce the models. A coloured picture of the real vehicle was included in the box of most early issues.

Well over a hundred different models were designed, the range being extended to include scale buildings and road signs. Production continued till the time that Tri-ang bought up Dinky Toys in 1967. After the cessation of UK production, some of the Spot-On dies went to New Zealand where some interesting versions were produced for a couple of years.

All Spot-On models are highly collectable today particularly commercial vehicles, buses and the Presentation and Gift Sets.

# Spot-On model identification

**Makers Name** and Trade Mark are clearly marked on base of the model ('SPOT-ON' and 'Models by Tri-ang'). Some New Zealand produced versions have nothing at all on the base.

**Model Name** is shown on the base (except some New Zealand versions) while the **Model Number** is usually shown on box but not always on the model.

**Baseplates** can be any of a variety of colours: black, silver, grey - even green has been observed on the base of a maroon version of No. 155 Taxi !

**Scale of models** is 1:42 (with very few exceptions) and is usually (but not always) shown on the base.

**Wheel hubs** on cars are usually turned aluminium with a raised 'hub cap'. Truck models usually have diecast and more accurate representations of real hubs. **Tyres** are mostly black rubber (occasionally plastic) on all the vehicle models. Rear twin wheels have special 'double tyres'.

**Number plates** are represented on most Spot-On models with the exception of those having plastic chassis (such as 266 Bull Nose Morris and 279 MG Midget). A large range of registration numbers were available to factory production staff and were applied randomly to most models. Different number plates are therefore to be expected on different examples of the same model and do not have any effect on the price.

**Windscreens and windows** are included in all vehicle models.
**Other features** include seats and steering wheel on most models, suspension on most cars, driver, other figures and lorry loads with some. Very few 'decals' or 'frills' is the norm.
**Colours** are all listed where known though different and

previously unknown colours still come to light occasionally.
**Colour Collector Cards**. These were included with all models supplied in all-card boxes until 1963.

**Prices** shown in the 'Market Price Range' column are for mint models in pristine boxes. These models are rare, hence their high market prices. The condition of models generally encountered tends towards the average and consequently command lower prices. Similarly, rare colours or combinations of colours puts the price into the higher part of the range with common colours achieving a more moderate price level.

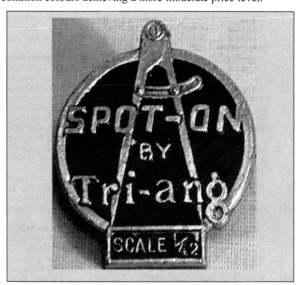

Spot-On Collector's Lapel Badge

| Model and details | MPR |
|---|---|

**100 Ford Zodiac** (without lights) (1959)
Red / Cream.................................. **£80-100**
Blue / Cream, Grey seats.............. **£80-100**
Red body, Cream seats .................. **£80-100**
Cream body .................................. **£80-100**
Yellow body, Cream seats ..........**£110-140**
Light Blue.................................. **£125-150**
Salmon-Pink ................................ **£80-100**
Green body .................................. **£80-100**
Bluish-Grey and
   Brownish-Pink body.............. **£100-125**
Light Blue over Grey, Red interior **£100-120**
TT White/Grey, Cream seats ...... **£100-140**
Grey / Sea Green, Cream seats...... **£125-150**
Lilac with Red seats .................. **£100-125**
Grey with Red seats .................. **£125-150**

**100sl Ford Zodiac** (with lights) (1959)
Grey/Turquoise, Cream seats ........ **£120-140**
Grey/Pink body............................ **£100-120**
Grey/White, Cream seats.............. **£100-120**
Grey/Light Blue, Cream seats ...... **£100-120**
Green/White body ........................ **£100-120**
Yellow, Cream seats .................... **£120-140**
Grey/Green .................................. **£100-120**
Two-tone Blue body .................... **£120-140**
Red body, Cream seats ................ **£100-120**
Pale Blue, Grey seats.................. **£120-140**
Two-tone Green, Cream seats ...... **£125-150**

**101 Armstrong Siddeley
236 Sapphire** (1959)
Blue/Grey, Cream seats .............. **£150-200**
Turquoise / Black ...................... **£150-200**
Blue / Black .............................. **£150-200**
Salmon Pink body ...................... **£125-150**
Lilac body .................................. **£150-200**
Salmon body, Black roof.............. **£150-200**
Mid-Green body, Dark Green
   roof, Cream interior .............. **£150-200**
Light Blue body, Dark Blue roof ... **£150-175**
Powder Green body...................... **£150-175**
Metallic Green / Black ................ **£150-175**
Bluish-Grey ................................ **£150-175**
Light Blue body .......................... **£150-175**
Light Blue / Black...................... **£150-175**
Grey / Black................................ **£175-225**
Pale Green and Metallic Charcoal.. **£150-175**
Deep Lilac / Black roof................ **£150-175**
Cream/Metallic Charcoal.............. **£150-175**
Metallic Blue / Black.................. **£150-175**
Yellow body, Black roof................ **£150-175**
Lilac/Grey, Black roof................ **£150-200**

**102 Bentley Continental
4-door Sports** (1959)
Metallic Green / Silver ................ **£150-200**
Metallic Grey / Blue.................... **£140-180**
Metallic Maroon / Silver.............. **£150-175**
Two-tone Grey............................ **£140-180**
Silver / Grey .............................. **£140-180**
Green / Grey .............................. **£140-180**
Silver / Light Blue ...................... **£175-225**
Grey / Light Blue body ................ **£120-150**
TT Light Blue/Silver, Red seats ..... **£180-220**

**103 Rolls Royce Silver Wraith** (1959)
Metallic Silver / Maroon,
   (White seats)........................ **£200-300**
Met. Silver / Met. Lt. Blue,
   (Cream seats).......................... **£175-225**
Met. Silver / Met. Green .............. **£175-225**

**104 M.G. 'MGA' Sports Car** (1959)
Beige body.................................. **£150-200**
Red body (Grey seats).................. **£150-200**
Mid-blue (White seats).................. **£150-200**
Pale Blue (White seats) ................ **£150-200**
Turquoise (White seats)................ **£150-200**

Cream body (White seats).............. **£150-200**
Salmon Pink (Grey seats) .............. **£200-250**
Bluish-Green body, (Lemon seats). **£150-200**
Greenish-Grey body,
   (Turquoise seats) .................. **£150-200**
Deep Green (White seats) ............ **£150-200**
Metallic Steel Blue body,
   (Grey seats)............................ **£150-200**

**105 Austin-Healey 100/6** (1959)
Yellow body,
   (White or Grey seats) ............ **£200-250**
Grey (Red seats) ........................ **£200-250**
Beige (Grey seats) ........................ **£200-250**
Metallic Blue, Cream side
   panels, Yellow seats.............. **£500-750**
Red body, Cream side
   panels, Cream seats .............. **£500-750**
Blue body, Grey seats.................. **£150-200**
Green body ................................ **£150-200**
Cream body ................................ **£150-200**
Turquoise body .......................... **£150-200**
Metallic Blue/Cream .................... **£500-750**
Metallic Green body .................... **£150-200**
Pink body.................................. **£150-200**
Light Blue body,
   (Royal Blue seats).................. **£150-200**
Turquoise body,
   (Light Grey seats).................. **£150-200**

**107 Jaguar XK-SS** (top down) (1960)
Metallic Blue or Metallic Green body,
   (Lemon seats, Black hood)............ **£225-275**
Cream body .............................. **£225-275**
Beige body ................................ **£225-275**
Red body, Cream seats ................ **£225-275**
Light Green, Grey seats................ **£225-275**
Dark Olive body, (Light
   Grey seats / hood) ................ **£225-275**
Pale Blue body,
   (Pale Grey seats / hood) ........ **£225-275**
Lilac body, (Grey seats,
   Black hood) .......................... **£225-275**
Light Blue body, (Dark
   Blue seats and hood) ............ **£225-275**
Light Grey body, (Pale
   Blue seats and hood) ............ **£225-275**
Fawn body, cast hubs have 'stick-on'
wheel trims that create a spoked
wheel and white-wall tyre effect ......... **NGPP**

**108 Triumph TR3a Sports** (1960)
Light Blue body, Dark Blue seats .. **£150-200**
Cream body, Dark Brown seats...... **£150-200**
Light Brown body, White seats...... **£150-200**
Pale Green body, Off-White seats .. **£150-200**
Apple Green body, Cream seats .... **£150-200**
Red body, Grey seats .................. **£150-200**
Fern Green, Grey seats ................ **£200-250**
Grey body, White seats................ **£150-200**
Metallic Green body, Lemon seats. **£150-200**
Pale Blue body, Pale Grey seats.... **£150-200**
Mid-Blue body, Mid-Grey seats..... **£150-200**
**NB** Two baseplate castings are
known with this model. One exposes
the axle ends near to the wheels, while
the other completely hides the axles.

**112 Jensen 541** (1960)
Red, Cream seats .......................... **£150-200**
Grey body .................................. **£125-150**
Lilac body .................................. **£125-150**
Pink body .................................. **£125-150**
Maroon / Black .......................... **£125-150**
Metallic Green body...................... **£125-150**
Light Blue, Red seats .................. **£125-150**
Pale Green, Cream seats.............. **£125-150**
Metallic Blue body ...................... **£125-150**
Lemon body, Black roof................ **£125-150**

Yellow body, Red seats.................. **£125-150**

**113 Aston-Martin DB3 Saloon** (1960)
Light Blue, Cream seats ................ **£140-160**
Grey body, Cream seats................ **£140-160**
Red body, Red seats ...................... **£225-275**
Light Green body.......................... **£140-160**
Dark Green body .......................... **£140-160**
Maroon body .............................. **£200-250**
Very Pale Pink, Cream interior...... **£160-190**
Deep Pink body, Cream interior..... **£160-190**
Deep Lilac, Blue seats.................. **£160-190**
Light Brown body ........................ **£160-190**
White body ................................ **£160-190**
Metallic Dark Green, Cream seats . **£160-190**
Metallic Silver Blue...................... **£160-190**
Yellow body, (Lemon interior,
   Red steering wheel)................ **£160-190**

**114 Jaguar 3.4 Mark 1 Saloon** (1960)
Metallic Blue body ...................... **£150-175**
Maroon body .............................. **£150-175**
Lilac body .................................. **£200-250**
Metallic Green body...................... **£150-175**
Pink body, Cream seats................ **£150-175**
Light Grey, Red seats .................. **£140-180**
Mid-Green body .......................... **£140-180**
Light Blue body............................ **£110-150**
Mid Blue, Cream seats ................ **£125-150**
Yellow body................................ **£110-150**
White body ................................ **£150-180**
Dark Red body............................ **£150-180**
Very Pale Pink body .................... **£150-200**
Deep Pink body .......................... **£150-200**
Sea Green, Cream seats................ **£150-175**

**115 Bristol 406 Saloon** (1960)
Orange body .............................. **£150-175**
Red body .................................... **£150-175**
Metallic Dark Steel body.............. **£150-175**
Yellow body................................ **£150-175**
Metallic Green body...................... **£150-175**
Grey body, Black roof,
   Cream seats .......................... **£150-175**

**118 BMW Isetta Bubble Car** (1960)
Pale Blue body............................ **£175-200**
Beige body.................................. **£175-200**
Grey body, Cream seats................ **£175-200**
Turquoise, White seats ................ **£175-200**
Dark Sea Green,
   Mid-Blue seats...................... **£175-200**
Metallic Green body...................... **£175-200**
Red body, Cream seats ................ **£175-200**
Pink body, Cream seats ................ **£175-200**
Pale Lemon, Cream seats ............ **£175-200**
Dark Blue, Cream seats .............. **£175-200**
Bright Green, Cream seats ........... **£175-200**

**119 Meadows Frisky Sport** (1960)
Orange / Grey .............................. **£125-150**
Blue / Grey .................................. **£125-150**
Turquoise / Black ........................ **£125-150**
Red / Light Grey .......................... **£125-150**
Red / Black .................................. **£125-150**
Light Blue / White........................ **£125-150**
Pale Blue / Black ........................ **£125-150**
Red / White ................................ **£125-150**
Yellow / Black ............................ **£150-200**

**120 Fiat Multipla Estate** (1960)
Blue (Cream seats) ...................... **£100-125**
Mauve (Red seats) ........................ **£100-125**
Pink body.................................... **£125-150**
Light Blue (Black seats)................ **£125-150**
Yellow body ................................ **£125-150**
Red body.................................... **£125-150**

| | |
|---|---|
| Dark Red body | £125-150 |
| Sea Green body | £150-200 |
| Pale Green body | £100-125 |
| White (Off-White seats) | £100-125 |
| Orange, White seats | £300-400 |
| Turquoise, Cream seats | £150-200 |

**131 Goggomobil Super Regent** (1960)

| | |
|---|---|
| Grey / Black | £150-175 |
| Yellow / Black | £150-175 |
| Mauve / Black | £150-175 |
| Blue / Grey | £150-175 |
| Blue body | £150-175 |
| Green body | £150-175 |
| Grey body | £150-175 |
| Metallic Green body | £150-175 |
| Beige body | £150-175 |
| Light Grey body | £150-175 |
| Pink body | £150-175 |
| Deep Salmon Pink body | £150-175 |
| Red body | £150-175 |
| Turquoise (Black seats) | £150-175 |
| Light Blue / Black | £175-225 |
| Red / Black | £175-225 |
| Dark Blue / Black | £175-225 |
| Green / Black | £175-225 |

**154 Austin A40 Farina Saloon** (1961)

| | |
|---|---|
| Green body | £100-125 |
| White (Cream seats) | £100-125 |
| Light Blue / White | £100-125 |
| Grey / Blue | £100-125 |
| Mid Grey, Red seats | £140-170 |
| Metallic Blue body | £100-125 |
| Beige body | £100-125 |
| Light Blue body | £100-125 |
| Navy body | £100-125 |
| Turquoise body | £100-125 |
| Pale Grey body, White interior | £100-125 |
| Metallic Green body, Cream interior | £100-125 |
| Red / Black | £100-125 |
| Blue / Black | £100-125 |
| Sea Green / Black | £100-125 |
| Lavender / Black | £100-125 |

'MAGGI' Promotional (1966),
Red body, Cream interior, 'MAGGI'
in yellow on front doors. Special
red / yellow box with leaflet .......... £200-300

**157 Rover 3-litre** (without lights) (1963)

| | |
|---|---|
| Mid Blue (Cream seats) | £150-175 |
| Mauve body | £150-175 |
| Beige body | £150-175 |
| Yellow body | £150-175 |
| Mid-Grey (Dk. Red seats) | £120-140 |
| Dark Grey body | £120-140 |
| Pale Grey body | £120-140 |
| Sea Green (Cream seats) | £120-140 |
| Dark Green body | £120-140 |
| Light Blue body | £120-140 |
| Deep Pink body | £120-140 |
| Dark Blue (Cream seats) | £150-175 |
| White body | £95-125 |

**157sl Rover 3-litre** (with lights) (1963)

| | |
|---|---|
| Light Blue (Cream seats) | £125-165 |
| Mid Blue (Cream seats) | £125-165 |
| Dark Blue (Cream seats) | £125-165 |
| Mauve (Cream seats) | £125-165 |
| Beige (Cream seats) | £125-165 |
| Red (Cream seats) | £125-165 |
| Yellow (Cream seats) | £125-165 |
| Pale Grey (Cream seats) | £125-165 |
| Grey (Cream seats) | £125-165 |
| Dark Grey (Cream seats) | £125-165 |
| Sea Green (Cream seats) | £125-165 |
| Dark Green (Cream seats) | £125-165 |
| Bright Green, Cream seats | £125-165 |
| White (Cream seats) | £125-165 |

**165/1 Vauxhall PA Cresta Saloon** (1961)

| | |
|---|---|
| Beige body | £120-150 |

| | |
|---|---|
| Red body | £120-150 |
| Maroon body | £120-150 |
| Pink body | £120-150 |
| Turquoise body | £120-150 |
| Yellow body | £120-150 |
| Blue body | £120-150 |
| Light Blue body | £120-150 |
| Grey body | £120-150 |
| Light Grey body | £120-150 |
| Plum Red body | £175-200 |
| Sea Green, Red interior | £175-200 |

**165/2 Vauxhall PA Cresta with roof rack** (1961)

| | |
|---|---|
| Beige body (Red seats) | £100-125 |
| Red body | £100-125 |
| Maroon body | £100-125 |
| Pink body | £100-125 |
| Turquoise (Cream seats) | £100-125 |
| Yellow body | £100-125 |
| Blue body | £90-120 |
| Light Blue (Red seats) | £90-120 |
| Grey body | £90-120 |
| Light Grey body | £90-120 |
| Plum Red body | £110-150 |
| Sea green body | £110-150 |

**166 Renault Floride Convertible** (1962)

| | |
|---|---|
| Blue (Grey seats) | £120-150 |
| Green body | £120-150 |
| Grey body | £120-150 |
| Dark Red (Grey seats) | £120-150 |
| White body | £120-150 |
| Yellow body | £120-150 |

**183 Humber Super Snipe Estate** (1963)

| | |
|---|---|
| Red, Cream seats | £100-125 |
| Beige body | £125-150 |
| Beige/White | £125-150 |
| Blue/White | £125-150 |
| Green/White | £125-150 |
| Turquoise, Cream seats | £125-150 |
| Blue/Black | £125-150 |
| Blue or Light Blue body | £125-150 |
| Metallic Bronze body | £125-150 |
| Two-tone Blue | £125-150 |

**NB** Some examples exist
fitted with wing mirrors.

**184 Austin A60 Cambridge** (1963)
(with 2 figures, skis on roof rack)

| | |
|---|---|
| Beige body | £110-140 |
| Green body | £110-140 |
| White body | £110-140 |
| Turquoise, White seats | £100-125 |
| Red (Grey rack/seats) | £100-125 |
| Light Blue (Grey rack) | £100-125 |
| Light Grey (Grey rack) | £100-125 |
| Lime Green | £90-120 |
| Greyish-Blue body, (Black or Grey rack) | £90-120 |

**185 Fiat 500** (1963)

| | |
|---|---|
| Light Blue (Cream seats) | £100-125 |
| Green (Cream seats) | £100-125 |
| Red (Cream seats) | £100-125 |
| Grey (Cream seats) | £100-125 |
| Yellow (Cream seats) | £120-150 |
| Dark Blue (Cream seats) | £120-150 |

**191 Sunbeam Alpine Convertible** (1963)

| | |
|---|---|
| Beige body | £150-175 |
| Mid-Blue body | £150-175 |
| Green (White seats) | £150-175 |
| Red body | £150-175 |
| Mauve body | £150-175 |
| Pink body | £150-175 |
| Turquoise (Cream seats) | £150-175 |
| Grey (Cream seats) | £150-175 |
| Light Blue (White seats) | £150-175 |
| Deep Salmon Pink body, (Red seats) | £150-175 |

| | |
|---|---|
| White with Red seats | £150-175 |
| Yellow with Cream seats | £150-175 |
| Yellow with Red seats | £225-275 |

**191/1 Sunbeam Alpine Hardtop** (1963)

| | |
|---|---|
| Red / White | £225-275 |
| Turquoise / Cream | £225-275 |
| Blue / Black | £225-275 |
| Blue / Cream | £225-275 |
| White / Black | £225-275 |
| Beige / White | £225-275 |
| Grey / Black | £225-275 |
| Dark Green (Red seats) | £225-275 |
| Metallic Green / Black | £225-275 |
| Pink (Cream seats) | £225-275 |
| Mauve (Cream seats) | £225-275 |
| Yellow (Cream seats) | £225-275 |
| Light Blue body | £225-275 |
| Light Blue/White | £225-275 |
| Pale Blue/White | £225-275 |

**193 N.S.U. Prinz** (1963)

| | |
|---|---|
| Turquoise (Cream seats) | £120-150 |
| Beige (Cream seats) | £120-150 |
| Pale Blue (Cream seats) | £120-150 |
| Light Blue (Cream seats) | £120-150 |
| Dark Blue (Cream seats) | £120-150 |
| Cream (Cream seats) | £120-150 |
| Grey (Red seats) | £120-150 |
| Red (White seats) | £120-150 |
| Dark Red, Grey seats | £100-120 |
| White (White seats) | £120-150 |
| Lime Green | £120-150 |
| Green, Grey seats | £100-120 |

**195 Volkswagen Rally Car** (1963)
With roof light, bonnet flags,
racing number '6', '9' or '23'.

| | |
|---|---|
| Beige (Off-White seats) | £200-250 |
| Cream body | £200-250 |
| Maroon body | £200-250 |
| Orange body | £200-250 |
| Red, racing number '11' | £200-300 |
| Metallic Bronze body | £200-300 |
| Light Blue body | £150-175 |
| Turquoise body, Off-White seats | £150-175 |
| Grey, Off-White seats | £175-200 |

**210 Morris Mini Minor** (1960)
Shown in catalogue but not issued..........NPP

**211 Austin Seven** (Mini) (1963)

| | |
|---|---|
| Light Blue body | £125-150 |
| Grey body | £125-150 |
| Red body | £125-150 |
| Yellow body | £125-150 |
| Pink body | £200-250 |
| White body | £160-180 |

**213 Ford Anglia Saloon** (1963)

| | |
|---|---|
| Beige body | £130-160 |
| Grey (Red seats) | £130-160 |
| Yellow body | £130-160 |
| White body | £130-160 |
| Turquoise body, Off-White seats | £130-160 |
| Light Blue body | £130-160 |
| Dark Blue body | £130-160 |
| Sky Blue, Off-White seats | £130-160 |
| Red body | £130-160 |
| Pink body | £130-160 |

**215 Daimler Dart SP250** (1961)

| | |
|---|---|
| Beige body | £120-150 |
| Green body (Red seats) | £160-190 |
| Yellow body | £120-150 |
| White (Red seats) | £160-190 |
| Light Blue (Blue seats) | £160-190 |
| Turquoise (White seats) | £100-125 |
| Red (Cream seats) | £100-125 |
| Grey (Cream seats) | £150-200 |

**216 Volvo 122s**
(with sliding roof) (1963)
Red (Cream seats) .......................... **£150-200**
Orange body ................................... **£150-200**
Blue (Off-White seats) ................... **£90-120**
Turquoise body .............................. **£90-120**
Grey body ...................................... **£100-125**
Bright Yellow body ........................ **£100-125**
Dark Green body,
   (Off-White seats) ......................... **£100-125**
Lime Green body, White interior .. **£150-200**

**217 Jaguar 'E' Type** (1963)
Beige (Cream seats) ...................... **£150-175**
Cream body ................................... **£150-175**
Light Green body ........................... **£150-175**
Green (Cream seats) ...................... **£150-175**
White body .................................... **£150-175**
Yellow / Black ............................... **£150-175**
Mid-Blue body ............................... **£150-175**
Light Blue body ............................. **£150-175**
Light Grey body ............................. **£150-175**
Red body, Cream interior .............. **£175-200**
Bright Green, Off-White seats ....... **£150-175**
Turquoise, Cream seats ................. **£150-175**

**218 Jaguar Mk.10** (1963)
Metallic Brown body ..................... **£140-170**
Light Blue body, (Mid-Blue seats) . **£140-170**
Dark Green body, (Cream seats) .... **£250-350**
Mid-Green body ............................ **£120-150**
Bronze body .................................. **£120-150**
White body .................................... **£120-150**

**219 Austin-Healey Sprite Mk.III**
(with driver figure) (1963)
Red (White seats) .......................... **£150-175**
Blue (Red seats) ............................. **£150-175**
Beige (White seats) ........................ **£150-175**
Off-White body .............................. **£150-175**
Light Blue body ............................. **£150-175**

**259 Ford Consul Classic** (1963)
White (Blue seats) ......................... **£100-125**
Beige (White seats) ........................ **£100-125**
Blue body ...................................... **£100-125**
Light Blue body ............................. **£100-125**
Red body ....................................... **£100-125**
Grey (Cream seats) ........................ **£100-125**
Green body .................................... **£100-125**
Turquoise, Off-White seats ............ **£100-125**

**260 Royal Rolls-Royce Phantom V** (1963)
Maroon body, Blue interior, two flags on
roof, Queen and Prince Philip in rear
seats, driver + attendant in front..... **£600-750**

**261 Volvo P1800** (1963)  Two versions
of this model exist (no price difference):
**1**: the bonnet and boot can be opened,
and a spare wheel is supplied;
**2**: only the bonnet can be opened.
Light Blue (Red or Grey seats) ...... **£100-130**
Mid-Blue body ............................... **£100-130**
Red (Grey seats) ............................ **£100-130**
Turquoise (White seats) ................. **£100-130**
Grey body ...................................... **£100-130**
Metallic Bronze body .................... **£100-130**
Tan body ....................................... **£100-130**
Red body, Grey interior ................. **£125-150**

**262 Morris 1100** (1963)
Dark Blue (Grey seats) .................. **£100-130**
Red (Grey or Cream seats) ............. **£120-140**
Bright Green (Red seats) ................ **£120-140**
Beige (Red seats) ........................... **£100-130**
Lime Green body ........................... **£100-130**
Light Blue body ............................. **£100-130**

**263 Bentley 4½ Litre** (Supercharged) (1964)
Green body, Union Jack,
number '27', '11' or '15' ................ **£80-100**

**266 'Bull Nose' Morris** 1923
(Scale 1:48) (1965)
Red / Black, Brown driver ................ **£70-80**
Yellow/Black, Brown driver............. **£70-80**

**267 M.G. 1100 Saloon** (1964)
White / Dark Green, (Red seats) .... **£150-175**
Red (Cream seats) ......................... **£150-175**
Green (Red seats) .......................... **£150-175**
Red / White (Red seats).................. **£150-175**
Royal Blue / White, (Red seats)..... **£350-450**
Royal Blue/Off-White,
   (Grey seats)................................. **£200-250**
Cream/Beige (Red seats)................ **£140-160**

**268 Vauxhall PB Cresta.** (1965).
Shown in catalogue but not issued
under this number, see 280.....................NPP

**270 Ford Zephyr 6 Mk.III**
(with poodle) (1965)
Pale Blue (Red seats)...................... **£250-350**
Cream body .................................... **£140-160**
Green body ..................................... **£140-160**
Greyish-Green (Red seats) ............. **£140-160**
Grey (Red seats) ............................. **£140-160**
Red (Grey  seats) ............................ **£250-350**
Off-White (Red  seats) .................... **£140-160**

**274 Morris 1100 and Canoe** (1965)
Green body ..................................... **£125-150**
Grey body ...................................... **£125-150**
Light Blue, (Red canoe) ................. **£125-150**
Dark Blue (Grey seats).................... **£125-150**
Red car, (Brown canoe)................... **£125-150**
Two-tone Blue body, (Red canoe).. **£125-150**
Red (Red/White canoe) .................. **£125-150**
Light Blue car with Blue / Red canoe,
Orange paddle (Set 703)........................GSP

**276 Jaguar 'S' type** (with 2 figures) (1964)
Metallic Bronze body, (Red  seats) **£150-200**
Metallic Blue body (Red  seats) ..... **£150-200**
Metallic Green body, Red interior.. **£150-200**
Silver body..................................... **£200-250**
Greyish Green body, Red interior .. **£200-250**

**278 Mercedes-Benz 230 SL**
(with 2 figures) (1965)
Metallic Red body .......................... **£150-175**
Cream body .................................... **£150-175**
Maroon body .................................. **£150-175**
Metallic Blue (Red  seats) .............. **£150-175**
Metallic Bronze body ..................... **£150-175**

**279 M.G. PB Midget** 1935
(scale 1:48) (1965)
Dark Blue body,
   Black wings / seats ...................... **£100-125**
Red body, Black wings and seats ... **£100-125**

**280 Vauxhall PB Cresta** (1963)
Cream / Red body, Red interior ..... **£140-160**
Dark Blue / White body,
   Red interior................................. **£140-160**
Grey / Green body .......................... **£140-160**

**281 M.G. Midget Mk.II,**
(plus policeman figure) (1966)
Blue body, White interior, driver.... **£150-200**
Red body, White interior, driver..... **£150-200**

**286 Austin 1800** (1965)
Light Blue, (Red seats) .................. **£125-150**
Dark Blue, (Red seats) ................... **£125-150**
Cream body, (Red seats)................. **£125-150**
Green  body, (Red seats) ................ **£125-150**
Beige body, (Red seats) .................. **£125-150**
Red  body, (Grey seats) .................. **£125-150**

**287 Hillman Minx**
(with Roof Rack and
two brown suitcases) (1965)

Pale Green, (Red seats) .................. **£125-150**
Beige body (Red seats).................... **£125-150**
Cream body (Red seats) ................. **£125-150**
Green body (Red seats) ................... **£125-150**
Red (Grey seats) ............................ **£150-175**
Greyish-Green body ....................... **£125-150**
**NB** This model is also known
   with the reference '287/1'.

**289 Morris Minor 1000** (1963)
Metallic Blue (Red seats) .............. **£150-200**
Light Blue body.............................. **£150-200**
Red body........................................ **£200-250**
Metallic Green body ....................... **£200-250**

**304 VW Variant Estate Car** (1967)
Mid-Blue body and plastic
   opening tailgate. See also 401/1... **£500-750**

**306 Humber Super Snipe Estate** (1964)
Same casting as 183 but with
roof-rack and two suitcases.
Beige (Cream seats)........................ **£150-175**
Blue body....................................... **£150-175**
Green body ..................................... **£150-175**
Red body........................................ **£150-175**
Metallic Bronze body, (Red seats) . **£150-175**
Light Blue body, (White
   roof-rack, Red seats) ................... **£100-125**
Turquoise body, (White roof-rack). **£100-125**
White / Turquoise, Grey rack ........ **£100-125**
Blue body, White roof .................... **£100-125**

**307 Volkswagen Beetle 1200** (1965)
Metallic Blue body ......................... **£200-250**
Metallic Dark Red body ................. **£200-250**

**308 Land Rover and Trailer** (1965)
Green (Tan canopy), trailer
   has Brown plastic body ............... **£125-150**

**401/1 VW Variant Estate Car** (1967)
Dark Blue body, White
   plastic opening tailgate................ **£300-500**

**405 'BEA' Vauxhall Cresta** (1966)
Dark Grey body, Red
   'BEA' logo, Red interior............... **£200-250**

**406 Hillman Minx with Dinghy**
Greyish-Green, Red seats .............. **£175-225**

**407 Mercedes-Benz 230 SL** (1966)
Brown body, Red interior,
   boot rack and luggage .................. **£70-80**

**408 Renault Caravelle** (1966)
Not issued...............................................NPP

**410 Austin 1800 and Rowboat**
(on roof) (1965)
Green car, Red or Orange boat....... **£100-140**
Blue car with Red or Orange boat.. **£100-140**
Red car with Red or Orange boat... **£100-140**
Beige car, Red or Orange boat ....... **£100-140**
Tan with red seats.......................... **£125-150**

# Spot-On Commercial Vehicles

**106a/0c  Austin Articulated Flatbed Lorry**
(1960)  with MGA in Crate
Light Blue, Dark Blue,
Red or Orange cab.................... **£250-400**

**106a/1  Austin Artic. Dropside Lorry**
(1959)  Light Blue, Green or
Orange cab/body ...................... **£200-250**

**106a/1c  Austin Artic. Flatbed Lorry**
with Crate Load
(1960)  Light Blue, Light Green or Orange
cab, 7 black plastic crates........... **£200-250**
Turquoise or Dark Blue body..... **£400-500**

**CB106  Four Wheel Trailer**
(1961)  Turquoise or Red body.............. **£150-175**

**109/2  E.R.F. 68g Flatbed Lorry**
(1960)  Turquoise, Light Grey or Blue ... **£160-190**
Maroon body .............................. **£350-400**

**109/2p  E.R.F. 68g Flatbed Lorry with Planks**
(1960)  Turquoise body
(Black cab roof on some)......... **£350-450**
Yellow body............................ **£800-1,100**

**109/3  E.R.F. 68g Dropside Lorry**
(1960)  Dk. Blue cab / Pale Blue body ... **£300-400**
Dark Blue cab / Silver body....... **£300-400**
Yellow body (Met. Grey roof).... **£160-190**
Light Green body (Green roof) .. **£160-190**
Blue body (Black roof)............... **£160-190**
Green body (Black roof) ........... **£160-190**
Deep Blue body, Silver chassis .. **£250-350**
Orange-Red body,
Light Grey chassis.................... **£350-450**
Lemon body, Silver chassis........ **£400-500**
Pale Green body, Silver chassis . **£300-350**
Turquoise body, Silver chassis .. **£300-350**

**109/3b  E.R.F. Dropside Lorry and Barrel load**
(1960)  Turquoise, Light Blue or Red
body (Silver truck bed on some),
ten Brown plastic barrels........... **£350-450**

**110/2  A.E.C. Mammoth Major 8**
Flatbed Lorry
(1960)  Dark Red (Black roof on some) . **£400-500**
Strawberry Red body................. **£500-750**

**110/2b  A.E.C. Lorry 'London Brick Co Ltd'**
(1960)  Red body, Black cab roof,
'brick' load, 'Phorpes Bricks'..... **£300-400**

**110/3  A.E.C. Lorry 'British Road Services'**
(1960)  Red body, Black cab roof on some,
Silver chassis / back, barrels ...... **£400-500**

**110/3d  A.E.C. Lorry with Oil Drums Load**
(1962)  Red body, Black cab roof........... **£500-600**
Red with Silver inner back and
chassis, Cream seats,
Red steering wheel ................... **£500-600**
Yellow cab and back, Dark Grey
chassis, Cream seats,
Black steering wheel ................ **£650-850**
Same but Light Grey chassis..... **£500-600**

**110/4  A.E.C. Tanker 'SHELL-BP'**
(1961)  Green cab, Red tank,
Black chassis and catwalk ......... **£400-500**
Yellow cab, White/Yellow tank,
Silver chassis / catwalk ............. **£500-750**

---

**111/a0g  Ford Thames with Garage Kit**
(1962)  Orange cab and truck body,
Silver chassis ........................... **£400-500**
Light Blue cab and truck body,
White garage ........................... **£400-500**

**111/a0t  Ford Thames Trader with**
Three Log Load
(1961)  Dark Blue or Red cab and truck
body, 3 logs ............................. **£300-400**
Light Blue cab and truck body ... **£300-400**
Light Yellow cab / truck body.... **£300-400**

**111a/1  Ford Thames Trader**
'British Railways'
(1959)  Maroon and White body,
'4884 BGM', 'M 1741 GT6' ... **£300-400**

**111a/1  Ford Thames Trader 'R.Hall & Son'**
Green body, door logo. Not issued?....NPP

**111a/1s  Ford Thames with Sack Load**
(1960)  Light Blue and Silver,
twelve brown plastic sacks....... **£300-400**
Dark Green body, Green inner
back, Black chassis................. **£500-750**
Two-tone Blue body,
Cream interior ......................... **£300-400**
Strawberry and Cream body,
Purple interior ........................ **£500-750**
Green with Cream interior and
inner back, black chassis ........... **£500-750**

**116  'CATERPILLAR' Tractor D9**
(1959)  Dark Yellow / Silver body,
Black rubber tracks, 'CAT D9',
information leaflet.............. **£1,000-1,500**

**117  'JONES' Mobile Crane**
(1963)  Cream cab and jib,
Red body and wheels,
Black chassis, Grey base.......... **£200-300**
Dark Red cab / body, White jib,
Light Grey chassis,
Silver wheels ........................... **£300-400**

**122  'UNITED DAIRIES' Milk Float**
(1961)  Red / White body, chains,
'Lada and New Yoghurt' ........... **£175-225**

**123  Bamford Excavator 'J.C.B.'**
(1959)  Red / Yellow. Not issued ...................NPP

**137  'MASSEY FERGUSON 65' Tractor**
(1962)  Red engine cover,
Grey chassis/engine,
Yellow hubs, Black tyres,
plastic seat ............................... **£500-700**

**158a/2  Bedford 'S' Type 2000 Gallon**
(1961)  'SHELL-BP' Tanker
Green cab, Red tank,
Black chassis, 'P33A37'........... **£400-500**
Yellow cab, White tank .......... **£700-1,000**
Dark Metallic Green cab,
Red tank, Black chassis............. **£500-600**

**158a/2C  Bedford Low Loader**
(1961)  Red, with cable drum. Not issued? .....NPP

**161  Land Rover (long wheel base)**
(1961)  Grey / White ............................ **£125-150**
Light Grey / White ................... **£125-150**
Blue / White.............................. **£125-150**

---

**210  Morris Mini Van**
(1961)  Bright Yellow, seats / steering
wheel, suspension.................... **£175-225**

**210/1  Morris Mini Van 'Royal Mail'**
(1962)  Red body,
Post Office crest, 'E-II-R' ......... **£175-225**

**210/2  Mini Van 'P.O. Telephones'**
(1962)  Olive-Green body, White interior,
Gold crown logo,
'TELEPHONE MANAGER' .... **£175-225**

**258  'R.A.C.' Land Rover**
(1963)  Dark Blue body,
'RADIO RESCUE'................... **£100-125**

**265  'TONIBELL' Ice Cream Van**
(1964)  Blue body, thick Red flash,
attendant ................................. **£300-350**

**271  'EXPRESS DAIRIES' Milk Float**
(1965)  Dark Blue / White, 3 wheels,
driver, crates and bottles,
'Drink Express Milk'................. **£300-400**

**273  Commer Van 'SECURITY EXPRESS'**
(1965)  Green / Gold, driver, seated
guard, coin slot in roof............. **£130-160**

**308  Land Rover and Trailer**
(1965)  Green (Tan plastic canopy),
trailer has Brown plastic body.... **£175-200**

**315  'GLASS & HOLMES' Commer Van**
(1965)  Blue / Yellow, 'Window Cleaning
Co. Est 1891', ladder and
figures...................................... **£200-250**

**402  Crash Service Land Rover**
(1966)  Orange body, 'MOTORWAYS
CRASH SERVICE' in Blue ..... **£100-150**

**404  Morris Mini Van**
(1966)  Yellow body, ladder, figure ........ **£500-700**
**404/1  Morris Mini Van 'SHELL'**
(1966)  As previous model but without
ladder and figure........................ **£500-700**
**404/2  Morris Mini Van 'AA'**
(1966)  In 1966 catalogue but never seen.....NGPP

# Spot-On miscellaneous models

## Buses, Coaches and Taxis

**145** 1963 **Routemaster Bus**, Red 'London Transport' bus, route '284',
'Ovaltine - The Worlds Best Nightcap'.
1st type has chrome moulded radiator.............................**£350-450**
2nd type has transfer print on plastic background ..........**£350-450**
**155** 1961 **Austin FX4 Taxi**, Maroon body, Cream steering wheel,
Green base, tin-plate hubcaps.....................................**£300-400**
Black body, Red seats, Grey base...................................**£80-100**
**156** 1961 **Mulliner Luxury Coach**, Pale Blue / Grey, Red flash,
'Tri-ang Tours' rear logo, 213 mm ...............................**£200-300**
Yellow / White body, Brown side flash........................**£900-1,200**
Sea Green / Cream, Red flash ...................................**£800-1,000**
Silver / Red / Dark Blue .............................................**£600-800**
Sky Blue / White body, Red flash ................................**£600-800**

## Boats, Caravans and Scooter

**135** 1961 **14ft Sailing Dinghy and Trailer**,
Blue / Grey, Dark Blue / Red, Dark Blue / White, or
Red / White boat (with or without cover), plastic trailer .....**£60-80**
**135** 1964 **14ft GP Sailing Dinghy**,
Brown or Yellow boat on trailer......................................**£60-80**
**139** 1960 **Eccles E.16 Caravan**, Blue body, White roof, 146 mm..........NPP
**229** 1966 **Lambretta**, Pale Blue body,
Red or White side panels, Black seat ............................**£175-225**
**264** 1962 **Tourist Caravan**, Blue body, White roof, 152 mm..........**£90-120**
Yellow or Cream body, White roof, Red trim .................**£130-160**
Tan body, White roof, Red trim....................................**£130-160**

## Emergency vehicles

**207** 1964 **Wadham Ambulance**,
Cream body, no Red crosses, with stretcher and patient..**£300-400**
White body with Red crosses, stretcher and patient ........**£400-500**
**256** 1966 **Jaguar 3.4 'POLICE' Car**, White or Black.
Very few exist with undamaged aerial or roof sign ........**£300-450**
**258** 1963 **'R.A.C.' Land Rover**, Dark Blue body,
'RADIO RESCUE', 108 mm .........................................**£100-125**
**309** 1965 **Police 'Z' Car**,
Ford Zephyr police car from the BBC-TV series 'Z-Cars'.
1st type with aerial and 'POLICE' sign, White body.......**£160-200**
2nd type with no aerial or police sign. Black body..........**£300-400**
2nd type (no aerial or police sign), White body..............**£300-400**
**316** 1966 **'FIRE DEPT' Land Rover**,
Red body, suspension, two firemen, 112 mm..................**£150-200**
**402** 1966 **Land Rover 'MOTORWAYS'**, Orange / Blue body,
hook, Blue 'CRASH SERVICE' logo ............................**£150-200**
**409** 1966 **Leyland 'Black Maria'**, Blue body, 'Police',
policeman and villain. Not issued ...................................... NPP
**415** **Land Rover 'R.A.F. Fire Service'**.
Greyish Blue, Grey interior ........................................**£175-225**

## Road Signs and Accessories

**L208/B** **Road Traffic Signs**:  20 different signs issued, each ............**£5-10**
**L1271/** **Road Direction Signs**:  /1 Portsmouth, /2 Guildford, /3 Bristol,
/4 Birmingham, /5 Biggar, /6 Dumfries..................................**£10-15**
**L151** **Police Public Call Box** .........................................**£75-100**
--- **Bus Stops**: No details available..............................................**£10-15**
--- **Road sections**: Straights, curves, T-junctions. Each ..................**£6-8**
--- **Plastic Figures**:  In groups set on a card. Figures include:
Garage Personnel, Newspaperman/Milkman/Postman,
Doctor/Parson/Schoolmaster, 2 Policeman and an RAC Man,
3 Schoolboys, 2 Children and a Man (in country clothes),
3 Roadmen and Brazier or 3 Roadmen and Road Drill/Planks/Walls.
Per card ....................................................................**£5-10**
Retailer's sheet of any six cards of figures........................**£100-125**

## Military models

**415** 1965 **R.A.F. Land Rover**, Blue/Grey, R.A.F. roundel,
hose/pump/attendant, 111 mm......................................**£300-400**
**416** 1965 **Leyland Army Ambulance**. Not issued...............................NPP
**417** 1965 **Military 'FIELD KITCHEN'**, Olive Green body,
squadron markings, suspension, 108 mm........................**£200-250**
**418** 1965 **Leyland Military Bus**, 'Army Personnel'. Not issued ..........NPP
**419** 1965 **Land Rover and Missile Carrier**,
Olive Green body, three White missiles ........................**£400-600**

## Garages and Equipment

**L146** 'SHELL' lamp standard ........................................**£20-25**
**L147** 'SHELL' sign ...................................................**£15-20**
**L148** 'SHELL' petrol pump...........................................**£15-20**
**L148** Trade pack, Blue card box of 6 of L148 pumps.................**£100-150**
**L149** Oil Dispenser Rack ...........................................**£10-15**
**L159** 'BP' Lamp Standard ...........................................**£20-25**
**162** 'BP' or 'SHELL' Filling Station .............................**£60-70**

**162/1/2/3** Garages, each..................................................**£20-30**
**163** 'BP' Petrol Pump..............................................**£15-20**
**164** 'BP' Forecourt Sign...........................................**£15-20**
**172a** 'SHELL' Garage Set...........................................**£75-100**
**172b** 'BP' Garage Set..............................................**£75-100**
**257** Garage Kit ...................................................**£150-175**
--- **Spot-On Garage**. Cardboard unit with white clock,
'GARAGE' in red, with 'The ONLY complete Highway System',
plus 'Number Plates' and 'Windows', plus 'Steering Wheels'
and 'Seats' on the 3 floor levels. Red/White/Blue sign
on roof 'Tri-ang SPOT-ON', 'Scale 1/45' ....................**£2,500-3,000**
'A' **Spot-On No. 'A' Garage**.
Cardboard/metal two-floor Garage ......................................**£150-200**

## 'Magicar' series

Plastic bodies, programmable mechanisms. Box has additional accessories.
**501** 1965 **Jaguar Mk.10**, Blue or Green body ...................................**£70-90**
**502** 1965 **Rolls-Royce Silver Cloud Mk.III**, Blue or Red body....**£100-125**
**503** 1965 **Bentley S3 Saloon**, Blue or Red body............................**£80-110**
**504** **Ferrari Superfast**, Blue or Red ..............................**£80-110**
**505** 1966 **Batmobile**, Black body with Batman and Robin figures .**£150-175**
? ? **Tric-Trac car**, Plastic bodied racing car ..........................**£80-110**

**MG1, MG2, MG3 Magicar Sets.** See 'Presentation and Gift Sets.

Spot-On models 155 Taxi and 184 Austin A60
Cambridge wiith Skis. The Taxi is shown with an early box;
the Austin is on a later design of box that has
illustrations of the model contained.

# Spot-On Presentation and Gift Sets

| Ref./Issued | Set name and details | Market Price Range |
|---|---|---|

Colours of individual items are not listed. It is possible to find virtually any factory colour that was available at the time of manufacture in Spot-On Gift Sets. Early sets should contain Picture Cards, Fleet Owners leaflets and Magazine Club leaflets.

**A**
**1960**
**Presentation Set 'A'**
102 Bentley, 108 Triumph TR3, 114 Jaguar 3.4, 118 BMW Isetta, 154 Austin A40............................................**£500-750**

**No.0**
**1960**
**Presentation Set**
106a/1 Austin Articulated Dropside Lorry, 100 Ford Zodiac, 103 Rolls-Royce Silver Wraith, 104 MGA, 113 Aston Martin ...............................................**£500-750**

**No.1**
**1960**
**Presentation Set**
100 Ford Zodiac, 101 Armstrong-Siddely, 103 Rolls-Royce and 104 MGA ...............**£800-1,000**

**No.2**
**1960**
**Presentation Set**
109/3 ERF Dropside Lorry, 101 Armstrong-Siddely, 102 Bentley Continental and 105 Austin-Healey 100/6 .......**£800-1,000**

**No.3**
**1960**
**Presentation Set**
Contains 111a/1 Ford Thames Trader, 101 Armstrong-Siddely, 104 MGA, 108 Triumph TR3a, 112 Jensen 541, 113 Aston Martin, 114 Jaguar 3.4 .........................**£800-1,000**

**No.4**
**1960**
**Presentation Set**
106a/1 Austin Articulated Dropside Lorry, 109/3 ERF, 100 Ford Zodiac, 107 Jaguar XK-SS, 112 Jensen 541 .........**£800-1,000**

**No.4a**
**1963**
**Presentation Set**
104 MGA, 105 Austin-Healey, 107 Jaguar and 108 Triumph TR3a .........................**£500-600**

**No.5**
**Presentation Set**
118 BMW Isetta, 119 Meadows Frisky Sport and 131 Goggomobil ................................................**£400-600**

**No.6**
**'Miniature' Presentation Set**
131 Goggomobil, 185 Fiat 500, 193 NSU Prinz, 211 Austin Seven ...............................................**£400-600**
Variation with 210/1 'ROYAL MAIL' Van instead of 193 NSU Prinz ................................................**£400-600**

**No.6a**
**'Miniature' Presentation Set**
131 Goggomobil, 185 Fiat 500, 119 Meadows Frisky and 211 Austin Seven ...............................................**£400-600**

**No.7**
**Rally Presentation Set**
166 Renault Floride, 191 Sunbeam Alpine, 211 Austin Seven, 213 Ford Anglia, 215 Daimler Dart, 217 Jaguar 'E'-type.......**£600-800**

**No.8**
**Presentation Set**
157 Rover, 191 Sunbeam, 213 Ford Anglia, 216 Volvo, 258 RAC Land Rover, petrol pumps .................................**£2,500-3,000**

**No.9**
**Presentation Set**
122 Milk Float, 145 Routemaster Bus, 193 NSU Prinz, 207 Wadham Ambulance, 211 Austin Seven, 256 Jaguar Police Car ...............**NGPP**

**No.10**
**Presentation Set**
122 Austin Seven, 145 Routemaster Bus, 157 Rover 3 litre, 158a/2 Bedford Tanker, 185 Fiat 500, 165 Vauxhall, 166 Renault, 211 Austin Seven, 215 Daimler Dart and 262 Morris 1100 ....**£500-750**

**No.14**
**Presentation Set**
211 Austin 7 Mini, 154 Austin A40, 156 Mulliner Coach, 191/1 Sunbeam, 122 Milk Float, 157sl Rover 3 Litre with lights ................................**£600-800**

**173**
**Terrapin Building Set**   A constructional set ...........................**£35-45**

**208/a**
**Road Construction Set**
4 workmen, brazier, hut, poles, road sections + 18 other small items ...............................................**£150-200**

**212**
**1963**
**Car, Dinghy and Trailer Set**
(1) Contains 165 Vauxhall PA Cresta (Red/Cream) and 135 GP Dinghy (Grey/White/Lemon) .....................**£200-225**
(2) Contains 270 Ford Zephyr 6 (Red) and 135 GP Dinghy (Red/White/Blue)................................**£300-400**
**NB** The price of a set depends on the rarity of the contents.

**259**
**Garage Set**   A constructional set ...............................................**£35-45**

**269**
**1965**
**Ford Zephyr and Caravan**
Contains 270 Ford Zephyr 6 (Red) plus 264 Caravan............**£400-500**

**308**
**1965**
**Land Rover and Trailer**
Green bodywork, Fawn cover......................................**£150-250**

**406**
**1966**
**Hillman Minx and Dinghy**
Contains 287 Hillman Minx and 135 GP Dinghy and trailer..**£150-250**

**701**
**'His, Her's, Junior's' Set**
219 Austin-Healey Sprite, 267 MG 1100, 280 Vauxhall Cresta, in 'window' box ...................................**£400-500**

**702**
**Gift Set 702**   270 Zephyr Six, 274 Morris 1100 and canoe, 286 Austin 1800 and 135 Dinghy ................................**£400-500**

**702(a)**
**Gift Set 702**   195 VW Rally, 217 Jaguar 'S' type, 261 Volvo P1800, 287 Hillman Minx...................................**£600-800**

**703**
**Gift Set 703**   Red Zephyr 6, Light Blue Morris 1100 with kayak and paddle, Lemon Humber Super Snipe, Dinghy on Trailer.............................................**£500-750**

**MG1**
**1966**
**'Magicar Motoring' Set**
501 Jaguar Mk.10 and 502 Rolls-Royce, roadway sections and traffic cones .....................**£200-250**

**MG2**
**'Magicar Motoring' Set**
503 Bentley S3 and 504 Ferrari Superfast, roadway sections and traffic cones .....................**£200-250**

**MG3**
**'Batman' Magicar Set (904)**
Batmobile with Batman and Robin figures .........................**£200-300**

**---**
**'Tric-Trac Devil Set' (Magicar)**
Two cars plus unapplied decal sheets ....................................**£200-250**

**?**
**Gift Set** originally from 'United Dairies' milkmen.
Jaguar 'S' Type, Zephyr 6, Morris 1100 with Kayak/paddle and a Vauxhall Cresta PB.........................................**£500-750**

---

# 'Tommy Spot' Gift Sets

All include a building kit and Tommy Spot figure.

**801** **'Home with Tommy Spot'** .......................287 Hillman Minx (with Mr Spot), 270 Ford Zephyr Six with driver, pictorial stand ........................**£450-500**
**802** **'Cops 'n' Robbers with Tommy Spot'** ....309 BBC-TV 'Z-Car' with driver and criminal, 276 Jaguar and driver, pictorial stand ................**£450-500**
**803** **'Superville Garage with Tommy Spot'** ..286 Austin 1800 with driver, 279 MG Midget, two garage workers, pictorial stand .............**£450-500**
**804** **'Sailing with Tommy Spot'**.....................280 Vauxhall PB Cresta and sailing dinghy with Tommy and Mr Spot, pictorial stand.................**£450-500**
**805** **'Fire with Tommy Spot'** ..........................316 Fire Dept Land Rover and trailer, two firefighters, pictorial stand .............................**£700-900**
**806** **'Royal Occasion with Tommy Spot'**.......260 Royal Rolls-Royce with chauffeur and royal passengers, 6 guardsmen, pictorial stand ..................**£1,200-1,500**
**807** **'Pit stop with Tommy Spot'** ...................Mercedes-Benz 230 SL and Jaguar 'S', two racing drivers, pictorial stand ......................**£1,200-1,500**
**808** **'Motorway Rescue with Tommy Spot'** ...402 'Crash Service' Land Rover and mechanic, A.A. van and man, pictorial stand ...................**£600-700**

# Spot-On 'Cotswold Village' series

Cotswold Village Series No.5, Antiques Shop

The 'Cotswold Village' items are rare and it is suggested that larger buildings (church, shop, etc) are likely to be in the region of **£125 - £150**, while smaller items might be anything from **£10 - £50** depending on size, complexity, etc.

These price levels can only be applied to pristine items in perfect original boxes.

| | | | |
|---|---|---|---|
| 1 | School | 10 | Farm House |
| 2a | Haystack | 11 | Manor House **£175-225** |
| 3 | 'Cornerstones' Cottage | 12 | Post Office |
| 4 | 'Fourways' Cottage | 13 | Church |
| 4b | 'The Cot' Cottage | 14 | Forge |
| 5 | Antiques Shop | 15 | Memorial Stone |
| 6 | General Store | 16 | Water Well |
| 7 | Bourton Town Hall | 16a | Stocks |
| 8 | Barn | - | Set of Trees |
| 9 | 'The King's Head' Public House | - | Bridge Sides |

# Catalogues, Leaflets and Pictures

| Issued | Publication details | Market Price Range |
|---|---|---|
| 1959 | **Early issue**  Red cover featuring a Target plus the dividers and diagram of Rolls Royce 'LTP 103'. Wording: '1/42' and 'SPOT-ON MODELS BY TRI-ANG'. Contains 8 pages | **£40-50** |
| 1959 | **'1st Edition'**  Village scene with Spot-On buildings and models, 'Tri-ang' logo in bright red, '6d', 'dividers' mark, 'SCALE 1/42'. Thick numbered pages with superb pictures | **£40-50** |
| 1960 | **'2nd Edition'**  As 1st Edition but 'Tri-ang' logo in maroon and pages not numbered | **£30-40** |
| 1961 | **'3rd Edition'**  **'100M/C.P.C./6.61'**.  Same as 2nd Edition | **£25-35** |
| 1963 | **'4th Edition'**  **'5a7383/DP'**  Royal Rolls-Royce on cover, '3d', Page 19 shows the new Presentation Sets 5-10 and 14 | **£20-30** |
| 1964 | **'5th Edition'**  Blue Austin 1800 (286) on cover, '2d', concertina type leaflet featuring new type of Black/Red window boxes for Gift Sets and single models | **£20-£30** |
| 1965 | **'6th Edition'**  Cover again features 286 Austin 1800 plus 289 Morris Minor, '2d', concertina type leaflet which includes 'Tommy Spot' and 'Magicar' listings and pictures | **£20-30** |
| 1966 | **'7th Edition'**  Booklet type featuring 407 Mercedes 230 SL and 287 Hillman Minx, '6d', 'Tommy Spot' featured with 'Royal Occasion' set and Car Spotters guide | **£20-30** |

## Leaflets and Model Pictures

The early 'blue boxes' for cars and small commercial vehicles and the early card boxes for the large commercial vehicles contained a model picture and a yellow / blue / white leaflet listing the models available. Prices of model picture cards can vary depending on the rarity of the model itself within a price range from **£5** to **£25**.
Spot-On 'Picture wallets' are to be found at **£15-20**.
It should be noted that no 'blue box' model or early large commercial boxed model is complete without the model picture.
Leaflets are not uncommon and may be obtained for, say, **£3-5**.

## Trade Display Material

Electric revolving Trade Display Unit.....**£300-400**
Glass shop-sign with 'SPOT-ON MODELS' in red/black/yellow design, 25 inches long .....**£150-200**

## Collector's Lapel Badge

'Spot-On by Tri-ang', Blue/Gold/Red, 2.5cm .....**£80-100**

Spot-On

E.R.F. Lorries

with different styles of boxes and showing various inserts, Collector Cards, etc.

When Tri-ang took over the production of Dinky Toys in 1967 they stopped production of Spot-On Models in the United Kingdom. Fourteen models were subsequently produced by the Tri-ang Pedigree company of New Zealand from the original dies sent out from the U.K.

New Zealand production lasted just two years and ceased in 1969 / 70. The New Zealand model reference numbers were different to their UK counterparts as listed in the Spot-On 7th Edition catalogue. Extras such as roof racks and luggage were not included with NZ issues and the models were housed in New Zealand yellow cellophane 'window' boxes. The following listing first appeared in 'Mini Cars' ('The News Sheet for Caledonian Autominologists'), dated September 1972 and was prepared by Eric Brockie in New Zealand. Thanks are due to James McLachlan (Club Secretary) for his kind permission to reproduce the listing.

| UK no. | NZ no. | Model name | Difference from UK version | NZ colour | Market Price Range |
|---|---|---|---|---|---|
| 289 | 101 | Morris Minor 1000 | Not manufactured in New Zealand | - | NPP |
| 219 | 102 | Austin-Healey Sprite | Colour only | White body, Red seats | £300-400 |
| 281 | 103 | MG Midget | No Policeman included | Dark Green or Red, White seats | £300-400 |
| 404 | 104 | Morris Mini Van | No 'Shell' logo, ladder or mechanism | Yellow | £200-300 |
| 267 | 105 | MG 1100 | Single colour only | Green | £150-200 |
| 262 | 106 | Morris 1100 | Same as UK issue | Blue | £150-200 |
| 287/406 | 107 | Hillman Minx | No roof rack or dinghy | Green | £150-200 |
| 280 | 108 | Vauxhall Cresta | Single colour only | Blue | £150-200 |
| 276 | 109 | Jaguar 'S' type | Same as UK issue | Metallic Blue | £200-300 |
| 286 | 110 | Austin 1800 | No lady driver or schoolboy | Light Brown or Mauve, White seats | £200-300 |
| 270 | 111 | Ford Zephyr 6 | Same as UK issue | White | £150-200 |
| 308 | 112 | Land Rover | No trailer included | Olive Green body, Pale Green tilt | £150-200 |
| 407 | 114 | Mercedes-Benz 230 SL | Not manufactured in New Zealand | - | NPP |
| 401 | 115 | Volkswagen Variant | No roof rack or skis | Dark Blue, Red int., White hatchback | £200-300 |
| 279 | 116 | MG PB Midget | Same as UK issue | Blue, Black, Red seats | £200-300 |
| 265 | 117 | 'TONIBELL' Ice Cream Van | Same as UK issue | Turquoise | £300-400 |
| 402 | 118 | Crash Service Land Rover | Same as UK issue | Orange, Blue | £200-300 |
| 316 | 119 | Fire Dept Land Rover | No Firemen | Red | £200-300 |
| 415 | 120 | RAF Land Rover | Not manufactured in New Zealand | - | NPP |

## TRI-ANG SPOT-ON SELECTED AUCTION RESULTS 2005 — 2007

### Vectis Auctions Ltd.
Fleck Way, Thornaby,
Stockton -on-Tees TS17 9JZ
Abbreviations: M = Mint, NM = Near Mint, EP = Excellent Plus,
E = Excellent, GP = Good Plus, G = Good, F = Fair

**SPOT-ON CARS**
**102 Bentley Saloon.** TT Light Blue/Silver, Red seats, NM in G box £190
**104 MGA Sports Car.** Pale Blue, Cream seats, M in E box £200
**104 MGA Sports Car.** Pink with Grey seats, EP in G box with ink stain £200
**105 Austin Healey.** Metallic Blue, Cream interior, M in E box £220
**105 Austin Healey.** Pale Blue, Grey seats, GP - E in G box £140
**105 Austin Healey.** Metallic Blue, Cream side panels,
pale yellow seats, L/CCC, NM in G box £680
**105 Austin Healey.** Red with Cream side panels, Cream seats,
L/CCC, M in G box £620
**107 Jaguar XKSS.** British Racing Green body, Grey seats, E in GP box £160
**108 Triumph TR3.** Olive Green, Cream seats, L/CCC, M in GP- E box £190
**108 Triumph TR3.** Cream, Brown seats, Orange PSW,
L/CCC, EP in E box £180
**112 Jensen 541.** Yellow/Black, EP in E box £110
**112 Jensen 541.** Pale Blue, ed seats, L/CCC, GP - E in GP box £130
**112 Jensen 541.** Lilac, Cream seats, L/CCC, GP - E in Fair box £100
**112 Jensen 541.** Pale Green, Cream seats, L/CCC, EP in GP box £130
**113 Aston Martin DB.** Lilac, Blue seats, L/CCC, EP in G box £110
**113 Aston Martin DB.** Red body and seas, L/CCC, GP - E in G box £200
**113 Aston Martin DB.** Light Blue, Cream seats,
L/CCC, GP - E in Fair box £130
**113 Aston Martin DB.** Pale Grey, Cream seats, L/CCC, EP in GP box £160
**113 Aston Martin DB.** Red body, Cream seats, L/CCC NM in GP box £320
**114 Jaguar 3.4 Saloon.** Pale blue, Cream seats, L/CCC, E in G box £100

**114 Jaguar 3.4 Saloon.** Lilac, Cream seats, L/CCC, NM in G box £180
**114 Jaguar 3.4 Saloon.** Light Grey, Red Seats, L/CCC, GP including box £130
**114 Jaguar 3.4 Saloon.** All Salmon Pink, Cream seats, CCC,
E in F Picture box £130
**118 BMW Isetta.** Red, Cream seats, L/CCC, M in E box £260
**118 BMW Isetta.** Mid Grey, Cream seats, L/CCC, EP in G - GP box £160
**118 BMW Isetta.** Turquoise, White seats, CCC, NM in GP box £160
**118 BMW Isetta.** Dark Sea Green, mid-Blue seats, L/CCC, M in E box £180
**119 Meadows Frisky.** Orange/Grey, Cream seats, CCC, GP in F box £110
**119 Meadows Frisky.** Blue, Grey hood, Cream seats, CCC, M in G box £180
**120 Fiat Multipla.** Sea Green, Cream seats, CCC, E in Fair box £140
**131 Goggomobile.** Mid Blue, Black hood, Cream seats, CCC, GP, E box £160
**154 Austin A40.** Blue, White seats, L/CCC, EP in G box £110
**154 Austin A40.** White, Cream seats, L/CCC, GP - E in GP box £100
**Austin A60 Cambridge.** Red, Pale Grey seats, LR, skis/sticks,
EP in G picture box £100
**185 Fiat 500.** Grey body, Cream seats, CCC, EP in E box £130
**185 Fiat 500.** Light Blue, Cream seats, CCC, NM in E box £90
**185 Fiat 500.** Red, Cream seat, CCC, M in G box £130
**191 Sunbeam Alpine.** Bright Green, White seats, CCC, E in G - GP box £90
**191 Sunbeam Alpine.** Turquoise, Cream seats, CCC, EP in G box £100
**191 Sunbeam Alpine.** Light Blue, Cream seats, CCC, NM in G box £140
**191 Sunbeam Alpine.** Red, White hood,/seats, L/CCC, EP in G box £110
**191 Sunbeam Alpine.** Met' Green, Black Hood, Cream seats,
L/CCC, EP in F box £90
**193 NSU Prinz.** Orange body, Cream seats, NM in EP box £110
**193 NSU Prinz.** Turquoise, White seats, CCC, GP in G box £70
**218 Jaguar Mk. 10.** Dk. Green, Cream seats, L/CCC, EP in E picture box £360
**218 Jaguar Mk. 10.** Light Blue, Mid Blue seats, figure,
NM in G picture box £130
**219 Austin Healey Sprite.** Pale Blue, Red seats, driver,

NM in EP window box ........................................... **£150**

**229 Lambretta Scooter**. Blue with white side panels, black seat,
NM in GP box........................................................ **£170**

**229 Lambretta Scooter**. Blue, red panels, black seat, NM in F box.. **£160**

**256 Jaguar 'Police' Car**. White, Cream seats, 2 x figures, roof box with
aerial, L/CCC, Excellent Plus in Good all card picture box ............... **£360**

**256 Jaguar 'Police' Car**. Black, Cream seats, 2 x figures, roof box with
aerial, L/CCC, Excellent Plus, in Fair all card box ............... **£240**

**259 Ford Consul Classic**. Grey, Cream seats, L/CCC, GP in G picture box **£80**

**260 Rolls Royce Phantom V**. Maroon, Pale Blue interior,
4 x figures inc. Queen and Price Phillip. Mint in EP Perspex box ....... **£520**

**261 Volvo P1800**. Turquoise, White seats, leaflet, GP in F picture box........ **£70**

**261 Volvo P1800**. Red, Grey seats, M in EP window box ......................... **£100**

**262 Morris 1100**. Dark Grey, Red seats, L/CCC, M in GP-E picture box. **£130**

**264 Tourist Caravan**. Yellow with White roof, M in E box...................... **£140**

**270 Ford Zephyr 6**. Red, Grey seats, 2 x figures,
GP in F scarce picture box.............................................. **£300**

**270 Ford Zephyr 6**. Pale Blue, Red seats, 2 x figures,
E in F scarce picture box .............................................. **£220**

**270 Ford Zephyr 6**. Greyish Green, Red seats, M in NM box................. **£170**

**274 Morris 1100 with Canoe**. Dark Blue, Grey seats,
NM, in GP-E window box ............................................... **£110**

**274 Morris 1100 with Canoe**. Red, Grey seats,
E, tray NM in GP - E window box .................................. **£100**

**274 Morris 1100 with Canoe**. Dark Green, Grey seats,
Mint, in GP-E window box ........................................... **£200**

**276 Jaguar 'S' Type**. Metallic Brown, Red seats, 2 x figures,
NM in E window box ..................................................... **£130**

**276 Jaguar 'S' Type**. Metallic Blue, Red seats, 2 x figures,
GP in GP window box .................................................... **£100**

**278 Mercedes-Benz**. Blue body, Red seats, M in GP window box ............ **£160**

**Vauxhall Cresta**. Dk. Blue, Cream roof, Red seats, NM in EP window box **£90**

**Vauxhall Cresta**. Cream, Red roof and seats, NM in G window box .......... **£90**

**281 MG Midget Mk.II**. Red, White seats, driver/policeman,
E in G window box ....................................................... **£120**

**286 Austin 1800**. Dark Blue, Red seats, 2 x figures, EP in G window box. **£150**

**286 Austin 1800**. Red, Grey seats, 2 x figures, NM in E window box ....... **£120**

**287 Hillman Minx**. Red, Grey seats, luggage rack,
EP, tray E in G window box ........................................... **£150**

**287 Hillman Minx**. Pale Green, red seats, no luggage rack,
M, tray E in G window box ............................................ **£80**

**306 Humber Super Snipe**. Blue Red seats, 2 x figures, luggage rack,
M in G window box ...................................................... **£80**

**309 Ford Zephyr 6**. 'Z Cars', White, Red seats, M in GP box .................. **£190**

**405 Vauxhall Cresta**. 'BEA', Grey, red seats, figure,
NM, tray GP in G window box ....................................... **£110**

**406 Hillman Minx and Dinghy**. Greyish Green, Red seats,
NM - M in E box .......................................................... **£90**

**COMMERCIAL VEHICLES** Unless stated differently all models in lift off
lid boxes with inner packaging.

**CB106 10-ton Trailer**. Red with Silver cast hubs, EP-NM in G box.......... **£190**

**106A/OC Austin Articulated Flatbed**.
'The British Motor Corporation Ltd', Dark Blue, Silver back, cast hubs.
Excellent including Turquoise, Grey seats, MGA sports car in
crate box, lift-off lid box. CCC .......................................... **£300**

**106A/1 Austin Artic. Dropside Lorry**. Light Blue cab and trailer,
black chassis, cast hubs, GP in G lift off lid box .................................. **£180**

**106A/1C Austin Lorry with Crate load**. Turquoise cab and trailer, black
chassis, cast hubs, 6 black plastic crates, G in Fair lift-off lid box .......... **£160**

**109/2P ERF 68G 8 wheel Flatbed with Plank Load**. Yellow cab and back,
Black chassis, Cream interior, cast hubs, GP-E, inner card tray Good.
G-GP lift-off lid box, L/CCC ............................................ **£950**

**109/2P ERF 68G 8 wheel Flatbed with Plank Load**.
Turquoise cab and back, Black cab roof, Grey chassis, cream seats,
E in G lift-off lid box, CCC........................................... **£380**

**109/2 ERF 68G 8Wheel Flatbed Truck**. Turquoise cab and back,
Silver chassis Cream interior, cast hubs, E in G - GP lift-off lid box... **£340**

**109/3B ERF 68G Dropside Lorry**. Turquoise, Silver inner back and
chassis, Cream interior, Red steering wheels, E in G box, CCC .......... **£300**

**109/3 ERF 68G Dropside Lorry**. Lemon, Dark Grey cab roof,
Silver inner back and chassis, Cream seats, EP in G box with leaflet.. **£400**

**109/3 ERF 68G Dropside Lorry**. Turquoise, Silver inner back and
chassis, red steering wheel, E in G box with leaflet ...................... **£260**

**109/3 AEC Mammoth Major 8 Lorry**. Dark Red cab and back,
Black cab roof, Silver chassis, GP-E in G-GP lift-off lid box, L/CCC **£320**

**109/3 AEC Mammoth 'British Road Services'**.
Strawberry Red, Black roof, Cream inner back, Silver chassis,
GP-E in G lift-off lid box, CCC. ..................................... **£460**

**110/3D AEC Mammoth Major 8 Lorry**. Red with Silver inner back and
chassis, Cream seats, red steering wheel, EP in G-GP box, CCC ........ **£440**

**110/3D AEC Mammoth Major 8 Lorry**. Yellow Cab and back,
Dark Grey chassis, Cream seats, Black SW, E-EP in G box, L/CCC... **£560**

**110/3D AEC Mammoth Major 8 Lorry**. Yellow cab/back,
Lt. Grey chassis, Cream seats, Black SW, EP in G-GP box, L/CCC.... **£900**

**110/4 AEC Tanker 'Shell BP'**. 'Petroleum Products', Green cab,
Red plastic tank, Black chassis and ladders, EP in G wrong box......... **£280**

**111A/OT Ford Thames Artic. with Log Load**. Pale Blue Cab/Trailer,
Black chassis, Cream interior, cast hubs, EP in G box, L/CCC .......... **£260**

**111A/1S Ford Thames Truck and Trailer**. Green with Cream interior and
inner back, black chassis, cast hubs, NM in GP box, L/CCC.............. **£620**

**111A/1S Ford Thames Truck and Trailer**. Light Blue Cab/trailer,
Black chassis, Silver trailer bed, red steering wheel, cast hubs,
cream interior, Near Mint in G-GP lift-off lid box............................ **£220**

**111A/1S Ford Thames Truck and Trailer**. Strawberry Red lower cab and
trailer, Cream upper cab and inside of trailer, purple cab interior,
cast hubs, L/CCC, E in G-GP lift-off lid box ................................ **£420**

**111A/OG Ford Thames Trader / Garage Kit**. Pale Blue, Black chassis,
cream interior, cast hubs, Excellent in GP lift-off lid box with L/CCC **£360**

**116 Caterpillar D9 Bulldozer**. Yellow with Silver blade,
Black rubber tracks, L/CCC, Excellent Plus in GP-E lift-up lid box **£1,100**

**122  Milk Float. 'UNITED DAIRIES'**, NM in GP picture box................. **£170**

**158A/2 Bedford 'S' Type 'Shell BP'**. Green/Black cab, Red tank,
cast hubs, L/CCC, Excellent Plus, inner tray and lift-off lid box E...... **£520**

**161 LWB Land Rover**. Grey, White seats and roof, CCC, E in G box....... **£120**

**210/1 Morris Mini Van**. 'Royal Mail', NM in GP picture  box .............. **£180**

**210/2 Morris Mini Van**. 'Post Office', EP in E picture box..................... **£190**

**265 Ice Cream Van**. 'Tonibell', figure, NM in E box............................... **£300**

**271 'Express Dairy' Van**. Dark Blue, White interior and crates, L/CCC,
NM in GP - E carded picture box .................................... **£480**

**273 Commer Van**. 'Security Express', dark Green, Grey interior,
cast hubs, figure, NM-M in GP window box .................................. **£130**

**GIFT SETS**

**No. 0 Presentation Set**. Models GP-NM in E-EP lift-off lid box.
MGA - Turquoise, White seats, Ford Zodiac - Pale Green, Cream seats,
Aston Martin - Lilac, Pale Blue seats,
Rolls Royce Wraith - Silver/Green, cream seats............................ **£480**

**No. 2 Presentation Set**. As per Catalogue:
Models NM - M in E lift-off lid box ............................. **£580**

**No. 4a Presentation Set**. Models:  GP-NM in G-GP lift-off lid box.
Jaguar XKSS - Green, Grey seats, MGA Sports Car - Orangey Red,
Cream seats, Austin Healey - Lemon, Grey seats,
Triumph TR3 - Turquoise, Grey seats ............................ **£360**

**212 Car and Dinghy Set**. Red/Cream Vauxhall, Red/White/Blue Dinghy,
Both NM in G window box ........................................... **£190**

**212 Car and Dinghy Set**. Orangey Red Ford Zephyr 6,
Grey/ White/ Lemon Dinghy, both M in G window box ..................... **£180**

**269 Gift Set**. Red/Grey Ford Zephyr 6, figure and Cream Caravan with
White roof, GP-E in G-GP window box ........................... **£460**

**308 Land Rover and Trailer Set**. Dark Brown, Green canopy,
Grey interior and Brown/Black trailer, NM-M in GP window box ...... **£160**

**406 Hillman Minx and Dinghy**. Greyish-Green, Red seats, luggage rack,
plus Red, Blue and White Dinghy, NM-M in G window box (RC) ..... **£190**

**701 'His, Hers and Juniors' Set**. Austin Healey - Red, White seats,
Vauxhall Cresta - Navy Blue/Cream, red seats, MG1100 - Beige/Cream,
Red seats, NM-M in G-GP window box ............................ **£620**

**702a Gift Set**. Jaguar S type- Met. Blue, Red seats, Austin 1800 - Sea Blue,
Red seats, Ford Zephyr 6 - Red, Grey seats, Morris 1100 - Pale blue,
Red seats and canoe, EP to Mint in Good to GP lift-off lid box .......... **£360**

**801 'Home with Tommy Spot'**. Ford Zephyr 6 - Red, Grey seats,
Hillman Minx - Greyish Green, red seats, M in G window box ......... **£320**

**803 'Service Tommy Spot'**. Austin 1800 - Blue, Red seats,
MG Midget - Red, White seats, M in G-GP window box ................... **£320**

**804 'Sailing with Tommy Spot'**. Vauxhall Cresta - Cream/Red, Red seats,
Dinghy on Trailer - Blue/White/Lemon, Mint in GP window box ...... **£380**

**805 'Fire Tommy Spot'**. Land Rover 'Fire Dept' with trailer, figures,
E - M in GP window box (RC) ....................................... **£360**

**806 Royal Occasion**. Model NM, internal stand and figures - EP,
outer box - Good Plus............................................... **£1,100**

**The 'Cotswold Village' Series**

**No, 4 Fourways Cottage**. Excellent Plus in Good window box................. **£120**

**No. 4b The Cot Cottage**. Excellent Plus in Good Plus window box .......... **£120**

**No. 5 Antique Shop**. Excellent Plus in Good Plus window box................. **£120**

**No. 7 Bourton Town Hall**. Excellent in Good - Good Plus window box .... **£120**

**No. 11 The Manor House**. Good Plus inc. window box - scarce issue ........ **£160**

**No. 12 Post Office**. Excellent Plus in Good - Good Plus window box........ **£120**

**No. 14 The Forge**. Excellent Plus in Good - Good Plus window box......... **£100**

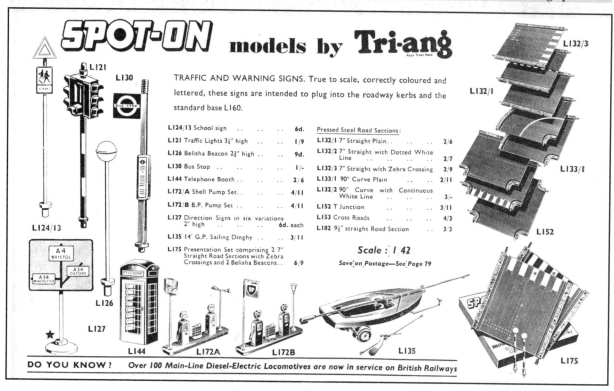

Contemporary advertisements for Tri-ang Spot-On models in the 'Eagle' comic. (ILLUSTRATION SUPPLIED BY JOHN RAMSAY)

Spot-On 120 Fiat Multipla.
PHOTO: VECTIS AUCTIONS LTD.

Many toys and models exist about which we know very little. The 1940s in particular saw a proliferation of small manufacturers (often only a one-man operation in a North London shed). In this post-wartime period the established manufacturers were engaged in an export drive that meant shortages of products at home. Not surprisingly, enterprising ex-servicemen and others turned their hands to toy production on a scale that they could manage. Their range was small (sometimes only one product) and they were often in business for only a year or two.

One outcome of this is that some toys and models discovered in attics or at swapmeets present us with a puzzle. Who made the item? When were they in production? Where was the maker's workshop? Very often there is no information at all on the product or simply a statement to the fact that it was 'Made in England'. Identification is sometimes diffcult – but is it impossible?

Since the 11th Edition was published, some very interesting additional information has been obtained and we are delighted to be able to pass on the details below. However, our lists below are far from complete and we do still require your help, so if you have any information on any of the manufacturers mentioned, please write to The Editor.

| | | | | | |
|---|---|---|---|---|---|
| Arbur | Condon | Johillco | Knight | Salco | Toby |
| Baxtoys | W.H.Cornelius | John Hill & Co. | Louis Marx | Scaledown | Toy Products |
| Betal | Cursor | Jolly Roger | Mafwo | Slikka | Tractoys |
| BMC | Denzil Skinner | Kenbo | Millbo | Sundaw | Trent Products |
| Bren L Toys | Eaglewall Plastics | Kenbro | Millbro | Tal Developments | Tudor Rose |
| Cherilea | Empro | Kemlow | Model Toys | Teddy Toys | Wardie |
| City Toys | Goody Toys | Kitmaster | Moultoys Ltd | Industries | |

**Astra Pharos Co.** (Shepherds Bush, London)
**Heavy 12 inch Howitzer**. Military Green, 11" long, 3 wooden shells, green lift-off lid box............................. **£100-125**
**Pom Pom Gun**. WWII Anti-aircraft style naval/land based weapon,............ **£100-125**
**WWII Mobile Unit**. Anti-Aircraft Gun + Searchlight Unit on trolley, boxed........ **£100-125**

**Automec**
**Bedford Flat Truck**. Orange cab/chassis, pale yellow back, red hubs ....................... **£50-75**
**Mobile Artillery Unit**. Bedford Military Truck, limber and field gun, all card pictorial display box. ........................... **£350-450**

**Betal**
**Saloon Car**. Clockwork motor in some ... **£15-20**
**Large Tinplate Trolleybus**. Red, Cream, silver poles, driver, CW, (28 cms) ........ **£250-350**
**AEC 'Q' type Bus with Lights.** Red/Cream/Silver, balloon tyres.......... **£200-300**

**BHL (British Home Life)**
**First Traffic Set**. Motorcycle Policeman and die-cast Road Signs, red box ............ **£60-80**

**Bradcars** (c1950-55)
Bradshaws Model Products. 1:75 scale. One-piece castings, no interiors. Boxed models:
**Austin A30, Riley 1.5 litre, Austin 7, Morris 6.**

**Brighton Manufacturing Co.**
**World's Warships Series Set 12.** Fifteen cast ships inc. a Hospital ship, boxed..... **£75-100**

**Brimtoy** (diecast issues)
1948-50 Vauxhall Saloon. Yellow body, cast wheels, plain card box with picture ...... **£100-150**

**Cherilea**
**Set 1001 'Spacemen'**. With rocket, 3 robots, 6 spacemen, 2 space animals. **£500-600**

**Condon**
These were based on the same chassis casting:
**Dumper Truck**, various colours .............. **£20-30**
**Site Crane**, various colours..................... **£20-30**
**Elevator Loader**, various colours........... **£20-30**

**Denzil Skinner**
**Nuffield Universal Tractor**. Made for the Morris Motors Agricultural Division.... **£300-500**

**Excella**
**Three Pigs' Houses**, with Pigs. House of Sticks, House of Bricks, House of Straw with Pigs

playing Flute, Violin and standing with trowel, indivual boxes......**As a set: £5,000-7,000**
**Big Bad Wolf and Three Pigs**.
Tied in box with lift-off lid ............ **£2,500-3,000**

**Gaiety Toys** (late 1940s)
Castle Art Products Ltd., Birmingham. Models may be found painted in various colours, often chromed, sometimes motorised. Models in boxes are rare. Products known:
**Morgan 3-wheel Sports Car**, 4.75in. ..... **£70-90**
**Racing Car**, single driver, 5in. long ........ **£30-40**
**Racing Car**, driver/co-driver, 4in. long ... **£30-40**
**Racing Car**, single driver, 3.25in. long ... **£20-30**
**Fire Engine**................................................NGPP

**Gilco**
**No. 1 Traffic Sign Set**. Ten items ............ **£30-40**
**No. 3 Traffic Signs Set**. Ten signs .......... **£70-90**
**No. 4 Traffic Sign Set**. Contains 24 items inc. Road Signs, Traffic Lights, Telegraph Poles, 2 Belisha Beacons. Pictorial card box. ... **£80-100**

**John Hill & Co. (Johilco)**
**Roman Gladiator Set**: Gold Chariot and Charioteer, 2 horses, 5 Centurion Gladiators + Officer in pale cream toga. Boxed........ **£125-150**
**Roman Chariot**: Gold Chariot/Charioteer, 2 horses, 2 Roman Soldiers ................... **£80-100**
**Coronation** (1935 Jubilee) **Coach Set**, 4 white horses + 2 riders, 6 'Beefeaters', 6 Footmen. The coach is 23cm long and contains figures of King George V & Queen Mary. Blue box marked 'Jubilee' ..........................NGPP
**Jubilee Coach**, King George V and Queen Mary in a 'coronation'-style coach with 4 horses, 2 riders, 6 mounted Life Guards, 6 Beefeaters, 6 footmen, blue box .............NGPP
**Mack Mail Van**. Red, Grey wheels ........ **£70-90**
**Racing Car**. Red ...................................... **£40-50**
**Tank**. Light Khaki, rubber tracks ........ **£100-125**
**Mack Gun Lorry**. Khaki / Black ..........**£90-110**
**Searchlight Lorry**. Khaki / Black ..........**£90-110**
**Mack Stake Truck**. Green / Yellow ........ **£40-50**
**Mack Concrete Truck**. Mustard Yellow . **£30-40**
**Ford 'T' Truck**. Dk. Blue, Gold screen..... **£60-70**
**Fargo Single Deck Coach**. Lt. Green...... **£30-40**
**'Millers' Series Set**. Windmill, Miller, Labourer with sack, Barrow man, Wheelbarrow, full and half full sacks corn bin, two mice .................................. **£150-200**
**Dirt Track Bike and Rider**. Pre-war, unpainted bike, Brown/Black rider........... **£70-90**
**Police Motorcycle and Sidecar**. Unpainted cycle, Blue sidecar, rider/passenger, white tyres............................................. **£100-125**
**Street Gas Lamp Set**. Gas Lamp,

Lamp Cleaner and Ladder, Box............ **£175-225**
**Father Christmas**.
65mm tall figure with toy sack ............ **£100-130**
**R.N.L.I. figures.** Three lifeboat men plus pincushion Lifeboat...................... **£100-125**

**Jolly Roger**
Made c1946/7 by Tremo Mouldings, Cardiff.
**Racing Car** (boxed) ...................................NGPP
**Saloon Car** (boxed) (picture opposite) ......NGPP

**Kay**
**'Safety First' Traffic Set**, boxed.
Two Petrol Pumps/Attendant, Signs ......... **£60-80**

**Kembo**
**Articulated Lorry**. Heavy lorry cab (tinplate base), open semi-trailer with curved front board and 'KEMBO TRANSPORT' paper labels. Minic-style tinplate wheels, rubber tyres. **£40-50**
**Saloon Car** Cast wheels, no base............. **£20-30**

**Kemlow** (1950s)
Kemlow's Diecasting Products Ltd., Wood Green, London. Distributors B.J. Ward Ltd. (trading as 'Wardie Products').
**'PICKFORDS' Removal Van**, 1:60..........NGPP
**Articulated Timber Truck**, 1:50...............NGPP
**Farm Tractor and Trailer**, 1:60 ..............NGPP
**Caravan**. 1:43.........................................NGPP
**Ford Zephyr Mk.I**, 1:43............................NGPP
**Thornycroft Mighty Antar**, 1:43 & 1:60 .NGPP
**Flat Truck**, 1:50 ......................................NGPP
**Armoured Car**, 1:60 ................................NGPP
**Field Gun**, 1:60 ......................................NGPP

**Milton Toys**
Made in India from old Corgi dies.
**Routemaster Bus**. Red, 'MILTON' logo. **£35-45**

**Minitoy**
**Racing Car**. Single piece casting includes cast stub axles for the cast wheels. 90mm. ........NGPP

**Moultoys Products (Great Britain)**
**'RAC' Patrol Cycle and Sidecar**.
Black/Silver cycle, Blue sidecar with 'RAC' cast in sides, patrolman. ........... **£100-125**
**'AA' Patrol Cycle and Sidecar**.
Black/Yellow/Silver bike, Yellow sidecar with 'AA' cast into sides ...................... **£100-125**
**Sports Motorcycle and Sidecar with Rider**.
Red/Yellow/Silver bike, Red/Yellow sidecar, Green/Black rider.................................. **£100-125**

**Sacul**
**'Rob Roy' Set**. This film-related boxed set con-

Photo: John King

ARBUR PRODUCTS          BREN L TOYS          TOBY          JOLLY ROGER

tains Rob Roy in full tartan with sword and an
English Redcoat with sword .......... **£1,000-1,250**
**'Bill and Ben' Set**. TV-related set with
Bill, Ben, Little Weed, 2 flower pots .... **£100-200**
**Andy Pandy Set**. With Andy Pandy,
Looby Loo and Teddy........................... **£200-250**

**Scaledown Models**
 **Fordson Major Roadless Halftrack**
 Blue body .............................................. **£100-125**

**Sentry Box Series**
 Three models in individual 'Sentry Box' boxes:
 Centurion Tank, Big Bedford Military Truck,
 25 pdr Field Gun .............................**each, 15-20**

**Skybirds** (1930s)
 **Army Truck** ......................................... **£80-100**
 **Anti-Aircraft Gun, 4 Gunners**, box ... **£400-500**
 **Lanchester Armoured Car**, box ......... **£500-600**
 **Tanker**, 6 wheels, rubber tyres...................NGPP
 **Military Refuelling Truck**.
 Gloss Olive Green, Extending Arm ...... **£100-125**
 **3A Civil Airline Personnel** Boxed Set
 plus RFC and other figures (12 in total).....NGPP
 **Sound Locator Unit**....................................NGPP
 **'39 Skybird League Challenge Trophy** ...NGPP
 **'40 11b Handley Page Hampden**, box .....NGPP
 **Skybird enamel badges**................. each, NGPP
 **Skybird books** Vols. 1, 2 and 3, etc. each, NGPP

**Sundaw Products** (c1950)
 H130 **Single-deck Motor Bus**. Red body,
 'TRANSPORT SERVICES', rubber wheels. Red/
 white end-flap box (picture) ................ **£250-350**
 H131 **Double-deck Motor Bus**. Green body,

'TRANSPORT SERVICES', rubber wheels.
Green/white end-flap box (picture) ...... **£400-600**
**NB** Similar models were sold by
Vectis Auctions Ltd in December 2000
for **£180** (H130) and **£600** (H131).

**Tractoys Models**
 **Ferguson 25 Tractor** ........................... **£175-200**

**True-to-Type Models** (similar in size to
 Matchbox 1:75s; all have unpainted
 cast wheels)
 **Cable-Layer Truck**.
 Green truck, Grey/Cream cable drum....... **£25-35**
 **Tip Cart Truck**. Red body and tipper ..... **£25-35**
 **Excavator Truck**.
 Green body, Blue back.............................. **£25-35**
 **NB** The three models listed above
 were sold by Vectis Auctions Ltd in
 2000 for **£800**!

**Tremo Models**    See also 'Jolly Roger'.
 **Set No.2 'Famous Fighting Ships
 of the Royal Navy'.**  Contains 5 ships:
 'Resolution', 'Defender', 'Dauntless',
 Grimsby Escort Veassel + 'Shark' Submarine.
 Green presentation box / packing.
 (picture opposite) ................................. **£250-300**

**Tudor Rose**
 **Heavy Duty Farm Tractor** Red /
 Yellow / Silver, Green driver, boxed .... **£100-150**

**Wardie Products Ltd.**
 **Oil Cabinets Set**, boxed.
 Twelve Oil Bins, 'Castrol', 'Shell', etc. **£200-250**

**Garage Personnel Set**, boxed.
Five various figures plus pumps, etc. ... **£300-400**
**'FINA' Petrol Pumps Set**, boxed.
Six blue pumps......................................... **£80-90**
**Traffic Signals Set**, boxed. Ten signs
with Traffic Light and Beacon................. **£30-40**
**Garage Equipment Set**, with 'BP' and
National Benzole' signs, boxed.
Two Pumps, 'DUNLOP' Tyre Rack',
'Castrol' Oil Cabinet ........................... **£200-250**
**Garage Equipment Set**, with 'ESSO' and
'OPEN' Signs, boxed. Three 'ESSO'
Pumps and an 'Essolube' Oil cabinet. ...... **£50-75**

**Wend-al Ltd.**
 **Horse-drawn Farm Vehicles**:
 Rake, Grass Cutter, Reaper................... ea. NGPP
 **Tumbrel Cart**, Red or Green Cart,
 dark brown Horse, driver, blue box ........ **£75-100**
 **Horse-drawn Plough Display Box**.
 Plough, Ploughman, white Horse ......... **£200-300**
 **Farmyard Display Box**. Includes
 Farmer's Wife, Poultry, Animals .......... **£200-300**
 **Farm Set** with Farmer and Land Girl,
 plus ten farmyard animals, boxed......... **£125-150**

**Unknown Diecast Manufacturer**
 (possibly Modern Products)
 **'Cinderella Coach to the Ball'** in lift-off
 lid box with colour wash line drawing.
 Early 1950s, Pink Coach and frame,
 blue spoked wheels, two cast-in footmen,
 four white horses, 6½' long. Box.......... **£175-225**

Gaiety Toys

Morgan 3-wheel
Sports Car
(clockwork).

Gaiety Toys Racer (clockwork) (above) and Gilco Traffic Signs Set (below).　　PHOTOS: VECTIS AUCTIONS LTD.

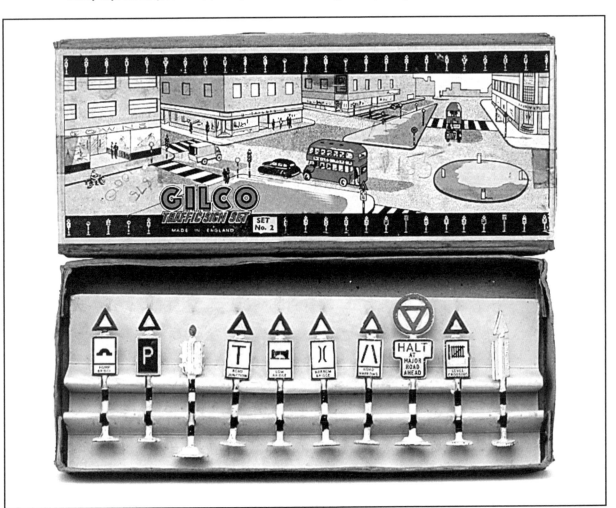

Kemlow items: (above) Artilliery Set; (below) Saloon Car and Caravan, and Armoured Car and Gun. PHOTOS: VECTIS AUCTIONS LTD.

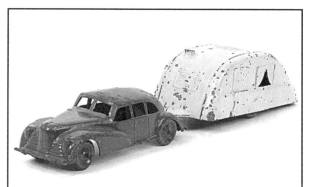

Sentry Box Series military items:

Tank, Army Lorry and Gun.

PHOTOS: VECTIS AUCTIONS LTD.

Kembo Saloon Car (left). The Betal Saloon Car (right) has been observed with and without a clockwork motor. PHOTOGRAPHS: JOHN KING

Above: Wardie set of 'Fina' Petrol Pumps. PHOTO: PETER BRIGHTY

Right: Denzil Skinner 'Nuffield' Tractor. PHOTO: BONHAMS LTD

True-to-Type Models: Cable Layer, Tip Cart and Excavator. PHOTOGRAPH: VECTIS AUCTIONS LTD.

## Vectis Auctions Ltd.
Fleck Way, Thornaby,
Stockton -on-Tees TS17 9JZ
Abbreviations: M = Mint, NM = Near Mint, EP = Excellent Plus,
E = Excellent, GP = Good Plus, G = Good, F = Fair

## BENBROS and ZEBRA TOYS
**10 Jaguar 'E' Type.** Blue, yellow interior,
NM in E Zebra Toys box .......................................... £280
**16 Ready Mixed Concrete Lorry.**
Red, Yellow including hubs, NM in E 'Zebra' box ..................... £130
**30 London Routemaster Bus.**
'Fina Petrol goes a long way', E in GP 'Zebra' box ................. £120
**52 'RAC' Motorcycle Patrol.**
Black, blue plastic rider, NM in E 'Zebra' box, ................... £220

## CHAD VALLEY
**Fordson Major E27N Tractor.**
Blue body Red Wheels., card box , GP in GP box ..................... £320
**Clockwork Double Deck Bus.**
E in F box Green body, cast hubs, with key.......................... £180
**Clockwork Double Deck Bus 1/76 Scale.**
'Wee-Kin' Series Blue body, E in G box ............................. £100

## SHACKLETON
**Foden FG6 Flatbed Lorry.**
Yellow/Red, working order, G - GP in GP box ........................ £500
**FG6 Tipper Lorry.** Blue and Red, G - GP in F box................. £460
**David Brown Tractor.**
Red body (restored), Black Tracks & trim, Excellent.............. £1,200

## HORNBY SPEEDBOATS
**'Racer 1'.** Cream with green engine cover, 9', working order.... £130
**'Racer 2'.**
Blue, white deck, windscreen, 12', working order F in P box... £130
**'Racer 3'.** Cream and Red, GP - E in F box....................... £130
**Limousine Boat No. 4 'Venture'.** Light green,
white deck/cabin roof, 16', working order F-G ...................... £140

## MECCANO OUTFITS
**No. 1 Constructor Car** as Saloon Coupé with hood.
Green with Yellow wings and hood. VG in G box ..................... £280
**No. 1 Constructor Car** as Saloon Coupé with hood.
Blue body, Cream wings and hood, G-VG.............................. £180
**No.2 Constructor Car.**
Red body, Blue cycle wings, E in F box ............................ £950
**No. 2 Constructor Car.**
Blue with Cream wings/running boards, driver, E.................... £580
**No. 2 Constructor Car.**
Green body and hubs, Yellow wings, E in G box ..................... £640
**No. 2A Aeroplane Constructor Outfit.**
Blue and White components, F-GP in F box .......................... £480
**2 Seater Sports Car.**
Blue. Red seats, Cream wings Excellent Plus, Box (GP) .......... £850
**2 Seater Sports Car.**
Cream with Red wings and running boards, E in G box ........... £680

## SUTCLIFFE BOATS
**'Grenville' Model Destroyer.** Grey hull/superstructure,
black lower body with tinplate stand.
GP in G original red card box. ..................................... £620
**'Bluebird II' Speedboat.**
Tri-hulled, Cream, lacks screen, key, EP in VG box................. £340
**'Bluebird' Speedboat with key.**

Single hull, Blue/Cream, gold trim, EP in F-G box .................. £150
**'Sprite' Day Cruiser.** Green hull, Cream deck, M in G box ...... £140
**'Sea Wolf' Submarine.**
Yellow, red deck fittings and bung, key, NM in E box .............. £100
**'Unda Wunda' Submarine.**
Light Blue, Gold effect trim/bung, key, M in E box ................ £120
**'Valiant' Battleship.** Black and Grey, EP in E box .............. £130

## TRI-ANG MINIC MODEL VEHICLES
**4M Sports Saloon.**
Pale Grey, petrol can, plated wheels, luggage rack, GP................ £70
**13M Racing Car.**
Pre-war, Pale Green, No. '6', red exhaust, white tyres, EP ........ £130
**15M Standard Petrol Tanker.**
Blue cab, Red back, Tri-ang transfers, plated wheels, EP........... £170
**17M Vauxhall Tourer.** Post-war, Red and Black,
E in F-G illustrated box .......................................... £140
**18M Vauxhall Town Coupé.**
Green with black wings/running boards, E in VG box .............. £170
**19M Vauxhall Cabriolet.** Post-war, Dark green with black
wings/running boards, VG in F box ................................. £130
**22M Delivery Van.**
'Carter Patterson & Pickfords' red cab, green body, F-G .......... £100
**22M Pre-war Delivery Van.**
Green cab, stone body 'Minic Transport', G......................... £120
**34M Pre-war Tourer.**
Dark Green, 4 passengers, luggage rack, plated wheels, GP ...... £320
**35M Taxi Cab** (see 39M). Blue, Black, plated wheels,
headlamp detached, EP ............................................. £220
**42M Rolls-Royce Sedanca.** Mid Green, White interior,
black roof/wings, cast hubs, G-GP ................................. £200
**48M Breakdown Lorry.**
Green cab with red body and green crane, E in VG box ........... £420
**48M Pre-war Breakdown Lorry.**
Red cab, green body with transfers, G ............................. £160
**48M Forward Control Breakdown Lorry.**
Red cab, Green back, red jib, cast wheels, VG ..................... £190
**52M Single Deck Bus 'Greenline'.**
Green body, 'Dorking', GP-E unboxed................................ £160
**52M Routemaster Single Deck Bus 'Greenline'.**
Green body, 'Dorking', Spot-On tyres, NM.......................... £380
**60M Double-Deck Bus.** All Red, 'London Transport',
'Pedigree Prams' etc., No. '14', E................................. £360
**62ME Pre-war Fire Engine.**
Electric lights, Red/Black, no hoses, E overall ................... £180
**66M 6-wheel Army Lorry.**
Standard cab, open lorry, camouflage finish, E in G box .......... £410
**71M Milk Tanker 'Minic Dairies'.** E in VG illustrated box ... £410
**73M Cable Lorry.**
Red with green trailer, 2 cable drums, VG in F-G box .............. £150
**74M Log Carrier.** Red cab, green trailer,
VG in F illustrated box ........................................... £100
**75M Forward Control Ambulance.**
White, 'LCC' to each side, red/white crosses, NM.................. £190
**81M 'LNER' Van.**
'LNER Express Parcel Service', plated wheels, GP- E .............. £320
**103M Shutter Van.**
Red cab 'Minic Transport' transfers, E in VG illustrated box .... £220
**107M 'British Railways' Van.**
Cream, Deep Red, 'Cheap Tickets and Excursions', EP ........... £170

## *Special Auction Services*
### SUTCLIFFE CLOCKWORK BOATS
'Nautilus' Submarine. Excellent in original Good box............................ £120
'Valiant' Battleship. Very Good - Excellent in Good box ......................... £140

## *Bonhams*
### CHAD VALLEY
Fordson Major E 27N Tractor. Blue, boxed with packing, G-E, box
G................................................................................................................... £456

### MATCHBOX TOYS  - 'MOKO'
Mechanical Drummer Boy. Model G, box F (incomplete) ...................... £456

## *Wallis & Wallis*
### SHACKLETON
Foden FG Truck. Dark Green with Red mudguards, grey chassis,
plus a Dyson Blue and Grey Trailer with red mudguards,
boxed, GC-VGC ..................................................................................... £460
David Brown Trackmaster 30. As per Catalogue,
AF - QGC some damage ........................................................................ £1,300
Foden Tipper. Pale Grey/ Red, GC for age, unboxed ............... £440

### TRI-ANG MINIC SHIPS
M892 SS 'United States' Set. As per Catalogue, complete,
VGC - Mint................................................................................................ £280

### HORNBY SPEEDBOATS
Hornby Racer II. Blue/Cream, good working order, Boxed VGC ........... £200
Hornby Racer III. Blue/Cream, Union flags to bow,
good working order, Boxed, VGC........................................................... £150

This Kembo Articulated Lorry has 'KEMBO' impressed into its tinplate base.

Tremo Models 'Famous Fighting Ships' set

Condon Dump Truck

## Minic Tinplate Model Toys
### An introduction by Mike Richardson

Minic road vehicles and accessories were introduced in June 1935 by the famous English 'Lines Bros.', company of, by then, Morden Road, Merton, Surrey. The name 'Minic' had been registered as a trademark a few months earlier and was derived from the words MINIature Clockwork - which accurately described the toys.

The tinplate material used for the models was always painted and never lithographed as had been the usual method before. Radiator grilles were plated, as were the front wings on many of the models. In a manner similar to the contemporary Dinky Toys, the first issues were not badged as being a model of any particular car or truck, they were just named 'Limousine', 'Tourer', etc. The first car to carry the name of the manufacturer came along in 1936, the Ford £100 Saloon and the Ford Light Van built on the same chassis. These were really delightful little models and over the production run, which continued after 1945, appeared in many colours.

1937 was the year when Minic brought out the named Vauxhall, Rolls-Royce, Bentley and Daimler models. The Vauxhalls were the previous 'Limousine' and others but with the grille and bonnet modified to represent the flutes of the full-size cars. The Rolls, Bentley and Daimler were totally new models and were known as the 'Quality Cars'. These were also offered, with a very few other models, with electric headlights.

Some of the rarest models were produced for only a very short time in 1940-1941 in camouflage colours. Except for one item, these were otherwise normal issue models except for the colouring. The green paint was sprayed all over the assembled model and then the brown shading was brushed on by hand. This of course means that probably no two models are exactly alike. The most desirable is the Balloon Barrage Wagon and Trailer (76) which had a large balloon supplied with it. Once the three pieces of the balloon had been sewn together the toy could not be put back in its box, which has made a boxed version extremely valuable now. Petrol companies were under government control during the war and the petrol was known as 'POOL'. Tri-ang issued both of their petrol tankers, the rigid and the articulated, in grey with 'POOL' on the tanks in white.

When production resumed in 1946 not all of the range was re-introduced. Restrictions on the supply of metal for toys affected all toy factories badly. The colours of paint post-war were generally much harsher in shade — gone were the soft blues, browns, beiges and greys, and in their place were red, green and dark blue. By 1948 over 40 models had been re-issued, but by the middle of 1948 the first plastic Minics had appeared. Plastic of course allowed for more realistic shapes to be made. This applied particularly to private car models as the real car manufacturers had introduced curves into their new models. There were no new tinplate Minic cars after the war.

The generic truck models all featured a 'normal control' cab and bonnet layout left over from the pre-war era until 1950 to 1951.

Minic followed the full-size trucks by changing to the more modern looking 'forward control' configuration. This was known in the US as 'cabover', where the driver sat high up alongside the engine rather than behind it. Both the articulated and the rigid trucks were treated this way, but many people feel that Minic trucks lost a lot of their charm at this time. Motors changed from clockwork to 'push and go' about this time also.

Probably the most attractive models of the post-war era were the Delivery Vans (model nos. 79 - 82) painted in the colours of the four independent railway operators. These were only sold from 1947 to 1949 and were correctly coloured and decalled. They also had advertising posters stuck on the van sides. They were replaced by a similar 'British Railways' van (107) in 1950, but this was only sold for one year before being replaced by the short bonnet version. For some unknown reason the G.W.R. and L.M.S. vans are more difficult to find than the other two. The long bonnet B.R. van is also very scarce.

Pre-war Minic also made a wide range of wooden garages, fire stations and other accessories to go with the models. The construction of these was similar to the Tri-ang dolls' houses and other wooden toys.

1936 saw the appearance of the No. 1 Construction Set which was supplied in a fitted wooden case with a lovely colour poster on the lid showing six models and a parts list. The models were supplied unpainted and unassembled but with all the necessary axles, wheels, grilles, decals etc., even including small pots of paint. A lovely toy and one which could, and probably did, provide some unusual colour combinations once the children, or more likely, their fathers got at them.

As all Minic vehicles can be carefully disassembled by loosening the tin tabs, many odd variations have appeared over the years. One well known batch of G.W.R. vans appeared on the short bonnet van. These were done openly to use up a batch of old shop stock which had got a bit rusty. When they were sold in about 1978 everyone knew they were repaints, but do all collectors around today, some 25 years later, know this? Remember the Construction Set models as well.

Some cars, taxis and trucks have been very carefully 'restored' by skilful operators and have been seen in collections, sold in auctions and at swapmeets. Just take the usual care and do not jump at a 'yes, it's a rare colour variation' without giving it a very good look.

Minic also illustrated proposed models in their advertising which never went into production. Three of these spring to mind immediately, the Trolley Bus (77M), the Coal Lorry (70M) and the long-bodied Ambulance (75M). Some collectors and artisans have made replicas of these to show what they would have looked like. They are lovely pieces in their own right but just remember they were not made by Tri-ang.

**1M**     **Ford £100 Saloon**
1936-41   Blue, green, beige,
          grey, red .................... **£150-200**
**1MCF**   1940-41   Camouflage finish........ **£400-500**
**1M**     1946-49   As pre-war
          civilian version............. **£75-100**

**2M**     **Ford Light Van**
1936-41   Blue, green, beige, red . **£200-300**
1946-49   As pre-war version...... **£100-125**

**3M**     **Ford Royal Mail Van**
1936-41   'Royal Mail'........ **£150-200**
1946-49   'E.R.',
          later 'G.R.' decals ....... **£100-125**

**4M**     **Sports Saloon**
1935-41   ..................................... **£150-200**

**5M**     **Limousine**
1935-41   ..................................... **£200-300**

**6M**     **Cabriolet**
1935-40   ..................................... **£300-400**

**7M**     **Town Coupé**
1935-41   Brown / beige.............. **£300-400**
1946-47   As pre-war version...... **£100-125**

**8M**     **Open Touring Car**
1935-41   Green / cream.............. **£200-300**
1946-47   As pre-war version...... **£100-125**

**9M**     **Streamline Saloon**
1935-41   Based on the Chrysler
          Airflow sedan.............. **£200-300**
1946-51   As pre-war version...... **£100-150**

**10M**     **Delivery Lorry**
1935-41   Green / cream ............. **£150-200**
1946-51   As pre-war version...... **£130-160**

**11M**     **Tractor**
1935-40   See also 83M............... **£200-300**
**11MCF**   1940-41   Camouflage finish........ **£500-600**

**12M**     **Learner's Car**
1936-41   Based on 8M............. **£250-350**
1946-50   Based on 17M ............. **£150-200**

**13M**     **Racing Car**
1936-40   Open cockpit............... **£150-200**
1947-55   Closed cockit.................. **£50-75**

**14M**     **Streamline Sports**
1935-41   Open version of 9M ..... **£250-350**
1946-51   ..................................... **£100-150**

**15M**     **Petrol Tank Lorry / Petrol Tanker**
1936-41   Long bonnet cab,
          'Shell' or 'B P' decals .. **£200-300**
1950-58   Short bonnet cab,
          'Shell' or 'B P' decals .. **£100-150**
**NB**   Some early post-war versions
have Tri-ang triangle decal only.

**15MCF**   **Petrol Tanker**
1940-41   Camouflage finish........ **£700-800**

**16M**     **Caravan**
1936-41   Non-electric................. **£150-200**
1947-55   Non-electric.................... **£50-75**

**17M**     **Vauxhall Tourer**
1937-41   8M but with Vauxhall
          grille and bonnet ......... **£250-350**
1947-55   ..................................... **£150-200**

**18M**     **Vauxhall Town Coupé**
1937-41   Green / beige.............. **£250-350**
1947-55   As pre-war version...... **£150-200**

**19M**     **Vauxhall Cabriolet**
1937-41   Green body,
          plated wings .............. **£300-400**

**19MCF**   1940-41   Camouflage finish........ **£500-700**
**19M**     1947-55   As pre-war version...... **£150-200**

**20M**     **Light Tank**
1935-41   ..................................... **£400-500**

**20MCF**   1940-41   Camouflage finish........ **£500-700**

**21M**     **'TRI-ANG TRANSPORT' Van /**
         **Delivery Van**
1935-41   ..................................... **£400-500**
1946-50   Replaced by 85M
          in 1951 ........................ **£100-125**
          'ATCO' version ...... **£1,000-1,500**

**21MCF**   **Delivery Van**
1940-41   Camouflage finish........ **£600-800**

**22M**     **'Carter Paterson & Co' Van**
1936-41   ..................................... **£350-450**
1946-51   ..................................... **£200-250**
**NB**   Early issues had
'Carter Paterson' decals, later:
'Carter Paterson & Pickfords'.

**23M**     **Tip Lorry**
1935-41   ..................................... **£200-250**
1946-50   Replaced by 86M......... **£100-150**

**24M**     **Luton 'MINIC' Transport Van**
1936-41   Green / red ................... **£400-500**
**24MCF**   1940-41   Camouflage finish....... **£800-1,000**
**24M**     1946-51   As pre-war version...... **£150-200**

**25M**     **Delivery Lorry with Cases**
All issues came with 6 wooden cases.
1936-41   Long bonnet cab .......... **£300-400**
1946-50   Long bonnet cab .......... **£150-200**
1950-56   Short bonnet cab .......... **£150-200**

**26M**     **Tractor and Trailer with Cases**
1936-41   11M Tracked Tractor ... **£300-400**
1946-51   11M Tracked Tractor ... **£150-200**
1951-55   67M Farm Tractor........ **£150-200**

**27M, 28M**        Numbers not allocated.

**29M**     **Traffic Control Car**
1938-41   As 4M, with driver,
          passenger, single horn
          loudspeaker on roof ..... **£200-300**
1947-52   With single horn
          loudspeaker on roof ..... **£150-200**
          With later smaller
          2-horn speaker ............ **£100-150**

**30M**     **Mechanical Horse & Pantechnicon**
1935-41   With 2-axle trailer,
          no decals ..................... **£150-200**
1946-51   'Minic Transport'........ **£150-200**
1951-55   With single-axle trailer,
          'Minic Transport' decals,
          short bonnet cab .......... **£150-200**
Rare 'BROCKHURST' issue. **£2,000-2,500**

**31M**     **Mechanical Horse & Fuel Oil Trailer**
(Mechanical Horse & Petrol Trailer)
1936-41   Long bonnet cab,
          'Shell BP Fuel Oil'....... **£300-400**
1946-51   'Shell', 'BP', 'Shell Fuel
          Oils', or 'BP Fuel Oil'.
          Long bonnet cab .......... **£150-200**
1951-58   Same, but with short
          bonnet cab ................... **£150-200**

**32M**     **Dust Cart / Refuse Lorry**
1936-41   With long bonnet ......... **£200-300**
1946-50   With long bonnet ......... **£100-150**
1950-56   With short bonnet......... **£100-150**

**33M**     **Steam Roller**
1935-41   Wooden wheels ........... **£175-225**
1946-55   Plastic wheels................. **£70-80**

**34M**     **Tourer with Passengers**
1937-40   8M + four lead figures . **£600-800**

**35M**     **Rolls Tourer**
Sometimes numbered '118M'
1937-41   ............................... **£1,000-1,200**
1946-52   ..................................... **£150-200**

**36M**     **Daimler Tourer**
1937-41   Red, black hood ..... **£1,000-1,200**
1946-52   As pre-war version....... **£150-200**

**37M**     **Bentley Tourer**
Sometimes numbered '39M'
1938-41   ............................... **£1,000-1,200**
1946-52   ..................................... **£150-200**

**38M**     **Caravan Set (non-electric)**
1936-40   5M Limousine with
          16M Caravan (see 113M
          for post-war version).... **£500-750**

**39M**     **Taxi / London Taxi**
1938-41   ............................... **£1,500-2,000**
1946-52   Post-war sometimes
          numbered 35M............. **£200-250**

**40M**     **Mechanical Horse & Trailer with Cases**
1941-41   Long bonnet cab (very
          few made in 1941) ....... **£300-400**
1946-51   Long bonnet cab .......... **£150-200**
1951-56   Short bonnet ................ **£100-150**

**41ME**     **Caravan with Electric Light & Battery**
1936-40   Battery not included,
          16M with light bulb ..... **£300-400**

**42M**     **Rolls Sedanca**
1937-41   Orange/beige or
          beige/black ............ **£1,000-1,500**
1947-52   As pre-war version....... **£250-350**

**43M**     **Daimler Sedanca**
1937-41   Red/black or
          beige/dark blue....... **£1,000-1,500**
1947-52   As pre-war version....... **£150-200**

**44M**     **Traction Engine**
1938-41   ..................................... **£200-300**
1946-55   ....................................... **£70-90**

**45M**     **Bentley Sunshine Saloon**
1938-41   Green/beige or
          dark green/black..... **£1,250-1,750**

**46M**     **Daimler Sunshine Saloon**
1938-41   Green / beige.......... **£1,250-1,750**
1946-52   As pre-war version...... **£500-700**

**47M**     **Rolls Sunshine Saloon**
1938-41   Beige / black ......... **£1,250-1,750**
1946-52   As pre-war version...... **£500-700**

**48M**     **Breakdown Lorry with**
         **Mechanical Crane**
1936-41   Long bonnet ................ **£300-400**
1946-50   Long bonnet ................ **£150-250**
1950-56   Short bonnet................ **£150-250**

**48MCF**   **Breakdown Lorry**
1940-41   Camouflage finish........ **£500-700**

**49ME**     **Searchlight Lorry with**
         **Electric Searchlight**
1936-41   Battery not included..... **£500-700**
**49MECF**   1940-41   Camouflage finish,
          battery not included ..... **£700-900**

**50ME**     **Rolls Sedanca with Electric Headlamps**
See also 42M.
1937-41   Red / black ............ **£1,000-1,500**

**51ME**     **Daimler Sedanca with**
         **Electric Headlamps**   See also 43M.
1937-41   Green / black.......... **£1,000-1,500**

Tri-ang Minic  1M '£100 Ford Saloon'          Photo: Vectis Auctions Ltd.

Early post-war Tri-ang Minic toys:  15M Petrol Tank Lorry and 25M Delivery Lorry          Photo: Vectis Auctions Ltd.

Tri-ang Minic  52M Single Deck Bus          PHOTO: VECTIS AUCTIONS LTD.

Tri-ang Minic  21M Delivery Van          PHOTO: VECTIS AUCTIONS LTD.

**52M** **Single Deck Bus / London Bus 'Red'**
1936-41  Duo-tone green, 'Green Line',
'London Transport' ...... **£350-450**
1946-58  Duo-tone green, early issues
have 'Green Line', later:
red 'London Transport' **£350-450**
Blue / Grey, 'Tri-ang
Transport' decals ................NGPP
1958-60  'Routemaster' front ...... **£350-450**

**53M** **Single Deck Bus**
1936-41  Red / stone livery,
'London Transport' ..... **£350-450**

**54M** **Traction Engine & Trailer with Cases**
All with 6 wooden cases
1939-41  44M & 2-axle Trailer... **£150-200**
1946-56  44M & 2-axle Trailer... **£125-150**

**55ME** **Bentley Tourer with Electric Headlamps**
1938-40  See also 37M.
Beige / black ......... **£1,500-2,000**

**56ME** **Rolls Sunshine Saloon with**
**Electric headlamps**
1938-40  See also 47M.
Duotone green ........................ **£1,500-2,000**

**57ME** **Bentley Sunshine Saloon with**
**Electric Headlamps**
1938-40  See also 45M.
Apple green / black band ....... **£1,500-2,000**

**58ME** **Daimler Sunshine Saloon with**
**Electric Headlamps**
1938-40  See also 46M.......... **£1,500-2,000**

**59ME** **Caravan Set (Tourer with Passengers)**
1937-40  34M with passengers
with 41ME Caravan
with Electric Lights... **£900-1,100**

**60M** **Double Deck Bus / London Bus**
1935-41  Red, maroon / stone,
'London Transport' ...... **£400-500**
1946-58  All-red, red/cream roof,
red-cream-red-cream body
with red roof,
red with cream lower windows,
red with cream upper windows;
all with 'London Transport'
decals............................ **£300-400**
Blue / cream ................. **£300-400**
1958-60  Routemaster front, red,
London transport or Tri-ang
Transport decals .......... **£250-350**

**61M** **Double Deck Bus**
1935-41  Green............................ **£400-500**

**62M** **London Fire Engine**
1936-41  ..................................... **£200-300**
1946-56  ..................................... **£175-225**

**62ME** **Fire Engine with Electric Headlamps**
1936-38  ..................................... **£300-350**

**63M** **Presentation Set No. 1**
1936-40  Contains 1M, 4M,
5M, 6M and 8M.... **£1,500-2,000**

**64M** **Presentation Set No. 2**
1936-40  Contains 1M, 2M, 5M,
13M, 15M, 20M, 21M,
22M and 23M ........ **£1,500-2,000**

**65M** **Construction Set No. 1**
1936-40  Wooden case containing
unpainted parts to assemble
5M, 6M, 9M, 10M, 11M and
21M models, including
paint, various transfers
and tools ............... **£1,500-2,000**

**66M** **Six-wheel Army Lorry**
1939-41  9M with 2 rear axles.... **£400-500**

**66MCF** 1940-41  Same model but in
camouflage finish......... **£400-500**

**67M** **Farm Lorry**
1939-47  9M with stake frame ... **£600-800**

**68M** **Timber Lorry**
1939-41  long bonnet cab, front
ladder / plank rack ....... **£250-350**
1946-51  long bonnet cab, front
ladder / plank rack ....... **£150-200**
1951-56  short bonnet, front
ladder / plank rack ....... **£100-150**

**69M** **Canvas Tilt Lorry**
1939-41  Model as 9M with 2 rear
axles and canvas tilt ..... **£500-600**

**69MCF** 1940-41  Same model but in
camouflage finish...... **£800-1,000**

**70M** **Coal Lorry**  Not issued.

**71M** **Mechanical Horse & Milk Tanker**
1939-41  Long bonnet cab, 'Minic
Dairies 3150 Gallons' .. **£400-500**
1946-51  Long bonnet cab .......... **£300-400**
1951-58  Short bonnet................. **£300-400**

**72M** **Mechanical Horse & Lorry with**
**Barrrels / Brewer's Trailer**
1939-41  Long bonnet cab .......... **£400-500**
1946-51  Long bonnet cab .......... **£400-500**
1951-56  Short bonnet................. **£300-400**

**73M** **Mechanical Horse & Cable Drum**
**Trailer / Cable Lorry**
1939-41  Long bonnet cab .......... **£400-500**
1946-51  Long bonnet cab .......... **£150-200**
1951-56  Short bonnet................. **£150-175**

**74M** **Mechanical Horse & Log**
**Trailer / Log Lorry**
1939-41  Long bonnet cab ................NGPP
1946-51  Long bonnet cab .......... **£150-200**
1951-56  Short bonnet................. **£100-150**

**75M** **Ambulance**
In 1939 trade catalogue but not issued.
1952-56  Short bonnet cab, based on
103M, red cross and
'LCC' decals ............... **£200-250**

**76M** **Balloon Barrage Wagon and Trailer**
1940-41  As 66M with winch, trailer
with 'gas' cylinders,
3-piece balloon
in stiffened fabric ... **£3,000-4,000**

**77M** **Trolley Bus.** In catalogue but not issued.

**78M** **'POOL' Petrol Tanker**
1940-41  As 15M, grey only, white
'POOL' decals ........ **£1,000-1,500**

**78M** **Jeep No. 1**
1946-56  Gloss or matt Olive.......... **£70-90**

**79M** **Mechanical Horse & 'POOL' Tanker**
1940-41  As 31M, grey only, white
'POOL' decals ........ **£1,000-1,500**

**79M** **G.W.R. Railway Van**
1947-49  Model as 21M ........ **£1,000-1,200**

**80M** **L.M.S. Railway Van**
1947-49  Model as 21M .............. **£500-750**

**81M** **L.N.E.R. Railway Van**
1947-49  Model as 21M .............. **£400-500**

**82M** **S.R. Railway Van**
1947-49  Model as 21M .............. **£400-500**

**83M** **Farm Tractor**
1947-56  Main body as 11M ......... **£75-100**

**84M** **---**  See Plastic Models.

**85M** **Forward Drive Van**
1951-55  Replaced 21M, short
bonnet version............. **£100-150**

**86M** **Forward Drive Tip Lorry**
1951-56  Replaced 23M.................. **£75-95**

**87M - 92M** **---**  Numbers not allocated.

**93M** **'O' Saloon**
1952-56  Small scale car ............. **£150-200**

**94M - 102M** **---**  See Plastic Models.

**103M** **Shutter Van**
1951-56  One piece lift-up rear
door; see 75M ............. **£175-225**

**104M - 106M**  See Plastic Models / No.2 Series.

**107M** **'British Railways' Van**
1950-51  Model as 21M with 'British
Railways' decals........... **£150-200**
1951-55  Model based on 85M ... **£100-150**

**108M - 112M** **---** See Plastic Models.

**113M** **Vauxhall Cabriolet and Caravan**
1950-51  19M + 16M .................. **£200-250**

**114M** **Mechanical Horse & Trailer**
**with Cruiser**
1950-51  Penguin plastic boat..... **£150-200**
1951-56  Short bonnet cab,
Penguin plastic boat..... **£150-200**

**119M** **Watney's Barrel Lorry**
1952-56  Long bonnet tractor unit with
barrel on roof, wooden
barrel artic. trailer; late
models had short bonnet cab
without barrel on roof .. **£250-300**

**123M** **British Road Services Lorry**
1951-56  Short bonnet 25M in red
with B.R.S. decals........ **£250-300**

**124M** **British Road Services Van**
1952-56  85M in green with
B.R.S decals................. **£250-300**

**145M** **Cement Mixer Lorry**
1951-56  Plastic mixer drum on
short bonnet truck
chassis / cab ................ **£100-125**

**30M base** **Mechanical Horse & Pantechnicon**
1937  'Brockhouse' promotional
based on 30M......... **£1,500-2,000**

**21M base** **'Atco Mowers' Van**  (promotional)
1951?  Based on 21M ........ **£1,000-1,500**
**21M base** **'Winstone Tiles' / Furniture Van**
1951?  New Zealand assembled
model, based on 21M . **£500-750**

**Other New Zealand issues**

**1M** **Ford Saloon**
1948?-51?  Red ..................................NGPP
**2M** **Ford Van**
1948?-51?  Blue .................................NGPP
**11M** **Tractor**
1948?-51?  Unpainted......................NGPP
**15M** **Petrol Tank Lorry 'SHELL'**
1948?-51?  Red / yellow ............. **£500-750**
**23M** **Tip Lorry**
1948?-51?  Red / purple-grey ...........NGPP
**16M** **Caravan**
1948?-51?  Red / white .....................NGPP
**18M** **Vauxhall Town Coupé**
1948?-51?  Purple-grey / red wings...NGPP
**19M** **Vauxhall Cabriolet**
1948?-51?  Duotone blue ...................NGPP

# Meccano Cars and Constructor Outfits

In 1932, Meccano introduced their 'Motor Car Constructor Outfit'. With its special parts (not compatible with standard Meccano), a small range of very sporty looking car models could be built. A year later, a smaller set, designated 'Motor Car Constructor Outfit No.1' appeared and the first set was given the superior 'No.2' tag. Features abounded: stylishly shaped mudguards and body panels, alternative radiators, working Ackermann steering, a driver; even working brakes! The kits included a powerful clockwork motor as standard and the whole lot could be driven 'at night' with the addition of the Motor Car Lighting Set that came along as early as 1933.

In addition, spare parts were available from Meccano dealers that enabled young builders to achieve different colour schemes. Body Sections were available in Orange and in Yellow, Wings in Orange and in Green, and Wheels in Orange or Yellow.
Ready-built models were available and are listed below. These were made up from parts relevant to the No.1 Outfit. A non-constructional Meccano Sports Car was also marketed at the time, as was a Motor Car Garage to house the vehicles, whether ready made or owner constructed.

Production quantities of the Outfits appear to have been somewhat limited in the latter half of the 1930s decade, thus surviving items are quite rare nowadays, especially in good and complete condition. All the Car Constructor Outfits were withdrawn from the Meccano Products Catalogue around 1940 and were never reintroduced.

### Motor Car Constructor Outfit.
Made from 1932 to 1933. No driver figure. Supplied in a strong green carton with a colourful label on the lid. In 1933, this set was promoted to 'Motor Car Constructor Outfit No.2'. Three colour options were available:
Red main components.............................................................**£400-500**
Blue main components ...........................................................**£400-500**
Green main components .........................................................**£400-500**

### Motor Car Constructor No. 1 Outfit.
Made from 1933 to 1940. No driver figure. Supplied in a strong green and yellow carton on the lid of which was a colourful label with an artist's impression of the Road Racer at speed. Outfits were supplied complete with a powerful clockwork motor. Four colour options were available:
Red and Light Blue main components ......................................**£300-400**
Light Blue and Cream main components ..................................**£300-400**
Green and Yellow main components ........................................**£300-400**
Cream and Red main components ............................................**£300-400**

**Ready-built models** were also available, made up from the No.1 Outfit:
| | | |
|---|---|---|
| 1/1 | **Sports Tourer** (with Hood), blue box, instruction sheet... | **£500-700** |
| 1/2 | **Saloon Coupé**, blue box with instruction sheet | **£500-700** |
| 1/3 | **Road Racer**, blue box with instruction sheet | **£500-700** |
| 1/4 | **Sports Tourer**, blue box with instruction sheet | **£500-700** |

### Meccano Two-seater Sports Car (non-constructional)
Length 8½". Clockwork motor. Available in three different colours:
Red, patterned green box has lift-off lid with full-colour label ........ **£900-1,100**
Blue, patterned green box has lift-off lid with full-colour label ........ **£900-1,100**
Cream, patterned green box has lift-off lid with full-colour label ..... **£900-1,100**

### Motor Car Constructor No. 2 Outfit.
Made from 1933 to 1941. Presentation and colours of parts were identical to those of the No.1 Outfit. As this set was developed from the 1932 Outfit, early versions have no driver figure. This enhancement (plus a few other minor modifications) appeared a few months later. The separately available spare parts also came in the same choices as for the No.1 set. However, it is very important to note that parts for the No.1 Outfit were **not compatible** with the No.2 Outfit (nor with standard Meccano parts).
Red and Light Blue main components ...........................................**£1,000-1,250**
Light Blue and Cream main components .......................................**£1,000-1,250**
Green and Yellow main components.............................................**£1,000-1,250**
Cream and Red main components .................................................**£1,000-1,250**

**Ready-built models** were also available, made up from the No.2 Outfit:
| | | |
|---|---|---|
| 2/1 | **Sports Tourer** (with Hood), blue box, instruction sheet... | **£700-900** |
| 2/2 | **Saloon Coupé**, blue box with instruction sheet | **£700-900** |
| 2/3 | **Road Racer**, blue box with instruction sheet | **£700-900** |
| 2/4 | **Sports Tourer**, blue box with instruction sheet | **£700-900** |

### Motor Car Lighting Set
Introduced in 1933. This set enabled the headlights in the No.2 Outfit to be illuminated using a 3 volt battery (not supplied).
Green box with lift-off lid ('M251'), instruction sheet........................**£150-300**

### Meccano Motor Car Garage
designed to accommodate Meccano Motor Cars (or others of a suitable size).
Inside dimensions: H 5in., L 13in., W 7 3/4in. Green box, lift-off lid . **£200-400**

See colour pages for more illustrations of Meccano Cars, Car Constructor Outfits, Aeroplane Constructor Outfits, accessories, and other Meccano Products.

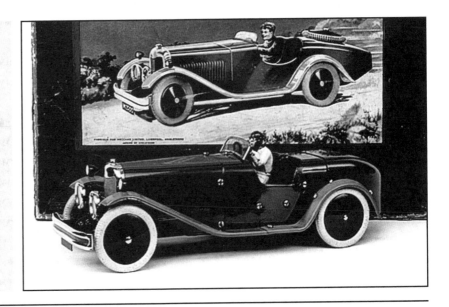

# Meccano Aeroplane Constructor Outfits

Meccano Aeroplane Constructor Outfits were introduced in October 1931 and were available in two varieties simply called Outfits No.1 and No.2. Unlike the Car Constructor Outfits, there was compatability between the No.1 and No.2 Aeroplane sets. This allowed the inclusion of a further set - No.1A Accessory Outfit which could convert the smaller one into the larger. Early wheels were actually standard Meccano pulleys painted red. There were a few other conventional Meccano parts in these Outfits (originally sprayed in silver paint) but the major components were specially designed for the purpose. For the No.1 set, the manual described three biplanes and three monoplanes that could be constructed. With its extra parts, which included diecast engine and seaplane floats, the No.2 manual suggested sixteen additional potential models. Early in 1932, two clockwork motors were introduced for use with these Outfits. The smaller of them just rotated the propeller, while the larger one actually provided sufficient motive power to the landing wheels to cause the model aircraft to taxi along the carpet runway.

A year later, much development work had produced better components. Special

wheels complete with stylish spats, for instance, replaced the unsuitable pulley wheels. Wing edges had become realistically rounded and wing tips and fuselages were enamelled in red.

1933 saw the introduction of Outfits No.OO and No.O as cheaper, simpler sets aimed at younger builders, and not interchangeable with Nos. 1 and 2. In the same year, the range was enlarged to include No.1 Special Outfit (twenty models) and No.2 Special Outfit (forty-four models). Available in various bright and attractive colours, the Special Outfits were very well endowed with new purpose-made components such as workable ailerons and rudders, passenger window panels, pilot's cabins, tail elevators, etc. There was even a model pilot for insertion into the open-cockpit model. Both civilian and military liveries were from time to time available in the late 1930s.

As with most Meccano items, the War brought production to a halt around 1940. Aeroplane Constructor Outfits were officially withdrawn in 1941 and sadly were never made again.

### No.00 Aeroplane Constructor Outfit
Made from 1932 to 1940. Designed for the younger builder, this set had a one-piece fuselage plus a few simple parts that were not compatible with Outfits No. 1 and 2. Supplied in a stout box with a two-colour label on the lid.
Red and cream components. Blue box with instructions ..................... **£200-300**
Green and cream components. Blue box with instructions.................. **£200-300**
Blue and white components. Blue box with instructions..................... **£200-300**

### No.0 Aeroplane Constructor Outfit
Made from 1932 to 1940. As the No.0 Outfit but with more parts (also not compatible with Outfits No. 1 and 2). Supplied in a stout box with a full-colour label on the lid.
Red and cream components. Blue box with instructions ..................... **£250-400**
Green and cream components. Blue box with instructions.................. **£250-400**
Blue and white components. Blue box with instructions..................... **£250-400**
Seville Grey components, RAF markings. Blue box + instructions ..... **£250-400**

### No.0P Aeroplane Hangar Outfit
Made from 1933 to 1940. The complete range of parts from Outfit No. 0, packed into a No.01 Aeroplane Hangar, then into a stout carton.
Red and cream components, blue box with lift-off lid, instructions..... **£350-500**
Green and cream components, blue box with lift-off lid, instructions . **£350-500**
Blue and white components, blue box with lift-off lid, instructions..... **£350-500**

### No.01 Aeroplane Hangar
Made from 1933 to 1940. To house a model aircraft made from Outfits No. 00, 0 or 01P. Single door, size (mm): 292(L) x 260(D) x 108(H) ...... NGPP

### No.02 Aeroplane Hangar
Made from 1933 to 1940. To house two models made from Outfits No. 00, 0 or 01P. Single door, size (mm): 546(L) x 279(D) x 159(H) ...... NGPP

### No.1 Aeroplane Constructor Outfit
Made from 1931 to 1932. Silver coloured components, standard Meccano pulley wheels (red). Wings and tailplanes have 'RAF markings. Manual shows 6 examples of mono- and biplanes that can be built. Supplied in a strong carton with a colourful label on the lid............... **£100-200**

### No.1 Aeroplane Constructor Outfit
Made from 1932 to 1940. Purpose-made wheels with enveloping spats replaced the Meccano pulley wheels. Wing and tailplanes edges were more rounded and realistic. Civilian as well as 'Military' models could also be built. Supplied in a strong blue carton with a colourful label on the lid.
Silver components (early production) ...................................... **£150-250**
Cream components, RAF roundels ......................................... **£250-400**
Blue and cream components, RAF roundels ......................... **£250-400**
Red and cream components................................................ **£250-400**
Green and cream components.............................................. **£250-400**

### No.1A Aeroplane Constructor Accessory Outfit
Made from 1931 to 1932. Silver components, sufficient to convert the No.1 Outfit into a No.2. Supplied in a strong carton with a colourful label on the lid .............................................................. **£100-200**

### No.1A Aeroplane Constructor Accessory Outfit
Made from 1932 to 1940. As the earlier set, but in the colours of the main Outfits available at the time Supplied in a strong carton with a colourful label on the lid................................................... **£100-200**

### No. 2 Aeroplane Constructor Outfit
Made from 1931 to 1932. Silver coloured components, red standard Meccano pulley wheels. Additional parts included seaplane floats and diecast engines. Wings and tailplanes have RAF markings. Manual shows 22 examples of mono-, bi- and seaplanes that can be built. Supplied in a strong carton with a colourful label on the lid.. **£100-200**

### No. 2 Aeroplane Constructor Outfit
Made from 1932 to 1940. As with the No. 1 Outfit, purpose-made wheels with spats replaced the original pulley wheels. Wing and tailplanes edges were more rounded and realistic. A much larger range of models could be built, including 'planes with 1, 2 or 3 engines, a Racing Seaplane, and a Giant Italian Bomber. Supplied in a strong blue carton with a colourful label on the lid.
Silver and blue components (early production) .................................. **£150-250**
Cream components, RAF roundels.......................................... **£300-400**
Blue and white components, RAF roundels ......................... **£500-750**
Red and Cream components.................................................. **£300-400**
Green and Cream components............................................... **£300-400**

### No.1 Special Aeroplane Constructor Outfit
Made from 1933 to 1940. In addition to the improved parts in the standard Outfits, new components in the 'Special' sets included engine cowlings, a pilot figure, passenger windows, moving ailerons and rudders. The manual (that covered both Outfits 1 and 2) showed twenty example models. Supplied in a strong blue carton with a colourful label on the lid.
Silver components (early production) ...................................... **£300-450**
Cream components, RAF roundels.......................................... **£300-450**
Blue and white components, RAF roundels ......................... **£300-450**
Red and Cream components.................................................. **£300-450**
Green and Cream components............................................... **£300-450**

### No.1AS Special Aeroplane Constructor Accessory Outfit
Made from 1933 to 1940. This set provided sufficient parts to convert the No.1 Special Outfit into a No.2. Supplied in a strong blue carton with a colourful label on the lid. .............................................. **£100-200**

### No.2 Special Aeroplane Constructor Outfit
Made from 1933 to 1940. As the No.1 Special Outfit, but with many additional parts that allowed the construction of the forty-four models shown in the manual, plus many others. Supplied in a strong blue carton with a colourful label on the lid.
Silver components (early production) ...................................... **£500-750**
Cream components, RAF roundels.......................................... **£500-750**
Blue and white components, RAF roundels ......................... **£500-750**
Red and Cream components.................................................. **£500-750**
Green and Cream components............................................... **£500-750**

### Meccano Aero Motor No.1
Produced from early 1932. Designed to fit in the fuselage component of Outfit Nos. 1 or 2, the clockwork motor would 'rotate the propeller at high speed, thus greatly adding to the realism of the model.'.............. **£30-40**

### Meccano Aero Motor No.2
Produced from early 1932. Suitable for use with Outfit Nos. 1 or 2, this was a more powerful clockwork motor that would spin the propeller and drive the landing wheels 'making the machines taxi along the floor in a most realistic manner.' An Adjustable Tailwheel was included with Aero Motor No.2............................................................ **£60-80**

### M236 Aeroplane Pilots.
Trade Box of six containing 2 red, 2 green and 2 blue...... **£200-300**

# Hornby Speed Boats

Hornby toy boats were introduced in the summer of 1932. In that year, only one model was available; it was simply called Speed Boat 'Hornby', having no reference number. A year later it was promoted to Speed Boat No.3, four new models having been designed to provide a range costing between 2/6 and 17/6 each. Hornby Racing Boats followed in 1934 along with a 'water toy' in the shape of a duck. This, like all the Hornby pre-war boats was operated by a clockwork motor. Also available were Pennants, Motors, Propellers and

Shafts for the customisation or scratch-building of model boats. Production of the original tinplate products ceased at the outbreak of war in 1939. In 1960, Hornby Speed Boats made a reappearance, but only as a small new range of plastic mouldings with extra detail and clockwork motors until 1965. A battery-operated model continued in production up to 1969, the range being dropped by Lines Brothers five years after their aquisition of Meccano.

| | | |
|---|---|---|
| 1932-32 | **Speed Boat 'Hornby'**, Red, Green or Blue, open cockpit, 16in long | NGPP |
| 1933-34 | **Speed Boat No. 3, 'Hornby'**, Red, Green or Blue, open cockpit, 16in long | NGPP |
| 1934-39 | **Speed Boat No.2, 'Condor'**, Red/Cream, 16½in long | **£90-120** |
| | **Speed Boat No.3, 'Gannet'**, Blue/White | NGPP |
| | **Speed Boat No.3, 'Curlew'**, Green/Ivory | NGPP |
| 1934-39 | **Speed Boat No.1 'Hawk'**, Red/cream, Blue/White or Green/Ivory 9¼in long | **£60-80** |
| 1947-?? | **Speed Boat No.1 'Gleam'**, Green/White, picture box | **£60-80** |
| 1947-?? | **Speed Boat No.1 'Naval Launch X46'**, Grey, picture box | **£60-80** |
| 1934-39 | **Speed Boat No.2 'Swift'**, (blue box, full-colour label), Red/Cream, Blue/White or Yellow/White, 12½in long | **£100-150** |
| 1934-39 | **Limousine Boat No.4, 'Venture'**, Red/Cream, Blue/White or Green/Ivory, 16½in long | **£120-170** |
| 1934-39 | **Cabin Cruiser No.5 'Viking'**, Red/Cream, Blue/White or Green/Ivory, 16½in long | **£200-300** |

| | | |
|---|---|---|
| 1934-39 | **Racing Boat No.1 'Racer I'**, Cream/Green, 8½in long | **£125-150** |
| 1934-39 | **Racing Boat No.2 'Racer II'**, Blue/Cream, 12½in long | **£125-150** |
| 1934-39 | **Racing Boat No.3 'Racer III'**, Red/Cream, 16½in long | **£150-200** |
| 1934-39 | **Hornby Water Toy (Duck)**, Superstructure is a tinplate pressing in the shape of a duck fitted to a 'Hawk' hull. 9¼in long | **£800-1,000** |
| 1960-62 | **Speed Boat No.3 River Launch**, Plastic moulding, 10in. long, clockwork motor | **£50-75** |
| 1960-62 | **Speed Boat No.4, Fast Patrol Launch**, plastic moulding, White hull, 'mahogany' deck, 10in. long, clockwork motor | **£60-80** |
| 1960-65 | **Speed Boat No.5 RAF Range Safety Launch**, plastic moulding, Black hull, Brown deck, 10in. long, clockwork | **£60-80** |
| 1963-69 | **Speed Boat**, plastic moulding, battery-operated motor | **£50-75** |

**See colour pages for illustrations of Hornby and Sutcliffe boats**

# Sutcliffe Model Boats

Sutcliffe Pressings was started in 1885, initially producing domestic and photographic sheet metal goods. Their famous oil cans came later, followed in 1920 by the first of their tinplate boats, the Valiant Battleship, the hulls of which were made as two pressings soldered together. In 1932 Sutcliffe pioneered the production of hulls made from a single pressing. A variety of

sizes of model boats were made but the majority were based on the 9 inch and 12 inch hulls. Production, mainly of boats, plus a smaller quantity of oil cans and other sheet metal work continued up to 1984.

| | | |
|---|---|---|
| 1920 | **'The Valiant Battleship'**. The first boat produced by Sutcliffe. Originally powered by a water circulatory boiler with the coil heated by methylated spirits | NGPP |
| 1928 | **'The Valiant Battleship'**. Clockwork | NGPP |
| 1978-80 | **'The Valiant Battleship'**, 12" hull. Modified re-issue with moveable rudder and gun turrets. Black/grey with three decals: 'Sutcliffe Models', 'Valiant', Union Jack | **£150-175** |
| 1978-80 | **'The Valiant Battleship'**. Electric powered (only 6 made) | NGPP |
| 1935 | **'Zip' Speedboat**, 9" hull with large clockwork motor | **£100-125** |
| c1978 | **'Zip' Speedboat**, 9" hull, (A batch of 100 were made) | **£75-95** |
| 1959-68 | **'Noddy'**, 9" hull | **£75-95** |
| 1963-80 | **'Merlin'** electric, 12" hull | **£75-95** |

| | | |
|---|---|---|
| 1950-59 | **'Viking' Liner**, 9" hull | **£75-95** |
| c1978 | **'Viking' Liner**, 9" hull. (A batch of 100 were made) | NGPP |
| ? | **'Victor' Motor Torpedo Boat**. Blue/White | **£150-175** |
| ? | **'Zodiac'**, large electric boat, plastic hull, wood deck | NGPP |
| ? | **'Zodiac'**, a very few were factory modified to clockwork | NGPP |
| ? | **'Minx' Cruiser** was smaller with a clockwork motor | NGPP |
| ? | **'Jupiter' Ocean Pilot Cruiser** | **£75-95** |
| ? | **'Racer'** | **£80-120** |
| ? | **'Hawk' Speedboat**. Turquoise hull, White deck | **£70-90** |
| ? | **'Hawk' Speedboat**. Light Green hull, White deck | **£160-190** |
| ? | **'Comet' Speedboat**. Yellow hull, dark blue hatch, red bung, early yellow box | **£125-150** |
| ? | **'Commodore' Cruiser**. Red hull, white superstructure | **£100-125** |
| ? | **'Merlin' Speedboat**. Red hull, white superstructure | **£100-125** |
| ? | **'Jupiter' Ocean Pilot**. Red hull, white deck | **£125-150** |
| ? | **'Diana' Speedboat**. Blue hull, white deck | NGPP |
| ? | **'Grenville' Destroyer**, Grey/black, tinplate stand | **£500-700** |
| ? | **'Snappy' Gunboat**, Red/grey | **£175-225** |
| ? | **'Sprite'**, Green and cream | **£125-150** |
| ? | **'Bluebird'**, single-hulled speedboat | **£150-200** |
| ? | **'Bluebird II'**, tri-hulled speedboat (picture at left) | **£300-400** |

**SUBMARINES**
These were boxed with a winding key and a 'periscope' rubber plug.

| | | |
|---|---|---|
| ? | **'Sea Wolf'**. Yellow with red deck fittings | **£125-150** |
| ? | **'Unda-Wunda'**. Light blue with gold trim | **£125-150** |
| c1960s | **'Nautilus'**, clockwork submarine. 'Nautilus, copyright Walt Disney Productions' transfer | **£120-180** |

**MISCELLANEOUS**

| | | |
|---|---|---|
| ? | **'Sutcliffe' Oil Cans**. Numerous types and sizes, each: | **£25-50** |
| ? | Sutcliffe **'Midget Oiler'**. Trade Box with 6 | **£200-250** |
| ? | **'Sutcliffe' Display Stand**. 'Sutcliffe Boats World Famous Models' | **£150-200** |

**SUTCLIFFE INFORMATION.** The listing above represents all the information we currently have on Sutcliffe. The Editors would welcome any contributions or new information that you may have for future inclusion.

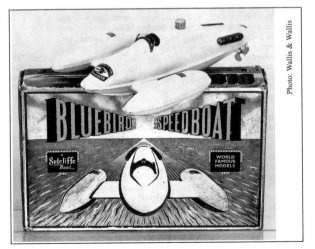

Photo: Wallis & Wallis

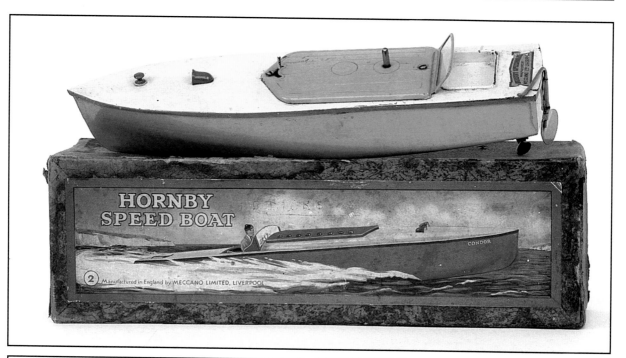

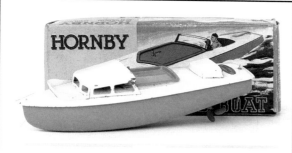

Hornby Speed Boats

Top: No.2 'Condor'    Left: No.1 'Hawk'    Right: 'Hornby Water Toy (Duck)'

Sutcliffe model Submarines

Left: 'Sea Wolf'    Right: 'Unda-Wunda'

**Gift Sets shown above sold by Vectis Auctions Ltd, Thornaby, Stockton-on-Tees**. Pictures reproduced by their kind permission.

**Models shown on opposite page sold by Lacy, Scott and Knight, Bury St Edmunds, Suffolk.**
Pictures reproduced by their kind permission.

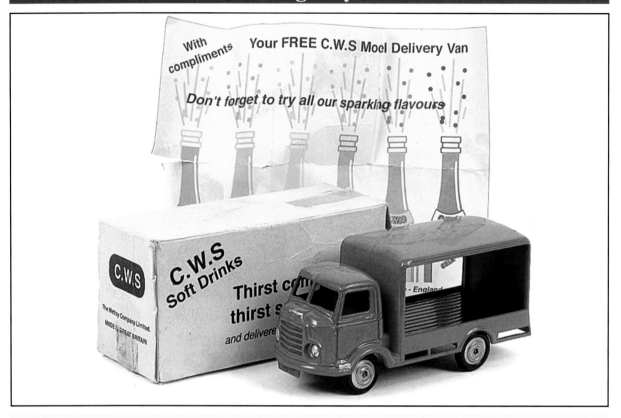

Early Mettoy Karrier Bantam 2-ton Van 'C.W.S.' promotional, 1957. This casting became Corgi Toys 455

Corgi Toys 436 Citroën ID19 Safari
1963 - 65

Trade box / counter display box of twelve Corgi Toys 155
'Embassy Shadow' Formula One Racing Cars, 1974 - 76

**Models shown on these two pages sold by Vectis Auctions Ltd, Thornaby, Stockton-on-Tees**.
Pictures reproduced by their kind permission.

Chipperfields Set 23 (first issue)
1962 - 66

Corgi Toys 321 'Monte Carlo' Mini Cooper 'S'
1966 - 67

Corgi Toys 391 James Bond Ford Mustang
1972

Corgi Toys 269 James Bond Lotus Esprit, 1977 - 83
and 272 James Bond Citroën 2cv, 1981 - 83

Corgi Toys H853 Magic Roundabout Playground, 1972 - 74

Mettoy Castoys Luxury Observation Coach.

Models shown on this page sold by Vectis Auctions Ltd, Thornaby, Stockton-on-Tees.

'The Man From U.N.C.L.E.'s 'Thrushbuster'. Corgi Toys 497, 1966 - 69.

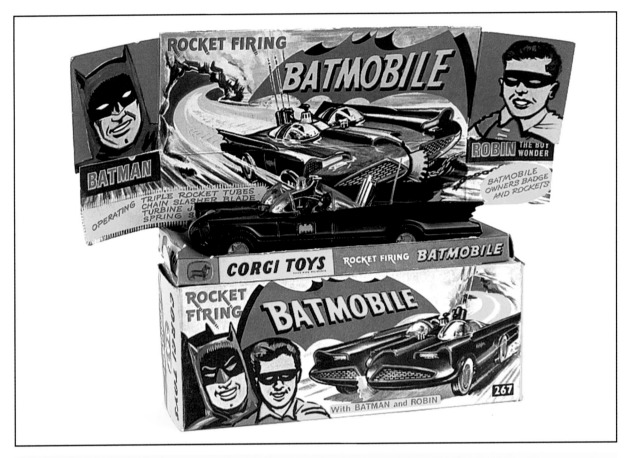

Corgi Toys 267 Batmobile with early 'diorama' box, 1966 - 67    PHOTO: VECTIS AUCTIONS LTD.

Corgi Toys 'Red Rose Coffee' 468 Routemaster Bus (Canadian promotional), 1966    PHOTO: VECTIS AUCTIONS LTD.

Crescent Toys 1288 Cooper-Bristol
1956 - 60   PHOTO: VECTIS AUCTIONS LTD.

Crescent Toys 1285 BRM Mk.II
1956 - 60   PHOTO: VECTIS AUCTIONS LTD.

Crescent Toys K665 Transport Ship
PHOTO: LACY, SCOTT & KNIGHT.

Crescent Toys 1803 Dexta Tractor and Trailer
1967 - 74   PHOTO: LACY, SCOTT & KNIGHT.

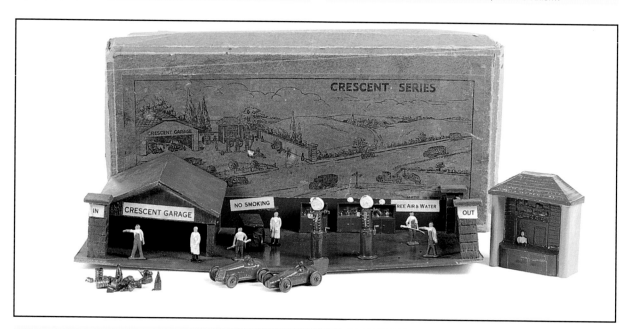

Crescent Garage Set   PHOTO: VECTIS AUCTIONS LTD.

# Matchbox Toys  (Moko and early Lesney)

Above: Massey-Harris 745D Tractor by Lesney.    Below: Moko Bulldozer, 'Jumbo the Walking Elephant' and 'Merry-go-Round'.

Above: a selection of Matchbox Miniatures buses.
Below: a selection of post-1969 'Superfast' models.

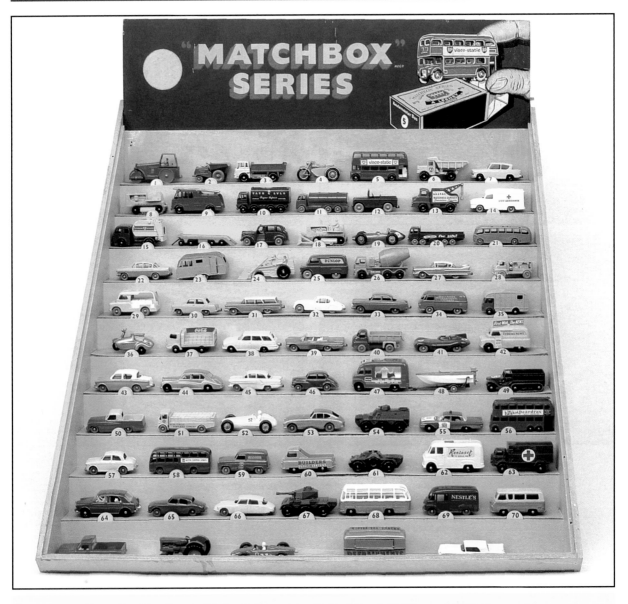

Above: Matchbox Counter Display Unit complete with the full early '1-75' range of Matchbox models.
Below: A selection of later Matchbox Miniatures.       PHOTOS: VECTIS AUCTIONS LTD.

# Matchbox Toys

Above: a selection of 'Regular Wheels' Matchbox Miniatures in early boxes.
Below: a selection of post-1969 'Superfast' models.

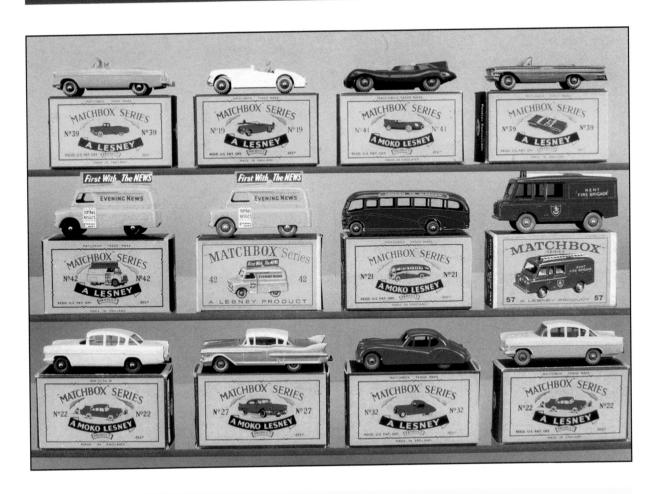

Above: a selection of 'Regular Wheels' Matchbox Miniatures in early boxes.
Below: a selection of later models showing development in box design.

# Matchbox Toys

Above: MB42 Bedford Van and MB37 Karrier Bantam Lorry. Note the metal/plastic wheel differences of both and the even/uneven load differences of the 'Coca-Cola' lorry.          Below: a selection of later 'Regular Wheels' models.

Matchbox Models of Yesteryear Y-1 to Y-16 in original counter display stand. PHOTOS: VECTIS AUCTIONS LTD.

Models of Yesteryear in rare colour combinations: Y11-3 Lagonda in gold and purple, and Y4-4 Duesenberg in white and red.

MB39 Ford Zephyr, MB44 Bentley and MB43 Hillman Minx

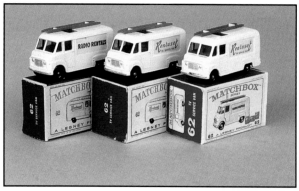

Three variations on the MB62 'Rentaset' theme.

MB36 Scooter and Sidecar; MB4 Motor Cycle and Sidecar

MB59 'British European Airways' Coach

Models of Yesteryear Gift Set G7

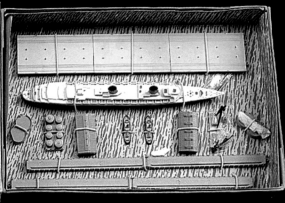

**Models sold by Vectis Auctions Ltd, Thornaby, Stockton-on-Tees.**   Pictures reproduced by their kind permission.

Spot-On 109/2p E.R.F. 68g Flatbed Lorry with Planks, 1960     PHOTO: VECTIS AUCTIONS LTD.

Spot-On Presentation Set No.0, 1960     PHOTO: VECTIS AUCTIONS LTD.

Cotswold Village No.3 'Cornerstones Cottage', 1960

Spot-On 107 Jaguar ;XK-SS', 1960

Spot-On 106a/1c Austin Articulated Lorry with Crate Load, 1960          PHOTO: VECTIS AUCTIONS LTD.

Spot-On 111/30g Ford Thames Trader with Garage Kit, 1962          PHOTO: VECTIS AUCTIONS LTD.

Spot-On 116 Caterpillar D9 Tractor with Bulldozer Blade, 1959     Photo: Vectis Auctions Ltd.

Spot-On 158a/2 Bedford 'S' type 2,000 gallon 'Shell-BP' Tanker, 1962     Photo: Vectis Auctions Ltd.

30M 'Minic Transport' Mechanical Horse and two-axle Pantechnicon.

119M Watney's Beer Lorry

**Models sold by Vectis Auctions Ltd, Thornaby, Stockton-on-Tees.**   Pictures reproduced by their kind permission.

113M Caravan and Limousine Set, comprising 19M Vauxhall Cabriolet and 16M (non-electric) Caravan.

39M London Taxi   (This model is sometimes seen with the reference 35M).

Salco items:  Horse-drawn Gipsy Caravan, Horse-drawn 'Toy Town Brewer's' Dray and 'Mickey's Fire Brigade'.
PHOTO: VECTIS AUCTIONS LTD.

Taylor & Barrett Trolley Bus     PHOTO: SPECIAL AUCTION SERVICES

Shackleton Foden FG6 Flatbed Lorry and Dyson Trailer.

David Brown 'Trackmaster 30' Tractor by Shackleton.

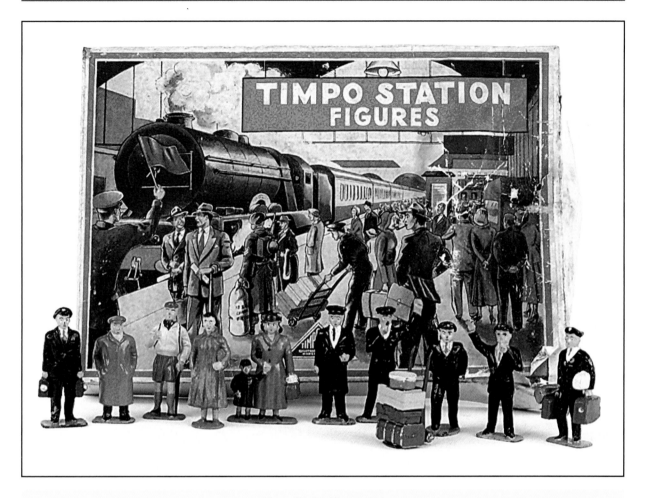

Timpo Station Figures Set

Sundaw Double Deck Bus (left);
Racing Car and Saloon Car by Jolly Roger (above).
PHOTOS: VECTIS AUCTIONS LTD.

Clockwise from top left:
Non-constructional Two-seater Sports Car (cream/red)
Non-constructional Two-seater Sports Car (red/blue)
Motor Car Model No.2 (Saloon / Coupé)
Aeroplane Constructor Outfit No.2 (Tri-motor model shown)
Aeroplane Constructor Outfit No.2 (cream/red/blue)
Spare Pilots     No.01P Hangar Outfit

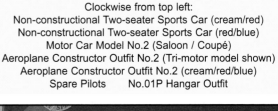

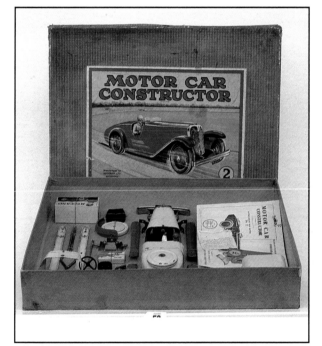

Meccano Motor Car Constructor Outfits

Top: No.1 Outfits as sold in England (left) and France (right)
Above: No.2 Outfit with cream and red components
Middle right: No.1 Outfit with black and red components
Right: a Motor Car Lighting Set

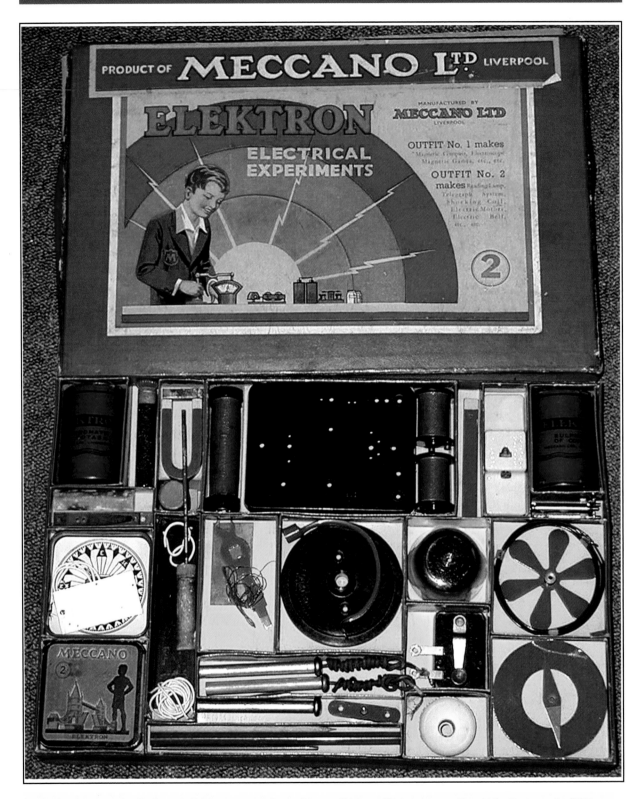

Meccano Elektron Outfit No.2. This pre-war set, in good to excellent condition, was recently sold by Bonhams for £341.
PHOTO: BONHAM'S AUCTIONS.